Ramsay's

Catalogue of

BRITISH DIECAST
MODEL TOYS

ELEVENTH EDITION

SWAPMEET

PUBLICATIONS

Swapmeet Publications
22 Foxgrove Lane, Felixstowe, Suffolk, IP11 7JU
Phone (01394) 670700, Fax: (01394) 670730
Web site: www.swapmeet.co.uk
E-mail: info@swapmeet.co.uk

Swapmeet Toys and Models Ltd., t/a Swapmeet Publications
Reg. No. 1715966. Reg. Office: 36 Rembrandt Way, Bury St Edmunds, Suffolk. Directors: E. J. Ramsay, S. E. Ramsay, Co. Sec. M. J. Ramsay, BA.

Originator and Editor
John Ramsay

Technical Editor
John King

1st Edition published 1983
2nd Edition published 1986
3rd Edition published 1988
3rd Edition Update published 1989
4th Edition published 1991
5th Edition published 1993
6th Edition published 1995
7th Edition published 1997
8th Edition published 1999
9th Edition published 2001
10th Edition published 2003
11th Edition published 2005

ISBN 09 54 99 25 - 0 - 4

Book designed by John King.
Origination by Swapmeet Publications, Felixstowe, Suffolk.
Printed by Warners Midlands plc., Bourne, Lincs.

Models featured on the front cover:
Dinky Toys No. 157 Jaguar XK120 Coupé,
Meccano Motor Car Constructor Outfit No. 1 (Pre-war French production)
Post-war Tri-ang Minic 30M Articulated Pantechnicon 'Minic Transport'

Contents

CONTENTS continued

Acknowledgements

The Editor would like to express appreciation to the following collectors, auctioneers and traders who very kindly took the time and trouble to provide updating information and photographs about new entries and colour variations, etc.

John Kinchen, Hampshire
David Cooke, Norwich
Derek Barratt, Norwich
Bruce Hoy, Queensland, Australia
Bryan Goodall and Simon Smith,
   Vectis Auctions Ltd, Stockton-on-Tees
Hugo Marsh, Christie's Model Auctions

Terry Durrant,
   Lacy Scott & Knight Model Auctions,
   Bury St Edmunds
Glenn Butler and Ray Strutt,
   Wallis & Wallis, Lewes, Sussex
Barry Potter of Barry Potter Auctions
Robert Newson, Wood Green, London
Mike and Sue Richardson, Windsor
Susan Pownall, Corgi Club
Herbert Bell, Western Australia
Andy Woodhall, Bury St Edmunds
Phillipe Salmon, Collectoys, France
Andrew Hilton and Nigel Mynheer,
   Special Auction Services, Reading
Vincent Espinasse, France

Horace Dunkley, Stamford, Lincs.
Nigel Cooper, Basingstoke
Trevor Bannister, Seaford
Leigh Gotch, Bonhams Auctioneers
Kevin McGimpsey (MICA),
   Deeside, Flintshire
Tony Murphy, DTCA
Norman Warnars, Tegelau, NL
Kevin Barwick, DTCA
Pierre Jacques Dujardin, France
Dale Sharp (by e-mail)
Jan Werner, DTCA
Hans Nuis, DTCA
John Anderson (by e-mail)
Major H.B (Bev) Stevens, Dorset

Introduction

Welcome to the 11th edition of 'British Diecast Model Toys Catalogue' which incorporates the following:

Updating and revision of the 10th edition

- The 10th edition model listings have been completely revised and the information on the model variations has been increased and improved.

- The vital 'Market Price Range' information has been totally revised and amended as appropriate by our team of valuation experts. The figures shown are supported by hundreds of meaningful auction results selected from a wide range of leading auction houses and from the internet.

- The colour section includes some the finest model pictures we have ever been able to feature.

Inclusion of British Tinplate Model Toys listings with Price Guides:

- Tri-ang Minic Toys - a completely new comprehensive listing of cars and vehicles especially produced for the catalogue by Mike Richardson.

- Meccano Contructor Toys – Outfits, Cars and Aeroplanes.

- Hornby Speedboats, Sutcliffe Model Boats etc.

- The Auction Results contain examples of many other makes.

The future – the launch of a Catalogue Updating Service.
- The new service will take the form of an updating publication and the first edition called the 'Model Price Review 2006' will become available in the autumn of 2006. (for more details see the information on page 66). We believe that the introduction of this updating service will be of greater benefit to catalogue users than any other improvement since the launch of the catalogue in 1983.

Do please advise us of what you would like to see included in the publication.

Based on the findings of the Market Surveys undertaken since 1983 virtually all the models have been given a 'Market Price Range'. The price gap between the lower and higher figures indicates the likely price range a collector should expect to pay for the model.

Models qualifying for a price at the top end of the range could include:

- Boxed models where both the model and the box are in pristine condition,
- A scarce or unusual colour
- An unusual component such as special wheels
- A model with pristine decals where this is unusual
- A model in an unusual or special box
- A model priced by a trader who disagrees with the price range quoted in the Catalogue (which is only a guide).

PRICES FOR MODELS IN LESS THAN MINT BOXED CONDITION

Many boxed models seen for sale fail to match up to the exacting standards on which the Market Price Range has been based, having slight model or box damage. In these instances models may be priced at 50% to 60% of the Market Price Range shown, and this is particularly relevant when a model is common. Boxed models with considerable damage or models lacking their original box will be priced much lower.

Note: It cannot be over-emphasised that irrespective of the price guidance provided by this Catalogue, collectors should not always expect to see prices asked within the price ranges shown. Traders will ask a price based on their trading requirements and will NOT be governed by any figures shown in this Catalogue, nor could they be reasonably expected to do so.

MODELS NOT GIVEN A 'MARKET PRICE RANGE'

It has not been possible to give every model a price range and these exceptions are as follows:

NPP   No Price Possible
This is shown alongside models never encountered in the survey or about which there is doubt as to their actual issue, even though a model may have been pictured in a catalogue. Readers will appreciate that unlike postage stamps or coins, no birth records are available in respect of all the die-cast models designed or issued.

NGPP   No Grading Possible at Present
Price grading may not be possible at present because:
i) The model or gift set is particularly rare and has not come to market in recent times. Consequently, no price grading has

been shown as the Compiler believes that to attempt one would be carrying rarity and value assessment into the realms of pure guesswork. As and when information becomes available concerning these rarities it will be included in the Catalogue.
ii) The model may have been recently introduced or announced in the model press or in a manufacturer's own literature, but a price has not yet been suggested or communicated to us.

GSP   Gift Set Price
If a model forms part of a Set (and is not available separately) the price range will be shown against the entry in the relevant Gift Set section and will refer to the complete set.

DESCRIPTION OF MODEL COLOURS

The descriptions of the various colours used to describe model colour variations have been derived from the following sources:
i)   Manufacturers colour descriptions.
ii) Colours commonly used and known to refer to certain models over a period of many years
iii) Colours which we in consultation with the trade or specialist collectors decide most closely describes a previously unrecorded genuine colour variation
iv) Colours given a model by an bonafide auction house. If this model is a previously unrecorded colour variation we will include the variation in future catalogue listings provided that:
a) The auctioneers are themselves satisfied that the model is genuine and not a repaint
b) Specialist dealers and collectors who view the model are satisfied that the colour variation is genuine and is not a repaint.

SCARCE COLOURS AND VARIATIONS

Collectors or traders who know of other variations which they believe warrant a separate listing are invited to forward this information to the Editor together with any supporting evidence.

AUCTION PRICE REALISATIONS
Prices of common models sold are often less than the Market Price Range figures shown. In many instances, the models have been purchased by the trade who will add their own mark-up.

Classifying the condition of models and boxes

The condition of a model and its accompanying box does of course have a direct bearing on its value which makes accurate condition grading a matter of key importance.

Unlike other collecting hobbies such as stamps or coins, no one universal grading system is used to classify the condition of models and boxes. Nevertheless, whilst several versions exist, there are really two main systems of condition classification in the UK as follows:

1. The 'Specific Condition' Grading System

The following example is fairly typical of the types of descriptions and gradings seen on Mail Order lists.

M.........Mint   AM......Almost Mint
VSC ....Very Slightly Chipped   SC ....Slightly Chipped
C ....Chipped   VC.......Very Chipped

If a model is described as Mint Boxed, the condition of its box is not normally separately described. However, it is expected to be in first class and as near original condition as is possible, bearing in mind the age of the model concerned.

If a box is damaged the flaws are usually separately described. This method has always seemed to work out quite well in practice, for all reputable dealers automatically offer a 'Sale or Return if not satisfied' deal to their clients, which provides the necessary safeguard against the misrepresentation of the model's condition. The Compiler would stress that the foregoing is only an example of a mail order condition grading system and stricter box grading definitions are known to exist.

2. The 'General Condition' Grading System

This method is often used by auctioneers although it is also to be seen used on the occasional mail order list.

(M)   Mint   (E)   Excellent
(G)   Good   (F)   Fair
(P)   Poor

Usually these gradings are separately applied to describe firstly the condition of the model and secondly the condition of the box. From our observations and purely for guidance purposes, we would suggest the following descriptions approximately represent the different grades.

MODEL CONDITION GRADINGS

1. MINT (M)
The model must be complete and as fresh, new and original in appearance as when first received from the manufacturers.

2. EXCELLENT (E)
The model is almost in mint condition and is only barred from that classification by having a few slight flaws, e.g., slight paintwork chipping in unimportant areas.

3. GOOD (G)
The model is in a complete and original condition and retains an overall collectable appearance despite having a few chips or rubbed paintwork.

4. FAIR (F)
The model may not be in its original state having, for example, a broken bumper, replacement radiator or windscreen, or it may have signs of metal fatigue. The paintwork may be faded, well chipped, retouched or repainted. There may be signs of rust. Unless the model is rare it is in a barely collectable condition.

5. POOR (P)
The model may be damaged, incomplete, repainted, altered, metal fatigued, or have a rusted baseplate or heavily chipped paintwork, etc. Unless the model is rare it has little real value to a collector other than as a candidate for a complete restoration or use as spares.

BOX CONDITION GRADINGS

1. MINT (M)
The box must be complete both inside and out and contain all the original packing materials, manufacturer's leaflet and box labels. It should look as fresh, new and original in appearance as when first received from the manufacturers.

2. EXCELLENT (E)
The box is in almost mint condition but is only barred from that classification by just the odd minor blemish, e.g., there may be slight damage to the display labels caused by bad storage. The original shop price label may have been carelessly removed and caused slight damage. The cover of a bubble pack may be cracked or there may be very slight soiling etc.

3. GOOD (G)
The box is complete both inside and out, and retains an overall attractive collectable appearance. Furthermore, despite showing a few signs of wear and tear, it does not appear 'tired'.

4. FAIR (F)
The box will have a 'tired' appearance and show definite signs of wear and tear. It may be incomplete and not contain the original packing materials or leaflets. In addition it may not display all the exterior identification labels or they may be torn or soiled or a box-end flap may be missing or otherwise be slightly damaged. In this condition, unless the model is particularly rare, it will not add much to the model's value.

5. POOR (P)
The box will show considerable signs of wear and tear. It will almost certainly be badly damaged, torn, incomplete or heavily soiled and in this condition, unless it is very rare, is of little value to a collector.

Model and Box Valuation Guidelines

The research has produced the following comparative price information concerning the values of both unboxed models and separate boxes in the various condition classifications.

The guidelines have been based on the 'General Condition' grading system as described in the previous section. The percentage value ranges are designed to reflect the relatively higher values of the rarer models and boxes.

UNBOXED MODEL CLASSIFICATION	% VALUE OF MINT BOXED MODEL
Mint	50% - 60%
Excellent	40% - 50%
Good	20% - 40%
Fair	10% - 20%
Poor	0% - 10%

BOX CLASSIFICATION	%VALUE OF MINT BOXED MODEL
Mint	40% - 50%
Excellent	30% - 40%
Good	20% - 30%
Fair	10% - 20%
Poor	0% - 10%

Note: The same model may have been issued in two or more types of box (Yesteryears for example). The model in the earlier box is usually (though not always) the more valuable.

Rare Models and Sets

The exceptions to the foregoing guidelines are in respect of rare models or boxes, or models seldom found in first class condition such as some pre-war models. In these situations rarity commands a premium and the asking price or the price realised at auction will almost certainly reflect it.

Selling models to the Trade

The model value figures produced by the Price Grading system always refer to the likely *asking prices* for models.

They have been prepared solely to give collectors an idea of the amount they might reasonably expect to pay for a particular model.

The figures given are *not* intended to represent the price which will be placed on a model when it is offered for sale to a dealer. This is hardly surprising bearing in mind that the dealer is carrying all the expense of offering his customers a collecting service which costs money to maintain.

Collectors should not therefore be surprised when selling models to the trade to receive offers which may appear somewhat low in comparison with the figures shown in the Catalogue.

Dealers are always keen to replenish their stocks with quality items and will as a result normally make perfectly fair and reasonable offers for models. Indeed, depending on the particular models offered to them, the actual offer made may well at times exceed the levels indicated in the Catalogue which are only *guidelines* and not firm figures.

One last point when selling models to the trade: do get quotations from two or three dealers, especially if you have rare models to be sold.

How to use the Catalogue

Identifying models from their lettering

All lettering shown in CAPITAL LETTERS indicates the actual lettering on the model itself. It may appear in either the Model Type (vehicle) or Model Features (description) column. Similarly *lettering in Italics* indicates that it is shown on the actual model.

Abbreviations

In this 9th Edition dependence on abbreviations has been reduced to a minimum but where necessary they are used to include information concisely. An Abbreviations list is included (near the back of the book) and provides additional and helpful information.

Catalogue omissions

Accurate birth records do not exist in respect of all the die-cast models issued. Therefore whilst every effort has been made to provide comprehensive information it is inevitable that collectors will have knowledge of models which have not been included. Consequently the Compiler will be pleased to receive details of these models in order that they may be included in future editions. Naturally, supporting evidence regarding authenticity will be required.

This Catalogue has been prepared solely for use as a reference book and guide to the rarity and asking prices of die-cast model toys.

Whilst every care has been taken in compiling the Catalogue, neither the Compiler nor the publishers can accept any responsibility whatsoever for any financial loss which may occur as a result of its use.

If you are really serious about buying or selling toys and trains, there is really only one place to visit . . .

Sandown Park

Europe's No.1 Toy Collectors Fair

Sandown Exhibition Centre, Sandown Park Racecourse, Esher, Surrey

10:30am - 4:00pm

2006 Sandown Dates

Saturday 4th March

Saturday 27th May

Saturday 5th August

Saturday 28th October

(2007 dates available later)

The finest 500 Stalls in Britain

Meet all the country's Top Dealers and Collectors and see the best of everything in Collectable Toys and Trains.

Sandown Park is only 5 miles from Junction 10 of the M25. Parking is available for 6,000 cars. Regular trains run from Waterloo to Esher.

Adults £4-50   Seniors £4-00   Children £2-00

Call us for a free detailed calendar of events on 01604 770025 or 01858 468459

BARRY POTTER
..... *Fairs* .....

Full details also available on our website: www.barrypotterfairs.com

When replying to advertisements, please mention 'John Ramsay's Catalogue'.

11

Guide to Advertisers

'Modern Diecast' information, contacts, collector clubs, etc.

CORGI CLASSICS
United Kingdom
Corgi Collector Club (Susan Pownall)
c/o Corgi Classics Ltd, Meridian East, Meridian
Business Park, Leicester, LE19 1RL
E-mail: micheala.staples@westquay.com

Australia
Corgi Collector Club, Hobbyco Ltd., PO Box Q99,
Queen Victoria Building Post Office, Sydney, NSW
2000.

New Zealand
Corgi Collector Club New Zealand, PO Box 63064,
Papatoetoe South, Auckland, New Zealand.

USA
Corgi Collector Club, c/o Corgi Classics Inc., Suite
205, 430W. Erie Street, Chicgao IL60610.
Canada
Corgi Collector Club, 4461, Highway No.7,
Unionville, Ontario, L3R 1M1.

LLEDO DAYS-GONE and VANGUARDS
Lledo Collectables
PO BOX 4000
Southampton, SO14 0ZR
Tel: 023 8024 8800
E-mail: rachel.wilson@westquay.com
Club website: www.lledodirect.co.uk
Manufacturer's website: www.lledo.com

EXCLUSIVE FIRST EDITIONS
For model information and subscriber service,
please address all correspondence to:
Gilbow (Holdings) Limited, 32 Woodhall Road,
Enfield, EN3 4LG

OXFORD DIE-CAST
Head office: Oxford Diecast Ltd, PO Box 62,
Swansea UK SA1 4YA TEL +44(0)1792 643500
Sales, etc.: 39 Westbury Street, Swansea,
UK SA1 4JW.
Phone : +44 (0) 1792 643500
Website: www.oxforddiecast.co.uk

Your comments are welcome!

The Editors hope that we have made this Catalogue as useful and as informative as is possible for the benefit of all our readers.

We could not have done this without the mass of contributions, information, photographs, etc. from collectors, dealers and toy enthusiasts around the world. Just as important are the suggestions, comments and requests that have been communicated to us. This contact with our readers is essential as it helps us to deliver the kind of Catalogue that our readers really want.

We shall be enhancing our service to collectors with the publication in 2006 of 'Model Price Review'. As we wish to make it particularly useful to Catalogue users, we welcome your suggestions, comments (good AND bad!), along with any new information that you may have. Please tell us what you would like to see, what you don't like, and anything else that you think we should know.

Every letter, note and e-mail will be read and ALL your comments will be thoroughly evaluated for use in Model Price Review 2006 and in future editions of the Catalogue. Please help us to make them the publications that YOU want to read! Write to:

    The Editors, British Diecast,
    Swapmeet Publications,
    22, Foxgrove Lane, Felixstowe, Suffolk, IP11 7JU.
or E-mail: info@swapmeet.co.uk

CALLING ALL DIE CAST MODEL ENTHUSIASTS

THE CORGI COLLECTOR CLUB is a must for all Corgi diecast model enthusiasts. Through the pages of our regular A4, full colour magazine, we bring you news of the latest releases from Corgi, fascinating features and background stories on the vehicles from which they are modelled, competitions, reader offers and much more.

CLUB BENEFITS INCLUDE:

- 10 issues of the Corgi magazine - Corgi Collector - for a year from the date your subscription is processed, with an automatic reminder when you need to renew.
- Free Corgi Collectables Catalogue, issued twice a year.
- A Free annual Limited Edition Corgi Collector Club model - exclusive to Club subscribers - sent to you separately and automatically when available during the year.

- Club membership card giving discount on Corgi purchases at selected Corgi Gold Star stockists.
- Family membership discount - 1 magazine per family - for one additional adult and up to 3 children - all living at the same address.
- Free gifts when you introduce new members.
- Invitations to selected Corgi previews in your area.
- The opportunity to buy Club merchandise and catalogues through the Club.

And especially for 1:76 Original Omnibus Company Bus enthusiasts

- The opportunity to purchase a Limited Edition 1:76 bus. The model is a Limited Edition of 1000 and exclusive to Corgi Collector Club members.
- Free Fleet List keeping

you up-to-date on all OOC models produced by Corgi, past and present.

Aviation Archive Collectors Club

Your annual subscription includes:

- Your membership card, giving you discount from selected Corgi stockists on your Aviation Archive purchases.
- Flight listing of all Aviation archive models produced to date.
- 6 copies of Flight Recorder, the full colour bi-monthly Aviation Archive newsletter.
- A free Aviation Archive catalogue.
- The opportunity to buy the exclusive Limited Edition Aviation Archive Club model, details published in Flight Recorder when available.

CORGI COLLECTOR CLUBS 2006 MEMBERSHIP APPLICATION FORM — CORGI

PLEASE TICK FEE BOX AS APPROPRIATE AND COMPLETE IN **BLOCK CAPITALS**

2006 CLUB FEES (Membership fee per year)

Please enrol me to the **Corgi Collector Club**

UK £21 ☐   Europe £23 ☐   Rest of world £25 ☐

Please enrol family members in addition to myself
Number of additional applicants: ☐

Family Membership per person (other than principal applicant)*
* Family membership is for Corgi Collector Club applications only

UK £3 ☐   Europe £4 ☐   Rest of world £5 ☐

Please enrol me to the Aviation Archive Club

UK £11 ☐   Europe £12 ☐   Rest of world £13 ☐

TOTAL £ (UK):	TOTAL £ (EUROPE):	TOTAL £ (REST OF WORLD):

Please allow 28 days from receipt of application for processing. Fees reflect postage by Air Mail for overseas members.

Occasionally, we may make our mailing list available to other Corgi Classic departments, whose products and services may be of interest to you. If you prefer not to receive such mailings, please tick this box ☐

Name: _____ Age: _____

Address: _____

_____

Postcode: _____ Country: _____

Daytime tel: _____ Evening tel: _____

E.mail: _____

Current Club Membership No. (if applicable) _____

If introduced by an existing fully paid up Corgi Collector Club member, please give:
Name: _____

Membership No.: _____
In the case of a family membership application*
(max 4 persons - 1 additional adult, other than full fee applicant and up to 3 children under 14 years of age) please give name of additional applicant(s):

1: _____ Age: _____
2: _____ Age: _____
3: _____ Age: _____
4: _____ Age: _____

PAYMENT DETAILS

I ENCLOSE PAYMENT AS FOLLOWS:

Membership Fees   Total £: _____

Payment Method (please tick relevant box)

Cheque ☐   Postal Order ☐   International Giro ☐

Cheques must be drawn on a British Bank and made payable to CORGI COLLECTOR CLUB

OR please debit my credit/debit card

Visa ☐   Mastercard ☐   Switch/Maestro ☐

for the sum of £: _____

Card No.: ☐☐☐☐ ☐☐☐☐ ☐☐☐☐ ☐☐☐☐

Valid From: ☐☐ ☐☐   Security No.: ☐☐☐

Expiry Date: ☐☐ ☐☐   Switch Issue No.: _____

Signature: _____

Date: _____

Membership valid for 12 months from the date of processing application. Please ensure your address details are complete above and return application form to **Corgi Collector Club, c/o Corgi Classics Ltd., Meridian East, Meridian Business Park, Leicester LE19 1RL. UK.**

Abbreviations

A

A.E.C.	Associated Equipment Company
AA	Anti-aircraft
A.A.	Automobile Association
ABC-TV	Associated British Cinemas (Television)
A.F.S.	Auxiliary Fire Service
AG	Amber glass
AMC	American Motor Corporation
APC	Armoured Personnel Carrier
ATV	Associated Television

B

BA	British Airways
BAC	British Airways Corporation
BB	Black base
BBC	British Broadcasting Corporation
BEA	British European Airways
BG	Blue glass
bhp	brake horsepower
BLMC	British Leyland Motor Corporation
BMC	British Motor Corporation
BMW	Bayrische Motoren-Werke
B.O.A.C.	British Overseas Airways
BP	British Petroleum
BPT	Black plastic tyres
BPW	Black plastic wheels
BR	British Railways
BRM	British Racing Motors
BRS	British Road Services
B.S.M.	British School of Motoring
BWW	Black WhizzWheels

C

CG	Clear glass
CLE	Certificated Limited Edition
cv	chevaux-vapeur (a measure of power; translated into English, it literally means 'horse-steams')
C.W.S.	Co-operative Wholesale Society
cwt.	hundred-weight
CWW	Chrome WhizzWheels

D

DCMT	Die Casting Machine Tools
DH	De Havilland
Dk.	Dark (shade of colour)
DUKW	An amphibious military vehicle developed by General Motors in WWII. The letters are not initials or an abbreviation but simply part of an early drawing office reference.

E

EEC	European Economic Community
e.g.	exempli gratia (= 'for example')
EMI	Electrical & Musical Industries
ER	Elizabetha Regina, (E II R, Queen Elizabeth II)
ERF	Edwin Richard Foden
Est.	Established (or estimate/d)

F

Fiat	(or FIAT) Fabbrica Italiana Automobile Torino
fig(s)	figure(s)

G

GB	Green box, or Grey base
G.B.	Great Britain
GER	Great Eastern Railway
GG	Green glass
GMC	General Motors Corporation
GP	Grand Prix
GPO	General Post Office
GPW	Grey plastic wheels
GR	Georgius Rex
GS	Gift Set
GSP	Gift Set price
GTO	Gran Turismo Omologato
GTV	Gran Turismo Veloce
GWR	Great Western Railway

H

HM	His/Her Majesty
HMS	His/Her Majesty's Ship
H.M.V.	'His Masters Voice'
hp	horse-power
H.W.M.	Hersham & Walton Motors

I

ICI	Imperial Chemical Industries
INTER	(or INTL) International
I.O.M.	Isle of Man

J

JB	James Bond
JCB	Joseph C. Bamford

K

K.D.F.	Kraft durch Freude
K.L.G.	Kenelm Lee Guinness
K.L.M.	Koninklijke Luchtvaart Maatschappij NV (Dutch airline)

L

L.A.P.D.	Los Angeles Police Department
LE	Limited Edition
LM	Le Mans
LMS	London Midland & Scottish Railway
LNER	London & North Eastern Railway
LNWR	London & North Western Railway
Lt.	Light (shade of colour)
Ltd.	Limited Liability Company
LWB	Long wheel-base

M

MB	Matchbox
Met.	Metallic
MG	Make of car, ('Morris Garages')
M.I.C.A.	Matchbox International Collectors Association
mm.	millimetres
MOY	Models of Yesteryear
MPR	Market Price Range
MW	Metal wheels

N

N	North
NAAFI	Navy, Army & Air Force Institutes
N.A.S.A.	National Aeronautics & Space Administration
NB	nota bene ('mark well')
NCO	Non-Commissioned Officer
NGPP	No guide price at present
nhp	(or n.h.p.) nominal horsepower
No.	Number
NPP	No price possible
NS	(or n/s) Nearside

O

OG	Orange glass
OS	(or o/s) Offside

P

PB	Propeller blade(s)
PG	Purple glass
P.I.	Private Investigator
PLC	Public Limited Company
PO	Post Office
PP	Packing piece(s), or plated parts
PSV	Public service vehicle
P.T.T.	Postes-Telephones-Telegraphes

R

RAC	Royal Automobile Club
RAF	Royal Air Force
R.C.M.P.	Royal Canadian Mounted Police
RHD	Right-hand drive
RM	Routemaster (bus)
RN(s)	Racing or Rally number(s)
RNLI	Royal National Life-boat Institution

S

S	South
SB	Silver base
SBRW	Solid black rubber wheels
SBX	Special box
SPW	Silver plastic wheels
SR	Southern Railway
St.	Saint or Street
SWB	Short wheel-base
SWRW	Solid white rubber wheels

T

TC	Twin carburettors
TDF	Tour de France
TK	Type of Bedford truck
TP	Twin Pack
TS	'Touring Secours'
TT	Two-tone (or Tourist Trophy)
TV	Television

U

UB	Unboxed, or Unpainted base
UK	United Kingdom
UN	United Nations
US	United States (of America)
USA	United States of America
USAAF	United States Army Air Force
USAF	United States Air Force
USS	United Space Starship
UW	Unpainted wheels

V

VW	Volkswagen

W

W	West
WB	Window box, or White base
WW	Wide wheels

Y

YB	Yellow box, or Yellow base
YMCA	Young Men's Christian Association

Official Company Acknowledgements

The names 'CORGI TOYS', 'CARS OF THE '50s', 'CORGITRONICS', 'CORGIMATICS', 'HUSKY', 'JUNIORS' and 'ROCKETS' are all acknowledged as trademarks of Corgi Classics Ltd.
'BRITAINS' is acknowledged as the trademark of Britains Ltd.
The name 'TRI-ANG' is acknowledged as a trademark of Hornby Hobbies Ltd., Margate, Kent.
The names 'MATCHBOX', 'MODELS of YESTERYEAR', 'DINKY TOYS' and 'SUPERFAST' are acknowledged as trademarks of Mattel Inc. USA.
The name 'MECCANO' is acknowledged as the trademark of MECCANO S.N., 73, rue Henri Barbusse, 92586 Clichy Cedex, France

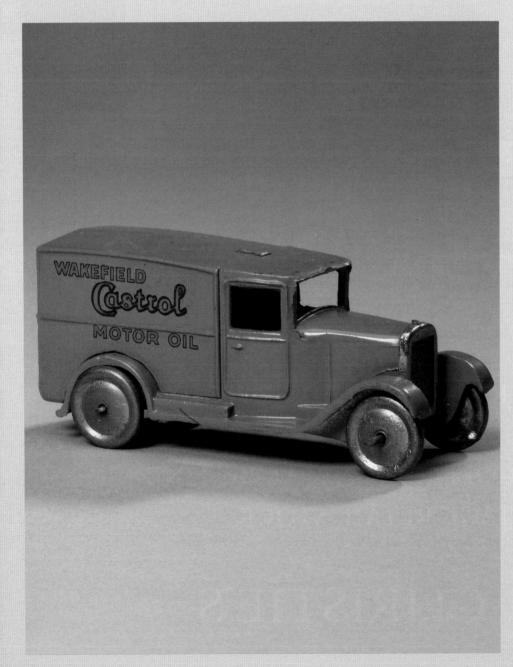

Dinky Toys Delivery Vans

22c Delivery Van
(no advertising)
1934 - 35

28c Delivery Van
'The Manchester Guardian'
Type 1, 1934 - 35

28d Delivery Van
'Oxo'
Type 1, 1934 - 35

28e Delivery Van
'Ensign Cameras'
Type 1, 1934 - 35

28e Delivery Van
'Firestone Tyres'
Type 1, 1934 - 35

28f Delivery Van
'Palethorpe's Sausages'
Type 1, 1934 - 35

28g Delivery Van
'Kodak Film'
Type 1, 1934 - 35

28b Delivery Van
'Pickfords Removals'
Type 1, 1934 - 35

28n Delivery Van
'Meccano'
Type 1, 1934 - 35

28L Delivery Van
'Crawford's Biscuits'
Type 1, 1934 - 35

28m Delivery Van
'Wakefield Castrol'
Type 1, 1934 - 35

28h Delivery Van
'Sharp's Toffee'
Type 1, 1934 - 35

Models shown above were sold by Christie's of South Kensington, London. Pictures reproduced by their kind permission.

Dinky Toys (pre-war)

22f Army Tank
1933 - 40

22e Farm Tractor
and Trade Box 'A966B'
1933 - 40

22g Streamlined Tourer
1935 - 41

24h Sports Tourer Two-Seater
1934 - 40

31 'Holland Coachcraft' Van
1935 - 36

24a Ambulance
1934 - 40

24e Super Streamlined Saloon
1934 - 40

22b Sports Coupé
1933 - 35

36b Bentley Two-seat Sports Coupé
with Driver and Footman
1937 - 41

23a Racing Car
1935 - 41

23a Racing Car
1935 - 41

23s Streamlined Racing Car
1938 - 40

Models sold by Christie's of South Kensington, London. Pictures reproduced by their kind permission.

Dinky Toys (post-war)

23b Hotchkiss Racing Cars
1946 - 48

30b Rolls-Royce
1946 - 50

30f Ambulance
1946 - 48

36f British Salmson
Four-seater Sports Car
1947 - 50

38f Jaguar SS100 Sports Car
1947 - 50

39c Lincoln Zephyr Coupé
1947 - 50

39cu Lincoln Zephyr Coupé
US issue 1950 - 52

39eu Chrysler Royal Sedan
US issue 1950 - 52

39eu Chrysler Royal Sedan
US issue 1950 - 52

101 Sunbeam Alpine Sports
1957 - 60

102 M.G. Midget Sports
1957 - 60

105 Triumph TR2 Sports
1957 - 60

Set 24 'Motor Cars', 1934 - 40

Trade box of 29a 'Marmite' Motor Buses, 1934 - 38

No. 4 Engineering Staff, 1932 - 39

62t (60v box) Armstrong-Whitworth Whitley Bomber, 1939 - 41

60t Douglas DC3 Air Liner, 1938 - 41

67a Junkers Ju89 Heavy Bomber, 1940 - 41

Dinky Toys

651 Centurion Tank (1954 - 70) in 1970 'window' box

The models shown on thses two pages were sold by Vectis Auctions Ltd, Thornaby, Stockton-on-Tees, TS17 9JZ. Pictures reproduced by their kind permission.

Left: 'Dolly Varden' Dolls House, 1935 - 40

Top row: 169 Studebaker Golden Hawk, 191 Dodge Royal, 105 Triumph TR2, 161 Austin Somerset
482 Bedford Van 'Dinky Toys', 465 Morris Van 'Capstan', 443 Tanker 'National Benzole', 455 Trojan Van 'Brooke Bond'
Bottom row: 504 Foden 14 ton Tanker, 905 Foden Flat Truck

Dinky Toys

923 Big Bedford Van 'Heinz'
1955 - 58

920 Guy Warrior Van 'Heinz'
1960 - 61

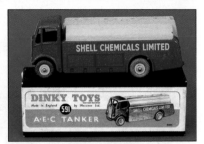

991 AEC Tanker
'Shell Chemicals Limited' 1954 - 55

482 Bedford 10cwt Van 'Dinky Toys'
1956 - 60

934 Leyland Octopus Wagon
1958 - 63

941 Foden 14 ton Tanker
1956

Top (all pre-war): 29c Double Deck Buses, 25f Market Gardener's Lorry, 36g Taxi, 33r 'GWR' Mechanical Horse and Trailer
2nd row (post-war): 230 Talbot-Lago, 193 Rambler, 555 Ford Thunderbird, 107 Sunbeam Alpine, 172 Studebaker Land Cruiser
3rd row: 413 Austin Wagon, 482 Bedford Van, 472 Austin A40 Van, 465 Morris Van, 492 Loudspeaker Van, 343 Farm Wagon
Bottom row: 914 AEC Articulated Lorry,   960 Lorry Mounted Cement Mixer,   942 Foden 14 ton Tanker 'Regent'

COLLECTOYS
International Antique Toy Auctions

The G. DULIN Collection of DINKY TOYS

Sales 22 October, 19 November & 16-17 December 2005

Each deluxe detailed catalogue including over 900 colour photos :
20€+6€ postage within Europe – Christmas double catalogue @ 30€+9€ VISA/MASTERCARD payment accepted

Absentee bids (Fax or E-Mail) or Telephone bids welcome

English & Italian Spoken

Where can you find the rarest English Dinky Toys?...

French Dinky Toys

22a Sports Roadster, 1933 - 37

22b Sports Coupé, 1934 - 37

22d Sports Coupé, 1934 - 37

23b Hotchkiss Racing Car, 1950 - 51

24h Two-seat Sports Car, 1936 - 37

24f Sportsman's Coupé, 1940 - 48

24N Citroën 11BL, 1958

24T Citroën 2cv, 1955 - 59

24S Simca 8 Sport, 1952 - 54

24U Simca 9 Aronde Elysée
1958 - 59

24UT Simca 9 Aronde Elysée Taxi
1956 - 58

24ZT Simca Ariane Taxi
1959

23H Talbot-Lago Racing Cars
with Trade Box, 1953 - 54

24Z Simca Vedette Versailles
1959

24V Buick Roadmaster
1956 - 59

French Dinky Toys

1406 Renault 4L Sinpar
'Michel Tanguy', 1968 - 71

24Y Studebaker Commander Coupé
1955 - 59

503 Touring Cars Gift Set
1963 - 64

1404 Citroén ID19
'Radio Tele Luxembourg' 1968 - 69

518 Renault 4L 'Pompiers de Paris'
1964

525 Peugeot 404 'Pompiers de Paris'
1964

14 Triporteur
1935 - 39

524 Renault Dauphine
with Trade Box, 1959 - 60

561 Citroën 'H' Van
'Baroclem' (promotional), 1964

The models shown above and on the opposite page were sold by Christie's of South Kensington, London.

510 Peugeot 204
Spanish production, 1977 - 78

559 Ford Taunus 17M
Spanish production, 1968 - 69

560E Citroën 2cv Azam Van
Spanish production, 1968 - 70

The three Spanish models shown above were sold by Collectoys, Hotel Frank Hornby, Bourges, France.

French Dinky Toys

1435E Citroën Présidentielle
in special presentation box, 1971

25-O Ford Milk Lorry 'Nestlés'
1950

588 Berliet Beer Lorry,
'Kronenbourg', 1964 - 70

24-56 'Tourisme' Gift Set, 1956

24-58 'Tourisme' Gift Set, 1958

1460 'Tourisme' Gift Set, 1968

No. 60 'Avions' Gift Set, 1937 - 40

Models shown on this page were sold by Collectoys, Hotel Frank Hornby, Place George Sand, Bourges, France.

Corgi Toys

'Jensen's' promotional Minis
225 Austin and 226 Morris

Corgi Toys Tractors 54, 50, 60 and 66 sold by Lacy Scott & Knight, Bury St Edmunds.

Early Mettoy version of 455
Karrier Bantam 'CWS' Lorry

8003 'Spindrift' Set for
Marks & Spencer, 1979

'Chipperfields' Gift Set 23, 1962 - 66

333 'R.A.C. International Rally'
Mini-Cooper 'S', 1966

453 Commer Refrigerated
Van 'Wall's', 1956 - 60

652 'Japan Airlines' Concorde
1973 - 81

468 'Red Rose Coffee'
Routemaster Bus, 1966

Corgi Toys

Gift Set 48 'Car Transporter with 6 Cars', 1969

Gift Set 12 'Grand Prix Racing Set', 1968 - 72

Models shown above and on the opposite page were sold by Vectis Model Auctions.

Corgi Toys Gift Sets 15 and 25 sold by Wallis & Wallis, Lewes, Sussex

Corgi Toys

203 Vauxhall Velox
1956 - 61

201M (motorised) Austin Cambridge
1956 - 59

202M (motorised) Morris Cowley
1956 - 59

200 Ford Consul
1956 - 61

206 Hillman Husky
1956 - 61

211S Studebaker Golden Hawk
1960 - 65

436 Citroën ID19 Safari
1963 - 65

319 Lotus Elan Coupé
1967 - 69

240 Fiat Jolly
1963 - 64

485 Mini Countryman with Surfer
1965 - 69

A selection of Corgi Toys Racing Cars
from the mid-1960s to early 1970s

1127 Bedford 'Simon Snorkel'
Fire Engine, 1967 - 69

Models shown above and on the opposite page were sold by Vectis Model Auctions.

447 'Wall's Ice Cream' Van
(Ford Thames), 1965 - 66

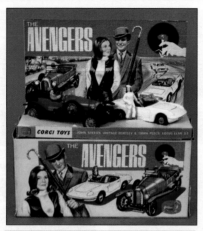

Gift Set 40 'The Avengers'
1966 - 69

Gift Set 14 'Daktari'
1969 - 73

'James Bond' Gift Set 22, 1980 - 82

'James Bond' Lotus Esprit
No. 269, 1977 - 83

'James Bond' Corgi Juniors
Nos. 40, 41, 60 and 73, late 1970s

422 Bedford 12cwt Van 'Corgi Toys'
1960 - 62

'James Bond' Corgi Juniors
No. 40 Aston-Martin, 1979 - 81

'James Bond' Aston-Martin DB5
No. 261, 1965 - 69

Corgi Toys

Gift Set 16 'Ecurie Ecosse' Racing Car Transporter
with three racing cars, 1961 - 65

497 'The Man from UNCLE' 'Thrushbuster'
1966 - 69

Top row: 339 Rally Mini, 205M Riley Pathfinder, 325 Ford Mustang, 475 Citroën Safari
Middle row: 403 Bedford Van 'Daily Express', 408 Bedford Van 'AA', 450 Austin Mini-van, 447 'Wall's Ice Cream' Van
Bottom row: 411 Karrier Bantam 'Lucozade' Van, 455 Karrier Bantam 2-tonner, 1133 Troop Transporter

Models sold by Vectis Auctions Ltd, Thornaby, Stockton-on-Tees, TS17 9JZ. Pictures reproduced by their kind permission.

37

Moko, Lesney and Matchbox Toys

Top: Moko Ruston-Bucyrus Excavator, Moko Excavator with Bucket Shovel and Moko Bulldozer.
Lower group: Lesney Massey-Harris Tractor, Lesney Prime Mover with Bulldozer on Trailer,
Moko 'Pop-Pop' Scooter and Moko Builders Crane.

MF1 Fire Station, 1963

No.11a E.R.F. Road Tanker, 1955

G-2 Transporter Set, 1965

No.46a Morris Minor 1000, 1958

No.5c Double Deck Bus, 1960
No.56a London Trolleybus, 1958

No.27c Cadillac Sixty Special, 1960

Models sold by Vectis Auctions Ltd, Thornaby, Stockton-on-Tees, TS17 9JZ. Pictures reproduced by their kind permission.

Matchbox Counter Display Unit complete with the full early '1-75' range of Matchbox models.

Photo:
Vectis Auctions Ltd.

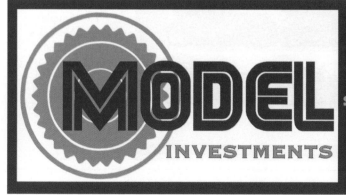

Matchbox 1-75s and 'Models of Yesteryear'

Two selections of late 1960s Lesney Matchbox models in the 1-75 Series.

Matchbox
'Models of Yesteryear'
Counter Display Unit
complete with:

Y1-3 Ford Model 'T'
Y2-2 Renault
Y3-2 Benz
Y4-3 Opel
Y5-2 Bentley
Y6-2 Bugatti
Y7-2 Mercer
Y8-2 Sunbeam
Y9-2 Simplex
Y10-2 Mercedes
Y11-2 Packard
Y12-2 Thomas
Y13-2 Daimler
Y14-2 Maxwell
Y15-1 Rolls-Royce
Y16-1 Spyker

Models sold by Vectis Auctions Ltd, Thornaby, Stockton-on-Tees, TS17 9JZ.

Lone Star, Chad Valley, Scalextric, Ranlite, Crescent

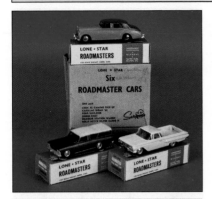

Lone Star Roadmaster Trade Box

Lone Star 'Gulliver County' Buses

'Chad Valley' Guy Van

Early (tinplate) Scalextric Cars

Ranlite Singer Saloon

Crescent Mercedes and Gordini

The models shown above were sold by Vectis Auctions Ltd, Thornaby, Stockton-on-Tees, TS17 9JZ.
The models shown below were sold by Lacy Scott & Knight, Bury St Edmunds, Suffolk.

Top row: Charbens Covered Wagons. Middle row: Britains Milk Cart, American Civil War Gun and Farmer's Gig.
Bottom row: Tri-ang Minic Ship, DCMT Cinderella's Coach, Morestone Stage Coach.

Britains

128F Fordson Tractor (rubber tyres)

2024 Light Goods Van with Driver

127F Fordson Tractor (spade wheels)

101v Petrol Pump and Oil Bin Set

1313 Volunteer Corps Ambulance

Motorcycle Dispatch Riders Set

Scamold, Johilco, Tri-ang Spot-On

Top row: Scamold 101 ERA, Scamold 103 Maserati, Johilco Land Speed Record Car
Middle row: Tri-ang Spot-On 100 Ford Zephyr, 217 Jaguar E-type, 271 'Express Dairies' Milk Float, 101 Armstrong-Siddeley
Bottom row: Tri-ang Spot-On 'Cotswold Village' Cottage, 156 Mulliner Luxury Coach

Morestone, Sundaw, Benbros, Barrett, Victory

Morestone Land Rovers
'Military Police' and 'Breakdown Unit'

Sundaw H131 Motorbus
'Transport Services'

Morestone Foden Petrol Tanker
'Esso'

Barrett Trolleybus

Victory Industries MG 'TF'

Benbros Qualitoys Articulated
Pantechnicon 'United Dairies'

The models shown above were sold by Vectis Model Auctions.

Meccano

No. 1 Outfit (blue/gold) plus lid for a Connecting Outfit

Early 'alphabetic' referenced Accessory Outfits

Meccano 'cat's whisker' Radio Reciving Set

An early 'starter' outfit, No. OOO (red/green)

Non-constructional Two-seater
Sports Car (clockwork)

Non-constructional Two-seater
Sports Car (clockwork)

Non-constructional Two-seater
Sports Car (clockwork)

Motor Car Model No.2 (Saloon/Coupé)

Motor Car Lighting Set for use with
Motor Car Construction Outfit No.2

No.O1P
Aeroplane
Hangar
Outfit

Pilots for
Aeroplane
Constructor
Outfits

Meccano

Motor Car Constructor Outfit No. 1

Motor Car Constructor Outfit No. 1

Outfit No. 1 as sold in France

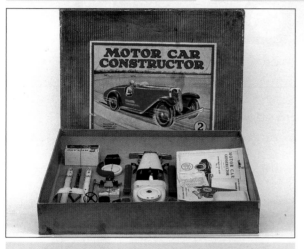

Motor Car Constructor Outfit No. 2

Aeroplane Constructor Outfit No. O

Aeroplane Constructor Outfit No. 2

'Tri-motor Bi-plane' built with Outfit No. 2

30M 'Minic Transport' Mechanical Horse and two-axle Pantechnicon

113M Caravan and Limousine Set, comprising 19M Vauxhall Cabriolet and 16M (non-electric) Caravan

Tri-ang Minic Tinplate Toys

39M London Taxi

(This model is sometimes seen with the reference 35M).

24M 'Minic Transport' Luton Van

49ME Searchlight Lorry with Electric Searchlight

21M 'Minic Transport' Van

21M 'Carter Paterson' Van

Models sold by Vectis Auctions Ltd, Thornaby, Stockton-on-Tees, TS17 9JZ. Pictures reproduced by their kind permission.

Hornby Speed Boats

Hornby Speed Boats
Top: No. 2 'Condor'   Left: No.1 'Hawk'   Right: 'Hornby Water Toy (Duck)'

Sutcliffe Model Boats

Sutcliffe Model Submarines
Left: 'Sea Wolf'   Right: 'Unda-Wunda'

Models sold by Vectis Auctions Ltd, Thornaby, Stockton-on-Tees, TS17 9JZ. Pictures reproduced by their kind permission.

Benbros and Zebra Toys

The following history and listings of Benbros and Zebra models have been provided by Robert Newson.

Benbros was started in the late 1940s by brothers Jack and Nathan Benenson, at Walthamstow in north-east London. They first called themselves 'Benson Bros.' and made diecast toys and lead figures (some of which are marked 'Benson'). The name Benbros was adopted in 1951. One of their best known die-cast toys was a miniature coronation coach, copied from the Moko-Lesney coach. Their range of large die-cast toys was expanded during the 1950s with re-issues of various Timpo Toys, for which Benbros had acquired the dies. The miniature

'T.V. Series' was introduced in late 1954, packed in individual boxes which resembled a 1950s television set. By 1956 there were 24 models in the T.V. Series, and soon after this the packaging was changed to red and yellow 'Mighty Midget' boxes. The Mighty Midgets were available up to 1965.

The Zebra Series was introduced in the 1960s in an attempt to update the range with better features and more accurate models. However, toy production was discontinued when Benbros was taken over in 1965.

NB See the 'Miscellaneous Models' colour section for additional pictures.

Benbros 'AA' Land-Rover,   **Benbros** 'AA' Motor Cycle Patrol,   **Zebra Toys** No.6 'AA' Triumph Motor Cycle and Sidecar

Benbros 'Mighty Midgets' ('Qualitoys' Series) 36 'ROYAL MAIL' Land-Rover, 13 Austin Champ, 30 AEC Army Box Van

Photographs: Vectis Auctions Ltd.

Benbros 'T.V. Series' and 'Mighty Midgets'

Most models came in a wide range of colours, so these have not been listed in the main, but full details of colours and other variations are given in the illustrated booklet 'Benbros T.V. Series & Mighty Midgets' by Robert Newson.

Ref	Model name	Colours, features, details	Price
1	Horse Drawn Hay Cart	With man and raves. Later models marked 'BENBROS'	£30-40
2	Horse Drawn Log Cart	With man and 'log', 'Made in England' under horse	£30-40
3	A.A. Motorcycle and Sidecar	With rider and separate windscreen. 'Made in England' under sidecar	£50-60
4	Stage Coach (with four horses)	'KANSAS STAGE' cast in, separate driver on some, 'BENBROS' on later models	£50-60
5	Horse Drawn Gipsy Caravan	No maker's name on model	£100-150
6	Horse Drawn Milk Cart	Milkman and horse, two separate or cast-in churns, 'BENBROS' on later models	£60-80
7	Three-wheeled Electric Milk Trolley	With milkman, 'EXPRESS DAIRY' cast in	£60-80
8	Foden Tractor and Log Trailer	With log (wood dowel)	£60-80
9	Dennis Fire Escape	Separate wheeled escape ladder	£30-40
10	Crawler Bulldozer	with rubber tracks	£20-30
11	Crawler Tractor with Hay Rake	Rubber tracks. Same basic casting as no. 10. No maker's name on model	£20-30
12	Army Scout Car	Separate or cast-in driver	£20-30
13	Austin Champ	Separate or cast-in driver	£20-30
14	Centurion Tank	with rubber tracks	£20-30
15	Vespa Scooter	With rider	£40-50
16	Streamlined Express Loco	('TV Series' only). Runs on four concealed wheels	£20-35
16	Chevrolet Nomad Station Wagon	('Mighty Midget' only). Most models have silver painted flash	£20-35
17	Crawler Tractor with Disc Harrow	Rubber tracks. Same tractor as no. 11. No maker's name on model	£20-30
18	Hudson Tourer	Same chassis as no. 16	£20-30
19	Crawler Tractor and Trailer	Rubber tracks. Same tractor as nos. 11 and 17. No maker's name on model	£20-30
20	Foden 8-wheel Flat Lorry	Early models in two-tone colours	£60-80
21	Foden 8-wheel Open Lorry	Early models in two-tone colours	£60-80
22	ERF Petrol Tanker	Similar to Matchbox 11a. No adverts or with 'Esso' transfer on one side	£60-80
23	AEC Box Van	No transfers. Open rear end	£50-60
23	Bedford Box Van	Without adverts or with 'Dunlop' transfers. Open rear end	£50-60
24	Field Gun	Solid wheels. No maker's name on model. Working firing mechanism	£15-25
25	Spyker	Similar to Charbens no. 2. Both models are marked with the maker's name	£20-30
26	1904 Vauxhall 5 hp	Same chassis as no.25. Colours observed: Silver or Yellow body, both with Black chassis; Red wheels	£20-30
27	1906 Rolls-Royce	Same chassis as no.25. Colours observed: Silver or Blue body, both with Black chassis; Red wheels	£20-30
28	Foden 8-wheel Flat Lorry with Chains	'Chains' are cast with the body; wheels may be unpainted metal or Black plastic	£70-90
29	RAC Motorcycle and Sidecar	Blue rider, separate windscreen and sidecar. 'Made in England' under sidecar, 'RAC' cast on front	£40-50
30	AEC Army Box Van	Same casting as no. 23 in Military Green paint; wheels may be painted or unpainted	£50-60
30	Bedford Army Box Van	Same casting as no. 23 in Military Green paint with red/yellow squadron transfer; wheels unpainted	£50-60
31	AEC Covered Lorry	Cast metal 'canvas' tilt, riveted in place. Colours seen: Red, Green, Metallic Blue, unpainted wheels	£50-60
31	Bedford Covered Lorry	Cast 'canvas' tilt, riveted in place. Colours seen: Red, Blue, Metallic Blue, unpainted wheels	£50-60
32	AEC Compressor Lorry	Body usually painted Yellow with unpainted metal wheels	£50-60
32	Bedford Compressor Lorry	Body usually painted Yellow with unpainted metal wheels	£50-60
33	AEC Crane Lorry	No hook cast. Colours seen: Orange, Metallic Brown, Metallic Blue, Metallic Green	£50-60
33	Bedford Crane Lorry	No hook. Colours (unpainted wheels): Green, Beige, Orange. With plastic wheels: Red, Yellow, Cream	£50-60
34	A.A. Land Rover	'AA ROAD SERVICE' cast in, open rear end. Bright or Dark Yellow; wheels may be painted or not	£50-60
35	Army Land Rover	Military-Green body and wheels (usually), open rear end, red/yellow squadron transfer on some	£50-60
36	Royal Mail Land Rover	Red body and wheels (usually), 'ROYAL MAIL E-II-R' cast in, open rear end	£50-60
37	Wolseley Six-Eighty Police Car	Black body, unpainted wheels, loud-hailers cast into roof. A little smaller than Budgie no. 5	£50-60
38	Daimler Ambulance	Similar to Matchbox 14b. Off-White (civilian) and Matt or Gloss Dark Green (military) versions	£50-60
39	Bedford Milk Float	Similar to Matchbox 29a. Orange or Red body, White crates. Wheels: White metal or Black plastic	£50-60
40	American Ford Convertible	Early issues: Light Blue or Red body with press-fit base, unpainted metal wheels	£50-60
		Later issues: Blue, Green or Silver body with rivetted base, Black plastic wheels	£50-60
41	Army Hudson Tourer	No. 18 in Military-Green, squadron transfer on some, unpainted metal wheels or Black plastic wheels	£50-60
42	Army Dispatch Motorcycle and Sidecar	Castings as nos. 3 and 29, 'Made in England' and 'AA' or 'RAC' cast on sidecar	£50-60
43-48	Bedford Articulated vehicles	Early issue tractor units are usually seen in Red, Orange or Yellow and have unpainted metal wheels. Later issue tractor units are usually seen in Blue, Beige, Green, Red or Yellow with Black plastic wheels.	
43	Bedford Articulated Box Van	Trailer colours seen: Yellow, Blue, Beige. 'Dunlop' transfers on some	£50-60
44	Bedford Articulated Crane Lorry	Yellow or Light Blue trailer with Silver plastic wheels; or Red or Cream trailer with Black plastic wheels	£50-60
	NB	The box for this model is marked 'Articulated Low Loader' and has an illustration showing such a vehicle carrying a load of wooden planks. The illustrated version was not put into production.	
45	Bedford Articulated Timber Lorry	With 'log' (wood dowel); various trailer colours, unpainted metal wheels or Black or Silver plastic wheels	£50-60
46	Bedford Articulated Petrol Tanker	Various shades of Red possible, without adverts or with 'Esso' transfer on one side only	£50-60
47	Bedford Articulated Dropside Lorry	Box description: 'Articulated Waggon'. Red, Blue or Light Blue trailer, metal or Black plastic wheels	£50-60
48	Bedford Articulated Lorry with Chains	'Chains' are cast with the model. Red, Blue or Beige trailer, Silver trim on some, Black plastic wheels	£50-60
49	Karrier Bantam Bottle Lorry	Similar to Matchbox 37a. 'Drink Coca-Cola' transfers. No maker's name, Black plastic wheels	£50-60
50	RAC Land Rover	Blue body, 'RAC ROAD SERVICE' cast in, open rear	NGPP

Benbros 'Zebra Toys'

Zebra Toys were introduced in the early 1960s and were manufactured along with the existing production of large scale Benbros vehicles. Zebra Toys were packaged in distinctive black and white striped boxes. Most of the models had jewelled headlights and some also had windows and plastic interiors.

The AA and RAC Mini Vans apparently had not been introduced when toy production by Benbros came to an end in 1965. They do not appear on a trade price list dated January 1965 but a small number of these models (probably a

trial run) were sold off with the remaining toy stocks and are now in the hands of collectors.

In the following list, numbers in brackets are those shown on Zebra boxes. The other numbers are cast on the models themselves. There seems to be no connection between the two numbering systems! Original retail prices (quoted in shillings and pre-decimal pence) are those given in 1964 and 1965 trade price lists. These models are rare in today's market.

Ref	Year(s)	Model name	Colours, features, details	Market Price Range
100 (16)		Foden Concrete Mixer	Red cab and chassis, Beige or Yellow barrel, 70 mm. (3s 1d)	£70-90
101 (36)		Scammell Scarab Articulated Van 'BRITISH RAILWAYS'	Maroon cab and trailer, Pale Orange or Mustard-Yellow tilt, 105 mm. (4s. 4d.)	£70-90
103 (10)		Jaguar 'E'-type	Metallic Light Green, Metallic Light Blue or Metallic Light Brown, 90 mm. (3s 0d)	£75-100
104 (30)		Routemaster Bus	Red, *Fina Petrol goes a long way* adverts, 111 mm. (4s. 11d.)	£60-80
106 (34)		Heinkel Bubble Car	Red or Blue body, 100 mm. (4s 4d)	£75-100
107 (27)		Daimler Ambulance	Cream body, 101 mm. (4s 1d)	£75-100
---	(20)	Bedford Cattle Transporter	Red cab and chassis, Light Brown body, 101 mm. (4s. 4d.)	£70-90
---		Lansing Bagnall Rapide 2000	Fork Lift Truck, Red body, 89 mm. (3s. 6d.)	£70-90
---		Field Gun	Dark Green, 'BENBROS' cast on model, 102 mm. (2s. 0d.)	£15-20
---	(1)	Police Patrol Motorcycle	(Triumph) 'Silver' plated, plastic rider, 'ENT 303' cast, 84 mm. (2s. 6d.)	£45-55
---		Rally Motorcycle	(Triumph) 'Silver' plated, plastic rider, 'ENT 303' cast, 84 mm. (2s. 6d.)	£45-55
---	(3)	Army Despatch Motorcycle	(Triumph) 'Silver' plated, plastic rider, 'ENT 303' cast, 84 mm. (2s. 6d.)	£45-55
---	(4)	Telegraph Boy Motorcycle	(Triumph) 'Silver' plated, plastic rider, 'ENT 303' cast, 84 mm. (2s. 6d.)	£45-55
---		'RAC' Triumph Motorcycle and Sidecar	Black bike, Blue sidecar, White fairing, plastic rider, 'ENT 303', 84 mm. (3s. 5d.)	£140-170
---	(6)	'A.A.' Triumph Motorcycle and Sidecar	Black bike, Yellow sidecar and fairing, plastic rider, 'ENT 303', 84 mm. (3s. 5d.)	£140-170
---	(60)	Austin Mini Van	'AA PATROL SERVICE', Yellow body. Opening side and rear doors	£150-200
---		Austin Mini Van	'RAC', Blue body. Opening side and rear doors	£150-200

Zebra Toys

104 Routemaster Bus,

101 Scammell Scarab Articulated Van 'BRITISH RAILWAYS'

100 Foden Concrete Mixer

Photo: Vectis Auctions Ltd.

'Qualitoys' and other Benbros model vehicles

This list includes all the other vehicles in the Benbros range, mostly large scale items. Many carried the name 'Qualitoy' as well as 'Benbros', and most were individually boxed. Dating of these models is quite difficult, since there were few contemporary adverts, and the only catalogues known are trade price lists for 1964 and 1965. The Timpo re-issues were probably no earlier than 1952, and the various motorcycles were introduced in late 1955. Where a retail price is shown (in shillings and pence) the model was still available on the 1964 and 1965 price lists.

Coronation Coach with 8 horses	'ER' cast on doors, 'MADE IN ENGLAND' on drawbar. Later boxes marked 'Zebra Toys', 116 mm (3s 7d)	£30-40
State Landau with 4 horses	Two separate footmen. 'MADE IN ENGLAND' under coach. 105 mm. (3s 7d)	£30-40
Father Christmas Sleigh	With four reindeer. Metallic green or metallic blue. 110 mm. (2s 6d)	£60-80
Covered Wagon with 4 Bullocks	Re-issue of a model by L. Brooks (Toys) Ltd. (1958). Hollow-cast lead bullocks (diecast on the Brooks model). 'MADE IN ENGLAND' lengthwise under, Cloth canopy, Green wagon, Yellow wheels, cowboy. 186 mm	£60-80
Covered Wagon with 4 Horses	Same wagon as above. Canopy plain or with 'BUFFALO BILL'S COVERED WAGON' or 'CALGARY STAMPEDE COVERED WAGON' printed. Red or Green wagon (Yellow shaft) or Metallic Green or Metallic Blue (Red shaft). Yellow wheels, two barrels, metal or plastic cowboy holding whip. 186 mm. (4s 8d)	£60-80
Rickshaw with two Passengers	Pulled by Ostrich or Zulu. Shown in the Joplin book* as Crescent, but believed to be Benbros. 150 mm	£125-175
Roman Chariot with two horses	With figure. Metallic Green or Yellow with Red wheels. About 135 mm	£60-80
Horse Drawn Farm Cart and man	Re-issue of Timpo model. Light Green farm cart, Brown horse	£60-80
Horse Drawn Water Wagon	Re-issue of Timpo model. Light Green wagon, Brown horse	£80-100
Horse Drawn Log Wagon with Log	Yellow with Red wheels, or Red with Yellow wheels, or Orange with Red wheels, Brown horse. 225 mm	£80-100
Stephenson's Rocket Loco and Tender	Metallic Brown, Gold or Silver 'plated' loco. Tender Metallic Green, Metallic Blue, Orange or Red. Boxed, 105 mm	£35-45
Caterpillar Tractor	Copy of early Lesney model. Red or Yellow or metallic Blue, rubber tracks, 97 mm. (3s 6d)	£30-40
Caterpillar Bulldozer	Copy of early Lesney model. Red tractor with Black blade, or metallic Blue with Red or Yellow blade. Rubber tracks. 118 mm. (4s 11d)	£30-40

Caterpillar Excavator with driver ......Orange (Green shovel) or metallic Blue (Red shovel), rubber tracks, Red or Green driver, 138 mm. (4s. 11d.)..............£30-40
Ferguson Tractor with driver.............No name on model. Yellow or Red with unpainted wheels, metallic Green or Yellow with Red wheels, Orange with
Black or Blue wheels. Driver Green, Brown, Blue, Metallic Blue or Grey. 73 mm. (2s 6d)....................£100-150
Ferguson Tractor with
Cab and Shovel ....No name on model. Red, Yellow or dark Green, unpainted wheels, Green or Brown driver. 100 mm £100-150
Ferguson Tractor and Log Trailer ......With driver and log. Tractor details as above. Red trailer (179mm) with yellow wheels. (4s 3d).......................£100-150
Ferguson Tractor with Roller.............With driver. No name on model. Former Timpo horse-drawn roller plus drawbar.
Tractor as above, Yellow trailer with Red rollers. Trailer length 109 mm. (3s 6d)....................£100-150
Ferguson Tractor with Harrow.........With driver. No name on model. Former Timpo horse-drawn harrow plus drawbar.
Tractor as above, Red or Yellow trailer, length about 110 mm. (3s 6d).......................£100-150
Euclid Dumper Lorry........................Copy of Dinky 965. Metallic Blue cab and chassis, Yellow or Orange tipper. 145mm. (5s 10d). Boxed £220-260
Muir Hill Dumper with Driver...........Orange (Green tipper, Blue wheels), Yellow (Red or Orange tipper, Blue wheels), Metallic Green
(Orange tipper, Blue wheels), or Red with Yellow tipper, Black wheels, 105 mm. (3s 11d)....................£50-60
A101 Army Land Rover and
Field Gun ....Open Land Rover has two figures cast, separate windscreen, metal wheels with rubber tyres.
Field gun marked 'BENBROS', solid rubber wheels. Matt Dark Green. 111 mm. and 102 mm £80-100
A102 Lorry with Anti-Aircraft Gun..Matt dark Green, Silver gun. 117 mm £25-30
A103 Lorry with Radar Scanner ......Matt dark Green, Silver radar dish. 117 mm £25-30
A104 Lorry with Searchlight..............Matt dark Green. 117 mm.....................£25-30
A105 Armoured Car and Field Gun..Dark Brownish-Green or matt dark Green. Field gun same as A101. 96 mm and 102 mm £30-40
A106 Army AEC Lorry with Tilt ....'SUNDERLAND' cast on cab sides. Dark Brownish-Green or matt dark Green, Green cloth tilt. 132 mm £125-150
A107 Army Closed Land Rover ....Casting as A101. Matt dark Green, Black roof. Opening side and rear doors. 111 mm....................£40-50
A110 Army Articulated
Low-Loader with Field Gun...........Matt Dark Green Low-loader as no. 221, Field Gun as no. A101 but with metal hubs and rubber tyres....................£30-40

220 AEC Flat Lorry with chains........'SUNDERLAND' cast on cab sides. Red cab and chassis, light Green, Blue, Beige or
Metallic Green body. 130 mm. (3s 6d)....................£125-150
221 Articulated Low Loader...............Re-issue of Timpo model. Red or Green cab with Red, Yellow or metallic Green trailer.
No name on model. 166 mm £25-30
223 Land Rover 'Royal Mail'............Red (Black roof). 'ROYAL MAIL E-II-R' cast on sides. Opening side and rear doors, 2 figures cast inside. 111mm..£140-170
224 Articulated Tanker ....Re-issue of Timpo model, no maker's name on model, 146mm (3s 6d). Red or Orange cab,
Green or metallic Green or Yellow trailer, 'MOTOR OIL ESSO PETROL' transfer £75-85
Green cab, Red trailer, 'SHELL PETROL' label.....................£75-85
Light Green cab, Red trailer, 'UNITED DAIRIES' transfer £75-85
225 AEC Dropside Lorry ....'SUNDERLAND' cast on cab sides. Red cab and chassis, light Green or Blue body. 132 mm. (3s 6d) £100-125
226 Petrol Tanker ....Re-issue of Timpo model. Red cab / chassis with Red or Yellow tank, light Green
cab / chassis with Yellow tank. 'Motor Oil Esso Petrol' or 'Fina Petrol Goes a Long Way'
transfer. No name on model. 117 mm. (3s 1d)....................£100-125
227 AEC Flat Lorry...........................Re-issue of Timpo model. 'SUNDERLAND' cast on cab sides. Red cab and chassis,
light Green, Blue or Cream body. 130 mm. (3s 1d)....................£100-150
228 AEC Lorry with Tilt....................As no.225 with plain cloth tilt. 132 mm....................£300-400
Forward Control Box Van ....Re-issue of Timpo model, no maker's name on model. 99 mm.
Green cab and chassis with light Green or Red body with 'Pickfords Removals' labels....................£140-170
Red cab, chassis and body, plain £30-40
Red cab and chassis, Green body, 'CHIVERS JELLIES' transfers £140-170
Articulated Box Van ....Re-issue of Timpo model, no maker's name on model. 145 mm.
Red or Green cab with Green, Red or Cream trailer. 'LYONS TEA' transfers. £140-170
Red cab with Green trailer. 'UNITED DAIRIES' transfers.....................£140-170
Light Green cab with Red or Orange trailer. 'BISHOP & SONS DEPOSITORIES LTD.' transfers....................£140-170
A.A. Land Rover...................................Casting as A107 and 223. 'AA ROAD SERVICE' cast on sides and roof sign. Opening side
and rear doors, two figures inside. Yellow with Black roof or all Yellow. 111 mm. (5s 10d)....................£125-150

310 Ruston-Bucyrus10-RB Crane......Maroon and Yellow body, dark Green chassis and jib, rubber tracks. 'BENBROS' cast underneath. (3s 6d)....................£70-80
311 Ruston-Bucyrus
10-RB Excavator ....Maroon and Yellow body, dark Green chassis and arms, rubber tracks. 'BENBROS' cast underneath. (3s 6d)....................£70-80
AEC Lorry and
Ruston-Bucyrus Crane ....'SUNDERLAND' cast on cab sides. Red cab and chassis, Yellow body. Crane as
no.310 with Maroon and Yellow body, dark green jib. 128 mm. (5s 10d)....................£125-150
AEC Lorry with Ruston-Bucyrus
Excavator.......................................'SUNDERLAND' cast on cab sides. Red cab and chassis, Yellow body. Excavator as
no.311 with Maroon and Yellow body, dark Green arms. 128 mm. (5s 10d)....................£125-150

A.A. Motorcycle Patrol ....Black cycle, AA badge cast on Yellow sidecar and windscreen, 'TTC147' cast on number plates. 84 mm.
(i) Fixed front forks, windscreen with plastic glazing, dark Brownish-Green metal rider....................£100-150
(ii) Steering front forks, windscreen with curved frame cast in place of glazing, plastic rider....................£100-150
RAC Motorcycle Patrol.......................Black cycle, RAC badge cast on Blue sidecar and windscreen. 'TTC147' cast on number
plates. Steerable front forks, windscreen with curved frame, plastic rider. 84 mm £100-150
Solo Motorcycle with Rider ....Fixed front forks, 'TTC147' cast on number plates. 84 mm.
(i) Police Patrol - Maroon cycle, Black metal rider £45-55
(ii) Telegraph Boy - Red cycle, Red metal rider £45-55
(iii) Army Despatch Rider - Dark Brownish-Green cycle and metal rider £45-55
(iv) Rally Rider - Green cycle, Blue metal rider £45-55
Solo Motorcycle with Rider ....Steerable front forks, 'TTC147' cast on number plates. Silver plated cycles with plastic riders
in four versions - Police Patrol, Telegraph Boy, Army Despatch Rider and Rally. 84 mm....................£45-55
Motorcycle and Sidecar......................Black / Cream, 'Express Window Service', figure dressed in Blue with flat cap £175-200

* Reference: 'The Great Book of Hollow-Cast Figures' by Norman Joplin (New Cavendish Books).

Britains Ltd.

BRITAINS MOTOR VEHICLES
by Mike Richardson

Most people are aware of the military vehicles made by Britains both before the War and after in 1/32 scale to go with their soldiers, but not so many are acquainted with the contemporary civilian models. Some of these models are only colour variations of the military versions, for example the 59F 'Four-wheeled Lorry with Driver' in the farm series is the same as 1335 'Lorry, Army, Four-wheeled type' but painted in a smart duotone colour scheme instead of khaki. Other models are only available in the civilian type, usually for the good reason that the army could not possibly have a use for a militarised version. A good example of this would be 1656 'John Cobb's Railton Wonder Car' (or 'Railton Mobil Special' as we know it!).

Britains are our oldest toy company which is still in business having been started in 1860 although the first of the famous soldiers did not appear until 1890. This still means over a hundred years continuous toy manufacture, surely a record. The motor lorry models appeared in late 1932 and were based on the Albion army lorries of the time with the familiar 'square' cab design which was to be a hallmark of the Britains lorries until the end of the decade. The range of 4, 6 and 10-wheel farm lorries are still illustrated in the 1940 catalogue. After the War the cab was brought up to date by a change to a more rounded Fordson type, not nearly so attractive.

The military ambulance was also used in civilian versions, a cream 'Corporation' and a blue 'Volunteer Corps' as alternative liveries to the khaki army one. The rarest version of this model is the red and black 'Royal Mail' van which was sold for a short time towards the end of the production run.

There are three civilian cars, a 'Two-seater Coupé' and two 'Sports Model Open Tourers' in the pre-war production. The coupé and the open sports car without driver and passenger do not have military equivalents, but when the open sports car has people in it then it is either a 'Mobile Police Car with 2 Officers'

(finished in green with black wings), or a 'Staff Car with 2 Officers' as the military offering. The occupants of the car are legless and their lower regions are covered with a tartan rug - how nice for them on cold days! After the War there was a one-piece casting version of the staff car and police car without the separate grilles of the pre-war models and these were rather plain by comparison.

The final group of models consists of the superb record cars 'Bluebird' and 'Railton Special'. These came out in the late 1930s and each is over 6 inches long. The Bluebird was produced in three versions; a) with fully detailed removable chassis, b) without this part, and c) a slightly smaller one (just over 5 inches), without underside detail. The Railton Mobil Special always had the removable chassis and was available painted silver for 1s.6d. or chrome plated for 2s.6d.

After the War two new farm tractor models appeared, a couple of Fordson Majors produced with the active co-operation of the Ford Motor Company. These are excellent models both finished in the correct shade of dark blue and with the name 'Fordson' applied to the front and sides of the radiator. One version has standard wheels but the other (rarer) one had the spiked or 'spud' wheels used on heavy ground.

All these models are to the same scale as the soldiers (1/32), but there is also a similar range in '00' gauge (1/76 scale) to go with model railways. The smaller models date mainly from the post-war era although a sports car and a fastback saloon were seen pre-war. The small scale trucks have a Fordson cab similar to the later large scale farm and army lorries.

The large scale pre-war models are very collectable and prices are consequently very high for rare items in excellent condition and with original lovely boxes. Some few years ago a batch of replicas of the coupé were made here in England so exercise care when buying this model. Spare parts are, or have been available for most of these toys to enable repairs to be carried out.

Britains No.1448 Army Staff Car with Officer and Driver   Photo: Vectis Auctions Ltd.

Britains Vehicles, Guns and Novelties, 1880 - 1916

BRITAINS VEHICLES, GUNS and NOVELTIES, 1880 - 1916

by James Opie

Although Britains is famous for manufacturing toy soldiers, it is not so widely known that they had produced toy vehicles before they made their first soldier. In one of their catalogues pre-dating toy soldier production, there are large and small Road Rollers, and probably manufactured even before these are a much larger and cruder Road Roller and Steam Crane, mostly built of tinplate (uncatalogued), and a Rotary Railway Express (uncatalogued), which was a lead die-cast floor toy rather than a toy train. All came boxed.

Dating in all probability from 1890 or earlier, the die-cast Road Rollers can lay claim to be the earliest attributable catalogued British die-cast toys.

Item	Market Price Range
The London Road Roller c.1890 to 1895	£2,500-4,000
The Miniature Road Roller c.1890 to1916	£750-1,000
The Rotary Railway Express c.1891 to 1894	£3,000-5,000

The next group of models, die-cast from lead alloy with steel and wire pins, springs, axles and ammunition, were the early guns and vehicles to accompany toy soldier production from 1895 to 1916. In fact, the first Britains spring gun was incorporated in a model soldier with a hollow rifle barrel and a steel spring set just behind the breech, so that a protruding piece of wire could be flicked through.

Set 28 included a three part mountain gun which loaded onto mules, set 39 was a Royal Horse Artillery set with a field gun and limber, and set 79 had the same gun as set 28, slightly modified with a wire towing eye to join to a small limber pulled by eight sailors. Set 144 used the same gun as set 39 with a modified limber as a Royal Field Artillery set. Sets 145 and 146 included a die-cast lead four wheel general purpose wagon. Sets 125 and 126 were Royal Horse Artillery sets made in a smaller size with a gun and limber, the gun from which, slightly modified without its towing hole, was also used in sets 148 and 149, and in small size second grade displays 04, 05 amd 06. Perhaps the most famous gun of all, the 4.7 inch Naval Gun, was at first made without a catalogue number. This was the gun used by H.G. Wells in his book 'Little Wars'. The field gun from set 39 was also available separately in an un-numbered box entitled 'Royal Artillery Gun'.

In 1906, Britains introduced a horse-drawn four wheel general service waggon, which was used in sets 145 and 146. In 1914, Britains produced their first civilian vehicle which was part of their standard scale figure range, the Boy Scout Trek Cart, two of which were included in both set 180 and in set 181. This would probably have been predated by the Coster's Barrow, which is almost the right scale, but produced as part of the novelty range
As the majority of these guns and vehicles came as part of sets, I will give both the price of the boxed sets and the price of the individual guns and vehicles when found separately.

Item	Market Price Range
Set 28 Mountain Artillery (oval base men), 1895-1908	£350-500
Set 28 Mountain Artillery (square base men), 1908-1916	£250-350
Mountain Artillery Gun (eight spoke wheels), 1895-1916	£30-50
Set 39 Royal Horse Artillery (shafted limber), 1896-1906	£1,500-2,000
Gun with bucket seats and Shafted Limber, 1896-1906	£250-400
Set 39 Royal Horse Artillery (centre pole limber), 1906-1916	£800-1,000
Gun and Centre Pole Limber, 1906-1916	£80-100

Item	Market Price Range
Royal Artillery Gun (boxed, no catalogue number), 1896-1916	£120-150
4.7 inch Naval Gun (boxed, no catalogue number), 1896-1916	£80-100
Set 79 Royal Navy Landing Party (oval base men), 1897-1916	£600-800
Landing Party Gun and Limber, 1897-1916	£100-150
Set 125 Royal Horse Artillery, full dress, small size, 1902-1916	£600-800
Set 126 Royal Horse Artillery, field dress, small size, 1902-1916	£600-800
Small size Gun and Limber, grey finish (from set 125), 1902-1916	£100-150
Small size Gun and Limber, khaki (from set 126), 1902-1916	£100-150
Set 144 Royal Field Artillery, bucket seats, 1906-1916	£1,500-2,000
Gun with bucket seats and Centre Pole Limber, 1906-1916	£300-400
Set 145 Royal Army Medical Corps Four Horse Ambulance Waggon, 1906-1916	£400-500
Set 146 Army Service Corps Two Horse Waggon, 1906-1916	£300-400
Four wheel General Service Waggon, 1906-1916	£60-90
Set 148 Royal Lancaster Regiment Game Set, with gun, 1907-1916	£6,000-7,000
Set 149 American Soldiers Game Set, with gun, 1907-1916	£6,000-7,000
Set 04 British Army Encampment, small size, 1910-1916	£400-500
Set 05 British Army Encampment, small size, 1910-1916	£500-600
Set 06 British Army Encampment, small size, 1910-1916	£600-700
Small size Gun, without towing hole, 1907-1916	£80-100
Set 180, Boy Scout Display with two trek carts, 1914-1916	£800-1,000
Set 181, large Boy Scout Display with two trek carts, 1914-1916	£3,000-4,000
Trek Cart with Boy Scout, 1914-1916	£150-200

Novelties, 1900 - 1916

Probably from around 1900 or even before, Britains produced cast alloy novelty toys. Exact dates of production are unknown. Those listed below (unboxed except where specified) were in the 1915 catalogue, but had no catalogue number quoted. The catalogue also stated 'Miscellaneous castings. Jockeys, Bicycles, Warships, Yachts, etc., in several qualities and sizes for Race Games, &c.'

Item	Market Price Range
Tea Pot, gilt, 1900-1916	£20-30
Coffee Pot, gilt, 1900-1916	£20-30
Kettle, gilt or black, 1900-1916	£20-30
Rocking Chair, 1900-1916	£30-40
Tea and Coffee Set, gilt, boxed, 1900-1916	£200-300
Saucepan, black, with lid, bright metal, 1900-1916	£30-40
Boiler with Lid, copper, gilt or black, 1900-1916	£20-30
Coal Vase with Tongs, copper, gilt or black, 1900-1916	£25-40
Watering Pot, red, 1900-1916	£20-30
Kettle on Stand, gilt, 1900-1916	£35-50
Large boxed Kitchen Set with kettles, 1900-1916	£300-500
Small boxed Kitchen Set with kettle, 1900-1916	£200-300
Baby's Chair, 1900-1916	£40-60
Push Chair, 1900-1916	£35-50
Caster's Barrow, blue or gold, 1900-1916	£40-60
Kitchen Steps, 1900-1916	£30-40
Football Association Cup, silver or gilt, 1904-1916	£750-1,000

An illustration from the January 1951 Britains Ltd. catalogue.

Illustration of Mechanical Unit driving No. 127F "Fordson Major" Tractor.

Illustration of Mechanical Unit driving No. 128F "Fordson Major" Tractor.

MANUFACTURED BY — IN LONDON.ENGLAND

TRADE — MARK

Regd No. 459993.

Britains Motor Vehicles (pre-war issues)

The models were constructed of a lead based alloy and the main body parts were hollow cast. However, parts such as wings and running boards were die-cast individually by hand. The Market Price Range figures refer to boxed models in excellent condition.

Civilian Vehicles

59 F   Four-wheeled Lorry with Driver
Back and doors open, rubber tyres, 6"..................**£150-200**

60 F   Six-wheeled Lorry with Driver
Two-tone Blue body, White cab roof, Silver radiator surround,
back and doors open, White rubber tyres, 6"...........**£150-200**

61 F   Ten-wheeled Lorry with Driver
Back and doors open, rubber tyres.........................**£200-250**

90 F   Builders Lorry
As 59 F plus builders name on side.
'DAVIS ESTATES LTD BUILDERS OF HOMES'...........**£2,000-3,000**

91F and 92F Builders Lorry
As 60F and 61F plus builders name on side. Never seen.........**NPP**

1398   Sports Model Open Tourer
Cream body, Black chassis and wheels,
White rubber tyres, 4.25"...................................**£750-1,000**

1399   Two-Seater Coupé (fitted bumpers)
Cream body, Tan roof, wings and running-boards,
Black hubs, White tyres, 4.5". (Also in other colours).......**£1,000-1,250**

1413   Mobile Police Car with two Officers
2-piece casting, Green body, Black wings, White tyres, 4.75".
(Also in other colours) **£500-600**

1470   The Royal Household Set
Coronation State Coach, King George VI plus the Queen
with twelve attendants....................................**£300-500**

1513   Volunteer Corps Ambulance with Driver,
Wounded Man and Stretcher
Blue body, 'AMBULANCE', Red/White cross, White tyres **£600-700**

1514   Corporation Type Motor Ambulance with
Driver, Wounded Man and Stretcher
Cream body, 'AMBULANCE', Red/White cross, White tyres .**£700-900**

1552   'ROYAL MAIL' Van with Driver
Post-Office Red body, Black bonnet, 'GR' plus crown design,
White tyres **£1,600-2,000**

---   1924 Wembley Exhibition Locomotive
Bronze finished diecast locomotive on plinth with '1924 Wembley
Exhibition', '240 tons - largest locomotive in the world' ....**NGPP**

Military Vehicles

Early issues of lorry and truck models in the ranges 1333 - 1433 and 1641 - 1643 had 'square' cabs, (post-war issues had 'rounded' cabs).

1321   Armoured Car with Gun
Military Green, solid metal wheels..........................**£100-125**

1333   Lorry, Army, Caterpillar Type with Driver
Military Green finish, rubber tyres, 6"....................**£150-200**

1334   Four-wheeled Tipper Lorry with Driver..............**£150-200**

1335   Lorry, Army, Six-wheeled Type with Driver
Military Green finish, rubber tyres, 6"....................**£150-200**

1392   Autogiro
Military Green, RAF roundels, pilot, three rotor blades..........**£750-950**

1432   Tender, Army, Covered, Ten-wheeled (with Driver)
Military Green finish, White rubber tyres, 6"...............**£150-200**

1433   Tender, Army, Covered, Ten-wheeled Caterpillar Type
(with Driver) Military Green finish, White rubber tyres, 6"..**£150-200**

1448   Staff Car
Military Green car with 2 Staff Officers,
White rubber tyres, 4".....................................**£350-450**

1641   Underslung Heavy Duty Lorry (18 wheels) with Driver
Military Green finish, 10"..................................**£350-450**

1641   Underslung Heavy Duty Lorry (18 wheels) with Driver
with 1749 Mounted Barrage Balloon Winch **£900-1,100**

1642   Underslung Heavy Duty Lorry (18 wheels) with Driver
with Mounted Searchlight, Military Green finish, 10".........**£350-450**

1643   Underslung Heavy Duty Lorry (18 wheels) with Driver
with Mounted Anti-Aircraft Gun (small)....................**£350-450**

1643   Underslung Heavy Duty Lorry (18 wheels) with Driver
with Mounted Anti-Aircraft Gun (large)....................**£600-800**

Autogiro and Record Cars (1:43 scale)

1392   Autogiro
Blue body, (other colours are known) including Military
Green with pilot and three detachable rotor blades **£750-950**

1936   Bluebird Record Car
(Napier-Campbell) Malcolm Campbell's car,
lift-off body, detailed engine, White tyres **£150-175**

1939   Napier Railton, John Cobb's car,
'350.20 mph World Land Speed Record' **£250-300**

'Circus' Series

'Mammoth Circus Roundabout'
Six horses (Black, Brown, White) plus riders, Green, Red and Yellow Carousel canopy.
Lead and card construction. Circa 1910 ....**£2,000-3,000**

'The Flying Trapeze' Set (No. 1141)
High wire act with balancing clown and suspended girl trapeze artiste, twirling paper parasol, wire
and card winder, marbled patterned box. 1936-39 ....**£2,000-3,000**

'Motor and Road' Series

Ref	Model name	Details	Price
1313	**Volunteer Corps 'AMBULANCE'**	Finished in Blue, with wounded man and stretcher	**£300-400**
2024	**Light Goods Van with Driver**	Various colours, 'BRITAINS LTD' logo	**£400-500**
2045	**Clockwork Van** (c1938)	Various colours, driver, opening rear doors. In Red box with Dark Yellow picture label	**£900-1,200**

NB   A boxed example of 2045 with red cab and green van body, Black 'BRITAINS' logo on White background, with driver and
original clockwork key sold at the Lacy, Scott & Knight 11/97 auction for **£1,050**

Britains 'Farm' series (post-war issues)

Motor-driven farm vehicles

59F	19??	**Farm Tipping Lorry with Driver,** Light Green or Blue, 4 wheels, 6" long	150-250
127F	19??	**Fordson 'MAJOR' Tractor with Driver,** fitted with spade-end wheels	£200-250
128F	19??	**Fordson 'MAJOR' Tractor with Driver,** with rubber-tyred wheels	£175-225
129 F	1955	**Timber Trailer with real log** Adjustable body. 8"	NGPP
130 F	1955	**Trailer with Racks (Tipping Hay Cart)** Two wheels, body tips, tailboard drops. 4.5"	NGPP
135 F	1955	**Disc Harrow** 2.5" ('Can be coupled in pairs to make tandem harrows, or to 136 F to make combination roller-harrow')	NGPP
136 F	1955	**Roller** 2.25". (See 135 F)	NGPP
137 F	1955	**Clockwork Set** Fordson Major Tractor with Driver, Mechanical Trailer (2041) and Tipping Hay Cart (130 F). 13.25"	NGPP
138 F	1955	**Four-Farrow Tractor Plough** (3-position adjustment of front wheel-arms possible)	NGPP
139 F	1955	**Clockwork Set** (Fordson Major Tractor with Driver and Mechanical Trailer (2041). 8.5"	NGPP

The following were all supplied in cellophane fronted landscape boxes.
NB Some of the same model numbers were used twice for different models.

9520	1965-70	**Fordson Major Tractor with Driver,** cast metal wheels, plastic outset lights	£75-85
9526	1965-70	**Ford Super Major '5000' Tractor** with Spade End Wheels, dark blue	£75-85
9527	1965-70	**Ford Super Major '5000' Tractor** with rubber tyres, dark blue	£65-75
9529	1965-70	**Massey-Ferguson 135 Tractor** with safety cab, red/white	£65-75
9596	1965-70	**Ford Super Major '5000' Tractor Set,** Ford Tractor plus nine implements	£100-150
9630	1965-70	**Ford Super Major '5000' Tractor** with cab and Shawnee-Poole Rear Dump Set	£85-95
9670	1965-70	**Dumper,** red with yellow wheels and blue driver	£20-25
9522	1970-80	**Massey-Ferguson 595 Tractor** with safety cab, red body, silver cab	£40-60
9524	1970-80	**Ford 6600 Tractor,** blue/white, blue driver	£60-70
9526	1970-80	**Deutz DX 110 Tractor,** green/black	£40-50
9527	1970-80	**Fiat Half-Track Tractor,** red/black, beige driver	£45-55
9528	1970-80	**Fiat Tractor,** red/black	£30-40
9529	1970-80	**Massey-Ferguson Tractor with Cab,** dark blue/white	£60-70
9569	1970-80	**Unimog Tractor/Lorry,** green/yellow	£30-40
9570	1970-80	**Massey-Ferguson 760 Combine Harvester,** red with driver	£100-130
9571	1970-80	**Farm Land-Rover, 'BRITAINS FARM'**	£30-35
9572	1970-80	**Massey-Ferguson 595 Tractor** with Front Loader, yellow with red front loader	£100-130
9576	1970-80	**Farm Land-Rover,** blue with cream canopy	£25-35
9584	1970-80	**Ford Tractor and Front Loader**	£45-55
9591	1970-80	**Massey-Ferguson 595 Tractor and 2 Wheeled Trailer,** red/white tractor with green/yellow trailer	£65-75
9595	1970-80	**Massey-Ferguson 595 Tractor** and Front Loader, red/white	£60-70

9597	1970-80	**Massey-Ferguson 595 Tractor and 8 Wheeled Trailer,** red/white	£65-75
9515	1980-85	**Volvo BM Valmet 805 Tractor,** red/black	£35-45
9517	1980-85	**Massey-Ferguson MF2680 Double Rear wheeled Tractor,** red/white	£45-55
9518	1980-85	**Renault TX145-14 Turbo Tractor,** orange/black/white	£30-40
9520	1980-85	**Massey-Ferguson MF2680 Tractor,** red/white	£40-50
9522	1980-85	**Renault Double Rear Wheeled Tractor,** orange/white	£40-45
9523	1980-85	**Ford TW20 Tractor,** blue/white	£35-45
9525	1980-85	**Mercedes-Benz Tractor,** yellow/black	£35-45
9530	1980-85	**Deutz Eight Wheeled Tractor,** green/black	£35-45
9529	1980-85	**Massey-Ferguson MF2680 Double Rear Wheeled Tractor,** red/grey	£45-55
9575	1980-85	**'New Holland' Combine Harvester,** yellow	£25-35
9580	1980-85	**Magirus Deutz Iveco Animal Transporter,** dark blue cab, red/grey back	£25-35
9581	1980-85	**Unimog Breakdown Truck,** white/orange/red	£15-25
9582	1980-85	**Magirus Deutz Iveco Flatbed Transporter,** white cab, grey back	£25-35
9583	1980-85	**Magirus Deutz Iveco Tipper Truck,** yellow/black	£20-30
9581	1980-85	**Unimog Breakdown Truck 'Recovery Service'**	£20-30
9584	1980-85	**Ford Tractor** with front loader	£40-50
9585	1980-85	**Fiat Tractor and Vacuum Tanker**	£40-50
9586	1980-85	**Volvo Tractor and Trailer**	£45-55
9587	1980-85	**Massey-Ferguson Tractor and Rear Dump**	£45-55
9588	1980-85	**Ford Tractor and Rotary Manure Spreader**	£45-55
9589	1980-85	**Deutz Tractor and Implements Set**	£100-125
9591	1980-85	**Fiat Tractor and Implements Set**	£100-125
9596	1980-85	**Deutz Tractor and Manure Spreader**	£45-55
9597	1980-85	**Ford Tractor and 8 wheeled trailer**	£50-60
9597	1980-85	**Mercedes-Benz Tractor with Tipper Hopper**	£40-50
9598	1980-85	**Massey-Ferguson MF2680 Tractor and Trailer**	£45-55
9599	1980-85	**Farm Tractor and Implements Set**	£100-125

Horse-drawn farm vehicles

4 F	1955	**Tumbrel Cart with Farm Hand & Horse** with removable Hay Racks & Backboard. 7.25"	NGPP
5 F	1955	**Farm Waggon with Farm Hand** plus two Horses, removable Backboard. 9.25"	NGPP
6 F	1955	**General Purpose Plough** with Farm Hand & two Horses. 10.75"	NGPP
8 F	1955	**Farm Rake with Driver & Horse** with lever operated Rake. 5.75"	NGPP
9 F	1955	**Farm Roller with Farm Hand & Horse** 5" long	NGPP
12 F	1955	**Timber Waggon with Farm Hand & two Horses** with Real log load. 11.75"	NGPP
20 F	1955	**Farmers' Gig with Horse & Farmer** Backboard drops. (Reins not supplied with 20F). 5.25"	NGPP
40 F	1955	**Farm Cart & Horse** 5" long	NGPP
45 F	1955	**Milk Float & Horse** (Churns No.588 were recommended but not supplied with this model). 5" long	NGPP
126 F	1955	**Horse Drawn Farm Cart** 5" long	NGPP
131 F	1955	**Horse Drawn Milk Float** with Milkman & two Churns. 5"	NGPP
142 F	1955	**Single Horse General Purpose Plough** with Ploughman. 10.25"	NGPP

'Lilliput' Series (1:76 scale)

Manufactured under license by Horton (Toys and Games) Ltd., Reno Works, Middlesborough, England.

LV 601	**Open Sports Car** 2.25" long	£60-70
LV 602	**Saloon Car** 2.25" long	£60-70
LV 603	**Articulated Lorry** 4" long	£60-70
LV 604	**Fordson Tractor with Driver** 1.5" long	£35-45
LV 605	**Milk Float and Horse** with Milkman. 2.25" long	£45-55
LV 606	**Tumbrel Cart and Horse** with Hay Racks and Carter. 2.75" long	£35-45
LV 607	**Austin 3-ton Covered Military Truck**	£35-45
LV 608	**Austin 3-ton Farm Truck**	£35-45
LV 609	**Austin Military Champ**	£65-75
LV 610	**Centurion Tank**	£35-45
LV 611	**Self-propelled 25-pounder Gun**	£25-35

LV 612	**Humber 1-1/2 ton Military Truck**	£35-45
LV 613	**Humber 1-1/2 ton Military Truck** Covered version	£35-45
LV 614	**Farm Trailer**	£15-25
LV 615	**Saracen Armoured Vehicle**	£15-25
LV 616	**1½ ton Truck**	£35-45
LV 617	**Civilian Ambulance.** Cream body with 'AMBULANCE' on sides, 'BRITAINS' on rubber tyres, Red plastic hubs	£100-125
LV 618	**Army Ambulance**	NGPP
LV 619	**'ROYAL MAIL' Van**	NGPP
LV 620	**3 ton Open Truck**	NGPP

'Clockwork' series

2041   **Clockwork Unit (2-wheeled trailer)**
'Will last 1 1/2 minutes when fully wound and capable of driving any other vehicle 20-30 feet' **£45-55**

2045   **Clockwork Van**
Finished in various colours with 'BRITAINS LTD' logo **£500-700**

'Motor & Road' series (civilian vehicles)

1513   **Volunteer Corps Motor Ambulance**
with Driver, Wounded Man and Stretcher, opening doors, finished in regulation Blue. 6" long ....NGPP

2024   **Light Goods Van with Driver**
various colours, opening doors, 'Britains Ltd' logos, 6" long ....NGPP

Petrol pumps

Each of the pumps 1v - 7v has a cast delivery nozzle attached by a flexible hose to the rotating top arm.

1v	**'SHELL'**	NGPP
2v	**'B.P.'**	NGPP
3v	**'ESSO'**	NGPP
4v	**'MOBILGAS'**	NGPP
5v	**'NATIONAL BENZOLE'**	NGPP
6v	**'FINA'**	NGPP
7v	**'DOMINION'**	NGPP
9v	**'CASTROL' Oil Cabinet**, sliding front / 3 pumps. 1.75" high.	NGPP
101v	**Stand with Three Pumps** 'SHELL', 'B.P.' and 'NATIONAL BENZOLE' pumps a base plus oil cabinet and operator.	NGPP
102v	**Stand with Three Pumps** 'ESSO', 'MOBILGAS' and 'FINA' pumps a base plus oil cabinet and operator	NGPP
103v	**Stand with Three Pumps** 'SHELL', 'ESSO' and 'MOBILGAS' pumps a base plus oil cabinet and operator	NGPP

Britains Military Vehicles and Guns (post-war issues)

Military vehicles

Post-war issues of lorry and truck models in the ranges 1334 - 1433 and 1641 - 1643 had 'rounded' cabs, (pre-war issues had 'square' cabs).

1334   **Four-wheeled Army Lorry with Tipping Body**
('rounded' cab) with Driver, 6" long **£150-200**

1335   **Six-wheeled Army Lorry with Tipping Body**
('rounded' cab) with Driver, 6" long **£150-200**

1433   **Covered Army Tender**
('rounded' cab) Caterpillar type with Driver, 6" **£150-200**

1448   **Army Staff Car**
with General and Driver, 4" long........................**£350-450**

1512   **RAMC Army Ambulance**
3rd version, split windscreen, driver, stretcher, patient **£200-250**

1791   **Royal Corps of Signals Motor Cycle Dispatch Rider**
sold unboxed **£25-35**

1791-DB **Royal Corps of Signals Motor Cycle Dispatch Riders**
Four motorcycles with revolving wheels in display box ....NGPP

1876   **Bren Gun Carrier with Driver, Gunner and 2nd Guard**
Carden-Vickers type suspension cast-in, separate gun, 3½" ...**£75-125**

1877   **Beetle Lorry and Driver** **£65-75**

1879   **'OO' gauge Lorry with Trailer and Hydrogen Cylinders**
Military Green, solid wheels, red cylinders ....NGPP

1897   **RAMC Motor Ambulance Set** (18 pieces)
With Driver, Orderlies, Nurses, Stretcher and Wounded ....NGPP

2048   **Military Set**
1877, 2041 and 2026 Gun **£150-175**

2150   **Centurion Tank**
Military Green **£300-400**

2150   **Centurion Tank**
Dark green finish, US star to turret......................**£80-100**

2154   **Centurion Tank, Desert Warfare**
Sand colour finish. Box has illustrated label **£225-275**

2156   **Centurion Tank**
Desert warfare finish **£400-500**

Guns and equipment

1201   **Gun of the Royal Artillery**
with shells, to fire with or without Amorce cap. 5.75" long ....NGPP

1263   **Gun of the Royal Artillery**
with shells, to fire with or without Amorce cap. 3.75" long ....NGPP

1264   **4.7 inch Naval Gun (mounted for field operations)**,
with shells, to fire with or without Amorce cap. 7.75" long ....NGPP

1292   **Gun of the Royal Artillery**
with shells, to fire with or without Amorce cap. 4.75" long ....NGPP

2026   **25-pounder Gun Howitzer**
with shells, to fire with or without Amorce cap. 4" long ....NGPP

Anti-aircraft Guns and equipment

1639   **Army Range Finder** (for all classes of Artillery)
a tripod mounted rangefinder with Operator ....NGPP

1640   **Searchlight**
with full movements, uses 3 volt torch battery. 2.5" high...........NGPP

1715   **25-pounder (40 mm.) Light Anti-Aircraft Gun**
'firing a metal shell with great accuracy'. Base 2" in diameter ...NGPP

1717   Mobile Unit 25-pounder
Light A.A. Gun (1715) on 4-wheel screw-jack chassis, 4.5" ....NGPP

1718   Searchlight
1640 on mobile screw-jack chassis, uses 3v battery. 4.5" long....NGPP

1728   **Predictor, with Operator**
Aircraft position predictor on a stand, for A.A defence ....NGPP

1729   **Height Finder, with Operator**
tripod mounted instrument for use with Predictor.....................NGPP

1731   **Spotting Chair (Swivelling)**
'with Man to lie down' (Service Dress, Shrapnel Helmet) ....NGPP

2052DB **Anti-Aircraft Unit** (15 pieces)
with usual personnel, 2 x 1728, 1 x 1729, 1 x (1639), 1 x 1731, 1 x 1640, Mobile A.A. Gun (1717) ....NGPP

Motor Cycles 1965 - 1975

All have plastic saddles, plated engines and 'diamond' headlights, and are packed in display boxes. Market Price Range for single boxed items **£20-30**

9640 **Two Go-Karts**, yellow/black or red/black ....
9695 **BMW with Policeman**, white with black/white rider ....
9696 **BMW with Civilian**, blue with white/blue rider ....
9671 **Racing Norton**, yellow with red/green rider ....
9674 **Chopper Trike**, yellow/gold/black ....
9677 **Long Fork Chopper**, red with blue rider ....
9679 **German Army Motor Cycle**, khaki ....
9680 **'Chopper' Motor Cycle**, black with pink rder ....
9681 **German Army B.M.W. Combination**, khaki with two blue riders ....
9682 **U.S. Army Motor Cycle**, black with khaki rider ....

9683 **Drag Motor Cycle**, gold with grey rider ....
9684 **Speedway Motor Cycles**, silver with black riders ....
9685 **Lambretta Scooter**, red/white with blue and red riders.............
9689 **Harley-Davidson**, red/white 'BUZZ' with red/blue/yellow rider .....
9690 **Triumph Thunderbird 650cc**, red with blue/brown/red rider.................
9691 **Gieves Challenger with Rider**, green with blue/brown rider ....
9692 **Honda Benly 125cc**, red with black/blue/yellow rider ....
9692/2 **U.S. Sheriff on Harley Davidson**, white with black/grey rider ....
9693 **B.M.W. 600cc**, silver with black/blue rider ....
9694 **Triumph Speed Twin with Rider**, yellow/blue with black rider ....
9697 **Police Patrolman on Triumph Thunderbird**, white with black rider.....
9698 **Dispatch Rider on Triumph Motor Cycle**, black, black/green rider......
9698/2 **MV-Augusta Motor Cycle**, red '7', green/yellow or white/blue rider...
9699 **BMW Racing Combination**, red/yellow with two black riders ....
9650 **Speedway Set** with four riders on motor cycles....................**£100-125**
9666 **Motor Cycle Boxed Set** with 3 different motor cycles..............**£80-100**

Britains Auction Results, 2003 - 2005

Britains models sold by VECTIS AUCTIONS
Vectis Auctions Ltd, Fleck Way, Thornaby, Stocton-on-Tees TS17 9JZ.

FARM MODELS (PRE-WAR ISSUES)
4f Tumbrel Cart – blue/red, brown horse, farm hand, E/UB....................**£200**
5f Farm Wagon – blue/red, 2 brown horses, carter, E/G **£260**
12f Timber Carriage – red/green, 2 horses and carter, E/VG **£190**
20f Farmers Gig – green/red, grey horse and farmer, E/VG **£190**
59f Home Farm Lorry – post war, light green, driver, VG/G......................**£235**
128f Fordson Major Tractor – dark blue/orange, E /VG **£240**

CIVILIAN MODELS (PRE-WAR ISSUES)
14 Salvation Army Girls (5) – with tambourines, etc., G – VG **£540**
638 Spiteful Cat – brown, and **562 Golfer** - brown suit, both VG **£110**
434 1931 Monoplane – R.A.F. roundels, 6 figures, G/G **£1,200**
435 1930 U.S. Monoplane – U.S. roundels, pilot, VG................................**£800**
1398 1935 Two Seater Sports Car, yellow/black, VG/VG **£1,000**
1399 Two Seater Coupé – Brown, tan wings, VG in G box **£1,295**
1472 H.M. King George V1, paint finish, E in VG box **£140**
Football Team – 1938 – Blackburn Rovers, 3 players etc., VG **£420**
1472 H.M. King George V1 – gilt finish, G in F box **£30**
1482 Racing Colours - pre-war - Lord Astor, VG in G box **£150**
2024 Light Goods Van - green, 'Britains Ltd', D, VG boxed **£480**
2024 Light Goods Van – blue, red hubs, 'Britains Ltd', E/G **£650**
2045 Light Goods Van – cream/blue, 'Britains Ltd', D/G/G......................**£360**
2045 Light Goods Van – blue/green, 'Britains Ltd', D, VG/G....................**£420**
1513 Volunteer Ambulance, early post war issue....................Estimate **£850**
1513 Volunteer Ambulance – 1937 version, square nose, Fair **£460**
1520 Short Monoplane Flying Boat 1937-39, E in G box **£9,200**
1552 'Royal Mail' Van – 1937 version, G in G ....Estimate **£3,000**
'Nestlés' – Map of the World Cow – 1924 promotional, VG......................**£160**
Cricketer – c 1910 - made for use with cricket game, VG **£320**
Snow White Cottage (large version) – made by Hugar, G **£2,800**
Snow White Cottage (small version) – made by Hugar, G **£500**
1654 Snow White and the 7 Dwarfs – E in VG orange box..................**£2,100**
Johnnie Walker Advertising Figure (Whisky Sales), VG **£140**

GARAGE ACCESSORIES (POST-WAR ISSUES)
101v Petrol Pumps – 'Shell', 'BP' and 'National Benzole', E/VG............**£220**
103v Petrol Pumps – 'Mobilgas', 'Shell' and 'Esso', E in VG box **£320**

MILITARY MODELS (PRE WAR ISSUES)
24 Boer Infantry Set - 1st version, G in F box **£1,300**
25 1910 Soldiers that will Shoot (4), G in G box................................**£2,000**
1254 Pontoon Section 1940 version, VG /G Whisstock box, ...**£1,800**
1329 RASC Wagon - 2 horse team, driver, wagon, VG/G........................**£400**
1330 Royal Engineers Wagon - 2 horse team, post war, G........................**£200**
1331 General Wagon - 2 horse team, driver, wagon, VG/G....................**£440**
1333 1934 Army Lorry – square nose, tipping body, D,VG/F **£260**
1433 1936 Army Covered Tender, square nose, VG/G..............................**£150**
1936 Army Autogiro – khaki, roundels, E in VG box **£1,600**
1450 RAMC Ambulance – 4 horse team, VG /VG **£2,000**
1512 1937 Army Ambulance, driver/patient, dark green, VG....................**£240**
1641 1940 Underslung Lorry - khaki, driver, VG in G box **£200**
1525 U.S. Airforce Biplane – 1937 version, VG overall **£1,200**
1698 Modern Army Display Set - 1938 version, E in VG box..............**£1,800**
1727 Howitzer Unit – 1433/1726/1725 all VG in VG box **£500**
1793 Motor Machine Gun Corps – VG in VG box **£425**
1877 Beetle Lorry, white tyres, driver, VG in VG box **£120**
1899 U.S. Army Autogiro – 1940 version, U.S. roundels, VG..................**£300**
1321 Armoured Car – khaki, white tyres, Good unboxed **£260**
Set 211 – (1920 issue), 10 horses, 18" Howitzer, VG boxed................**£2,950**

MILITARY VEHICLES (POST WAR ISSUES)
1334 4 wheeled Army Lorry – split windscreen, E in E box....................**£190**
1335 6 wheel Army Lorry – round nose version, D, E/F **£160**
1433 Covered Army Tender – split windscreen, E/UB..............................**£230**
1433 Covered Army Tender – round nose, D, VG unboxed **£110**
1448 Army Staff Car with Officer and driver, rubber tyres, VG/G........**£310**
1512 Army Ambulance – 1948 version, round nose, G **£340**
1641 Underslung Lorry –blue body, square nose, VG/VG **£660**
1855 Winch Lorry with metal Barrage Balloon, E/G **£460**
1879 Gas Cylinder Lorry & Trailer, red cylinders, G/VG **£420**
2102 Austin Champ - Excellent in Poor box **£90**
2150 Centurion Tank – dark green finish, U.S. star, E U/B......................**£120**
2154 Centurion Tank – sand coloured finish, E in G box **£310**
Covered Tender – 2nd version, rounded radiator, E in E box **£145**

LILIPUT - CIVILIAN VEHICLES
LV603 Articulate Lorry - green, E in good box **£40**
LV604 Fordson Tractor, dark blue body, orange hubs, NM/E **£140**

LV617 'Ambulance' – cream with brown decals, G-VG/UB......................**£90**
LV619 'Royal Mail' Van – black cab, red body 'ER', E/UB......................**£80**
LV608 3 ton Farm Lorry – black cab, yellow back, G/UB **£70**
LV609 3 ton Farm Lorry – green cab, red back, E/UB **£80**
Motor Vehicle Set – six models, E in E box **£825**

MODERN FARM (POST WAR ISSUES)
9522 Massey-Ferguson 595 Tractor – red, grey, driver, M/NM............**£60**
9527 Ford Super Major Diesel Tractor – blue/grey, EP/GP..................**£110**
9524 Ford 6600 Tractor – blue/grey, NM in GP box **£60**
9576 Farm Land Rover – olive green, tan tilt, D/GK, VG/F **£280**
9596 Gift Set with Ford Super Major Tractor, etc., EP/GP **£750**
9565 Farm Elevator – Lister, blue/red battery operated, GP/F **£360**
Fordson Tractor with plastic cab plus **Shawnee Poole Rear
    Dump Trailer** – both yellow with grey hubs, Excellent Plus..............**£580**
Fordson Major Tractor with spud type wheels – blue with
    orange wheels, plus **Kay Turner Rake** – orange/white, EP..............**£480**

HUNTING SETS
235 'Full Cry' – 4 riders, 12 hounds and a fox, E in E box......................**£520**
236 'The Meet' and 'Full Cry', large display set, E in F-G box **£850**

PRE-WAR RACING COLOURS (in White boxes with Dark Blue lettering)
1480 - HM The King - dark blue, red sleeves, VG in VG box **£260**
1481 - Lord Derby – dark blue, white cap, Excellent in VG box..............**£130**
1482 - Lord Astor – blue, pink cap, Excellent in VG box **£160**
1483 - Major Furlong – white, blue cap/sleeves,VG in B box **£110**
?   Lord Londonderry - grey/yellow, Excellent in VG **£260**
?   Lord Woollavington - white/red, Excellent in VG box **£160**
?   J V Rank – yellow, blue cap, Excellent in VG box **£160**
?   Foxcatcher Farm – blue/yellow hoops, Fair unboxed................**£40**
?   E S Tattersall – pink, black sleeves/cap, VG ....Estimate **£80**
?   HH The Aga Khan – blue, brown hoops, F-G, UB **£30**
?   Mrs J De Selincourt, red/green, white sleeves, G/UB................**£30**
?   Hon. Dorothy Paget – blue, yellow hoop, G/UB **£80**

POST-WAR RACING COLOURS (in White boxes with Red lettering)
RC6 – Lord Roseberry – green, pink hoops, VG in F box **£110**
RC15 – Glen Riddle Farm – blue, yellow hooped sleeves, E/E................**£260**
RC16 – Green Tree Stables – pink and dark blue, E in VG........................**£180**
RC24 – Mr Alfred Venderbilt – white and red, E in VG box....................**£240**
RC63 – HH The Aga Khan – grey horse, blue rider, G in F box **£130**
RC67 – Mr H.J. Joel – blue with red cap, E in VG box **£260**
RC142 – Duke of Norfolk – mid blue, VG in G box **£160**
RC144 – Mrs M. Boussac – red, blue cap, E in GP box **£140**
RC14 – Mr J.L. Jarvis – blue, pink sleeves, E in G box **£240**

MISCELLANEOUS ITEMS
Farm Series Set – 35 items strung onto card, no lid, VG/P....................**£740**
Catalogue - January 1951 - 106th edition, G..**£100**
Catalogue - January 1953 - 108th edition, VG..**£80**

Britains models sold by CHRISTIE'S,
Christie's, 85 Old Brompton Road, South Kensington, London SW7 3LD.
1641 Square Nosed Lorry (1947) – light blue, G-VG in F-G **£358**
BRITAINS GARDEN LOTS
Rockery Sections – 11 different variations, Good....................................**£179**
Garden Pieces – lily pond, trees, hedges etc (13), G-VG **£203**
Garden Fence with Trellis Sections – 9 pieces..**£203**
Garden Flowers – sunflowers, lobelias, roses, etc., (42) G-VG **£203**
Lawn and Wooden Block sections – 87 pieces, G-VG............................**£203**
Garden Flowers – gladioli, alyssium, daffodils, etc., (105) G-VG **£203**
Flower Bed Sections – 13 pieces, G-VG..**£203**
Garden Flowers – poppies, delphiniums, geraniums (53), G-VG **£203**
053 Span Roof Greenhouse – green and white, VG in VG box **£262**
028 Garden Shelter and two Cold Frames, F-G......................................**£203**

Britains models sold by BONHAM'S,
Bonham's, Montpelier Street, Knightsbridge, London SW7 1HH.
1940 issue 6 Wheel Farm Lorry- mid blue, E in E box **£1,000**
1939 issue 4 Wheel Farm Lorry – green, E in E box **£470**

Britains model sold by G. KIDNER,
The Old School, The Square, Pennington, Lymington, Hants SO41 8GN
1879 Gas Cylinder Lorry, G in G box **£140**

Britains models sold by SPECIAL AUCTION SERVICES,
Kennetholme, Midgham, Nr Reading Berkshire RG7 5UX
2175 - Self Propelled Gun – VG in F box **£256**
2154 Centurion Tank in desert warfare finish, G in G box......................**£240**

Chad Valley

The Chad Valley company (makers of board games and wooden toys) produced tinplate toy vehicles from 1932 incorporating the year of manufacture in the registration number on the number plates.

Their first 'Wee-Kin' diecast toy vehicles were produced around 1949 and had 'CV 1949' as the registration number. They were fitted with a key-wound clockwork motor and were designed more as toys than models having generic titles like 'Open Lorry' or 'Fire Engine'. The cars issued between 1951 and 1954 as Rootes Group promotionals are much better attempts at models and

were sold at Rootes Group garages as well as normal toy shops. The tractors produced from 1952 are particularly fine and well detailed models. The years shown below indicate the periods in which Chad Valley offered them for sale though not all the toys were available for the whole of the period and some were still in the shops well after production ceased in 1956.

(This introduction to Chad Valley was written by Sue Richardson who also provided the basic listing. Additional listing information came from the Cecil Gibson archives and John G. Butler of Berkhampstead, Herts.).

Diecast clockwork toys and model vehicles

220	1949-53	**Razor Edge Saloon.** Various colours, no. plates 'CV 1949', approximate. scale 1:43	**£140-180**
221	1949-53	**Traffic Control Car.** Casting as 220 plus loudspeaker, 'CV 1949'	**£100-150**
222	1949-53	**'POLICE' Car.** As 220 plus loudspeaker	**£100-150**
223	1949-53	**Track Racer.** 'CV 1949' on number plates	**£100-150**
224	1949-53	**Double Decker Bus.** Red, 'CV 1949', 1:76	**£100-150**
225	1949-53	**Open Lorry.** Various colours, 'CV 1949'	**£100-150**
226	1949-53	**Low-Loader.** Green / Red, 'CV 1949', 3 cases	**£100-150**
227	1949-53	**Timber Wagon.** 'CV 1949'	**£100-150**
228	1949-53	**Cable Layer.** Red cab, Green body, 'CV 1949'	**£100-130**
229	1949-53	**Breakdown Lorry.** 'CV 1949'	**£100-130**
230	1949-53	**Milk Float.** 'CV 1949', eight milk churns	**£150-180**
231	1949-53	**Fire Engine.** Red body, 'CV 1949'	**£100-130**
232	1949-53	**Tower Repair Wagon.** All-Green, 'CV 1949'	**£125-175**
233	1949-53	**Milk Tanker.** Blue / White, 'CV 1949'	**£150-175**
234	1949-53	**Petrol Tanker.** 'CV 1949'	**£150-175**
239	1949-53	**Dust Cart.** Tinplate sliding panels, 'CV 1949'	**£140-180**
-	1951-54	**Guy Van.** Dark Blue / Cream, tinplate doors, *'Lyons Ice Cream Cadby Hall London W11'*	**£300-500**
-	1951-54	**Guy Van.** Red body, Blue hubs, tinplate doors, Red *'CHAD VALLEY'* logo	**£300-500**
-	1951-54	**Guy Van.** Green body, tinplate doors, Yellow *'Guy Motors Ltd, Commercial Vehicle Manufacturers'*	**£500-750**

Other issues (with or without motor)

--	1950-55	**Hillman Minx Saloon**	**£100-125**
--	1950-55	**Humber Super Snipe**, blue / grey body	**£90-120**
--	1950-55	**Guy Truck**	**£80-120**
--	1950-55	**Sunbeam Racer**	**£100-125**
--	1950-55	**Humber Hawk**	**£100-125**
--	1950-55	**Rolls-Royce Razor Edge Saloon**	**£100-125**
--	1950-55	**Routemaster London Bus**	**£100-125**
--	1950-55	**Commer Avenger Coach**	**£100-125**
--	1950-55	**Guy Truck 'LYONS ICE CREAM'**	**£300-400**
--	1950-55	**Sunbeam-Talbot Saloon**, metallic pale brown	**£100-125**
--	1950-55	**Guy Milk Tanker**, blue /cream, 'MILK'	**£200-300**
--	1950-55	**Guy Cable Lorry**	**£100-150**
--	1950-55	**Guy Petrol Tanker 'REGENT PETROL'**	**£300-400**
--	1950-55	**Guy 'FIRE' Engine**	**£300-400**
--	1950-55	**Guy Container Lorry**	**£100-150**
	1950-55	**Guy Refuse Lorry**	**£100-150**

Rootes Group promotional models (scale 1:43)

236	1949-53	**The Hillman Minx** Grey or Metallic Dark Blue body	**£100-140**
237	1949-53	**The Humber Super Snipe** Metallic Dark Green or Red body	**£100-140**
238	1949-53	**The Sunbeam-Talbot** Light Blue or Metallic Dark Green. Base has wording 'A Rootes Group Product' plus usual CV marks	**£140-180**
240	1949-53	**Commer Avenger Coach** Blue, Red or Green body, (1:76 scale)	**£200-250**
242	1949-53	**The Commer Hands** (6-wheel artic.) Red body with 'Commer Hands' sticker	**£125-150**
507	1951-54	**The Humber Hawk** Met. Dark Blue, Met. Dark Green, or mid-Green	**£100-140**

Chad Valley model Tractors

1952	**Fordson Major E27N** Dark Blue body, Orange wheels, rubber tyres (2 types of tread on rear), steering, towbar with pin, clockwork wound by starting handle. Scale 1:16. Illustrated box or plain box with small label	**£300-400**
1955	**Fordson Major E27N** Red and Yellow with driver, clockwork, scale 1:43, boxed. Made under licence by 'Raybro & Sturdy Products S.A.', Johannesburg, South Africa (model marked 'Chad Valley GB')	**£200-300**
1954	**Fordson Major DDN** Mid-Blue body, Orange wheels, rubber tyres, working steering, lifting bonnet, towbar/pin, hydraulic lift at rear (detachable centre arm), clockwork wound through rear hub. Scale 1:16. Illustrated box or plain box with small label	**£300-400**
	Static version: As previous model but without clockwork operation. Illustrated box or plain box plus small label. The word 'working' is deleted from all sides of box	**£200-300**
	Chrome version: Static (non-clockwork) version in chrome plate, with or without wooden plinth. Thought to be a ploughing trophy or Ford presentation model	**£250-400**
1955	**Ford Dexta** Mid-Blue, Orange wheels, radiator panels and 'Fordson Dexta', not steerable, rubber tyres, hook, 1:16. Illustrated box	**£400-600**
1955	**Ferguson** Green, Red wheels, 'Ferguson' on sides, steering, hook, 1:16. Illustrated box inscribed 'Ferguson'. Promotional	**£500-700**
	Grey body, Grey wheels, hydraulic lift at rear	**£600-800**
1950-55	**Massey Ferguson Tractor**, with or without motor	**£400-600**
1950-55	**Fordson Major Tractor**, Red or Blue, motor in some	**£400-600**
	Bright Yellow/Orange, Red wheels, key, boxed	**£1,750-2,250**

Chad Valley 231 Fire Engine
Photo: Vectis Auctions Ltd.

Charbens Toys

The following history and listings have been researched by Robert Newson. The firm of Charbens & Co. was started around 1928 by Charles and Benjamin Reid and was based at Hornsey Road, Holloway, London N7. They made hollow-cast lead figures, and a few lead vehicles were also produced in the 1930s. After the war zinc die-casting was introduced, and some items exist in both lead and zinc versions (the latter from new dies). Zinc castings by Charbens very often have metal failure as a result of contamination from the lead that was still used extensively in the factory.

The 'Old Crocks' series of miniatures was introduced in 1955. After 1967 all vehicle models were deleted from the catalogue except for a few items included in sets with plastic figures. Production of figures was discontinued in 1973. Model numbers were allocated around 1954, so items which had already been withdrawn are not numbered. Dates of issue have been taken from catalogues or adverts, but inevitably are incomplete. Most pre-war items have 'RD' cast in, most post-war items have 'CHARBENS' cast underneath. Most were boxed.

Ref	Year(s)	Model name	Colours, features, details	Market Price Range

Pre-war issues (part hollow-cast, part diecast construction)

Ref	Year(s)	Model name	Colours, features, details	Market Price Range
---	---	**Motorcycle Policeman**	Solid cast machine with green petrol tank	£40-60
---	---	**Police Motor Cycle and Sidecar**	Solid cast machine, rider and passenger in black / white uniforms, black sidecar	£40-60
---	---	**Soap Box Racer**	Solid cast brown base, four red wheels (six spokes), Cub Scout pushing, Cub Scout rider + another	£400-600
---	---	**Goat Cart with Girl**	Blue or red cart and girl, brown or white goat, yellow 6-spoke wheels	£80-100
---	---	**Road Workers Set**	Contains Horse Roller (green / orange / brown), orange / black tar boiler truck with 6-spoke wheels, plus 4 workmen, a nightwatchman, hut, brazier, 'Road up' sign, pipe and 2 barriers	£200-300
---	---	**Gypsy Caravan**	Blue / white caravan with white horse, yellow wheels (smaller at front) plus orange / black seated Gypsy woman with baby, standing man, linen line with washing, cooking pot	£400-600
---	---	**The Farm Wagon**	Green / yellow four-wheel wagon with two hay racks, brown carthorse, cream / black carter figure. In red card box with cream label	£125-150
---	---	**Tumbril Cart** (two wheels)	Green / yellow cart with two hay racks, brown horse, cream / black carter, cream card box	£100-125
---	---	**Coster Cart with Donkey**	Green / yellow cart, solid sides, grey donkey, costermonger figure (see 24 below)	£100-125
---	---	**Organ Grinder's Cart** (two wheels)	Brown / yellow organ, grey donkey, red monkey with mug, brown / green organ-grinder	£150-175
---	---	**Governess's Cart** (two wheels)	Yellow / black, cream / red or brown / black cart, 2 children, donkey, zoo-keeper figure	£100-125
---	---	**Milk Float** (two wheels)	Yellow / red cart with 'PURE MILK' cast in. Brown horse, milkman figure (see 25)	£80-100
---	---	**Milk Float** (four wheels)	Orange / white body with 'UNITED DAIRIES', 'PASTEURISED MILK' and 'CREAM' logo. 8-spoke wheels with rubber tyres, brown horse, white / blue milkman with bottle	£400-600
---	---	**Milk Handcart**	with 'MILK' logo and Milkman	£200-300
---	---	**Bread Handcart**	with 'HOVIS' logo and Delivery-man	£200-300
---	---	**Cape Cart** (two wheels)	Enclosed dark blue body and roof, brown horse, mid-blue figure	£80-100
---	---	**Tree Wagon** (four wheels)	Yellow / red log carrier, 12-spoke wheels, 4 horses, 2 white figures with poles, (see also 1)	£200-300
---	---	**Dairy Float** (four wheels)	Mid-blue, 'EXPRESS DAIRY', 'PURE MILK', 'BUTTER & EGGS', white shafts, brown horse, 8-spoke wheels, rubber tyres, white / blue milkman holding bottle	£400-600
---	---	**Coal Cart** (four wheels)	Black cart, coalman and coal sack, white / orange horse, 12-spoke wheels, 6 spare sacks	£400-600
---	---	**Coffee Stall** (four wheels)	Orange / yellow stall, silver chimney, brown / white horse, tea urn and crockery	£150-175
---	---	**Railway Wagon** (four wheels)	Grey / red open wagon, 'London Midland Scottish Railway' cast in, driver, white horse	£400-600
---	---	**Horse-Drawn Grass Cutter**	Yellow / red cutter, brown driver and horse (see also 3)	£100-125
---	---	**Horse-Drawn Roller**	Green / yellow roller, brown driver and horse (see also 2)	£100-125
---	---	**Horse-Drawn Delivery Van**	Blue / white, 'HOVIS', four wheels, brown horse, driver	£400-600
---	---	**Gamekeeper with Dog**	Gamekeeper with cap and shotgun, brown/white dog with bird in mouth	£100-125
---	---	**Flower Seller**	Seated female figure with bunch of flowers, separate casting of basket of flowers	£100-125
---	---	**Jack's Band**	Nine assorted musicians plus conductor	£400-600
---	---	**Circus Clown Set**	Clowns on Stilts, Clown on Unicycle, Clown climbing Ladder, Clown standing, Policeman clown	£75-100
---	---	**Circus Single Figures**	Liberty Horses, Performing Elephants, Seal with Balls, Strongman, Boxing Midgets, Acrobats, Parrot, Dog, Ringmaster	each: £15-20
---	---	**Hay Cart**	Yellow / green cart, grey / black horse, beige / black figure	£100-125
---	---	**Walking Barrow Boy**	A clockwork toy. Green / blue / red / yellow. Boxed	£80-100

Charbens No. 36, '3-wheel Pedestrian Electric Vehicle'. Photo: Vectis Auctions Ltd.

Pre-war Motor Vehicles (all cast in lead)

6   **Petrol Tanker**. Red, blue, yellow..£300-400
524 **Fire Engine**. Cast-in driver, separate ladder, rubber tyres £200-300
525 **Car and Caravan**. Six-light saloon car (red, green or yellow); Caravan copied from Dinky Toys 30g, yellow with orange lower half......£300-400
526 **Motor Van**. No details..£150-250
728 **Ambulance**. Man cast on rear step. Green or brown £200-300
864 **Racing Car**. Pale blue, green or yellow..£75-100
865 **Breakdown Lorry**. No details..£120-150
---   **Bentley Ambulance**. Copy of Dinky Toys 24a in off-white........£120-150
---   **1935 Bluebird**. Blue body...£300-400
---   **Armoured Car**. Six wheels, brown £80-100

---   **Caterpillar Tractor**. Copy of Tootsietoy but larger.
      'MIMIC TOY' cast underneath £150-250
---   **Tank**. Copy of Tootsietoy. 'MIMIC TOY' cast underneath.
      Very dark blue..£80-100
---   **Mack Stake Lorry**. Copy of Tootsietoy. Green and red.............£100-125
---   **Mack Lorry with AA Gun**.
      Copy of Tootsietoy. Light brown, black and silver.............£150-200
---   **Mack Searchlight Lorry**. Copy of Tootsietoy.
      Light brown and black..£150-200
---   **Mack Barrage Balloon Set**. No details.
      Johillco made a similar set £300-400

Post-war issues (Boxed models, mostly all-diecast construction)

-   late 1940s **Packard Saloon**. 'JAVELIN' cast under. Red or green..£40-60
-   late 1940s **Petrol Tanker**. Different from the pre-war tanker.
      Red, Green or Blue £40-60
-   late 1940s **Station Wagon**. Tan with dark brown bonnet and
      wings, spare wheel at rear £40-60
-   1959 **British Paratrooper and Motorcycle**. Military-green
      motorcycle and rider's uniform (red beret) £100-150

1 1940s-60 **Horse-Drawn Log Wagon**. Yellow, red wheels, with man, 2 tandem horses, wooden log, cream card box ...£80-100
2 1940s-67 **Horse-Drawn Roller**. Yellow with green or red roller, with horse and man (seated)...£80-100
3 1940s-67 **Horse-drawn Grass Cutter**. Yellow, red wheels, unpainted cutter, with horse and man (seated).............£80-100
4 1940s-67 **Horse-drawn Two-wheel Farm Wagon with Raves**. Green wagon, yellow shafts and wheels £80-100
5 1940s-67 **Horse-drawn Four-wheel Farm Wagon with Raves**. Green wagon, yellow shafts and wheels £80-100
6 1940s-67 **Tractor with Driver**. Red or orange with metal wheels or blue with rubber wheels.................................£80-100
7 1940s-62 **Horse-drawn Van with Man**. Blue with cream upper half, metal wheels, 'HOVIS BREAD' or 'PURE MILK' labels; or Orange with light brown upper half, rubber wheels, 'HOVIS BREAD' labels...£300-400
8 1940s-62 **Tipper Lorry**. Cab/tipper colours include: red/cream, blue/cream, dark green/yellow, orange/yellow...............£40-60
9 1940s-62 **Motor Coach**. Yellow with red flash, dark red with cream flash, dark blue with green flash, light green with blue flash, beige with green flash......................................£150-200

10 to 14   **Light Vans**. Two castings known. The first was a small boxy van with no rear windows. The second (from the early 1950s) was larger and more rounded, resembling a Ford E83W, with two rear windows.
10 1940s-60 **Royal Mail Van**. Red, 2nd casting with black bonnet, 'ROYAL MAIL', 'G-VI-R' paper labels £100-125
11 1940s-62 **'AMBULANCE'**. Cream, Red Cross (paper labels) ..£100-125
12 1940s-62 **'Carter Paterson' Van**. Dark green, 'CARTER PATERSON' on paper labels £100-125
13 1940s-60 **'Police' Van**. Dk. blue, 'POLICE GR' paper labels ..£100-125
14 1940s-62 **Post Office Telephones Van**. Green, 'POST OFFICE TELEPHONES' on paper labels.......£100-125
15 1940s-62 **Fire Engine and Wheeled Escape**. Red or orange-red, unpainted ladders, three firemen and hose £100-125
16 1940s-67 **Covered Wagon with Four Horses and Driver**. Green or red wagon, yellow wheels, cloth canopy, metal shaft and horses. Red box, full-colour label......£100-125
      Same, but Orange wagon, plastic shaft and horses £100-125
17 1940s-67 **Tractor and Log Trailer with Driver**. Tractor as No.6, Trailer as No.1 but with drawbar in place of shafts £150-200
18 1940s-62 **Tractor and Grass Cutter with two Drivers**. Tractor as No.6, Trailer modified from No.3 ....£150-200
19 1940s-67 **Tractor and Reaper with two Drivers**. Tractor as No.6, green Reaper (yellow or red metal blades) or light blue Reaper (red plastic blades), or all plastic £150-200
20 1954-67 **Mobile Crane**. Red body, green chassis, unpainted or yellow jib £40-60
      Orange body, light blue chassis, yellow jib....................£40-60

21 1954-67 **Muir-Hill Dumper with Driver**.
      Beige or orange with green or yellow dumper...............£40-60
      Red with yellow plastic dumper......................................£40-60
22 1954-67 **Travelling Zoo**. Elephant towing two cages with two lions, two polar bears, man. Red chassis, unpainted cages, yellow roofs, metal or plastic animals.............£100-125
      With orange chassis, light blue cages, yellow roofs ...£100-125
23 1955-58 **Water Pistol**. no details..£5-10
24 1954-55 **Costermonger's Cart**. Dark green cart, red or yellow wheels, donkey, man and basket.....................................£40-60
25 1955-? **Horse-drawn Milk Cart**. Yellow with red wheels, 'PURE MILK' labels. With man and churn £100-125
26 1954-62 **Armoured Car**. Green or beige, metal or rubber wheels ..£40-60
27 1955-67 **Large Tractor**. Cast in two halves. Red with yellow wheels or orange with light blue wheels £200-300
28 1954-67 **Diesel Road Roller**. Green or pale green, red wheels, unpainted flywheel..£60-80
29 1954-62 **Mincer**. Toy kitchen equipment, yellow............................£5-10
30 1955 **Scammell Mechanical Horse and Trailer**. Blue with 'LNER' labels, or dark brown cab with beige trailer and 'GWR' labels.......................................£60-80
31 1955-62 **Articulated Low-loader with Cable Drum**. Red or green cab, yellow trailer..£60-80
32 1955-62 **Alfa-Romeo Racing Car**. Hollow-cast lead, red with rubber wheels.....................£50-75
33 1955-62 **Cooper-Bristol Racing Car**. Hollow-cast lead, green with rubber wheels £50-75
34 1955-62 **Ferrari Racing Car**. Hollow-cast lead, blue (yellow) nose, rubber wheels £50-75
35 1954-67 **Horse-drawn Log Wagon**. As No.1 but single horse £50-75
36 1940s-55 **3-wheel Pedestrian Electric Van**. Dark blue, 'PURE MILK' or 'EXPRESS DAIRIES' printed on sides; milkman, crate and bottles £120-160
      Orange, 'HOVIS' on sides, man, tray of loaves.........£120-160
36 1957-62 **Maudslay Horse Box**. Dark red, 'HORSE TRANSPORT' printed on sides, horse and driver £120-160
      Green/Red body, 'NEWMARKET HORSEBOX' £120-160
36 1967 **Steam Roller Large scale**. Green body, red 12-spoke wheels, unpainted roller, black chimney, card box £300-400
37 1960-62 **Articulated Low-loader with Rocket Missile**. Dark green cab / trailer, orange / black missile launcher. No makers name on model...£90-120
38 1955-60 **'Shoot and Save' Money Box**. Savings bank, with gun to fire coin into bank £90-120
39 1955 **Telephone Kiosk**. Red kiosk with opening door, unpainted telephone £15-20
40 1940s-55 **Fire Engine with Ladder and Firemen**. Different from No.15. Red body, unpainted 2-part ladder..........£90-120
41 1955 **Fireplace**. Dolls house item £5-10
445 c1955 **'Auto Race Set' 'Andover series'**. Made only for the Flare Import Corporation, 230 Fifth Ave., New York. Contains 3 (Dinky style) racing cars, 6 mechanics, man with chequered flag. 43mm scale, hollow-cast. Card box has Formula I race scene on colour label...................£300-400
519 c1950 **'The Hiker's Camp Set'**. Green metal tent ('The Hikery'), Male Hiker resting, Male Hiker walking with backpack and stick, Female Hiker walking with backpack and stick, Female Hiker reading a book, 2 plates, 2 cups. Brown card box with b/w picture label on lid.................NGPP

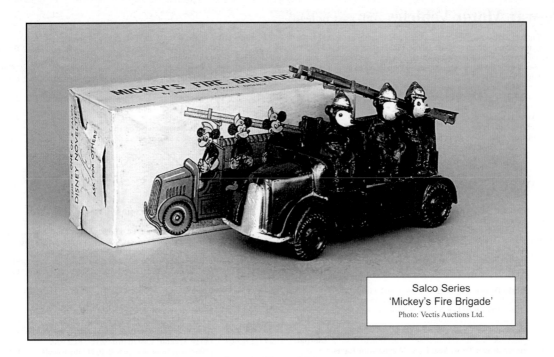

Salco Series
'Mickey's Fire Brigade'
Photo: Vectis Auctions Ltd.

Salco Series

---	**Mickey's Fire Brigade**	Red fire engine with unpainted ladder, 3 painted Mickey Mouse figures. All card picture box £1,250-2,000
---	**Mickey and Minnies' Piano**	Cream piano with operating handle, Mickey and Minnie Mouse figures.
		Black/Blue/Yellow/White all card picture box £1,250-2,000
---	**Mickey and Minnies' Barrel Organ**	Red organ with Yellow wheels, Mickey and Minnie Mouse figures. All card picture box £1,000-1,500
---	**Milk Cart with Pluto and Donald Duck**	........£200-300
---	**'Mickey and Minnie on the River'**	Green boat, 2 seats, Mickey and Minnie £750-1,000
---	**'Mickey and Donald's Garden' Set**	Blue wheelbarrow, spade and rake. Boxed £750-1,000
---	**Horse-drawn Brewer's Dray**	Light Blue dray with Yellow detachable brewery sign marked 'TOY TOWN BREWERS', six unpainted barrels, black bowler-hatted driver and brown horse £300-400
	Donald Duck's Dairy	A cart with Donald and Pluto. Yellow / red / blue / white £300-450

'Old Crocks', Military models and 'Miniature Lorries'

'OLD CROCKS' series

1 **1904 Darracq.** Dark Blue, Red or Orange, open 2-seater £10-25
2 **1904 Spyker.** Yellow 4-seater open car £10-25
3 **1914 'Old Bill' Bus.** 2-piece casting, or single casting plus separate top deck, Red or Orange £10-25
4 **1907 Ford Model T.** 2-piece casting, tin chassis, Dark Blue £10-25
  Single casting, no separate chassis, Dark Blue £10-25
5 **1907 Vauxhall.** Green open 2-seater £10-25
6 **1906 De Dion Bouton.** Light Green or Violet open 2-seater £10-25
7 **1898 Panhard.** Light Green or Brown 2-seater £10-25
8 **1906 Rolls-Royce Silver Ghost.** Silver 4-seater open car £10-25
9 **1903 Standard 6hp.** Dark Red or Maroon with Beige roof £10-25
10 **1902 Wolseley.** Light Blue 4-seater open car £10-25
11 **1908 Packard Runabout.** Light Green open 2-str £10-25
12 **1905 Vauxhall Hansom Cab,** Orange / Beige £10-25
13 **1900 Straker Flat Steam Lorry.** Light Green, packing case £10-25
  1900 Straker Lowside Steam Lorry. Light Blue, three barrels £10-25
14 **Stephenson's 'Rocket' Locomotive.** Yellow / Black £10-25
15 **Tender for 'Rocket',** colours as 14 ....£10-25
16 **1909 Albion.** Dark or Light Blue open truck £10-25
17 **1912 Rover.** Orange 2-seater open sports car £10-25
18 **1911 Mercedes-Benz.** Dark Green open 2-seater £10-25
19 **Bedford Horse-Box.** Brown, *'HORSE TRANSPORT'* cast on sides, *'H.G. IVORY'* on tailgate £15-25

20 **1910 Lanchester.** Light Blue 4-seater sports tourer £10-25
21 **1922 Morris Cowley.** Beige 2-seater open car £10-25
22 **1900 Daimler.** Maroon 2-seater £10-25
23 **1904 Autocar.** Dark Blue, open 3-wheeler £10-25
24 **1870/80 Grenville Steam Carriage.** Green or Light Green £10-25
25 **1905 Napier.** Violet or Purple 2-seater racer £10-25
26 **Fire Engine and Escape.** Red or Orange £10-25
27 **Articulated Breakdown Lorry.** Dark Green cab, Light Blue trailer, Orange crane £10-25
28 **Mercer Runabout.** Dark Blue or Green 2-seater sports £10-25

MILITARY MODELS

30 **Searchlight on 4-wheel Trailer.** Green and Silver £10-25
31 **Twin Bofors Gun on Trailer.** Green and Silver £10-25
32 **Radar Scanner on Trailer.** Green and Silver £10-25
33 **Field Gun on Trailer.** Green and Silver £10-25
34 **Rocket Gun on Trailer.** Green and Silver £10-25
35 **Armoured Car.** Green £10-25

'MINIATURE LORRIES' (not issued)

40 **Articulated Tanker.** Listed in 1960 catalogue ....NPP
41 **Articulated Lorry.** Listed in 1960 catalogue ....NPP
42 **Six-wheeled Lorry.** Listed in 1960 catalogue ....NPP
43 **Six-wheeled Tanker.** Listed in 1960 catalogue ....NPP

Mettoy
Corgi Toys

Corgi Toys were launched in 1956 by the Mettoy Company which had itself been founded in Northampton by Phillip Ullmann in 1933. The 'Mettoy' name was derived from the first three letters of 'Metal' plus 'toy' - the company's main product range being composed of lithographed metal toys. In 1948 Mettoy produced their first cast metal toys and called them 'Castoys'. The Castoys models contained a clockwork motor and when the first Corgi Toys models were introduced they also contained a mechanism. This, plus the introduction of window glazing, gave Corgi a competitive edge against their great rivals, Dinky Toys.

Corgi Toys were named after the Welsh breed of dogs and this logo will be found on virtually all the Corgi packaging. The models were produced in Swansea by Mettoy Playcraft Ltd., hence baseplates are marked 'Made in Gt. Britain'.
The development of the Corgi Toys product range was largely instigated by Howard Fairbairn, a Mettoy Company Director. Prior to his director appointment, he had been Head of Development at the Birmingham Aluminium Casting Co. and had considerable diecasting experience. The first truly Corgi Toys product was No.200 Ford Consul in 1956.

Corgi have always been famed for their model innovations. This was especially true when they were able to promote their models as 'The Ones With Windows'. Additionally, greater realism was achieved over time with, for example, better detailing of their wheel hubs.

Corgi introduced various model ranges which have stood the test of time. Today, virtually all the Corgi models produced in the 1950s and 1960s are highly sought after. In particular, model such as the range of 'Monte Carlo' Minis, the Gift Sets, Farm Tractors and the 'Chipperfield's Circus' subjects are

Corgi Toys shop display card

Photo: Vectis Auctions

very collectable. In addition, television and film related models such as 'Batman', 'James Bond' and similar items fetch very high prices at auction.

In 1983, the Mettoy company went into receivership and Corgi Toys became the subject of a management buy-out. From this time, the emphasis changed from the mass-production of toy vehicles to mainly the development of authentic limited edition models aimed at adult collectors - the 'Corgi Classics' range. Regrettably these items fall outside the scope of this publication. However, collectors requiring information on Corgi Classics are recommended to join the Corgi Collectors Club.

The Editor wishes to thank all who have contributed to the greatly revised listings.

Market Price Range

Please note that the prices shown refer to pristine models and boxes.

Items failing to match this standard will sell for less.

Note also that boxes must still contain all their original additional contents.

Corgi Toys Identification

Often referred to as 'the ones with windows', Corgi Toys were the first manufacturer to produce models with that refinement. Some of their first models also had a mechanical motor. Spring suspension was introduced from 1959 and in 1960 the first die-cast model to have an opening bonnet. The first models were based on real cars of the period. Similarly, with the launch of the 'Corgi Major Toys' in 1959, models of real commercial vehicles were available and competed with the Dinky 'Supertoys' range.

In the 1960s Corgi produced many successful film and TV-related models. Probably the best remembered was the 'James Bond' Aston Martin which sold in huge quantities in the autumn of 1965. Indeed, such was the popularity of the model that a version was still available in 1992!

Corgi introduced many new features in the 1960s such as: jewelled headlights, opening bonnet revealing detailed engine, opening boot revealing spare, self-centering steering, ruby rear lights, etc. One particularly attractive model was the Midland Red Motorway Express Coach. The detailed interior even incorporated a toilet! Needless to say good examples of this model are highly sought after by bus collectors. Similarly the 'Chipperfields Circus' collection of models were beautifully produced and are highly prized today.

Innovations were frequent and imaginative in the 1960s. 'Golden Jacks' for instance, a built-in jacking system which enabled models to have 'Take-Off' wheels. And 'Trans-O-Lites' whereby light rays were captured and fed through prisms to illuminate the headlights. 'WhizzWheels' and the slightly larger scale of 1:42 were introduced in the 1970s.

A market strategy unique to Corgi was the launching a replica model car simultaneously with the real car. To date simultaneous launches have occurred with Austin Metro, Ford Escort, Triumph Acclaim, Ford Sierra and the MG Maestro 1600, which is a unique record. Corgi were the first die-cast manufacturers to introduce the dimensions of light, sound and movement into their models by using the micro-chip in their 'Corgitronic' range. The models 'come alive', for example by just pushing down on the rear axle or, in the case of the Road Repair Unit, by pressing the workman to activate the pneumatic drill sound. Others (like the Sonic Corgi Truck) can be operated from a remote control handset.

Mechanical. Some early Corgi Toys were produced in either the normal form or with a friction type flywheel motor. Exceptions were the sports cars and trucks which could not be converted to take the flywheel. The mechanisms were not robust and were phased out in 1959.

Boxes. July 1956 - Blue box, January 1959 - Yellow/Blue box (Two-tone cars were first to use them) December 1966 - Window box (2 square window ends) May 1973 - Angled window box (one square window end, coloured lines around box) 1980 - Yellow window box, 1987 New style Corgi logo box.

Box contents. Model boxes often contain much more than just the basic model. Prices shown in the Catalogue assume that not only is the model in pristine condition, but that it is accompanied by all the original additional contents. These can include: extra card packing, inner card or polystyrene trays, pictorial stands, plastic protectors, transit card protection intended for removal by the retailer, instruction and information leaflets, catalogues, consumables (such as unopened packets of rockets, decals, etc.). This particularly applies to some Novelty and Film/TV models, e.g., Nos. 268, 277, 497, 511, 1123, 1139, 1144 and Gift Sets 3, 10, 20 and 21. A further example relates to the early 'Blue box' models each of which should contain a concertina catalogue leaflet plus a 'Join the Corgi Club' leaflet. If original items are missing, e.g., the plastic dome protector included with 511 Chipperfields Poodle Truck or card protectors with other models, it will affect the price that a model will achieve.

Whilst every effort has been made to describe models and, where known, their accompanying contents, any further information would be welcomed.

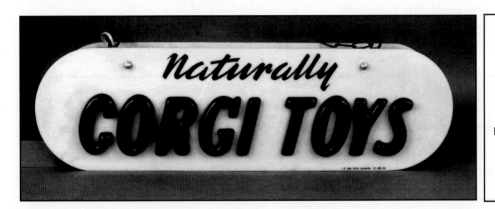

Corgi Toys advertising sign. This illuminated plastic and metal sign is fitted with chains for hanging. The yellow background has the wording 'Naturally' in red and 'Corgi Toys' in blue.

Photo: Vectis Auctions Ltd.

Castoys were produced by the Mettoy Company between 1948 and 1958 and were instigated by a request from Marks and Spencers for a robust, long lasting toy. The models were made of zinc alloy and were initially advertised as 'Heavy Cast Mechanical Toys'.

Generally, they had windows, a clockwork motor and brake, plus black rubber tyres on cast hubs. Of the original issues, only two models, No. 840, the 'Eight Wheel Lorry' and 870 'Delivery Van' remained in production after 1951 and these were packaged in attractive Yellow/Red boxes which displayed a picture of the model inside. The later issues of the Delivery Van with their various attractive body designs are now rare and sought after items.

The following listing contains all the information available at present. The Editor would welcome any additional information on body colours and variations.

NB See the 'Miscellaneous Models' colour section for pictures.

Ref	Year(s)	Model name	Colours, features, details	Market Price Range

Large Scale Models 1:35

Presented in Yellow/Red endflap boxes each displaying an excellent picture of the model contained within.

Ref	Year(s)	Model name	Colours, features, details	Market Price Range
-	-	Milk Handcart	with 'MILK' logo and Milkman	£150-175
718	1956-58	Luxury Observation Coach	Metallic Blue and Gold body with Silver raised roof section and base, Red door with Brown plastic male passenger Destination board shows 'PRIVATE' and registration 'MTY 718'	£250-350
			Metallic Brown and Pink body with Silver raised roof section and radiator, with Green female passenger	£200-300
810	1948-51	Limousine	Cream, Red or Green body, 'MTY 810'	NGPP
820	1948-51	Streamline Bus	Cream, Green or Red body, clockwork mechanism, Red pressed tin seating, solid rubber wheels, unpainted chassis. Registration No 'MTY 820'	£100-200
			As previous model but with opening door and registration No 'MTY 720'	£100-200
830	1948-51	Racing Car	Light Green, 6, long approx, 'METTOY' cast in base, tinplate hollow printed wheels with motor and brake	£100-200
840	1948-58	8 Wheel Lorry	Metallic Blue cab with Grey rear body, Silver radiator and hubs	£100-200
850	1948-51	Fire Engine	Red body, Silver ladder and crank	£100-200
			Red body, Silver extending ladder, no crank	£100-200
860	1948-51	Tractor	No models seen but shown in 1951 catalogue with Yellow/Red body	NGPP
863		Ferguson TE20 Tractor and Trailer	Red/Blue tractor, Yellow trailer, Red hubs, painted plastic driver	£150-200
870	1948-51	Delivery Van	No models seen but shown in 1948 catalogue with plain Dark Blue body	£100-150
	1952-55	'EXPRESS DELIVERY'	Yellow or Blue body with Red logo and design on sides	£150-200
	1955-58	'POST OFFICE TELEPHONES'	Green body, White logo, Royal crest in Gold, Silver two part extending ladder	£200-300
	1955-58	'ROYAL MAIL'	Red body, Silver trim, Yellow logo and Royal crest, 'MTY 870'	£200-300
	1955-58	'AMBULANCE'	Cream body with Black logo on sides	£100-200
	1956-58	'BOAC'	Blue body, Silver trim, White 'Fly By BOAC' on roof	£250-350

Small Scale Models 1:45

Ref	Year(s)	Model name	Colours, features, details	Market Price Range
---	1955-57	Soft Drinks Van	Dark red body, number plate 'CWS 300', Silver wheels, Logo on rear: 'CWS SOFT DRINKS - THIRST COME - THIRST SERVED'	£75-95

Special 1:18 scale issue for Marks and Spencer

Ref	Year(s)	Model name	Colours, features, details	Market Price Range
---	1958	'VANWALL' Racing Car	Diecast body, perspex screen, driver, 'VANWALL' transfers, 'push and go' motor in some. 'Vanwall the famous British Grand Prix Winner' cast in base.	
			i) Green body, racing number '7' or '18', no Mettoy logo on base	£300-350
			ii) French Blue body, racing number '20', no Mettoy logo on base	£300-350

The 'Miniature Numbers' series

The range of models produced between 1951 an 1954 was based on just two vehicles - the Standard Vanguard and the Rolls Royce. Models were issued in two sizes and featured a clockwork motor plus brake, adjustable steering (controlled by moving the central fog lamp sideways) and moulded grey plastic wheels. Both diecast and plastic bodies have been observed on some examples. They were packaged in attractive window boxes. The following listing has been taken from the 1951 Mettoy Catalogue and the Editor would welcome any additional information.

Ref	Year(s)	Model name	Colours, features, details	Market Price Range
502	1951	Standard Vanguard Saloon	Shown with Green body in catalogue (2 7/8 inches long)	£50-75
505	1951	Rolls-Royce Saloon	Red or Blue body, Silver trim (3 inches long)	£50-75
510	1951	Standard Vanguard Police Car	Black with White 'POLICE' logo on doors; roof siren and bell	£50-75
511	1951	Standard Vanguard Taxi	Shown in 1951 catalogue with Yellow body and Red roof rack	£50-75
512	1951	Standard Vanguard Fire Chief	Red, White 'FIRE CHIEF' on doors; single Silver ladder on roof	£50-75
602	1951	Standard Vanguard Saloon	Blue body shown in catalogue (large scale version of 502, 4¼ inches long)	£50-75
603	1951	Standard Vanguard Saloon	As 602 but with automatic to and fro bump feature	£50-75
605	1951	Rolls-Royce Saloon	Yellow body shown in catalogue (large scale version of 505, 4½ inches long)	£50-75
606	1951	Rolls-Royce Saloon	As 605 but with automatic to and fro bump feature	£50-75

NEW!
Catalogue users Updating Service

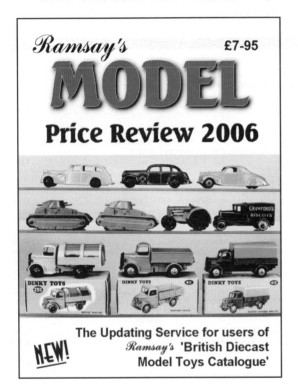

Ramsay's £7-95

MODEL
Price Review 2006

The Updating Service for users of
Ramsay's 'British Diecast
Model Toys Catalogue'

NEW!

Keep up to date! Times have changed and there is now a need for an updating service between Catalogue editions.

This will take the form of a new publication called '**Model Price Review**' which will become available in the autumn of 2006.

Make sure you are fully up to date with all the latest information, market trends, auction results and new discoveries in the world of model and toy collecting. Order your copy of '**Model Price Review 2006**' now!

See also 'Novelty, Film and TV-related' section.

Ref	Year(s)	Model name and details	Market Price Range

150 1957-61 **Vanwall Racing Car**
Green body, Yellow seat, large or small '*Vanwall*', flat hubs, RNs '1', '3' or '7', clear or Blue screen. 'Made in Gt Britain' or 'British Made' and large 'CORGI TOYS VANWALL' cast along base. Blue box with leaflet **£100-120**
Mid-Green body, Silver seat, small '*Vanwall*', clear screen. 'Made in Great Britain' cast along base. 'CORGI TOYS VANWALL' small across base. Flat hubs. RN '3' **£100-120**
Vermillion Red body, Silver or Yellow seat, small or large '*Vanwall*', Blue or clear screen. RN '1', '3' or '7'. 'CORGI TOYS VANWALL' cast small across or large along base. Flat or spoked hubs. Blue/Yellow box......**£150-200**

150 S 1961-65 **Vanwall Racing Car**
Vermillion Red body, Blue/White bonnet design plus Black RN '25', White driver, Silver seat, small '*Vanwall*', 'Made in Gt. Britain' cast along the base. '150S CORGI TOYS VANWALL' across base **£100-120**
Same model, but with Crimson body **£150-200**
Promotional: 'Vandervell Products' finish ....NGPP

150 1972-74 **Surtees TS9 Formula 1**
Metallic Purple or Metallic Blue body, 'BROOKE BOND OXO' logo, 8-spoke WhizzWheels **£30-35**
Metallic Turquoise body, cast 8-stud WhizzWheels.......**£15-20**
1975-76 Blue/Yellow body, '*DUCKHAMS*', (in GS 29 only)...........GSP

151 1958-61 **Lotus XI Le Mans Racing Car**
Blue body, Red or Maroon seats, clear or Blue-tinted windscreen, racing numbers '1', or '3'......................**£200-250**
Silver body, Red seats, RN '3'. Blue tinted screen **£120-150**
Red body, Beige seats, RN '1'. Blue tinted screen.....**£200-250**
151 A 1961-65 **Lotus XI Le Mans Racing Car**
Blue body, Red seats, Red/White bonnet stripe, White driver, Black racing number '7' **£100-150**
Blue body, no bonnet stripe, Red seats, White driver, Black racing number '7' **£100-150**
Lemon body, racing number '3', driver.....................**£130-160**

151 1974-76 **Yardley Mclaren M19A**
White body, 'YARDLEY', racing number '55', 8-spoke or stud WhizzWheels......................................**£35-45**
With Blue stripe on White helmet, WW, (GS30 only) ....GSP

152 1958-61 **B.R.M. Racing Car**
Light or Dark Green body, Yellow seat, no driver, racing numbers '1', '3' or '7'. Blue box with leaflet.....**£90-110**
1961-65 Turquoise body, Silver trim, Union Jack on bonnet, RN's '1', '3' or '7'. Blue/Yellow box, no leaflet **£90-110**
152 S 1961-65 **B.R.M. Racing Car**
Turquoise body, Union Jack on bonnet, White driver, RNs '1', '3' or '7', Blue/Yellow box, no leaflet..........**£140-160**

152 1974-75 **Ferrari 312 B2**
Red body, 'Ferrari/Shell' logo, RN '5', White driver, Orange/Blue helmet, 8-spoke or 8-stud cast hubs **£30-35**

153 1960-61 **Bluebird Record Car**
Blue body, UK and US flags on nose, metal hubs **£85-95**
153 A 1961-65 **Bluebird Record Car**
Blue body, UK and US flags on nose, plastic hubs.........**£85-95**
Blue body with two Union Jacks on nose, plastic hubs ..**£85-95**

Market prices shown here are for guidance only. They refer ONLY to mint models in pristine boxes that are complete with all of their original contents.

WW = WhizzWheels   RN = Rally or Racing Number

---

153 1972-74 **Team Surtees TS 9B**
Red body, Blue or Blue/White driver (Rob Walker), RN '26', 8-stud hubs **£40-50**
Red body, '*NORRIS*' logo, (Gift Set 30 only) ....GSP

154 1963-72 **Ferrari Formula 1**
Red body, Ferrari bonnet badge, White driver, RN'36' ..**£40-60**

154 1974-79 **'JOHN PLAYER SPECIAL' Lotus**
Black body, Gold trim, RN '1' or '4', 'JPS' logo, Black/Red helmet, 8-stud hubs, drivers Emerson Fittipaldi or Ronnie Petersen'Fittipaldi' on box **£30-35**
'JPS' logo, Black or Blue helmet, 'Petersen' on box......**£30-35**
'JPS TEXACO' logo, Red helmet **£30-35**
'JPS TEXACO', Black helmet, 12-spoke hubs ......(GS32 only)
'JPS SHELL' logo, Black/Red helmet, (GS30 only)..........GSP
Marks & Spencers issue:
No 'Corgi' on base, 'TEXACO' logo, Orange (?) helmet...GSP

155 1964-69 **Lotus Climax Racing Car**
British Racing Green body, Yellow stripe on bonnet, White driver, Blue helmet, racing number '1'...............**£30-35**
155 1974-76 **'SHADOW' Formula 1**
Black body, 'UOP', racing number '17', driver (Jackie Collins) White/Maroon helmet **£30-35**

156 1967-68 **Cooper-Maserati**
Dark Blue body, RN '7', White driver, Blue helmet **£30-35**
156 1974-79 **Graham Hill's Shadow**
White/Red body, RN'12', '*EMBASSY RACING*' **£30-35**
Special issue:
Model in box with outer sleeve as presented at the National Sporting Club showing name 'MENU' **£300-500**

158 1969-73 **Lotus Climax Racing Car**
Orange and White body, Blue driver, White helmet, Black number '8' and bonnet stripe...............................**£35-45**
158 1975-78 **Elf Tyrrell Ford F1**
Blue body, RN '1', '*ELF*', Jackie Stewart driving **£30-35**

159 1969-72 **Cooper-Maserati**
Yellow and White body, Black bonnet stripe, Blue driver, White helmet, cast wheels, Yellow racing number '3' **£30-35**
159 1974-76 **Indianapolis Racing Car**
Red body, racing number '20', Patrick Eagle driving **£30-35**

160 1975-78 **'HESKETH' 308 F1**
White body, Black helmet, 4-spoke or 8-stud hubs........**£30-35**
Yellow body, 'CORGI TEAM' logo, Orange driver (James Hunt), Black helmet, Blue belts, (GS26 only) ....GSP
Marks & Spencers issue: White body and driver, no 'CORGI' on some, Orange helmet ....GSP

161 1971-73 **Santa Pod 'COMMUTER'**
Red 'Dragster' body, Chrome engine, RN '2', WW **£25-30**
161 1977-78 **'ELF-TYRRELL' P34**
Blue and Yellow body, 'ELF' logo, Red or Blue helmet, 8-stud hubs, Yellow racing number '4' **£25-30**
162 1978-79 **'ELF-TYRRELL' P34**
Blue / White body, 'FIRST NATIONAL BANK' logo, Red or Orange helmet **£25-30**
Marks & Spencers issue:
As previous model but no 'Corgi' on base, 8-stud hubs......GSP

162 1971-72 **'QUARTERMASTER' Dragster**
Green and White body, aerofoil, driver, plastic hubs **£50-60**
163 1971-73 **Santa Pod Dragster 'GLOWORM'**
White body, Blue trim, Red chassis, driver **£30-35**
164 1972-73 **Ison Bros Dragster '*WILD HONEY*'**
Yellow/Black body, Green tinted glass, WhizzWheels....**£40-50**
165 1972-74 **Adams Brothers '*DRAG-STAR*'**
Red/Yellow body, 4 x V-8 engines, WhizzWheels **£30-35**

166 1971-74 **Ford Mustang 'ORGAN GRINDER'**
Yellow/Green body, racing number '39', driver.............**£30-35**

167 1973-74 **USA Racing Buggy**
White/Red body, racing number '7', driver, US flag **£40-50**

169 1974-77 **'STARFIGHTER' Dragster**
Blue/Silver/Red body, *'FIRESTONE'*.............................**£30-35**

170 1974-77 **John Woolfe's Dragster**
'RADIO LUXEMBOURG', '208' **£40-50**

190 1974-77 **'JOHN PLAYER' Lotus**
1:18 scale, Black/Gold, RN '1', driver, removable wheels, tools included in box..**£35-40**

191 1975-80 **'TEXACO MARLBORO' F1 Mclaren**
1:18 scale, White/Red, RN '5', removable wheels, tools included in box...**£35-40**

200 1956-61 **Ford Consul** (This was the first 'Corgi Toys' model)
Smooth cast hubs, no suspension, leaflet with early issues.
Cream body **£140-180**
Dark or Pale Green body **£140-180**
Tan or Dark Tan body **£140-180**
Blue body **£140-180**
Light Greyish-Brown body **£140-180**
Bright Green body..**£140-180**

200M 1956-59 **Ford Consul** (with flywheel motor)
Smooth cast hubs, no suspension, leaflet with early issues.
Two-tone Green..**£140-180**
Green/Cream **£140-180**
Silver/Cream..**£140-180**
Pale Grey over Green **£140-180**
Blue body **£140-180**
Dark Green or Bright Green **£140-180**

200 1976-78 **BLMC Mini 1000**
Metallic Blue body, Silver roof, Red or White interior...**£20-25**

200A 1978-83 **BLMC Mini 1000**
Metallic Blue or Silver body, White or Red interior, Union Jack stripe on roof, WhizzWheels **£25-35**

201 1956-61 **Austin Cambridge**
No suspension, leaflet with early issues.
Pale Blue body **£140-180**
Turquoise body..**£140-180**
Light Grey or Mid-Greybody...............................**£140-180**
Green/Cream **£175-225**
Two-tone Green..**£140-180**
Silver over Metallic Green....................................**£200-250**

201M 1956-59 **Austin Cambridge** (with flywheel motor)
Leaflet with early issues.
Cream body **£140-180**
Red body **£140-180**
Slate Grey or Medium Grey body **£140-180**
Silver or Metallic Blue...**£140-180**
Burnt Orange body..**£300-400**

201 1970-72 **The Saint's Volvo**
White body, White 'Saint' logo on red label, WhizzWheels, driver, Red/Yellow 'window' box **£140-160**

201 1979-82 **BLMC Mini 1000**
Silver body, with or without 'TEAM CORGI' and '8'....**£15-25**
As previous model but with Orange body **£15-25**
Dark Blue body without 'TEAM CORGI' **£15-25**
Dark Blue with 'ESSO' and 'MICHELIN' labels **£15-25**

202 1956-61 **Morris Cowley**
Smooth cast hubs, no suspension, leaflet with early issues.
Bright Green body..**£140-170**
Grey body...**£140-170**
Blue body **£140-170**
Grey/Blue body..**£140-170**
Blue/Cream body...**£140-170**
Pale Green/Blue body **£140-170**
White/Blue body **£140-170**

202M 1956-59 **Morris Cowley** (with flywheel motor)
Leaflet with early issues.
Pale Green or Medium Green or Dark Green body.....**£140-170**
Off-White body **£140-170**

202 1970-72 **Renault 16TS**
Blue/Silver body, Yellow interior, WhizzWheels **£25-30**

203 1970-72 **De Tomaso Mangusta**
Metallic Dark Green, Gold stripes, racing number '1'....**£25-35**

203 1956-61 **Vauxhall Velox**
Smooth cast hubs, leaflet with early issues.
Red body **£140-170**
Cream body **£140-170**
Yellow body **£140-170**
Yellow/Red body..**£140-170**

203M 1956-59 **Vauxhall Velox** (with flywheel motor)
Smooth cast hubs, leaflet with early issues.
Red body **£200-250**
Orange body **£250-300**

203 1971-72 **De Tomaso Mangusta**
Green/Gold body, White interior, WhizzWheels **£25-30**
Green body, White interior, Silver base, WhizzWheels ..**£25-35**

204 1956-61 **Rover 90**
Smooth cast hubs, leaflet with early issues.
Cream or Off-White body £150-175
Light or Dark Grey body, flat hubs...........................£150-175
Mid or Dark Green body, flat hubs...........................£150-175
Metallic Green body, flat hubs................................£150-175
Metallic Red lower body, with Cream upper body......£150-175
Metallic Cerise over Grey body................................£150-175

204M 1956-59 **Rover 90** (with flywheel motor)
Smooth cast hubs, leaflet with early issues.
Bright Mid-Green or Dark Green body £160-190
Grey body...£160-190
Metallic Green body..£200-250

204 1972-73 **Morris Mini-Minor**
Dark Blue body, Lemon interior, WhizzWheels............£80-100
Deep Blue body, Lemon interior, WhizzWheels £200-250
Metallic Blue body, Lemon interior, WhizzWheels £100-125
All-Orange body, Lemon interior, WhizzWheels £100-125
Orange body, Black roof, WhizzWheels....................£120-150

205 1956-62 **Riley Pathfinder**
Smooth cast hubs, leaflet with early issues.
Red body £130-160
Blue body...£130-160

205M 1956-59 **Riley Pathfinder** (with flywheel motor)
Smooth cast hubs, leaflet with early issues.
Red body £200-250
Mid Blue body £200-250
Navy Blue body £200-250

206 1956-59 **Hillman Husky Estate**
Smooth cast hubs, leaflet with early issues.
Tan or Greyish Light-Brown body...........................£100-140
Metallic Blue and Silver body £130-170

206M 1956-59 **Hillman Husky Estate** (with flywheel motor)
Smooth cast hubs, leaflet with early issues.
Cream body £150-190
Mid-Blue body £150-190
Grey body...£150-190
Turquoise body..£250-300

207 1957-62 **Standard Vanguard III**
Smooth cast hubs, leaflet with early issues.
White body (Red roof) £120-140
Grey body (Red roof)..£120-140
Red over Green body £120-140

207M 1957-59 **Standard Vanguard III** (with flywheel motor)
Smooth cast hubs, leaflet with early issues.
Primrose Yellow body £190-230
Pale Green body, Red roof pillars............................£145-175

208 1957-60 **Jaguar 2.4 litre**
Smooth cast hubs, leaflet with early issues.
White body £120-150

208M 1957-60 **Jaguar 2.4 litre** (with flywheel motor)
Smooth cast hubs, leaflet with early issues.
Metallic Dark Blue body..£150-175

208 S 1960-63 **Jaguar 2.4 litre** (with spring suspension)
Lemon body, smooth hubs £120-150
Pale Lemon body, shaped spun hubs £120-150

210 1957-60 **Citroën DS19**
Smooth cast hubs, leaflet with early issues.
Yellow body, Red roof, Grey or Silver baseplate £120-160
Metallic Dark Green body, Black roof.......................£120-160
As previous but with bulge to take flywheel motor.
Note that a '210M' was not produced.........................£120-160

210 S 1960-65 **Citroën DS19** (with spring suspension)
Red body, Lemon interior, Grey baseplate £100-120

211 1958-60 **Studebaker Golden Hawk**
Smooth cast hubs, leaflet with early issues.
Blue body, Gold rear wing flashes...........................£120-150
White body, Gold rear wing flashes.........................£100-125

211M 1958-59 **Studebaker Golden Hawk** (with flywheel motor)
Smooth cast hubs, leaflet with early issues.
White/Gold body £150-200

211 S 1960-65 **Studebaker Golden Hawk** (with spring suspension)
Gold ('plated') body, Red interior, White flash,
shaped hubs £125-150
Gold (painted) body, shaped hubs...........................£125-150

212 1958 **Road Racer** Not released, one example known to exist....NPP

214 1959-65 **Ford Thunderbird Hardtop**
Smooth cast hubs, leaflet with early issues.
Pale Green (Cream hardtop), '1959' rear no. plate......£100-120
Grey (Red hardtop), '1959' on rear number plate £100-120
Pale Green (Cream hardtop), blank rear no. plate £100-120

214M 1959-60 **Ford Thunderbird Hardtop** (with flywheel motor)
Smooth cast hubs, leaflet with early issues.
Pink (Black hardtop), '1959' on rear number plate £200-250
Pale Green body, Cream hardtop £170-200

214 S 1962-64 **Ford Thunderbird Hardtop** (with spring suspension)
Metallic Grey/Red body, Lemon interior....................£100-120
Black/Red body, Lemon interior...............................£100-120

215 1959-62 **Thunderbird Open Sports**
White body, Blue interior.......................................£100-120
Blue body, Silver interior.......................................£100-120

215 S 1962-64 **Thunderbird Open Sports** (with spring suspension)
Red body with Yellow interior and driver £140-180

499 'Winter Olympics' Citroën
with tobogganist

258 The 'Saint's' Car
(Volvo P1800)

216 1959-62 **Austin A40**
Smooth cast hubs, leaflet with early issues.
Two-tone Blue body.....................................**£100-120**
Red body, Black roof **£100-120**

216M 1959-60 **Austin A40** (with flywheel motor)
Smooth cast hubs, leaflet with early issues.
Red body, Black roof **£130-160**
All-Red body **£130-160**

217 1960-63 **Fiat 1800 Saloon**
Light Blue (Lemon interior), smooth or shaped hubs **£80-90**
TT Blue (Lemon interior), smooth or shaped hubs **£80-90**
Light Tan body, Lemon interior **£80-90**
Mustard Yellow body, Bright Yellow interior............**£100-120**

218 1960-62 **Aston Martin DB4**
Red body (bonnet vent on some), flat or shaped hubs ..**£80-100**
1961-62 Red body, Red interior, cast 'spoked' hubs..................**£80-100**
Primrose Yellow body with bonnet vent,
Red interior, flat spun hubs.......................**£80-100**
Same model, but with cast 'criss-cross' wheels..........**£140-170**

219 1959-63 **Plymouth Suburban Sports**
Cream with Fawn roof, Red interior.............................**£80-100**

220 1960-65 **Chevrolet Impala**
Metallic Red body, Red or Lemon interior,
spun hubs, leaflet.............................**£70-80**
Same, but Powder Blue body.......................**£70-80**
Pink body, Lemon interior, spun hubs **£70-80**
Sky Blue body, Red interior, spun hubs........................**£80-90**

221 1960-63 **Chevrolet Impala Cab**
Yellow body, *'NEW YORK TAXI'*, Red interior,
smooth/shaped spun hubs, roof box **£90-110**

221 1960-63 **Chevrolet Impala State Patrol**
See 'Emergency Vehicles' section.

222 1959-65 **Renault Floride**
Dark Red body; Red, White or Yellow
interior, flat or shaped hubs...................**£60-70**
Maroon body, Red, White or Yellow
interior, flat or shaped hubs....................**£60-70**
Metallic Blue body, Red interior, shaped hubs...............**£60-70**

224 1961-65 **Bentley Continental**
Opening boot with removable spare, special lights.
Cream over Metallic Apple Green, Red interior.........**£120-140**
Black over Silver body, Red interior **£120-140**
Two-tone Green or Gold body **£120-140**
Metallic Green and White body **£120-140**
Cherry Red body, Lemon interior **£120-140**

225 1961-65 **Austin 7 (Mini) Saloon**
Red body, Yellow interior, spun hubs **£75-85**
Primrose-Yellow body, Red interior, flat hubs............**£500-600**
Mid-Blue body, Red interior, shaped hubs **£400-500**
Danish promotional: 'JENSEN'S',
Red body, Lemon interior, flat spun hubs.............**£1,000-1,200**

226 1960-68 **Morris Mini Minor**
Pale Blue body, Cream or Yellow interior,
flat or shaped hubs **£60-70**
Red body, flat or shaped hubs **£60-70**
Metallic Maroon, Lemon interior, detailed cast hubs.....**£70-80**
Yellow body **£200-250**
Danish promotional: 'JENSEN'S',
Pale Blue body, Red interior, flat spun hubs **£1,200-1,400**
Deep Blue body, (only in Gift Set 11) ....GSP
NB The Light Blue version of 226 was also used for
a short time by a US games manufacturer in a table-top
racing game. This version has a large drive-pin hole in
the base and has 'EAST AFRICAN RALLY' stickers
on the bonnet, RN '3'. Not separately boxed **£200-300**

227 1962-65 **Mini Cooper Rally**
Bright Blue body, White roof and bonnet, Red interior,
spun hubs, Union Jack and chequered bonnet flags,
racing numbers '1', '3' or '7'......................................**£200-300**
Same but Bright Blue body and bonnet, White roof ...**£200-300**
Primrose Yellow body, White roof and bonnet,
with flags and racing number '3' or '7' **£200-300**
Primrose Yellow body and bonnet, flags, RN '1'.......**£200-300**
Green body, White roof. Not seen ....NPP

228 1962-65 **Volvo P-1800**
Beige body, Red interior, spun hubs **£65-75**
Red body, Lemon interior, spun hubs **£80-100**
Pink or Dark Pink body, Lemon interior **£55-65**

229 1961-66 **Chevrolet Corvair**
Mid-Blue body, Bright Yellow interior, spun hubs..........**£60-70**
Pale Blue body, Lemon or Red interior, shaped hubs **£60-70**
Gold body, (in 'Golden Guinea' set)...................................GSP

230 1962-64 **Mercedes-Benz 220 SE**
Shaped spun hubs, spare wheel in boot.
Cream (Red interior)................................**£70-80**
Metallic Red body, Lemon interior..............................**£70-80**
Black body, Lemon interior **£70-80**
Dark Blue body, Lemon interior **£70-80**

231 1961-65 **Triumph Herald**
Gold top and bottom, White in centre, Red interior **£100-130**
Mid-Blue top and bottom, White centre, Red interior....**£70-80**
All Pale Blue (other details required, please) ....NGPP

232 1961-63 **Fiat 2100**
Pale Pink with Mauve roof, Lemon interior, spun hubs ..**£60-70**

233 1962-72 **Heinkel Trojan**
Spun hubs or detailed cast hubs.
Red body, Lemon interior **£75-80**
Blue body, Lemon interior **£75-80**
Lilac body, Lemon interior **£100-140**
Orange body, Lemon interior **£100-140**
Pink body, Lemon interior **£100-140**
Metallic Blue body, spun hubs **£100-125**
Fawn body, spun hubs **£100-125**
Turquoise body, spun hubs **£100-125**
NB This was the first Corgi model to have
'By Special Request' flash on the box.

234 1961-65 **Ford Consul Classic**
Beige body, Pink roof, Lemon interior, or Gold body.....**£70-80**

235 1962-66 **Oldsmobile Super 88**
All with spun hubs.
Black body, White side flash **£85-95**
Metallic Steel Blue, White side flash, Red interior **£85-95**
Light Blue body, Red interior, White side flash **£85-95**

236 1964-68 **'CORGI' Motor School** (Austin A60)
Light Blue body, 2 figures, 'Highway Code' leaflet,
right-hand drive **£90-110**
Export issue: Dark Blue, left-hand drive, leaflet..............**£125-150**

238 1962-67 **Jaguar Mk10**
All issues have spun hubs, luggage in boot.
Blue/Yellow box with leaflet.
Pale Blue body, Red interior...................................**£100-120**
Mid-Green body, Red interior.....................................**£100-120**
Deep Blue body, Red interior **£100-120**
Kingfisher Blue body, Lemon interior........................**£100-120**
Sea-Green body, Red interior....................................**£200-300**
Metallic Steel (Blue-Grey) body, Red interior............**£125-150**
Metallic Deep Blue body, Red or Lemon interior **£125-150**
Metallic Sea-Green body, Red interior **£175-200**
Metallic Cerise body, Lemon interior **£120-140**
Metallic Silver body, Red interior.............................**£175-200**
Metallic Green body, Red interior **£100-125**

239 1963-68 **VW 1500 Karmann Ghia**
Spare wheel/suitcase in boot, spun hubs.
Cream body (Red interior)...**£80-90**
Red body (Yellow interior)...**£80-90**
Gold body, Red or Yellow interior.................................**£90-100**
Red body, White or Yellow interior.................................**£80-90**
Plum body, Red interior..**£90-100**
Orange body, Yellow interior......................................**£130-160**

240 1963-64 **Fiat 600 Jolly**
Spun hubs, two figures.
Metallic Light Blue, Silver/Red top, Red interior **£150-200**
Metallic Dark Blue body, Red interior......................**£120-140**
Blue body, Red interior..**£120-140**
Yellow body, Red interior **£120-140**

241 1963-69 **Chrysler Ghia L64**
All have shaped spun hubs or detailed cast hubs
and a Corgi dog on the rear shelf.
Metallic Blue/White body, Cream interior.....................**£70-80**
Metallic Green body, Cream interior **£70-80**
Metallic Gold body..**£70-80**
Metallic Silver Blue body (Red interior) **£70-80**
Metallic Copper..**£70-80**
Lime Green, Yellow interior **£80-100**

242 1965-66 **Ghia Fiat 600**
Orange-Yellow body, Red interior, two figures in
swim gear, windscreen but no canopy **£250-350**

245 1964-68 **Buick Riviera**
Model has 'Trans-O-Lites' and towbar
Metallic Gold body, Red interior, spoked hubs **£70-80**
Same, but with cast hubs..**£110-130**
Metallic Steel Blue (Red interior) body.........................**£70-80**
Metallic Greenish Blue body..**£70-80**
Pale Blue body, spun or cast hubs **£70-80**

246 1965-68 **Chrysler Imperial Convertible**
Shaped spun or detailed cast hubs. All issues should
include driver/passenger, golf trolley in boot,
Blue/Yellow box with inner packing.
Metallic Deep Red body, Pale Blue or Green interior...**£80-100**
Metallic Turquoise body, Green interior.....................**£80-100**
Metallic Blue body, Pale Blue interior.......................**£110-130**
Metallic Kingfisher Blue body, Green interior **£175-225**

247 1964-69 **Mercedes-Benz 600 Pullman**
Metallic Maroon body, Cream interior,
windscreen wipers, instruction sheet **£80-90**
Metallic Red body, Cream interior, spun hubs **£80-90**

248 1965-67 **Chevrolet Impala**
Brown body, Cream roof/interior, shaped spun hubs **£45-55**

249 1965-69 **Morris Mini-Cooper DeLuxe**
Black body, Red roof, Lemon interior,
wickerwork panels, spun or cast hubs **£125-150**

251 1963-66 **Hillman Imp**
Model has spun hubs and luggage.
Metallic Blue body, Yellow interior...............................**£85-95**
Metallic Bronze body, White side stripe and interior ..**£100-125**
<u>Danish promotional</u>: 'JENSEN'S',
Light Blue body, Yellow interior, logo **£1,000-1,200**

252 1963-66 **Rover 2000**
Model fitted with spun hubs; leaflet in box.
Metallic Light Blue or Steel Blue body, Red interior **£90-110**
Metallic Maroon body, Red or Yellow interior...........**£230-280**

253 1964-68 **Mercedes-Benz 220 SE**
Metallic Maroon body, luggage, spare wheel **£80-100**
Metallic Blue body, luggage, spare wheel **£80-100**

255 1964-68 **Motor School A60**
Dark Blue body, left-hand drive, 5 language leaflet,
(USA issue of 236)...**£100-125**

256 1965-68 **Volkswagen 1200 Rally**
Orange body, RN '18', 'EAST AFRICAN RALLY',
steering wheel on roof, rhinoceros...............................**£250-300**

258 1965-70 **The Saint's Volvo P1800**
See 'Novelty, Film and TV-related' section.

259 1966-69 **Citroën 'Le Dandy'**
Metallic Dark Red, Yellow interior, wire wheels **£125-150**
Metallic Blue body, White roof and boot **£125-150**

260 1969-? **Renault 16 TS**
Metallic Red, Yellow interior, cast hubs **£35-45**

261 1965-69 **James Bond's Aston-Martin**
See 'Novelty, Film and TV-related' section.

262 1967-69 **Lincoln Continental Executive Limousine**
Box should also contain a picture strip for use
with the on-board 'TV set'.
Metallic Gold/Black body **£150-175**
Light Blue/Tan body **£175-225**

263 1966-69 **Rambler Marlin Sports**
Red body, Black roof White interior, spun or cast hubs ..**£40-50**
White body, Blue roof, (in Gift Set 10) ....**GSP**

264 1966-69 **Oldsmobile Toronado**
Metallic Medium or Dark Blue body,
smooth or cast spoked hubs, Cream interior..................**£35-45**

269 1977-83 **James Bond Lotus Esprit**   See 'Novelty, Film and
270 1968-78 **James Bond Aston-Martin**   TV-related' section for
271 1978-92 **James Bond Aston-Martin**   these models.

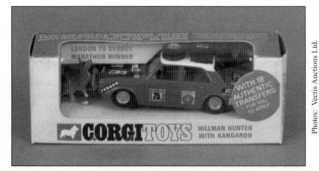

302 Hillman Hunter Rally Car with 'Golden Jacks', a kangaroo
and 18 additional transfers

513 Citroën Safari 'Alpine Rescue Car'
with St Bernard dog and handler

Photos: Vectis Auctions Ltd.

272	1969-69	**Ghia Mangusta De Tomaso**
		Blue/White body with Gold stripes, aerial **£80-100**
		Orange-Red body, aerial **£80-100**
272	1981-83	**James Bond Citroën 2cv**
		See 'Novelty, Film and TV-related' section.
273	1970-?	**Rolls-Royce Silver Shadow**
		With 'Golden Jacks', 'Take-Off wheels', spare wheel.
		Metallic Silver/Blue **£75-95**
		Pearlescent White over Grey, Blue interior **£65-85**
273	1982-83	**Honda Ballade 'BSM' Driving School Car**
		Yellow body with Red side stripes................................. **£25-35**
274	1970-72	**Bentley 'T' Series**
		Bright Pink body, Cream interior, special lights, WW **£45-55**
275	1968-70	**Rover 2000 TC**
		With 'Golden Jacks', 'Take-Off wheels', spare wheel.
		Metallic Olive Green body, Brown or Red interior,
		Amber roof panel **£75-85**
		Same as above but with White interior........................ **£90-120**
		White body, Maroon interior, Amber roof panel **£120-150**
		Metallic Maroon body... **£90-120**
		Gold plated version **£150-250**
275	1981-84	**Mini Metro**
		Blue, Purple or Red body, Yellow interior...................... **£10-15**
		Gold body.. **£45-50**
		'Royal Wedding' Metro
		Mauve body with Silver 'Charles & Diana' crest,
		special Mauve box **£20-25**
276	1968-72	**Oldsmobile Toronado**
		With 'Golden Jacks', 'Take-Off wheels'.
		Metallic Blue or Red body... **£50-70**
		Metallic Gold body, Cream interior **£45-65**
		Metallic Green body, Cream interior **£45-65**
		Metallic Brown body, Cream interior **£45-65**
276	1982-83	**Triumph Acclaim**
		Metallic Blue, or Cream body, steering control............... **£7-10**
277	1982-	**Triumph Acclaim 'BSM' Driving School Car**
		Yellow body, Black 'wheel' steering control on roof **£15-20**
278	1982-?	**Triumph Acclaim 'CORGI MOTOR SCHOOL' Car**
		Yellow body, with steering control, logo **£25-35**
279	1980-?	**Rolls-Royce Corniche**
		Metallic Dark Red body, opening doors/bonnet/boot...... **£20-25**
280	1970-78	**Rolls-Royce Silver Shadow**
		Metallic Silver upper body, Blue lower body,
		Brown interior, WhizzWheels **£35-40**
		Metallic Blue body, Brown interior, WhizzWheels.......... **£30-35**
281	1971-72	**Rover 2000 TC**
		Metallic Red body, Yellow interior,
		amber or clear roof, WhizzWheels **£60-75**
		Lacquered Purple body, Amber roof............................. **£100-125**
281	1982-	**'DATAPOST' Metro**
		Blue/White body, rally number '77', various adverts........ **£9-12**
282	1971-74	**Mini Cooper Rally**
		White/Black/Yellow, rally number '177',
		special lights, WhizzWheels **£55-65**
283	1971-74	**DAF 'City' Car**
		Red/Black body, White interior, WhizzWheels **£15-20**
284	1970-76	**Citroën SM**
		Green body, Pale Blue interior, spoked wheels **£55-75**
		Metallic Cerise, Pale Blue interior, spoked wheels **£55-75**
285	1975-81	**Mercedes-Benz 240 D**
		Silver, Blue, Bronze or Beige (all Metallic), WW........... **£25-35**
286	1975-79	**Jaguar XJC V-12**
		Blue/Black, Red/Black, Red, Pearl,
		Blue or Orange (all Metallic), WhizzWheels **£25-35**
287	1975-78	**Citroën Dyane**
		Metallic Green, duck decal, WhizzWheels.................... **£25-35**
		Metallic Yellow/Black, duck decal, WhizzWheels......... **£25-35**
		Metallic Bronze, duck decal, WhizzWheels **£25-35**

288	1975-79	**Minissima**
		Beige/Black/Yellow body **£25-35**
289	1976-80	**VW Polo 'DBP'** (German issue)
		Yellow/White body, left-hand drive, WW **£55-75**
289	1977-81	**Volkswagen Polo**
		Lime Green or Orange body **£25-35**
289	1977-81	**VW Polo 'ADAC'** (German issue)
		As previous model but Yellow body............................... **£55-75**
290	1976-77	**Kojak Buick**
		See 'Novelty, Film and TV-related' section.
290	1977-82	**Starsky & Hutch Ford Torino**
		See 'Novelty, Film and TV-related' section.
291	1977-80	**AMC Pacer**
		Metallic Red body, opening doors and hatchback **£20-25**
291	1982-?	**Mercedes Benz 240 Rally**
		Muddy Cream body, RN '5',
		'EAST AFRICAN RALLY' or *'E.A.R.'* logos **£20-25**
293	1977-80	**Renault 5 TS**
		Orange, Silver or Silver/Blue body, WhizzWheels **£20-25**
		French issue:
		Light Blue body, Dark Blue roof, 'SOS MEDICINS'...**£80-100**
294	1980-84	**Renault 5 TS Alpine**
		Black body with White stripe **£10-15**
298	1982-83	**Magnum P.I. Ferrari 308GTS**
		See 'Novelty, Film and TV-related' section.
299	1982-?	**Ford Sierra 2.3 Ghia**
		Metallic Light Brown/Black stripe, Dark Brown or Grey
		interior, Brown or Dark Grey base.
		Issued in a special two-tone Blue 'Ford' box **£20-25**
		Metallic Light Brown, Metallic Blue, Red or Yellow
		body, packed in White/Red 'Ford' box or normal
		Black/Yellow/Red box **£15-20**
300	1956-65	**Austin Healey 100-4**
		Smooth hubs, leaflet supplied with early issues.
		Red with Cream interior.. **£200-300**
		Cream with Red interior.. **£200-300**
		Blue body with Cream interior **£175-225**
300	1970-70	**Chevrolet Corvette Stingray**
		Model has 'Golden Jacks' / 'Take-Off Wheels', luggage.
		'Plated' Bright Green, Dark Red or Green body **£85-95**
		Metallic Red body, Black bonnet................................... **£65-75**
		Metallic Green body, Black bonnet **£65-75**
		NB Models without box header cards contained instructions.
300	1979-82	**Ferrari 'DAYTONA'**
		Green, multicoloured flash, RN '5', opening doors **£25-35**
301	1956-61	**Triumph TR2**
		Cream body with Red seats **£150-200**
		Red body with Cream seats **£150-200**
		Deep Green body with Cream seats............................ **£150-200**
301	1970-73	**Iso Grifo 7 litre**
		Metallic Blue body, Black bonnet, White interior,
		Silver or Black roll-bar, WhizzWheels **£30-35**
301	1979-82	**Lotus Elite Racing Car**
		Yellow/Red body, racing number '7', *'FERODO'* **£20-25**
302	1957-65	**MG 'MGA'**
		Red (Cream seats) smooth or chrome spun hubs,
		(paint shades exist).. **£200-240**
		Cream with Red seats... **£200-240**
		Mid or Dark Metallic Green body (Cream or
		Yellow seats), smooth or shaped spun hubs **£200-240**
302	1969-72	**Hillman Hunter Rally**
		Blue body, White roof, Matt-Black bonnet, RN '75',
		equipment, kangaroo, 'Golden Jacks', transfers,
		toolbox, leaflet, instructions....................................... **£100-130**
302	1979-82	**VW Polo**
		Metallic Brown/Red body, RN '4', various adverts **£20-25**
303	1958-60	**Mercedes-Benz 300 SL** (Open Roadster)
		Off-White body, Blue seats, smooth hubs, Blue box....**£125-150**
		Blue body, White seats, smooth hubs, Blue box **£100-125**
		Cream body, Blue seats, smooth hubs, Blue box........**£100-125**
		NB Models in rare plain overprinted box, add **£20-30**.

303 S 1961-63 **Mercedes-Benz 300 SL** (Open Sports)
Off-White body, Yellow interior, Red bonnet stripe,
racing numbers '1' to '12'..**£100-125**
Mid-Blue body, Yellow interior, Red bonnet stripe,
racing numbers '1' to '12'..**£150-175**

NB 'Open Sports' models were housed in
303S 'Open Roadster' boxes.

303S2 1963-64 **Mercedes-Benz 300 SL** (Open Sports with Driver)
With driver dressed in Grey suit, White shirt and Red
bow-tie. White body, Yellow interior,
Red bonnet stripe, racing numbers '1' to '12'.............**£100-130**
Blue body, Yellow interior, Red bonnet stripe,
racing numbers '1' to '12'...**£100-130**
Chrome plated body, Lemon/Brown interior, Red
bonnet stripe, spoked or cast hubs, RNs '1' to '12' **£175-225**

303 1970-72 **Roger Clark's Ford Capri**
White body, Black bonnet, RN '73', decal sheet,
WhizzWheels...**£70-80**
As previous model but with Red spot hubs.
Yellow/Red box with '9 transfers for you to apply!'.....**£90-110**

304 1959-61 **Mercedes-Benz 300 SL Hardtop**
Yellow body, Red hardtop, spun hubs, no suspension.**£100-125**
Yellow body and hardtop, flat spun hubs **£300-400**

304 S 1961-63 **Mercedes-Benz 300 SL Hardtop**
Chrome body, Red hardtop, stripe,
smooth/shaped/spoked hubs, RN '3' or '7' **£100-130**
White body, Red hardtop, RN '7', shaped hubs **£300-400**

304 1971-72 **Chevrolet Camaro SS350**
Dark Blue body, White bonnet band,
interior and detachable roof, special lights **£40-50**

305 1960-63 **Triumph TR3**
Metallic Olive Green or Cream body, Red seats,
smooth or shaped hubs...**£150-175**

305 S 1962-63 **Triumph TR3** (with spring suspension)
Light Green or Cream body, shaped spun hubs..........**£175-225**

305 1972-73 **Mini Marcos GT 850**
White body, Red interior, Blue/White stripes,
racing number '7', WhizzWheels **£30-35**

306 1971-73 **Morris Marina 1.8 Coupé**
Metallic Red body, Cream interior, WhizzWheels **£45-55**
Metallic Lime Green body, Cream interior, WW **£40-45**

306 1980-81 **Fiat X1/9S**
Metallic Blue body with Red/Yellow bands,
racing number '3' or '6'...**£15-20**

307 1962-64 **Jaguar 'E' type**
Metallic Grey body with Red removable hard-top,
spun hubs, inner packing...**£90-100**
Plum to Red body and hard-top, inner packing...........**£100-125**

307 1981-82 **Renault Turbo**
Yellow/Red body, RN '8', 'CIBIE', other adverts...........**£10-15**

308 1972-76 **Mini Cooper 'S' 'MONTE CARLO'**
Yellow body, RN '177', two spare wheels on
roof-rack, WhizzWheels, (339 update) **£100-125**
Gold 'plated' body. Only 144 thought to exist **£1,000-1,500**

308 1982-82 **BMW M1**
Yellow and Black body, RN '25', 'TEAM BMW' **£10-15**

309 1962-65 **Aston-Martin DB4 Competition**
Turquoise/White body, Lemon interior,
UK flags on bonnet, spun hubs, RN '1', '3' or '7'......**£150-175**
Variation with spoked hubs..**£150-175**

309 1982- **VW 'TURBO'**
White and Orange body, RN '14', Red decals **£10-15**

310 1963-67 **Chevrolet Corvette Stingray**
Metallic Cerise, Lemon interior, shaped hubs **£70-80**
Metallic Silver body, Lemon interior, 'wire' wheels.......**£70-80**
Metallic Bronze body, Lemon interior, 'wire' wheels.**£100-125**

310 1982- **'PORSCHE' 924 Turbo**
Black/Gold, 'GOODYEAR'...**£10-15**

311 1970-72 **Ford Capri V6 3-litre**
Orange body, Gold wheels with Red WW hubs,
Black interior..**£80-90**
Fluorescent Orange body, WhizzWheels **£50-60**
Fluorescent Orange body, Red WhizzWheel hubs **£70-90**
Red body, Black bonnet, Red WhizzWheel hubs **£70-90**

312 1964-68 **'E' type Jaguar**
Silver (vacuum plated) body, racing number '2',
driver, spoked hubs **£90-120**

312 1971-74 **Marcos Mantis**
Metallic Red body, White interior, spoked hubs..............**£20-30**

312 1983- **Ford Capri 'S'**
White, RN '6', hinged parcel shelf, various adverts **£10-15**

313 1970-73 **Ford Cortina GXL**
Metallic Blue body, Black roof, Black/White interior,
Graham Hill figure, WhizzWheels.................................**£60-70**
Bronze body, Black roof, White interior........................**£60-70**
Yellow body, Black roof **£175-200**
Metallic Pale Green body, Black roof, White interior.....**£80-90**
Promotional: Tan body, Black roof, Red interior,
left-hand drive, 'CORTINA' number plate **£250-350**

314 1965-72 **Ferrari Berlinetta 250 LM**
Red body, racing number '4', wire wheels, suspension ..**£60-70**

314 1976-79 **Fiat X1-9**
Metallic Lime Green/Black body, suspension, hook.......**£25-35**
Silver/Black body, suspension, hook **£25-35**

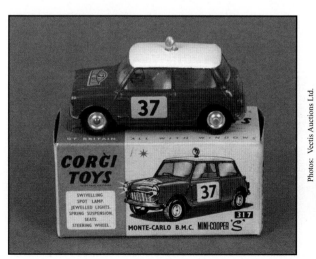

317 'Monte Carlo Rally' BMC Mini-Cooper 'S'

318 Lotus Elan S2 with driver

Photos: Vectis Auctions Ltd.

Market prices shown here are for guidance only. They refer ONLY to mint models in pristine boxes that are complete with all of their original contents.

314 1982- **Supercat Jaguar XJS-HE**
Black body, Red or Tan interior, opening doors **£10-15**

315 1964-66 **Simca 1000 Sports**
Plated Silver, Red interior, RN '8',
Red/White/Blue racing stripes **£70-80**
Metallic Blue body, RN '8', Red/White/Blue stripes ..**£120-140**

315 1976-79 **Lotus Elite**
Red or Yellow with White seats, suspension **£20-25**

316 1963-66 **NSU Sport Prinz**
Metallic Red body, Yellow seats, spun hubs............**£50-60**

316 1971-73 **Ford GT 70**
Lime Green and Black body, White interior,
racing number '32', (unapplied) decal sheet **£30-40**

317 1964-65 **Mini Cooper 'S' 'MONTE CARLO 1964'**
Red body, White roof, Yellow interior, RN '37',
roof spotlight. (*Paddy Hopkirk*)...............**£150-175**
Red body, Pink roof variation **£200-250**

318 1965-66 **Mini Cooper 'S' 'MONTE CARLO 1965'**
Red body, White roof, 'AJB 44B',
racing number '52', no roof spotlight...........**£175-200**

318 1965-67 **Lotus Elan S2 Open Top**
Metallic Steel Blue, RN '6' or '8', driver, 'tiger' decal,
'I'VE GOT A TIGER IN MY TANK' logo on boot lid,
Blue/Yellow box, unapplied decals.............**£125-150**
White body, Black interior, same 'tiger' decal,
spun hubs, unapplied decal sheet (RN '7'), figure **£500-600**

318 1965-68 **Lotus Elan S2 Open Top**
Dark Green body, Yellow stripe with Black or
Red interior (Gift Set 37) ....**GSP**
White body, Black interior (GS40), 'tiger' label,
unapplied decals **£250-300**
Metallic Copper body, unapplied decals..............**£200-250**
Yellow body, Green stripe, Black interior, spun hubs .**£150-200**

318 1981-? **Jaguar XJS**
Blue/Cream body with Red line....................**£15-20**

318 1983-? Black/Red/White body, racing number '4',
'MOTUL', *'JAGUAR'*...................**£15-20**

319 1967-69 **Lotus Elan S2 Hardtop**
Yellow body (Green top), shaped hubs................**£1250-150**
Blue body (White top), shaped hubs................**£1250-150**
Red body, White top, cast hubs....................**£90-120**
Red body, Red top, cast hubs **£90-120**
Blue body, White top, cast hubs **£90-120**
Green and Yellow lift-off body **£90-120**
Red body with White top, WhizzWheels...........**£75-85**

NB 1967-69 boxed issues should include a sheet of
self-adhesive racing numbers '1' to '12'.

319 1973-74 **Lamborghini P400GT**
Metallic Silver body, Purple/Yellow stripes, '7', WW **£25-30**

319 1978-81 **Jaguar XJS**
Metallic Red body, Black roof, suspension **£15-20**

320 1965-67 **Ford Mustang Fastback 2+2**
Opening doors, suspension, Corgi dog, sliding windows.
Silver (Red interior), detailed cast hubs **£70-85**
Metallic Deep Blue (Cream interior) detailed cast hubs .**£70-85**
Metallic Deep Blue (Cream interior), spoked hubs........**£70-85**
Light Green body (Cream interior), spoked hubs...........**£70-85**
Metallic Purple body, (Cream interior), spoked hubs........**£70-85**
Metallic Deep Yellow body, Black bonnet and
interior, cast hubs **£500-750**

320 1978-81 **The Saint's Jaguar XJS**
See 'Novelty, Film and TV-related' section.

321 1965-66 **Mini Cooper 'S' 'MONTE CARLO 1965'** (*Timo Makinen*)
Red body, White roof without spotlight,
'AJB 44B' on bonnet, rally number '52'. **£200-250**
Same, but in 317 picture box with 'No. 321' and
'MONTE CARLO WINNER' flash...........**£350-450**
Red body, White roof with spotlight,
rally number '52', in 321 regular box..............**£200-250**

321 1966-67 **Mini Cooper 'S' 'MONTE CARLO 1966'**
Red body, White roof with rally number '2' and
'TIMO MAKINEN' and *'PAUL EASTER'* signatures,
no spotlight. Box flashed with white sticker with
'1966 MONTE CARLO RALLY AUTOGRAPHED
MINI-COOPER 'S' in Red lettering............**£250-350**
As previous issue but in 321 pictorial box with
'RALLY' text printed in Red panel............**£350-450**

321 1978-81 **Porsche 924 Saloon**
Metallic Green body with hook **£40-45**
Red body **£20-25**
Metallic Light Brown body, Red interior....................**£60-70**

241 Ghia L.6.4,   332 Lancia Fulvia Sport Zagato,   236 Austin A60 Motor School Car with Corgi 'Highway Code'.

322   1967-67   **Rover 2000 'MONTE CARLO'**
Metallic Maroon body, White roof, Red interior,
rally number '136', rally plaques, leaflet....................**£250-300**
As previous model but with Green interior ....NGPP
Model boxed in rare 252 box with 322 labels
over the box ends **£300-350**

          1967   **'INTERNATIONAL RALLY FINISH'**
White body, Black bonnet, Red interior,
White/Orange label on doors with Black RN '21',
cast hubs, 322 box with Red 'ROVER 2000
INTERNATIONAL RALLY FINISH' and box flash.
Paint shade differences are known........................**£400-500**

323   1965-66   **Citroën DS19 'MONTE CARLO 1965'**
Pale Blue with White roof, Lemon interior,
rally plaques and number '75', suspension...............**£200-250**

323   1974-78   **Ferrari Daytona 365 GTB/4**
White/Red/Blue body, RN '81', opening doors..............**£10-15**

324   1966-69   **Marcos Volvo 1800 GT**
White body, two Green stripes, Cream interior **£35-40**
Blue body, two White stripes and bonnet, Blue interior..**£40-50**
    NB   Boxed models should include an unused decal
sheet with racing numbers '4' and '8'.

324   1973-75   **Ferrari Daytona Le Mans**
Yellow body, racing number '33', 'A.BAMFORD' **£25-35**

325   1965-69   **Ford Mustang Competition**
White body, double Red stripe on bonnet, roof and boot.
Blue interior, spun hubs or 'wire' wheels or
cast 'alloy' wheels **£70-80**
White body, double Red stripe on bonnet, roof and
boot + Red side stripe, cast 'alloy' wheels **£200-300**
    NB   An unused sheet of four racing numbers should
be enclosed with each model.

325   1981-   **Chevrolet Caprice**
Metallic Light Green or Dark Green body **£20-25**
Metallic Silver over Dark Blue (US market)..................**£70-80**

327   1967-69   **MGB GT**
Dark Red body, Blue or Yellow interior,
spoked wheels, Brown suitcase, leaflet **£150-175**

327   1980-81   **Chevrolet Caprice Taxi**
Yellow body, 'THINK TWA', fare table on door.............**£15-20**

328   1966-67   **Hillman Imp 'MONTE CARLO 1966'**
Metallic Dark Blue/White, 'FRW 306 C',
rally plaques and number '107', spun hubs **£150-175**
    NB   If 'HILLMAN IMP 328' Yellow/Red advertising
card is with model, expect price to be **20%** higher.

329   1973-76   **Ford Mustang Rally Car**
Metallic Green, White roof, RN '69', (391 special)........**£25-30**

329   1980-82   **Opel Senator**
Dark Blue or Bronze body, opening doors **£15-18**
Silver body **£25-30**

330   1967-69   **Porsche Carrera 6**
White body, Red bonnet and doors,
racing number '60', cast hubs, Blue engine cover **£60-80**
White body, Dark Blue bonnet and doors,
racing number '60', cast hubs, Orange engine cover ..**£110-130**

331   1974-76   **Ford Capri GT Rally**
White body, Black bonnet, 'TEXACO', RN '5' **£55-65**

332   1967-69   **Lancia Fulvia Zagato**
Metallic Green, Metallic Blue, or Orange, cast hubs **£60-70**
Yellow body, Black bonnet, cast hubs **£100-125**

333   1966   **Austin Mini Cooper 'S' 'SUN - RAC Rally'**
Red body, White roof (without spotlight), RN '21' and
'SUN RAC INTERNATIONAL RALLY' decals, 225 box
with White label '1966 RAC INTERNATIONAL
RALLY' in Blue. (Tony Fall / Mike Wood) **£300-400**
As previous model but with Morris grille **£600-900**

334   1968-70   **Mini Cooper 'Magnifique'**
Metallic Dark Blue or Green, jewelled lights,
sunshine roof, Cream interior **£70-90**

334   1981-   **Ford Escort 1.3 GL**
Blue, Green or Yellow body...**£12-15**
Red body with 'AVIS' logo on roof...............................**£25-35**

335   1968-70   **Jaguar 4.2 litre 'E' type**
Metallic Dark Red body, Black interior,
spoked wheels, wing flap bubble pack **£100-125**
Metallic Blue, Black interior, wing flap bubble pack..**£100-125**
Orange body, Black roof, wing flap bubble pack ....NGPP

336   1967-69   **James Bond Toyota 2000GT**
See 'Novelty, Film and TV-related' section.

337   1967-69   **Chevrolet Stock Car**
Yellow body, Red interior, RN '13', 'STINGRAY' **£45-60**

338   1968-71   **Chevrolet SS 350 Camaro**
Metallic Lime Green/Black (Red interior),
Gold/Black or Bronze/Black, 'Golden Jacks'.................**£45-60**

338   1980-83   **Rover 3500**
Metallic Blue, Red/Black or Bronze/Brown body..........**£20-35**

339   1967-71   **Mini Cooper 'S' 'MONTE CARLO 1967'**
    (i)   Red body, White roof, RN '177', 2 spare wheels on
roof-rack, Austin grille, cast hubs, in 227 box with White
flash label with '1967 MONTE-CARLO WINNER
B.M.C. MINI-COOPER 'S' in Red lettering,
Red '339' flash on box end **£300-400**
    (ii)   As (i) but shaped spun hubs, slight Silver detail **£300-400**
    (iii)   As (i) but with Morris grille.....................................**£300-400**
    (iv)   As (i) but in 339 picture box with winner's text
in Red lettering on box front. Special leaflet enclosed
with each model **£300-400**
    (v)   As (i) but in 339 box with the winners text
in Red panel **£300-400**

340   1967-69   **Sunbeam Imp 'MONTE CARLO 1967'**
    (i)   Metallic Blue, RN '77', spun or cast hubs, flashed 328
box with '1967 MONTE CARLO SUNBEAM IMP
WINNER PRODUCTION CARS UP TO 1000cc' text
in Blue capitals plus model no. '340' **£200-300**
    (ii)   As (i) but in 340 pictorial box with 'winner' text
printed in Red on box front plus cast detailed hubs **£200-300**
    (iii)   As (i) but Metallic Dark Blue body, cast detailed
hubs, 'winner' text in Red panel on box front...........**£250-350**

340   1981-84   **Rover 'TRIPLEX'**
White/Red/Blue, RN '1', hinged parcel shelf.................**£15-20**

341   1968-70   **Mini Marcos GT 850**
Metallic Maroon body (Cream seats),
'Golden Jacks' and 'Take-off' wheels............................**£60-70**

341   1981-82   **Chevrolet Caprice**
Red/White/Blue body, RN '43', 'STP', White tyres **£10-15**

342   1970-72   **Lamborghini P400 Miura**
Red body, White interior, Black plastic fighting bull figure,
WhizzWheels. 1st type box: Blue/Yellow box has
'Revised specification' label for 'Take-off' wheels........**£85-95**
2nd type box: Red/Yellow box with
'Revised specification' label **£50-60**
Lime Green body, Red interior, with bull figure **£50-60**

342   1980-82   **'The Professionals' Ford Capri**
See 'Novelty, Film and TV-related' section.

343   1969-73   **Pontiac Firebird**
Metallic Silver/Black, Red seats,
Gold/Red 'Take-Off wheels', 'Golden Jacks' **£35-45**
With Red-hub WhizzWheels..**£50-60**

343   1980-81   **Ford Capri 3 litre**
Yellow or Silver body, Black designs **£30-35**

344   1969-73   **Ferrari Dino Sports**
Yellow with Black doors (number '23'), WhizzWheels..**£40-50**
Red with White doors (number '30'), WhizzWheels **£40-50**
With Red-hub WhizzWheels.......................................**£50-60**

345   1969-?   **MGC GT Competition**
Yellow body, Black bonnet/tailgate/interior, spoked
wheels, Black suitcase. 'MGB GT' on box overprinted
'NEW MGC'. Self-adhesive numbers enclosed.........**£150-175**
Orange body, Black interior, spoked wheels.
In early Car Transporter Gift Sets 41 and 48 only ....GSP

345 1981-82 **Honda Prelude**
Metallic Blue body, sunshine roof £10-15
Cream/Green body, sunshine roof £10-15
Metallic Yellow body, sunshine roof £10-15

346 1982-84 **Citroën 2cv**
Yellow/Black body £10-15
Burgundy/Black body £10-15
Red/White body £10-15
Grey/Red body £10-15
German promotional:
Yellow body, Black roof, 'REISGOLD' label £100-120

347 1969-74 **Chevrolet Astro Experimental**
Metallic Dark Blue body, Red-hub WhizzWheels..........£40-50
Metallic Green body, Red-hub WhizzWheels £40-50
As previous models but with plain WhizzWheels £30-40

348 1968-69 **Ford Mustang 'Pop Art' Stock Car**
Blue body and interior, Red/Orange 'Flower-Power'
labels, RN '20'. Not shown in catalogues £100-150
Light Blue body without labels....................................£60-70

348 1980-81 **'Vegas' Ford Thunderbird**
See 'Novelty, Film and TV-related' section.

349 1967-67 **'POP ART' Morris Mini**
Red body, Lemon interior, 4 psychedelic labels,
'MOSTEST' logo, few only produced...................£2,250-2,750
Pre-production issue:
Blue body, Red interior, cast hubs £1,750-2,250

370 1982-? **Ford Cobra Mustang**
White/Black/Red/Blue, 'MUSTANG',
with or without tailgate stripe £10-15

370 1982- **Ford Cobra Mustang**
White body, Red interior, Blue/Red design £10-15

371 1970-73 **Porsche Carrera 6**
White/Red, racing number '60', plated Blue
engine cover, WhizzWheels, (330 update) £20-25

372 1970-72 **Lancia Fulvia Zagato**
Orange body, Black bonnet, Black interior, WW £40-50

373 1981- **Peugeot 505**
Red body, Silver or Black lining, suspension £10-15

374 1970-76 **Jaguar 'E' type 4.2 litre**
Red or Yellow body, WW, (2+2), (335 update) £50-60

374 1973- **Jaguar 'E' type 5.3 litre**
Yellow or Metallic Yellow body 'New' on box label £50-60

375 1970-72 **Toyota 2000 GT**
Metallic translucent 'candy' Blue body, White interior,
WhizzWheels, (modified 336), leaflet £50-60
Metallic Purple body, White interior, WhizzWheels £45-55

376 1970-72 **Chevrolet Corvette Stock Car**
Silver body, racing number '13', 'GO-GO-GO',
WhizzWheels, (337 update) £40-50
Metallic Blue body, Red interior, RN '13', WW............£40-50

377 1970-72 **Marcos 3 litre**
Yellow body, Black bonnet and interior, Whizzwheels,
(324 conversion)..£60-70
White body, Grey sunroof, Whizzwheels £80-90
Metallic Blue-Green body, Black interior,
bonnet decal, WhizzWheels £60-70

378 1970-72 **MGC GT**
Red body, Black bonnet, interior and suitcase,
WhizzWheels, (345 update)...£80-90
Orange body, (this version only in Gift Set 20)................GSP

378 1982- **Ferrari 308 GTS**
Red or Black body, pop-up headlights...........................£20-30

380 1970-74 **Alfa Romeo P33**
White body, Gold roll bar, Red seats, WhizzWheels.......£25-30

380 1983- **'BASF' BMW M1**
Red/White, racing number '80', aerofoil.........................£7-10

381 1970-76 **VW Beach Buggy**
Metallic Red/White, Blue/White, Orange/White or
Red/White, 2 Maroon surfboards, WhizzWheels £15-20

381 1983- **'ELF' Renault Turbo**
Red/White/Blue, racing number '5', 'FACOM'..............£10-15
Blue/White, racing number '13', 'ELF' £10-15

382 1970-75 **Porsche Targa 911S**
Metallic Silver-Blue body, Black roof with Gold stripe,
WhizzWheels..£25-30
Metallic Olive-Green body, Black roof with or without
Gold stripe, WhizzWheels £25-30

382 1983- **Lotus Elite 22**
Metallic Blue body, 'Elite 22', number plates................£10-15

383 1970-76 **VW 1200 'Flower Power'**
Red body with psychedelic Grenadine and Green daisy
labels on bonnet and doors..£75-85
Red body, Green base, White interior, no flower decals .£25-35

383 1970-73 **Volkswagen 1200 'ADAC'**
Yellow/Black, 'ADAC' (German equivalent of 'AA') ..£80-100
Volkswagen 1200 'PTT'
Yellow/Black, Red interior, logo, Swiss issue £80-100

383 1977-78 **Volkswagen 1200 Rally**
Blue body, rally number '5', chequered roof and sides...£10-15

384 1978- **Volkswagen 1200 Rally**
Blue body, rally number '5', chequered stripes.............£35-45
As previous model but with 'CALEDONIAN
AUTOMINOLOGISTS' logo £100-125
Blue body, Cream interior, WhizzWheels,
'40th Anniversary 1938 - 1978'.................................£160-190

384 1970-73 **Adams Brothers Probe**
Red body, Silver base, WhizzWheels £30-40
Metallic Gold body, WhizzWheels £30-40
Green body, White interior...£30-40

384 1983-84 **Renault 11 GTL**
Dark Cream body, (export issue) £25-30
Maroon or Metallic Mauve body £25-30

385 1970-76 **Porsche 917**
Metallic Blue or Red body, racing number '3',
cast or WhizzWheels, with leaflet £30-35

386 1971-74 **Bertone Barchetta**
Yellow/Black 'RUNABOUT', aerofoil, WhizzWheels ...£20-25

387 1970-73 **Corvette Stingray Coupé**
Metallic Blue body, Black bonnet, roof emblem, WW ...£35-45
Metallic Pink body, Black bonnet, Black interior..........£35-45

388 1970-74 **Mercedes-Benz C111**
Orange/Black body, WhizzWheels £20-25

389 1971-74 **Reliant Bond 'BUG' 700 ES**
Orange body, 'BUG' labels, Cream interior, WW..........£35-45
Lime Green body, WhizzWheels £65-75

391 1972-72 **James Bond Ford Mustang**
See 'Novelty, Film and TV-related' section.

392 1973-76 **Bertone Shake Buggy**
Pink and Green body, detailed engine, flag, WW...........£25-30
Yellow body, Black or Green interior £25-30

393 1972-79 **Mercedes-Benz 350 SL**
White body, Pale Blue interior, chrome spoked wheels ..£25-30
Metallic Blue or Dark Blue body, chrome disc wheels ...£25-30
Metallic Green body, Brown interior..............................£65-75

394 1972-77 **Datsun 240 Z 'Safari Rally'**
'East African Safari Rally' finish: Red body,
rally number '11', 'CASTROL' and 'JAPAN' logos £25-30

395 1972-73 **Fire Bug**
Orange body, Whizzwheels, Red/Black or
Pink/Black stripe, Yellow ladder (381 Beach Buggy) £20-30

396 1973-76 **Datsun 240 Z 'US Rally'**
'US Rally' finish: Red/White body, rally number '46',
'JOHN MORTON' and 'DATSUN' logos £40-50

**Market prices shown here are for guidance only. They refer
ONLY to mint models in pristine boxes that are complete with
all of their original contents.
WW = WhizzWheels   RN = Rally or Racing Number**

397 1974-76 **Porsche-Audi 917-10**
White/Red body, 'L&M', RN '6', *'CORGI'*, driver........**£25-30**

400 1974-75 **Volkswagen 1300 *'CORGI MOTOR SCHOOL'***
Metallic Red body, roof steering wheel, cones............**£80-100**
Metallic Blue body version..**£40-50**
Metallic Blue, 'CORGI FAHR SCHULE', (German).**£100-120**
401 1975-77 **Volkswagen 1300**
Same as C400 but supplied with 24 'bollards' and
diorama for miniature driving practice **£45-55**

406 1957-62 **Land Rover '109 WB'**
Yellow body, Black roof, smooth hubs, thin tyres..........**£70-90**
Metallic Dark Blue body, Cream roof,
smooth or shaped hubs, thin or thick tyres **£60-70**
Green body with Tan tinplate cover, smooth hubs,
thin or thick tyres **£60-70**
'ETENDARD' variant:
As previous issue but with 'ETENDARD' decals, plus
Red/White/Green roundels on front wings ....NGPP
406s 1963 **Land Rover '109 WB'**
Yellow body, Red seats, shaped hubs, suspension..........**£60-70**

411 1976-79 **Mercedes Benz 240 D**
Orange/Black or Cream body, *'TAXI'* on roof................**£10-15**
German issue:
Black body, Red *'TAXI'* roof sign, *'TAXI'* on doors........**£35-45**
415 1976-78 **Mazda Camper**
Red body with drop-down tailboard, White caravan......**£25-30**

418 1960-65 **Austin FX4 'TAXI'**
Black body, flat or shaped hubs, no driver **£50-60**
Black, flat or shaped hubs, 'younger' driver figure.........**£40-50**
Black body, flat or shaped hubs, 'older' driver figure.....**£35-45**

419 1978-79 **AMC Jeep CJ-5**
Metallic Green body with White plastic top,
or Metallic Dark Green body **£25-35**

420 1962-66 **Ford Thames 'Airborne' Caravan**
Two-tone Green, Brown interior or Blue/Pale Grey,
Red interior or Blue/Green, Brown interior....................**£70-80**
Two-tone Lilac, Beige interior **£70-80**
421 1977-80 **Land Rover Safari**
Orange body, Black roof rack with ladder, spare wheel..**£20-25**
Red body, White roof rack with ladder,
'FOREST FIRE WARDEN' logo **£20-25**
Land Rover Workman's Bus
Yellow/Red body, no roof rack or ladder ....NGPP

424 1961-65 **Ford Zephyr Estate**
Pale Blue body, Dark Blue bonnet and side flash,
Lemon interior, luggage, flat or shaped spun hubs........**£90-110**
425 1978 - **London Taxi**
FX4 type taxi with Black body, *'TAXI'*, WhizzWheels.**£10-15**
Maroon body, Red interior, WhizzWheels....................**£80-100**

430 1962-64 **Ford Bermuda 'TAXI'** (Ford Thunderbird)
White body, Yellow and Red canopy...........................**£100-130**
White body, Lime Green and Red canopy..................**£100-130**
White body, Blue and Red canopy.............................**£100-130**
Metallic Blue body, Red canopy **£200-300**

436 1963-65 **Citroën ID19 'SAFARI'**
Yellow body, driver and passenger, detailed interior,
roof luggage, 'Wild Life Reservation' logo **£100-125**

438 1963-77 **Land Rover 109 WB**
Model has plastic canopy. Earlier issues have metal
towhooks (plastic later), suspension.
Dark Green body Grey or Tan canopy,
Lemon interior, shaped hubs...................................**£100-125**
Dark Green body Cream canopy,
Lemon interior, spun hubs......................................**£175-200**
Dark Brown body, Light Brown canopy,
Red interior, shaped hubs.......................................**£100-125**
Metallic Green body, Olive-Green canopy,
Yellow interior, shaped hubs.....................................**£60-80**
Metallic Green body, Olive-Green canopy,
Chrome hubs **£60-80**
Metallic Green body, Olive-Green canopy, WW...........**£60-70**
Red body, Brown tilt, Red interior, shaped hubs...........**£60-70**
'LEPRA' variant:
Metallic Green body, Tan canopy with 'LEPRA' logo,
Yellow interior, shaped hubs, Silver steering wheel....**£500-750**
Red body, Blue canopy, (in Gift Set 19)............................GSP
Promotional:
with '10 MILLIONTH CORGI LAND ROVER' label....NGPP

440 1966-69 **Ford Consul Cortina Estate**
Metallic Dark Blue with Brown side panels,
plastic golfer, caddie and trolley **£125-150**
440 1979- **Mazda Custom Pick-Up**
Orange/Yellow/Red, US flag.......................................**£15-20**
441 1979-83 **'GOLDEN EAGLE' Jeep**
Brown/Tan or Gold/White, spare wheel on some.........**£15-20**

443 1963-65 **Plymouth Suburban USA Mail**
Blue/White body, Red interior,
'ADDRESS YOUR MAIL CAREFULLY' **£125-150**
445 1963-66 **Plymouth Suburban Sports Station Wagon**
Pale Blue or Eggshell Blue body, Red roof,
Lemon interior, Silver side stripe, spun hubs...............**£90-110**
Beige body, Tan roof..**£55-65**

447 1983 **'RENEGADE' 4x4 Jeep**
Yellow body, RN '5' (As 448 but without hood) ....In GS 36
448 1983 **'RENEGADE' 4x4 Jeep**
Yellow body, Red hood, racing number '5'......................**£8-10**

450 1983-? **Peugeot Taxi**
Beige with Blue label, *'739:33:33'*, (French issue) **£30-35**
451 19?? **Ford Sierra Taxi**
Cream body ....NGPP
457 1981-83 **Talbot Matra Rancho**
Red/Black or Green/Black, tilt seats............................**£10-15**
457 1984-? **Talbot Matra Rancho**
Orange/Black or White/Blue body, Brown seats **£20-25**
475 19?? **Citroën Safari**
See Novelty, Film and TV-related section.

480 1965-66 **Chevrolet Impala Taxi**
Yellow body, Red roof, spun hubs, roofbox, aerial **£100-125**
As previous model but with detailed cast wheels........**£100-125**
485 1965-69 **Mini Countryman with Surfer**
Sea-Green body, Lemon interior, 2 surfboards on
roof-rack, male figure, special leaflet **£140-160**
As previous model but with unpainted grille.............**£140-160**

491 1966-69 **Ford Consul Cortina Estate**
All have Brown/Cream side/rear panels.
Metallic Red, Metallic Blue or Metallic Dark Grey **£90-110**
NB No golf equipment issued with this model (see 440).

497 1966-69 **'The Man From UNCLE' Car**
See 'Novelty, Film and TV-related' section.
507 1969 **Chrysler Bermuda Taxi**
Shown in catalogue but not issued.....................NPP

C801	82	**1957 Ford Thunderbird**, White/Tan, Cream/Orange or Cream/Black **£15-25**	
C802	82	**Mercedes 300 SL**, Burgundy or Silver body, with suspension............**£15-25** Red body, no suspension **£15-25**	
C803	83	**1952 Jaguar XK120 Sports**, Red body/Black hood **£15-25**	
C803/1	83	**1952 Jaguar XK120 Rally**, Cream body, RN '56' ....**£15-25** White body, rally number '56' **£15-25**	
C804	83	**Jaguar 'Coupé des Alpes'**, Cream/Grey RN '56' or '414' ....**£15-25** Same but with rear wheel 'spats' **£15-25**	
C805	83	**1956 Mercedes 300SC**, Black body, Tan hood.....................**£15-25**	
	84	Maroon body **£15-25**	
	86	Beige body and hood.....................**£15-25**	
	87	Grey (Black hood), export model **£15-25**	

C806	83	**1956 Mercedes 300SL**, Black body, Grey/Black hood **£15-25**
	86	Black/Green body, Beige seats.........**£15-25**
	86	Red, (Cream interior), export model.**£15-25**
	86	Blue body **£15-25**
C810	83	**1957 Ford Thunderbird**, White body **£15-25**
	84	Pink body **£15-25**
	87	Red body.....................................**£15-25** Cream body, Orange roof ....**£15-25** Black/White, Red/White interior......**£15-25**
C811	84	**1954 Mercedes SL**, Silver body......**£15-25**
	86	Red body.....................................**£15-25**
	87	Grey body, export model.................**£15-25**
C812	85	**1953 MG TF**, Green/Tan seats **£15-25**
C813	85	**1955 MG TF**, Red/Black **£15-25**
	87	Cream/Red, export model **£15-25**
C814	85	**1952 Rolls-Royce Silver Dawn**, Red/Black **£15-25**

	86	White/Beige.................................**£15-25**
	86	Silver/Black, export model...............**£15-25**
C815	85	**1954 Bentley 'R' type**, Black or Cream body **£15-25**
	86	Dark Blue and Light Blue body **£15-25**
	86	Cream/Brown, export model ....**£15-25** White body, Black roof **£15-25**
C816	85	**1956 Jaguar XK120**, Red body, Black tonneau, '56' ....**£15-25** Red body, Cream hardtop.................**£15-25**
C819	85	**1949 Jaguar XK120**, White body, Black hood, '7' **£15-25**
C825	85	**1957 Chevrolet Bel Air**, Red body, White roof and flash **£15-25**
	87	Black/White, export model...............**£15-25**
C869	86	**MG TF Racing Car**, Royal Blue body, Beige seats, RN '113' **£15-25**
C870	86	**Jaguar XK120**, Green body, Yellow seats, RN '6', export model **£15-25**

ORIGINAL ISSUES. A factory fire ended production in 1969 of this original series of 'Classics' cars. Boxes are of two types: one with separate lid with coloured line-drawings printed on it and containing a separate picture of the model; and type two which has the model attached to a sliding-drawer style base in an outer box with half-flaps (similar printing to 1st type). Early issues have reference numbers '901' onwards which were changed to '9001' etc. just before release.

9001	1964-69	**1927 3-litre Bentley**...................	British Racing Green, racing number '3', detachable hood, driver..............................	**£50-65**
9002	1964-68	**1927 3-litre Bentley**...................	Red body, civilian driver, no racing number, detachable hood	**£50-65**
9004	1967-69	**'WORLD OF WOOSTER'** Bentley..........................	As previous model but in Green or Red and with Jeeves and Wooster figures	**£100-150**
9011	1964-68	**1915 Model 'T' Ford**	Black body, driver, passenger, spoked wheels, brass radiator................................	**£50-65**
9012	1965-68	**Model 'T' Ford**	Version with Yellow/Black body, Black or Yellow wheels................................	**£50-65**
9013	1964-69	**1915 Model 'T' Ford**	Blue/Black body, detachable hood, spare wheel, driver cranks..............................	**£50-65**
9014		**1915 'LYONS TEA' Van**	Appeared in 1967/68 catalogue but was not issued...	NPP
9021	1964-69	**1910 38 hp Daimler**	Red body, driver and 3 passengers, folded hood, detailed chassis	**£50-65**
9022		**1910 38 hp Daimler**	Appeared in the 1966 catalogue but not issued	NPP
9031	1965-68	**1910 Renault 12/16**	Lavender/Black body with carriage lamps, spoked wheels	**£50-65**
9032	1965-69	**1910 Renault 12/16**	Same as previous model but Primrose Yellow and Black body...................	**£50-65**
9041	1966-70	**1912 Rolls-Royce Silver Ghost** .	Silver and Black body, carriage lamps, spoked wheels..........................	**£50-65**
		variant:	Maroon body, Silver roof and bonnet	**£75-85**

RE-INTRODUCED ISSUES. Four of the 'Classics' were re-introduced in 1985 when original tools were discovered. They have new numbers, 'SPECIAL EDITION' on their baseplates and are packed in Grey/Red boxes which do not contain a picture of the model. 13,500 of each colour were made.

C860 (9041)	1985	**1912 Rolls-Royce Silver Ghost**....................Silver, Black or Ruby Red body		**£15-25**
C861 (9002)	1985	**1927 3-litre Bentley open top** ....British Racing Green, Black or Ruby Red body		**£15-25**
C862 (9031)	1985	**1910 Renault 12/16**................................Yellow, Pale Blue, Cream or Brown body		**£15-25**
C863 (9012)	1985	**1915 Model 'T' Ford** ....Black, Red or Blue body		**£15-25**

These packs combine standard models with (mainly) similar 'Junior' models. Launched early in 1982 in France with the name 'Les Plus de Corgi', the packs later became available in the UK in Woolworths as 'Little and Large; the Little One Free'.
See also 'Novelty, Film and TV-related' section for additional details.

No.53 **Triple Pack** (1982), 'Stunt Bikes':
171 Street Bike, 172 Police Bike, 173 Café Racer....

'Les Plus de Corgi' Duo Pack range:

1352	Renault 5 (307) Metro (C275)..........**£15-25**	
1353	Austin Metro...................................**£15-25**	
1354	Texaco Lotus (C154) Junior 53 ....**£15-25**	
1355	Talbot Matra Rancho (457)..............**£15-25**	
1356	Fiat XI/9 (306).................................**£15-25**	
1357	Golden Eagle Jeep (C441)................**£15-25**	
1358	Citroën 2cv....................................**£15-25**	
1359	Ford Escort (334), Junior 105...........**£15-25**	

F.W. Woolworth's 'Little & Large'
Promotional Duo Pack selection:

1352	Renault 5 (307) Metro (C275)..........**£15-25**
1353	Austin Metro...................................**£15-25**
1355	Talbot Matra Rancho (457)..............**£15-25**
1356	Fiat XI/9 (306).................................**£15-25**
1359	Ford Escort (334), Junior 105...........**£15-25**
1363	Buck Rogers (607)...........................**£50-60**
1364	Space Shuttle 'NASA' (648)............**£20-30**
1365	469 Routemaster Bus, E71 Taxi **£20-30**
1371	Volkswagen Turbo (309)..................**£15-25**

Other Duo Packs (most available in UK).

1360	Batmobile (267)............................**£100-125**
1361	James Bond Aston-Martin, Silver.......................................**£90-120**
1362	James Bond Lotus Esprit (269) **£80-100**
1363	Buck Rogers (607)...........................**£50-60**
1364	Space Shuttle 'NASA' (648)............**£20-30**
1365	469 Routemaster Bus, E71 Taxi **£15-25**
1372	Jaguar XJS (319)............................**£15-25**

1372	'Magnum PI' Ferrari (298) **£80-100**
1373	Ford Capri (312) Junior 61 ....**£15-25**
1376	Starsky & Hutch Ford Torino **£70-80**
1378	Porsche 924, Yellow **£15-25**
1380	Mercedes 240D, Metallic Grey **£15-25**
1381	Ferrari 308GTS, Red **£15-25**
1382	Ford Mustang (320).........................**£15-25**
1383	Mack Fire Pumper **£15-25**
1384	Ford Thunderbird, Cream/Orange ....**£15-25** Ford Thunderbird, Cream/Black **£15-25**
1385	Austin Metro 'DATAPOST' **£15-25**
1389	Ford Sierra (299) Junior 129 ....**£15-25**
1390	Porsche 924, Black **£15-25**
1393	447 Jeep and E182 Jeep...................**£15-25**
1394	448 Jeep and E183 Jeep..................**£15-25**
1395	495 Mazda, E184 Range Rover........**£15-25**
1396	Space Shuttle **£15-25**
1397	BMW M1 'BASF' (380)...................**£15-25**
1401	Lotus Elite and E10 TR7 ....**£15-25**
1402	1133 Tipper plus E85 Skip Truck......**£20-30**
1403	Mercedes Tanker, E185 Van **£15-25**
1405	Jaguar **£15-25**

Market prices shown here are for guidance only. They refer ONLY to mint models in pristine boxes that are complete with <u>all</u> of their original contents.   WW = WhizzWheels.   See also 'Gift Sets' and 'Novelty, Film and TV-related' sections.

Ref	Year(s)	Model name and details	Market Price Range
100	1957-65	**Dropside Trailer** Cream/Red or Yellow body, drawbar	**£50-60**
101	1958-63	**Platform Trailer** Grey/Yellow or Silver/Blue or Silver/Lemon body, drawbar and axle swivel	**£60-70**
109	1968-69	**'PENNYBURN' Trailer** Blue body, Yellow chassis, accessories, leaflet	**£40-50**
403	1956-60	**Bedford 12 cwt Van 'DAILY EXPRESS'** Dark Blue body. Blue box with leaflet	**£150-200**
		As previous model but Deep Blue body	**£150-200**
403M	1956-60	**Bedford 12 cwt Van 'KLG PLUGS'** Bright Red body, flywheel motor. Leaflet in box	**£150-200**
403	1974-79	**Thwaites Skip Dumper** Yellow/Green tipping body, driver, WhizzWheels	**£40-50**
404	1956-62	**Bedford Dormobile** Smooth or ribbed roof, smooth or shaped hubs. Early issues have divided windscreen. Blue box with leaflet.	
		Cream (Blue roof on some)	**£80-100**
		Turquoise	**£80-100**.
		Blue	**£80-100**.
		Red or Metallic Red	**£80-100**.
		Yellow body with Pale Blue roof, flat hubs	**£120-140**
		Yellow lower half, Blue upper half	**£150-200**
		All-Yellow body, with suspension	**£80-100**
404M	1956-60	**Bedford Dormobile** (with flywheel motor) Blue box also contains leaflet.	
		Red or Metallic Red	**£130-160**
		Turquoise body	**£130-160**
		Blue body	**£130-160**
405		**Bedford Van 'AFS'** See 'Emergency Vehicles' section.	

Ref	Year(s)	Model name and details	Market Price Range
405	1981-?	**Ford Transit Milk Float 'DAIRY CREST'** 'MILK MARKETING BOARD' logo on each side and 'MILK' on rear	**£20-30**
405	1982-?	**Ford Transit Milk Float** 'LOTTA BOTTLE' on Blue/White body	**£10-15**
406	1971-75	**Mercedes-Benz Unimog**	
		Yellow/Green body with Blue interior	**£25-35**
		Yellow/Red body with Blue interior	**£25-35**
		Blue/Red body with Blue interior	**£25-35**
407	1957-62	**Smiths Karrier Bantam** *'HOME SERVICES HYGIENIC MOBILE SHOP'*, Pale Blue body, Red logo, smooth hubs	**£140-170**
408	1957-59	**Bedford 'AA' Service Van** Yellow/Black, divided windscreen, smooth hubs, Blue box, leaflet	**£140-180**
		As previous model but in Blue/Yellow box	**£180-220**
	1959-63	Same, but shaped hubs, Blue/Yellow box, no leaflet	**£140-180**
		Same, but single windscreen, ridged roof, spun hubs	**£120-140**
409	1959-65	**Forward Control Jeep** Light Blue body, Red grille, smooth or shaped hubs	**£80-90**
409	1976-77	**Unimog Dumper** White/Red or Blue/Yellow body, suspension, hook	**£20-30**
409	1981-?	**'ALLIS CHALMERS' Forklift** Yellow body, pallets/load/driver	**£15-20**
411	1958-62	**Karrier Bantam Van 'LUCOZADE'** Yellow body, Grey shutter, smooth hubs, Blue box	**£130-160**
		Same, but with shaped hubs, Blue/Yellow box	**£120-140**
413	1960-64	**Smiths Karrier Bantam Mobile Butchers** White/Blue van, spun hubs, *'FAMILY BUTCHERS'*, meaty decals. Blue box with leaflet	**£150-175**
		As previous model but with suspension	**£150-175**

Corgi Toys Major Pack 1130, Bedford TK Horse Transporter 'Chipperfield's Circus'   Photo: Christie's, South Kensington

413 1976-78 **Mazda Motorway Maintenance**
Yellow/Black body, figure, road signs, bollards,
decal sheet enclosed, (modified 478/493).......................**£25-35**

416 1959-61 **R.A.C. Land Rover**
Blue body, *'RADIO RESCUE'* on cab roof sign,
metal canopy, smooth hubs, Blue/Yellow box **£120-140**
Blue body, no cab roof sign, *'RADIO RESCUE'*
on canopy, shaped hubs..**£160-200**
Belgian issue:
Yellow body, Green metal canopy,
'TS RADIO' decals on doors **£1,000-1,250**

416s 1962-64 **R.A.C. Land Rover**
Blue body, Lemon interior, suspension,
'RADIO RESCUE' on plastic canopy..........................**£75-95**
Belgian issue:
Yellow body, Grey plastic canopy, suspension,
'TS RADIO' decals on doors **£1,000-1,250**

417 1960-62 **Land Rover 'BREAKDOWN SERVICE'**
Red body, Yellow tinplate canopy, spun hubs **£90-100**

417s 1963-65 **Land Rover 'BREAKDOWN SERVICE'**
Red body, Yellow tinplate canopy, shaped hubs,
suspension...**£160-190**

420 1962-66 **Ford Thames 'Airborne' Caravan**
Two-tone Green, Brown interior or Blue/Pale Grey,
Red interior or Blue/Green, Brown interior **£70-80**
Two-tone Lilac, Beige interior **£70-80**

421 1960-63 **Bedford 12 cwt Van 'EVENING STANDARD'**
Black body, Silver ridged roof, undivided windscreen,
smooth hubs...**£150-175**
Black lower body, Silver upper body and roof **£110-130**
Medium Blue body, 'AVRO BODE' logo **£250-300**

422 1960-62 **Bedford 12 cwt Van 'CORGI TOYS'**
Yellow body, Blue roof, smooth or shaped hubs **£300-400**
reversed colours:
Blue body, Yellow roof, smooth wheels..................**£400-500**
variation: Blue lower half with Yellow upper body **£400-500**

424 1977-79 **Security Van**
Black/Yellow/White body, *'SECURITY'*.........................**£10-15**

426 1962-64 **'CHIPPERFIELDS CIRCUS' Mobile Booking Office**
Karrier Bantam in red and blue, with clown and
circus posters, spun hubs. Blue/yellow card box **£300-400**
As previous model but with shaped hubs....................**£250-300**

426 1978-81 **Chevrolet Booking Office Van 'PINDER'**
Yellow/Red/Blue body, 'PINDER JEAN RICHARD',
WhizzWheels, two loudspeakers.....................................**£35-45**
NB The 'clown's face' poster may be at the front or the
rear on the nearside of the model.

428 1963-66 **Karrier Ice-Cream Van 'MR SOFTEE'**
Blue/White body, detailed chassis, salesman swivels .**£200-250**

431 1964-66 **Volkswagen Pick-Up**
Yellow body, Red or Olive-Green canopy,
Red 'VW' emblem...**£60-70**
Metallic Gold body, Red 'VW' emblem,
Red canopy, Red interior, spun hubs...........................**£250-350**

431, 432, 433 **Chevrolet Vans**
('VANATIC', 'VANTASTIC' and 'VANISHING POINT').
See 'Novelty' section.

433 1962-64 **Volkswagen Delivery Van**
Red/White body, Red or Yellow interior........................**£60-70**
Dutch promotional issue:
'VROOM & DREESMAN', Grey body, spun hubs **£400-500**

434 1962 **Volkswagen Kombi**
Metallic Pale Grey over Green body,
Red interior, spun hubs...**£65-75**
1963-66 Two-tone Green, Red or Yellow interior **£60-70**

435 1962-63 **Karrier Bantam Van**
Blue/White/Yellow, *'DRIVE SAFELY ON MILK'* **£100-120**

437 1979-80 **Chevrolet Van 'COCA-COLA'**
Red body, White logo, tinted roof windows, crates.........**£20-25**

440 1979-80 **Mazda Custom Pick-up**
Yellow body, Red roof...**£15-20**

441 1963-67 **Volkswagen Van 'CHOCOLATE TOBLERONE'**
Blue body, Lemon interior, 'Trans-o-lite' headlamps **£80-100**

443 1963-66 **Plymouth Suburban US Mail**
Blue/White body,
'ADDRESS YOUR MAIL CAREFULLY'.........................**£65-75**

447 1965-66 **'WALLS ICE CREAM' Van**
Blue/Cream Ford Thames van, salesman, boy, spare
transfers. Blue/Yellow card box, inner base, leaflet.....**£250-350**

450 1964-67 **Austin Mini Van**
Green body with unpainted grille, Red interior **£55-65**
Green body with painted grille, Red interior.................**£90-110**
Green body, Austin Countryman grille, Red interior **£90-110**
Promotional:
Metallic Green body, Grey base, Red interior, White
'FDR1.2009/17' logo. In original 450 box with
club slip. Thought to be a Dutch promotional **£300-400**

452 1956-63 **Commer Dropside Lorry**
Red and Cream body, (raised ridge on some cab roofs),
smooth or shaped hubs **£80-100**
Blue body, Cream back **£80-100**

453 1956-60 **Commer Refrigerated Van 'WALLS ICE CREAM'**
Dark Blue cab, Cream back, smooth roof,
flat spun hubs..**£175-200**
Light Blue cab, Cream back, cast roof,
flat spun hubs..**£125-150**

454 1957-63 **Commer Platform Lorry**
Metallic Blue cab and chassis, Silver-Grey platform,
flat hubs, leaflet...**£80-100**
Yellow cab and chassis, Silver platform **£80-100**

455 1957-60 **Karrier Bantam 2-ton**
Blue, Red or Grey body, Red platform, smooth hubs ..**£120-140**
Early Mettoy issue:
Red body with *'C.W.S. SOFT DRINKS'* logo on rear ..**£120-140**

456 1960-63 **ERF 44G Dropside Lorry**
Yellow cab and chassis, Metallic Blue back,
smooth/shaped hubs...**£70-80**

457 1957-65 **ERF 44G Platform Lorry**
Two-tone Blue or Yellow/Blue body, smooth hubs **£80-100**

458 1958-66 **E.R.F. Earth Dumper**
Red / Yellow, 'ERF' cast-in, smooth or shaped hubs.....**£80-100**

459 1958-60 **ERF 44G Van 'MOORHOUSES LEMON CHEESE'**
Yellow/Red **£150-200**

459 1973-78 **Raygu Rascal Roller**
Yellow/Green body, *'Road Roller'*................................**£15-20**

460 1959-61 **E.R.F. Neville Cement Tipper 'TUNNEL CEMENT'**
Lemon cab/chassis, Silver base and metal filler caps......**£40-50**
As previous version, but with Red plastic filler caps **£70-80**

462 1970-? **Commer Van 'CO-OP'**
White/Blue body, Blue/Yellow box..............................**£80-100**

462 1971-? **Commer Van 'HAMMONDS'**
Green/Blue/White promotional model, cast hubs **£110-130**

465 1963-66 **Commer Pick-Up Truck**
Red/Yellow, Yellow/Red or Green/Grey, 'Trans-O-Lites' ..**£50-60**

466 19?? **Commer Milk Float**
White cab, chassis and load; Blue rear roof and sides...**£80-100**
Promotional issue: As previous model but with
'CO-OP' labels. Plain card box **£80-100**

470 1965-72 **Forward Control Jeep**
Blue/Grey, Mustard Yellow, Pale Green or
Light Blue body, detachable canopy **£35-40**

471 1965-66 **Karrier Bantam Snack Bar**
Blue/White, 'JOE'S DINER', figure, opening hatch...**£140-170**
Belgian issue: Blue/White, 'PATATES FRITES' **£200-250**

Market prices shown here are for guidance only. They refer
ONLY to mint models in pristine boxes that are complete with
all of their original contents.

---

474 1965-68 **Musical 'WALLS ICE CREAM' Van**
Ford Thames van in Blue/Cream, musical movement
(must function for top price), diorama but no figures.
Blue/Yellow card box **£250-300**

477 1966-68 **Land Rover Breakdown**
Red, Yellow tilt, spare wheel on some, hook, WW **£40-50**

478 1965-68 **Jeep Tower Wagon** (Forward Control)
Green, Yellow and Silver body, figure **£40-50**

479 1968-71 **Commer Mobile Camera Van**
Blue/White body, shaped hubs, *'SAMUELSON FILM
COMPANY LTD'*, camera and operator **£150-175**
As previous model but with cast hubs **£150-175**

483 1968-72 **Dodge Tipper Truck**
White cab, Blue tipper, *'KEW FARGO'*, cast hubs **£70-80**

484 1967-69 **Dodge Livestock Transporter**
Beige/Green body, *'KEW FARGO'*, 5 pigs **£35-45**

486 1967-69 **'KENNEL CLUB' Truck**
White/Orange Chevrolet Impala with 'Vari-View'
dachshund picture, 4 dogs, cast hubs **£110-140**

493 1975-78 **Mazda B 1600 Pick-Up**
Blue/White or Silver/Blue body **£20-25**

494 1967-72 **Bedford Tipper**
Red cab/chassis, Yellow tipper.....................................**£60-70**
Red cab/chassis, Silver tipper......................................**£90-110**
Yellow cab/chassis, Blue tipper...................................**£110-130**
Blue cab/chassis, Yellow tipper...................................**£130-150**

508 **Commer Minibus 'Holiday Camp Special'**
White/Orange, Green luggage, spun hubs, leaflet.................**£80-90**

Major Packs

1100 1958-63 **Bedford 'S' Carrimore** (Low-loader)
Yellow cab, Metallic Blue low-loader trailer,
smooth or shaped hubs **£140-170**
Red cab, Metallic Blue low-loader trailer, winch **£140-170**

1100 1971-73 **Mack Truck 'TRANS-CONTINENTAL'**
Orange cab, Black/Orange/Silver trailer **£40-50**
Orange and Metallic Lime Green version......................**£70-80**

1101 1957-62 **Bedford 'S' Carrimore Car Transporter**
Blue cab, Yellow transporter body,
'CORGI CAR TRANSPORTER'..................................**£140-170**
Red cab, Blue transporter body, smooth hubs.............**£140-170**

1101 1976-81 **Mobile Crane**
Yellow/Blue body, *'Warner & Swasey'*..........................**£25-30**

1102 1958-62 **'EUCLID' TC-12 Bulldozer**
Yellow body, Pale Grey tracks. Box has inner lining ..**£120-140**
As previous model but with Black tracks **£120-140**
Pale Lime-Green body...**£120-140**

1102 1974-76 **Crane Freuhauf**
Yellow cab, Orange dumper body,
'Road Maker Construction' logo, (Berliet Dumper)........**£30-35**

1103 1960-65 **'EUCLID' Crawler Tractor**
Yellow or Pale Lime-Green body, Pale Grey tracks **£150-175**
As previous model but with Black tracks **£150-175**

1104 1958-63 **Bedford 'S' Carrimore Machinery Carrier**
Red cab, Silver trailer, smooth hubs, operable winch .**£140-170**
Blue cab, Silver trailer, smooth hubs **£140-170**

1104 1974-77 **Bedford 'TK' type Horse Transporter**
Green or Metallic Green, *'NEWMARKET'*,
four horses and boy **£50-60**

1105 1962-66 **Bedford 'TK' type *'Corgi Car Transporter'***
Red cab, Blue/White trailer, collapsible decks **£175-225**

1105 1976-80 **Berliet Racehorse Transporter**
Brown/White, *'NATIONAL RACING STABLES'*,
four horses **£40-50**

1106 1972-77 **Mack Container Truck 'ACL'**
Yellow/Black/White body, two Red containers **£40-50**
Promotional issue for the '3M' company **£120-140**

1107 1963-66 **'EUCLID' with Dozer**
Yellow body, Black or Grey tracks, driver...................**£150-200**
Red body..**£150-200**
Lime-Green body...**£80-100**

1107 1978-79 **Berliet Container Lorry 'UNITED STATES LINES'**
Blue cab, White chassis, 2 Grey containers, ...**£30-40**

1108 1982 **Ford Truck 'MICHELIN'**
Blue/White articulated body, two containers **£40-50**

1109 1979 **Ford Truck 'MICHELIN'**
Blue/Yellow articulated body, two containers.................**£40-50**

1110 1959-64 **Bedford 'S' Tanker 'MOBILGAS'**
Red/White articulated body, detachable cab **£150-200**
As previous model but with shaped spun hubs...........**£150-200**

1110 1965-67 **Bedford 'TK' Tanker 'SHELL BENZEEN'**
Blue/White articulated tanker, Dutch model.........**£1,500-2,000**

1110 1976-80 **'JCB' Crawler Loader**
Yellow/White body, Red bucket, Black tracks, driver **£30-40**

1110 1976-80 **'JCB' Crawler**
Yellow and White body, driver.......................................**£30-40**
Light Blue/Orange with Light Blue chassis, driver **£30-40**
Yellow body, Light Blue cab, Red bucket....................**£30-40**
Red body, Light Blue cab and bucket **£30-40**
Orange body, *'BLOCK CONSTRUCTION'* logo **£30-40**

1113 1981-86 **'HYSTER' Handler**
Yellow or Black/White main body, *'US Lines'*, hoist..**£100-125**
1986-87 Yellow or Black/White main body, *'SEALINK'*,
container, export model **£100-125**
1986-87 White/Dark Blue/Yellow, *'MICHELIN'*, container......**£100-125**

1116 1979-? **Refuse Lorry** (Shelvoke and Drewry Revopak)
Orange/Silver or Red/Silver body **£15-20**
1988 Blue cab, White tipper, *'BOROUGH COUNCIL'*.............**£5-10**

1117 1980-85 **'FAUN' Street-sweeper**
Orange and Yellow or All-Yellow, with operator............**£15-20**

1119 1983 **Mercedes Load Lugger**
Yellow/Red body, *'CORGI'* **£15-20**

1121 1983 **Ford Transit Tipper**
Orange/Beige body, *'CORGI'*, (Corgimatic) **£15-20**

1126 1961-65 **Racing Car Transporter 'ECURIE ECOSSE'**
Metallic Dark Blue body, logo in Yellow lettering **£200-250**
later version: with logo in Orange lettering **£130-160**
with logo in White lettering **£130-160**
with logo and raised ridges in Light Blue..................**£130-160**
Metallic Light Blue body with logo in Red lettering...**£130-160**

1128 1963-76 **'PRIESTMAN' Cub Shovel**
Red/Yellow body, driver...**£100-125**

1129 1962-65 **Bedford 'S' Tanker 'MILK'**
Blue/White articulated body, detachable cab **£200-250**

1131 1963-66 **Bedford 'TK' Carrimore** (Machinery Low Loader)
Blue cab, Silver trailer, Yellow detachable rear
axle unit, spun hubs..**£120-140**
Same, but Black detachable rear axle unit **£80-100**

1132 1963-65 **Bedford 'TK' Carrimore**
Yellow cab, Red low loader trailer,
spare wheels, no winch...**£120-140**

1137 1966-69 **Ford Articulated Truck 'EXPRESS SERVICES'**
Blue/Silver/Red body, 'H' series tilt-cab....................**£100-120**

1138 1966-69 **Ford Articulated Transporter 'CORGI CARS'**
Red body, Silver tilt cab, two-tone Blue trailer **£145-175**

1140 1965-67 **Bedford 'TK' Petrol Tanker 'MOBILGAS'**
Red/Silver/White articulated body, tilting cab,
Box includes inner packing **£175-200**

81

1141 1965-67 **Bedford 'TK' Milk Tanker 'MILK'**
Blue/White articulated body, tilting cab......................**£200-250**

1142 1967-74 **Holmes Wrecker Recovery Truck**
White/Red/Gold body, 2 mechanics..........................**£100-125**

1145 1969-76 **Unimog Goose Dumper**
Yellow/Red body, *'406'*...**£30-35**

1146 1970-73 **Scammell Carrimore Mk.V**
Orange/White/Blue Tri-deck Transporter articulated
transporter with 3 collapsible decks............................**£125-150**

1147 1969-72 **Scammell Truck**
Yellow/White body, *'FERRYMASTERS
INTERNATIONAL HAULIERS'* **£60-80**

1148 1969-72 **Scammell Carrimore Mk.IV**
Red/White car transporter body with Yellow chucks.....**£90-110**

1150 1971-77 **Mercedes** (Unimog 406) **Snowplough**
Green/Black, 2 Red flags, Orange/Silver plough.............**£30-35**
Yellow cab and back, Red chassis, Silver plough...........**£30-35**

1151 1970 **Scammell Truck 'Co-operative Society'**
Blue/White body, promotional **£120-140**

1151 19?? **Mack Tanker 'EXXON'**
Red/White body, striped window box **£60-70**

1152 1971-76 **Mack Tanker 'ESSO'**
White/Red/Blue, Gloster Saro Tanker (detachable).........**£40-50**
As previous model but with 'EXXON' logo....................**£70-80**

1152 1983- **'BARRATT' Tipper**
Green/White body, tipper section tips.............................**£5-10**

1153 1973-74 **'PRIESTMAN' Crane**
Red/Orange body, *'Higrab'*...**£60-70**

1153 1983-84 **'WIMPEY' Tipper Truck** (Scania)
Green/Silver body (later Yellow), tipping section tips.......**£5-10**

1154 1974-76 **Priestman Crane Truck**
Yellow/Red body, Silver boom, hook **£45-55**

1154 1979 **Giant Tower Crane 'BLOCK CONSTRUCTION'**
Orange/Yellow crane, White body **£55-65**

1155 1975-79 **'Skyscraper' Tower Crane**
Yellow/Red body, Black tracks **£35-40**

1156 1977-79 **Volvo Concrete Mixer**
Yellow/Red/Orange body, *'RAPIER'* **£30-35**

1156 1980 Orange/White body, *'BLOCK CONSTRUCTION'* **£30-35**

1157 1976-81 **Ford Tanker 'ESSO'**
White/Red articulated body.......................................**£25-35**

1158 1976 **Ford Tanker 'EXXON'**
White/Black articulated body, US issue only..................**£50-60**

1159 1976-79 **Ford Car Transporter**
Metallic Blue/White or Metallic Green artic. body **£60-70**

1160 1976-78 **Ford Tanker 'GULF'**
White/Orange articulated body **£30-40**

1161 1976-78 **Ford Tanker 'ARAL'**
Blue/White/Black artic. body, German export model......**£60-80**

1169 1982 **Ford Tanker 'GUINNESS'**
Red/Cream/Black articulated body **£60-80**

1170 1982 **Ford Car Transporter**
Red/White/Yellow articulated body **£50-60**

Market prices shown here are for guidance only. They refer
ONLY to mint models in pristine boxes that are complete with
<u>all</u> of their original contents.

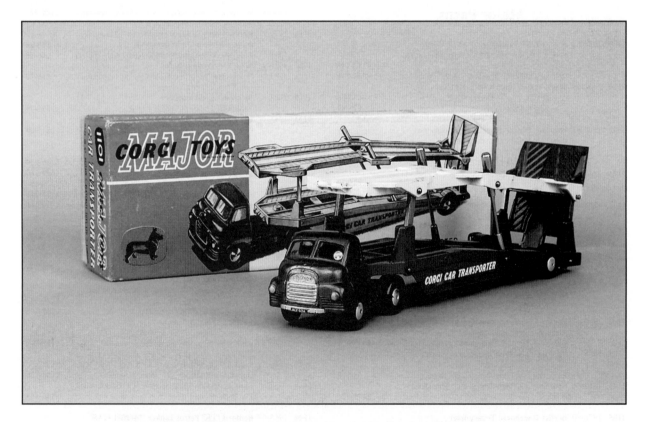

Corgi Toys Major Pack 1101, Bedford S-type 'Carrimore' Car Transporter
Photo: Vectis Auctions Ltd.

Emergency Vehicles

Police, Fire, Ambulance and other Emergency Vehicles, etc.

See also 'Corgi Commercial Vehicles' (for other breakdown recovery vehicles, etc.), and the 'Corgi Gift Sets' section.

Ref	Year(s)	Model name and details	Market Price Range
209	1958-61	**Riley Pathfinder Police Car** Black and Silver body, bell, *'POLICE'*	**£100-150**
213	1959-61	**Jaguar Fire Chief's Car** Red body, bell, Grey aerial, roof sign, smooth spun hubs	**£150-200**
213s	1961-62	**Jaguar Fire Chief's Car** (with suspension) As previous model but with shaped spun hubs	**£150-200**
		Deep Cherry Red, Lemon interior, spun hubs	**£500-600**
223	1959-61	**Chevrolet Impala 'State Patrol'** Black body, Silver stripe, Lemon interior, Grey aerial. Box also contains internal packing	**£100-120**
237	1962-66	**Oldsmobile Sheriff's Car** Black body, White roof, *'COUNTY SHERIFF'*, clear or Blue light. Box also contains internal packing	**£80-90**
260	1979-81	**Buick 'POLICE' Car** Metallic Blue/White body, *'CITY OF METROPOLIS'*, two flashing light bars	**£30-40**
284	1982-83	**Mercedes-Benz 240 D** Red body, *'NOTRUF 112'*, flashing lights, German export model	**£20-25**
293	1977-80	**Renault 5 TS** Metallic Orange or Two-tone Blue body, WW	**£15-25**
293	1980-81	**Renault 5 TS** Two-tone Blue body, roof light, *'S.O.S. MEDICINS'*	**£25-35**
295	1982-83	**Renault 5 TS Fire Chief** Red/White *'SAPEURS POMPIERS'*, French export	**£15-20**
297	1982-86	**Ford Escort 'Panda' Car** Light or Dark Blue, White doors, Blue warning lights, *'POLICE'*	**£15-20**
326	1980-81	**Chevrolet Caprice Police Car** Black/White body, *'POLICE'*, suspension	**£20-30**
332	1980-81	**Opel Doctors Car** White/Red body, *'NOTARTZ'*, opening doors	**£30-40**
339	1980	**Rover 3500 Police Car** White and Red body, *'POLICE'*	**£20-25**
373	1970-76	**VW 1200 Police Car** Green and White body, Red interior, *'POLIZEI'*, Blue roof light, WhizzWheels	**£45-60**
		White body, Red interior, Silver base, Blue roof light, *'POLIZEI'*	**£130-160**
		Black/White/Blue body, *'POLITIE'*, WhizzWheels	**£120-140**
		White body, Red interior, Blue roof light, Black *'POLICE'* lettering on White decal	**£50-60**
		Same, but White *'POLICE'* lettering on Blue decal	**£50-60**
		White body, Black hatch/bonnet stripes, Red interior, 2 figures, *'POLICE'*	**£50-60**
383	1970-73	**VW 1200 'ADAC'** Yellow body, Black roof with '1341', *'ADAC STRASSENWACHT'* logo on doors	**£75-85**
386	1987	**Mercedes 'POLIZEI'** Green/White body, two Blue warning lights, German export model	**£30-40**
395	1972-73	**Fire Bug** Orange body, Whizzwheels, Red/Black or Pink/Black stripe, Yellow ladder (381 Beach Buggy)	**£20-30**
402	1972-77	**Ford Cortina GXL Police Car** White/Red body, *'POLICE'* labels, (updated 313)	**£55-65**
		White/Red body, *'POLIZEI'*, German issue	**£75-85**
405	1956-60	**Bedford Fire Tender 'A.F.S.'** Bright or Dark Green body, divided windscreen, Silver or Black ladder, smooth or shaped hubs. (Utilicon). Blue box with leaflet	**£150-180**

Ref	Year(s)	Model name and details	Market Price Range
405M	1956-59	**Bedford Fire Tender** Red body, divided windscreen, Silver or Black ladder, *'FIRE DEPT'*, smooth or shaped hubs, friction motor. (Utilicon). Blue box with leaflet	**£120-150**
405	1978-80	**Chevrolet Ambulance** White/Orange, patient on stretcher and two attendants	**£20-25**
406	1980-81	**Mercedes Bonna Ambulance** White body, Red/Black design, opening doors, stretcher, ambulancemen, *'AMBULANCE'*	**£15-20**
		German issue: Cream body, *'KRANKENWAGEN'*	**£30-40**
		Danish issue: Red/White/body, *'FALCK'*	**£30-40**
		Swedish issue: White/Red/Black body, *'SDL 951'*	**£30-40**
407	1980	**Mercedes Bonna Ambulance** White body, Red/Black design, opening doors, stretcher, ambulancemen, *'AMBULANCE'*	**£15-20**
408	1957-59	**Bedford 'AA' Service Van** Yellow/Black, divided windscreen, smooth hubs, Blue box, leaflet	**£140-160**
	1958-59	Yellow/Black, undivided windscreen, smooth or shaped hubs, Blue box, leaflet	**£100-125**
	1959-63	Yellow/Black, undivided windscreen, shaped hubs, Blue/Yellow box, no leaflet	**£90-110**
	late issue:	Yellow/Black, single windscreen, ridged roof, flat spun hubs	**£90-110**
412	1957-60	**Bedford 'AMBULANCE'** Cream 'Utilicon' body, divided windscreen, smooth hubs. Blue box with leaflet	**£140-160**
		As previous model but with one-piece windscreen	**£160-190**
		Factory error: A few examples of 412 were issued with *'HOME SERVICES'* front labels	**NGPP**
412	1976-79	**Mercedes Police Car** White/Black body, 'POLICE' logo, Blue roof lamp	**£30-35**
		Green/White body, 'POLIZEI' logo, Blue roof lamp, German issue	**£35-45**
414	1975-77	**Jaguar XJ12-C** White/Blue body, *'COASTGUARD'*	**£10-15**
416	1959-61	**R.A.C. Land Rover** Blue body, *'RADIO RESCUE'* on cab roof sign, metal canopy, smooth hubs, Blue/Yellow box	**£140-160**
		Blue body, no cab roof sign, *'RADIO RESCUE'* on canopy, shaped hubs	**£150-190**
		Belgian issue: Yellow body and metal canopy, 'TS' decals on sides, 'RADIO' on roof	**£250-300**
416s	1962-64	**R.A.C. Land Rover** Blue body, Lemon interior, suspension, *'RADIO RESCUE'* on plastic canopy	**£65-75**
		Belgian issue: Yellow body, Grey plastic canopy, suspension, 'TS RADIO' decals on doors	**£250-300**
416	1977-79	**Buick Police Car** Blue body or Metallic Blue body, *'POLICE'*, two policemen	**£25-30**
419	1960-65	**Ford Zephyr Motorway Car** White or Cream body, smooth or shaped hubs, *'POLICE'*, aerial, large or small roof light	**£100-125**
		Export issues: with *'POLITIE'* or *'RIJKS POLITIE'* logo (Dutch)	**£150-200**
421	1977-79	**Land Rover Station Wagon** Red body, White roof-rack, *'FOREST WARDEN'*	**£20-25**
422	1977-80	**Riot Police Wagon** Red/White body, number '6' and *'RIOT POLICE'* on doors, water cannon	**£15-20**

423	1960-62	**Bedford 12cwt. Tender**	
		Red body, Black ladder, undivided windscreen, smooth or shaped hubs, 'FIRE DEPT.'	**£140-160**
		Red body, unpainted ladder, undivided windscreen, shaped hubs	**£125-150**
424	1976-79	**'SECURITY' Van**	
		Black/Yellow/White body, mesh windows, WW	**£10-15**
428	1978-80	**Renault Police Car**	
		Black/White body, 'POLICE', (export isssue)	**£55-65**
429	1978-80	**Police Jaguar XJ12-C**	
		White/Red/Blue body, 'POLICE', aerial, lights	**£25-35**
430	1978-80	**Porsche 924 'Police'**	
		Black/White body, 'POLICE', warning light	**£15-20**
430	1978-80	**Porsche 924 'Polizei'**	
		White/Green body, 'POLIZEI', (export isssue)	**£55-65**
437	1962-65	**Cadillac Superior Ambulance**	
		Cream over Red body, 'AMBULANCE' on side windows, Amber roof light	**£80-90**
	1965-68	Light Blue over White body, 'AMBULANCE' on sides, Red cross on bonnet, Red roof light	**£100-125**
		Metallic Red over Metallic Silver body	**£100-125**
439	1963-65	**Chevrolet Impala**	
		Red body, 'FIRE CHIEF', White stripe, Lemon interior, aerial, Yellow roof light, firemen, with White painted door labels with 'FIRE DEPT'	**£140-170**
		White rectangular label on front doors 'FIRE DEPT'	**£80-100**
		with round Red label on front doors 'FIRE DEPT'	**£80-100**
448	1964-69	**Austin Police Mini Van**	
		Dark Blue body, Red interior, shaped or cast hubs, aerial, White 'POLICE' logo, policeman and dog, pictorial stand and internal support packaging	**£150-175**
461	1972-79	**'Police' Vigilant Range Rover**	
		White/Blue, warning lights, policemen, 8 'POLICE' emergency signs + bollards	**£25-35**
		White/Red body, 'LANGZAAM', policemen, emergency signs, Dutch model	**£50-60**
463	1964-66	**Commer 'AMBULANCE'**	
		Cream or White body, Red interior, Blue tinted windows and roof light	**£120-140**
464	1967-68	**Commer 'POLICE' Van**	
		Dark Blue, 'COUNTY POLICE', window bars, clear roof light, leaflet	**£100-125**
		Same, but Metallic Light Blue, with Blue roof light	**£100-125**
		Dark Blue, window bars, Red roof light, 'CITY POLICE', instruction leaflet	**£175-200**
		Dark Blue, 'open' windows, Blue roof light, White 'POLICE' cast into sides, with instructions	**£90-110**
		Deep Green body, 'POLICE', export model, opaque rear/side windows	**£400-500**
		Metallic Green body, 'POLIZEI', German issue	**£150-175**
		Metallic Blue body, 'SECOURS', French issue	**£150-175**
		Metallic Blue body, window bars, 'RIJKSPOLITIE', Dutch issue	**£150-175**
477	1966-67	**Land Rover Breakdown**	
		Red body, Yellow canopy with spotlight and 'BREAKDOWN SERVICE' logo, rubber (or later plastic) 'tyre' crank, shaped or cast hubs	**£45-55**
		Same, but with large or small Silver crank, WW	**£35-40**
481	1965-69	**Chevrolet Police Car**	
		White/Black body, 'POLICE PATROL', Red roof lights, two policemen	**£100-125**
482	1966-69	**Chevrolet Impala**	
		Red over White body, Chrome stripe, bonnet logo, Blue light, Grey aerial, rectangular 'FIRE CHIEF' label on front doors, detailed cast or shaped spun hubs	**£75-95**
		With round label on front doors 'FIRE CHIEF'	**£75-95**
482	1974-77	**Vigilant Range Rover**	
		Red and White body with 'AMBULANCE' logo	**£25-30**
		White body with Blue side stripe and 'AMBULANCE' logo, stretcher and 2 ambulancemen	**£25-30**

483	1979	**Belgian Police Range Rover**	
		White body, Red stripes, warning lights, policemen, emergency signs	**£75-85**
484	1978-80	**AMC Pacer 'RESCUE'**	
		White/Orange/Black body, number '35', 'RESCUE'	**£10-15**
		As previous issue but with 'SECOURS' logo	**£40-50**
489	1980	**Volkswagen Polo**	
		White/Green body, 'POLIZEI', (export issue)	**£50-55**
		Variation with 'ADAC' logo, (export issue)	**£50-55**
490	1967-69	**Volkswagen Breakdown**	
		Unpainted fittings, Chrome tools, Red 'VW' emblem, Red/Yellow stripe label, two spare wheels.	
		Avocado body, shaped hubs, 'BREAKDOWN SERVICE' labels, spun or cast hubs	**£90-110**
	1968-72	Same, but with 'RACING CLUB' labels (in GS 12)	**GSP**
492	1966-70	**VW 1200 Car**	
		Green body, White roof, White 'POLIZEI' on bonnet, No '18' logo	**£80-95**
		White body with Black 'POLIZEI' on doors and bonnet, (Germany)	**£200-250**
492	1966-69	**VW European Police Car**	
		Dark Green body, White roof and wings, Red 'POLIZEI', Blue lamp	**£90-110**
	NB	Box should contain 'True Scale Steering' Red/Yellow cardboard roof fitting.	
		All-White body, Light Brown interior, driver, crest on doors, 'POLITIE', Blue lamp, Dutch model	**£175-225**
		All-White body, Light Brown interior, driver, crest on doors, 'POLITZIE', Blue lamp, Swiss model	**£175-225**
506	1968-69	**Sunbeam Imp 'Panda' Car**	
		White body, Black bonnet and roof, Blue roof light	**£80-90**
		White body, Black roof, 'luminous' door panels, Blue roof light	**£80-90**
		Light Blue body, White roof, 'luminous' door panels, Blue roof light	**£80-90**
509	1970-75	**Porsche 911s Targa Police Car**	
		White/Red body, Black roof, 'POLICE' logo	**£65-75**
		White/Red body, 'POLIZEI', siren, warning lights	**£65-75**
		'RIJKSPOLITIE' export issue	**£90-110**
513		**Citroën Safari 'ALPINE RESCUE' Car**	
		White/Red car, skis and sled on roof-rack, skier, St Bernard dog, Blue/Yellow 'window' box	**£90-110**
700	1974-79	**Motorway Ambulance**	
		White/Red body, 'ACCIDENT', Red Cross	**£15-20**
702	1975-79	**Breakdown Truck**	
		Red/Black, single bumper, hook, 'ACCIDENT'	**£10-15**
703	1976-78	**Hi-Speed Fire Engine**	
		Red body, Yellow ladder, warning lights	**£10-15**
911	1976-80	**Air-Sea Rescue Helicopter**	
		Blue/Yellow body, Black 'flick-spin' rotor, 'N 428'	**£15-20**
921	1975-81	**Hughes OH-6A Helicopter**	
		White/Red, 'POLICE', 'RESCUE', warning lights	**£15-20**
921/1	1975-80	**'POLIZEI' Helicopter**	
		White/Blue, 'POLIZEI', Black 'flick-spin' rotor, German issue	**£25-30**
921/2	1975-80	**'POLITIE' Helicopter**	
		White/Blue, 'POLITIE', Black 'flick-spin' rotor, Dutch issue	**£25-30**
921/4	1975-80	**'ADAC' Helicopter**	
		Yellow body, 'D-HFFM', Black 'flick-spin' rotor	**£25-30**
921/6	1975-80	**Swiss Red Cross**	
		Red helicopter body, Black blades, 'flick-spin' rotor	**£25-30**
922	1975-78	**Casualty Helicopter**	
		Sikorsky Skycrane with Red/White body	**£25-30**
923	1975-78	**Casualty Helicopter**	
		Army Sikorsky Skycrane with Olive/Yellow body	**£25-30**
924	1977-81	**Air-Sea Rescue Helicopter**	
		Orange/Yellow/Black body, 'RESCUE'	**£25-30**
927	1978-79	**Surf Rescue Helicopter**	
		Blue/White body, 'SURF RESCUE'	**£25-30**
931	1979-80	**Jet Ranger Helicopter**	
		White/Red, 'POLICE RESCUE', 'flick-spin' rotor	**£25-30**

Major Packs (Emergency Vehicles)

1001 1980-82 **HCB Angus Firestreak**
Red body, Yellow ladder, 2 firemen plus equipment **£60-70**

1103 1976-81 **Chubb Pathfinder**
Red/Silver, *'AIRPORT CRASH TRUCK'*,
operable pump and siren, orange logo **£60-70**
Same model but non-working siren, Brick-Red logo **£50-60**
Red/Silver, *'NEW YORK AIRPORT'* logo **£80-90**

1118 1981-83 **Chubb Pathfinder**
Red body, *'AIRPORT FIRE SERVICE'*,
operable water pump **£60-70**

1126 1977-81 **Dennis Fire Engine 'SIMON SNORKEL'**
Red/White/Yellow, turntable, ladder, 6 firemen...............**£55-65**

1127 1964-74 **Bedford Fire Engine 'SIMON SNORKEL'**
Red/Yellow/Silver, turntable, ladder, 6 fireman..........**£100-125**

1140 1982 **Ford Transit Wrecker**
White/Red, *'24 Hour Service'*, operable winch, hook,....**£15-20**
As previous model but logo changed to *'RELAY'* **£15-20**
1982 Red/Yellow, *'ABSCHLEPPDEENST'*, export model......**£15-20**

1142 1967-74 **'HOLMES WRECKER'**
Red/White/Blue, Grey or Gold twin booms,
ladder, 2 spare wheels..**£90-110**

1143 1968-80 **'AMERICAN LA FRANCE'**
Articulated Fire Engine in Red/White/Yellow,
shaped spun or detailed cast wheels, 4-part extending
ladder, 5 firemen, plain early box **£90-120**
As previous model but in later striped window box **£80-100**

1144 1975-78 **Berliet Wrecker Recovery**
Red/White/Gold body, with Gold or Grey hoists............**£60-70**

2029 1980-83 **Mack Fire Engine**
Red body, warning light, detachable ladder,
'HAMMOND FIRE DEPT' **£15-25**

Corgi Toys 513

Citroën Safari

'ALPINE RESCUE' Car

Photo:
Vectis Auctions Ltd.

Aircraft

Helicopters and Space Vehicles are also listed in the Emergency Vehicles, Novelty and Military Sections.

Ref	Year(s)	Model name and details	Market Price Range
650	1973-80	**'BOAC' Concorde**, White/Blue with Gold tail design, all-card box with 'BRITISH AIRWAYS', box has inner packing	**£70-80**
		White/Blue with Red/White/Blue tail, display stand, 'G-BBDG'	**£50-60**
		Version with White stripes on tail	**£15-25**
		Version with crown design on tail	**£15-25**
651	1973-81	**'AIR FRANCE' Concorde**, White/Blue with Gold tail design, all-card box	**£70-80**
		White body, Red/White/Blue tail, display stand	**£40-50**
652	1973-81	**'JAPAN AIRLINES' Concorde**, White/Red/Blue/Black, all-card box, inner packing	**£150-200**
653	1973-81	**'AIR CANADA' Concorde**, White/Red/Blue/Black, all-card box, inner packing	**£150-200**
1119	1960-62	**HDL Hovercraft 'SR-N1'**, Blue/Grey/White body, Yellow rudders and wheels (Major Pack)	**£100-130**
1301	1973-77	**Piper Cherokee Arrow**, Yellow/Black with White wings, or White/Blue, 'N 286 4 A'	**£35-45**
1302	1973-77	**Piper Navajo**, Red/White or Yellow/White, 'N 9219 Y'	**£35-45**
1303	1973-77	**Lockheed F104A Starfighter**, Silver or Camouflage with Black crosses	**£35-45**
1304	1973-77	**Mig-21 PF**, Silver or Blue, number '57', Red stars, retractable undercarriage	**£25-35**
1305	1973	**Grumman F-11a Tiger**, Blue 'NAVY', or Silver with US stars	**£25-35**

Ref	Year(s)	Model name and details	Market Price Range
1306	1973-77	**North American P51-D Mustang**, Silver or Camouflage, Black props, US stars, moveable controls	**£25-35**
1307	1973-77	**Saab 35 X Draken**, Silver or Camouflage, retractable undercarriage, Swedish markings	**£35-45**
1308	1973-77	**BAC (or SEPCAT) Jaguar**, Silver or Camouflage, retractable wheels, moveable control surfaces	**£35-45**
1309	1973-77	**'BOAC' Concorde**, Dark Blue/White, retractable wheels	**£45-55**
1310	1973-77	**'AIR FRANCE' 'BOEING 707B'**, White/Blue body, Silver wings, retractable wheels	**£55-65**
1311	1973-77	**Messerschmitt ME410**, All Silver body, Black Iron Crosses on wings and fuselage	**£35-45**
1312	1973-77	**Boeing 727 'TWA'**, White body, Silver wings, retractable wheels	**£35-45**
1313	1973-77	**Japanese Zero-Sen A6M5**, Green or Silver with Red circles, retractable wheels	**£35-45**
1315	1973-77	**'PAN-AM' Boeing 747**, White body, Silver wings, hinged nose, retractable wheels	**£35-45**
1315/1		**'BRITISH AIRWAYS' Jumbo Boeing 747**, White/Silver, Blue logo, hinged nose, retrac. wheels	**£55-65**
1316	1973-77	**McDonnell Douglas F-4c5**, Phantom II in Silver or Camouflage with retractable undercarriage	**£35-45**
1320	1978-80	**'BRITISH AIRWAYS' VC-10**, White/Silver with Red tail, Blue logo, retractable wheels	**£35-45**
1325	1978-80	**'SWISSAIR' DC-10**, White/Silver with Red stripe and tail, retractable wheels	**£35-45**

Military and R.A.F. models

Unless described otherwise, all models in this listing are finished in Military-Green or Olive-Drab camouflage.

Ref.	Years	Model details	Market Price Range
350	1958-62	**Thunderbird Missile**, Blue, Green or Silver missile with Red tip, Air Force Blue loading trolley	**£65-75**
351	1958-62	**RAF Land Rover**, Blue body, RAF roundel, spare wheel, windows, flat spun hubs	**£90-110**
		Same model but with suspension, flat spun hubs	**£90-110**
352	1958-62	**RAF Vanguard Staff Car**, Blue bodied Standard Vanguard with RAF roundel	**£80-100**
353	1959-61	**Decca Radar Scanner**, Blue/Orange, scanner rotates	**£35-45**
354	1964-66	**Commer Military Ambulance**, Military Green body, Red Interior, Red cross, driver, Blue tinted glazing	**£125-150**
355	1964-65	**Commer Van 'US MILITARY POLICE'**, Red interior, driver, Blue roof light, leaflet	**£125-150**
356	1964-66	**VW Personnel Carrier**, Military Green body, Red interior, driver, Blue roof light, 'US Personnel'	**£125-150**
357	1964-66	**Land Rover**, Military Green body, Lemon interior, driver, White star, aerial, 'Weapons Carrier'	**£240-280**
358	1964-68	**Oldsmobile Staff Car**, Red interior, White star, 'HQ STAFF', driver, 3 passengers, aerial	**£150-180**
359	1964-66	**Commer Army 'FIELD KITCHEN'**, Blue interior, US star on roof, driver/attendant, 'US ARMY'	**£150-200**
414	1961-63	**Bedford Dormobile Military Ambulance**, Olive drab body, Red crosses, smooth hubs	**£100-125**
		Same model but with shaped hubs and suspension	**£100-125**
500	1963-64	**US Army Land Rover**, Rare version of model 357	**£175-225**
900	1974-78	**German Tiger MkI Tank**, Brown/Green, rubber tracks, fires shells (12 supplied) aerial, '144'	**£30-40**
901	1974-78	**Centurion Mk.I Tank**, rubber tracks, fires shells (12 supplied) aerial, Union Jacks	**£30-40**
902	1974-80	**American M60 A1 Tank**, rubber tracks, fires shells (12 supplied)	**£30-40**
903	1974-80	**British Chieftain Tank**, fires shells (12 supplied), rubber tracks	**£30-40**
904	1974-78	**German King-Tiger Tank**, 'B 34', rubber tracks, fires shells (12 supplied) Black crosses	**£30-40**
905	1975-76	**Russian SU100 Tank Destroyer**, Grey, Red Star, fires shells (12 supplied), rubber tracks	**£30-40**
906	1975-76	**Saladin Armoured Car**, rubber tracks, fires shells (12 supplied) elevating gun	**£30-40**
907	1976-80	**German Rocket Launcher**, Steel Blue/Red, half-track, detachable limber, fires rockets (12)	**£30-40**
908	1977-80	**French AMX Recovery Tank**, crane, lifting dozer blade, equipment, 3 figures	**£40-50**
909	1977-80	**Tractor Gun and Trailer**, Sand-coloured British gun and trailer, fires shells (12 supplied)	**£40-50**
920	1975-78	**Bell Army Helicopter**, Military-Green with Army markings, Black or Green rotor	**£15-20**
922	1975-78	**Casualty Helicopter**, Red/White/Yellow Sikorsky helicopter, number '3', Red crosses	**£15-20**
923	1975-78	**Sikorsky Sky Crane**, Military-Green, Red cross, 'ARMY' marking	**£15-20**

MAJOR PACKS - (Military models)

Ref.	Years	Model details	Market Price Range
1106	1959-61	**Karrier Decca Radar Van**, Cream body, 4 Orange bands, rotating scanner, aerials, box has interior packing	**£125-175**
		Same, but with 5 Orange bands	**£100-125**
1108	1958-60	**Bristol Bloodhound Guided Missile and Launching Ramp**, Green ramp, Yellow/Red/White Guided Missile, RAF markings	**£150-175**
1109	1959-61	**Bristol Bloodhound Guided Missile and Loading Trolley**, Green ramp, Yellow/Red/White Guided Missile, RAF markings	**£150-175**
1112	1959-62	**Corporal Guided Missile on Launching Ramp**, Military-Green mechanical base, White missile, Red rubber nose cone, instruction sheet in box	**£200-250**
	1960-62	Same but with separately boxed 1408 Percussion Head and instructions	**£200-250**
1113	1959-62	**Corporal Guided Missile Erector Vehicle**, with lifting mechanism and Missile, spare wheel, leaflet	**£250-350**
1115	1958-61	**Bristol Ferranti Bloodhound**, Yellow/Red/White Guided Missile with RAF markings	**£65-75**
1116	1959-61	**Bloodhound Launching Ramp**, launching ramp for 1115. Rotates, has lifting mechanism	**£55-65**
1117	1959-61	**Bloodhound Loading Trolley**, for use with 1115. Military-Green, spare wheel, drawbar pivots	**£55-65**
1118	1959-64	**International Tow Truck**, Military-Green with British markings (US markings on box picture)	**£125-150**
		Dutch issue with Silver grille and sidelights	**£125-150**
		US Army issues	**£125-150**
1124	1960-61	**Launching Ramp for Corporal Guided Missile**, Military-Green, operable mechanisms, in plain 'Temporary Pack' box	**£100-125**
1133	1965-66	**Troop Transporter**, International six wheeled truck, 'US 7811332', hook	**£175-200**
1134	1965-66	**'US ARMY' Fuel Tanker**, Olive Bedford 'S' Type Artic, US Army star, 'NO SMOKING'	**£225-275**
1135	1965	**Heavy Equipment Transporter**, Bedford Carrimore, Military Green, US Army star, driver, Red interior	**£225-275**

> Market prices shown here are for guidance only.
> They refer ONLY to mint models in
> pristine boxes that are complete with
> all of their original contents.

Corgitronics and Corgimatics

These models have 'Battery-operated Micro-Chip Action'.

Ref	Year	Model details	Market Price Range
1001	1982	**HCB Angus Firestreak**, Red/Yellow/White, 'RESCUE', electronic siren, on/off switch	**£60-70**
1002	1981	**Sonic Corgi Truck Set**, Yellow/White/Black/Red, SHELL SUPER OIL', 'BP OIL', remote control	**£25-30**
1002	1981	**'YORKIE' Truck Set**, White/Yellow/Blue/Orange, 'MILK CHOCOLATE YORKIE', remote control	**£25-30**
1003	1981	**Ford Road Hog**, Black, Yellow/White twirls, 2-tone horn, press-down start	**£15-20**
1004	1981	**'Beep Beep Bus'**, Red, 'BTA WELCOME TO BRITAIN', 2-tone horn, press-down start	**£20-25**
	1983	Red body with 'WELCOME TO HAMLEYS' logo	**£20-25**
1005	1982	**Police Land Rover**, White/Red/Blue, 'POLICE', electronic siren, press-down start	**£15-20**
1006	1982	**'RADIO WEST' Roadshow**, 'Your Local Radio 605', AM radio, advertised but not issued	**NPP**

Ref	Year	Model details	Market Price Range
1006	1982	**'RADIO LUXEMBOURG'**, Red/White, 'RTL 208', AM radio, 3 loudspeakers	**£25-30**
1007	1982	**Road Repair Unit Land Rover and Trailer**, Yellow/Red/Silver, 'ROADWORKS', press start, road drill and sound	**£25-35**
1008	1982	**Fire Chief's Car**, Red/White/Yellow/Silver, 'FIRE DEPARTMENT', press-down start, siren	**£15-20**
1009	1983	**MG Maestro 1600**, Yellow/Black, press start, working front and rear lights	**£15-20**
		Red/Black body. Sold in Austin-Rover Group box	**£20-25**
1024	1983	**'Beep Beep Bus'**, Red, 'BTA', supplied exclusively to Mothercare shops	**£20-25**
1121	1983	**Ford Transit Tipper Lorry**, Orange/Black, flashing light and working tipper	**£20-25**

Agricultural models also appear in the Gift Sets section.

Ref.	Years	Model details	Market Price Range
50	1959-66	**Massey-Ferguson 65 Tractor**, Bright Red bonnet, seat and metal hubs, Pale Grey chassis, Black plastic steering wheel	**£160-200**
		Bright Red bonnet, bare metal seat, Red metal hubs, Grey plastic steering wheel	**£100-125**
		Dark Red bonnet, Silver metal steering wheel and seat, Fawn engine, Red plastic hubs	**£140-160**
NB		A variation with Copper metal seat is known to exist	NGPP
50	1974-77	**Massey-Ferguson 50B Tractor**, Yellow/Black/Red body, windows	**£60-80**
51	1959-64	**Massey-Ferguson Tipper Trailer**, Red chassis, Yellow or Grey body, Red metal or plastic wheels	**£40-45**
53	1960-66	**Massey-Ferguson 65 Tractor with Shovel**, Bright Red bonnet without decals, Grey plastic steering wheel, Silver metal seat/shovel, fawn engine, fawn rams with Black decals, Red metal hubs	**£120-150**
		As previous model, but Bright Red bonnet has thin Black outline decals, Red plastic hubs	**£100-125**
		Same but Bright Red bonnet has thin Black outline decals, bare metal rams / shovel, Red plastic hubs	**£100-125**
		Red bonnet with White/Black decals, Silver metal steering wheel, Fawn engine and rams, Fawn bucket with Silver interior, Red plastic hubs	**£150-180**
54	1974	**Massey-Ferguson 50B Tractor with Shovel**, Yellow and Red body and shovel	**£60-80**
54	1962-64	**Fordson Power Major Tractor** (Roadless Half-Tracks), Blue body, Orange rollers and wheels, Black rubber tracks, lights in radiator grille. Plain 'early' box	**£250-300**
		Same but with Grey rubber tracks, lights at sides of grille, picture box	**£250-300**
55	1961-63	**Fordson Power Major Tractor**, Blue/Grey/Red body, Orange metal hubs, Silver seat/steering wheel	**£400-500**
		Blue/Grey/Red body, Dull Orange plastic hubs, Silver seat/steering wheel	**£200-225**
55	1977	**David Brown Tractor 1412**, Black/Red/White body, steering wheel	**£60-80**
56	1961-63	**Four-Furrow Plough**, Red/Brown/Yellow body	**£30-35**
56	1977	**Farm Tipper Trailer**, Red/Yellow or Red/White body with drop-down tailboard	**£10-15**
57	1963-66	**Massey Ferguson 65 Tractor with Fork**, Red/Silver/Cream body, Red hubs, driver, steering wheel	**£160-180**
		Same model but with Orange hubs	**£125-150**

Market prices shown here are for guidance only. They refer ONLY to mint models in pristine boxes that are complete with all of their original contents.

Ref.	Years	Model details	Market Price Range
58	1965-72	**Beast Carrier**, Red/Cream/Blue body, four calves	**£45-55**
60	1964-71	**Fordson Power Major Tractor**, Blue body and steering wheel, bare metal seat, driver, Red plastic hubs	**£250-350**
61	1964-71	**Four-Furrow Plough**, Blue/Silver body	**£30-35**
62	1965-72	**Ford Tipper Trailer**, Red/Yellow body, two raves	**£20-25**
64	1965-69	**Forward Control Jeep**, Red body, Yellow/White working conveyor, farmhand figure	**£80-100**
66	1966-72	**Massey-Ferguson '165' Tractor**, Red/Blue/White body, engine sound	**£120-140**
67	1967-72	**Ford Super Major Tractor**, Blue/White/Silver body, 'FORD 5000', instructions	**£320-360**
69	1967-72	**Massey-Ferguson '165' Tractor and Shovel**, Red/Blue body, Silver shovel, driver	**£350-400**
71	1967-72	**Fordson Disc Harrow**, Yellow/Red/Silver body	**£30-35**
72	1971-73	**Ford 5000 Tractor and Towbar**, As Corgi 67 but with frame, bucket and pipes	**£200-250**
73	1970-73	**Massey-Ferguson Tractor and Saw**, As Corgi 66 plus Yellow rotating saw	**£250-300**
74	1969-72	**Ford 5000 Tractor and Scoop**, As Corgi 67 plus Yellow/Silver scoop	**£140-170**
100	1957-61	**Dropside Trailer**, Yellow/Red/Grey body	**£40-50**
101	1958-61	**Platform Trailer**, Yellow/Grey or Blue/Grey body	**£40-50**
102	1958-59	**Rice's Pony Trailer**, Red body, Brown chassis, wire drawbar, smooth hubs, plastic pony	**£70-80**
		Red body, Silver chassis, wire drawbar, smooth hubs, plastic pony	**£60-70**
	1959-65	Red body, Black chassis, wire or cast drawbar, smooth or shaped hubs	**£60-70**
		Red body, Silver chassis, wire or cast drawbar, smooth or shaped hubs	**£60-70**
		Cream body, Red chassis, wire or cast drawbar, smooth or shaped hubs	**£60-70**
	1961-68	Tan/Cream body, Silver chassis, cast drawbar, shaped hubs	**£60-70**
112	1969-72	**Rice Beaufort Horse-Box**, Blue/White horse-box with mare and foal	**£25-30**
484	1967-69	**Dodge Livestock Transporter**, Beige/Green/Graphite Grey body, spun hubs, 'KEW FARGO', 5 pigs. Blue/Yellow card box	**£70-80**
		Later issue with cast hubs. Blue/Yellow window box	**£70-80**

Corgi Toys 60 Fordson Power Major Tractor and 51 Massey-Ferguson Tipper Trailer

Photo: Vectis Auctions Ltd.

Major Packs
(and large Agricultural Models)

See also 'Gift Sets' section.

Ref.	Years	Model details	Market Price Range
1111	1959-60	**M-F Combine Harvester**, Red/Yellow, Yellow metal wheels, metal tines, box has internal packing	**£100-150**
1111	1960-61	**M-F '780' Combine Harvester**, Red/Yellow, Yellow metal wheels, plastic tines, box has internal packing	**£100-150**
	1961-64	Red/Yellow, Red plastic wheels, Yellow plastic tines, box has internal packing	**£175-225**
1112	1977-78	**David Brown Tractor and Combine Harvester**, Corgi 55 Tractor with Red/White/Black combine harvester	**£150-175**

Novelty, Film and TV-related models

Ref	Year(s)	Model name	Colours, features, details	Market Price Range
107	1967-70	Batboat on Trailer	Black boat (tinplate fin cover) with Batman and Robin figures, gold trailer (suspension, cast wheels). Blue/yellow pictorial box also contains black accessory towing hook for attachment to Batmobile	£125-150
	1974-81		Black boat (plastic fin) with Batman and Robin figures, gold trailer (no suspension, Whizzwheels), striped window box	£90-110
201	1970-72	The Saint's Volvo	White body, White 'Saint' logo on red label, WhizzWheels, driver, Red/Yellow 'window' box	£200-225
258	1965-68	The Saint's Volvo P1800	White body, Black 'Saint' logo (transfer), Red interior, driver, spun hubs, Blue/Yellow card box	£250-300
	1968-70		White body, White 'Saint' logo on Red label, Red interior, driver, cast hubs, Blue/Yellow card box	£250-300
	1968-70		As previous version but white 'Saint' logo on blue label	NGPP
	1970-71		White body, White logo on Red label, Yellow interior, WhizzWheels	£155-175
259	1979-80	Penguinmobile	White car with 'Penguin' and Red/Yellow parasol, Black/Yellow 'window' box	£35-40
260	1979-81	Superman Police Car	Blue/White body, 'CITY of METROPOLIS', Black/Yellow pictorial window box	£35-40
261	1965-69	James Bond's Aston-Martin	Bright Gold body (metal roof), Red interior, wire wheels. With James Bond at the wheel, passenger seat ejector (with bandit figure). Accessories: envelope with 'secret instructions', spare bandit figure, self-adhesive '007' badge, (plus 'Model Car Makers to James Bond' Corgi Catalogue in earlier boxes). Blue/Yellow picture box has inner pictorial stand. From the film 'Goldfinger'	£400-500
	variant:		As previous model but the opening roof component is made of plastic	NGPP
261	1979-81	Spiderbuggy	Red/Blue jeep body with crane, Spiderman and Green Goblin figures. Black/Yellow pictorial window box	£75-100
262	1967-69	Lincoln Continental Executive Limousine	Metallic Gold/Black body, with picture strip for onboard 'TV set'	£125-150
			Light Blue/Tan body, with picture strip for onboard 'TV set'	£150-175
262	1979-80	Captain Marvel's Porsche	White with flames and stars, driver, Black/Yellow 'window' box	£35-40
263	1979-81	Captain America's Jetmobile	White/Red/Blue body, Red wheels, Black/Yellow 'window' box	£25-30
264	1979-82	Incredible Hulk Truck	Bronze Hulk in Red cage on Mazda pick-up, Black/Yellow 'window' box	£45-55
			As previous model but Hulk in Grey cage	£55-65
	NB		Dark Bronze Hulk is rare – add **£10** to price.	
265	1979-82	Supermobile	Blue/Red/Silver body, Superman at the controls, moving fists'. Black/Yellow pictorial 'window' box has 10 spare rockets / instruction leaflet	£40-50
266	1968-72	Chitty Chitty Bang Bang	Chrome, Brown and Red body (162 m), Red/Yellow retractable 'wings', figures of Caractacus Potts, Truly Scrumptious, a boy and a girl Pictorial Blue/Yellow 'window'box comes in two sizes	£250-300
	1992	25th Anniversary replica:	model on 'mahogany' display stand. Direct mail offer from Corgi	£60-70
266	1979-83	Spider Bike	Red/Blue motorcycle, Spiderman rider, Black wheels, Black or Red handlebars forks, Black or Blue seat and fairing, amber or clear windshield, rocket launchers.	
		Box 1:	Black/Yellow pictorial 'window' box with header card, 10 spare rockets on sprue	£100-125
		Box 2:	Black/Yellow 'window' box without header card, 10 spare rockets on sprue	£100-125
		Box 3:	Black/Red/Yellow striped 'window' box without header card, 10 spare rockets on sprue	£100-125
266	1980-82	Spider Bike	As previous model but with White wheels	£100-125
267	1966-67	Batmobile (i):	Gloss Black body, Red 'Bat' logo on doors and on gold cast hubs, Batman and Robin figures, 'pulsating exhaust flame', sealed secret instructions concealed in box base. 12 spare rockets (Red or Yellow) attached to sprue, self-adhesive 'Batman' badge. Pictorial card box with diorama, earliest versions had 'features' leaflet within	£500-700
		(ii):	As previous model but with Matt Black body	£600-750
	1967-72	(iii):	As (i) but with towing hook cast into base. Blue/Yellow 'window' box (some in earlier card boxes)	£300-350
	1967-72	(iv):	As (i) but with cast Silver wheels. Black/Blue/Yellow 'window' box	£350-350
	1973	(v):	As (iv) but with Red WhizzWheels (with Chrome hubs) and without pulsating 'flame' effect. Blue/Yellow 'window' box with missiles and instructions	£400-600
	1974-77	(vi):	As (v) but with Black WhizzWheels and without pulsating 'flame' effect. Copyright information cast in base Dark Blue/Yellow 'window' box (header card on some), spare rockets, no instruction sheet	£150-200
	1977-79	(vii):	As (vi) casting but wider WhizzWheels, no Robin figure. Black/Red/Yellow 'window' box	£150-200
	1979-80	(viii):	Gloss Black, Gold slasher blade and tow hook, aerial, Batman and Robin figures, wide WhizzWheels, striped 'window' box	£125-175
268	1978-80	Batman's Batbike	Black/Red rocket-firing motorcycle with Red or Grey Batman figure. Black and Yellow 'window' box (header card on some), spare rockets	£80-100
	1980-83		As previous versions but in Black/Red/Yellow striped 'window' box	£50-70
268	1967-72	The Green Hornet's 'Black Beauty'	Black body, Green interior, driver and Green Hornet figures, transfer on roof, spun or cast detailed hubs. Fires missiles from front, radar spinners from rear. Four of each, plus 'secret instructions' are in Blue/Yellow pictorial card box which should also include a greaseproof paper roof decal protector, and inner pictorial card	£200-300
269	1977-83	James Bond Lotus Esprit	White body, Black windows, operable fins and rocket mechanism. From the film 'The Spy Who Loved Me'. Early Black/Yellow pictorial 'window' box with plain base must contain instruction sheet and 10 spare rockets attached to sprue	£125-165
			Later pictorial 'window' box has instructions printed on base, 10 spare rockets	£100-130
	1977		10 gold-plated versions of 269 were presented to VIPs at the film's launch. The models had special mountings and boxes	£1,000-1,500
		Pre-production model:	Demonstration model in a case. Red/Yellow/Blue/Green	£1,000-1,400

270	1968-76	James Bond's Aston-Martin DB5	Silver body (slightly larger than 261). Features as 261, plus revolving number-plates and extending tyre slashers. Box must contain inner pictorial stand, James Bond leaflet, sealed 'secret instructions' packet, unused '007' lapel badge (different from 261), set of unapplied number plates and bandit figure. Variations include Gold or Silver coloured bumpers, metal or plastic spoked rear wheels.

Box 1: Pictorial wing-flap box. Model sits on card platform under vac-formed bubble (fragile, few made)......**£400-500**
Box 2: Blue/Yellow 'window' box (some with card 'upstand' till 1973, few made).................................**£500-750**
Box 3: Black/Blue/Yellow striped 'window' box (1973-76)...**£250-350**

270 1977-78 .... As previous version but with fixed number plates, 'solid' chrome WhizzWheels, no tyre-slashers, no 'secret instructions'. Striped window box, ejectable passenger lodged in box inner **£100-130**

271 1978-81 **James Bond Aston-Martin**........ Silver body (1:36 scale), Red interior, Gold radiator/bumpers, WhizzWheels ('spoked' detail or 'alloy racing'). Early Black/Yellow boxes had '1:36' printed on window tag, plus header card **£70-80**
Later Black/Yellow boxes did not have the window tag **£50-60**
Final issues were in Black/Red/Yellow striped window boxes **£40-50**

271 1990 ....'MODELAUTO' promotional: Silver body, Red interior with 2 figures, Blue logo 'National Motor Museum Holland' **£180-220**
? 1991-92 **James Bond Aston-Martin**........ Reissue of C271 in clear plastic display box with plastic '007' badge **£20-30**
271/1 **James Bond Aston-Martin**........ Silver body (1:36 scale), small 4-spoked wheels...**£80-100**

272 1981-83 **James Bond Citroën 2cv** .... Yellow body, opening bonnet, WhizzWheels From film 'For Your Eyes Only'.
Box (1): Black/Red/Yellow 'window' box with pictorial header card..**£30-40**
Box (2): Black/Red/Yellow 'compact' box with pictorial top flap...**£30-40**
272 1981 ....Gold plated version: (12 only produced). Strada Jewellry Certificate should be with model **£2,000-3,000**

277 1968-72 'MONKEES' Monkeemobile.... Red body, White roof, Yellow logo, cast detailed windows. Figures of Mike, Mickey, Davy and Pete plus red plastic 'Monkees' guitar. Blue/Yellow 'window' box. **£300-400**
As above, but without the 'Monkees' guitar...**£300-400**
In Blue/Yellow 'window' box with clip-in cardboard header as used for shop display purposes **£800-900**
NB Pre-production model with plastic engine exists.
278 1981- **Dan Dare's Car**........................ Red/Yellow space vehicle. Planned but not produced..NPP

290 1976-77 **Kojak Buick** .... Bronze body (various shades), 4-spoke or disc type wheel hubs, 'gunfire' sound, self-adhesive 'Lieutenant' badge, figures of Kojak (no hat) and Crocker (blue jacket). Black/Yellow pictorial 'window' box **£80-100**
1977-80 .... Same but Kojak figure has a hat and Crocker has a Black jacket. 'New' tag on some boxes....................**£40-50**
292 1977-82 **Starsky & Hutch Ford Torino**.. Red/White body, figures of Starsky, Hutch, and a suspect. Black/Yellow pictorial 'window' box **£100-150**
1986 .... Reissued as an export model (20,000) **£10-15**
298 1982-83 **Magnum P.I. Ferrari**................ Red Ferrari 308GTS with 4-spoke or disc wheels. Black/Red/Yellow pictorial 'window' box **£20-30**

320 1978-81 **The Saint's Jaguar XJS** .... White body, standard or 'dished' WhizzWheels. Black/Yellow 'window' box (yellow or black inner) **£50-60**
336 1967-69 **James Bond's Toyota 2000 GT**.. White body, Red aerial, 2 figures, rocket launchers in boot. From film 'You Only Live Twice'. Diorama box must have card reinforcements to protect aerial, 8 spare rockets on sprue, sealed envelope marked 'Secret Instructions' which also contains self-adhesive '007' badge.........................**£300-350**

342 1980-82 'The Professionals' Ford Capri Metallic Silver body, dished or disc hubs, figures of Cowley, Bodie, Doyle. Pictorial 'window' box **£125-150**
As previous model but with chrome wheel hubs..**£150-175**
Finished in Matt Silver, Dark Red interior **£125-150**
348 1980-81 'Vegas' Thunderbird .... Red body with Dan Tanner figure Black/Yellow pictorial 'window' box **£60-80**
391 1972-72 **James Bond Ford Mustang Mach I** .... Red body, Black bonnet, White interior and base, WhizzWheels (2 types known).
From film 'Diamonds Are Forever'. Red/Yellow 'window' box has '007' Red sticker **£200-250**
As previous model but with 'CORGI TOYS' shop display stand...**£200-250**

431 1978-79 'VANATIC' .... White Chevrolet van, polychromatic side labels **£15-20**
432 1978-79 'VANTASTIC'........................... Black Chevrolet, Yellow/Red design **£15-20**
433 1978 'VANISHING POINT' .... Chevrolet van shown in 1978 catalogue but not issued..NPP
434 1978-80 'CHARLIE'S ANGELS' Van ... Pink Chevrolet Custom van, Yellow or Brown interior, 4-spoke or disc wheels. Black/Yellow pictorial 'window' box **£50-75**
435 1979-80 'SUPERMAN' Van .... Metallic Silver Chevrolet 'SuperVan'. Black/Yellow pictorial 'window' box (printing variations seen) **£35-45**
436 1979-80 'SPIDERVAN'......................... Blue Chevrolet van, 'Spiderman' design, 4-spoke or disc wheels. Black/Yellow pictorial 'window' box...**£35-45**
437 1979-80 'COCA COLA' .... Red Chevrolet van, White design, tinted roof windows, crates **£30-35**
NB Various other labels were designed for the Chevrolet 'van' series. Some prototype labels were printed but not officially used. Some of these may have found their way on to repainted van castings - they are NOT official Corgi issues. Logos include: 'Apache Patrol', 'Light Vantastic', 'Vanilla Treat', 'Cosmos', 'Columbia', 'Aquarius', 'Centaur', 'Colorama', 'Rocket Van', 'Centaur', plus four other unlettered 'psychedelic' designs.

436 1963-65 **Citroën 'WILDLIFE SAFARI'** Yellow Citroën ID19, driver and passenger, detailed interior, roof luggage, 'Wild Life Reservation' logo..**£70-80**
447 1965-66 'Walls Ice Cream' Van .... Ford Thames van in Blue/Cream, salesman, boy, spare transfers. Blue/Yellow card box, inner base, leaflet **£175-225**
448 1964-69 **Austin Police Mini Van** .... Dark Blue body, Red interior, shaped or cast hubs, aerial, White 'POLICE' logo, policeman and dog, pictorial stand and internal support packaging..**£115-130**
450 1968-71 **Lunar Bug** .... Red, White, Blue. Blue/Yellow window box includes inner packing **£60-70**
472 1964-66 'VOTE FOR CORGI' .... Corgi 438 Land Rover in Green/Yellow, Red interior, 2 figures, Blue/Yellow card box..................**£100-120**
474 1965-68 **Musical 'Walls Ice Cream' Van** Ford Thames van in Blue/Cream, musical movement (must function), diorama but no figures. Blue/Yellow card box with packing ring and packing piece, plus unused sticker sheet....................**£175-250**
475 1964-65 'Olympic Winter Sport' .... White/Yellow Citroën Safari, '1964', roof-rack, skier, skis. Diorama 'By Special Request' box **£90-110**
475 1965-68 'CORGI SKI CLUB'................. Citroën Safari with Off-White body, Red roof-rack, 4 White skis and 2 poles, bonnet transfer, Brown dashboard/rear seats, Green front seats **£110-130**
475 1965-68 'CORGI SKI CLUB'................. Citroën Safari with White body, Yellow Roof-rack, 4 Red skis and 2 poles, Green dashboard/rear seats, Brown front seats **£110-130**

479	1967-71	**Mobile Camera Van**	Blue/White Commer van, spun hubs, camera/operator, 'Samuelson Film Services', equipment case..... **£100-125**
479	1967-71		As previous model but with detailed cast hubs **£80-90**
486	1967-69	**'KENNEL CLUB' Truck**	White/Orange Chevrolet Impala with 'Vari-View' dachshund picture, 4 dogs **£50-60**
487	1965-69	**'CHIPPERFIELDS'** Parade Vehicle......................	472 Land Rover in Red/Blue, *'CIRCUS IS HERE'* label, chimpanzee, clown, Blue/yellow card box **£200-250**
497	1966-66	**'The Man From UNCLE's 'Thrush Buster'**...................	Oldsmobile (235) with White body, cast wheels, cast spotlights, 'UNCLE' logo, gun sound, figures of Napoleon Solo and Ilya Kuriakin. Blue/Yellow pictorial card box (which must include internal packaging, roof packing, and 3-D 'Waverley' ring) **£600-700**
497	1966-69		Same but Metallic Purplish-Blue body, cast or plastic spotlights **£300-350**
499	1967-69	**'1968 Winter Olympics'**............	White/Blue Citroën, 'Grenoble Olympiade', Red or Yellow roof rack, Yellow or Red skis/poles, male tobogganist, female skier. Blue/Yellow 'window' box with instruction sheet...... **£200-250**
503	1964-70	**'CHIPPERFIELDS'** Giraffe Transporter	Red/Blue Bedford 'TK', cast or spun wheels, 2 giraffes. Blue/Yellow card box **£100-150**
	1970-71	....	As previous model but larger 'stepped' front wheels **£130-170**
			Window box variation **£200-300**
510	1970-73	**Team Manager's Car**	Red Citroën, *'Tour De France'*, figures, spare wheels, *'Paramount'* **£70-80**
511	1970-71	**'CHIPPERFIELDS'** Poodle Truck	Blue/Red Chevrolet Impala Pick-Up, *'PERFORMING POODLES'* labels, cast wheels, female trainer (Mary Chipperfield, 4 White and 2 Black poodles. Blue/Yellow 'window' box (should include a plastic dome over dogs).................. **£350-400**
513	1970-72	**Citroën 'Alpine Rescue'**...........	White/Red car, Yellow roof-rack, St Bernard, sled, skis, male figure. Blue/Yellow 'window' box **£250-300**
607	1963-68	**'CHIPPERFIELDS'** Elephant Cage....................	A Corgi Kit with Brown plastic cage and elephant parts, instruction leaflet. Blue/Yellow card box **£50-75**
647	1980-83	**Buck Rogers Starfighter**	White/Blue, Yellow retractable wings, Wilma Dearing and Tweaky figures, Black/Yellow pictorial 'window' box, 10 spare rockets **£40-45**
648	1981-82	**NASA Space Shuttle**................	White/Black body, 'USA Satellite', opening hatch **£20-25**
649	1979-82	**James Bond Space Shuttle**........	White body (C468 casting), separate satellite (early versions retained by nylon strap). From film 'Moonraker' Larger pictorial Black/Yellow box.. **£50-75**

This illustration of the Corgi Constructor Set is taken from the 1966 Corgi catalogue.

681	1972	Stunt Bike	Gold body, Blue and Yellow rider, Red trolley, 'window' box, (19,000 made) £125-150
700	1974-80	Motorway Service Ambulance	White/Red futuristic vehicle, WhizzWheels £8-12
701	1974-80	Inter-City Mini-Bus	Orange body, Yellow labels, WhizzWheels £8-12
801	1969-69	Noddy's Car	Yellow/Red car with dickey-seat, cast hubs, chrome bumpers. Figures of Noddy, Big-Ears, and black-faced Golly Pictorial Blue/Yellow, 'window' box £1,000-1,500
			As previous model but Golly has Light Tan face £750-1,000
			As previous model but Golly has Grey face £350-500
	1969-73		As previous model but Master Tubby (light or dark brown) instead of Golly £200-300
802	1969-72	Popeye's Paddle-Wagon	Yellow/White body, Red wings, Blue paddle covers, White or Yellow rear wheels, anchors, moving figures of Popeye, Olive Oyl, Swee'Pea, Bluto and Wimpey. Blue/Yellow pictorial 'window' box £300-400
803	1969-72	The Beatles Submarine	Yellow/White, psychedelic design, hatches (Yellow rear, White front) open to show John, Paul, George and Ringo, pictorial window box with Blue-Green inner lining £250-350
	1970-71		As previous model but with Red hatch covers £300-400
	1970-71		With one red hatch and one white hatch £500-600
804	1975-78	Noddy's Car	Red/Yellow car, no dickey-seat, no rear bumper. Figure of Noddy only. Dark Blue/Yellow pictorial 'window' box £125-150
805	1970-71	Hardy Boys Rolls-Royce	9041 Silver Ghost casting in Red, Blue and Yellow, plated wheels. Bubble-pack of five Hardy Boys figures also contained in the Blue/Yellow 'window' box £150-200
806	1970-72	Lunar Bug	Red/White/Blue, 'Lunar Bug', windows, drop-down ramps £65-75
807	1971-73	Dougal's Magic Roundabout Car (based on 510 Citroën)	Yellow/Red, with Brian, Dougal and Dylan. Yellow/Blue 'window' box with decal sheet £225-250
	1973-74		As previous model but in Black/Yellow 'window' box, with decal sheet £130-160
808	1971-73	Basil Brush's Car	Red/Yellow car with hand-painted Basil figure, 'Laugh tapes' and soundbox are in separate printed box within pictorial Blue/Yellow 'window' box £175-200
809	1973-73	Dick Dastardly's Car	Blue/Red/Yellow racing car with Dick and Muttley figures. Dark Blue/Yellow 'window' box £150-175
811	1972-74	James Bond Moon Buggy	Blue/White body, Yellow WhizzWheels, Red scanner. Roof opening mechanism should be working. Blue/Yellow pictorial window box £250-350
H851	1972-74	Magic Roundabout Train	Red/Blue, Mr Rusty and Basil in the locomotive (engine sound), Rosalie and Paul in the carriage and Dougal in the van. Blue/Yellow pictorial 'window' box with Blue nylon tow-rope £300-400
H852	1972-74	Magic Roundabout Carousel	Red/Yellow/Blue working roundabout with Swiss musical movement playing the TV theme. Dylan, Paul, Rosalie, Florence and Basil figures. Blue/Yellow pictorial card box £450-550
H853	1972-74	Magic Roundabout Playground	Contains a modified H852, H851 (with the figures), plus Zebedee, Dylan, four kids, see saw, park bench, 3 Blue and 3 Orange shrubs and 2 flowers. Operating carousel and track. Theme music plays when Dylan is wound up £1,250-1,500
H859	1972-74	Mr McHenry's Trike	Red/Yellow trike and trailer, Mr McHenry and pop-up Zebedee figures, Blue and Yellow pictorial 'window' box with blue towing cord and instruction sheet £175-225
H860-H868			
	1972-74	Magic Roundabout figures	Figures packed in individual clear plastic tubs: 860 Dougal, 861 Florence, 862 Zebedee, 863 Mr Rusty, 864 Brian the Snail, 865 Basil, 866 Ermintrude the Cow, 868 Dylan the Rabbit ...... Each: £25-35
925	1976-81	Batcopter	Black body, Red 'Bat' rotors, Batman figure, operable winch, 143 mm £65-75
9826	1978-80	Stromberg Helicopter	Black body/rotors, ten spare rockets. From 'The Spy Who Loved Me'. Black/Yellow 'window' box £60-70
927	1978-80	Chopper Squad Helicopter	White/metallic Blue Jet Ranger helicopter, operating winch. Black/Yellow pictorial 'window' box £35-45
928	1981-82	Spidercopter	Blue/Red body, 'spider legs', retractable tongue. Black/Yellow pictorial 'window' box £40-50
929	1979-80	'DAILY PLANET' Jetcopter	Red/White body, rocket launchers, Black/Yellow pictorial 'window' box contains 10 spare rockets £50-60
930	1972-80	'Drax' Helicopter	White body, 'Drax' logo, ten spare rockets. From the film 'Moonraker'. Black/Yellow 'window' box £60-70
9004	1967-69	'The World of Wooster' Bentley	Green 9002 Bentley with figures of Jeeves and Wooster, plated wheels. Bubble-packed in display base £70-90

Major Packs

Original internal packaging for securing model and accessories must all be present before model can be considered complete and therefore to achieve the best price. See Corgi model identification page.

1121	1960-62	'CHIPPERFIELDS' Crane Truck	Red body, Raised Blue log and wheels, operable grey tinplate jib and hook, instruction leaflet. Blue/Yellow lidded box with packing £125-150
	1963-69		Red body, raised Blue logo and wheels, operable chrome tinplate jib and hook, instruction leaflet. Blue/Yellow card box with end flaps £125-150
1123	1961-62	'CHIPPERFIELDS' Circus Cage	Red body, Yellow chassis, smooth hubs, red diecast end and middle sliding doors, 2 plastic lions (in stapled bags), animal name decals, instruction sheet. Blue/Yellow lidded box with packing £100-125
	1963-68		Red body, Yellow chassis, smooth or spun hubs, Blue plastic end and middle sliding doors, 4 animals (lions, tigers or polar bears in stapled bags), animal name decals. Blue/Yellow card box with end flaps £75-100
1130	1962-70	'CHIPPERFIELDS' Horse Transporter	Bedford TK truck, Red/Blue, Green or Red 'horse-head' design at rear, cast or spun hubs, 6 Brown or Grey horses, Blue/Yellow card box with card packing around horses £175-225
	1970-72		As previous model but with larger 'truck' wheels £150-175
1139	1968-72	'CHIPPERFIELDS' Menagerie Transporter	Scammell Handyman MkIII, Blue/Red cab, Blue trailer with 3 plastic cages, 2 lions, 2 tigers and 2 bears. Blue/Yellow pictorial 'window' box with packing to hold animals, plus spare self-adhesive securing tape for animals £300-400
1144	1969-72	'CHIPPERFIELDS' Crane and Cage with Rhino	Red/Blue Scammell Handyman MkIII, 'COME TO THE CIRCUS' on n/s, silver jib and hook, stepped 'truck' front wheels on some, Grey rhinoceros in plastic cage. Blue/Yellow 'window' box with pre-formed blister-pack around animals £400-500
1163	1978-82	Human Cannon Truck	Red and Blue body, 'MARVO' figure £30-40
1164	1980-83	Berliet 'DOLPHINARIUM'	Yellow cab, Blue trailer, Clear plastic tank, 2 dolphins, girl trainer. Black/Yellow 'window' box with header card on some £100-150
			Yellow cab, Yellow trailer, 'window' box with header card on some £100-150

Novelty, Film and TV-related models

Marks & Spencer issues

In 1978 a special series of models and sets were produced for sale through selected M & S stores. They were packed in attractive non-standard boxes and had unique liveries. They were issued in small quantities.

SINGLE MODELS

8800	1979	Custom Van	No details available	£25-35
8801	1979	Spindrift Helicopter	Black body with Yellow chassis, floats and rotor blades	£25-35
8802	1979	Massey Ferguson Tractor	Red/Black body with White arms and Red shovel	£40-50
8803	1979	Buick 'FIRE CHIEF' Car	Red body with 'City Fire Department' logo on bonnet	£50-75

SMALL SETS

8000	1978	F1 Racing Set	Includes 162 'ELF' Tyrrell (Dark Blue) and 160 Hesketh F1 (White)	£75-100
8001	1978	Wings Flying Team	Includes 301 Lotus Elite (Green) and Nipper aircraft (White) on Grey trailer	£100-150
8002	1978	Motorway Police Patrol	C429 'POLICE' Jaguar (Green) and Blue Fiat X1-9	£60-80
8003	1979	Spindrift Power Boat Team	301 Ferrari Daytona (Yellow) and Yellow power boat on trailer	£60-80

MEDIUM SETS

8100	1978	Racing Team	C421 Land Rover (White with 'FORMULA' logo), 338 Rover, and 301 Lotus on trailer	£150-200
8101	1978	Wings Flying School	C421 Land Rover (Grey with 'WINGS' logo) Grey helicopter and Nipper aircraft on Grey trailer	£150-200
8102	1978	Motorway Breakdown	C429 'POLICE' Jaguar, 293 Renault 5 (Yellow) plus Berliet Wrecker with 'RESCUE BREAKDOWN SERVICES'	£100-150
8103	1979	Spindrift Power Boat Team	Includes Spindrift 301 Ferrari, Helicopter and Dinghy	£150-200

LARGE SETS

8400	1978	Grand Prix Racing	Includes 160 Hesketh (White) 162 'ELF' Tyrrell (Dark Blue) Fiat X1-9 (Blue) and Land Rover (White with 'FORMULA 1 RACING TEAM' logo)	£250-350
8401	1978	Wings Flying Club	Land Rover, Helicopter, Tipsy Nipper aircraft on trailer plus Lotus Elite	£250-300
8402	1978	Motorway Rescue	Includes 'POLICE' Jaguar, Berliet Wrecker, Renault 5 and Fiat X1-9	£250-300
8403	1979	Spindrift Power Boat Team	Includes Ferrari Daytona (Yellow) Yellow power boat on trailer, Yellow/Black helicopter, plus MF Tractor and 'RESCUE' dinghy	£250-300

Trophy Models (Marks & Spencer special 'plated' issues)

The models were specially produced in 1961 to be sold by Marks & Spencer. The set consisted of five vacuum-plated 'gold' models taken from the existing Corgi product range, each mounted on a detachable black moulded base with a gold name label. The models were packaged in white boxes with red/grey design plus 'St Michael Trophy Models' in red. They did not sell well at the time of issue but are keenly sought after by present day collectors.

150 S	1961	**Vanwall Racing Car**	Gold vacuum-plated body, Red wheels and radiator grille	£100-200
152	1961	**BRM Racing Car**	Gold vacuum-plated body, Red wheels and radiator grille	£100-200
300	1961	**Austin-Healey Sports Car**	Gold vacuum-plated body, plastic windscreen, Red wheels and grille	£100-200
301	1961	**Triumph TR2 Sports Car**	Gold vacuum-plated body, plastic windscreen, Red wheels and grille	£100-200
302	1961	**MG 'MGA' Sports Car**	Gold vacuum-plated body, plastic windscreen, Red wheels and grille	£100-200

The 'Exploration' Range

D2022	1980	'SCANOTRON'	Green/Black/Yellow	£15-25
D22023	1980	'ROCKETRON'	Blue/Yellow, Black tracks	£15-25
D2024	1980	'LASERTRON'	Orange/Black/Yellow	£15-25
D2025	1980	'MAGNETRON'	Red/Black	£15-25

'The Muppets Show' models

D2030	1979-80	**Kermit's Car**	Yellow car with a famous Green frog, bubble-packed	£40-45
	1980-82		Same model but in Red/Yellow pictorial 'window' box	£35-40
D2031	1979-80	**Fozzie Bear's Truck**	Red/Brown/White truck, Silver or Black hooter, bubble-packed	£35-40
	1980-82		Same model but in Red/Yellow pictorial 'window' box	£30-35
D2032	1979-80	**Miss Piggy's Sport Coupé**	Pink sports car, Red or Pink dress, bubble-packed	£40-45
	1980-82		Same model but in Red/Yellow pictorial 'window' box	£35-40
D2033	1979-80	**Animal's Percussionmobile**	Red traction-engine, Yellow or Red wheels, Yellow or Black chimney, Yellow or Silver cymbal. Bubble-packed	£35-40
	1980-82		Same model but in Red/Yellow pictorial 'window' box	£30-35

Duo Packs (Film and TV-related models)

1360	1982-?	**Batmobile**	267 plus a Corgi juniors version, Black/Red/Yellow 'window' box	£150-175
1361	197?-?	**James Bond Aston-Martin**	271 plus a Corgi juniors version, Black/Red/Yellow 'window' box	£125-150
1362	197?-?	**James Bond Lotus Esprit**	269 plus a Corgi Juniors version, Black/Red/Yellow 'window' box	£125-150
1363	1982-83	**Buck Rogers Set**	647 plus a smaller version Black/Yellow pictorial 'window' box	£50-60
1376	1982-83	**Starsky & Hutch Ford Torino**	292 plus a Corgi Juniors version	£70-80

Miscellaneous Corgi models

104	1965-68	**Dolphin Boat on Trailer**	Blue/White boat, Red trailer	£50-75
171	1982-	**Street Bike**	Red, Silver and Black body, multicoloured swirl	£5-10
172	1982-	**'POLICE' Bike**	White/Black/Silver body	£5-10
173	1982-	**Cafe Racer**	Silver and Black racing number '26', '750 cc Class'	£5-10
391	1972-73	**'FIREBUG'**	Orange body, Yellow ladder, 'FIREBUG', WhizzWheels	£15-25
423	1978-78	**'ROUGH RIDER'**	Yellow Chevrolet van, motorcycle side labels	£20-25
450	1968-71	**Lunar Bug**	Red, White, Blue. Blue/Yellow window box includes inner packing	£60-70
806	1970-72	**Lunar Bug**	Red/White/Blue, 'Lunar Bug', windows, drop-down ramps	£65-75

Qualitoys

A range of sturdy toys made up from the same basic parts. First issued in 1969, they were aimed at the pre school age group. They were publicized as being from the 'makers of Corgi Toys' and did not form part of the Corgi range as such. They have little collectable value at the present time.

Q701 **Pick Up Truck** ....
Q702 **Side Tipper** ....

Q703 **Breakdown Truck** ....
Q704 **Tower Wagon** ....
Q705 **Horse Box** ....
Q706 **Giraffe Transporter** ....
Q707 **Fire Engine** ....
Q708 **Pick Up Trailer** ....

Accessories

Corgi Kits

601	1961-68	Batley 'LEOFRIC' Garage	£20-25
602	1961-66	'A.A.' and 'RAC' Telephone Boxes	£50-60
603	1961-66	Silverstone Pits	£30-40
604	1961-66	Silverstone Press Box	£50-60
605	1963-67	Silverstone Club House and Timekeepers Box	£60-70
606	1961-66	Lamp Standards (2)	£5-10
607	1963-67	Circus Elephant and Cage	£45-55
608	1963-66	'SHELL' Filling Station Building	£35-45
609	1963-66	'SHELL' Filling Station Forecourt Accessories	£25-35
610	1963-66	Metropolitan Police Box and Public Telephone Kiosk	£60-70
611	1963-66	Motel Chalet	£25-35

Spare wheels for 'Take-off Wheels' models; bubble-packed on card.

1341	1970	for 344 Ferrari Dino Sport. Shown in 1969 catalogue but model issued with WhizzWheels	£10-15
1342	1968	for 300 Chevrolet Corvette	£10-15
1351	1968	for 275 Rover 2000 TC	£10-15
1352	1968	for 276 Oldsmobile Toronado	£10-15
		for 338 Chevrolet Camaro	£10-15
		for 343 Pontiac Firebird. Shown in 1969 catalogue but model not issued with 'Take-off Wheels'	£10-15
1353	1970	for 342 Lamborghini P400	£10-15
		for 302 Hillman Hunter Rally	£10-15
1354	1970	for 273 Rolls Royce Silver Shadow	£10-15
1361	1968	for 341 Mini Marcos GT 850. (This was the first 'Take-Off Wheels' model)	£10-15

Corgi 'Cargoes'   Bubble-packed on card.

1485	1960	Lorry Load - Planks	£10-15
1486	1960	Lorry Load - Bricks	£10-15
1487	1960	Lorry Load - Milk Churns	£10-15
1488	1960	Lorry Load - Cement	£10-15
1490	1960	Skip and 3 Churns	£10-15

Figures

1501	1963-69	Racing Drivers and Pit Mechanics (6)	£10-15
1502	1963-69	Silverstone Spectators (6)	£10-15
1503	1963-69	Race Track Officials (6)	£10-15
1504	1963-69	Press Officials (6)	£10-15
1505	1963-69	Garage Attendants (6)	£10-15

Self-adhesive accessories

1460	1959	'A' Pack (66 items) including Tax Discs, Number Plates, 'GB' and 'Running-In' labels, etc	£10-15
1461	1959	'B' Pack (36 items) including White-wall tyre trim, 'Styla Sportsdiscs', Number Plates, etc	£10-15
1462	1959	'C' Pack (69 items) including Number Plates, Commercial & Road Fund Licences (A, B and C), 20 and 30mph Speed Limit and Trailer Plates, etc	£10-15
1463	1959	'D' Pack (100 items) including Number Plates, 'Corps Diplomatique' and 'L' Plates, Touring Pennants, etc	£10-15
1464	1961	'E' Pack (86 items) including Assorted Badges, Take-Off Wheels, Trade and Licence Plates, etc	£10-15

Spare tyre packs

1449	1970-71	New Standard 15 mm	£10-15
1450	1958-70	Standard 15 mm	£10-15
1451	1961-70	Utility Vehicles 17 mm	£10-15
1452	1961-70	Major Models 19 mm	£10-15
1453	1965-70	Mini Cars 13 mm	£10-15
1454	1967-70	Tractor wheels (Rear) 33 mm	£10-15
1455	1967-70	Tractor wheels (Front) 19 mm	£10-15
1456	1967-70	Racing wheels (Rear) 16 mm	£10-15
1457	1967-70	Racing wheels (Front) 14 mm	£10-15
1458	1967-70	Commercial (Large) 24 mm	£10-15
1459	1967-70	Commercial (Medium) 19 mm	£10-15

Miscellaneous

1401	1958-60	Service Ramp (operable)	£15-20
1445	1962	Spare Red bulb for 437 Ambulance	£2-3
1441	1963	Spare Blue bulb for 464 Police Van	£2-3
1443	1967	Red flashing bulb for 437 Ambulance	£2-3
1444	1967	Blue flashing bulb for 464 Police Van	£2-3
1445	1967	Spare bulb for 'TV' in 262 Lincoln	£2-3
1446	1970	Spare tyres for 1150 Snowplough	£2-3
1480	1959	Spare nose cone for Corporal Missile	£2-3
1497	1967	James Bond Spares 2 Bandits + lapel badge (261)	£15-25
1498	1967	James Bond Spares Missiles for 336 Toyota	£10-15
1499	1967	Green Hornet Spares Missiles & scanners (268)	£10-15
?	1960s	Corgi Club Badge. Gold Corgi dog on Red backing	£20-25
?	1962-64	'SHELL' Filling Station and Garage in Blue, Red and White, single floor, plastic 'SHELL' logo	£300-400
?	1962-64	Corgi Garage in Bright Blue, Yellow, Red and White, three floors, 'SKYPARK' and 'CENTRAL PARK GARAGE' logos	£300-400
24205	1967	Batmobile Accessory Pack (sprue of missiles)	£25-35

A page from an early 1960s Gamages catalogue illustrating some of the Corgi accessories that were available.

Routemaster Buses

Only models thought to have been 100% produced by Corgi have been included in the listings.

Identification of Routemaster Double-Decker Bus models

1ST CASTING, 1964 - 1975
MODEL No. 468 ONLY – CLOSED TOP MODEL

Length 114 mm, die-cast body comprised of two separate castings which make up the lower and upper decks. The castings are separated by a white plastic joint.

The baseplate is die-cast, painted grey and stamped 'Corgi Toys', 'LONDON TRANSPORT', 'ROUTEMASTER', 'MADE IN ENGLAND' plus the Patent No. 904525. The early issues had turned metal wheels with rubber tyres. These lasted until 1973 when cast metal wheels were introduced with plastic tyres and in 1974/75 WhizzWheels were seen.

Early issues also had jewelled headlights which were replaced in 1973 by the cast-in type painted silver. The decals are of the transfer printed variety and there is a board at the front only. The model has spring suspension, windows, a metal platform handrail and a driver and clippie. The interior seats are white or cream.

2ND CASTING, 1975 ONWARDS
CLOSED TOP AND OPEN TOP MODELS

MODEL Nos: C460, C463, C464, C467, C469, C470, C471, C473, C475, C476, C477, C479, C480, 1004 and all the numbers allocated to the 'Specials'.
Length 123 mm, die-cast body comprised of two separate castings which make up the lower and upper decks. The castings are separated by a cream plastic joint for normal issues and very often by a coloured joint for 'Specials'. Until Model No. 480 was issued as an AEC Renown in 1983 the plastic baseplates were stamped 'CORGI', 'LONDON TRANSPORT', 'ROUTEMASTER' and 'MADE IN ENGLAND'. However 'LONDON TRANSPORT' and 'ROUTEMASTER' were removed from this time onwards.

The logos were originally stick-on labels followed by tampo printing in the mid-eighties. The seats were normally white or cream but other colours are used for the 'Specials' (eg. Red in the 'BRITISH DIE-CAST MODEL TOYS CATALOGUE' Special). The model has silver painted cast-in headlights, spring suspension, windows, a metal platform handrail but apart from the very early issues does not have a driver or clippie.
The wheels are of the WhizzWheel type. The early issues were of a close fitting type e.g. 'BTA', 'SWAN & EDGAR', 'DISNEYLAND'. However by the time the model was issued they had become protruding. The wheel hubs are either chrome (earlier models) or painted with plastic tyres.

Routemaster Buses, 1964-1975, (1st casting)

468	1964-66	'NATURALLY CORGI', Red, London Transport, *'CORGI CLASSICS'* ads	**£60-70**
468	1964	'NATURALLY CORGI', (Australian), Green/Cream/Brown, 'NEW SOUTH WALES', *'CORGI CLASSICS'* adverts	**£900-1,100**
468	1966	'RED ROSE COFFEE', (Canadian promotional), Red body, driver and clippie, 1st type box	**£400-500**
468	1967	'OUTSPAN ORANGES', (Australian issue) Green/Cream/Brown body	**£200-300**
468	1967-75	'OUTSPAN ORANGES', Red, London Transport, '10', (diecast or WhizzWheels)	**£50-60**
468	1968	'GAMAGES', Red, London Transport, '10'	**£175-200**
468	1969	'CHURCH'S SHOES', Red, London Transport, '10', Union Jacks	**£150-175**
468	1970	'MADAME TUSSAUDS', Red, London Transport, '10'	**£125-150**
468	1975	'THE DESIGN CENTRE', Red, London Transport, '10'	**£70-80**
468	?	'cokerchu', '2d', Red, London Transport, promotional	**£175-200**

469 Routemaster Bus (2nd casting),
'Mettoy Welcomes Swiss Buyers to Corgi Factory'

Photo: Vectis Auctions Ltd.

Routemaster Buses, 1975 – 1983, (2nd casting)

C467	1977	'SELFRIDGES', Red, London Transport, '12'. Box 1 – standard; Box 2 – 'SELFRIDGES' own	**£20-25**
C469	1975-76	'BTA WELCOME TO BRITAIN', Red, London Transport, '11', driver, clippie	**£15-20**
C469	1976	'THE DESIGN CENTRE', Red, LT, '11', driver, clippie, *'Visit The Design Centre'* in black or red	**£125-150**
C469	1977	'CADBURYS DOUBLE DECKER', Orange, on-pack offer, special box	**£12-18**
C469	1977	'METTOY', 'Mettoy Welcomes Swiss Buyers to Swansea'	**£300-400**
C469	1979	'SELFRIDGES', Red, London Transport, '12'. Re-issue of C467 (see above)	**£20-25**
C469	1979	'LEEDS PERMANENT' BUILDING SOCIETY', 'LEEDS', '22'	**£15-20**
C469	1979	'SWAN & EDGAR', Red, London Transport, '11'	**£25-35**
C469	1979	'HAMLEYS', Red, London Transport, '11'	**£15-20**
C469	1980	'HAMLEYS', Five clowns advert., '6'	**£10-15**
C469	1978-80	'BTA', Red, London Transport, ('7', '11' or '12')	**£10-15**
C469	1982	'BLACKPOOL', Cream/Green, 'Blackpool Illuminations', '21'	**£30-40**
C469	1983	'CORGI COLLECTORS VISIT'	**£300-400**
C469	1983	'GAMLEYS', Red, *'Toyshop Of The South'*	**£10-15**
C469	1983	'EAGLE STAR', White/Black, '1 Threadneedle Street'	**£10-15**
C469	1983	'REDGATES', Cream/Brown (Red seats) '25'	**£30-40**
C469	1983	'L.T. GOLDEN JUBILEE', Red/White/Silver, 21, *'1933-1983 '*, (1,000)	**£30-40**
C469	1983	'BLACKPOOL PLEASURE BEACH', Cream/Green, Blackpool Transport, '23', *'Britain's No.1 Tourist Attraction'*	**£35-45**
C469	1983	As previous model but with open top	**£50-55**
C469	1983	'NORBROOK MOTORS', Dark Blue (White seats) route '57'	**£12-18**
C469	1983	As previous model but Red version	**£12-18**
C469	1983	'DION DION', Dark Blue, *'Saves You More'*. S. African issue: incorrect label *'Saves You Money'*	**£10-15** / **£15-20**
C469	1983	'THORNTONS', Brown/Cream, route '14'	**£10-15**
C469	1983	'MANCHESTER LIONS', Cream, route '105BN Manchester'	**£15-20**
C469	1984	'NEW CORGI COMPANY', Red, '29th March 84', *'South Wales - De Cymru'*, (2,000)	**£15-20**
C469	?	'COBHAM BUS MUSEUM', no details	**£25-35**
C470	1977	'DISNEYLAND', Yellow open top	**£10-15**
C471	1977	'SEE MORE LONDON', Silver, '25', *'The Queen's Silver Jubilee London Celebrations 1977'*	**£10-15**
C471	1977	'WOOLWORTHS', Silver, '25', *'Woolworths Welcome The World'*, *'Queens Silver Jubilee 1977'*	**£20-30**
C523	1986	'BRITISH DIECAST', Red, *'British Diecast Model Toys Catalogue'*	**£10-15**
C638	1989	'Great Book of CORGI', Yellow/Blue, '1956-1983'. Originally only available with book	**£25-35**

Corgi Gift Sets

Original internal packaging for securing models and accessories must all be present before sets can be considered complete and therefore to achieve the best price. See Corgi Toys model identification page.

Ref	Year(s)	Set name and details	Market Price Range
1	1957-62	**Transporter and 4 Cars** 1101 Blue/Yellow Bedford Carrimore Transporter plus 201 Austin Cambridge, 208 Jaguar 24, 301 Triumph TR2 (or 300 Austin-Healey) and 302 MGA, plus two Yellow/Black 'Corgi Toys' dummy boxes	**£500-700**
1a	1957-62	**Transporter and 4 Cars** 1101 Red/Two-tone Blue Transporter, 200 Ford Consul, 201 Austin Cambridge, 204 Rover 90, 205 Riley Pathfinder, 2 Yellow 'Corgi Toys' dummy boxes	**£400-500**
1b	1959-62	**Transporter and 4 Cars** 1101 Red/Two-tone Blue Transporter, 214 Thunderbird Hardtop, 215 Thunderbird Convertible, 219 Plymouth Suburban, 220 Chevrolet Impala. (US issue set)	**£400-500**
1c	1961-62	**Transporter and 4 Cars** 1101 Red/Two-tone Blue Transporter, 210s Citroën (or 217 Fiat 1800), 219 Plymouth Suburban Sport, 226 Mini, 305 Triumph TR3. (US issue set)	**£400-500**
1	1966-72	**Farm Set** Ford 5000 Tractor + 58 Beast Carrier, pictorial stand	**£100-120**
1	1983	**Ford Sierra Set** Ford Sierra 299 with Blue body, Blue/Cream Caravan	**£20-30**
2	1958-68	**Land Rover and Pony Trailer** 438 Land Rover (Green, Beige tin tilt) and 102 Rice Pony Trailer (Red/Black)	**£200-250**
		As previous but with All Red Land Rover	**£175-220**
		with Light Brown Land Rover (Apricot plastic tilt), Light Brown/Cream trailer	**£175-220**
2	1971-73	**Unimog Dumper and Shovel** 1128 Mercedes Tipper and 1145 Unimog Goose Dumper. Yellow/Blue 'window' box	**£60-70**
2	1980-81	**Construction Set** 54 Tractor, 440 Mazda, tool-box and cement mixer	**£30-35**
	1980-80	**Construction Set** French export: 1110 and 1156 plus cement mixer	**£30-40**
3	1959-63	**Thunderbird Missile Set** 350 Thunderbird Missile and 351 Land Rover. Blue/Yellow card box	**£200-300**
3	1967-69	**Batmobile and Batboat** 1st issue: 267 Batmobile with 'Bat' wheels, plus 107 Batboat, in plain Blue 1st issue 'window' box with inner tray and 4 figures, instruction sheet	**£600-800**
		2nd issue: 267 Batmobile with Red wheels (without 'Bat' design), plus 107 Batboat. Yellow/Blue 'window' box should also contain unopened instruction pack	**£1,000-1,500**
	1980	3rd issue: 267 Batmobile (plain cast wheels), and 107 Batboat (WW), two figures. Striped 'window' box should also contain instructions in unopened packet	**£300-400**
3	1986-88	**'British Gas' Set** Ford Cargo Van, Ford Escort Van (2nd), compressor	**£20-25**
4	1958-60	**Bristol Ferranti Bloodhound Guided Missile Set** Contains: 351, 1115, 1116, 1117 (see 'Military Vehicles' section). Blue/Yellow card box	**£350-450**
4	1974-75	**Country Farm Set** Models 50 and 62 plus hay load, boy and girl. Striped 'window' box	**£100-125**
5	1959-60	**Racing Car Set** 150 (Red), 151 (Blue), 152 (Green). Smooth hubs. Yellow/Blue lift-off lid box, vac-formed inner	**£300-400**
	1960-61	150 (Red), 151 (Blue with Red bonnet stripe), 152 (Green). Flat or cast spoked wheels. Yellow/Blue box with polystyrene inner tray	**£250-350**
5s	1962-63	**Racing Car Set** 150s (Red), 151a (Blue), 152s (Turquoise). Yellow/Blue box with 'Gift Set 5s' stickers, inner polystyrene tray	**£500-600**
5	1967-72	**Agricultural Set** 484 Livestock Transporter and pigs, 438 Land Rover (no hood) 62, 69, 71, accessories 1490 skip and churns, 4 calves, farmhand and dog, 6 sacks. Box has inner pictorial stand	**£275-325**
5	1976-77	**Country Farm Set** As Farm Set 4, but minus boy, girl and hay load	**£100-150**
6	1959-60	**'Rocket Age' Set** Contains: 350, 351, 352, 353, 1106, 1108, 1117 (see 'Military' section)	**£3,000-4,000**
6	1967-69	**Cooper-Maserati Set** Contains 490 VW Breakdown Truck plus 156 Maserati on trailer. 'Window'/flap box	**£150-175**
7	1959-64	**Tractor and Trailer Set** Contains 50 Massey-Ferguson 65 Tractor and 51 Trailer. Yellow/Blue all-card box	**£300-400**
7	1968-76	**'DAKTARI' Set** 438 Land Rover in Green with Black Zebra stripes, spun or cast hubs. 5 figures: Paula, Dr Marsh Tracy with chimp Judy on his lap, a Tiger on the bonnet, and Clarence The Short-Sighted Lion (with spectacles!). Yellow/Blue 'window' box	**£200-250**
		Version with WhizzWheels. Striped box	**£100-125**
8	1959-62	**Combine Harvester, Tractor and Trailer Set** Contains 1111, 50 and 51. Tractor has Copper seat, Red metal hubs	**£250-300**
8	1968-74	**'Lions of Longleat' Set** Land Rover with shaped hubs, keeper, 3 lions, plastic den, 3 joints of meat. Yellow/Blue 'window' box with header card and inner packing	**£225-275**
		Same but WhizzWheels. Striped 'window' box	**£100-125**
9	1959-62	**Corporal Guided Missile Set** Contains: 1112, 1113, 1118 (see 'Military Vehicles')	**£400-600**
9	1968-72	**Tractor, Trailer and Shovel Set** Contains 66 Ferguson 165 Tractor with 69 Shovel and 62 Tipper Trailer with detachable raves. Yellow/Blue all-card box with inner pictorial stand	**£200-250**
9	1979-82	**'RNLI' Rescue Set** Land Rover and Dinghy on trailer. White, Blue, Red, Black. Striped 'window' box	**£75-95**
9	19??	**3 Racing Minis Set** Yellow, White and Blue, numbers/stripes/adverts, special Red 'Hamleys' box	**£90-110**
10	1968-69	**Marlin Rambler Set** Blue/White 319 with Trailer, 2 canoes (1 with figure). Yellow/Blue box, inner packing, pictorial tray	**£250-300**
10	1973-78	**Tank Transporter Set** Contains 901 Centurion Mk.I Tank and 1100 Mack articulated transporter. Picture card box	**£100-120**
10	1982	**Jeep Set** Red 441 plus motorcycle on trailer	**£20-25**
10	1985	**Sierra and Caravan Set** C299 Sierra + Pale Brown caravan	**£25-35**
11	1960-64	**ERF Dropside and Trailer** 456 and 101 with cement and planks load. Yellow/Blue picture box with inner card stand	**£150-200**
		As above but with WhizzWheels	**£90-110**
11	1971-72	**London Transport Set** Contains 418 Taxi, 468 'OUTSPAN' Bus, 226 Mini (Deep Blue), policeman on stand, Striped 'window' box with inner tray	**£140-160**
	1980-82	C425 Taxi with C469 Bus 'B.T.A.' and policeman	**£35-45**
12	1961-64	**'Chipperfields Circus' Set** 1121 Circus Crane Truck 'CHIPPERFIELDS' and 1123 Circus Cage, plus instructions. Yellow/Blue all-card picture box	**£150-175**
12	1968-71	**Grand Prix Racing Set** 155, 156 and 330 with 490 Volkswagen tender, 3 mechanics, 16 bollards and hay bales. Yellow/Blue 'window' box also contains cones in bag, instructions, 'Mr Retailer' card and inner polystyrene tray	**£400-500**
	1971-72	158, 159 and 330 (or 371) with 490 Volkswagen tender, 3 mechanics, 16 bollards and hay bales. The artwork on the box and the vac-formed base are different from previous issue	**£300-400**

12 1981- **Glider and Trailer Set**
345 with Trailer and Glider **£50-60**

13 1964-66 **Fordson Tractor and Plough Set**
Contains 60 Fordson Power Major Tractor and
61 Four Furrow Plough in Blue, Orange plastic front
and rear hubs. Yellow/Blue box with inner tray..............**£300-400**

13 1968-72 **Renault 16 Film Unit**
White/Black, *'TOUR DE FRANCE'* , *'PARAMOUNT'*,
cameraman, cyclist. Yellow/Blue box with inner
tray plus plain orange card backdrop **£175-225**

13 1981-82 **Tour de France 'RALEIGH' Team Car**
373 Peugeot, White body, Red/Yellow 'RALEIGH'
and 'TOTAL' logos, racing cycles and Manager
with loudhailer **£180-220**

14 1961-64 **Tower Wagon Set**
409 Jeep, Yellow cradle, lamp standard and
electrician. Yellow/Blue card box....................................**£100-120**

14 1969-73 **Giant 'DAKTARI' Set**
Gift Set and items plus 503 and 484 transporters (spun
hubs), large and small elephants. Blue/Yellow window
box with pictorial header card and inner tray.................**£300-400**
Version with WhizzWheels. Striped 'window' box
with pictorial header card and inner tray........................**£150-200**

15 1963-64 **Silverstone Set**
150s, 151a, 152s, 215s, 304s, 309, 417s,
3 buildings, plain box (no picture) **£1,500-2,500**
1964-66 150s, 154, 152s, 215s, 304s, 309, 417s,
3 buildings, layout shown on box..............................**£1,500-2,500**

15 1968-77 **Land Rover and Horsebox Set**
Contains 438, 112, spun hubs, mare and foal.
Yellow/Blue box contains inner polystyrene tray **£100-125**
Version with WhizzWheels. Striped 'window' box
contains inner card packing...**£55-75**

15 1986 **'TARMAC' Motorway Set**
'Motorway Maintenance' Green/Black 1128 Mercedes
Tipper, Mazda Pickup and a compressor..........................**£20-30**

16 1961-65 **'ECURIE ECOSSE' Set**
1126 Transporter with 3 individually boxed racing cars
in all-card lift-off lid box with instruction leaflet and
internal packing.
i) Metallic Dark Blue 1126 Transporter (with Orange
lettering), 150 Vanwall (Red, RN '25'), 151 Lotus XI
(Blue, RN '3'), 152 BRM (Turquoise, RN '3') **£400-500**
ii) Metallic Dark Blue 1126 Transporter
(with Yellow lettering), 150s Vanwall,
151a Lotus XI (Blue, RN '7'), 152s BRM....................**£400-500**
1965 iii) Metallic Light Blue 1126 Transporter
(with Red Lettering), 150s Vanwall, 152s BRM,
154 Ferrari (Red, number '36')....................................**£350-400**
iv) Metallic Dark Blue 1126 Transporter
(with Light Blue lettering and ridges),
150s Vanwall, 152s BRM, 154 Ferrari **£300-350**

17 1963-67 **Ferrari Racing Set**
438 Land Rover in Red with Green top,
Red 154 Ferrari F1 on Yellow trailer.
Yellow/Blue box has inner tray **£275-325**

17 1977-80 **Military Set**
Contains 904, 906, 920 (see 'Military' section)..................**£40-50**

18 1961-63 **Ford Tractor and Plough Set**
Contains 55 Fordson Power Major Tractor and 56 Four
Furrow Plough in Blue/Red/Yellow. Drab Orange front
and rear hubs. Yellow/Blue box with inner tray.............**£200-250**

18 1975-80 **Emergency Gift Set**
Contains 402, 481, C921 (see 'Emergency Vehicles')........**£60-70**

18/1 19?? **3 Mini Racers Set**
CHELSEA', *'PARK LANE'* and *'PICADILLY'* logos..........**£20-30**

18/2 19?? **Mini Special Editions Set**
with *'RED HOT'*, *'RITZ'* and *'JET BLACK'* logos **£20-30**
NBC18/1 and C18/2 were sold (in long 'window' boxes)
exclusively by Woolworths.

19 1962-68 **'CHIPPERFIELDS' Cage Set**
438 Land Rover (plastic tilt) and 607 Elephant and
cage on trailer. Blue/Yellow picture box has inner
card tray and additional packing.....................................**£200-300**

19 19?? **'RNLI' Set**
438 Land Rover plus Orange dinghy on trailer
with *'Mumbles Lifeboat'* logo **£60-70**

19 1972-77 **Land Rover and Nipper Aircraft**
438 Land-Rover (Blue/Orange, tinplate tilt) + trailer.
Blue/Orange/Yellow plane *'23'* or Blue/Orange/White
plane *'23'*. Yellow/Blue 'window' box............................**£60-70**

19 1973-77 **'CORGI FLYING CLUB'**
As previous model but Land-Rover has a plastic tilt.........**£45-60**

19 1979-82 **Emergency Gift Set**
Contains C339 and C921. Striped 'window' box..............**£40-60**

19 1980-82 **Emergency Gift Set**
C339 and C931 in Red/White. Striped 'window' box **£40-60**

20 1961-64 **'Golden Guinea' Set**
Gold-plated 224 Bentley Continental, 234 Ford Consul,
229 Chevrolet Corvair, Catalogue, 2 Accessory Packs.
Inner card tray with lower card packing,
outer Dark Green sleeve with window **£400-500**

20 1970-73 **Tri-Deck Transporter Set** (Scammell Handyman Mk.III)
1st issue contains 1146 Transporter with six
'WhizzWheels' cars: 210 'Saint's' Volvo,
311 Ford Capri, 343 Pontiac, 372 Lancia, 377 Marcos,
378 MGC GT (Red body).
Instruction sheet, 'Mr Retailer' transit card protector.....**£600-700**
NBGS 20 may be found with widely differing contents
as Corgi used up excess stock in this Set.
Harrods set: Late issue set with: 1146 Transporter,
382 Porsche Targa (Silver Blue), 313 Ford Cortina
GXL (Bronze/Black), 201 Volvo (Orange 'Saint' label),
334 Mini (Orange) and 377 Marcos (Silver Green).
Box also has instruction sheet and
'Mr Retailer' transit card protector..................................**£600-700**

20 1978-80 **Emergency Gift Set**
Contains C429, C482, C921 (see 'Emergency
Vehicles' section). Box has inner tray **£35-45**

21 1962-66 **ERF Dropside and Trailer**
456 and 101 with milk churns and self-adhesive
accessories. Yellow/Blue box with inner card stand **£225-275**

21 1969-71 **'Chipperfields' Circus Set**
Contains 1144 Crane and Cage, and 1139 Menagerie
Transporter. Yellow/Blue box with internal
packaging and 'Mr Dealer' box protector card **£1,000-1,250**

21 1980-82 **Superman Set**
Contains 260, 265 and 925, plus inner tray and
plastic rockets on sprue **£100-125**

22 1962-65 **Farming Set**
Contains 1111 M-F Combine Harvester,
406 Land-Rover and Trailer, 51 Tipping Trailer,
101 Platform Trailer, 53 M-F 65 Tractor with Shovel,
1487 Milk Churns, 1490 Skip and 3 churns,
plus models in Gift Set 18 above. Lift-off lid
all-card picture box with inner polystyrene tray **£3,000-3,500**

22 1980-82 **James Bond Set**
Contains 269 Lotus Esprit, 271 Aston-Martin DB5
and 649 Space Shuttle plus rockets and 2 spare
bandit figures. Box has inner tray **£400-600**

23 1962-66 **'CHIPPERFIELDS' Set**
1st issue: 1121 Crane Truck, 2 x 1123 Animal Cages
(2 lions, 2 polar bears), plus Gift Set 19 and
426 Booking Office. All-card lift-off lid picture box
with inner polystyrene tray **£500-750**
1964 2nd issue: as 1st issue but 503 'TK Giraffe Truck'
replaces 426 Booking Office, inner polystyrene tray......**£400-600**

23 1980-82 **Spiderman Set**
261 Spiderbuggy, 266 Spiderbike, 928 Spidercopter with
figures, missiles on sprue. In striped 'window' box........**£150-200**

24 1963-68 **Commer Constructor Set**
2 cab/chassis units, 4 interchangeable bodies, milkman,
accessories. Yellow/Blue picture box with lift-off
lid and inner polystyrene tray **£100-130**

24 1976-78 **Mercedes and Caravan**
Contains 285 in Metallic Blue plus 490 Caravan in
White. Striped 'window' box..**£40-50**
1979 285 in Metallic Brown plus 490 Caravan in Bronze.
Striped 'window' box..**£40-50**

25 1963-66 **BP or Shell Garage Set**
224, 225, 229, 234 and 419 all in Blue/Yellow boxes
plus: 601 Batley Garage, 602 'AA' and 'RAC' Boxes,
606 Lamp Standards (2), 608 Filling Station,
609 accessories, 1505 Figures.
Plain card box with or without layout picture **£1,000-1,500**

25 1969-71 **Racing Car and Tender**
159 and VW Tender, 2 sets of decals in stapled bags.
Blue/Yellow window box, inner plastic tray **£120-140**

25 1980-81 **Talbot Rancho Set**
457 plus two motorcycles on trailer **£15-20**

26 1971-76 **Beach Buggy Set**
381 plus Red Sailing Boat with Blue sail.
Orange/Yellow 'window' box...**£40-50**

26 1981-83 **Corgi Racing Set**
457 Talbot Matra Rancho, 160 Hesketh (Yellow),
'Corgi Racing Team' trailer **£35-45**

27 1963-72 **Priestman Shovel on Machinery Carrier**
1128 and 1131 (Bedford Machinery Carrier).
Blue/Yellow box with inner tray **£225-275**

28 1963-65 **Transporter and 4 Cars**
1105 Bedford TK Transporter with 222 Renault Floride,
230 Mercedes-Benz, 232 Fiat, 234 Ford Classic,
2 dummy 'Corgi Toys' boxes, instructions.
Pictorial box, internal card packing................................**£400-500**

28 1975-78 **Mazda B1600 Dinghy Set**
493 Mazda + dinghy and trailer. Striped 'window' box......**£50-60**

29 1963-65 **Massey-Ferguson Set**
Contains 50 Massey-Ferguson Tractor with driver and 51
Tipper Trailer - Cream/Yellow, Red plastic rear hubs.
Yellow/Blue all-card box with inner tray **£250-300**

29 1981-82 **'CORGI' Pony Club**
Contains 441 Jeep, 112 trailer, girl on pony, 3 jumps,
3 hay bales. Striped 'window' box **£55-65**

29 1975-76 **'DUCKHAMS' FI Racing Set**
Surtees Racing Set with 323 Ferrari Daytona and
150 Ferrari in Blue/Yellow *'DUCKHAMS RACING
TEAM'* livery. Striped 'window' box....................................**£50-75**

30 1973-73 **Grand Prix Gift Set**
'Kit' versions of 151 Yardley (1501), 154 JPS (1504),
152 Surtees (1502) plus 153 Surtees (1503)? in
unique Norris livery. Picture 'window' box.
Mail order only **£100-120**

30 1979-80 **Circus Gift Set**
Land Rover and Trailer...**£60-75**

31 1964-68 **Buick Riviera Boat Set**
245 Buick, Red boat trailer, and Dolphin Cabin Cruiser
towing lady water-skier. Pictorial sleeve box with
internal packing display tray around models..................**£375-425**

31 1976-80 **Safari Land Rover Set**
C341 Land Rover with animal trailer, Warden and Lion.
Box has inner polystyrene tray **£55-65**

32 1965-68 **Tractor, Shovel and Trailer Set**
54 Massey-Ferguson 65 Tractor, 69 Shovel, 62 Tipping
Trailer with detachable raves - Red/Cream/Yellow.
Yellow/Blue picture box with inner pictorial stand........**£250-300**

32 1976-79 **Lotus Racing Set**
C301 Lotus Elite, and C154 JPS Lotus on trailer **£125-175**

32 1979-83 **Lotus Racing Set**
C301 Lotus Elite, and C154 Texaco Lotus on trailer.........**£70-85**

33 1965-68 **Tractor and Beast Carrier**
Contains 55 and 58 ....**£100-125**
1968-72 Contains 67 and 58 ....**£70-80**

33 1980-82 **'DLRG' Rescue Set**
White/Red 421 Land Rover and boat on trailer **£25-30**

34 1976-79 **Tractor & Tipping Trailer**
Contains 55 and 56 ....**£55-65**

35 1964-68 **London Traffic Set**
418 Taxi with 468 *'Corgi Toys'* or *'Outspan'* Bus,
policeman on stand. Yellow/Blue box, inner tray **£150-175**

35 1978-79 **'CHOPPER SQUAD' Surf Boat**
Contains 927, 419, trailer, rescue boat **£30-40**

36 1967-70 **Marlin Rambler Set**
Contains 263 and Boat...**£45-65**

36 1967-71 **Oldsmobile Toronado Set**
276 (Greenish-Blue), Chrome trailer, Yellow/Blue
'SWORDFISH' boat, 3 figures. Yellow/Blue box..........**£100-125**

36 1983 **Off-Road Set**
447 (Dark Blue/Cream, RN '5') + power-boat on trailer....**£25-35**

36 1976-78 **Tarzan Set**
Light Green 421 Land Rover and trailer, paler Green 'zebra'
stripes, Tarzan, Jane, Cheetah (chimp), boy, dinghy with
hunter, elephant, snake, vines, etc. Yellow/Blue 'window'
box with inner pictorial backking display **£250-350**

37 1966-69 **'Lotus Racing Team'**
490 VW Breakdown Truck, Red trailer with cars
318, 319, 155, plus 2 sets of spare racing numbers
('5' and '9' or '4' and '8'), a 1966 illustrated checklist,
a sealed pack of cones, set of bollards and a spare
Lotus chassis unit. Yellow/Blue 'window' box has
inner polystyrene tray **£400-500**

37 1979-80 **Fiat X-19 Set**
Fiat X-19 and Boat 'Carlsberg' **£30-40**

38 1977-78 **Mini 1000 Camping Set**
Cream Mini with 2 figures, tent, barbecue in
inner display stand **£90-110**

38 1965-67 **'1965 Monte Carlo Rally'**
318 Mini Cooper 'S', 322 Rover 2000, and 326
Citroën DS19. Monte Carlo Rally emblem on
each bonnet. Yellow/Blue all-card box contains
pictorial stand and inner card packing............................**£500-750**

38 1980 **Jaguar XJS Set**
319 with Powerboat on Trailer **£20-30**

40 1966-69 **'The Avengers' Set**
John Steed's Bentley (Green body, Red wire wheels),
Emma Peel's Lotus Elan (Black/White body),
Steed and Emma Peel figures, 3 Black umbrellas.
Yellow/Blue picture box with inner pictorial stand........**£500-600**
With Red/Black Bentley with Silver wire wheels..........**£350-450**

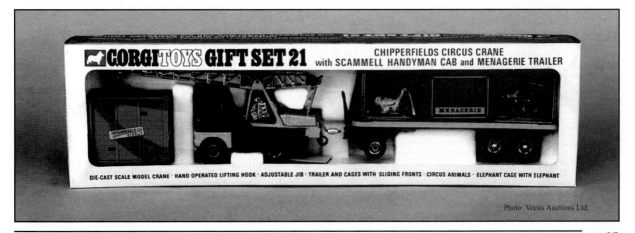

Photo: Vectis Auctions Ltd.

40 1976-82 **'Batman' Gift Set**
Contains modified 107 Trailer plus 267 Batmobile (WW)
and 925 Helicopter. 12 missiles on a sprue.
Striped box also has inner tray with card packing **£500-600**

41 1966-68 **Carrimore Car Transporter with Ford Tilt Cab**
1138 Transporter (Red/Two-tone Blue),
252 Rover 2000 (Metallic Plum),
251 Hillman Imp (Metallic Bronze),
440 Ford Cortina Estate (Metallic Blue),
226 Morris Mini-Minor (Light Blue),
321 Austin Mini Cooper 'S' (Red, RN '2', '1966 Monte Carlo
Rally', with roof signatures),
249 Morris Mini Cooper DeLuxe (Black/Red,
'wickerwork' panels).
Pictorial lift-off lid box with inner polystyrene tray.
Only sold by mail order....................................**£500-750**

41 1969-69 **Carrimore Car Transporter with Scammell Cab**
1148 Transporter (Red/Two-tone Blue),
226 Morris Mini-Minor (Metallic Maroon),
345 MGC GT (Orange in earliest sets, Yellow/Black later),
340 Sunbeam Imp (1967 Monte Carlo,
Metallic Blue, RN '77'),
258 Saint's Volvo P1800 (White with Orange label),
249 Morris Mini Cooper DeLuxe (Black/Red with
'wickerwork' panels), 339 Mini Cooper 'S' ('1967
Monte Carlo Rally', RN '177'), plus sealed bag of
cones and leaflet. Pictorial lift-off lid box with inner
polystyrene tray. Only sold by mail order **£500-750**

41 1977-81 **Silver Jubilee Set**
The State Landau with HRH Queen Elizabeth and
Prince Phillip (and a Corgi!)...................................**£15-20**

42 1978-79 **Agricultural Set**
Contains 55 David Brown Tractor plus 56 Trailer,
Silo and Elevator **£100-125**

43 1979-80 **Silo and Conveyor Set**
'CORGI HARVESTING COMPANY LTD' **£40-50**

44 1978-80 **Metropolitan Police Set**
421 Land Rover, 112 Horsebox plus Policeman on
horse. Striped 'window' box.................................**£80-90**

44 1978-80 **Mounted Police Set**
French issue with Policeman on horse **£75-100**

45 1966 **'All Winners' Set**
261 James Bond's Aston-Martin, 310 Chevrolet Stingray,
324 Marcos Volvo, 325 Ford Mustang Competition,
314 Ferrari Berlinetta. Yellow/Blue 'window' box **£350-450**

45 1978-79 **Royal Canadian Police Set**
Land Rover (421), Trailer (102), 'Mountie' on horse **£125-150**

46 1966-69 **'All Winners' Set**
264 Oldsmobile Toronado (Metallic Blue),
307 Jaguar 'E'-type (Chrome finish, RN '2', driver),
314 Ferrari Berlinetta (Red, RN '4'),
337 Chevrolet Stingray (Yellow, RN '13'),
327 MGB GT (Red/Black, suitcase). Box should
contain unopened bag of cones and decal sheets **£225-275**

46 1982 **Super Karts Set**
Red Kart, Purple Kart, with Silver/Red driver in each ....**NGPP**

47 1966-71 **Ford 5000 Tractor and Conveyor Set**
Contains 67, trailer with conveyor belt, figure,
accessories plus inner display card..................................**£200-250**

47 1978-80 **Pony Club Set**
421 Land Rover and Horsebox in Metallic Bronze,
girl on pony figure **£25-30**

48 1967-68 **Carrimore Car Transporter with Ford Tilt Cab**
1138 Transporter (Orange/Silver/Two-tone Blue) with
252 Rover 2000 (Metallic Plum),
251 Hillman Imp (Metallic Maroon),
440 Ford Cortina Estate (Metallic Blue),
249 Morris Mini Cooper DeLuxe (with 'wickerwork' panels),
226 Morris Mini-Minor (Metallic Maroon),
321 Mini Cooper 'S' ('1966 Monte Carlo Rally'),
Red/White, RN '2'. Blue/Yellow 'window' box with
inner polystyrene packing....................................**£600-800**

1968 **'SUN/RAC' variation:**
As previous set but 321 Mini Cooper is replaced by
333 SUN/RAC Rally Mini. 251 Hillman Imp is changed
to Metallic Gold with White stripe and the 226
Austin 7 Mini is now Metallic Blue with RN '21' **£700-900**

48 1969 **Carrimore Car Transporter with Scammell Cab**
1148 Transporter (Red/White) with 345 MGB (Orange),
340 Sunbeam Imp (1967 Monte Carlo,
Metallic Blue, RN '77'),
258 Saint's Volvo P1800 (White with Orange label),
249 Morris Mini Cooper DeLuxe (with 'wickerwork' panels),
339 Mini Cooper 'S' ('1967 Monte Carlo Rally', RN '177'),
226 Morris Mini-Minor (Metallic Maroon),
plus sealed bag of cones and leaflet. Blue/Yellow
'window' box with inner polystyrene packing...............**£600-800**

48 1978-80 **'PINDER' Circus Set**
Contains C426, C1163, C30, ringmaster, artistes, animals,
seating, and cardboard cut-out 'Jean Richard Pinder'
'Big-Top' circus tent. Striped 'window' box **£125-150**

49 1978-80 **'CORGI FLYING CLUB'**
Metallic Green/White Jeep (419) with Blue/White
Tipsy Nipper Aircraft...**£50-60**

51 19?? **'100 Years of the Car' Set**
3 Mercedes: C805 (White), C806 (Black),
C811 (Red) (Originally for Germany).......................**£20-25**

? 1978-80 **'The Jaguar Collection'**
C804 (Cream), C816 (Red),
C318 (Mobil Green/White). ('UNIPART' stores) **£30-35**

53 19??-?? **Land Rover and Thunderbirds Missile Set**
Models as listed **£500-750**

54 1978-80 **Swiss Rega Set**
Bonna Ambulance and Helicopter...............................**£30-35**

55 1978-80 **Norway Emergency Set**
Police Car, Breakdown Truck, Ford Transit Ambulance,
'UTRYKKNINGUSSETT'.......................................**£20-30**

56 1978-80 **Swedish Set**
Ford Sierra 'POLIS', Bonna Ambulance............................**£12-18**

57 1978-80 **Swedish Set**
Contains Volvo and Caravan..................................**£12-18**

57 1978-80 **Volvo 740 and Caravan**
Red Volvo, White/Red/Blue Caravan. Swedish export.......**£15-20**

61 1978-80 **Swiss 'FEUERWEHR' Set**
1120 Dennis Fire Engine, Sierra 'POLITZEI',
Escort Van *'NOTRUF'*...**£30-35**

64 1965-69 **FC Jeep 150 and Conveyor Belt**
Jeep (409) Yellow/White Conveyor **£100-130**

65 1978-80 **Norway Set**
Ford Transit Ambulance plus Helicopter.......................**£20-30**

67 1978-80 **Cyclists Sets**
Sold in France, 2 Cars, 2 Bicycles.
Three sets: 67/1, 67/2, 67/3.................Each set: **£20-30**

70 1978-80 **Danish 'FALCK' Set**
Bonna Ambulance and Ford Breakdown Truck **£20-30**

72 1978-80 **Norway Set**
Contains C542 plus Helicopter *'LN OSH'* **£20-30**

1151 1970 **Scammell 'Co-op' Set**
Blue/White 1147, 466 & 462. Promo in brown box **£150-175**

? 1967 **Monte Carlo Game**
Fernel Developments game with two Lavender 226 Minis,
'1967 Rallye Monte Carlo' bonnet labels, RNs 1 and 4,
plastic/paper winding roads, cards, dice shakers,
Blue/White/Red box. Scandinavian set **£350-450**

? 1980 **Construction Site Set**
Contains 54 with 440 (Mazda Pick-Up)............................**£30-35**

US EXPORT SETS — made exclusively for FAO Schwarz of America.
FAO-012
c1966 **'BEST IN SHOW' Animal Gift Set**
Contains: GS2 Land-Rover with Rice's Pony Trailer,
484 Dodge Kew Fargo and 486 Chevrolet Impala
'Kennel Club'. Blue/Yellow individual card boxes,
Blue/Yellow presentation box...................................**£1,500-2,000**

FAO-804
c1968 **'CIRCUS' Set**
Contains: GS7 'Daktari' Set, 470 Forward Control Jeep,
1123 'Chipperfields' Circus Animal Cage and GS19
'Chipperfields' Circus' Land-Rover and Elephant Cage on
Trailer. Blue/Yellow individual boxes,
Blue/Yellow presentation box...................................**£1,750-2,250**

'Husky' models and 'Corgi Juniors'

Husky models were introduced by Mettoy Playcraft in 1965 to compete with the Matchbox 1-75 range. These small-scale models have plenty of detail and action-features and the range includes cars, commercials, military and Film/TV specials.

The models have either a plastic or die-cast chassis together with various types of regular wheels and WhizzWheels. Models could only be obtained from 'Woolworths' stores and were only sold in blister packs. Production under the 'Husky' trade name ceased in 1969 and the range was reissued in 1970 as 'Corgi Juniors'. To facilitate this change, 'HUSKY' was removed from the baseplates which were then re-engraved 'CORGI JUNIORS'.

The models were mostly fitted with 'WhizzWheels' to enable them to be used on the 'Rocket Track' and to compete against the new Matchbox 'Superfast' range. Corgi Juniors were blister packed on blue/white card for the 'regular' issues and red/white card for the 'specials'. Each pack incorporated a 'Collectors Card' picture of the real vehicle and these could be cut out and pasted into a special collectors album.

The Market Price Range shown for 'Husky' and 'Corgi Juniors' refers only to mint condition models in unopened blister packs (and later in pristine boxes).

'Husky' models 1965 - 1969

1	1965-69	**Jaguar Mk.10**	
		All have Yellow interior.	
1-a1	1965-66	(small casting), Metallic Blue body, GPW	**£20-25**
1-a2	1966	(small casting), Red body, GPW	**£40-45**
1-b1	1967	Light Metallic Blue, GPW	**£20-25**
1-b2	1967	Blue body, GPW	**£25-30**
1-b3	1968	Light Metallic Blue body, tyres	**£25-30**
1-b4	1968	Cream body, tyres	**£45-55**
1-b5	1969	Dark Blue body, tyres	**£25-30**
1-b6	1969	Dark Maroon body, tyres	**£30-35**
2	1965-69	**Citroën Safari with Boat**	
2-a1	1965-66	(small casting) Pale Yellow body, Tan boat, GPW	**£20-25**
2-b1	1967	Metallic Green body, Brown boat, GPW	**£45-50**
2-b2	1967	Metallic Gold body, Blue boat, GPW	**£40-45**
2-b3	1968-69	Metallic Gold, Blue boat, tyres	**£20-25**
3-a1	1965-67	**Mercedes 220** Pale Blue, GPW	**£15-20**
3-bt	1967-68	**Volkswagen Police Car** White/Black doors, smooth hubs with tyres	**£25-30**
3-b2	1969	With detailed hubs / tyres	**£25-30**
4	1965-69	**Jaguar Fire Chief**	
4-a1	1965-66	(small casting), Red body, chrome siren, 'Fire', GPW	**£25-30**
4-bl	1967	as previous model	**£25-30**
4-b2	1968-69	Same but with tyres	**£30-35**
5-a1	1965	**Lancia Flaminia** Red, GPW	**£40-45**
5-a2	1965-66	Blue, GPW	**£15-20**
5-b1	1967-69	**Willys Jeep**, Metallic Green, Grey windshield	**£15-20**
5-b2	1967-69	With Yellow windshield	**£25-30**
6-a1	1965-67	**Citroën Safari Ambulance**, White, Red cross, GPW	**£20-25**
6-b1	1968-69	**Ferrari Berlinetta** Red body, tyres	**£25-30**
6-b2	1968-69	Maroon body, tyres	**£25-30**
7-a1	1965-66	**Buick Electra** Orange-Red, GPW	**£15-20**
7-b1	1967	**Duple Vista 25 Coach** Green/White, GPW	**£20-25**
7-b2	1968-69	Same but with tyres	**£20-25**
8-a1	1965-66	**Ford Thunderbird** (open) Pink, Black open body, Grey plastic wheels	**£20-25**
8-b1	1967	**Ford Thunderbird Hardtop** Yellow, Blue top, GPW	**£30-35**
8-c1	1967-69	**Tipping Farm Trailer** Yellow, Red back, tyres	**£10-15**
9-a1	1965-67	**Buick 'Police' Patrol** Dark Blue, GPW	**£20-25**
9-b1	1968-69	**Cadillac Eldorado** Light Blue, tyres	**£20-25**

10-a1	1965-67	**Guy Warrior Coal Truck** Red, GPW	**£15-20**
10-a2	1968-69	Same model	**£15-20**
11-a1	1965-67	**Forward Control Land Rover** Green body (shades), metal or plastic base, rear corner windows, GPW	**£15-20**
11-a2	1968-69	Same, but Metallic Green, no corner windows, GPW	**£15-20**
12-a1	1965-66	**Volkswagen Tower Wagon** Yellow/Red, GPW	**£20-25**
12-b1	1967	**Ford Tower Wagon** Yellow, Red tower, GPW	**£30-35**
12-b2	1967	White, Red tower, GPW	**£15-20**
12-b3	1968-69	White, Red tower, tyres	**£20-25**
13-a1	1965-66	**Guy Warrior Sand Truck** Yellow, GPW	**£15-20**
13-a2	1967-68	Blue, GPW	**£15-20**
13-a3	1969	Blue, tyres	**£20-25**
14-a1	1965-66	**Guy Warrior Tanker 'Shell'** Yellow, round tank, GPW	**£20-25**
14-b1	1967	Same, but square tank	**£20-25**
14-b2	1967	**Guy Warrior Tanker 'Esso'** White, square tank, GPW	**£20-25**
14-b3	1968-69	Same, but with tyres	**£20-25**
15-a1	1965-66	**Volkswagen Pick Up**, Turquoise body, GPW	**£15-20**
15-b1	1967-68	**Studebaker Wagonaire TV Car** Yellow body, GPW	**£20-25**
15-b2	1968	Metallic Blue body, GPW	**£25-30**
15-b3	1969	Metallic Blue body, tyres	**£25-30**
16-a1	1965-66	**Dump Truck/Dozer** Yellow, Red back, GPW	**£15-20**
16-a2	1966	**Dump Truck/Dozer** Red, Grey back, GPW	**£20-25**
17	1965-69	**Guy Warrior 'Milk' Tanker**	
17-a1	1965-66	White, round tank, GPW	**£20-25**
17-b1	1967	White, square tank, GPW	**£20-25**
17-b2	1968	Cream, round tank, GPW	**£20-25**
17-b3	1969	Cream, round tank, tyres	**£20-25**
18-a1	1965-66	**Plated Jaguar** (small casting) Chrome, GPW	**£20-25**
18-bi	1967-68	Same, but larger casting	**£20-25**
18-b2	1969	Larger casting, tyres	**£30-35**
19-a1	1966	**Commer Walk Thro' Van** Red body, GPW	**£40-45**
19-a2	1966-67	Green body, GPW	**£25-30**
19-b1	1968-69	**Speedboat on Trailer** Gold trailer, Red, White and Blue boat, tyres	**£15-20**
20-a1	1965-66	**Ford Thames Van** Red, Yellow ladder, GPW	**£20-25**
20-b1	1967	**VW 1300 with Luggage** Tan body, tyres	**£30-35**
20-b2	1967-69	With Blue body	**£20-25**
21-a1	1966-67	**Forward Control Military Land Rover**, GPW	**£15-20**
21-b1	1968-69	**Jaguar 'E'-type 2+2** Maroon body, tyres	**£20-25**

22-a1	1965-66	**Citroën Safari Military Ambulance**, GPW	**£20-25**
22-b1	1967-68	**Aston-Martin DB6** Metallic Gold body, GPW	**£25-30**
22-b2	1968-69	**Aston-Martin DB6** Purple body, tyres	**£30-35**
23-a1	1966-67	**Guy Army Tanker**, GPW	**£15-20**
23-b1	1968	**Loadmaster Shovel** Orange body, BPW	**£25-30**
23-b2	1968-69	Yellow body, BPW	**£15-20**
24-a1	1966-67	**Ford Zephyr Estate** Blue body, GPW	**£15-20**
24-a2	1968-69	**Ford Zephyr Estate** Red, GPW	**£25-30**
25-a1	1966-67	**SD Refuse Van** Light Blue body, GPW	**£15-20**
25-a2	1968	Red body, GPW	**£30-35**
25-a3	1968-69	Red body, tyres	**£40-45**
26-a1	1966-67	**Sunbeam Alpine** Metallic Bronze body, Blue hard top, GPW	**£25-30**
26-a2	1967	Same, but Red body, GPW	**£40-45**
26-a3	1968-69	Red body, Blue top, tyres	**£50-55**
27-a1	1966-67	**Bedford Skip Lorry** Maroon body, GPW	**£20-25**
27-a2	1967	**Bedford Skip Lorry** Dark Green body, GPW	**£50-60**
27-a3	1967	Orange body, GPW	**£20-25**
27-a4	1968-69	Orange body, tyres	**£20-25**
28-a1	1966-67	**Ford Breakdown Truck** Blue, metal jib, GPW	**£15-20**
28-a2	1968-69	Blue, Gold jib, tyres	**£20-25**
29-a1	1966-67	**ERF Cement Mixer**, Yellow, Red barrel, GPW	**£15-20**
29-a2	1968-69	Yellow, Red barrel, tyres	**£20-25**
30-a1	1966-67	**Studebaker Wagonaire Ambulance**, White, Red Cross, stretcher, GPW	**£25-30**
30-a2	1968-69	Same, but with tyres	**£25-30**
30-a3	1969	**Studebaker Wagonaire** Pale Green body, tyres	**£35-40**
31-a1	1966-67	**Oldsmobile Starfire Coupé** Olive Green body, GPW	**£15-20**
31-a2	1968-69	Same but with tyres	**£20-25**
32-a1	1966-67	**Volkswagen Luggage Elevator** White body, Yellow conveyor, GPW	**£25-30**
32-a2	1967	With Blue conveyor, GPW	**£30-35**
32-a3	1968-69	Red, Blue conveyor, GPW	**£35-40**
33-a1	1967	**Farm Trailer and Calves** Olive Green, tyres	**£10-15**
33-a2	1968-69	Turquoise, tyres	**£10-15**
34-a1	1967	**Tractor** Red, Red exhaust, tyres	**£20-25**
34-a2	1968-69	Red, Black exhaust, tyres	**£20-25**
35-a1	1967	**Ford Camper** Yellow, GPW	**£20-25**
35-a2	1967	Metallic Blue, GPW	**£25-30**
35-a3	1968-69	Metallic Blue, tyres	**£25-30**

36-a1	1967	**Simon Snorkel Fire Engine**	
		Red, GPW £20-25	
36-a2	1968-69	Red, with tyres £20-25	
37-a1	1968-69	**NSU Ro80**	
		Metallic Blue, tyres.............£25-30	
38-a1	1968	**Rices Beaufort Single Horse Box**	
		Turquoise, tyres..................£10-15	
38-a2	1969	Metallic Green body, tyres...£20-25	

39-a1	1969	**Jaguar XJ6 4.2**	
		Yellow, Red interior, tyres ...£45-55	
40-a1	1969	**Ford Transit Caravan**	
		Red body, tyres....................£25-35	
40-a2	1969	Lime green body, tyres.........£25-35	
41-a1	?	**Porsche Carrera 6**	
		In catalogue but not issued ......NPP	

42-a	1969	**Euclid Truck**	
		Yellow body, Red dumper....£40-45	
43-a	?	**Massey-Ferguson 3003**	
		no details £40-45	

See also following section and 'Corgi Rockets'.

1001-a1	1967	**James Bond Aston Martin DB6**	Silver, Red interior, 2 ejector figures, Grey plastic wheels	£180-200
1001-a2	1968-69	**James Bond Aston Martin DB6**	Silver, Red interior, 2 ejector figures, tyres	£180-200
1002-a1	1967-69	**Batmobile**	Black, Batman and Robin figures, tow hook, Grey plastic wheels	£150-160
1003-a1	1967-69	**Batboat**	Black boat, Red fin, Batman and Robin figures, Grey plastic wheels	£150-160
1004-a1	1968-69	**Monkeemobile**	Red, White roof, 4 figures, 'Monkees' on doors, tyres	£160-180
1005-a1	1968-69	**Man From UNCLE Car**	Blue, 3 Missiles on sprue, 2 figures, tyres	£160-175
1006-a1	1969	**Chitty Chitty Bang Bang**	Chrome, Dark Grey base, Red wings, Yellow fins, 4 figures, tyres	£140-180

Corgi Juniors 1970 - 1972

Note: The models in this list were each accompanied by a colourful Picture Card, the lack of which could adversely affect the model's potential price.

1-a1	1970	**Reliant TW9 Pick Up**	
		Beige body, Black WW £20-25	
1-a2	1970-72	Orange body, Black WW £15-20	
2-a1	1970	**Citroën Safari with** (white) **Boat**	
		Blue body, tyres...................£25-30	
2-a2	1970	With Black WhizzWheels...£20-25	
2-a3	1971-2	Yellow body, BWW £20-25	
2-a4	1971-2	Purple body, BWW £20-25	
3-a1	1970	**Volkswagen 1300 Police Car**	
		White body, tyres £30-35	
3-a2	1970	With Black WhizzWheels....£20-25	
3-a3	1971-72	With chrome WhizzWheels .£20-25	
3-a4	1971-72	With chrome WhizzWheels ..£15-20	
4-a1	1970-72	**Zeteor 5511 Tractor**	
		Orange, Red base, BPW £10-15	
5-a1	1970	**Willys Jeep**	
		Tan body, Brown interior,	
		tyres......................................£15-20	
5-a2	1970	With Black WhizzWheels....£10-15	
5-a3	1971	With chrome WhizzWheels .£10-15	
5-a4	1970	Orange body, Brown interior,	
		Black WhizzWheels.............£10-15	
5-a5	1971	Same, chrome Whizzwheels.£10-15	
5-a6	1971-72	Red body, Yellow interior,	
		chrome WhizzWheels £10-15	
6-a1	1970	**De Tomaso Mangusta**	
		Lime Green, BWW £10-15	
6-a2	1970	Metallic Purple, Black WW.£10-15	
6-a3	1971-2	Metallic Purple, CWW £10-15	
7-a1	1970	**Duple Vista 25 Coach**	
		Red body/White roof, tyres..£20-25	
7-a2	1970	Yellow/White, Black WW ..£12-15	
7-a3	1971-2	Purple/White, chrome WW.£12-15	
7-a4	1971-2	Orange/White, chrome WW £12-15	
8-a1	1970	**Tipping Farm Trailer**	
		Blue, Orange back, tyres......£10-15	
9-a1	1970	**Cadillac Eldorado**	
		Metallic Green body,	
		Red interior, tyres................£25-30	
9-a2	1970	With Black WhizzWheels....£15-20	
9-a3	1970	White/Black, BWW £15-20	
9-a4	1971	White/Black, chrome WW..£15-20	
9-b1	1971-72	**Vigilant Range Rover**	
		White body, chrome WW ...£12-15	
10-a1	1970	**Guy Warrior Coal Truck**	
		Orange body, tyres £15-20	
10-b1	1971-2	**Ford GT7O**	
		Orange body, CWW.............£10-12	

11-af	1970	**Austin Healey Sprite Le Mans**	
		Red body, Blue interior, Grey	
		base, RN '50', sticker pack,	
		Black WhizzWheels...............£30-35	
11-a2	1971	Yellow int., chrome WW £30-35	
11-a3	1971-2	Red body, Yellow interior,	
		Black base, CWW..................£30-35	
12-a1	1970	**Reliant-Ogle Scimitar GTE**	
		White body, Black WW £20-25	
12-a2	1970	Metallic Blue, chrome WW .£20-25	
12-a3	1971-2	Matt Blue, chrome WW.......£20-25	
13-a1	1970	**Guy Warrior Sand Truck**	
		Blue body, tyres £15-20	
13-a2	1971-72	Red body, chrome WW........£12-15	
14-a1	1970	**Guy Warrior Tanker 'ESSO'**	
		(square tank), White, tyres...£15-20	
14-a2	1971-2	White, chrome WW £12-15	
15-a1	1970	**Studebaker Wagonaire TV Car**	
		Metallic Turquoise , tyres £35-40	
15-a2	1970	Yellow body, Black WWs....£25-30	
15-a3	1970	Met. Lime Green, BWW £25-30	
15-a4	1971-2	Met. Lime Green, CWW £25-30	
16-a	1970-2	**Land Rover Pick Up**	
		Metallic Green, CWW £10-12	
17-af	1970	**Volkswagen 1300 Beetle**	
		Metallic Blue body,	
		'flower' decals.....................£45-50	
17-a2	1970-72	Metallic Green body £20-25	
19-a1	1970	**Speedboat on Trailer**	
		Blue trailer, Red,White and	
		Blue boat, tyres £15-20	
19-a2	1970	With Black WhizzWheels....£10-15	
19-a3	1971-2	With chrome WhizzWheels .£10-15	
20-a1	1967	**Volkswagen 1300 with Luggage**	
		Mustard Yellow body, tyres.£25-30	
20-a2	1967-69	Red body, Black WW £20-25	
21-a1	1971-72	**BVRT Vita-Min Mini Cooper S**	
		Metallic Purple, CWW £25-30	
22-a1	1970	**Aston-Martin DB6**	
		Purple body, tyres.................£45-50	
22-a2	1970	Metallic Olive body, tyres....£45-50	
22-b1	1971-72	**Formula 1 GP Racing Car**	
		Yellow body, WW...............£12-15	
23-a1	1970-2	**Loadmaster Shovel**	
		Yellow body, BPW..............£10-12	
24-a1	1971-2	**Aston-Martin DBS**	
		Green body, chrome WW £20-25	
25-a1	1970-72	**SD Refuse Van**	
		Orange / chrome, tyres.........£15-20	
26-a1	1971-72	**ERF Fire Engine Water Tender**	
		Red body, chrome WW........£12-15	

27-a1	1970	**Bedford Skip Lorry**	
		Orange, Silver skip, tyres.....£20-25	
28-a1	1970	**Ford Breakdown Truck**	
		Blue body, tyres £20-25	
28-a2	1970	Blue body, Black WW £15-20	
28-a3	1970	Turquoise, Black WW..........£15-20	
29-a1	1971-72	**Simon Snorkel Fire Engine**	
		Red body, chrome WW £12-15	
30-a1	1970	**Studebaker Wagonaire**	
		Ambulance, White body,	
		removable stretcher, tyres £25-30	
30-a2	1970	With Black WhizzWheels....£20-25	
30-a3	1970	With non-removable stretcher,	
		Black WhizzWheels.............£15-20	
30-a4	1971	Non-removable stretcher,	
		small CWW..........................£15-20	
30-a5	1971-72	Same as previous model £15-20	
31-a1	1970-71	**Land Rover Breakdown**	
		Purple body £12-15	
31-a2	1972	Red body £12-15	
32-a1	1970-71	**Lotus Europa**	
		Metallic Green, CWW £15-20	
32-a2	1972	Green body, CWW..............£15-20	
33-a1	1970	**Farm Trailer and Calves**	
		Orange, tyres £10-15	
33-b1	1970-72	**Jaguar 'E'-type Series 2**	
		Yellow, CWW......................£12-15	
34-a1	1970-72	**B.M. Volvo 400 Tractor**	
		Red, Yellow wheels, tyres....£15-20	
35-a1	1970	**Ford Camper**	
		Turquoise body, chrome back,	
		tyres......................................£25-30	
35-a2	1970-2	Same, but Black WW............£15-20	
35-a3	1970-2	Red body, Cream back,	
		Black WhizzWheels.............£20-25	
36-a1	1970	**Simon Snorkel Fire Engine**	
		Red body, tyres.....................£20-25	
37-a1	1970	**NSU Ro80**	
		Metallic Blue body, Green	
		tinted windows, tyres £25-30	
37-a2	1970	Metallic Mauve body,	
		Black WhizzWheels.............£15-20	
37-a3	1970	Purple body, Black WW £15-20	
37-a4	1971-2	Purple body, CWW £15-20	
37-a5	1971-2	Metallic Copper body, Amber	
		tinted windows, CWW.........£15-20	
38-a1	1970	**Rices Beaufort Single Horse Box**	
		Metallic Green body, tyres...£15-20	
38-a2	1970	Red body, tyres.....................£15-20	
38-a3	1970	Red body, Black WW £10-15	
38-a4	1971-72	Metallic Copper, CWW £10-15	

39-a1	1970	**Jaguar XJ6 4.2** Yellow, Red interior, tyres ...**£30-35**
39-a2	1970	Silver, Red interior, BWW...**£20-25**
39-a3	1971-72	Silver, Red interior, CWW...**£20-25**
39-a4	1971-72	Metallic Red, Yellow interior, chrome WhizzWheels......**£20-25**
39-a5	1971-72	Red body, Yellow interior, chrome WhizzWheels **£20-25**
4d-a1	1970	**Ford Transit Caravan** Yellow body, Blue interior, Silver rear door, tyres..........**£25-30**
40-a2	1970	Yellow body, Cream interior, Black WhizzWheels.............**£20-25**
40-a3	1970	Blue body, Cream interior, Black WhizzWheels.............**£20-25**
40-a4	1971-72	Blue body, Cream interior, chrome WhizzWheels **£20-25**
40-a5	1971-72	Metallic Pale Blue body, Cream interior, CWW **£15-20**
40-a6	1972	Metallic Pale Blue body, Cream interior, Black plastic base, chrome WhizzWheels.**£15-20**
41-a1	1970	**Porsche Carrera 6** White body, clear canopy, RN '19', tyres **£20-25**
41-a2	1970	Blue tinted canopy, BWW ...**£15-20**
41-a3	1971-72	Blue tinted canopy, CWW ...**£15-20**
42-a1	1970	**Euclid Dumper** Yellow cab, Red back, Dark Grey base, Black wheels......**£15-20**
42-a2	1970	Red cab, Yellow back, unpainted base, CWW **£10-15**
42-a3	1971-72	Yellow cab, Red back, Dark Grey base, BWW **£10-15**
42-a4	1971-72	Blue cab, Silver back, Dark Grey base, CWW **£10-15**
42-a5	1971-72	Blue Cab, Yellow back, Dark Grey base, CWW **£10-15**
43-a1	1970	**Massey Ferguson Tractor Shovel** Yellow body, Red interior, Black plastic wheels............**£12-15**
43-a2	1971-72	Yellow body, Red shovel and interior, BPW **£10-15**
44-a1	1970-72	**Raygo Rascal Road Roller** Blue / Orange, BPW **£10-12**
45-a1	1970	**Mercedes 280SL** Metallic Silver, Red interior, tyres......................................**£30-35**
45-a2	1970	Metallic Blue body, Red interior, Black WW......**£20-25**
45-a3	1970	Yellow body, Red interior, unpainted base, BWW **£15-20**
45-a4	1970	Yellow body, Red interior, White base, BWW **£15-20**

45-a5	1970	Red body, Cream interior, Black WhizzWheels.............**£25-30**
45-a6	1971-72	Red body, Cream interior, chrome WhizzWheels **£25-30**
45-a7	1971-72	Blue body, Cream interior, unpainted base, CWW **£20-25**
46-a1	1970	**Jensen Interceptor** Maroon body, Yellow interior, unpainted base, tyres............**£35-40**
46-a2	1970	Maroon body, Black WW **£25-30**
46-a3	1971	Orange body, unpainted base, CWW **£25-30**
46-a4	1972	Metallic Green body, unpainted base, CWW **£25-30**
47-a1	1971-72	**Scammell Concrete Mixer** White / Red, CWW **£10-15**
48-a1	1971-72	**ERF Tipper Truck** Red cab, Silver back, unpainted base, CWW **£10-15**
48-a1	1971-72	Blue cab, Orange back, chrome Whizzwheels...........**£10-15**
48-a1	1971-72	Blue cab, Orange back, Dark Grey base, CWW **£10-15**
48-a1	1971-72	Blue cab, Yellow back, Dark Grey base, CWW **£10-15**
49-a1	1971-72	**Pininfarina Modulo** Yellow, Red stripe, CWW....**£10-12**
50-a1	1971-72	**Ferrari 5l2s** Metallic Red, CWW **£10-12**
51-a1	1971-72	**Porsche 917** Gold, RN '23', CWW **£10-12**
52-a1	1971-72	**Adams Probe 16** Metallic Pink, CWW............**£10-12**
54-a1	1971-72	**Ford Container Wagon** Red, Yellow skip, CWW **£10-12**
55-a1	1970-72	**Daimler Fleetline Bus** Red, 'Uniflo', CWW............**£10-12**
56-a1	1970-72	**Ford Capri Fire Chief** Red, White bonnet, 'Fire' decal on door, White interior, CWW **£25-30**
56-a2	1970-72	With 'Fire Chief' decal **£25-30**
56-a3	1970-72	All-Red, 'Fire Chief' on door, Yellow interior, CWW **£25-30**
57-a1	1970-72	**Caddy Hot Rodder** Metallic Blue, 'Caddy Hot Roddy' on doors, sticker pack, CWW **£12-15**
57-a2	1970-72	Metallic Pink body, CWW...**£12-15**
58-a1	1971-72	**G.P. Beach Buggy** Metallic Red, Cream interior, CWW **£10-12**
58-a2	1971-72	Same, but Yellow interior **£10-12**

59-a1	1971-72	**The Futura**, Orange, 'Futura' on sides, Black base, sheet of stickers, CWW **£10-12**
60-a1	1971-72	**VW Double Trouble Hot Rod** Metallic Pink, CWW...........**£12-15**
61-a1	1970-72	**Mercury Cougar Police Car** White/Black, 'Sheriff', chrome WhizzWheels **£12-15**
62-a1	1970	**Volvo P1800** Red, Yellow int., CWW **£35-40**
62-a2	1971-72	Red, Blue interior, CWW....**£25-30**
62-a3	1972	Red, Cream interior, CWW .**£45-50**
63-a1	1970-72	**Ford Escort Monte Carlo Rally Car**, Met. Blue, RN '32', Red interior, sheet of stickers, chrome WhizzWheels **£35-40**
63-a2	1972	With Yellow interior, CWW **£45-50**
63-a3	1972	With Cream interior, CWW .**£45-50**
64-a1	1971-72	**Morgan Plus 8** Yellow, CWW **£20-25**
64-a2	1971-72	Red, RN '20', CWW **£20-25**
65-a1	1971-72	**Bertone Carabo** Metallic Purple, White interior, CWW..........**£12-15**
65-a2	1971-72	Orange interior, CWW........**£10-12**
67-a1	1971-72	**Ford Capri 'Hot Pants' Dragster** Yellow body, CWW **£35-40**
70-a1	1971-72	**US Racing Buggy**, Blue, chrome WhizzWheels.**£10-12**
71-a1	1971-72	**Marcos XP** Orange, chrome WW **£12-15**
72-a1	1971-72	**Mercedes-Benz C111** Red, chrome WW............**£10-12**
73-a1	1971-72	**Pininfarina Alfa Romeo P33** Blue body, chrome WW **£10-12**
74-a1	1971-72	**Bertone Barchetta** Orange, chrome WW **£10-12**
75-a1	1971-72	**Superstock Car** Silver, Blue base, Union Jack, sticker pack, CWW **£20-25**
76-a1	1971-72	**Chevrolet Astro** Metallic Red, CWW **£12-15**
77-a1	1971-72	**Bizzarrini Manta** Pink, CWW **£10-12**
78-a1	1971-72	**Old MacDonald's Truck** Red, Brown back, CWW **£25-30**
1017-a1,	1971-72,	**Holmes Wrecker and Towing Cradle**, Yellow cab, Red back, 'Auto Rescue' decals, Gold booms, Red cradle ..**£100-120**

Major Models

2001	1968-69	**'HUSKY' Multi Garage**............	A set of four garages (no cars), 'Husky' on base...**£15-20**
	1970-75	Corgi Juniors issue:	As previous model but with 'CORGI' logo, 'Juniors' on base...**£10-15**
2002	1967-69	**'HUSKY' Car Transporter**.......	Hoynor MkII, White/Blue/Orange, detachable cab, 'Husky' on base..**£30-40**
	1970-72	Corgi Juniors issue:	As previous model but with 'CORGI' logo, 'Juniors' on base...**£25-35**
2003a	1968-69	**Machinery Low-Loader**...........	Red/Blue/Yellow, detachable cab, drop-down ramp, 'Husky' on base...**£25-35**
2003b	1970-73	Corgi Juniors issue:	As previous model with metal wheels or WhizzWheels, 'Juniors' on base.....................................**£25-35**
2004a	1968-69	**Removals Delivery Van**	Red or Blue cab, plated box, *'HUSKY REMOVALS'*, metal wheels, 'Husky' on base **£45-55**
2004b	1970-72	Corgi Juniors issue:	As previous model but *'CORGI REMOVALS'*, WhizzWheels, 'Juniors' base....................................**£20-30**
2006	1970-79	**Mack 'ESSO' Tanker**	White body and tank, WhizzWheels, 'Juniors' on base **£10-15**

Husky Accessories

1561/2	1968-69	**Traffic Signs** **£20-30**
1571	1968-69	**Pedestrians**..................**£10-15**
1572	1968-69	**Workmen** **£10-15**
1573	1968-69	**Garage Personnel**.......**£10-15**
1574	1968-69	**Public Servants**...........**£10-15**
1580	1968-69	**Husky Collector Case** storage for 48 models ...**£15-25**

| 1585 | 1968-69 | **Husky Traveller Case,** opens to form Service Station (this item never seen)........NPP |
| 2001 | 1968-69 | **'HUSKY' Multi Garage,** A set of four garages, ...(no cars), 'Husky' on base ..**£20-25** |

| | 1970-75 | As previous model but with 'CORGI' logo, 'Juniors' on base ....**£10-15** |
| --- | 1970s | **USA Dealer Display Unit**. A wooden revolving unit with lighting, brown/black, *'Collect Husky Models'*............**£200-300** |

Corgi Juniors Film and TV-related models, 1970 - 1972   See also preceeding section and 'Corgi Rockets'.

1001-a1	1970	**James Bond Aston-Martin DB6**	Silver, Red interior, 2 ejector figures, Grey plastic wheels	**£180-200**
1001-a2	1970	**James Bond Aston-Martin DB6**	Silver, Red interior, 2 ejector figures, Black WhizzWheels	**£180-200**
1001-a3	1971-72	**James Bond Aston-Martin DB6**	Silver, Red interior, 2 ejector figures, chrome WhizzWheels	**£160-180**
1002-a1	1970	**Batmobile**	Black, Batman and Robin figures, tow hook, Grey plastic wheels, 'Corgi Junior' label on base	**£150-160**
1002-a2	1970	**Batmobile**	Black, Batman and Robin figures, tow hook, Black WhizzWheels	**£150-160**
1002-a3	1971-72	**Batmobile**	Black, Batman and Robin figures, tow hook, chrome WhizzWheels	**£150-160**
1003-a1	1970	**Batboat**	Black boat, Red fin, Batman and Robin figures, GPW, 'Corgi Junior' label on base	**£140-150**
1003-a2	1970	**Batboat**	Black boat, Red fin, Batman and Robin figures, Black WhizzWheels	**£130-140**
1003-a3	1971-72	**Batboat**	Black boat, Red fin, Batman and Robin figures, chrome WhizzWheels	**£140-150**
1004-a1	1970	**Monkeemobile**	Red, White roof, 4 figures, 'Monkees' on doors, tyres, 'Corgi Junior' label on base	**£160-180**
1004-a2	1970	**Monkeemobile**	Red, White roof,4 figures, 'Monkees' on doors, tyres, 'Corgi Junior' base	**£160-180**
1004-a3	1971	**Monkeemobile**	Red, White roof, 4 figures, 'Monkees' on doors, tyres, Black WhizzWheels	**£150-160**
1005-a1	1970	**Man From U.N.C.L.E. Car**	Blue, 3 missiles on sprue, 2 figures, tyres, 'Corgi Junior' label on base	**£125-150**
1006-a1	1970	**Chitty Chitty Bang Bang**	Chrome, Dark Grey base, Red wings, Yellow fins, 4 figures, tyres	**£140-180**
1006-a2	1971	**Chitty Chitty Bang Bang**	Chrome, Dark Grey base, Red wings, Yellow fins, 4 figures, Black WhizzWheels	**£140-180**
1007-a1	1971-72	**Ironsides Police Van**	Blue, 'San Francisco' logo, Ironside in back, chrome WhizzWheels	**£160-180**
1008-a1	1971-72	**Popeye's Paddle Wagon**	Yellow, Blue, Popeye with Olive and Sweet Pea, chrome WhizzWheels	**£120-130**
1010-a1	1972	**James Bond Volkswagen**	Orange, Green stripe / 'Corgi Toys' on roof, RN '5', Yellow interior, chrome WhizzWheels	**£750-1,000**
1011-a1	1971-72	**James Bond Bobsleigh**	Yellow, '007' decal, Grey plastic bumper, George Lazenby figure, Black WhizzWheels	**£500-750**
1012-a1	1971-72	**S.P.E.C.T.R.E. Bobsleigh**	Orange, 'Boars Head' decal, Grey plastic bumper, Blofleld figure, Black WhizzWheels	**£750-1,000**
1013-a1	1971-72	**Tom's Go Cart**	Yellow, Tom figure, chrome WhizzWheels	**£50-60**
1014-a1	1971-72	**Jerry's Banger**	Red, Jerry figure, chrome WhizzWheels	**£50-60**

Husky and Corgi Juniors Gift Sets 1968 - 1970

3001	1968-69	**4 Garage Set**	Contains 23, 27, 29, or 9, 30 or 36	**£75-100**
3002	1968-69	**Batmobile Set**	1002 Batmobile and 1003 Batboat on trailer	**£300-350**
3002	1970	**'Club Racing' Set**	Juniors set of 8 racing cars inc Mini Cooper 'S' (Metallic Mauve), Ford Capri, Morgan, etc	**£150-250**
3003	1968-69	**Car Transporter Set**	2002 Husky Car Transporter plus 16, 26, 6-2, 21-2, 22-2, 26	**£150-200**
3004	1968-69	**4 Garage Set**	Contains 23-2, 29	**£60-80**
3004		**James Bond 'OHMSS' Set**	Contains 1004, 1001, 1011, 1012 plus un-numbered VW Beetle in Red with Black No'5' on White circle on sides. (From film 'On Her Majesty's Secret Service')	**£5,000-6,000**
3005	1968-69	**Holiday Time / Leisure Time**	Contains 2-2, 5-2, 7-2, 15-2, 19-2, 20-2, 21-2, 35-1	**£150-200**
3006	1968-69	**Service Station**	Contains 14-c, 22-2, 28	**£60-80**
3007	1968-69	**'HUSKY MULTIPARK'**	In 1968 catalogue but not issued	**NPP**
3008	1968-69	**Crime Busters Set**	Contains 1001, 1002, 1003, 1005	**£500-700**
	1970	Corgi Juniors issue:	As previous set	**£400-600**
3011		**Road Construction Set**	Gift Set containing seven models	**£120-140**

Husky and Corgi Juniors Catalogues and listings

HUSKY CATALOGUES

Mettoy Playcraft (Sales) Ltd 1966	**Leaflet (single fold)**	Red, illustrating No.1 Jaguar Mk.10 on cover and Nos.1-29 inside. '1/9 each'	**£20-25**
Mettoy Playcraft (Sales) Ltd 1966	**Leaflet (Belgian issue)**	As previous leaflet but Nos.1-32 shown, printed in French	**£20-25**
Mettoy Playcraft (Sales) Ltd 1966	**Booklet (10 pages)**	Front/rear covers feature a row of garages and cars. Good pictures of 1002 Batmobile and 1001 James Bond's Aston-Martin, plus Nos.1-36	**NGPP**
no ref. 1967	**Catalogue (24 pages)**	Cover features boy with Husky vehicles and sets. Good pictures of all the rare models and Gift Sets plus accessories and models 1-41	**£30-40**

CORGI JUNIORS CATALOGUES

Mettoy Playcraft 1970	**Catalogue (16 pages)**	Blue cover with 10 models featured. Contains excellent pictures of all the rare early models including GS 3004 James Bond 'O.H.M.S.S.' Set etc	**£30-40**
no ref 1970	**Corgi Juniors Collectors Album**	28 pages. To hold cards cut from Corgi Junior bubble packs. Has details of featured models below space for card. Centre two pages have 'Corgi Toys' adverts plus articles, etc.	**£10-15**

Corgi Juniors Twin-Packs   Corgi Juniors bubble-packed in pairs from 1977 approximately.

2501	London Bus and Taxi	**£20-30**	2511	Sting Helicopter and Scout Car	**£20-30**	2523	Police Car and Helicopter	**£25-35**
2502	Land Rover Breakdown and Jaguar XJS	**£30-40**	2512	Space Shuttle and Star Ship 'Liberator'	**£40-50**	2524	Custom Van Twin	**£25-35**
2503	Land Rover and Horse Box	**£20-30**	2513	Fire Tender and Ambulance	**£20-30**	2525	Triumph TR7 + Dinghy on Trailer	**£40-50**
2504	Land Rover Breakdown and AMC Pace Car	**£30-40**	2514	Building Set	**£25-35**	2526	Dumper Truck + Shovel Loader	**£25-35**
			2515	Citroën and Speedboat	**£25-35**	2527	'Kojak' and Police Helicopter	**£50-60**
2505	'DAILY PLANET' Van and Helicopter	**£20-30**	2516	Tractor and Tipping Trailer	**£25-35**	2528	Starsky and Hutch Twin Pack	**£50-60**
2506	Supermobile and Superman Van	**£50-60**	2518	Mercedes and Caravan	**£25-35**	2529	James Bond Lotus + Helicopter	**£100-150**
2507	Tom's Cart and Jerry's Banger	**£20-30**	2519	Batmobile and Batboat	**£150-200**	2530	Rescue Range Rover and Helicopter	**£30-40**
2508	Popeye's Tugboat and Olive Oyl's Aeroplane	**£20-30**	2520	Rescue Set	**£30-40**	2506	AMF 'Ski-daddler' Snowmobile and trailer	**£100-150**
2510	F1 and F5000 Racing Cars	**£30-40**	2521	James Bond Lotus and Aston-Martin DB5	**£150-200**	2538	Buck Rogers Starfighter and NASA Columbia Shuttle	**£40-50**
			2522	Army Attack Set	**£30-40**			

Corgi Juniors 1975 - 1983

Market Price Range - scarcer items as shown, otherwise under £15. These models are fitted with WhizzWheels.

E2	80-81	Blake's Seven Liberator...**£75-100**	
E3	77-81	Stromberg's Helicopter......**£25-35**	
E6	79-80	'Daily Planet' Helicopter ...**£15-20**	
E11	79-85	Supermobile....................**£20-30**	
E17-2	79-81	Metropolis 'POLICE' Car .**£25-35**	
E19	80-82	Pink Panther Motorcycle...**£15-20**	
E20-2	79-81	Penguinmobile...................**£20-30**	
E21	79-80	Charlie's Angels Van **£15-20**	
E23	79-81	Batbike.............................**£100-125**	
E24	79-80	'SHAZAM' Thunderbolt ..**£40-50**	
E25	79-80	'Capt. America' Porsche ..**£40-50**	
E32	70-74	The Saint's Jaguar XJS **£65-85**	
E33	79-80	'Wonderwoman's Car **£30-40**	
E38	80-83	Jerry's Banger **£15-20**	
E40-2	79-81	J. Bond's Aston-Martin..**£125-150**	
E41	79-81	J. Bond Space Shuttle **£15-20**	
E44-2	79-80	Starship Liberator **£50-75**	
E45	77-81	Starsky and Hutch	
		Ford Gran Torino.............**£15-20**	
E49-2	81-83	Woody Woodpecker's Car.**£15-20**	
E50	79-80	'Daily Planet' (Leyland) Van,	
		Red or Silver **£15-20**	
E52-2	82-83	Scooby Doo's Vehicle.........**£20-25**	
E56	79-80	Chevrolet 'SPIDERVAN'..**£20-25**	
E57-2	79-80	Spiderbike **£20-25**	

E59-1	80-83	Tom's Cart......................**£15-20**
E60	77-79	James Bond Lotus Esprit
		1: with side & rear wings.**£100-125**
		2: without wings; some have
		'TURBO' side design...**£100-125**
E64	80-82	'The Professionals'
		Ford Capri **£15-20**
E67-2	80-83	Popeye's Tugboat...............**£15-20**
E68	77-79	Kojak's Buick Regal.........**£20-25**
E69	76-80	Batmobile **£100-125**
E72-2	79-83	Jaguar XJS, Blue or Red .....NGPP
		Jaguar XJS, Red with White
		'MOTOR SHOW' logo **£20-30**
E73	80	'DRAX' Helicopter **£20-25**
E75	77-80	Spidercopter **£20-30**
E78	76-81	Batcopter **£60-70**
E79-2	80-83	Olive Oyl's Aeroplane **£15-20**
E80	79-80	'MARVEL COMICS' Van .**£20-25**
E82-2	81-82	Yogi Bear's Jeep **£20-30**
E84-2	80-83	Bugs Bunny Vehicle............**£15-20**
99	79-81	Jokermobile.....................**£30-40**
100	81-83	Hulk Cycle **£30-40**
E115	81-83	James Bond 2cv Citroën **£40-50**
128	82-83	Fred's Flyer **£25-35**
131	82-83	Ferrari 308GTS,

		'Magnum PI'.....................**£25-35**
133	82-83	Buick Regal 'POLICE'
		Car, 'Magnum PI' **£25-35**
134	82-83	Barney's Buggy, Red/Orange,
		(The Flintstones') **£25-35**
E148	83-84	USS Enterprise **£15-20**
E149	83	Klingon Warship...............**£15-20**
E151	83	Wilma's Coupé..................**£25-35**
198	83	James Bond Citroën 2cv **£50-75**
E2009	?	James Bond 'Aerocar' ('The
		Man With the Golden Gun').
		NB: Not a licensed product..........**£200-300**

GERMAN ISSUES:

E119	83	'FLUGHAFEN-FEURWEHR'
		Fire Engine **£15-20**
120	?	Leyland Van, 'Eiszeit' **£15-20**
120	83	Ice Cream Van,
		'FRESHLICHE' **£15-20**
121	83	Chevrolet Van,
		'TECHNISCHER'...........**£15-20**
126	82-83	Ford Transit Breakdown,
		'ABSCHIEPPDIENST'.....**£15-20**
127	82-83	'ADAC' Car **£20-25**

Corgi Juniors Sets

2601	**Batman Triple-Pack** **£200-300**
E2001	**Multi Garage Complex.** 4-garage complex (plastic)...........**£30-35**
E3001	**Multi Garage and three cars** **£45-55**
E3005	**Leisure Time Set** **£100-125**
E3009	**Service Station and three cars** **£80-100**
E3013	**Emergency Rescue Set** (Rescue Station + 3 models)..........**£70-85**
E3109	**Agricultural Set.** Contains: 2 Tractors, Land-Rover,
	3 Trailers, 2 Huts...**£90-110**
3019/1	**James Bond 'Octopussy' Set**, 1983-84......................**£300-400**
E3021	**Crimefighters Gift Set** (E45, E60, E68, E69, E75, E78) .**£400-600**
E3023	**Mercedes Transporter plus 4 cars** **£75-100**
E3024	**Construction Gift Set** (6 vehicles).............................**£75-100**
E3026	**Emergency Gift Set** (6 vehicles)................................**£75-100**
E3030	**James Bond 'The Spy Who Loved Me' Gift Set**, 1976-77
	(E3, E60, 'Jaws' Van, Mercedes, Speedboat)..................**£300-400**
E3040	**Superman 'City of Metropil' Adventure Set** **£100-125**
E3071	**'Growlers' 6-Car Speed Set.** Ford GT70, Ferrari 312s,
	Marcos XP, CanAm Racer, Jaguar 'E'-type, Porsche 917 .**£100-150**

E3080	**Batman Gift Set**, 1980-82
	(E20, E23, E69, E78, E99) **£400-500**
E3081	**Superman Gift Set** (E6, E11, E17, E47, E50) **£125-150**
E3082	**James Bond 'Goldfinger' Gift Set**, 1980-82,
	(E40, E41, E60, E73, plus 'Jaws' van).............................**£400-500**
E3084	**Cartoon Characters Set** (E19, E38, E58, E67, E79) **£100-125**
E3100	**Construction Gift Set** (7 items) **£75-100**
E3101	**Fire Gift Set** (6 items) **£75-100**
E3103	**Emergency Gift Set** (6 items) **£75-100**
E3105	**Transporter Gift Set** (Mercedes Transporter + 4 cars)......**£75-100**
3107	**'Sports Cars'.** Five pieces in set....................................**£30-40**
E3108	**'Scoobie and His Friends' Set** Contains 5 items **£75-100**
E3114	**'Superheroes' Gift Set** (Batman / Superman vehicles)....**£100-125**
E3116	**'Crimefighters' Gift Set** (Starsky & Hutch,
	James Bond and Buck Rogers vehicles)............................**£125-150**
E3184	**'Data Post' Set** Contains 6 items **£40-50**

Corgi Super Juniors and Superhaulers

FORD D SERIES TRUCK (1970-75)

2002	Car Transporter, White cab,
	Blue lower, Red deck **£20-25**
	Red cab, White deck **£40-50**
2003	Low Loader, Blue...............**£20-25**
2004	'CORGI' Removals Van,
	Red cab, Silver trailer.......**£40-50**
	Light Blue cab..................**£40-50**
2007	Low Loader, Red cab,
	Blue trailer with Orange
	Junior digger load..............**£25-35**
2012	Low Loader, Military
	Green with US vehicle ....NGPP

FORD D SERIES SETS (1970-76)

3003	Car Transporter Set, White
	or Red cab, 5 Juniors........**£40-50**
3011	Low Loader Set, Red cab,
	plus 6 Juniors....................**£50-60**
3024	Low Loader Set, Blue cab,
	Yellow trailer (1976),
	6 Juniors **£50-60**
3025	Car Transporter Set, Yellow
	cab, Orange deck (1976),
	5 Juniors **£30-35**

MACK TRUCKS (issued 1971-75)

2006	'ESSO' Tanker, White **£10-15**
2010	'EXXON' Tanker, White..**£20-25**
2011	'US' Army Tanker,
	Military Green body.........**£20-25**
2027	'RYDER RENTALS',
	Yellow cab + box trailer....**£10-15**

MERCEDES TRACTOR UNITS, CAR TRANSPORTER (issued 1976)

2014/15	White cab and deck,
	Blue chassis....................**£20-25**
2015	White cab, Yellow deck,
	Red chassis.....................**£20-25**
N.B. Car Transporter Sets 3023,
	3015, 3105 ....**£30-35**

MERCEDES TANKERS (1983-84)

Market Price Range - as shown
otherwise **£10-15**. Liveries issued:

1130	'CORGI CHEMCO',
	Red or White cab ......
1130	'SHELL' Yellow or White cab......
1166	'GUINNESS' ....
1167	'DUCKHAMS'...........................
1167	'7 UP' **£20-25**

MERCEDES BOX TRAILERS (issued 1978-85)

Market Price Range as shown otherwise
£10-15. Liveries issued:

1111	'SAFEWAY'.....................**£15-20**
1129	'ASG SPEDITION' ....
1129	'CORGI' Black or White cab ......
1131	'CHRISTIAN SALVESON'.........
1137	'SOUKS SUPERMARKET'
	(Saudi issue)....................**£25-30**
1139	'HALLS FOOD' ....
1144	'ROYAL MAIL PARCELS' ....
1145	'YORKIE'..............................
1146	'DUNLOP' ....
1166	'ARIA DAIRY' ....
1175	'INTERNATIONAL'........**£70-80**
1175	'TI RALEIGH' ....
1176	'ZANUSSI' ....
1177	'WEETABIX' ....
1178	'MAYNARDS' ....
1202	'PICKFORDS HOMESPEED'
	....**£70-80**
2028	'GERVALS DANONE' ....
2020	'BIRDS EYE' ....
---	'B. H. S.' **£20-30**
---	'CARTERS Lemonade'.....**£25-35**

MERCEDES SETS

1200	'DUCKHAMS' & 'GUINNESS'
	Tanker plus 3 Scammells ..**£40-50**
1403	'CORGI CHEMCO',
	plus Junior Van **£25-30**
3128	'DUCKHAMS' & 'YORKIE',
	plus 10 Juniors **£40-50**

RECOMMENDED READING

'CORGI SUPER JUNIOR and SUPERHAULER GUIDE' provides full details plus pictures of all the variations compiled by Andy and Pat Browning, 3 Waterside Terrace, Ninn Lane, Great Chart, Ashford, Kent, TN23 3DD. Tel: (01233) 643461.

NB All the profits from this publication go to a children's charity.

Corgi Rockets

This model range was issued between 1970 and 1972 to compete against Mattel 'Hot Wheels' and similar products. The models had 'WhizzWheels' and featured a special 'Tune-Up' system which increased the play value and speed of the virtually frictionless wheels. In addition they were very robust, being advertised as 'four times stronger' than most other diecast racers. To begin with, seven Corgi Juniors were adapted as Rockets and five of those received a vacuum metallised finish. A range of accessories was also issued in the form of 'Speed Circuits' etc, and each car was provided with a special 'Golden Tune-Up Key' which released the base. The bubble-packed models are difficult to find in top condition and the prices reflect their scarcity.

Ref	Year	Model name and details	MPR
D 901	1970-72	**Aston-Martin DB-6**, Metallic Deep Gold body, Green interior	**£60-70**
D 902	1970-72	**Jaguar XJ-6**, Metallic Green, Cream interior	**£80-100**
D 903	1970-72	**Mercedes-Benz 280 SL**, Metallic Orange body, White interior	**£60-70**
D 904	1970-72	**Porsche Carrera 6**, Orange-Yellow body, Black number '19'	**£60-70**
D 905	1970-72	**'The Saint's Volvo P1800**, White body, Blue/White 'Saint' label on bonnet	**£80-100**
D 906	1970-72	**Jensen Interceptor**, Metallic Red, Yellow interior	**£60-70**
		Pink / Cream body	**£80-100**
D 907	1970-72	**Cadillac Eldorado**, Met. Copper, White interior	**£60-70**
D 908	1970-72	**Chevrolet Astro**, Metallic Red/Black body	**£40-50**
D 909	1970-72	**Mercedes-Benz C111**, Red or Blue, White interior	**£40-50**
D 910	1970-72	**Beach Buggy**, Orange body, Black interior	**£30-40**
D 911	1970-72	**Marcos XP**, Gold body, Chrome interior	**£30-40**
?	1970-72	**Ford Capri**, Purple body	**£40-50**
D 913	1970-72	**Aston-Martin DBS**, Metallic Blue, Yellow interior	**£70-90**
D 916	1970-72	**Carabo Bertone**, Met. Green/Blue, Orange interior	**£20-30**
D 917	1970-72	**Pininfarina Alfa-Romeo**, Metallic Purple/White	**£20-30**
D 918	1970-72	**Bitzzarini Manta**, Met. Dark Blue, White interior	**£20-30**
D 919	1970-72	**'Todd Sweeney' Stock Car**, Red/Purple, Yellow/Black front, RN '531'	**£100-125**
D 920	1970-72	**'Derek Fiske' Stock Car**, White/Red, Silver bonnet, Red logo, RN '304'	**£100-125**
D 921	1970-72	**Morgan Open Sports**, Met. Red body, Black seats	**£60-75**
D 922	1970-72	**Rally Ford Capri**, Yellow body, Orange/Black stripe, RN '8'	**£100-125**
		Green body, Black bonnet, (GS 2 model)	**£60-75**
D 923	1970-72	**'James Bond' Ford Escort**, White body, Pale Blue stripes, racing number '7', 'JAMES BOND', White '007' and 'SPECIAL AGENT' logos (From film 'On Her Majesty's Secret Service')	**£700-800**
D 924	1970-72	**Mercury Cougar XR7**, Red body with Black roof, Yellow interior	**£30-40**
		'James Bond' issue: Red/Black with Yellow side flash, interior and skis on roof rack (From film 'On Her Majesty's Secret Service')	**£700-800**
D 925	1970-72	**'James Bond' Ford Capri**, White body with Black/White check design, 2 bonnet stripes and RN '6'. (From film 'On Her Majesty's Secret Service')	**£700-800**
D 926	1970-72	**Jaguar 'Control Car'**, Metallic Brown body, Red roof blade, Blue/White figures	**£200-250**
D 927	1970-72	**Ford Escort Rally**, White body, Red RN '18', 'DAILY MIRROR' labels on doors, '1970 Mexico World Cup Rally Winner'	**£400-500**
D 928	1970-72	**Mercedes 280 SL 'SPECTRE'**, Black body with Red 'SPECTRE' logo, plus boars head design	**£300-400**
D 930	1970-72	**Bertone Barchetta**, Metallic Green over White body, Red interior	**£40-50**
D 931	1970-72	**'Old MacDonald's Truck'**, Yellow cab, Brown rear, Silver engine	**£75-100**
D 933	1970-72	**'Holmes Wrecker'**, White or Blue cab, White back, *'AUTO RESCUE'*	**£150-180**
D 937	1970-72	**Mercury Cougar**, Metallic Dark Green body, Yellow interior and spoiler	**£20-30**

Gift Sets

D 975	1970	**Super Stock Gift Set 1**, Contains D 905, D 919, Trailer and 3 figures	**£250-350**
D 976	1970	**Super Stock Gift Set 2**, Contains Green/Black D 922, D 920, Trailer, 3 figures	**£250-350**
D 977	1970	**Super Stock Gift Set 3**, Contains D 926, D 919, D 920 and 5 figures	**£300-400**
D 978		**'OHMSS' Gift Set**............, Models of cars in the James Bond film 'On Her Majesty's Secret Service': D 923 and D 925 (as driven in the ice-racing scene), D 924 (as driven by 'Tracey'), D 928 (as driven by the Chief of 'SPECTRE')	**£5,000-6,000**
	NB	Male skier has red metal base, red/yellow skis, yellow poles.	

Accessories (Introduced in 1970. All NGPP)

D 2051 Action Speedset, One car, 'Autostart', 12 ft of track ....
D 2052 Super Autobatics Speedset, One car, 'Autostart', 16 ft of track plus 'leaps' etc ....
D 2053 Clover Leaf Special Speedset, One car, 'Autostart', track plus 'clover-leaf leaps' etc............
D 2058 Race-Abatic Speedset, Two cars, 'Autostart', 2 x 16 ft of track plus 'leaps' etc ....
D 2071 Jetspeed Circuit, One car, 'Superbooster', 16 ft of track + 'leaps' etc
D 2074 Triple-Leap Speed Circuit, One car, 19 ft, 6 in of track....................
D 2075 Grand Canyon Speed Circuit, One car, 12 ft of track....................
D 2079 World Champion Speedset, Two cars, 2 x 16 ft of track, 2 Boosters..

D 1928	**Rocketlube Tune-up Kit** ..	**D 1963**	**Track** (16ft) ....
D 1931	**Superleap**	**D 1970**	**Super Booster** ....
D 1934	**Autofinish**	**D 1971**	**Hairpin Tunnel** ....
D 1935	**Connections** (3)................	**D 1976**	**Quickfire Start** ....
D 1936	**Space Leap**	**D 1977**	**Lap Counter** ....
D 1937	**Autostart**	**D 1978**	**Pitstop**...........................
D 1938	**Super Crossover**	**D 1979**	**Spacehanger Bend**...........
D 1945	**Adaptors** (3).....................		

Corgi Rockets Catalogues

1969	**8-page booklet** listing the first 7 issues, Green model on cover	**£20-25**
1970	**16-page booklet** most issues, good pictures of rare models, sets, accessories......	**£30-35**

Corgi Rockets
Stock Cars
and
Sports Cars

Photo:
Swapmeet Publications.

Catalogues (UK Editions)

Information taken from the Cecil Gibson Archives and this Catalogue compiler's own collection of reference material.
Note: 'Concertina' leaflets were issued with models sold in the early Blue boxes.

Year	Publication	Reference number and details	Market Price Range
1956	Concertina leaflet	No ref. Blue cover, famous Corgi dog, shows first 14 models, no prices	£20-25
1956	Concertina leaflet	No ref. Blue cover with Red/Gold Corgi dog. Depicts first 14 models; shows prices of both normal and mechanical models	£20-25
1957	Concertina leaflet	50/157/K1. Blue cover with Red/Gold Corgi dog. Depicts ten models and lists the mechanical models in red	£20-25
1957	Concertina leaflet	40/257/K1. Blue cover with Red/Gold Corgi dog. Depicts ten models but does not list mechanical models	£20-25
1957	Concertina leaflet	40/257/K2. As previous leaflet but with the addition of 208	£20-25
1957	Concertina leaflet	50/557/K3. As 40/257/K2 plus 100,150, 408, 454, 'WOW! CORGI TOYS' logo	£20-25
1957	Catalogue Leaflet	20/657/C2. Unfolded size (11" x 8 3/4"). Cover shows 1st type blue box for 208 Jaguar	£20-25
1957	Concertina leaflet	100/1057/K3. Blue cover showing 100, 150, 207, 208, 302, 405, 408, 453, 455	£20-25
1957	Concertina leaflet	50/1057/K4. Blue cover, 'WOW! CORGI TOYS' logo. Listings include models 102, 406/7, and first 'MAJOR' toy (1101)	£20-25
1957	Concertina leaflet	50/1157/K4. Cover shows 102, 210, 406, 407, 412, 1101, 'WOW! CORGI TOYS' logo	£20-25
1957	Four-fold leaflet	25/257/C1/UK. 'Blue box' 208 Jaguar on cover, 15 model pictures inside	£30-40
1957	Four-fold leaflet	25/257/C2/UK. As previous leaflet but with 24 model pictures	£30-40
1957	Four-fold leaflet	50/1057/C3/UK. Shows GS 1 Bedford Transporter and 6 cars on Blue/Yellow cover.	£30-40
1957	Four-fold leaflet	25/1157/C4/UK. As previous leaflet plus 101 and 102	£30-40
1958	Catalogue Leaflet	15/158/C4. Unfolded size (1' x 11"). 1101 Car Transporter on cover	£20-25
1958	Catalogue Leaflet	10/258/C5. Unfolded size (1' x 11"). 1101 Car Transporter on cover	£20-25
1958	Catalogue Leaflet	40/258/C5. Same as previous	£20-25
1958	Concertina leaflet	52/258/K5. Cover shows GS 1 and 2, 101, 211, 302, 457, 459, 1100, 1401, 1450	£20-25
1958	Box Insert	52/258/K5. 1401 Corgi Service Ramp on cover	£15-20
1958	Box Insert	52/258/K6. 350 'Thunderbird' Guided Missile on cover	£15-20
1958	Concertina leaflet	52/258/K6. Cover shows GS 1 and 2, 101, 211, 302, 457, 459, 1100, 1401, 1450, plus 350, 351	£20-25
1958	Concertina leaflet	300/658/K7. Shows GS 3, 151, 209, 458, 'NEW CORGI TOYS' logo and prices	£20-25
1958	Box Insert	3.350/658/K7. 1401 Corgi Service Ramp on cover	£15-20
1958	Four-fold leaflet	No ref. Shows GS 1 Bedford Transporter and 6 cars on Blue/Yellow cover, plus 211 No prices or car listing	£30-40
1958	Box Insert	5/658/K7. 458 E.R.F. Truck & 209 Police Car on cover	£15-20
1958	Catalogue	650/858/C8. First 'book' catalogue Cover depicts boy playing with Bloodhound Missile, many other vehicles	£40-50
1958	Box Insert	10/658/K7. 458 E.R.F. Truck & 209 Police Car on cover	£15-20
1958	16 page Catalogue	40/1058/C8. Boy and large collection on cover.	£20-25
1958	Box Insert	120/1058/K8. 458 E.R.F. Truck & 209 Police Car on cover	£15-20
1959	Four-fold leaflet	No ref. Blue cover with 'THE ROCKET AGE WITH CORGI TOYS' (issued with Rocket Age models)	£20-30
1959	Interim leaflet	No ref. September 1959. Lists 152, 50 Tractor, 350 Thunderbird, new Ford TT van and accessories	£20-30
1959	16 page Catalogue	UK 9/59. Cover features Massey Ferguson Tractor No. 50 and BRM No. 152. Agricultural and 'MAJOR' issues listed	£40-50
1959	20 page Catalogue	No ref. Racing Car and Tractor design on cover	£30-35
1959	Single page leaflet	No ref. Features Renault Floride plus 'STRAIGHT FROM THE MOTOR SHOW' logo	£20-30
1959	Two fold leaflet	No ref. Features 'AUTHENTIC ROCKET AGE MODELS' logo and models plus 1102 Tractor Dozer	£20-30
1960	Interim leaflet	No ref. Depicts M1 Motorway scene	£20-30
1960	20 page Catalogue	No reference number, otherwise as next item	£25-35
1960	20 page Catalogue	UK 9/60. Cover has motorway bridge scene and Corgi models. First listings of 'CHIPPERFIELDS' issues	£50-60
1960	Interim Leaflet	No ref. 1119 H.D.L. Hovercraft, etc. on cover	£20-25
1961	24 page Catalogue	No reference number, otherwise as next item	£40-50
1961	24 page Catalogue	UK 9/61. Racetrack scene on cover. Listings and pictures include new Sports Cars, Express Coach and Kits	£40-50
1961	Price List	No ref. Single double-sided sheet (size as catalogue), 'Revised price list as from August 1961'. 'UK' on back	£1-2
1961	Interim Leaflet	No ref. 231 Triumph Herald, etc. on cover	£20-25
1962	Two-fold Checklist	No ref. Front depicts Blue/Yellow 'CORGI TOYS' plus seven models. Red/Grey interior plus first check list	£20-30
1962	Interim Leaflet	No ref. 224 Bentley + 304s Mercedes on cover	£20-25
1963	32 page Catalogue	C/100/62. Cover depicts schoolboy (in red cap and blazer) crossing road with Corgi dog. No catalogue date shown on front	£50-60
1963	32 page Catalogue	No ref. Same cover as C/100/62 but boy's cap and blazer are Blue. '1963-64' is shown on front cover	£40-50
1963	40 page Catalogue	As previous item, but expanded to 40 pages	£40-50
1964	Interim Leaflet	Playcraft Toys Ltd 1964. 251 Hillman Imp, etc. on cover.	
1964	40 page Catalogue	Playcraft Toys Ltd 1964. Cover logos: 'CORGI TOYS', 'CORGI CLASSICS', '1965'. Classics / first Routemaster listed	£30-40
1964	Two-fold Checklist	Playcraft Toys Ltd 1964. Leaflet with Blue/Yellow 'Corgi Toys' design on cover featuring 241 Ghia	£25-35
1965	Interim Leaflet	Playcraft Toys Ltd 1965. 155 Lotus Climax Racing Car, etc.	£20-25
1965	40 page Catalogue	No reference number or text, otherwise as next item	£20-25
1965	40 page Catalogue	Playcraft Toys Ltd 1965. Cover shows model 261 James Bond's Aston Martin DB5. Rallye Monte Carlo issues. 'Price 3d'	£30-40
1965	Two-fold Checklist	Mettoy Playcraft (Sales) Ltd 1965. Leaflet with six model cars from six different nations featured on the cover	£20-25
1966	48 page Catalogue	C2017/9/66. Cover and contents feature 'BATMAN' and 'THE AVENGERS' etc. Includes price list. 190 x 78mm., '4d'	£30-40
1966	Leaflet	C2038/66. Cover proudly states 'MODEL CAR MAKERS TO JAMES BOND'	£20-25
1966	Four-fold Checklist	C2039/4/66. Leaflet similar to previous with 'MODEL CAR MAKERS TO JAMES BOND'. 1127 Simon Snorkel featured	£20-30
1967	Three-fold Checklist	Mettoy Playcraft (Sales) 1967. Front shows 'NEW' in 5 languages plus 1142 Holmes Wrecker	£20-30
1967	48 page Catalogue	C/2017/7/67. Lincoln Continental (262) on both covers. 'Price 6d'. Unissued 9022 Daimler and 9014 'Lyons Tea' shown	£30-40
1967	Interim Leaflet	No ref. 1142 'Holmes' Wrecker on cover	£20-25
1968	48 page Catalogue	C2017/9/68. Cover features 268 'Chitty Chitty Bang Bang'. 803 'Yellow Submarine' and 'Take-off Wheels' issues listed	£30-40
1969	Seven-fold Checklist	Mettoy Playcraft (Sales) Ltd 1969. Unfolded size 2'6" x 8 3/4". Leaflet has 'Concorde' model on cover plus 302 Hillman Hunter. Listings include 'Corgi Comics', 'CHIPPERFIELD' and Scammell Transporter Set No.48	£30-40
1970	48 page Catalogue	The Mettoy Co Ltd 1970. Cover depicts 388 Mercedes-Benz C111, first 'WhizzWheels' models listed	£30-40
1971	Two-fold Checklist	1970 Mettoy Co Ltd. Leaflet with 6 WhizzWheels models on the cover. The final 'Take-Off Wheels' issues are listed	£15-20

Corgi Toys UK Catalogues

Year	Catalogue	Description	Price
1972	48 page Catalogue	C2017 Petty 7/71/LOI7b. Cover shows 1972 Car models. Excellent 'CORGI COMICS' pictures inside	£20-25
1972	48 page Catalogue	C2017 Petty 7/71/LOI7B (2nd). Cars across both covers	£20-25
1972	4-page Brochure (A4)	'Corgi Juniors with WhizzWheels' No ref. Includes 'Juniors Extra' section of TV models	£10-15
1973	40 page Catalogue	1973 Mettoy Co Ltd. F1 Racing Cars featured on the cover. Good Racing/Rally pictures within	£10-15
1974	40 page Catalogue	C2107. 'Corgi '74' on cover	£10-15
1974	40 page Catalogue	C2111. 'Corgi '74' on cover	£10-15
1974	40 page Catalogue	1974 Mettoy Co Ltd. 'John Player' Lotus on cover, good Military and Aircraft pictures	£10-15
1975	Catalogue Leaflet	No ref. Unfolded size 2' x 8½". 'Corgi 75' on cover	£10-15
1975	Three-fold leaflet	1975 Mettoy Co Ltd. Helicopters, Noddy's Car, etc on the cover. Numbers given 'C' prefix	£10-15
1976	Three-fold leaflet	1976 Mettoy Co Ltd. First page features 'KOJAK'. Good Roadmaking and Public Services listings	£10-15
1977	48 page Catalogue	C2210. Silver Jubilee Coach on cover. Large section listing Corgi 'Juniors'	£10-15
1977	48 page Catalogue	C2211. 'Corgi 77' on cover	£10-15
1977	32 page Catalogue	C2222. 'Corgi 77' on cover	£10-15
1978	48 page Catalogue	The Mettoy Co Ltd. James Bond's Lotus on cover, 'JEAN RICHARD PINDER' models within	£10-15
1979	48 page Catalogue	C2250. James Bond's Space Shuttle C649 'MOONRAKER' on the cover. 'SUPERMAN' + 'THE MUPPETS' listed inside	£10-15
1980	48 page Catalogue	C2270. Rover 3500 'POLICE' C339 and C1001 HCB ANGUS on cover. Foreign 'POLICE' issues listed	£10-15
1980	48 page Catalogue	C2275. Fire 'RESCUE' Vehicle plus '1980/81' on cover	£10-15
1980	32 page Catalogue	C2282. As previous, but no Juniors included	£10-15
1980	32 page Catalogue	C2283. Same as previous	£10-15
1981	32 page Catalogue	C2285. 'CORGI' container on cover. Listings feature Film/TV models	£10-15
1981	32 page Catalogue	C2290. 'Corgi' Container on cover	£10-15
1981	32 page Catalogue	C2292. 'Corgi' Container on cover	£10-15
1982	32 page Catalogue	C2337. Cover features 'Gull-wing' Mercedes (C802), 'Corgitronics' within	£10-15
1983	36 page Catalogue	Mettoy Co PLC. Boxed models on cover, new Mercedes and Scania trucks inside	£10-15
1984	32 page Catalogue	No ref. 'CORGI '84' + boxed models on cover. '800' series cars listed. The last catalogue to display the Corgi Dog emblem	£5-10
1985	48 page Catalogue	No ref. Cover shows new 'CORGI' trade name logo. The new 'CLASSICS' Commercials range is listed	£5-10

Trade Catalogues

Catalogues for trade purposes have been produced for some years and occasionally are offered for sale to collectors. No information is available on catalogues issued before 1980 but those from the 1980-90 decade tend to be in the £5 to £15 range.

Newsletters and Club Magazines

Mettoy Corgi Newsletters	£5-6
Corgi Club Magazines	
1950s	£20-25
1960s	£15-18

An imaginative illustration features on the cover of this 1966 Corgi catalogue.   Photo: Swapmeet Publications.

IDENTIFICATION of OVERSEAS CATALOGUES

The overseas editions are comprised of specially amended U.K. editions and there are many versions. They may be identified by:

- All the text being in the relevant language.
- A special reference number (but not always) e.g. 52/258/K5 AUSTRALIA.
- An adapted checklist/pricelist in the language/currency of the country concerned.
- The name of the country either on the cover, on page two, or on the checklist.
- Some complete catalogues were issued with all the text being in the language concerned, e.g. French, German, etc.
- Normally overseas editions, unlike U.K. editions, do not display the catalogue price on the cover. The exception to this rule being those issued with all the text in the language concerned.

As stated above, the overseas editions are basically the same as the U.K. editions. Similarly the catalogues, leaflets and box inserts issued in any one particular year were the same for all overseas countries. The only differences being the reference numbers, the type of language and currency shown.

The following listing of overseas editions correspond with the country by country listings and will assist collectors identify the various editions. The reference codes shown, e.g. '52/258/K5' are common to all countries with a country reference being added as required, e.g. '52/258/K5 EAST AFRICA'. The '258' part refers to the month and year of issue, i.e. Feb. 1958.

TYPES of CATALOGUES LISTED

Box Inserts - These were inserted in the early blue box issues circa 1957-1959. They have a single fold and contain a checklist with prices in the local currency, plus a few pictures of the latest models.
Catalogue Leaflets - These are large, full colour leaflets, usually listing the full range available, together with pictures plus a checklist with prices.
Catalogues - These may contain 16, 20, 32, 40 or 48 pages and are full colour booklets containing the complete current range.
Interim Leaflets - Usually a double folded leaflet issued to supplement the main catalogues. These contain six pages, plus a checklist of the latest issues.

The information contained in these listings has been obtained from Corgi archive material. Whilst many issues have been listed, we believe others exist and we would welcome any such information.

Overseas catalogues were produced in much smaller numbers than were the U.K. editions. Consequently as they seldom appear for sale, it is not possible to give their individual market prices. For guidance purposes however, some have been known to sell for prices in excess of **£100**. As a result the extremely rare issues such as British East Africa, West Africa, Malta, Hong Kong, etc. may be expected to attract a premium.

African issues

English text - local currency

BRITISH EAST AFRICA
1959 **16 page Catalogue '8/59'**. 'British East Africa 8/59' on cover, along
 with a tractor and racing car **£80-100**
1960 **20 page Catalogue '9/60'**. 'British East Africa 9/60' on cover **£60-80**
1962/63 **Interim Leaflet** (no ref.). 'British East Africa' on checklist.............**£25-35**
1961/62 **Interim Leaflet** (no ref.). 'British East Africa' on top of page two...**£25-35**

EAST AFRICA
1958 **Box Insert '52/258/K5 East Africa'**. 'East Africa' on checklist............**£25-35**
1965 **Interim Leaflet** (no ref.). 'East Africa' + 'Mettoy 1965' on checklist ...**£20-25**
1964/65 **40 page Catalogue** (no ref.). 'East Africa 8/64' on checklist **£35-45**

KENYA, UGANDA & TANGANYIKA
1958 **Catalogue Leaflet '15/158/C3 KUT'**.
 'Kenya, Uganda and Tanganyika'......................................**£30-35**
1958 **Box Insert '3.350/658/K7/KEN.-UG-TAN'** **£30-35**

RHODESIA
Early Distributors: Coombe & Dewar Pty Ltd. P.O. Box 1572,
Bulawayo and P.O. Box 663, Salisbury.
1961/2 **Interim Leaflet** (no ref.). 'Rhodesia' top of page two......................**£25-35**
1962/3 **Interim Leaflet** (no ref.). 'Rhodesia' on checklist..............................**£25-35**
1962 **32 page Catalogue 'C/100/62'**.
 'Rhodesia 1/63' on checklist. Red suited boy on cover....................**£60-80**
1964 **Interim Leaflet** (no ref.). 'Rhodesia' + 'Playcraft 1964' on checklist...**£20-30**
1965 **Interim Leaflet** (no ref.). 'Rhodesia' + 'Mettoy 1965' on checklist **£20-30**

RHODESIA, ZAMBIA & MALAWI
1965/66 **40 page Catalogue** (no ref.).
 'Rhodesia/Zambia/Malawi 8/65' on checklist, + '1965' on cover **£50-60**

SOUTH AFRICA & RHODESIA
1958 **Box Insert '52/258/K5 South Africa/Rhodesia'**.
 'South Africa/Rhodesia' on checklist..**£25-35**
1958 **Box Insert '52/258/K6 South Africa/Rhodesia'**.
 'South Africa/Rhodesia' on checklist..**£25-35**

SOUTH AFRICA
1958 **Box Insert '10/658/K7/S. Africa'**. 'S. Africa' on checklist page **£25-35**
1958/59 **16 page Catalogue '40/1058/C8/S. Africa'**. 'S. Africa' on back **£60-80**
1961/62 **Interim Leaflet** (no ref.). 'South Africa on page two.....................**£25-35**
1962/63 **Interim Leaflet** (no ref.). 'South Africa' on checklist **£25-35**
1964 **Interim Leaflet** (no ref.). 'S. Africa' and
 'Playcraft Toys Ltd. 1964' on checklist **£25-35**
1965 **Interim Leaflet** (no ref.). 'South Africa' + 'Mettoy 1965' on checklist.**£25-35**
1966 **48 page Catalogue 'C/2017/9/66'**.
 'South Africa' on checklist and cover...**£40-50**
1967 **Interim Leaflet** (no ref.). 'South Africa' on cover, plus
 'Mettoy, etc. 1967' on last page **£25-35**
1971 **2-fold checklist '© 1970 Mettoy Co Ltd'**. 'Corgi Toys with
 WhizzWheels' plus 'Australia', 'S.Africa' and 'USA' on cover.
 Checklist has prices in all three currencies.....................................**£15-20**
NB As listed under CANADA, a catalogue was issued in 1970 with a combined CANADA and SOUTH AFRICAN checklist.

Australia

Address of Corgi Club in 1959: The Secretary, Corgi Model Club (Australian Section), P.O. Box 1607, M. Melbourne C1.
1957 **Catalogue Leaflet '20/657/C2/AUS'**. Checklist dated 1.6.57.
 Cover shows early 'Blue Box' with model 208 ....**£25-35**
1958 **Box Insert '52/258/K5/Australia'**. Cover shows Model 350 ....**£25-35**
1958 **Box Insert '52/258/K6/Australia'**. 1401 Service Ramp on cover...**£25-35**
1958 **Box Insert '10/658/K7/Aus'**. Cover shows Models 209 & 458 .....**£25-35**
1959 **16 page Catalogue** (no ref.). Australia 8/59 on cover **£80-100**
1961/62 **Leaflet** (no ref.). 'Australia' on top of page two.........................**£25-35**
1962/63 **Leaflet** (no ref.). 'Australia' on checklist....................................**£25-35**
1967 **Leaflet** (no ref.). 'Australia' on cover **£20-25**
1971 **2-fold Checklist '© 1970 Mettoy Co Ltd'**. 'Corgi Toys with
 WhizzWheels' plus 'Australia', 'S.Africa' and 'USA' on cover.
 Checklist has prices in all three currencies **£10-15**

Austria

German Text. 'Kontrolliste fur den sammler'
1957 **Leaflet '20/657/C2/A'**. 'Austria' on checklist **£30-35**
1961/62 **Interim Leaflet** (no ref.). 'Austria' on top of page two **£20-25**
1964 **Interim Leaflet** (no ref.). 'Austria' on checklist **£20-25**
1964/65 **40 page Catalogue** (no ref.). 'Austria 9/64' on checklist.................**£35-45**
1965 **Interim Leaflet** (no ref.). 'Austria' on checklist **£20-25**

Belgium

Early distribution:
Joets Eisenmann, S.A., 111/113 Rui Masui, Bruxelles, Teleph: (02) 15.48.50.
1958 Belgian Corgi Club: M. Le Secretaire du Club Corgi, Jouets Eisenmann, 20 BD M. Lemonnier, Bruxelles.

English Text - (French Checklist). 'Liste de Contrôlle pour le Collectionneur'
1958 **Box Insert '52/258/K6/Belgium'**. 'Belgium' on checklist..............£30-35
1958 **Box Insert '5/658/K7/Belg.'**. 'Belg' on checklist.....................£30-35
1967 **Leaflet** (no ref.). 'Belgium' on cover £20-25

English Text (Flemish Checklist). 'Kontroleer zo de Verzameling'
1966 **48 page Catalogue 'C/2017/9/66'**.
    'Belgium' on cover and on checklist......................£35-45
1967 **Leaflet** (no ref.). Belgium (Flemish) on cover £20-25

English Text (separate French and Flemish checklists)
1961/62 **Interim Leaflet** (no ref.). 'Belgium' on top of page two...........£20-25
1962/63 **Interim Leaflet** (no ref.). 'Belgium' on checklist.....................£20-25
1963/64 **40 page Catalogue** (no ref.). 'Belgium 8/63' on checklist £40-50
1964 **Interim Leaflet** (no ref.). 'Belgium' and 'Playcraft 1964'
    on checklist £20-25

1965 **Interim Leaflet** (no ref.). 'Belgium' and 'Mettoy 1965' on checklist£20-25
1967 **Leaflet** (no ref.). 'Belgium' on cover...................................
1967/68 **48 page Catalogue 'C/2017/7/67'**. 'Belgium (French) 1967' on
    checklist £35-45
1967/68 **48 page Catalogue 'C2017/7/67'**. 'Belgium 8/67' on Flemish
    checklist and 'Belgium (French) 8/67' on French checklist £35-45

1974 **40 page Catalogue** (no ref.). 'C2103 Belgium' on Flemish checklist
    plus '2107' on French checklist £15-25

English Text (French/Flemish combined checklist)
1957 **Catalogue Leaflet '20/657/C2/B'**. 'Belgium' on checklist £25-35
1958 **Catalogue Leaflet '20/258/C5/B'**. 'Belgium' on checklist £25-35

French Text - French checklist
1958 **Box Insert '120/1058/K8/Belg'**. No. 458 E.R.F. on cover..............£25-35
1960 **20 page Catalogue** (no ref.). 'Belgium 9/60' and
    'Frs.3.' - on cover...£40-50
1961 **24 page Catalogue** (no ref.). 'Belgium 9/61'
    and 'Frs.3.' - on cover...£40-50
1965/66 **40 page Catalogue** (no ref.). 'Belgium 8/65' on checklist £30-40

Canada

English text - local currency
1958 **Catalogue Leaflet '40/258/C5/CA'**. 'Canada' on checklist.............£30-35
1958 **Box Insert '52/258/K5/Canada'**. 'Canada' on checklist.................£30-35
1958 **Box Insert '52/258/K6/Canada'**. 'Canada' on checklist.................£30-35
1958 **Box Insert '5/658/K7/CAN'**. 'CAN' on checklist £30-35

1960 **20 page Catalogue 'Canada 9/60'**. 'Canada 9/60' on cover............£50-60
1960/61 **Interim Leaflet 'Canada'**. 'Canada' on checklist £30-35
1961/62 **24 page Catalogue 'Canada 9/61'**. 'Canada 9/61' on cover.........£60-70
1961/62 **Interim Leaflet 'Canada'**. 'Canada' on checklist £30-35
1963 **32 page Catalogue 'C/100/62'**. 'Canada 1/63' on checklist.............£50-60
1964 **Interim Leaflet 'Canada'**.
    'Canada' and 'Playcraft Toys Ltd. 1964' on checklist £30-35

1965 **Interim Leaflet 'Canada'**. 'Canada' and
    'Mettoy etc. 1965' on checklist £30-35
1964/65 **40 page Catalogue 'Canada 9/64'**.
    'Canada 9/64' on checklist plus '1965' on cover...............£50-70
1965/66 **40 page Catalogue 'Canada 8/65'**.
    'Canada 8/65' on checklist plus '1966' on cover...............£50-70
1966 **48 page Catalogue 'C2017/9/60'**. 'Canada' on cover and checklist £50-70
1967 **Interim Leaflet 'Canada'**.
    'Canada' on cover plus 'Mettoy 1967' on last page £25-35
1969 **7-fold Leaflet 'Canada'**. Concorde featured on cover;
    '8/69' on checklist £60-70

French Text Issue
1966 **48 page Catalogue 'C/2017/9/66'**. 'Canadian (French)' on cover £60-70

Combined Canadian and South African checklist
1970 **48 page Catalogue** (no ref.). 'Canada, South Africa' on checklist.
    'The Mettoy Co. Ltd. 1970' on rear cover £60-70

Denmark

All the text in Danish
1960 **20 page Catalogue** (no ref.). 'Denmark 9/60' and '25 re' on cover £50-60
1961/62 **24 page Catalogue** (no ref.). 'Denmark 9/61' and '25 re' on cover ..£50-60
1977 **48 page Catalogue 'C2214'**. 'Katalog' and 'Corgi '77' on cover.........£10-15

English text - Danish checklist. 'Samlerers Kontrolliste'
1960/61 **Interim Leaflet** (no ref.). 'Denmark' on checklist...........................£20-25
1961/62 **Interim Leaflet** (no ref.). 'Denmark' on page two £20-25
1963/64 **40 page Catalogue** (no ref.).
    'Denmark 8/63' on checklist plus '1963-64' on cover £60-80
1964 **Interim Leaflet** (no ref.). 'Denmark' & 'Playcraft 1964' on checklist...£20-25
1964/65 **40 page Catalogue** (no ref.).
    'Denmark 9/64' on checklist plus 1965 on cover......................£50-60
1965/66 **40 page Catalogue** (no ref.).
    'Denmark 8/65' on checklist plus 1966 on cover......................£40-50
1966 **48 page Catalogue 'C2017/9/66'**. 'Denmark' on cover and checklist..£30-40

1974 **40 page Catalogue 'C2105 1974'**.
    Danish checklist + 'Corgi '74' on cover...........................£10-15
1980/81 **48 page Catalogue 'C2271'**. Danish checklist + 1980/81 on cover .£10-15
1981/82 **30 page Catalogue 'C2292'**. Danish checklist + 1981-82 on cover .£10-15

Eire

1958 **Box Insert '52/258/K6/EIRE'**. 'Eire' on checklist....................£20-25
1958 **Box Insert '5/658/K7/EIRE'**. 'Eire' on checklist....................£20-25
1960/61 **Interim Leaflet** (no ref.). 'Eire' on checklist £20-25
1962/63 **Interim Leaflet** (no ref.). 'Eire' on checklist £15-20
1964/65 **Interim Leaflet** (no ref.). 'Eire' plus 'Playcraft 1964' on checklist ..£15-20

Finland

English Text - local currency
1963/64 **40 page Catalogue** (no ref.).
    'Finland 8/63' on checklist plus '1963-64' on cover £30-40
1965 **Interim Leaflet** (no ref.). 'Finland 6/65' & 'Mettoy 1965' on checklist .£15-20

France

English Text - French checklist
1961/62 **Interim Leaflet** (no ref.). 'France' on page two £30-40
1962/63 **Interim Leaflet** (no ref.). 'France' on checklist £30-40
1963/64 **40 page Catalogue** (no ref.).
    'France 8/63' on checklist plus 1963-64 on cover £80-100
1964/65 **Interim Leaflet** (no ref.). 'France' & 'Playcraft 1964' on checklist ..£30-40
1965 **Interim Leaflet** (no ref.). 'France' and 'Mettoy 1965' on checklist £30-40

French Text and checklist   'Liste de Controle pour le Collecteneur'.
1965 **40 page Catalogue** (no ref.). 'France 8/65' on checklist plus
    'Playcraft Toys Ltd. 1965' on rear cover......................£60-70
1968 **48 page Catalogue 'C2017/8/67'**. French text - 1968 on cover £40-50
1969 **48 page Catalogue 'C2017/9/68'**. French text - 1969 on cover £30-40
1973 **40 page Catalogue** (no ref.). French text - 1973 on cover..................£20-30
1974 **40 page Catalogue 'C2107 1974'**. French text - 1974 on cover £20-30
1975 **Catalogue Leaflet** (no ref.). French text - 'Corgi '75' on cover £10-15
1977 **16 page Catalogue 'C2222'**. French text plus 'Corgi '77' on cover £20-30

1980/81 **48 page Catalogue 'C2275'**.
    French text plus 1980/81 on cover (includes Juniors) £25-35
1980/81 **32 page Catalogue 'C2282'**. French text plus 1980/81 on cover......£20-30
1981/82 **32 page Catalogue 'C2290'**.
    French text plus '1981 Mettoy' on rear cover...................................£20-30

Holland / Netherlands

Agent for Holland: N.V.S/O, Herengracht 25, Amsterdam.

Dutch Text throughout
1959 **20 page Catalogue** (no ref.).
'Holland 8/59' plus 'FL.O.10' on cover plus Dutch text **£80-100**
1961 **24 page Catalogue** (no ref.).
'Holland 9/61' plus 'F.O.10' on cover plus Dutch text **£60-80**

French Text - Dutch checklist. 'Kontroleer zo de Verzameling'.
1980/81 **48 page Catalogue 'C2281'.**
French text, Dutch checklist, plus '1980 Mettoy' on rear cover........**£20-30**
1981/82 **30 page Catalogue 'C2291'.**
French text, Dutch checklist, plus '1981 Mettoy' on rear cover........**£20-30**

English Text with French and Dutch checklists
1974 **40 page Catalogue** (no ref.). 'C2107 1974' on French checklist.
'C2103 1974' on Dutch checklist **£20-30**

English text - Dutch checklist
1957 **Catalogue Leaflet '20/657C2/NL'.** 'Holland' on checklist **£20-30**
1958 **Catalogue Leaflet '15/158/C4/H'.** 'Holland' on checklist **£25-30**
1958 **Box Insert '52/258/K5/HOLLAND'.** 'Holland' on checklist **£25-30**
1958 **Box Insert '52/258/K6/HOLLAND'.** 'Holland' on checklist **£25-30**
1958 **Box Insert '5/658/K7/HOL.'.** 'HOL' on checklist **£25-30**
1960/61 **Interim Leaflet** (no ref.). 'Holland' on checklist **£25-30**
1961/62 **Interim Leaflet** (no ref.). 'Holland' top of page two **£25-30**
1962/63 **Interim Leaflet** (no ref.). 'Holland' on checklist **£25-30**
1963/64 **40 page Catalogue** (no ref.). 'Holland 8/63' on checklist................**£60-80**
1964 **Interim Leaflet** (no ref.). 'Holland' on checklist **£25-30**
1964/65 **40 page Catalogue** (no ref.). 'Holland 9/64' on checklist...............**£25-30**
1965 **Interim Leaflet** (no ref.). 'Holland' on checklist **£25-30**
1966 **48 page Catalogue 'C2017/9/66'.** 'Holland' on cover and checklist....**£50-60**
1967 **Interim Leaflet** (no ref.). 'Holland' on cover..................................**£20-25**
1967/68 **48 page Catalogue 'C2017/7/67'.** 'Holland 8/67' on checklist **£50-60**
1969 **48 page Catalogue 'C2017/9/68'.** 'Holland 10/68' on checklist **£30-40**
1974 **40 page Catalogue 'C2211 1974'.** Dutch text in checklist..................**£20-25**
1974 **40 page Catalogue** (no ref.).
C2107 on French checklist plus C2103 on Dutch checklist **£20-25**

Hong Kong

1961 **Catalogue** (no ref.). 24 pages, 'Hong Kong 9/61' on cover.................**£80-100**
1961/62 **Interim Leaflet** (no ref.). 'Hong Kong' on page two....................**£20-25**
1963 **Catalogue 'C/100/62'.** 24 pages, 'Hong Kong 3/63' on checklist.........**£60-80**
1963 **Interim Leaflet** (no ref.). 'Hong Kong' on checklist **£20-25**
1964 **Interim Leaflet** (no ref.). 'Hong Kong' on checklist **£20-25**
1965/66 **40 pages** (no ref.). 'Hong Kong 8/65' on checklist......................**£60-80**
1966 **Catalogue 'C2017/9/66'.** 48 pages, 'Hong Kong' on
cover and checklist **£60-80**

Italy

1963 Concessionairia per l'Italia: Ditta 'Guimar' via Disciplini 7, Milano (303). 'Distinta di Controllo per l'Collezzionisti'.
1958 **Box Insert '52/258/K5 ITALY'.** 'Italy' on checklist............................**£25-35**
1958 **Box Insert '52/258/K6 ITALY'.** 'Italy' on checklist............................**£25-35**
1958 **Box Insert '5/658/K7 ITALY'.** 'Italy' on checklist.............................**£25-35**
1959 **Catalogue** (no ref.). 20 pages, 'Italy 8/59' on cover **£50-75**
1960/61 **Interim Leaflet** (no ref.). 'Italy' on checklist **£20-25**
1961 **Catalogue** (no ref.). 24 pages, 'Italy 9/61' on cover **£40-50**
1961/62 **Interim Leaflet** (no ref.). 'Italy' on page two **£20-25**
1962/63 **Interim Leaflet** (no ref.). 'Italy' on checklist **£20-25**
1963/64 **Catalogue** (no ref.). 40 pages, 'Italy 8/63' on checklist................**£80-100**
1964 **Interim Leaflet** (no ref.). 'Italy' on checklist **£20-25**
1964/65 **Catalogue** (no ref.). 40 pages, 'Italy 9/64' on checklist.................**£40-50**
1965 **Interim Leaflet** (no ref.). 'Italy' on checklist **£20-25**
1967 **Interim Leaflet** (no ref.). 'Italy' on cover.
'ATTENDETE OGNIMESE LE NOVITA 'CORGI'.....................**£20-25**

1974 concessionaria per l'Italia:
Toyuro s.n.c., Via S. Vittore 45, Milano (20123).
1974 **Catalogue 'C2112 1974'.** 40 pages, 'Italia' reference on checklist.......**£15-20**
1980/81 **Catalogue 'C2278'.** 48 pages, Italian text throughout..................**£10-15**
1981/82 **Catalogue 'C2293'.** 32 pages, Italian text throughout..................**£10-15**

Japan

1968 **Folded Leaflet** **£50-60**
1973 **Catalogue** (no ref.). 40 pages, Japanese text throughout **£30-40**

Malta

1964 **Leaflet** (no ref.). 'Malta' on checklist...**£25-35**
1964/65 **Catalogue** (no ref.). 40 pages, 'Malta 8/64' on checklist.................**£60-70**
1965 **Leaflet** (no ref.). 'Malta' in checklist...**£25-35**

New Zealand

1964/65 **Catalogue** (no ref.). 40 pages, 'New Zealand 8/64' on checklist......**£60-70**
1965 **Leaflet** (no ref.). 'New Zealand' on checklist...................................**£25-30**
1965/66 **Catalogue** (no ref.). 40 pages, 'New Zealand 8/65' on checklist......**£50-60**

Norway

'Se dem alle 1 den nye Katalogen, Samlers Liste'.
English Text - Norwegian checklist
1961/62 **Leaflet** (no ref.). 'Norway' on page two......................................**£25-35**
1962/63 **Leaflet** (no ref.). 'Norway' on checklist.......................................**£25-35**
1964 **Leaflet** (no ref.). 'Norway' on checklist...**£20-25**
1964/65 **Catalogue** (no ref.). 40 pages, 'Norway 9/64' on checklist.............**£30-40**
1965 **Leaflet** (no ref.). 'Norway' on checklist...**£20-25**
1966 **Catalogue** (no ref.). 40 pages, 'Norway 8/65' on checklist.................**£30-40**
1966 **Catalogue 'C2017/9/66'.** 48 pages, 'Norway' on cover and checklist....**£35-45**
1967/68 **Catalogue 'C2017/7/67'.** 48 pages, 'Norway 8/67' on checklist......**£35-45**
1970 **Catalogue** (no ref.). 48 pages, 'Norway' on checklist.......................**£25-30**
1974 **Catalogue 'C2113'.** 40 pages, Norwegian checklist...........................**£15-20**
1980/81 **Catalogue 'C2272'.** 48 pages, Norwegian checklist **£10-15**
Norwegian text throughout
1975 **Catalogue Leaflet** (no ref.). Text plus '1975 Mettoy'.......................**£10-15**

Portugal

'Lista de controle para o colecionador'.
English Text - Portuguese checklist.
1957 **Catalogue Leaflet '25/257/C2/P'.** 'Portugal' on checklist **£25-35**
1960 **Leaflet** (no ref.). 'Portugal' on checklist..**£20-25**
1961/62 **Leaflet** (no ref.). 'Portugal' on page two.....................................**£20-25**
1962/63 **Leaflet** (no ref.). 'Portugal' on checklist......................................**£20-25**
1963/64 **Catalogue** (no ref.). 40 pages, 'Portugal 8/63' on checklist............**£35-45**
1964 **Leaflet** (no ref.). 'Portugal' on checklist..**£20-25**
1967/68 **Catalogue 'C2017/7/67'.** 48 pages, 'Portugal 8/67' on checklist **£35-45**

Singapore and Malaya

1958 **Box Insert '52/258/K5 SINGAPORE/MALAYA',**
'Singapore/Malaya' on checklist **£25-35**
1958 **Catalogue Leaflet '10/258/C5/SM'.** 'Singapore/Malaya' on checklist ..**£25-35**
1958 **Box Insert '3.350/658/K7 SING-MAL'.** 'Sing.-Mal' on checklist **£25-35**
1960 **Catalogue** (no ref.). 20 pages, 'Singapore Malaya 9/60' on cover......**£80-100**
1960 **Leaflet** (no ref.). 'Singapore/Malaya' on checklist **£25-30**
1961 **Catalogue** (no ref.). 24 pages, 'Singapore/Malaya 9/61' on checklist ..**£70-90**
1962/63 **Leaflet** (no ref.). 'Singapore/Malaya' on checklist **£25-30**
1962/63 **Catalogue 'C/100/62'.** 32 pages, 'Singapore/Malaya 2/63'
on checklist **£60-80**
1965 **Leaflet** (no ref.). 'Singapore/Malaya' on checklist **£20-25**

Spain

Spanish Text and checklist. 'Lista de Coleccionistas'.
1961 **Checklist.** 24 pages, 'Spanish 9/61' on cover **£30-40**

English Text - Spanish checklist "Lista de Precios para Coleccionistas"
1962 **Checklist 'C/100/62'.** 'Spanish' on checklist **£25-30**
1980/81 **Checklist 'C2273'.** Spanish text in checklist..................................**£10-15**

Sweden

'Kontrollista för Samlaren'.
English text - Swedish checklist
1958 **Box Insert '52/258/K5/SWEDEN'**. 'Sweden' on checklist £25-35
1958 **Box Insert '52/258/K6/SWEDEN'**. 'Sweden' on checklist £25-35
1958 **Box Insert '5/658/K7/SWEDEN'**. 'Sweden' on checklist £25-35
1959 **Catalogue** (no ref.). 16 pages, 'Sweden 8/59' on cover £40-50
1960/61 **Leaflet** (no ref.). 'Sweden' on checklist £20-25
1961 **Catalogue** (no ref.). 24 pages, 'Sweden 9/61' on cover £40-50
1961/62 **Leaflet** (no ref.). 'Sweden' on page two £20-25
1962/63 **Leaflet** (no ref.). 'Sweden' on checklist £20-25
1963/64 **Catalogue** (no ref.). 40 pages, 'Sweden 8/63' on checklist...............£60-80
1964/65 **Catalogue** (no ref.). 40 pages, 'Sweden 9/64' on checklist.............£50-60
1965 **Leaflet** (no ref.). 'Sweden' on checklist £20-25
1966 **Catalogue** (no ref.). 40 pages, 'Sweden 6/65' on checklist £35-45
1966 **Catalogue 'C2017/9/66'**. 40 pages, 'Sweden' on cover and checklist ...£35-45
1967 **Leaflet** (no ref.). 'Sweden' on cover..£20-25
1974 **Catalogue 'C2106 1974'**. 40 pages, Swedish text on checklist............£15-20
1975 **Leaflet** (no ref.). Swedish text throughout......................................£10-15
1980/81 **Catalogue 'C2277'**. 48 pages, Swedish text throughout.................£10-15

Swedish text - Norwegian checklist
1981/82 **Catalogue 'C2287'**. 32 pp, Swedish text + Norwegian checklist......£10-15

Switzerland

English Text - English/Swiss checklist
1957 **Catalogue Leaflet '20/657/C2/CH'**. 'Switzerland' on checklist £80-100
1958 **Box Insert '52/258/K5/Switzerland'**. Reference on checklist £25-35
1958 **Box Insert '52/258/K6/Switzerland'**. Reference on checklist £25-35
1958 **Box Insert '5/658/K7/SWITZ'**. Reference on checklist £25-35
1958 **Catalogue '25/1058/C8/SWITZ'**.
    16 pages, 'Switz' on checklist. New issues in French £80-100
1958 **Catalogue Leaflet '5/658/C5/CH'**. 'Switzerland' on checklist £25-35
1960/61 **Leaflet** (no ref.). 'Switzerland' on checklist £25-30
1961 **Catalogue** (no ref.). 24 pages, 'Switzerland 9/61' on cover..................£40-50
1961/62 **Leaflet** (no ref.). 'Switzerland' on page two £20-25
1962/63 **Catalogue 'C100/62'**. 32 pages, 'Switzerland 1/63' on checklist....£40-50
1962/63 **Leaflet** (no ref.). 'Switzerland' on checklist £20-25
1964 **Leaflet** (no ref.). 'Switzerland' on checklist £20-25
1964/65 **Catalogue** (no ref.). 40 pages, 'Switzerland' on checklist £25-35
1965 **Leaflet** (no ref.). 'Switzerland' on checklist £20-25
1966 **Catalogue** (no ref.). 40 pages, 'Switzerland 8/65' on checklist £30-40
1966 **Catalogue 'C/2017/9/66'**. 48 pages, 'Switzerland' on
    cover and checklist £30-40
1967 **Leaflet** (no ref.). 'Switzerland' on cover.......................................£20-25
1969 **Catalogue 'C2017/9/68'**. 48 pages, 'Switzerland 10/68' on checklist...£30-40

United States of America

1958 Sole Distributor for U.S.A.: Reeves International Incorp., 1107 Broadway, New York 10, N.Y.
1958 **Catalogue Leaflet '20/458/C5/U.S.A.'**. 'U.S.A.' on checklist £30-40
1958 **Box Insert '20/658/K7/U.S.A.'**. 'U.S.A.' on checklist...........................£30-40
1959 **Catalogue 'USA 8/59'**. 16 pages, pictures of tractor and
    racing car on cover £80-100
1961 **Catalogue 'USA 9/61'**. 24 pages, 'U.S.A. 9/61' on cover....................£60-80
1961/62 **Leaflet**. 'U.S.A.' on page two £25-30
1962/63 **Catalogue 'C/100/62'**. 32 pages, Cover shows boy in red with
    corgi dog. 'U.S.A. 5/63' on checklist £80-100
1962/63 **Leaflet 'USA 8/65'**. 'U.S.A.' on checklist £25-30
1964 **2-fold Checklist** (no ref.). Ghia L 6.4 featured on cover.
    'USA' and '© Playcraft Toys 1964'..£25-30
1964/65 **Catalogue** (no ref.). 40 pages, Green 9001 Bentley and
    Ghia L6.4 on cover. 'USA 8/64' on checklist £65-75
1965/66 **Catalogue** (no ref.). 40 pages, 'U.S.A. 8/65' on checklist £65-75
1967 **Leaflet** (no ref.). 'U.S.A.' on cover...£20-25
1968/69 **Catalogue 'C2017/9/68'**. 48 pages, Chitty-Chitty-Bang-Bang on cover.
    'USA 10/68' on checklist £40-50
1971 **2-fold Checklist '© 1970 Mettoy Co Ltd'**. 'Corgi Toys with
    WhizzWheels' plus 'Australia', 'S.Africa' and 'USA' on cover.
    Checklist has prices in all three currencies £25-30

International Issues 1981 - 1985

The catalogue listings are printed in English, French and German.
Catalogue 'C2293' was issued as a miniature booklet.

1965 Corgi Club addresses

Canada: ....Kleinberg Agencies 1085 St. Alexander St., Montreal'Can,
                 Quebec, Canada.
South Africa:.....PO Box 6024, Johannesburg,
U..S.A.: ....1107 Broadway, New York 10, N.Y.

The 1966 UK Catalogue 'C2017/9/66' is in the unusual size of 190 x 78 mm.
Photo: Swapmeet Publications.

Shop display and 'point-of-sale' items

Year(s)	Item, reference, details	Market Price Range
1957-59	**Display stand, wooden** Ten cream 'corrugated' hardboard shelves, pale blue display background with yellow/blue plastic 'CORGI TOYS' sign screwed to top of display, (30 x 29 x 12 inches)	**£200-250**
1957-59	**Display card/sign** Tin/cardboard, yellow/blue with gold 'dog' logo, 'Wow! Corgi Toys - The Ones With Windows'	**£100-125**
1957-59	**Display card/sign** As previous item but with 'New Corgi Major Toys - The Ones With Windows'	**£100-125**
1957-59	**Wooden display unit** Two shelf stand with Blue backing logo 'CORGI TOYS', 'THE ONES WITH WINDOWS', 'MODEL PERFECTION' and 'NEW' plus the early gold Corgi dog on red background	**£200-250**
1957-59	**Counter display unit** Cardboard, single model display card with Dark Blue inner display area, 'new - CORGI TOYS' logo	**£75-100**
1957-59	**Counter display unit** Cardboard, 2 tier unit with 'New - CORGI MAJOR TOYS' yellow/blue design	**£200-300**
1957-59	**Counter display unit** Cardboard, 2 tier unit, 'COLLECT CORGI TOYS' and 'New MODELS EVERY MONTH' logos in yellow/blue design	**£200-300**
1957-59	**Counter display unit** Cardboard, Renault Floride (222) pictorial display card with '1959 MOTOR SHOW' and 'EARLS COURT' logos	**£300-400**
1957-59	**Counter display unit (cardboard)** Citroën (475) pictorial display card with 'new - THE CITROËN' and 'OLYMPIC WINTER SPORTS' logos	**£200-300**
c.1959	**Display unit** Shows picture of Gift Set 8 'Combine Harvester Set'. 'At work in the field' logo	**£150-175**
1957-67	**Metal display stand** Tiered stand 75cm x 30cm x 45cm high, three 'CORGI TOYS' and Black logos, + three early gold Corgi dog emblems	**£175-200**
1960	**Counter Display Box** Stand for GS1 Bedford Carriemore (1101) and 4 cars	**£300-400**
c.1960	**Window display sign** Yellow background with 'Naturally Corgi Toys' in Red and Blue, illuminated. 27" long x 8" high. (Possibly Belgian market)	**£500-700**
1960-61	**Window sticker** 'NEW MODELS EVERY MONTH'	**£25-30**
1960s	**Metal display stand C2034** Stand has 'Corgi Display C2034' on the back	**NGPP**
1966-69	**Window sticker** Window bills advertising new releases	**£15-20**
1960-69	**Oblong window sign** Glass or plastic with 'CORGI TOYS' and 'PRECISION DIE-CAST SCALE MODELS' logos plus gold Corgi 'dog' logo in blue/yellow/red design	**£200-250**
1960s	**Tinplate stand** 5 Grey tiers topped by 'CORGI TOYS'/Gold dog header	**£200-300**
1960-69	**Glass display sign** Square sign, gold corgi dog on Red panel within Blue lined glass surround	**£150-175**
1961	**Corgi Dog** Moulded dog standing on hind feet holding a 'CORGI CHRISTMAS CARD'	**£200-300**
1968-83	**Metal display stand** Tiered stand 75 cm x 3.5 cm c 45 cm high, with three 'CORGI TOYS' Black/Yellow logos, plus three White/Red late Corgi dog emblems	**£145-175**
1971-73	**Oblong sign** Plastic, with 'CORGI' and 'TESTED BY THE CORGI TECHNOCRATS' logos plus white Corgi 'dog' logo on red square, yellow background plus 3 'Technocrats' faces	**£100-125**
1963-65	**Display stand, C2001/2** For self-selection, 7 tray unit, large 'CORGI TOYS' header sign	**£200-300**
1963-65	**Display stand, rotary, C2003** Self-selection, 4 columns, 4 compartments (45 x 30 in.), large 'CORGI TOYS' header boards	**£200-300**
1963-65	**Display stand, rotary, C2004** Self-selection, 4 column, 72 compartments (72 x 30 in.)	**£200-300**
1963-65	**Display stand, rotary, C2005** Self-selection, 2 column, 36 compartments (72 x 30 in.)	**£150-200**
1963-65	**Display stand, rotary, C2006** Self-selection, 2 column, 36 compartments (55 x 30 in.)	**£100-150**
1963-65	**Display stand, plastic, C2007** Large moulded plastic counter display to house up to 50 models, large black header display board with 'NATURALLY CORGI TOYS' on yellow/blue background, and 'JOIN THE CORGI MODEL CLUB' on display front	**£200-300**
1960s	**Display stand, revolving, C2008** Glass fronted large electric display to house 100-120 models with light and dark simulated wood panels with four 'CORGI' logos, (38 x 24 x 24 in.)	**£400-600**
1957-66	**Showcase, glass, C2009** 3 glass shelves, 3 'CORGI TOYS' logos (black/blue) plus gold Corgi 'dog' logo on red background, (20x15x9 in.)	**£200-300**
1970s	**Corgi Juniors unit, E9051** Yellow plastic (21.75 x 21.75 in.), displays 48 models, logo 'LOOK FOR WHIZZWHEELS MODELS'	**£100-150**
1975	**Army diorama** Plastic unit for displaying tank models	**£140-160**
1976	**Kojak's Buick** Card counter-display unit	**£80-90**
?	**Window poster** Advertising new model 428 'MR SOFTEE' Ice Cream Van	**£60-80**
?	**Shop Display Card** 'Mr SOFTEE Ice Cream free with this Corgi Toy'	**£300-400**
?	**Shop Display Stand** 'New! Chrysler Imperial'	**£150-200**
?	**Shop Display Stand** 'New! the Bentley Continental'	**£500-600**

NB The Editor would welcome any further information on Corgi display material.
NOTABLE AUCTION RESULT
19?? 'Avengers Gift Set' No. 40
Advertising card, 11"x33" sold at auction in 2004 for **£330**

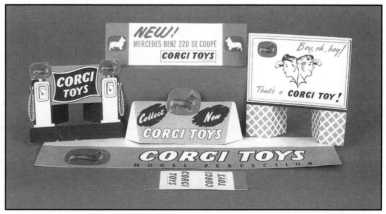

Presentation and display material for Corgi Toys retailers

Photo: Vectis Auctions Ltd.

Corgi Toys Numerical Index

Refer first to the Contents List (page 3) for quick guidance to main sections. Sets, for example, are not listed in this Index since that section is easily found and items in it are listed numerically. A quick check through this general (alphabetical) list may also prove helpful.

These Auction Results are provided to support the Market Price Range guidance throughout the Catalogue.

Vectis Auctions Ltd.

Fleck Way, Thornaby, Stockton -on-Tees TS17 9JZ

Abbreviations: **M** = Mint, **NM** = Near Mint, **EP** = Excellent Plus,
E = Excellent, **GP** = Good Plus, **G** = Good.
WW = Whizzwheels, **RN** = Racing Number, **B/Y** = Blue/Yellow box.

CARS

150 Vanwall Formula 1, green, M in NM box	£190
151 Lotus Mark 11, silver/red, M in GP box	£170
151A Lotus Mark 11, blue, red seats, M in E box	£280
152S BRM, turquoise, M in NM blue/yellow box	£160
200M Ford Consul, M in G box	£140
203M Vauxhall Velox, red/yellow, M in E blue/yellow box	£300
204 Rover 90, grey, E in E blue box	£160
205M Riley Pathfinder, dark blue, M in GP box, leaflet	£170
206 Hillman Husky, brown, M in E box	£130
208M Jaguar 2.4, blue, M in E box	£150
211 Studebaker Golden Hawk Saloon, gold, E in E blue box	£200
211M Studebaker Golden Hawk Saloon, gold, M in GP blue box	£200
218 Aston-Martin DB4, yellow, open vent, M in E box	£120
225 Austin Seven Mini 'Jenson's', red, M in NM box	£1,100
225 Morris Minor 'Jenson's', blue, M in GP box	£1,300
227 Morris Mini Cooper, primrose yellow, NM in GP box	£220
238 Jaguar Mark X, silver, M in E box	£240
238 Jaguar Mark X, steel blue, M in E box	£110
275 Rover 2000TC, white, Take-off Wheels, M in E box	£190
300 Austin-Healey, red, cream seats, M in NM box	£320
302 MGA Sports Car, red, cream seats, M in NM box	£240
309 Aston-Martin DB4, white, turquoise, M in GP box	£220
310 Chevrolet Corvette, metallic bronze, E in NM box	£180
317 Mini-Cooper Rally, signatures issue, M in GP box	£320
322 Rover 2000, 'International Rally' issue, white/black, M in M box	£420
322 Rover 2000, 'Monte-Carlo' issue, M in NM box	£240
333 Mini-Cooper, 'Sun Rally', NM in flashed B/Y box	£210
335 Jaguar 'E' Type, red, M in bubble pack	£150
339 Mini-Cooper 'S' Rally, red/white, '177', M in NM box	£180
345 MGC-GT, 'Competition', yellow/black, M in E box	£110

MILITARY VEHICLES

356 VW 'US Personnel' Carrier, M in GP box	£180
357 Land Rover Weapons Carrier, M in E box	£240
358 Oldsmobile 'HQ Staff Car', M in G box	£180
359 'US Army' Field Kitchen, M in GP box	£280
1119 Hovercraft SR-N1, silver, M in E box	£160
1112 Corporal Guided Missile Launcher, E including box	£320
1113 Corporal Guided Missile Vehicle, NM overall	£440
1116 Bloodhound Guided Missile Launcher, M in G box	£170
1124 Corporal Missile Launcher Platform, NM in GP box	£170
1133 Troop Transporter, leaflet, M in GP box	£200
1134 Bedford 'S' Fuel Tanker 'US Army', M in G box	£240
1135 Bedford Equipment Transporter, M in E - GP	£280

NOVELTY, FILM and TV-RELATED

107 'Batman's Batboaat/Trailer, M in GP striped box	£50
258 'The Saint's Volvo, black decal, M in NM B/Y box	£200
261 'James Bond's Aston-Martin DB5, M in E box	£260
267 Batmobile, red wheels, M in EP striped box	£700
267 Batmobile, WhizzWheels, M in M striped box	£140
268 The Green Hornet, M in NM picture box	£240
270 'James Bond's Aston-Martin DB4, silver, M in bubble pack	£460
336 'James Bond's Toyota 2000GT, NM in in EP picture box	£260
391 'James Bond's Ford Mustang, E in E box	£160
426 Booking Office, EP in GP blue/yellow box	£150
487 Parade Land Rover, E in GP box	£90
497 'Man from Uncle' Car, blue, Waverley ring, M in G box	£280
497 'Man from Uncle' Car, white, Waverley ring, NM in GP box	£600
503 Giraffe Transporter, NM in E box	£140
511 Poodle Truck, EP in E box	£220
802 'Popeye's Paddle Wagon, GP in E box	£220
803 Yellow Submarine, red hatches, GP in E box	£180
804 Noddy's Car with Big Ears and Tubby, NM in E box	£260
805 'Hardy Boys' 1912 Rolls-Royce, M in E box	£150
811 'James Bond's Moonbuggy, EP in E box	£320

EMERGENCY VEHICLES

209 Riley Pathfinder Saloon 'Police', M in GP box	£145
213S Jaguar 'Fire Service', red, NM in E B/Y box	£200
354 Commer 'Ambulance', green, M in GP box	£200
405 Bedford Van 'AFS', green	£120
408 Bedford Van 'AA Services', M in NM blue box	£140
448 BMC Mini Van 'Police', dark blue, M in M box	£260
412 Bedford 'Ambulance', M in E blue box	£190
464 Commer 'County Police' Van, NM in G Box	£70
1127 Simon Snorkel Fire Engine, M in E packing	£190

COMMERCIAL VEHICLES

403 Bedford Van 'Daily Express', M in M blue box	£220
404 Bedford Dormobile, yellow, NM in E blue box	£140
407 Karrier Bantam 'Mobile Shop', M in GP B/Y box	£130
411 Karrier Bantam 'Lucozade' Van, NM in GP box	£120
416S Land Rover 'Touring Secours', M in E box	£1,000
428 Karrier 'Mister Softee' Van, with badge, M in M box	£380
453 Commer 'Walls', light blue cab, M in GP box	£80
471 Karrier Van 'Patates Frites', M in GP box	£200
1101 Bedford 'S' Transporter, red/blue, EP in GP box	£100
1129 Bedford 'S' Tanker, M in G (grubby) box	£180
1142 Holmes Wreck Truck, M in E striped box	£140

BUSES

468 Routemaster, 'Red Rose Coffee', MB	£400
468 Routemaster, 'Red Rose Tea', MB	£40
468 Routemaster, 'Corgi Classics', MB	£500
468 Routemaster, 'Cokerchu', E boxed	£160
C469 Routemaster, 'Mettoy Welcomes Swiss Buyers'	£260
C469 Routemaster, 'Collectors Visit', M in E box	£260

Special Auction Services

Midgham, Reading, Berkshire RG7 5UX.

Abbreviations:
M = Mint, **E** = Excellent, **VG** = Very Good, **G** = Good, **F** = Fair.

205 Riley Pathfinder, red E-M in VG box	£120
261 Gold 'James Bond's Aston-Martin, E-M in VG-E box	£280
266 Chitty Chitty Bang Bang, E in G-VG window box	£150
268 Green Hornet, E-M in G box	
300 Austin-Healey, red E-M in G-VG box	£140
317 BMC Mini Cooper S Monte Carlo Rally, E-M in G box	£130
342 'The Professsionals' Ford Capri, E-M in VG box	£90
485 BMC Mini Countryman, E-M in G box	£140
801 Noddy's Car with Tubby, E-M, box F-G	£165
802 Popeye's Wagon, E in G window box	£220
803 Beatles' Submarine, VG - E in F-G box	£160
853 Magic Roundabout Playground, E in VG box	£500
GS 1 Ford 5000 Tractor Set, G in G box overall	£120
GS 3 Batmobile Set, 3rd issue E-M in G window box	£240
GS 4 Bloodhound Set, G-VG in F box	£150
GS 14 'Daktari' Set, E in G box	£180
GS 19 Corgi Flying Club, E-M in E-M box	£70
GS 25 Garage Set (minus Ford Classic), VG in F-G box	£500
GS 48 Scammell Transporter Set, E in F-G box	£480
1012-al Juniors 'James Bond's Bobsleigh, orange M in VG-E box	£420
11012-al - same as previous only yellow	£430
3030 Juniors 'James Bond's 'Spy Who Loved Me', E-M in G box	£180

CORGI TOYS - Formerly owned by Arthur Katz, co-founder of Mettoy/Corgi:
Gold Plated Prsentation James Bond Lotus Esprit produced for the world premiere ot the 'The Spy Who Loved Me' on 7th July 1977. Registaton No. 'PPW 306R' and mounted on blue and black perspex base with secret drawer for rockets at back. Good ... £1,075

Gift Set 1 Car Transporter – 4 cars All VG – E in G box	£540
Gift Set 3 Batmobile and Batboat, E in VG box	£705
G.S. 15 Siverstone Racing Layout – E , boxes E, set box VG	£1,057
G.S. 21 'Chipperfields Circus' – Crane/Trailer, VG in E	£705
G.S. 23 'Chipperfields Circus' with Booking Office, VG/G	£411
268 Routemaster Bus 'New South Wales' – VG in G-VG box	£587

DJ Auctions

66 Scarborough Rd, Driffield, East Yorkshire YO25 5DS.

109 **Tool Trailer**, mint, boxed...£35
214S **Ford Thunderbird**, metallic grey/red, lemon interior.......£108
263 **Rambler Marlin**, red with black roof £40
303s **Mercedes-Benz 300SI Sports Car**, blue body.............£125
303S2 **Mercedes-Benz 300SI Sports Car**, silver body £300
307 **Jaguar 'E' Type**, metallic grey, red top......................£108
309 **Aston-Martin DB4**, blue/white, excellent model and box.....£182
314 **Ferrari Berlinetta 250 Le Mans** £35
439 **Chevrolet Impala 'Fire Dept.'** £115
475 **Citroën Safari Olympic Sports** with accessories................£103

Collectoys

Editoys, BP 22 - 18001 Bourges Cedex, France.

Condition Grading System: Models shown as A. B. C. & D.
Boxes - a. b. c. d. Unboxed o.

54 **Fordson Power Major**, A.b. £140
57 **Massey Ferguson 65**, B.b. £90
66 **Massey Ferguson 165**, A.a. £40
74 **Ford 5000 Super Major Tractor**, A.b. £180
213 **Jaguar Fire Chief's Car**, A. b. £80
227 **Mini Cooper Rally**, blue/white, A,a. £150
259 **Citroën 'Le Dandy'**, metallic blue/white, A.a £180
261 **'James Bond's Aston-Martin DB5**, A.a.a. £300
262 **Lincoln Continental**, blue/gpld, A.b. £210
267 **Batmobile**, 1st. issue, red bat wheels, A.b. £480
268 **Black Beauty**, A.b. £180
277 **Monkeemobile**, A.b. £120
302 **MGA Sports Car**, red body, cream, seats £130
336 **'James Bond's Toyota 2000 GT**, A.a. £300
302 **Hillman Hunter Rally**, B.b. £125
391 **'James Bond's Ford Mustang Mach 1**, B.b. £165
339 **Mini Cooper 'S' Monte Carlo Rally**, A.a. £350
416 **Land Rover**, yellow, 'TS Radio', C unboxed £120
435 **Karrier Bantam, 'MILK' Truck**, A.b. £240
447 **Ford Thames, 'Walls Ice Cream'**, A.b. £250
448 **Austin 'POLICE' Van**, A..c. £120
471 **Karrier Bantam 'PATATES FRITES'** £300
499 **Citroën ID 19, '1968 GRENOBLE OLYMPICS'**, C.d. £110
513 **Citroën ID 19, 'ALPINE RESCUE'**, B.b. £275
1101 **Bedford Car Transsporter**, blue/yellow B.b. £110
1126 **Racing Car Transporter**, light blue logo £150
1126 **Car Transporter**, Mint in good box £180
339 **Mini Cooper S Rally**, M in M box £410
1109 **Bloodhound Missile**, M in VG box £130
1133 **Troop Transporter**, E in VG box £75
GS 37 **Lotus Racing Team Set**, A.c. £230
1142 **Ford Holmes Recovery Truck**, A.b. £75
GS 38 **'Monte Carlo Rally' Set**, 317/322/323, B, unboxed..........£655
GS 48 **'JEAN RICHARD' Circus Set**, A.b. £110

Christie's South Kensington

85 Old Brompton Road, London SW7 3LD.

Abbreviations: M = Mint, E = Excellent, VG = Very Good,
G = Good, F = Fair.

1140 **Bedford Tanker**, E in VG box..................................£600
GS 16 **Transporter Set**, orange lettering, E in E box £500
270 **'James Bond's Aston Martin DB5**, M in E wing display box £500

Bonhams

Montpelier Street, Knightsbridge, London SW7 1HH

204M **Rover 90 Saloon**, metallic green, E in E box £230
227 **Mini-Cooper**, primrose yellow, E in E box £220
301 **Triumph TR2 Sports Car** – cream with red seats, E in E box ...£170
200 **Ford Consul Saloon** – cream, flat spun hubs, E in E box £160
206 **Hillman Husky** – grey, flat spun hubs, E in G box £105
211 **Studebaker Golden Hawk** – blue/gold E in G box £75
261 **'James Bond's Aston Martin DB5**, complete, G-E box G-E £180
305 **Triumph TR3** plus 2 x 430 Taxis, all E in E boxes............£200
267 **'Batmobile'**, E in E window box £270
270 **'James Bond's Aston-Martin**, E in E window box £260
301 **Triumph TR2 Sports**, cream with red seats £170
GS5 **British Racing Cars**, models E in G box £290
GS5 **Agricultural Set**, models good in torn box £210
1110 **Bedford 'Mobilgas' Tanker 'S'-type**, E in G box £210
GS23 **Circus Set**, models all G-E in G box £410
1106 **Decca Airfield Radar**, E in G box £75
GS 40 **The Avengers** – lacks umbrellas, G-E in G-f box £160
267 **Batmobile** in window box - E in E box £270
925 **Batcopter** in window box, E in G box £120
497 **Man from Uncle with Waverley ring**, blue, G-E in G box £210
290 **Kojak's Buick** – E in E box £80
1120 **'Midland Red' Motorway Express Coach** – E in G box £85
1126 **Ecurie Ecosse Racing Car Transporter** – E in G box £240
204 **Rover 90** plus 305 **Triumph TR3** – both E in G boxes £320
513 **Citroen Safari Alpine Rescue Car**, dog, etc., G-E in G box ...£180
301 **Austin Healey** (red), plus two 301 **Triumph TR3s**, all E/G ..£420
GS 27 **Machinery Carrier & Priestman Shovel**, G-E in G box.........£100
GS24 **Commer Constuction Set** – G-E in G box £75
GS28 **Carrimore Car Transporter and Cars**, G-E in G box £380
GS27 **Priestman Shovel and Machinery Carrier** – E in G box £120
GS13 **Fordson Tractor and Furrow Plough** – G-F in F box............£160

Wallis & Wallis

West Street Auction Galleries, Lewes, Sussex, BN7 2NJ.
Abbreviations: M = Mint, (V)GC = (Very) Good Condition.

201 **Austin Cambridge**, silver/green, box and model GC £160
204 **Rover 90**, mid grey, boxed, VGC £60
204 **Rover 90 Saloon**, metallic cerise, VGC, box minor wear £140
211 **Golden Hawk**, blue/gold, VGC in VGC box £80
256 **VW Safari Car**, VGC in VGC box £110
259 **Citroën Le Dandy**, metallic dark red, VGC, boxed. £130
261 **'James Bond's Aston-Martin DB5**, 1st issue, M in VGC box £340
268 **Green Hornet**, complete, boxed VGC £170
270 **'James Bond's Aston-Martin DB5**, 2nd issue, M in VGC box £330
270 **'James Bond's Aston-Martin DB5**, whizzwheels, VGC, boxed £70
336 **'James Bond's Toyota 2000GT**, boxed, GC - VGC £130
345 **MGC GT**, bright yellow, boxed, VGC £70
359 **US Army Kitchen**, mint boxed £210
407 **Karrier Bantam Mobile Shop**, VGC, box worn £95
440 **Cortina Golfers Estate**, VGC - M, boxed £205
416 **RAC Land Rover**, 1st issue, tin tilt, boxed, VGC £140
420 **Thames Caravan**, two-tone lilac, boxed, VGC £85
426 **Booking Office**, boxed, VGC £90
452 **Commer Lorry with trailer** (100), VGC, boxes GC £110
464 **Commer Police Van**, raised white letters, M, boxed £100
497 **Oldsmobile 'Man From Uncle' Car**, metallic blue, VGC, boxed...£220
1100 **Bedford Transporter**, blue/yellow,VGC, boxed £140
1118 **6 x 6 Army Truck**, boxed, VGC £120
1121 **Circus Crane Truck**, VGC, minor wear £100
1130 **Circus Transporter**, VGC - M, minor box wear £120
GS 4 **Bloodhound Set**, GC - VGC, some box wear.....................£240
GS 10 **Marlin Rambler Set**, VGC, worn box £85
GS 15 **Silverstone Racing Set** *, M, boxed, complete, unmade kits..£1,450
GS 25 **Shell / BP Garage Set** *, M, boxed, complete, unmade kits....£1,250
GS 23 **Circus Set**, 2nd issue, VGC, some box wear £280
GS 24 **Constructor Set**, M, minor box wear £140
GS 32 **Tractor & Shovel Set**, VGC, minor box wear £230
GS 37 **Lotus Racing Team**, boxed VGC - Mint £300
GS 40 **Avengers Set**, rare with all red wheels, M, boxed £480
GS 40 **Avengers Set**, standard wheels, boxed, VGC - M £320
* See page 33 for colour pictures of GS 15 and GS25.

Crescent Toys

The Crescent Toy Company was founded in July 1922 by Henry G. Eagles and Arthur A. Schneider in a workshop 30 feet square at the rear of a private house at 67 De Beauvoir Crescent, Kingsland Road, London N1.

They manufactured model soldiers, cowboys, kitchen sets, etc. from lead alloy. These were hollow castings, hand painted, packed one dozen to a box, and sold to wholesalers at six shillings per dozen boxes. The small firm prospered and eventually opened up a factory in Tottenham. With the second World War came a ban on metal toys and production was changed to munitions. After the War the firm resumed making metal hollow-cast toys and in addition marketed the diecast products of a firm called DCMT (Die Casting Machine Tools Ltd).

As a consequence early post-war models had 'DCMT' cast into the underside of the body. In 1948 the firm opened a modern factory on a four-acre site at Cymcarn, a Welsh mining village near Newport, Monmouth (now Gwent) and two years later transferred all production there, maintaining only an office in London. From this time Crescent toys made their own diecast products without 'DCMT' on them. Hence it is possible to find the same models with or without 'DCMT' cast in. Die Casting Machine Tools went their own way and from 1950 produced models under the name of 'Lone Star'.

Crescent Toys will be best remembered for their excellent ranges of military models and farm equipment but probably most of all for their superb reproductions of the racing cars of the 1950s.

The following post-war model listings have been extracted from a unique collection of original trade catalogues (1947-80) most kindly provided by Mr. J. D. Schneider, the former Managing Director of Crescent Toys Ltd. All of the original research and actual compiling of the lists was undertaken by Ray Strutt.

The Editor would also like to thank Les Perry of Rochdale for additional information.

Ref.	Year(s)	Details	MPR

EARLY POST-WAR MODELS (various colours)

Ref.	Year(s)	Details	MPR
223	1948	**Racing Car**	**£40-60**
422	1949	**Sports Car**	**£40-60**
423	1949	**Oil Lorry**	**£40-60**
424	1949	**Truck Lorry**	**£40-60**
425	1949	**Saloon Car**	**£40-60**
800	1947-49	**Jaguar**	**£40-60**
802	1947-49	**Locomotive**	**£40-60**
803	1947-48	**Locomotive**, Silver	**£40-60**
804	1948-49	**Police Car**, Black	**£40-60**
1221	1949	**Fire Engine**, Red body	**£40-60**
---	---	**Garages**, retailing at 1/-, 1/6, 2/6 and 4/-. Complete with Modern Pumps, Motor Cars and Garage Attendants, *'CRESCENT GARAGES'* logo	NGPP
FC 330	---	**Domestic Iron and Stand**	**£20-30**
---	---	**Zulu-drawn Rickshaw**. Red/Green rickshaw, 'Zulu' with wheel attached to foot, colonial couple in tropical dress/pith helmets in rickshaw	**£125-175**
---	---	**Milk Bar Set**	**£300-400**
---	---	**Barber Shop Set**	**£300-400**

FARM EQUIPMENT (various colours)

Ref.	Year(s)	Details	MPR
1802	1949-60	**Tractor and Hayrake**	**£75-100**
1803	1967-74	**Dexta Tractor and Trailer**	**£75-100**
1804	1950-59	**Tractor and Disc Harrow**	**£75-100**
1805	1950-61	**Tractor**	**£65-85**
1806	1950-60	**Hayrake**	**£10-15**
1807	1950	**Disc Harrow**	**£10-15**
1808	1950-56	**Platform Trailer**	**£10-15**
1809	1950-56	**Ricklift Trailer**	**£10-15**
1809	1962-80	**Dexta Tractor**	**£45-55**
1810	1950-80	**Box Trailer / Farm Trailer**, (No.148 1968-74)	**£15-20**
1811	1950-67	**Animal Trailer / Cattle Trailer**, (No.148 1968-71)	**£10-15**
1811	1975-81	**Dexta Tractor and Trailer**	**£60-70**
1813	1950	**Timber Wagon** (Horse Drawn)	**£75-95**
1814	1950-60	**Plough Trailer**, (No.150 1968-71)	**£20-30**
1815	1950	**Hayloader**	**£20-30**
1816	1950	**Roller Harrow**	**£20-30**
1817	1950-56	**Timber Trailer**	**£20-30**
1818	1954-60	**Tipping Farm Wagon**	**£20-30**
1819	1954-55	**Large Farm Wagon**	**£30-40**

DIECAST ACTION TOYS (various colours)

Ref.	Year(s)	Details	MPR
1219	1954-59	**'Milking Time' Set**. 2 Milkmaids, 2 cows, calf. Card box with picture on lid	**£100-125**
1222	1954-59	**Builders & Decorators Truck** (red handcart), unpainted ladder and bucket, beige figure on green base. Grey card box with drawing of set	**£100-125**
1268	1954-59	**Mobile Space Rocket**	NGPP
1269	1954-59	**Mobile Crane**	**£80-100**

Ref.	Year(s)	Details	MPR
1272	1954-59	**Scammell Scarab and Box Trailer**	**£80-90**
1274	1954-59	**Scammell Scarab and Low Loader**	**£80-90**
1276	1955-59	**Scammell Scarab and Oil Tanker**	**£80-90**
2700	1956-60	**Western Stage Coach**	**£80-90**
2705	1955	**Western Stage Coach**	**£80-90**
-		**Scammell Scarab Set**, Mechanical Horse, Box Trailer and Low Loader	**£100-150**

MILITARY MODELS (All in military colours)

Ref.	Year(s)	Details	MPR
155	1960-68	**'Long Tom' Artillery Gun**	**£20-35**
235	1946	**Cannon**, operable	**£20-25**
F 355	1938	**Tank and Cannon Set**	**£100-125**
650	1954-59	**Military Set**: two 696 British Tanks, one 698 Scout Car, one 699 Russian Tank	**£150-200**
NN656/2	1938-40	**Field Gun and Gunner**	**£40-50**
NN692	1938-40	**Deep Sea Diver**, with equipment	**£40-60**
NN693	1938-40	**A.R.P. Searchlight Unit**, 3 personnel, boxed	**£120-150**
NN694	1938-40	**A.R.P. Rangefinder Unit**, 2 personnel, boxed	**£90-120**
695	1938-40	**A.R.P. First Aid Post**: a tent, two stretcher bearers and patient, Red Cross nurse	**£125-150**
F 695	1946	**Howitzer**, unpainted, with spring and plunger, *'CRESCENT'* cast-in	**£10-20**
696	1954-59	**British Tank**	**£40-50**
698	1954-56	**Scout Car**	**£30-40**
699	1954-56	**Russian Tank**	**£40-50**
NN700	1938-40	**Royal Engineers Field Set**: Engineers (2 standing, 2 kneeling), telegraph pole, transmitter, aerial. Box has colour picture of set on lid	**£125-150**
701	-	**GPO Telephone Engineers Set**: 4 men, telegraph pole, hut, cart, accessories. Box has colour picture of set on lid	**£125-150**
702	-	**Sound Locator Unit**, operator figure, boxed	**£60-80**
K 703	1938-40	**Field Wireless Unit** with two Soldiers	**£90-120**
K 704	1938-40	**R.A.M.C. Stretcher Party**, 2 Soldiers and Patient	**£90-120**
1248	1957	**Field Gun**	**£5-10**
1249	1958-79	**18-pounder Quick-Firing Gun**	**£10-15**
1250	1958-80	**25-pounder Light Artillery Gun**	**£10-15**
1251	1958-80	**5.5" Medium Heavy Howitzer**	**£10-15**
1260	1976-79	**Supply Truck**	**£40-60**
1263	1962-80	**Saladin Armoured Scout Car**	**£50-60**
1264	1975-80	**Scorpion Tank**	**£12-16**
1265	1977-80	**M109 Self-Propelled Gun**	**£12-15**
1266	1978-79	**Recovery Vehicle**	**£12-15**
1267	1958-63	**'Corporal' Rocket and Lorry**	**£90-120**
1270	1958-60	**Heavy Rescue Crane**	**£50-60**
1271	1958-60	**Long Range Mobile Gun**	**£30-40**
1271	1976-80	**Artillery Force**	**£20-30**
2154	1962-74	**Saladin Armoured Patrol** (No.1270 1975-80)	**£60-75**

HISTORICAL MODELS (in regal colours)

1300	1975-76	**Royal State Coach**	£20-30
1301	1977-79	**Royal State Coach**, (Commemorative box)	£20-30
1302	1977	**Royal State Coach and Figures**	£20-30
1450	1956-60	**Medieval Catapult**	£20-30
1953	1954-60	**Coronation State Coach**	£40-65

Miniature 'WILD WEST' Transport

906	1956	**Stage Coach**, various colours	£30-40
907	1956	**Covered Wagon**, various colours	£30-40

G.P. RACING and SPORTS CARS

1284	1956-60	**Mercedes-Benz**, all-enveloping silver body, racing number '12'	£90-120
1285	1956-60	**B.R.M. Mk.II**, bright green, '7'	£90-120
1286	1956-60	**Ferrari**, orange-red	£90-120
1287	1956-60	**Connaught**, dark green, racing number '8'	£90-120
1288	1956-60	**Cooper-Bristol**, light blue, racing number '2'	£90-120
1289	1956-60	**Gordini**, French blue, racing number '14'	£90-120
1290	1956-60	**Maserati**, cherry red, racing number '3'	£90-120
1291	1957-60	**Aston-Martin DB3s**, white/light blue	£100-150
1292	1957-60	**Jaguar 'D' type**, dark green	£100-150
1293	1958-60	**Vanwall**, dark green, racing number '10'	£150-200
6300	1957	**Racing Cars Set**, 1284 - 1289 in display box	NGPP
	1958-60	Same set but 1290 replaces 1284	NGPP

LONG VEHICLES (various colours)

1350	1975-80	**Container Truck**	£20-25
1351	1975-80	**Petrol Tanker**	£20-25
1352	1975-80	**Girder Carrying Truck**	£20-25
1353	1975-80	**Flat Platform Truck**	£20-25

'TRUKKERS' (various colours)

1360	1976-81	**Cement Mixer**	£5-20
1361	1976-81	**Covered Truck**	£5-20
1362	1976-81	**Tipper Truck**	£5-20
1363	1976-81	**Recovery Vehicle**	£5-20
1364	1976-81	**Super Karrier**	£5-20

CRESCENT AIRCRAFT

O 2	1940	**Spitfire Set**. Two Spitfires with two Pilots and two Mechanics	£100-200
Q 2	1940	**Spitfire Set**. As O 2 but new ref. no.	£100-200
U 2	1940	**Aircraft Set**. Five Aircraft plus three Pilots and six Groundcrew	£200-300
FC 38	1946	**Aeroplane**, Spitfire	£25-35
FC 89	1946	**Aeroplane**, Mosquito	£25-35
FC 90	1946	**Aeroplane**, Lightning, 3" x 2", US markings	£25-35
FC 179	1946	**Khaki Bomber**	£15-20
FC 372	1946	**Aeroplane**, Lightning, 4.75" x 3", US markings	£25-35
FC 663	1946	**North Sea Patrol**. Aeroplane with pilot and one other crew member	£80-100

Photo: Vectis Auctions Ltd.

CRESCENT SHIPS

BATTLESHIPS

---		**HMS 'King George V'.** Grey hollow-cast, with main armament only, boxed	£20-30
---		Same but additional separately cast secondary armament	£20-30
---		**HMS 'Vanguard'.** Grey / black / white, solid, *'CRESCENT'*' cast-in	£10-15
Q 3	1940	**Battleship Set.** Battleship plus four Sailors	£80-100
S 3	1940	**Warships Set.** Battleship and Destroyer plus eight Sailors	£100-200
NN 691		**HMS 'Malaya'.** Grey hollow-cast, black funnels, boxed	£20-35

AIRCRAFT CARRIERS

-		**HMS 'Victorious'.** Grey hollow-cast body, separate unpainted aircraft, boxed	£20-35
NN 667		**HMS 'Eagle'.** Grey hollow-cast body, unpainted aircraft, Union Jack sticker attached to box	£20-35

OTHER WARSHIPS

---		**'H' or 'I' Class Destroyer.** Unpainted solid cast body, *'CRESCENT'*' cast into bow	£20-30
---		**'H' or 'I' Class Destroyer.** As previous model plus three lead figures of naval personnel	£40-60
---		**'V' and 'W' Class Destroyer.** Grey hollow-cast body	£5-8
A 34		**Gunboat.** Grey hollow cast body	£5-8
234		**Submarine.** Unpainted, conning tower and deck gun, 4"	£20-30
C 310		**'County' Class Cruiser, 'Cumberland',** Grey hollow-cast	£10-20
K 664		**'County' Class Cruiser,** Grey hollow-cast body	£10-20
K 665		**War Transport Ship,** Grey hollow-cast body, boxed	£20-30

PASSENGER SHIPS

---		**'Queen Mary'.** Black / white / red, hollow-cast body, boxed	£50-75
---		**'Dunnottar Castle'.** Mauve / white / red, hollow-cast, boxed	£50-75
---		**'Athlone Castle'.** Mauve / white / red, hollow-cast, boxed	£50-75

'Dunnottar Castle' and 'Athlone Castle' were part of the 'Union Castle' fleet and the models were sold in souvenir boxes, probably on board.

SHIP MODEL IDENTIFICATION. Crescent Ships are of rather crude manufacture and have virtually no identifying features. Only the HMS 'Vanguard' and the 'H' or 'I' Class Destroyer are known to have *'CRESCENT'* cast in. A few of the early models had a little paper 'Crescent' half-moon label. Ship models were packed in cream cardboard boxes of varying quality.

MISCELLANEOUS models and sets

'Dodgem' Car	Blue version seen, other colours possible	£100-200
'Tower Bridge'	Solid cast model of the famous landmark, in various colours	£20-30
'Dial 999' Police and Robbers Set.	Contains black police car with loudhailer on roof and four semi-flat action figures (policeman running, policeman and dog, two fleeing villains, (one with swag). Packed in card box with black and white label	£200-300
'Dan Dare' Set.	With figures of Dan Dare, Miss Peabody, Dan Dare in spacesuit, 2 Treens (1 silver, 1 gold), rocket and launcher. Packed in card box	£400-500
'Wild Animals' Set.	no details	NGPP
'Model Farm' Set.	no details	NGPP
Trade Box	for 6 x No.363 'Shell-BP' clip-on signs. Green/red/blue card box with lid	£30-40

Meccano
Dinky Toys

Dinky Toys represent by far the largest and most important of all the model collecting series – there are thousands of variations to collect. The listings are structured on a thematic basis. This enables models to be identified that much quicker and for collectors to specialise on a particular favourite theme be it cars, commercials or aircraft, etc.

Today Dinky Toys are bought and sold across the world by thousands of collectors for whom there is nothing quite so rewarding as a new variation to add to their collection. It has been estimated that the average value of top quality rare boxed models have increased by as much as 20% in the twelve month period 2004/5. The growth of traditional and Internet auctions has had a major effect on prices of rare items. As a consequence, this Catalogue's largest ever Auction Results Section contains hundreds of examples of the prices achieved by rare and desirable toys and models. This auction reporting information refines and underpins the Market Prices shown against model descriptions. In order to maintain our accurate recording of the ongoing price changes in the market, we will be making new and updated information available to collectors on an annual basis, through the medium of 'Model Price Review', the next edition of which will be published in 2006.

All of this is a very long way indeed from Frank Hornby's original vision of a range of miniature vehicles which would complement his model railway layouts!

HISTORY OF DINKY TOYS

In 1931, Meccano Ltd introduced a series of railway station and trackside accessories to accompany their famous 'HORNBY' train sets. These 'Modelled Miniatures' were in sets numbered 1 – 22 and included railwaymen, station staff, passengers and trains. Set number 22 was comprised of six vehicles which were representative rather than replicas of actual vehicles. It was first advertised in the Meccano Magazine of December 1933.

At about this time 'Tootsie Toys' of America were introducing model vehicles into the United Kingdom and they were proving to be very popular. Consequently Meccano Ltd decided to widen their range of products and issue a comprehensive series of models to include vehicles, ships and aircraft. 'Modelled Miniatures' therefore became 'Meccano Dinky Toys' and set number 22 the first set of 'Dinky Cars'. The first 'Dinky Toys' advertisement appeared in the April 1934 edition of the Meccano Magazine. The first Dinky car produced after the change of name was 23a in April 1934. It was probably based on an early MG but was again generally representative rather than an accurate model. Set 22 cost 4/- and consisted of: 22a Sports Car, 22b Sports Coupé, 22c Motor Truck, 22d Delivery Van, 22e Tractor and 22f Tank and is today highly sought after.

The range of models produced grew quickly so that the Meccano Magazine of December 1935 was claiming that there were 200 varieties to choose from! Although the phrase 'Dinky Toys' became a household name, the actual range was of course far greater and was not limited to cars; it even included dolls house furniture. Indeed, by the time the famous Binns Road factory in Liverpool finally closed its doors in November 1979 over 1,000 different designs had been produced. Pre-war models are rare today and fetch high prices, which reflects how difficult it is to find a model in really good condition. This is because so many 1930s models were made from an unstable alloy which has tended to crystallise and disintegrate. Fortunately the post-war models do not suffer from the same problem and much of today's collecting interest is centred around the delightful models produced in the fifties and sixties with Gift Sets being particularly sought after. Most Dinky Toys boxes were made by McCorquodale in Northern Ireland.

In 1987 the Dinky trade name was bought by Matchbox who were at the time part of the Universal International Co. of Hong Kong. They introduced the 'Dinky Collection' in 1988 with some very fine models in a constant scale of 1:43. On the 7th May 1992 it was announced in the 'New York Times' that 'Tyco Toys Inc.' had acquired by merger the 'Universal Matchbox Group' and with it the famous 'Dinky Toys' brand name.

In 1998, Mattel bought the Matchbox brand and in 1999 disclosed that all new car models will be classified as 'Dinky Toys', including those previously included in their Matchbox Models of Yesteryear range. At the beginning of 2001 however, both of those famous names have been all but buried in favour of Mattel's 'Hot Wheels' brand since most of their products have been aimed at the US toy market.

Market Price Range
**Please note that the prices shown refer to pristine models and boxes.
Items failing to match this standard will sell for less.
Note also that boxes must still contain all their original packing pieces
and additional contents where appropriate.**

Common Features. There are several features common to various groups of models and to avoid unnecessary repetition in the listings they are shown below. Exceptions to these general indications are noted in the listings.

'Dinky Toys', 'Meccano Ltd', or 'Meccano Dinky Toys'.
These wordings are to be found cast or stamped on the base-plate or chassis or in the case of early models without a base they are cast into the model itself. Some very early models have 'HORNBY SERIES' cast-in (e.g, those in the 22 series).

Wheel hubs. Solid one-piece wheel/tyre castings were fitted to the 'Modelled Miniatures' and first pre-war 'Dinky Toys'. They had 'Hornby' or 'Meccano' cast onto their rims and were covered in a thin colour wash or silver-plated. This casting was soon replaced with more realistic cast hubs (having a smooth convex face) fitted with white (sometimes coloured) rubber tyres. Pre-war hubs may be black, coloured or sometimes silver-plated. Post-war hubs were of the 'ridged' type having a discernible ridge simulating a hub cap. They were painted and usually fitted with black rubber tyres.

Supertoys hubs and tyres. When Supertoys were introduced in 1947 the ridged type of hub was used on the Fodens with black 'herringbone pattern' tyres, and on the Guys with smooth black tyres. Fodens graduated to the use of 'fine radial-tread' tyres first in black, later in grey, then to black again but with a more chunky 'block' tread. Supertoys later acquired plastic hubs and plastic tyres.

Hub materials. Lead was used originally for a short time, the majority of models from the mid-1930s to the early 1960s having diecast mazak hubs. Small models like motor-cycles or the 35b Racer were fitted with solid one-piece wheel/tyre moulding (white or black rubber pre-war, black post-war). In 1958/9 aluminium hubs were introduced and some models (such as 131, 178, 179, 180, 181, 182 and 290 Bus) appeared fitted with either type. Plastic hubs replaced the diecast versions on racing cars numbered 230-235 while the Austin A30 and Fiat 600 were given solid one-piece wheel/tyre plastic injection mouldings. **Speedwheels** were introduced in the 1970s and some model can be found fitted with metal wheels or Speedwheels. The former are more collectable.

Baseplates are tinplate or diecast unless described otherwise. Plastic moulded baseplates are generally restricted to a few models made after 1970. **Model Numbers** appear on many Dinky Toys baseplates but not all. The **Model Name** however appears on virtually every post-war Dinky Toy. Pre-war models usually had neither (the 38 and 39 series are exceptions having the model name on their baseplates).

Construction Materials. All models assumed to be constructed at least in part of a diecast alloy. Some pre-war models were made of a lead alloy like the 22 and 28 series plus the few odd models such as 23 a Racing Car and 23m Thunderbolt. The Blaw-Knox Bulldozer was one of the very few produced (right at the end of its production) in plastic.
Windows. Pre-war and early post-war models had tinplate or celluloid windscreens. Moulded plastic windscreens appeared in the 1950s on open car models. The first Dinky to be fitted with all-round plastic window glazing was the Austin A105 Saloon. Some models in production at the time were fitted with glazing later and may therefore be found with or without it.

Hooks were not fitted to the first Supertoys Foden models (1947). Small hooks were fitted in early 1948, the usual (larger) hook appearing in mid-1948.

Axles were all 'crimped' pre-war and on these series of models post-war: 23, 25, 29, 30, 34, 35, 36, 37, 38, 39, 40 and 280. Otherwise models had rivet-ended axles until the advent of Speedwheels. Early Guy models had tinplate clips to retain the front axles. Pre-war axles are generally thinner than post-war at 0.062mm diameter while post-war axles are 0.078mm in diameter.

Size of models (where shown) is in millimetres and refers to the longest overall measurement (usually the length). In the case of pre-war models slight inaccuracies may occur from expansion of the casting as it ages in the course of time.

The Scale of Dinky Toys was originally 1:43 (with a few exceptions). Supertoys Foden and Guy vehicles (introduced in 1947) were in a scale of 1:48 while military models issued from 1953 were smaller at 1:60. Most aircraft models before 1965 were around 1:200 and ships 1:1800. In the late 1960s and early 1970s the 1:36 scale was introduced, mostly for cars.

Dinky Numbering System. The dual/triple reference numbers used on some Dinky Toys and Supertoys (for example 409 / 521 / 921 Bedford Articulated Lorry) refers to the basic model type and casting and not to model colours. The renumbering by Meccano was an administration process to re-catalogue production of existing lines and introduce new models. New colours on existing castings which arise at about the time of renumbering are therefore coincidental with it rather than a consequence of it.

Identification of early post-war Dinky Toys cars.
Note that pre-war wheel hubs may be smooth diecast or the rare chrome ('Tootsie-Toy' type) hubs which attract a premium.

Post-war 30 Series
Circa 1946.........Open chassis with smooth black wheel hubs.
Circa 1948.........Plain chassis with ridged black wheel hubs.

36 Series
Circa 1946.........Moulded chassis with smooth black wheel hubs.
Circa 1948.........Moulded chassis with ridged black wheel hubs.

38 Series
Circa 1946........With pre-war lacquered metal base, silvered sidelights, smooth black hubs, spread spigots not rivets.
Circa 1946.........Solid steering wheels, smooth black hubs, silvered sidelights, black painted baseplate.
Circa 1947.........As above but with silver-edged windscreen.
Circa 1948-49....Open or solid steering wheel, ridged hubs, black painted baseplate.
Circa 1950.........As above but with coloured wheel hubs.

39 Series
Circa 1946.........'Gold' pre-war baseplate, smooth black wheel hubs, silver door handles and radiator cap.
Circa 1948.........Black painted baseplate, ridged black wheel hubs.
Circa 1950.........As above but with coloured wheel hubs.

Box Types Introduction

A mint condition model car without its correct box is worth but a fraction of its mint boxed equivalent. Furthermore, as model boxes made from card do not survive as well as their die-cast contents, pristine box examples are scarce and becoming scarcer. The condition of a box is of paramount importance and attention is drawn to the section in the catalogue introduction, namely: 'Classifying the Condition of Models and Boxes'.

The following listing provides collectors with a working knowledge of the range of box types issued. In addition details are given of their dates of issue, their design and of the models which used them. See also the colour sections for examples of many types of boxes.

Whilst every care has been taken in preparing the listing, other variations may exist and information on them is welcomed. Similarly, with no 'dates of birth' available the dates of issues shown are approximate and again any further information is welcomed.

Box Identification

Model colour identification marks - colour spots

These are shown on the box lid end flap and take the form of a circular colour spot. This may be either a single colour or, in the case of the later two-tone car issues, a two-tone colour spot. Colour spots were used until the early 1960s.

NB The dual numbered 234/23H box displays the **Ferrari** model name against a blue panel which matches the main body colour.

Dual numbered boxes 1953 - 1954

A new numbering system was introduced which resulted in models being issued displaying both the old and new reference numbers. The information was shown on the box end flaps as follows:

Old model number shown in red letters on either side of a larger white number set on a black oval background, e.g. 40J **161** 40J. Dual numbered boxes were only issued for a short period and may attract a premium. The numbers may be large or small.

Pre-war issues

Apart from special issues such as 23m Thunderbolt Speed Car and 23p Gardner's M.G. Record Car, individual models were sold unboxed. They were usually packaged in half-dozen retailers trade packs (see the section on Trade Packs). Models were also sold in boxed sets (see the Gift Set Section).

Post-war After the second world war models continued to be sold unboxed from trade boxes until 1953/54 when the first individual boxes were introduced. The boxes have been catalogued into three types as follows:

Type 1: Card boxes with tuck-in flaps
Type 2: Display boxes -Blister packs, rigid plastic packs,
vacuform packs and card window boxes.
Type 3: Export Issue boxes.

Type 1 1953 – 1975 All card box with tuck-in end flaps

(i) 1953- 1954 Deep yellow box with 'DINKY TOYS' in red plus the model's name and type in black. A white reference number on a black oval background is on the box end flaps but no reference number is shown on the box face. The model is pictured on the box sides but without a white shaded background. Colour spots shown on box-end flaps as applicable. Foreign language information is shown on one of the end flaps of the early issue boxes. Box in general use during the model renumbering period. Consequently, dual numbered boxes will be found. It would appear that only models 23f, g, h, j, k and n, and 40j were housed in individual boxes prior to renumbering. Please supply details of any other models housed in boxes displaying just their old reference number.

(ii) 1955 - 1956 Same as (i) but a white reference number on a black oval background is shown on the face of the box to the left of the model picture. Also as (i) but with a white reference number on a red oval background and placed either to the left or right of the model picture. Box in general use for all issues.

(iii) 1956 - 1960 Same as (ii) but model pictures are displayed against a white shadow background. In some instances only one picture. had a shadow, e.g. 171 Hudson Commodore and in others both pictures were given a shadow; e.g. 152 Austin Devon. Box in general use for all issues. Later issues display 'WITH WINDOWS', caption in a red line features box.

(iv) c1960 Deep yellow plain box with no model picture, 'DINKY TOYS' and text in red; rarely used. Colour spots shown as applicable. We believe these boxes may have been used for mail-order or possibly export purposes. The Editor would welcome any new information. Known examples: 103, 108, l09, 163, 178 and 191.

(v) 1959–1961 Plain lighter yellow box with no model picture. It has two yellow and two red sides. 'DINKY TOYS' is shown in yellow on red sides. Colour spots shown as applicable. Models recorded: 105, 109, 131, 150, 157, 165, 169, 173. 174, 176, 178, 187, 189, 191, 192 and 230 to 235. The special issue 189 Triumph Heralds used this box.

(vi) 1960 - 1966 Yellow box with a separate red line features box placed to the right of the model picture. Colour spots still in use on early 1960s issues. Foreign language text on one box end flap and 'WITH WINDOWS' captions on box face. Models recorded: 105, 112, 113, 131, 144, 148, 155, 157, 164–167, 176–178, 181/2, 184, 186, 191-195, 197, 199, 230-235, 237, 239 and 449. Later issues without colour spots. Boxes used for some South African issues display both English and Afrikaans text.

(vii) c.1962 – 1963 Lighter yellow box similar to (v) but colour spots not in use. A scarce issue box which may attract a premium. Model recorded: 166.

(viii) 1962 – 1963 Yellow box with a red end features panel around the left side of the box. Recorded models: 113, 147 and 198.

(ix) 1962 – 1963 (?) Yellow/red box similar to previous items, but has yellow ends, yellow top and bottom panels and red side panels, the latter virtually filled with the text: *'DINKY TOYS'*. Colour spots not seen. See page vii of the colour section for an illustration of this box (containing 178 Plymouth Plaza).

(x) 1963 – 1970 Yellow box with a red end features panel around the right side. The panel is bisected by the model picture and is with or without a large or small white arrow design. Models recorded: 112-114. 120, 127-130, 133-139, 140-148, 198, 240-243, 268, 273 and 274. Some South African issues used this box, e.g. 141 Vauxhall Victor Estate Car. They display both English and Afrikaans text. The rare Triumph 2000 Saloon promotional issues will be found in this box. Some have an applied white label on the box face showing the colour of the model, e.g. Olive-Cactus.

(xi) 1966 – 1969 Detailed full colour picture box with pictorial scene on two sides with 'DINKY TOYS' in red letters. Recorded issues: 133, 136, 183, 212, 214, 225 plus Hong Kong issues 57/001-57/006.

(xii) 1968 – 1974 White-fronted box with a thin yellow band across the box face. A yellow laurel leaf design on a black background is a main box feature. The white face of the box may contain features information such as '1st AGAIN' and 'SPEEDWHEELS'. Variation exists with a semi-pictorial box face (probably an export special) e.g. 176 NSU R80. Models recorded: 157, 159 165/6, 169, 174/5, 179, 183, 192, 205 and 212. NB. A variation of this box exists with a large red 'DINKY TOYS' and number to the left of the picture and no yellow band across the face, e.g. 138 Hillman Imp.

Type 2 1962 – 1980 Display boxes, Blister packs, Rigid plastic and Vacuform packs, Window boxes

(i) 1962 – 1964 Blister Card Packs used for racing cars nos. 205210. Red/yellow display card with chequered flag design.

(ii) 1967 – 1971 Rigid plastic 'see-through' case with lift-off lid. models displayed on a card base with a black 'roadway' surface. The base sides are yellow with 'DINKY TOYS' in red. Recorded issues: 110, 116, 127, 129, 131/2, 142, 152-154, 158, 161, 163/4, 168, 175, 187-189, 190, 208, 210, 213, 215, 216, 220/1 and 223/4.

(iii) 1972 – 1976 Vacuform Packs. Models displayed on a black base with a blue surface with 'DINKY TOYS' in red/white letters. The model is covered by a close fitting plastic cover. Known issues: 129, 131, 149, 168, 178 and 192 plus 1:25 issues 2214, 3162 and 2253.

(iv) 1976 – 1979 Window Box with 'see-through' cellophane front and blue and red header card with a 'DINKY DIECAST TOYS' in yellow letters. Variations exist with a model picture on the header card e.g. 112 'Purdey's TR7'. Known issues: 113, 120, 122/3/4, 128. 180, 192, 207/8, 211, 221/2/3 and 226/7.

(v) 1968 – 1969 Plastic see-through red box made in a garage shape to house 'Mini Dinky' issues.

(vi) 1979 Bubble Pack 219 'Big Cat' Jaguar.

Dinky Toys Cars – Box Types (continued)

Type 3   1966 – 1980   Export issue boxes

(i) 1966 – 1980 An all yellow card and cellophane 'see-through' display box with outward-folding ends. 'DINKY TOYS' and four diagonal stripes plus 'A MECCANO PRODUCT MADE IN ENGLAND' are in red on the box face. The box display base may be either yellow or have a black 'roadway' design.

Whilst generally used for export issues it was specifically used for the U.S. export series 'MARVELS IN MINIATURE - which appeared in red letters on the box front. Later issues listed the models on the base of the box.

A box variation exists with just 'DINKY' and 'A MECCANO PRODUCT' on the face of the box plus the model name and number. The base of the box is yellow. The box was issued with a card protection strip which stated: 'Mr DEALER PLEASE REMOVE THIS STRIP'. Models known to have been issued in this box include: 110-115, 120, 127/8, 133-138, 141/2. 151, 161, 170-172, 190, 192, 196, 215, 237, 240-243, 257/8, 57/006. **NB** We believe this box was probably used in the UK but would be grateful for confirmation.

(ii) 1966 – 1968 All gold card and cellophane 'see-through' display box with just 'DINKY' in gold letters set in a red panel on the box front plus red and black diagonal stripes. 'A MECCANO PRODUCT MADE IN ENGLAND' in black is also on the front of the box. Only used for a short time so models in these boxes often sell at a premium. The known issues are: 112, 113, 148, 193, 215, 238, 240-243, 340 and 448.

(iii) 1979 – 1980 A flat yellow box with blue end flaps. Used to house the Swiss promotional issue No. 223 Hesketh F1 Racing Car 'OLYMPUS CAMERAS'.
Export issue: 449 has been observed in an 'all gold' box.

40 Series issues distribution, renumbering and packing

Models in the 40 Series were initially sold unboxed from retailers' trade boxes of 6 models as follows:

i)   1947-50   Plain Brown card box with lift-off lid. On the end of the lid was a Yellow label displaying the quantity, the model's name and its reference number, e.g., '6 RILEY SALOON 40a'.

ii)   1950-54   All Yellow card box with lift-off lid. The contents were printed in Black on the end of the box lid.

iii)   1954   Models renumbered. When the 40 Series models were renumbered, the final all-Yellow card boxes for six displayed both the original number and its new number, for example: '158 RILEY SALOON 40a'.

iv)   1954-60   The renumbered models were individually boxed in the first type of Yellow end-flap boxes as follows:
    a) Displaying the dual numbers for a short time, e.g., '40a 158 40a' on the end flap.
    b) Displaying just the model's new number, e.g., '158' plus the correct colour spot for the model.

Dublo Dinky Toys usually came in yellow boxes with a distinctive red band around each end.
Exceptions include the 071 VW Delivery Van and 070 AEC Mercury Tanker 'SHELL-BP' shown in this picture.
Also illustrated here is the box for Dinky Toys 772 British Road Signs.
Photo: Barry Potter Auctions.

Dinky Toys Cars – Identification of casting types

Chassis types, 1934 – 1950

| **1934 - 1935**
'Criss-cross' chassis
1st type
with or without
slot for spare wheel | **1935 - 1936**
'Criss-cross' chassis
2nd type
with or without
slot for spare wheel | **1936 - 1940**
Open chassis
with or without
slots for figures | **1946 - 1947**
Plain chassis, no
slots for figures,
hole for caravan
drawbar | **1948 - 1950**
'Moulded'
(detailed) chassis,
hole for caravan
drawbar |

24 Series radiator grille types, 1934 – 1940

| **1st type**
1934 - 1938
With diamond shape
in centre of bumper
No radiator badge
No over-riders | **2nd type**
1934 - 1938
No diamond shape in
centre of bumper
No radiator badge
No over-riders | **3rd type**
1938 - 1940
'Bentley' style
with radiator badge
and over-riders |

The first and second type grilles will be found on the both the first and second type chassis.
The later third type grille will be found with the second type chassis.

Dinky Toys Cars – Identification of wheel types

1935 - 1941.
Pair of smooth-hub diecast wheel hubs as fitted to all car models. Crimped axle ends.

1935 - 1941.
Pair of smooth-hub diecast wheel hubs as fitted to 23a Racing Car. Note the 'arrow-head' or 'herring-bone' tyre treads.

1947 onwards.
Ridged-hub diecast wheel as on all early post-war issues. Rounded axle ends. Smooth tyres. French versions are often referred to as 'convex' and are sometimes plated.

1958
Treaded plastic wheel fitted to 160 Austin A30. Smooth (non-treaded) wheels were also fitted to this model.

c1958.
Treaded tyre design as fitted to 111 Triumph TR2.

c1959.
Spun aluminium hubs as fitted to many car models.

c1967.
16-spoke cast wheel as on 281 Fiat Pathé News car.

c1970.
No. 100 Lady Penelope's 'FAB 1' 2nd type wheel shown. 1st type has six raised studs in a 'starfish' pattern.

c1968.
Cast wheel used on No. 13 Ferrari in the 'Mini-Dinky' series.

c1972.
Detailed cast wheel as fitted to 252 Pontiac Parisienne Police Car.

Dinky Toys Cars

Ref	Year(s)	Model name and details	Market Price Range
22a	1933-35	**Open Sports Car** 'Modelled Miniature' with 'HORNBY SERIES' cast into lead body, solid metal wheel/tyre castings (thinly painted in metallic blue, purple, green, yellow or red, or not painted at all) lead windscreen surround, tinplate radiator (grille may be same colour as body, or overpainted with the colour of the mudguards).	
		Blue body, Yellow seats and mudguards	**£400-600**
		Blue body, Red seats and mudguards	**£400-600**
		Cream body, Red seats and mudguards	**£400-600**
		Cream body, Green seats and mudguards	**£400-600**
		Cream body, Blue seats and mudguards	**£400-600**
		Red body, Cream or Blue seats and mudguards	**£400-600**
		Yellow body, Green seats and mudguards	**£400-600**
		Orange-Brown body, Cream seats and mudguards	**£400-600**
		Green body, Yellow seats and mudguards	**£400-600**
22b	1933-35	**Closed Sports Coupé** 'Modelled Miniature' with 'HORNBY SERIES' cast into lead body, solid metal wheel/tyre castings (coloured or plain, as 22a) tinplate radiator (painted in main body colour).	
		Cream body, Red roof and mudguards	**£600-900**
		Cream body, Green roof and mudguards	**£600-900**
		Green roof and mudguards	**£600-900**
		Red body, Blue roof and mudguards	**£600-900**
		Red body, Cream roof and mudguards	**£600-900**
		Blue body, Red roof and mudguards	**£600-900**
		Blue body, Yellow roof and mudguards	**£600-900**
		Yellow body, Green roof and mudguards	**£600-900**
		Orange body, Green roof and mudguards, Gold washed wheels	**£600-900**
22g	1935-41	**Streamline Tourer** Model has cast steering wheel and windscreen, smooth diecast hubs which may be painted as body colour or a contrasting colour. Some have chrome hubs. Body colours: Green, Maroon, Red, Light or Dark Blue, Cream, Buff or Black	**£300-400**
		Turquoise body, Blue hubs, White tyres	**£500-750**
22h	1935-41	**Streamlined Saloon** A saloon version of 22g (no steering wheel). Wheels may be painted as body colour or a contrasting colour. Red, Maroon, Blue or Cream	**£300-400**
23	1934-35	**Racing Car** (1st casting) Lead body, no racing number, no driver, 0, 2, 3 or 4 exhausts stubs (without pipe), coloured tyres on some. Cream or White body with either Blue, Cream, Green, Orange or Red top and nose flash	**£200-300**
		Yellow body with Blue upper body flash, 3 exhaust stubs	**£200-300**
23a	1935-41	**Racing Car** (23 re-issued) As 1st casting but diecast body, no driver, no number, Black or White tyres, 4 exhausts. White body and hubs, Blue top flash and circle on nose	**£200-300**
		Cream body and hubs, Red top flash and circle on nose	**£200-300**
		Blue body, White top flash and circle on nose	**£200-300**
		Orange body, Green top flash and circle on nose	**£200-300**
		Yellow body, Dark Blue flash and circle on nose	**£200-300**
		Brown body, Cream top flash	**£200-300**
		Silver body, Green racing number '8'	**£200-300**

Ref	Year(s)	Model name and details	Market Price Range
23a		**Racing Car** (2nd casting) With driver plus raised circles for racing numbers, 6 exhausts in fishtail. *Colour type 1:* With minor colour sidestripes and perhaps coloured tyres. (Sometimes known as 'humbug' version). *Colour type 2:* Broad nose flash, even width top rear flash. (Also sometimes known as 'humbug' version). *Colour type 3:* Broad flash at cockpit and pointed ends top flash, cast circle on nose. Variations:	
		Type 1, Cream body, Red stripes, number '9'	**£400-600**
		Type 2, Blue with White stripes / driver, RN '11'	**£400-600**
		Type 2, Yellow body, Dark Blue top flash, racing number '7' or '1'	**£200-300**
		Type 2, Blue body, White top flash, racing number '11', '4' or '5'	**£200-300**
		Type 2, Yellow with Blue stripes, racing number '7', silvered 'Tootsie Toy' type hubs	**£750-1,000**
		Type 2, Orange with Green stripes, racing number '10', silvered 'Tootsie Toy' type hubs	**£750-1,000**
		Type 3, White body, Blue nose/circle/top flash, racing number '2'	**£200-300**
		Type 3, Cream body, Red nose/circle/top flash, racing number '3'	**£200-300**
		Type 3, Red body, Cream nose/top flash, no number, no transverse ribs	**£200-300**
		Type 3, White body, Green nose/circle/top flash, racing number '6'	**£200-300**
		Type 3, Orange body, Green nose/circle/top flash, racing number '4'	**£200-300**
		Casting variation with driver, raised racing number circle on nearside only, no detailed exhaust, Orange body, Green nose circle, Green RN '4'	**£150-175**
		Orange body, long Green upper body flash, 3 exhaust stubs, Green RN '4' or '10'	**£150-175**
		Yellow body, long Dark Blue upper body flash, plated hubs	**£200-250**
23a	1946-52	**Racing Car** (3rd casting) With transverse body ribs, no raised circle for racing numbers, and only issued in colour type 3, with or without racing numbers. (Re-introduced in 1954 as 220). Red or Red/Green body, Silver nose circle, top flash and side circle (Red RN '4'), Red hubs	**£40-50**
		Silver body, Red nose circle, top flash and side circle (Silver RN '4'), Red hubs	**£40-50**
		Red body, Cream flashes, Black hubs	**£40-50**
23b	1935-41	**Hotchkiss Racing Car** Blue body with Dark Blue, Red or Silver flash and racing number '2', '5' or '8'	**£150-200**
		Cream body with Red flash and RN '1'	**£150-200**
	1935-41	Yellow body with Blue flash and RN '3'	**£150-200**
		Orange body with Green flash and RN '6'	**£150-200**
		Green body with Yellow flash and RN '5'	**£150-200**
		Turquoise body with Blue flash and RN '4'	**£150-200**
	1946-48	Red with Silver flash and RN '5'	**£40-50**
		Silver with Red flash and RN '5'	**£40-50**
23c	1936-38	**Mercedes-Benz Racing Car** Red, Light Blue, Silver, Yellow or Light Green body with contrasting body flashes, with or without racing numbers '3', '4' or '5', driver cast-in, Black hubs, treaded tyres	**£200-250**
	1938-40	As previous model but with rivetted baseplate bearing information	**£150-200**
	1946-50	('Large Open Racing Car'). Re-issued 23c in Blue or Silver, with various racing numbers	**£40-50**

Cars

23d 1936-38 **Auto-Union Racing Car**
Early pre-war issues without driver:
Red, Turquoise, Pale Green, Yellow or Silver body,
racing numbers on some, clipped-in tinplate base ...**£200-300**
1938-41 Later pre-war issue with driver, rivetted baseplate ..**£200-300**
1946-50 Early post-war issue with driver:
Red or Silver body, with or with racing number,
Black or White tyres...**£60-70**
Later post-war issue without driver...........................**£50-60**

23e 1936-38 **'Speed Of The Wind' Racing Car**
Red, Blue, Light Blue, Green, Yellow or Silver body,
plain clipped-in tinplate base, driver, with or without
racing numbers '3' or '6', Black hubs and
herringbone tyres. Lead fakes exist.............................**£50-75**
1938-41 With rivetted baseplate bearing information................**£50-75**
1946-49 Red or Silver, rivetted informative baseplate,
Red hubs, Grey tyres **£35-45**
1950-54 (Renumbered to 221)
Silver body and hubs, plain base................................**£35-45**

23f 1952-54 **Alfa-Romeo Racing Car**
Red body, White racing number '8',
Red diecast hubs..**£85-95**
1954 (Renumbered to 232)

23g 1952-54 **Cooper-Bristol Racing Car**
Green body, White RN '6', Green ridged hubs **£85-95**
1954 (Renumbered to 233)

23h 1953-54 **Ferrari Racing Car**
Blue body, Yellow nose, RN '5' and ridged hubs........**£85-95**
1954 (Renumbered to 234)

23j 1953-54 **H.W.M. Racing Car**
Light Green body, Yellow '7', Green ridged hubs......**£85-95**
1954 (Renumbered to 235)

23k 1953-54 **Talbot-Lago Racing Car**
Blue body, Yellow RN '4', Blue diecast hubs.............**£85-95**
1954 (Renumbered to 230)

23m 1938-41 **'Thunderbolt' Speed Car**
Silver body, Black detailing, Union Jacks on tail,
Silver baseplate. In original Blue box dated '2-38',
code: 'A2247' **£125-150**
Red body, Silver detailing **£300-400**

23n 1953-54 **Maserati Racing Car**
Red, White flash and RN '9', Red diecast hubs **£85-95**
1954 (Renumbered to 231)

23p 1939-40 **Gardner's MG Record Car**
Dark Green, White flash and 'MG' logo, Union Jacks,
'MG Magnette' on lacquered unpainted tinplate
baseplate, Yellow box, dated '9-39', 104 mm..........**£150-200**
1946-47 Dark Green, Union Jacks, no flash,
'MG Record Car' on base, not boxed **£80-100**

23s 1938-40 **Streamlined Racing Car**
Light Green body, Dark Green detailing, lead........**£100-125**
Light Blue. Dark Blue or Silver detailing, lead **£100-125**
Orange body, lead...**£100-125**
Light Green, Light Blue, Red or Orange body,
mazak diecasting **£75-100**
23s 1948-54 Light, Mid or Dark Green, Silver or Green flashes **£50-65**
Navy Blue, Silver or Green flashes..........................**£50-65**
Silver body with Red, Green or Blue flashes..............**£50-65**
Red body with Silver or Black flashes, Black base **£50-65**
1954 (Renumbered to 222)

24a 1934-40 **Ambulance** See 'Emergency Vehicles' Section.

24b 1934-38 **Limousine**
Types 1 or 2: criss-cross chassis.
Types 1, 2 or 3: grille, no sidelights, no spare wheel,
3 side windows, 3 'stacked' parallel horizontal bonnet
louvres. Blue, Black or plated 'Tootsie-Toy' hubs.
Body/chassis colours:
Maroon/Dark Maroon, Maroon/Grey, Maroon/Black,
Blue/Yellow, Dark Blue/Black, Yellow/Brown......**£300-500**

1937-40 casting change:
Same colours but no spare wheel slot,
3 parallel bonnet louvres, open chassis,
'Bentley' grille and bumper.....................................**£200-400**

24c 1934-38 **Town Sedan**
Types 1 or 2: criss-cross chassis.
Types 1, 2 or 3: grille, spare wheel, no sidelights,
separate windscreen/steering wheel casting,
smooth Blue, Black or plated 'Tootsie-Toy'type hubs.
Body/chassis colours:
Green/Black, Green/Yellow, Pale Green/Red,
Dark Blue/Dark Blue, Cream/Dark Blue,
Cream/Black, Dark Blue/Black **£300-500**
1937-40 casting change:
Same colours but open chassis, no spare wheel slot,
narrower boot, shorter door handles.........................**£200-400**

24d 1934-38 **Vogue Saloon**
Types 1 or 2: criss-cross chassis.
Types 1, 2 or 3: grille, with nearside spare wheel,
no sidelights. Smooth Blue, Black or plated hubs
with White tyres.
Body/chassis colours:
Blue/Dark Blue, Blue/Black, Blue/Maroon,
Cream/Blue, Brown/Green, Pink/Green, Red/Grey,
Green/Blue, Green/Black, Maroon/Black **£300-500**
1937-40 casting change:
Same colours but open chassis,
higher 'domed' roofline, no spare wheel.................**£200-400**

24e 1934-38 **Super Streamlined Saloon**
Types 1 or 2: criss-cross chassis.
Types 1, 2 or 3: grille, no spare or sidelights,
12 bonnet louvres. Smooth Blue, Black or
plated 'Tootsie-Toy' type hubs.
Body/chassis colours:
Maroon/Black, Red/Maroon, Green/Maroon,
Red/Black, Green/Blue, Red/Brown, All Maroon ...**£300-400**
1937-40 casting change:
As previous model but with 13 bonnet louvres **£300-400**

24f 1934-38 **Sportsmans Coupé**
Criss-cross chassis, with spare wheel,
no sidelights, smooth hubs.
Blue/Blue, Blue/Black, Yellow/Brown,
Cream/Dark Blue, Tan/Brown...............................**£200-400**
1937-40 casting change:
Open chassis, higher 'domed' roofline,
no spare wheel **£200-400**

24g 1934-38 **Sports Tourer Four-seater**
Types 1 or 2: criss-cross chassis.
Types 1, 2 or 3: grille, spare wheel hub cast-in,
no sidelights, open tinplate windscreen, separate
dashboard/steering wheel casting. Blue or Black
smooth hubs or plated 'Tootsie-Toy'type hubs.
Body/chassis colours:
Yellow/Black, Yellow/Blue, Yellow/Brown,
Blue/Brown, Cream/Green, Cream/Brown,
Black/Cream, Blue/Maroon...................................**£300-500**
1937-40 casting change:
Open chassis, filled-in windscreen,
cast impression of spare wheel..............................**£300-500**

24h 1934-38 **Sports Tourer Two-seater**
Types 1 or 2: criss-cross chassis.
Types 1, 2 or 3: grille, spare wheel hub cast-in,
no sidelights, open tinplate windscreen, separate
dashboard/steering wheel casting. Plated, Blue or
Black smooth hubs.
Body/chassis colours:
Red/Red, Green/Dark Green, Yellow/Green,
Yellow/Blue, Yellow/Black, Yellow/Brown,
Black/Cream, Cream/Green, Red/Green,
Blue/Brown, Yellow/Purple...................................**£400-600**
1937-40 casting change:
Open chassis, filled-in windscreen,
cast impression of spare wheel..............................**£400-600**

Note: The rarest of the 24 Series have coloured tyres matching the body colour and a higher value can be expected.

25j	1947-48	**Jeep**

Red body, Black, Red or Blue hubs **£80-100**
Green body, Black or Red hubs **£80-100**
Aqua or Sky Blue body, Black or Yellow hubs **£100-150**

25y 1952-54 **Universal Jeep**
Red body, Blue hubs...**£80-100**
Red body, Red hubs...**£80-100**
Dark Green body, Mid-Green hubs **£80-100**
Dark Green body, Maroon hubs **£80-100**
1954 (Renumbered to 405)

27d 1950-54 **Land Rover**. See 'Farm and Garden Models'.
27f 1950-54 **Estate Car**. See 'Farm and Garden Models'

30a 1935-40 **Chrysler 'Airflow' Saloon** (renumbered to 32)
No chassis, separate bumper units, lead versions exist,
smooth plain or silvered hubs.
Turquoise, Maroon, Cream, Green,
Purplish Blue, Red, (hubs may be any colour) **£300-400**
With 'Tootsie-Toy' type plated chrome hubs **£300-400**
1946 Cream or Green body, smooth hubs, White tyres ...**£250-300**
1946-48 Blue, Cream or Green body,
ridged hubs usually Black **£200-250**

30b 1935-40 **Rolls-Royce**
Open chassis, no sidelights, authentic radiator,
smooth Black hubs or coloured hubs.
NB: Models with coloured hubs attract a premium.
1935-40 Cream/Black, Red and Maroon, Blue/Black,
Dark Blue/Black, Fawn/Black, Tan/Dark Brown,
Red/Black, All Black **£300-400**
Yellow/Brown, Red/Red, Grey/Grey,
Green/Light Green, Pale Green/Black **£250-350**
Light Blue body, smooth Black wheel hubs...........**£250-350**
Fawn body, Black hubs, Black open chassis...........**£250-350**
1946 Fawn body, Black open chassis and smooth hubs ..**£150-200**
Fawn, Black open chassis, ridged Silver hubs........**£200-250**
1946-50 Plain (closed) chassis, ridged hubs, Mid-Blue/Black,
Violet-Blue/Black, Greyish-Brown/Black,
Dark Blue/Black, Light Blue/Black, Fawn/Black, ..**£150-200**

30c 1935-40 **Daimler**
Open chassis, no sidelights, authentic radiator,
smooth hubs.
1935-40 Cream/Black, Blue/Black, Dark Blue/Black,
Yellow/Black, Fawn/Black **£200-300**
Turquoise/Black, Fawn/Black, Light Green/Black ..**£200-300**
Pink/Maroon, Red/Red **£175-250**
Two-tone Grey or two-tone Green **£300-500**
1940-41 Pale Tan body, Black chassis and hubs **£200-250**
1945-46 Beige body, smooth black hubs.........................**£300-400**
Green or Fawn body, smooth or ridged hubs............**£90-120**
1946-50 Plain (closed) chassis, ridged hubs.
Dark Green/Black, Cream/Black, Fawn/Black,
Beige/Black, Grey/Black, Light Green/Black.........**£100-150**
Medium Green body, Pale Green ridged hubs **£100-125**

30d 1935-40 **Vauxhall**
Open chassis, no sidelights, spare wheel in wing,
'egg box' or 'shield' grille.
1935-38 Green/Black, Blue/Black, Grey/Black,
Yellow/Black, Brown/Black **£200-300**
Yellow/Brown, Cream/Brown, Tan/Brown **£200-300**
Two-tone Grey or two-tone Green **£300-400**
1938-40 Radiator change: As previous model but with
'shield' grille, Black or coloured chassis **£200-300**
1946 Dark Olive Green body, open chassis,
smooth Black hubs, White tyres.............................**£100-125**
1946-50 Plain (closed) chassis, no spare wheel,
Green/Black, Dark Brown/Black, Maroon/Black,
Yellow/Black, Grey/Black, Olive-Green/Black,
Blue/Black **£100-125**
Hub variation: Dark Olive Green body,
Black chassis, Silver ridged hubs, thick axles **£200-250**

30e 1935-48 **Breakdown Car** See 'Commercial Vehicles' section.
30f 1936-41 **Ambulance** See 'Emergency Vehicles' section.
30g 1936-50 **Caravan** See 'Accessories (Pre-War)' section.

32 1934-35 **Chrysler 'Airflow' Saloon** (renumbered from 30a)
Maroon (lead) body, no chassis, separate bumpers ..**£200-250**
Same model, but diecast body................................**£200-250**

34a 1935-40 **'Royal Air Mail' Service Car**
See 'Commercial Vehicles and Vans' section.

35a 1936-40 **Saloon Car**
Some versions may have spare wheel cover
in a darker shade of the main colour.
Mid-Blue, Dark Blue, Maroon, Grey, Yellow, Red,
Turquoise, Black or White solid rubber wheels..........**£65-75**
1946-48 Grey or Light Blue body (spare wheel cover not
enhanced), Black rubber wheels................................**£50-60**

35az 1939-40 **Fiat 2-seater Saloon**
Red, Blue or Green, White rubber wheels,
'Simca 5' cast inside. French issue **£80-100**

35b 1936-39 **Racer**
Red, Silver, Yellow or Blue body, with or without
driver, White solid rubber wheels, Red grille and
steering wheel..**£65-75**
35b 1939-54 **Midget Racer**
Silver body, Red grille, Brown driver,
solid Black rubber wheels only **£65-75**
Same, but with Silver driver.................................**£65-75**
Green body, Black tyres **£150-175**
1954 (Renumbered to 200)

35c 1936-40 **MG Sports Car**
Red, Pale or Dark Green, Turquoise, Yellow,
Dark Blue or Maroon, Silver detailing,
White solid rubber wheels (Black later) **£75-100**
1946-48 Red or Green body, Silver on radiator only,
Black rubber wheels only.....................................**£40-50**

35d 1938-40 **Austin 7 Car** (open tourer)
Wire windscreen frame, Black or White rubber wheels,
Silver radiator and steering wheel, hole for driver.
Light Blue, Dark Blue, Turquoise, Grey,
Lime Green, Maroon or Yellow,
(Yellow may have Orange spare wheel cover) **£50-60**
1946-48 No wire windscreen frame, no hole for driver.
Light Blue, Grey or Yellow body,
Silver on radiator only, Black rubber wheels only......**£35-45**
As previous model, but Fawn body **£45-55**

36a 1937-41 **Armstrong-Siddeley Limousine with Driver and Footman**
Detailed chassis with slots, tinplate figures,
sidelights, Black smooth hubs.
Red/Dark Red, Grey/Dark Grey,
Maroon/Dark Maroon, all-Maroon..................**£1,000-1,500**
1946 Grey body, Black smooth wheel hubs,
moulded chassis with or without slots, no figures ...**£100-130**

> **Notable Auction Result**: In 2001, Christie's sold an
> all-maroon 36a Armstrong-Siddeley with Driver
> and Footman for **£2,350**

36a 1947-50 **Armstrong-Siddeley**
(no slots or figures), moulded chassis, ridged hubs
(black or coloured), plated radiator.
Mid-Blue/Black, Grey/Black, Maroon/Black,
Red/Maroon, Light Blue/Black, Powder Blue/Black,
Saxe-Blue/Black, Olive-Green/Black,
Turquoise/Black, Blue/Blue **£175-200**

36b 1937-41 **Bentley 2 seat Sports Coupé with Driver and Footman**
Detailed chassis with slots, tinplate figures,
sidelights, smooth black hubs.
Cream/Black, Yellow/Maroon, Grey/Grey........**£1,000-1,500**
1946 Light Green or Saxe Blue body, smooth black
hubs, moulded chassis (slots on some), no figures ..**£200-300**

36b 1947-50 **Bentley**
Moulded chassis (no slots/figures), ridged hubs,
plated radiator.
Green/Black, Dark Blue/Black, Light Blue/Black,
Grey/Black, Fawn/Black, Light Fawn/Black **£175-200**

36c 1937-41 **Humber Vogue Saloon with Driver and Footman**
Detailed chassis with slots, tinplate figures,
sidelights, plated radiator.
Green/Dark Green, Blue/Dark Blue,
all Royal Blue, smooth Black hubs...................**£1,100-1,400**
1946 Early post war issues with smooth Black hubs,
moulded chassis with or without slots, no figures ...**£100-150**

36c 1947-50 **Humber Vogue**
Dark Brown/Black, Blue/Black, Grey/Black,
Maroon/Black, no slots or figures, ridged hubs **£120-150**
Light Blue body, Black moulded chassis,
ridged Black hubs, plated radiator **£150-200**

36d 1937-41 **Rover Streamlined Saloon with Driver and Footman**
Detailed cast chassis with slots, tinplate driver and
passenger, sidelights, Black smooth hubs.
Light Green body, mid-Green wings,
White tyres..**£1,000-1,500**
Red Green body, Maroon wings, White tyres.........**£400-600**
1946 Early post war issues with smooth Black hubs
and moulded chassis with or without slots **£150-200**

36d 1947-50 **Rover**
No slots or figures, ridged hubs.
Dark, Saxe, Mid or Bright Blue/Black,
Light or Mid-Green/Black....................................**£130-170**
Green body with Light Green hubs.........................**£200-250**
Dark Blue body, Black wings, Light Blue hubs......**£300-350**
Navy Blue body, Black wings, Black hubs.............**£300-350**

36e 1937-41 **British Salmson Two-seater Sports Car with Driver**
Detailed chassis, hole in seat for driver,
cast Red or Green driver, Black hubs,
solid windscreen, sidelights, spare wheel on some.
Royal Blue/Black, Blue/Dark Blue, Black/Red,
Grey/Dark Grey, Silver/Black, Red/Maroon......**£1,000-1,500**

1946 **British Salmson**
Early post war issues with smooth Black hubs,
moulded chassis, no driver......................................**£125-175**
Rare Brown issues **£400-600**

36e 1947-50 **British Salmson Two-seater Sports Car**
Moulded chassis, no hole in seat,
tinplate windscreen, ridged hubs.
Red/Black, Light, Mid or Dark Green/Black,
Fawn/Black, Mid-Blue/Black,
Sky-Blue/Black or Saxe-Blue/Black **£90-150**
Red or Brown body **£300-400**

36f 1937-41 **British Salmson Four-seater Sports Car with Driver**
Detailed chassis, hole in seat for driver, cast driver,
sidelights, Black smooth hubs and solid
windscreen, cast-in spare wheel at rear.
Red/Maroon, Green/Dark Green,
Grey/mid-Grey, Deep Blue/Black **£1,000-1,500**

36f 1947-50 **British Salmson Four-seater Sports Car**
No hole or driver, tinplate windscreen, ridged hubs.
Black moulded chassis. Body colours:
Light or Mid-Green, Brown, Grey, Fawn,
Greenish-Grey or Light Grey **£150-200**

36f

Photo: Vectis Auctions Ltd.

**NB Early Post War Issues 38 and 39 Series:
see the Model Identification section for details.**

38a 1940-41 **Frazer Nash BMW Sports**
Red body, smooth Black hubs,
Red or Maroon seats..**£200-300**
Light Green with Dark Green seats........................**£200-300**
Dark Blue body and smooth Black hubs, Fawn seats **£150-250**
Light Grey body, Brown seats.................................**£150-250**
1946 Special issue:
Dark Blue body, Light Blue seats, spread spigot
not rivet, 'Hornby Series' tinplate sheet base **£150-250**
1947-50 Regular issues:
Black base, Black ridged hubs, celluloid windscreen:
Light or Dark Blue (Fawn or Grey seats) **£75-95**
Grey (Fawn, Khaki or Blue seats)............................**£150-200**
Grey (Red seats and hubs) or Blue (Blue hubs) **£150-200**
Light Grey (Blue seats, Black hubs) **£150-200**
Blue with Putty seats..**£150-200**
38a 1950-55 As previous models but made for export only........**£120-160**
1955 (Renumbered 100)

38b 1940-41 **Sunbeam Talbot Sports**
NB All 38b issues may be found with or without
silver edging to the windscreen.
Red (Maroon tonneau), Red or Black smooth
hubs, lacquered metal base......................................**£200-300**
1946 Grey body, Fawn seats or Green with Dark Green
tonneau, Black smooth hubs...................................**£300-400**
1947-49 From 1947, most have Black ridged hubs and
Black tinplate baseplate. Body/tonneau colours:
Red/Maroon **£120-160**
Maroon/Grey **£120-160**
Light Green/Green..**£120-160**
Brown/Blue...**£120-160**
Green/Dark Yellow...**£120-160**
Light Grey (Grey or Dark Blue tonneau)................**£120-160**
Dark Grey (Grey or Light Blue tonneau).................**£120-160**
Yellow body and hubs with matt Fawn tonneau **£200-300**
Deep Yellow body and hubs with
Dark Green tonneau, Silver edged screen................**£200-300**
Dark Blue body, Light Grey tonneau **£150-200**
Light Blue body, Dark Grey tonneau **£150-200**
Mid-Blue body, Grey tonneau.................................**£150-200**
Brown/Blue, Silver edged windscreen **£150-200**
1950 Late post war issues with coloured hubs,
e.g., Yellow body, Green tonneau, Yellow hubs or
Red body, Maroon tonneau, Red hubs **£100-150**
Red body, Dark Green tonneau, Red hubs..............**£100-150**
38b 1950-55 As previous models but made for export only........**£120-160**
1955 (Renumbered 101)

38c 1946 **Lagonda Sports Coupé**
Early post war issues with smooth Black hubs........**£120-160**
1947-50 From 1947, most have ridged Black hubs.
Green body, Black or Dark Green seats...................**£120-160**
Grey body, Fawn or Maroon seats **£120-160**
Maroon body, Dark Blue or Grey seats...................**£120-160**
Light Grey body, Mid or Dark Grey seats **£120-160**
38c 1950-55 As previous models but made for export only........**£120-160**
1950 Late post war issues with coloured hubs,
e.g., Green body with Light Green hubs.................**£120-160**
1955 (Renumbered 102)

38d 1940-41 **Alvis Sports Tourer**
Green body, Black seats and hubs, lacquered base ..**£200-250**
Maroon body, Red seats, lacquered base **£200-250**
1946 Early post war issues **£120-160**
1947-50 From 1947, all had a Black painted baseplate.
Green/Dark Green **£120-160**
Green/Brown..**£120-160**
Green body, Black seats, Black or Green hubs........**£120-160**
Maroon/Grey, Red hubs **£120-160**
Maroon/Red **£120-160**
Light Blue/Dark Blue **£120-160**
Blue/Grey...**£120-160**
Grey/Blue...**£120-160**
38d 1950-55 As previous models but made for export only........**£120-160**
1955 (Renumbered 103)

38e 1940 ? **Triumph Dolomite**
Planned and catalogued but not issued ....NPP

38e 1946 **Armstrong Siddeley Coupé** ('Hurricane')
Early post war issues with Black smooth hubs........**£100-150**
1947-50 From 1947, all have a Black painted baseplate.
Body / interior colours:
Grey/Deep Blue...**£120-160**
Light Grey/Blue..**£120-160**
Light Grey/Green..**£120-160**
Light Green/Grey...**£120-160**
Grey/Dark Green..**£120-160**
Bright Green/Grey..**£120-160**
Red/Maroon...**£120-160**
Cream/Blue...**£120-160**
Dark Green body and interior **£120-160**
Royal Blue body, Dark Green interior **£120-160**
Apple Green body, Dark Grey interior....................**£120-160**
1950 Light Green body, Apple Green hubs................**£250-300**
Light Green body, Grey interior, Mid-Green hubs ..**£250-300**
Light Grey body, Dark Green interior, Grey hubs ...**£250-300**
Grey body, Dark Blue interior, Red hubs................**£250-300**
Grey body, Dark Blue interior, Pale Blue hubs........**£250-300**
Grey body, Dark Blue interior, Mid-Blue hubs........**£250-300**
38e 1950-55 As previous models but made for export only........**£250-300**
1955 (Renumbered 104)

38f 1940-41 **Jaguar (SS100) Sports Car**
2 celluloid windscreens, clear lacquered baseplate.
Some windscreen edges have silver detailing.
Khaki/Blue, Blue/Grey, Light Blue/Grey, Grey/Blue,
Grey/Black, Red/Maroon, Dark Brown/Black........**£300-400**
1946 Early post-war issues with Black smooth hubs
(later issues are ridged) **£120-150**
1947-50 From 1947, all have a Black painted baseplate.
Light, Mid- or Dark Blue body,
Grey or Putty interior...**£120-150**
Light Brown body, Blue interior **£120-150**
Red body, Maroon interior **£120-150**
Brownish-Grey body, Black interior **£150-200**
Grey body, Red interior, Red hubs..........................**£250-300**
1950 Late post-war issues with coloured hubs,
e.g., Light Blue body, Putty interior (Blue hubs) or
Red body, Maroon interior (Red hubs) **£250-350**
38f 1950-55 As previous models but made for export only........**£200-300**
1955 (Renumbered 105)

39a 1939-41 **Packard Super 8 Tourer**
Smooth hubs, Silver or lacquered baseplate.
Light Green, Grey, Black, Yellow, Blue.................**£300-400**
1946 Early post-war issues with Black smooth hubs........**£100-125**
1947-50 All have a Black painted baseplate, ridged hubs.
Dark Brown, Green or Olive-Green body...............**£100-125**
1950 Late post-war issues with coloured ridged hubs.....**£200-250**

39b 1939-41 **Oldsmobile 6 Sedan**
Black, Maroon, Yellow, Mid Blue,
Light or Mid-Grey or Green, Silver base................**£150-200**
1946 Early post-war issues with smooth Black hubs........**£100-150**
1947-50 All have Black baseplate (open at rear), ridged hubs.
Grey, Brown, Green or Fawn body **£100-125**
Cream body **£125-150**
Violet-Blue..**£130-170**
1947-50 US issue: Light Blue body, Black hubs **£200-300**
1950 Late post-war issues with coloured ridged hubs **£200-250**
1952 Export issue: Beige body and hubs,
closed rear baseplate...**£200-300**
39bu 1950-52 **Oldsmobile Sedan** (US issue)
Cream with Dark Blue wings, Black baseplate **£600-800**
Cream body, Tan wings,
Black baseplate (closed at rear), Black hubs **£800-1,000**
Tan body and hubs, baseplate closed at rear...........**£600-800**
Light Blue body, Dark Blue wings, Lt. Blue hubs...**£600-800**

39c 1939-41 **Lincoln Zephyr Coupé**
Lacquered baseplate, smooth Black hubs.
Grey/Black, Yellow Red or Green body **£150-175**
1946 Early post-war issues with smooth Black hubs........**£100-150**
1947-50 Black painted baseplate, ridged hubs.
Light Grey, Brown, Maroon or Red body................**£90-120**
1950 Late post war issues with coloured ridged hubs,
Light 'Riley' Green with darker Green hubs or Red
body with Red hubs or Yellow with Green hubs **£200-400**

39cu 1950-52 **Lincoln Zephyr Coupé** (US issues)
All have Black painted baseplate.
Red body and ridged hubs, Maroon wings **£2,500-3,000**
Cream body and ridged hubs, Brown wings...........**£700-900**
Tan with Brown wings, Black ridged hubs.............**£700-900**

39d 1939-41 **Buick Viceroy Saloon**
Lacquered baseplate, smooth Black hubs.
Grey, Green, Maroon, Cream or Blue....................**£200-300**
1946 Early post-war issues with Black smooth hubs.....**£100-125**
1946 Olive body, smooth hubs.....................................**£100-125**
1947-50 All have Black painted baseplate, ridged hubs.
Light or Dark Green, Maroon, Fawn, Blue,
Beige or Grey body, matching ridged hubs............**£100-150**
Mustard body, Mustard ridged hubs......................**£150-200**
Greyish-Brown body, Light Brown ridged hubs.....**£150-200**
Apple Green body and matching ridged hubs.........**£150-200**
1950 Late post-war issues with coloured ridged hubs,
e.g., Light 'Riley' Green body with darker green
hubs or Brown body with Green or Yellow hubs ...**£200-400**

39e 1939-41 **Chrysler Royal Sedan**
Lacquered baseplate, smooth Black hubs.
Black, Green, Royal Blue or Grey body **£100-150**
Yellow body, Black hubs...**£400-600**
1946 Early post-war issues with smooth Black hubs.....**£100-125**
1947-50 All have ridged hubs.
Light Blue, Mid-Blue, Dark Blue, Light Green,
Mid-Green, Dark Green or Dark Grey body,
Black ridged hubs and baseplate **£85-110**
As previous models but with Silvered baseplate **£250-350**
Cream body, Light Green hubs, Black baseplate **£500-750**
1950 Late post-war issues with coloured ridged hubs,
e.g., Light 'Triumph 1800' Blue with Blue hubs **£200-250**
39eu 1950-52 **Chrysler Royal Sedan** (US issues)
Black baseplate, Blued axles.
Yellow with Red wings, Yellow hubs **£1,500-2,000**
Two-tone Green body, Light Green hubs..........**£1,000-1,400**

39f 1939-41 **Studebaker State Commander**
Lacquered baseplate, smooth Black wheel hubs.
Yellow, Green or Dark Grey body **£200-250**
1946 Early post-war issues with smooth Black hubs.......**£100-150**
1946 Yellow body, smooth Black hubs........................**£250-350**
1947-50 From 1947, all have Black baseplate, ridged hubs.
Green, Olive or Maroon body **£90-120**
Dark Grey or Light Grey body, Black hubs.............**£90-120**
Dark Maroon body, Black hubs...............................**£90-120**
Very Dark Blue or Navy Blue body, Black hubs......**£90-120**
Tan body, Black ridged hubs.................................**£120-150**
Mid-Blue body, Mid-Blue hubs **£200-250**
Dark Green body, Black hubs................................**£120-140**
1950 Late post-war issues with coloured ridged hubs.....**£200-250**

39eu

39c

Photos: Vectis Auctions Ltd.

40a   **Riley Saloon**

1947-50   *1st baseplate*: Tinplate baseplate '40A' has small
lettering and the rear wheels are retained by cast pillars.

Light, Mid or Dark Grey body, Black hubs...................**£80-90**
Light Grey body, Tan hubs **£80-90**
Mid-Green body, Black hubs..**£80-100**

1950-53   *2nd baseplate*: with '40A' and large lettering.
Also with tow-hook aperture.

Dark Blue or Mid-Blue body, Black hubs **£80-100**
Grey body, Black hubs...**£150-175**
Dark Green body, Black hubs..**£80-100**
Cream body, Mid-Green hubs..**£80-100**

1954   *40a renumbered 158*

40b   **Triumph 1800 Saloon**

1948-49   Small baseplate lettering, rear axles held by cast
pillars (see diagram).

Light, Mid or Dark Grey body, Black hubs.................**£80-100**
Light, Mid or Dark Grey body, Grey hubs...................**£80-100**
Mid-Blue body and hubs **£100-130**
Light Blue body, Blue or Fawn hubs...........................**£90-110**
Fawn body, Black or Fawn hubs **£80-100**
Black body, Black hubs **£400-600**

1949-54   *2nd baseplate*:
Small lettering on baseplate,
rear axle held by baseplate tabs.

Mid or Dark Blue body, Fawn hubs **£80-100**
Light Blue body and hubs...**£80-100**
Fawn body, Green hubs **£80-90**

1954   *40b renumbered 151*

> Casting with rear axle pillars (1948 - 50),
> Small lettering on baseplate, as illustrated (1948 - 53)
> Large lettering on baseplate (not illustrated) (1954 - 60),
> Two raised rails on baseplate, as illustrated (1948 - 53)
> No raised rails on baseplate (not illustrated) (1954 - 60)

40c   **Jowett Javelin**

1940   Factory drawing exists but model not issued ....NPP

40d   **Austin (A40) Devon**

1949-54   Small baseplate lettering, rear axle held by the baseplate.

Maroon body and hubs **£80-90**
Red body, Maroon hubs...**£400-600**
Light Grey-Green body and hubs **£90-110**
Light Grey-Green body, Beige hubs............................**£90-110**
Light Blue body, Mid-Blue hubs **£90-110**
Mid-Blue body, Light Blue hubs **£90-110**
Dark Green body, Cream hubs **£80-90**
Luminous Blue body, Mid-Blue hubs.........................**£120-140**

1954   *40d renumbered 152*

---

158   **Riley Saloon** (renumbered from 40a)

1954-55   158 baseplate has large lettering; no tow-hook aperture.

Cream body, Mid-Green hubs......................................**£150-200**
Mid-Green body, Green hubs **£150-200**
Light Green body and hubs **£150-200**
Light Green body, Mid-Green hubs.............................**£150-200**
Dark Blue body, Mid-Blue hubs..................................**£150-200**
Light Grey body and hubs **£150-200**

> See also the 'Dinky Toys Cars - Box Types' and
> 'Model Identification' information pages.

---

151   **Triumph 1800 Saloon** (renumbered from 40b)

1954-60   151 baseplate has large lettering.

Beige body, Green hubs **£90-110**
Dark Blue, Light Blue hubs **£90-110**
Light Blue body, Mid-Blue hubs **£90-110**
Light Blue body, Fawn hubs **£90-110**
Light Blue body, Grey hubs **£90-110**
Mid-Blue body, Light Blue hubs **£90-110**

---

152   **Austin (A40) Devon** (renumbered from 40d)

1954-59   Large baseplate lettering (see example diagrams).
'DEVON' cast into underside of roof.

Suede Green body and hubs **£150-200**
Dark Blue body, Mid-Blue hubs..................................**£150-200**
Tan body, Suede Green hubs **£500-700**
Maroon body, Red hubs...**£175-200**
Light Blue body and hubs...**£400-500**
Dark Blue body, Light Blue hubs **£150-200**
Light Green body, Mid-Green hubs.............................**£150-200**
Dark Green body with Fawn hubs................................**£150-200**

1956-59   *Two-tone issues*:

Blue upper body and hubs, Yellow lower body..........**£200-300**
Cerise lower body, Green upper body, Cream hubs...**£200-300**

40e / 153   **Standard Vanguard**

> Casting with open wheel arches
> (no spats) (1948 - 50)

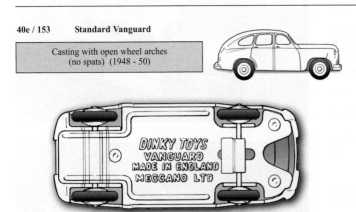

> Tinplate clip secures rear axle (1948 - 49)
> Small lettering on baseplate (1948 - 53)
> Baseplate has raised rails (1948 - 53)

> Baseplate tabs secure rear axle (1949 - 60)
> Large lettering on baseplate (1954 - 60)
> No raised rails on baseplate (1954 - 60)
> Body casting includes rear wheel spats (1951 - 60)

40e   **Standard Vanguard**
1948   *1st casting*: Open rear wheel arches, small baseplate
         lettering, rear axle secured by tinplate clip.
         Fawn body and hubs...£125-150
         Fawn body, Red hubs..£150-175
1949-50 *baseplate change*: Open rear wheel arches, small or
         large base lettering, rear axle held by baseplate tabs.
         Fawn body and hubs...£80-100
         Mid-Blue body and hubs...£80-100
         Maroon body and hubs..£80-100
         Dark Blue body, Fawn hubs....................................£500-600
1950-54 *2nd casting*: Closed rear wheel arches.
         Light Blue body, Fawn hubs...................................£100-150
         Fawn body with Fawn hubs....................................£100-150
1954   *40e renumbered 153*

153   **Standard Vanguard** (renumbered from 40e)
1954-60 'VANGUARD' cast into underside of roof,
         large baseplate lettering.
         Mid-Blue body, Cream, Blue or Fawn hubs..............£100-150
         Dark Blue body, Fawn hubs....................................£200-250
         Fawn body, Fawn hubs...£100-150
         Cream body, Cream hubs...£100-150
         Maroon body, Fawn hubs..£100-150
         Maroon body, Maroon hubs...................................£750-1,000
   NB The ridge which appears on the boot of some
         Vanguard models is the result of worn die replacement.

> Please note that the illustrations on these two pages
> are not all to the same scale.

40f   **Hillman Minx**
1951-54 *1st baseplate*:
         Small baseplate lettering (see diagram).
         Tan body, Fawn hubs...£150-175
         Mid-Green body, Light Green hubs.........................£150-175
         Light Green body and hubs.....................................£150-175
         Light Green body, Mid-Green hubs.........................£150-175
         Dark Tan body, Green hubs.....................................£150-175
         Dark Tan body, Cream hubs....................................£150-175
         Light Tan body, Cream hubs...................................£150-175
         Dark Green body, Mid-Green hubs.........................£150-175
1955   *40f renumbered 154*

154   **Hillman Minx** (renumbered from 40f)
         'HILLMAN MINX' cast into underside of roof.
1955-59 *2nd baseplate*:
         Large baseplate lettering (see diagram).
         Dark Tan body, Cream or Green hubs......................£110-140
         Pale Tan body, Blue or Yellow hubs.........................£110-140
         Light Green body and hubs.....................................£175-200
         Dark Green body, Light Green hubs........................£175-200
         Pale Green body, Light Green hubs.........................£175-225
         Light Green body, Mid-Green hubs........................£175-225
         Two-tone issues:
         Pale Blue lower body and hubs, Cerise upper body...£200-250
         Lime Green lower body, Cream upper body & hubs.£200-250

> 1951 - 54: Small lettering on baseplate,
> Two raised rails on baseplate, Rear axle secured by baseplate tabs

> 1954 - 59: Large lettering on baseplate,
> No raised rails on baseplate, Rear axle secured by baseplate tabs

40g   **Morris Oxford**
1950-54 Small baseplate lettering.
         Fawn body, Grey hubs...£80-100
         Grey body and hubs..£80-100
         Green body, Light Green hubs.................................£80-100
         Green body, Fawn hubs...£80-100
1954   *40g renumbered 159*

159   **Morris Oxford** (renumbered from 40g)
1954   Small baseplate lettering, 'MORRIS OXFORD'
         cast into underside of roof.
         Dark Green body and hubs......................................£140-175
         Green body, Light Green hubs...............................£140-175
         Beige body and hubs (Export issue)........................£500-800
         Blue body, Grey hubs...£1,500-2,000
         Fawn body, Grey or Stone hubs.............................£120-140
         Two-tone issues:
         Green upper body and hubs, Cream lower body......£150-175
         Cream upper body and hubs, Cerise lower body £150-175
         Turquoise upper body, Cream lower body,
         Turquoise-Green hubs...£500-700

> See also the 'Dinky Toys Cars - Box Types' and
> 'Model Identification' information pages.

40h   **Austin Taxi (FX3)**
1952-54 Diecast chassis with cast-in driver and model number.
         All-Yellow body and hubs, Black chassis,
         interior and driver £100-125
         All-Yellow body and hubs, Brown chassis,
         interior and driver £150-250
         Dark Blue body, Light Blue hubs, Black chassis,
         interior and driver £250-350
         Mid-Blue body and hubs, Black chassis,
         interior and driver £400-600
1954   *40h renumbered 254*

254   **Austin Taxi (FX3)** (renumbered from 40h)
1956-59 Blue body, Light Blue hubs £500-750
         Black body, spun hubs, Grey chassis ('254'),
         interior and driver £110-130
         Two-tone issue:
         Yellow upper body and hubs, Dark Green lower
         body, Black chassis ('254'), interior and driver £90-120

40j   **Austin (A40) Somerset**
1953-54 Large lettering on baseplate.
         Pale Blue body and hubs...£80-100
         Red body and hubs...£80-100
         Mid-Blue body and hubs...£80-100
         Dark Blue body, Mid-Blue hubs...............................£80-100
1954   *40j renumbered 161*

161   **Austin (A40) Somerset** (renumbered from 40j)
1954   Large baseplate lettering, 'AUSTIN SOMERSET'
         cast into underside of roof.
         Pale Blue body, Mid or Dark Blue hubs....................£80-100
         Red body and hubs...£80-100
1956-59 *Two-tone issues*:
         Red lower body and hubs, Yellow upper body..........£200-250
         Cream lower body and hubs, Black lower body £200-250

101 1957-60   **Sunbeam Alpine** (touring finish)
Maroon body, Cream interior,
Cream diecast hubs, Grey driver.............................£120-140
Same model, but with spun hubs £200-300
Light Turquoise body, Dark Blue interior,
Mid-Blue diecast hubs, Grey driver........................£120-140
Same model, but with spun hubs £150-175
Light Blue body, Blue diecast hubs £120-140

102 1957-60   **MG Midget** (touring finish)
Deep Yellow body, Red interior,
Red diecast hubs, Grey driver................................£150-175
Pale Green body, Cream interior,
Cream diecast hubs, Grey driver............................£250-350
Late issues with spun aluminium hubs,
in plain or lighter yellow boxes..............................£250-350

103 1957-60   **Austin Healey 100** (touring finish)
Red body, Grey interior, diecast hubs and driver.....£250-300
Cream body, Red interior and hubs, Grey driver.....£250-300

104 1957-60   **Aston-Martin DB3S** (touring finish)
Light Blue body, Dark Blue interior,
Mid-Blue hubs, Grey driver £150-200
Salmon-Pink body, Red interior and diecast hubs,
Grey driver, Matt or Gloss baseplate £150-200

105 1957-60   **Triumph TR2** (touring finish)
Grey body, Red interior and hubs, Grey driver........£250-300
Same, but with spun hubs and plastic steering
wheel. 'Plain' printed or late lighter yellow box......£300-400
Lemon Yellow body, Pale Green interior,
Mid-Green hubs, Grey driver £250-300
     1959-60   As before but with spun hubs, in 'plain' printed box
with Yellow spot, or in late lighter Yellow box £350-450

106 1954-58   **Austin A90 Atlantic** (Renumbered from 140a)
Light Blue body, Cream interior, Cream hubs........£125-150
Light Blue body, Red interior, Red or Cream hubs .£200-250
Light Blue body, Dark Blue interior,
Cream or Dark Blue hubs......................................£125-150
Black body, Red interior and hubs, White tyres £125-150
Pink body, Cream interior, Cream hubs,
'106' on baseplate...£100-120
NB Interiors may have a gloss or matt finish.

107 1955-59   **Sunbeam Alpine Sports** (competition finish)
Pale Blue, Beige or Cream interior,
Cream hubs, '26', racing driver £125-150
Deep Pink body, Grey interior, Cream hubs,
RN '34', racing driver £125-150
NB See also 'Factory samples' listing at the
end of this section.

108 1955-59   **MG Midget** (competition finish)
Red body, Tan interior, Red hubs,
RN '24', racing driver £150-200
Cream body, Red interior, Red hubs,
RN '26' or '28', racing driver £150-200
NB The version of 108 issued in the US is numbered 129.

109 1955-59   **Austin-Healey 100** (competition finish)
Cream body, Red interior and hubs,
racing driver and racing number '22' or '23'..........£150-200
Yellow body, Blue interior and hubs,
racing driver and racing number '21' or '28'..........£150-200

110 1956-59   **Aston-Martin DB3S** (competition finish)
Grey body, Blue interior and hubs,
racing driver and number '20'................................£150-175
Mid-Green body, Red interior,
Red ridged hubs, racing number '22' or '25'..........£150-200
Light Green body, Red interior,
Red ridged hubs, RN '22' or '25' £200-250

110 1966-67   **Aston-Martin DB5**
Metallic Red, Cream or Black interior,
'110' on base, spoked wheels £100-120
     1967-71   Metallic Red or Blue, Cream or Black interior,
plain base, spoked wheels £100-120
NB See also 'Factory samples' listing at the
end of this section.

> **Note: Models produced in South Africa should all**
> **be housed in boxes that have both**
> **English and Afrikaans printed wording.**

111 1956-59   **Triumph TR2 Sports Car** (competition finish)
Salmon-Pink body, Blue interior and hubs,
racing driver and RN '29' £200-250
Turquoise body, Red interior and hubs,
racing driver and racing number '25' £200-250

112 1961-66   **Austin-Healey Sprite Mk.II**
Red body, Cream interior, spun hubs £125-175
South African issues: (English / Afrikaans on box)
Turquoise body, Cream interior, spun hubs £500-750
Light or Dark Blue, Cream interior, spun hubs........£500-750
Lilac (Pink) body, Cream interior, spun hubs £500-750

113 1962-69   **MG 'MGB' Sports Car**
Cream body, Red interior,
Grey plastic driver, spun hubs...............................£100-125
South African issues: (English / Afrikaans on box)
Mid-Blue body, Red interior, spun hubs £750-1,000
Red body, Cream interior, spun hubs £750-1,000
Ivory body, spun hubs £750-1,000

114 1963-71   **Triumph Spitfire**
Sports car with Blue lady driver (plastic),
spun hubs, jewelled headlamps.
     1963-66   Metallic Silver-Grey body, Red interior...................£120-140
Red body, Cream interior £120-140
     1966-70   Metallic Gold body, Red interior,
'Tiger In Tank' on bootlid £120-140
     1966-70   Metallic Gold body, without bootlid logo................£120-140
     1970-71   Metallic Purple body, Gold interior £150-200

115 1965-69   **Plymouth Fury Sports**
White open body, Red interior, cast wheels,
driver and passenger, 'window' box...........................£70-80

116 1966-71   **Volvo P 1800 S**
Red body, White interior, wire wheels.......................£60-75
Metallic Red, Light Blue interior, wire wheels........£100-130

120 1962-67   **Jaguar 'E' type**
Red body, detachable Black or Grey hardtop plus
optional Cream or Grey folded soft-top, spun hubs.£100-130
Metallic Blue and White, Black, Grey or
Cream body, spun hubs £100-130
Metallic Light Blue and Black body,
White interior, spun hubs £700-900

122 1977-78   **Volvo 265 DL Estate**
Metallic Blue (Brown interior), or Cream with
'265DL' wing badges, cast hubs................................£30-35
     1979-80   Orange version without '265 DL' (made in
Italy by Polistil), Brown box....................................£40-50
NB See also 'Factory samples' listing at the
end of this section.

123 1977-80   **Princess 2200 HL**
Metallic Bronze with black roof side panels,
plastic wheels...£30-35
All White £30-35
White body, with Blue roof OR Blue side panels.......£30-35

124 1977-79   **Rolls-Royce Phantom V**
Metallic Light Blue,
boot opens - bonnet does not (see 152)......................£35-45

127 1964-66   **Rolls-Royce Silver Cloud Mk.3**
Metallic Blue or Metallic Green body,
White interior, spun hubs £65-75
     1966-69   Metallic Gold body, White interior, cast hubs £55-65
     1969-72   Metallic Red body, White interior, cast hubs...............£55-65

> **Market prices shown here are for guidance only. They refer ONLY to**
> **mint models in pristine boxes (where appropriate) that are complete**
> **with all of their original contents.**

128 1964-67 **Mercedes-Benz 600**
Metallic Maroon body, White interior, spun hubs,
three figures/luggage **£45-55**

1967-75 Metallic Maroon body, White interior, Blue base,
spun hubs or Speedwheels, driver only **£30-40**

1975-79 Metallic Blue, White interior, driver, Speedwheels **£30-35**

129 1954? **MG Midget** (US issue)
White body, Maroon or Red interior and tonneau,
Red hubs, no driver or racing number (see 108).
Yellow box with '129' **£700-900**
Red body, Tan interior and tonneau, Red hubs,
no driver or RN (see 108), Yellow box with '129' ..**£700-900**

129 1965 -72 **Volkswagen 1300 Sedan**
Metallic Blue body, White interior, spun hubs,
registration plate 'K.HK 454' **£45-55**

1972-76 Metallic Bright Blue, White interior, Speedwheels **£30-35**

130 1964-66 **Ford Consul Corsair**
Red or Metallic Wine Red body,
Off-White interior, spun hubs.........................**£65-75**

1966-69 Pale Blue, Metallic Dark Grey base,
Off-White interior, spun hubs.........................**£45-55**
NB Baseplates may have rounded or dimpled rivets.

131 1956-61 **Cadillac Eldorado**
Yellow body, Cerise interior, Grey or Brown driver,
Grey or Cream diecast hubs, packing also in box....**£110-140**
Salmon-Pink body, Grey interior, Grey driver,
Beige diecast hubs, packing piece also in box **£110-140**

1962-63 As previous models but with spun hubs **£300-400**

131 1968-70 **Jaguar 'E'-type 2+2**
White body, Light Blue or Red interior,
Gold base, cast spoked wheels **£90-110**

1970-75 Metallic Copper body, Blue interior,
Gold base, cast spoked wheels or plastic wheels........**£70-80**

1975-76 Metallic Purple body, Light Blue interior,
cast spoked wheels....................................**£80-100**

1976-77 Bronze body, Speedwheels...............................**£70-90**

1977-77 Metallic Red or Post Office Red body,
Blue interior, Speedwheels **£80-100**

132 1955-61 **Packard Convertible**
Light Green body, Red interior and hubs,
Grey driver...**£110-140**
Pale Tan body, Red interior and hubs, Grey driver ..**£110-140**

1962-63 As previous models but with spun hubs **£130-160**

132 1967-74 **Ford 40 RV**
Metallic Silver body, Red interior, spoked wheels **£30-40**
Fluorescent Pink body, Yellow engine cover,
White interior, spoked wheels **£35-45**
Metallic Light Blue body, Red or Yellow interior **£30-40**
NB Early models have red headlight recesses.

133 1955-60 **Cunningham C5R**
White body, Dark Blue stripes, Brown interior,
RN '31', Blue hubs, Light Blue driver **£65-75**
Off-White body, Blue interior and driver...................**£65-75**
As previous models but with spun aluminium hubs **£70-80**

133 1964-66 **Ford Cortina** (issued to replace 139)
Metallic Gold/White body, Red interior, spun hubs, ..**£60-70**

1966-68 Pale Lime body, Red interior, spun hubs **£65-75**

134 1964-68 **Triumph Vitesse**
Metallic Aqua Blue body, White side stripe,
Red interior, spun hubs................................**£70-85**
Metallic Aqua Blue body, White side stripe,
Grey interior, spun hubs **£80-90**
Indian issues:
Manufactured in India and fully licensed by Meccano.
Sold as 'Dinky Toys' and not the later 'Nicky Toys'.
Box marked 'Licenced Manufacturer & Registered User
in India, S. Kumar & Co., Registered Proprietors of
Trade Mark Meccano Ltd.' Model base also marked
'Licensee in India S. Kumar & Co.'. Variations:
Green body, White flash, cast hubs, rubber tyres **£300-400**
Red body, cast hubs, rubber tyres **£300-400**

135 1963-69 **Triumph 2000 Saloon**
Red interior, Grey base, spun hubs, wipers, luggage.
Normal colours: Metallic Green with White roof or
Metallic Blue with White roof, spun hubs **£70-90**
Gift Set 118 colour: White body, Blue roof,
Red interior, spun hubs, individually boxed............**£110-140**
Promotional colours: Each promotional issue was
packed in a standard Yellow/Red card picture box.
Black body, Cactus-Green or White roof................**£350-500**
Blue Grey body, Black roof **£350-500**
Light Green body with Lilac roof **£350-500**
Metallic Green with White roof **£350-500**
Brown body, Light Green roof **£350-500**
British Racing Green, White roof **£350-500**
Red or Cherry Red body, White roof, Blue interior.**£350-500**
White body, Black roof, Blue interior.......................**£350-500**
White body, Light Green roof, Blue interior...........**£350-500**
White body, Light Grey roof, Blue interior **£350-500**
White body, Wedgewood Blue roof, Blue interior....**£350-500**
Dark Green body, Cactus-Green roof.....................**£350-500**
Gunmetal body, Black roof,
with 'Gunmetal/WD' label on box **£350-500**

136 1964-65 **Vauxhall Viva**
White-Grey body, Red interior, spun hubs................**£60-75**

1965-68 Metallic Bright Blue body, Red interior, spun hubs **£55-65**

1969-73 Pale Metallic Blue body, Red interior, spun hubs.......**£50-65**

137 1963-66 **Plymouth Fury Convertible**
Green body, Cream hood, spun hubs **£70-85**
Metallic Grey body, Cream hood, spun hubs...............**£70-85**
Pink body, Cream hood, spun hubs..........................**£70-85**
Blue body, Cream hood, spun hubs..........................**£70-85**

138 1963-66 **Hillman Imp**
Metallic Silver-Green body, Red or White interior,
luggage, spun hubs, cast headlamps...........................**£75-85**

1966-68 Metallic Red body, luggage, spun hubs,
jewelled or plastic headlamps **£70-90**

1968-73 Metallic mid-Blue body,
luggage, spun hubs, jewelled headlamps **£70-90**
As previous issue but with Blue interior,
in picture box with white background.....................**£175-200**
Late issue: Metallic Deep Blue body, Red interior,
bare metal baseplate, spun hubs **£175-225**

139 1963-64 **Ford Consul Cortina**
Pale Blue body, Off-White interior, spun hubs,
cast headlamps..**£65-75**

1964-65 Metallic Blue body, Fawn interior, spun hubs **£65-75**
South African issues: English / Afrikaans on box.
Bright Green body, Fawn interior, spun hubs **£750-1,000**
Dark Green body, Fawn interior, spun hubs **£800-1,100**

139a 1949-54 **Ford Fordor Sedan**
All have small lettering on the black baseplates
which may be gloss or matt.
Yellow, Red, Green or Tan body,
(all with matching hubs)................................**£80-100**
Green body, Yellow hubs................................**£80-100**
Brown body, Red hubs **£80-100**
Tan body, Maroon hubs.................................**£80-100**
Red body, Maroon hubs **£80-100**
NB Later issues have 'Ford Sedan' cast into
underside of roof.
1954 (Renumbered to 170)

139am 1950-54 **US Army Staff Car** See 'Military Vehicles' section.

139b 1950-54 **Hudson Commodore**
Dark Blue body, Stone roof and hubs **£80-100**
Dark Blue body, Tan roof and hubs **£80-100**
Deep Cream body, Maroon roof and hubs **£80-100**
Royal Blue body, Pale Tan roof and hubs..............**£100-130**
Grey lower body, Light Blue roof
(as 151 (40b) Triumph Renown Blue) ....NGPP
Dark Blue body, Grey roof and hubs ....NGPP
1954 (Renumbered to 171)

> **Note: Models produced in South Africa should all
> be housed in boxes that have both
> English and Afrikaans printed wording.**

Cars

140a 1951-53 **Austin A90 Atlantic**
Mid-Blue body, Red interior, Cream hubs **£300-400**
Mid-Blue body and hubs, Dark Blue interior **£1,200-1,500**
Mid-Blue body, Maroon interior, Cream hubs ...**£1,000-1,250**
Deep Blue body, Red interior and hubs **£1250-150**
Red body, Maroon interior and hubs **£1,200-1,500**
Light Blue body, Red interior, Cream hubs **£250-350**
Red body, Cream interior and hubs **£100-120**
Light Blue body, Red interior and hubs **£100-120**
Pink body, Cream interior and hubs **£100-120**
Black body, Red interior and hubs **£100-120**
NB Interiors may have a gloss or matt finish.
1954 (Renumbered to 106)

140b 1951-54 **Rover 75 Saloon**
Maroon body and hubs. Sold unboxed...................**£100-125**
Maroon body, Red hubs. Sold unboxed **£100-125**
Cream body and hubs. Sold unboxed...................**£100-125**
Cream body, Blue hubs.
Supplied in dual-numbered box ('140b/156')..........**£140-180**
Red body, Maroon hubs.
Supplied in dual-numbered box ('140b/156')....**£1,000-1,250**
1954 (Renumbered to 156)

140 1963-69 **Morris 1100**
Light Blue or Dark Blue, spun hubs **£50-65**
South African issues: English and Afrikaans on box.
White body, Blue roof, Red interior, spun hubs......**£500-700**
Caramel body, Red interior, spun hubs **£500-700**
Sky Blue body, Red interior, spun hubs..................**£500-700**

141 1963-67 **Vauxhall Victor Estate Car**
Yellow body, Blue interior, spun hubs **£50-65**
1963 South African issues: English / Afrikaans on box.
Pink, Ivory or Yellow body,
all with Blue interior, spun hubs **£400-600**
US promotional: Dark Red body, Blue interior,
spun hubs. Paper labels with Yellow wording:
'LIGHTNING FASTENERS LTD',
'TECHNICAL SERVICES' **£500-750**

142 1962-68 **Jaguar Mk.10**
Metallic Light Blue or Mid-Blue,
Red interior, spun aluminium hubs **£50-65**
1963 South African issues: English and Afrikaans on box.
Ivory body, spun hubs **£500-750**
Green body with White roof, spun hubs **£500-750**
Sky Blue body, Red interior, luggage,
Cream base, spun hubs......................................**£800-1,100**
NB Gold, US export issue 'see-through' window
boxes. Model nos. 134, 138 and 142 housed in
these boxes may attract a premium of 50%.
See 'Cars - Box Types' for a complete listing.

143 1962-67 **Ford Capri**
Turquoise body, White roof, Red interior, spun hubs ..**£60-70**

144 1963-67 **Volkswagen 1500**
Off-White body, Red interior, luggage, spun hubs **£55-65**
Metallic Gold or Bronze body, Blue interior,
luggage, spun hubs **£55-65**
Metallic Gold or Bronze body, Red interior,
luggage, spun hubs **£100-125**
1963 South African issues: English and Afrikaans on box.
Metallic Green body, spun hubs...........................**£500-750**
Caramel body...**£500-750**

145 1962-67 **Singer Vogue**
Metallic Light Green body, Red interior, spun hubs **£70-80**
Yellow body, Red interior, spun hubs **£1,500-2,000**

146 1963-67 **Daimler 2.5 litre V8**
Metallic Pale Green body, Red interior, spun hubs......**£80-90**

147 1962-69 **Cadillac '62**
Metallic Green body, Red or White interior
spun hubs **£60-75**

148 1962-65 **Ford Fairlane**
(Non-metallic) Pea Green body, Cream interior,
open or closed windows, spun hubs...........................**£75-85**
As previous model but with Red interior................**£100-125**
1963 South African issues: English and Afrikaans on box.
Bright Blue body, closed windows,
spun hubs, White tyres **£500-800**
Dark Blue body, Light Grey interior,
spun hubs, no base number, White tyres.................**£500-800**
Heather Grey body, Light Grey interior,
spun hubs, no base number, White tyres **£500-800**
1965-67 Light Metallic Green, Pale Cream interior,
open windows, spun hubs..................................**£125-150**
US issue: Metallic Emerald Green body,
spun hubs, Gold 'see-through' window box **£300-400**

149 1971-75 **Citroën Dyane**
Metallic Bronze body, Black roof and interior,
Speedwheels **£30-35**
1971-75 Light Grey body, Dark Grey or Black roof................**£25-30**

150 1959-64 **Rolls-Royce Silver Wraith**
Two-tone Grey body, suspension, spun hubs,
Chromed metal bumpers **£55-65**
Later issues with plastic bumpers **£60-85**
NB The French version of 150 (French reference 551)
was cast from English-made dies, was assembled in
France, and has 'Made in France' on the baseplate.

151 1954-59 **Triumph 1800 Saloon** (renumbered from 40b)
See '40 Series' pages.

151 1965-69 **Vauxhall Victor 101**
Pale Yellow body, Red interior, spun hubs.................**£80-100**
Metallic Red body, White interior, spun hubs...........**£80-100**

152 1954-59 **Austin (A40) Devon** (renumbered from 40d)
See '40 Series' pages.

152 1965-67 **Rolls-Royce Phantom V**
Navy Blue body, Beige interior, chauffeur and two
passengers, spun hubs or cast hubs **£100-125**
1967-77 Design change: Very Dark Blue body,
White interior with Chauffeur but no passengers,
Blue base, cast hubs **£40-50**

153 1954-59 **Standard Vanguard** (renumbered from 40e)
See '40 Series' pages.

153 1967-71 **Aston-Martin DB6**
Metallic Silver Blue body, Red interior,
spoked wheels...**£60-70**
Metallic Turquoise body, White interior,
spoked wheels..**£80-100**

154 1955 **Hillman Minx** (renumbered from 40f)
See '40 Series' pages.

154 1966-69 **Ford Taunus 17M**
Yellow body, White roof, Red interior,
rounded spun hubs or cast wheels.............................**£40-50**

155 1961-66 **Ford Anglia 105E**
Turquoise or Green body, Red interior, spun hubs ..**£100-125**
Turquoise body, Pale Blue interior, spun hubs...........**£80-100**
Very Pale Green body, Red interior, spun hubs.
In mail-order box with correct spot........................**£350-450**
NB Meccano issued a batch to Ford to mark the
first Ford made on Merseyside on 8th March 1963.
Some were fixed on plinths and given as souvenirs.
1963 South African issues: English and Afrikaans on box.
Caramel body, Red interior, spun hubs **£500-750**
Off-White body, Red interior, spun hubs **£500-750**
Light Blue body, Red interior, spun hubs **£500-750**

Market prices shown here are for guidance only. They refer ONLY to mint models in pristine boxes (where appropriate) that are complete with all of their original contents.

156	1954-56	**Rover 75** (renumbered from 140b)

156 1954-56 **Rover 75** (renumbered from 140b)
Red body, Maroon hubs £750-1,000
Green body, Cream hubs £200-250
Maroon body, Cream hubs £130-150
1956-59 Two-tone issues:
Light Green upper body, Mid-Green lower body
and hubs, treaded tyres £150-175
Dull two-tone Green body,
Mid-Green hubs '156' to base £300-400
Light Green upper body, Turquoise lower body,
Mid-Green hubs...£750-1,000
Mid-Blue upper body, Cream lower body and
hubs, treaded tyres £175-225
Dark Blue upper body, Cream lower body and
hubs...£250-350
Violet-Blue upper body, Cream lower body and
hubs...£400-600

156 1968-71 **Saab 96**
Metallic Red or Metallic Blue body, spun hubs...........£65-75

157 1954-57 **Jaguar XK120**
Yellow body, Light Yellow hubs £125-150
Red body, Red diecast hubs £150-175
White body, Fawn hubs...£125-150
Dark Sage Green body, Beige or Fawn hubs £150-200
1957-59 Two-tone issues: Turquoise lower body,
Cerise upper body, Red hubs..............................£250-350
Yellow lower body, Light Grey upper
body and hubs..£250-350
1959-62 Red body, spun hubs...£250-350
Dark Sage Green body, spun hubs £250-350

157 1968-73 **BMW 2000 Tilux**
Box has inner pictorial stand.
Blue/White, Red interior, cast hubs £55-65
Metallic Blue with Gold upper half £90-120
Pale Blue body, Red interior, spun hubs ....NGPP

158 1954-55 **Riley Saloon** See '40' Series information.

158 1967-70 **Rolls-Royce Silver Shadow**
Metallic Red, White interior, cast hubs £45-55
1970-73 Metallic Bright Blue, White interior, cast hubs £55-65
Metallic Light Blue, White interior, cast hubs...........£55-65

159 1954 **Morris Oxford** See '40' Series information.

160 1958-62 **Austin A30**
Smooth or treaded solid grey plastic wheels.
Turquoise body...£90-120
Pale Beige body..£90-120
NB A version of the Austin A30 has been reported
with spun hubs, but is not confirmed.

160 1967-74 **Mercedes-Benz 250 SE**
Metallic Blue body, working stop-lights.....................£30-40
1974 Metallic Blue body, White interior,
bare metal baseplate, spun hubs, bubble-packed £100-125

161 1954 **Austin (A40) Somerset** See '40' Series information.

161 1965-69 **Ford Mustang Fastback**
White (Red seats), 'MUSTANG' decal badge on
wings, chrome detailed wheels.................................£70-90
1969-73 Yellow body, Blue seats, cast-in logo replaces decal...£60-70
Orange body (without decal), Speedwheels................£40-50

162 1956-60 **Ford Zephyr Mk.I**
Cream upper body, Dark Green lower body,
Cream hubs...£100-120
Cream upper body, Lime Green lower body,
Cream hubs...£110-140
Two-tone Blue body, Grey hubs..............................£100-125
NB Rear number plate may be plain or Silver.

162 1966-70 **Triumph 1300**
Light Blue body, Red interior, spun aluminium hubs ..£65-75

163 1956-60 **Bristol 450 Coupé**
British Racing Green body, Light Green hubs,
racing number '27' £70-90

163 1966-70 **Volkswagen 1600 TL**
Red or Dark Metallic Red, cast detailed hubs £40-50
Metallic Blue body, Speedwheels £60-70

164 1957-60 **Vauxhall Cresta**
Maroon lower body, Cream upper body,
Cream hubs...£100-125
1957-60 Green lower body, Grey upper body, Grey hubs £100-125
NB Rear number plate may be plain or Silver.

164 1966-71 **Ford Zodiac Mk.IV**
Metallic Silver body, Red interior,
Yellow or Black chassis, cast wheels........................£50-60
Pale Met. Blue body, Yellow chassis, cast wheels.......£75-85
Metallic Copper body, Red interior,
Yellow chassis, cast wheels, rigid plastic case............£50-60

165 1959-60 **Humber Hawk**
Black and Green lower body,
Black roof, spun hubs...£125-150
Maroon and Cream lower body,
Maroon roof, spun hubs £100-125
NB Both versions have been observed with or
without a front number plate.
1959-63 Black lower body, all Green upper body, spun hubs,
with front number plate casting,
in late issue lighter Yellow box with Green spot £200-250

165 1969-76 **Ford Capri**
Metallic Green body, Orange interior, Speedwheels....£50-60
Metallic Purple body, Orange interior, Speedwheels....£50-60
Met. Turquoise body, Yellow interior, Speedwheels....£60-70

166 1958-63 **Sunbeam Rapier**
Yellow lower body, Deep Cream upper body,
Beige hubs £80-100
Same but with spun hubs.......................................£100-125
Blue lower body, Turquoise upper body,
Blue hubs..£100-125
Same but with spun hubs.......................................£100-125

166 1967-70 **Renault R16**
Metallic Blue, spun hubs...£40-50

167 1958-63 **A.C. Aceca Sports Coupé**
Grey body, Red roof, Red hubs................................£80-100
Cream body, Reddish-Maroon roof, Silver hubs £100-125
Deep Cream body, Dark Brown roof, Cream hubs..£100-125
All Cream body, spun aluminium hubs.
In lighter Yellow box with Cream spot £125-150
Cream body, Maroon roof, spun hubs £125-150
Cream body, Dark Brown roof, spun hubs.............£125-150
Grey body, Red roof, spun hubs.
In plain Red/Yellow box......................................£125-150

168 1959-63 **Singer Gazelle Saloon**
Deep Brown lower, Cream upper body,
spun aluminium hubs £90-110
Dark Green lower, Grey upper body,
spun aluminium hubs £90-110
Black body, spun aluminium hubs, Silver trim.............NGPP

168 1968-70 **Ford Escort**
Pale Blue or White, cast detailed hubs......................£45-55
1970-74 Metallic Red body, spun aluminium hubs.................£67-75
1974-75 Metallic Blue body, Speedwheels £67-75

169 1958-63 **Studebaker Golden Hawk**
Tan body, Red rear side panel and hubs,
White tyres, plain Yellow/Red box...........................£90-110
Same, but with spun aluminium hubs, White tyres ...£90-120
Light Green body, Cream rear side panel and hubs,
White tyres...£90-120
Same, but with spun aluminium hubs, White tyres .£100-130

169 1967-69 **Ford Corsair 2000 E**
Silver body, Black textured roof £70-85

Two paint schemes exist for two-colour issues on
models 170, 171 and 172:

1: Lower colour covers wing tops and doors up to
windows (generally known as 'Highline') and

2: Lower colour extends only up to ridge
on wings/doors ('Lowline').

---

170 1954-56 **Ford Fordor Sedan** (renumbered from 139a)
Tan body, Red hubs **£120-150**
Yellow body, Red hubs...**£120-150**
Green body, Red hubs **£120-150**
Red body, Red hubs...**£120-150**

1956-58 'Highline' versions:
Red lower body, Cream upper body, Red hubs......**£200-250**
Blue lower body, Pink upper body, Blue hubs........**£200-250**

1958-59 'Lowline' versions:
Red lower body, Cream upper body, Red hubs......**£150-200**
Blue lower body, Pink upper body, Blue hubs........**£150-200**

170m 1954-54 **Ford US Army Staff Car** See 'Military Vehicles' section.

170 1964-70 **Lincoln Continental**
Metallic Bronze body, White roof,
Blue interior, cast wheels **£75-85**
Light Blue body, White roof,
Mid-Blue interior, cast wheels **£75-85**

170 1979 **Ford Granada Ghia**
Not issued, but a Metallic Silver factory publicity
sample was sold by Vectis Auctions in 1999 for £470.

171 1954-56 **Hudson Commodore Sedan** (renumbered from 139b)
Dark Blue body, Pale Tan upper body and hubs......**£100-125**
Royal Blue body, Pale Tan upper body and hubs **£200-250**
Light Blue body, Pale Tan upper body, Fawn hubs ..**£400-600**
Cream body, Dark Maroon upper body and hubs **£100-125**
Cream body, Dark Maroon upper body, Red hubs,
large lettering on baseplate......................................**£100-125**

1956-58 'Highline' versions:
Turquoise lower body, Red upper body, Red hubs ..**£250-350**
Blue lower body, Red upper body, Red hubs...........**£250-350**
Blue lower body, Maroon upper body, Red hubs......**£250-350**
Light Grey lower body with Mid-Blue upper body,
Blue hubs **£250-350**

1958-59 'Lowline' versions:
Turquoise lower body, Maroon upper body,
Red hubs **£250-350**
Light Grey lower body with Mid-Blue upper body,
Blue hubs **£250-350**

171 1965-68 **Austin 1800**
Metallic Blue body, Red interior, spun hubs................**£60-80**
Light Blue body, Red interior, spun hubs **£60-80**

172 1954-56 **Studebaker Land Cruiser**
Light Green body, Mid-Green or Mid-Blue hubs **£90-110**
Blue body, Fawn or Beige hubs **£130-160**
Light Beige body, Cream hubs................................**£250-350**

1956-58 'Highline' versions:
Beige lower body, Maroon upper body,
Cream hubs..**£150-200**
Beige lower body, Tan upper body, Cerise hubs......**£150-200**

1958-59 'Lowline' versions:
Cream lower body and hubs, Maroon upper body...**£150-200**
Cream lower body and hubs, Lt. Tan upper body....**£150-200**

172 1965-69 **Fiat 2300 Station Wagon**
Two-tone Blue body, Red interior, spun hubs.............**£60-80**

173 1958-62 **Nash Rambler Station Wagon**
Turquoise body with Cerise flash, Grey hubs,
no number on later baseplates **£90-110**
Pink body with Blue flash, Cream hubs,
no number on later baseplates **£90-110**
As previous issues but with spun hubs,
in plain Yellow/Red box without picture **£90-120**
Beige body, Blue side flash,
spun hubs, White tyres **£200-300**

173 1969-72 **Pontiac Parisienne**
Metallic Maroon body, Lemon interior,
retractable aerials, cast wheels **£80-100**
Metallic Blue body **£80-100**

174 1958-63 **Hudson Hornet**
Red lower body, Cream roof and side flash,
Beige hubs, White tyres...**£90-110**
Yellow lower body, Dark Grey roof and flash,
Cream hubs, White tyres **£100-125**
Later issues with spun aluminium hubs **£140-170**

174 1969-72 **Ford Mercury Cougar**
Blue or Metallic Dark Blue body,
cast hubs or Speedwheels.......................................**£55-75**

175 1958-61 **Hillman Minx**
Grey lower body, Mid-Blue upper body and hubs...**£100-125**
Grey lower body, Mid-Blue upper body, spun hubs .**£200-250**
Pale Brown body, Green roof and boot,
Beige hubs **£100-125**
Pale Brown body, Green roof and boot, spun hubs .**£200-250**

175 1969-73 **Cadillac Eldorado**
Metallic Purple body, Black roof, Orange interior,
cast or Speedwheels..**£70-90**
Metallic Sea-Green body, Black roof,
Orange interior, cast or Speedwheels.........................**£70-90**

176 1958-63 **Austin A105 Saloon**
First Dinky Toys car to have full window glazing.
Body sides have a contrasting panel line.
Treaded tyres may be Black or White.
1958-59 Cream body, Navy Blue panel line, Cream hubs **£90-110**
Pale Grey body, Red panel line, Red hubs..............**£130-160**
1959-63 Cream body, Dark Blue roof and panel line,
Cream hubs..**£100-125**
Cream body, Mid-Blue roof and panel line,
Cream hubs..**£150-175**
Cream body, Dark Blue roof and panel line,
spun aluminium hubs **£150-175**
Cream body, Mid-Blue roof (but no panel line) **£150-175**
Pale Grey body, Red roof and panel line,
Light Grey hubs...**£150-175**
Pale Grey body / roof, Red panel line, spun hubs ...**£125-175**

176 1969-74 **N.S.U. Ro80**
Metallic Red body, spun hubs, luminous seats,
working lights..**£40-50**
Metallic Blue body **£100-150**

177 1961-66 **Opel Kapitan**
Light Greyish-Blue body, Red interior, spun hubs **£60-75**
1963 South African issues: English and Afrikaans on box.
Mid or Dark Blue body, Red interior,
spun hubs **£1,000-1,200**
Caramel body, Red interior, spun hubs **£1,000-1,200**
Pale Yellow body, Red interior, spun hubs........**£1,000-1,200**

178 1959-63 **Plymouth Plaza**
Light Blue body, Dark Blue roof and side flash,
Gloss Black baseplate, spun hubs..........................**£110-140**
Salmon Pink body, Light Green roof and
side flash, spun hubs..**£150-190**
Light Tan body, Light Green roof and side flash,
matt-Black base, spun hubs **£150-200**
Light Blue body, White roof and flash, spun hubs,
White treaded tyres, Yellow/Light Yellow box **£175-225**
Pale Blue body, White roof and flash,
spun hubs, late issue – no number on baseplate **£140-170**

178 1975-79 **Mini Clubman**
Bronze body, opening doors,
jewelled headlights on some, Speedwheels **£40-50**
Red body version, Speedwheels..............................**£100-125**

179 1958-63 **Studebaker President**
Light Blue body, Dark Blue flash,
Cream hubs, White tyres...**£90-120**
Yellow body, Blue flash and hubs, White tyres **£90-120**
Late issues with spun hubs **£120-150**

179 1971-75 **Opel Commodore**
Metallic Blue body, Black roof, Speedwheels £55-75

180 1958-63 **Packard Clipper**
Cerise upper body, Cream lower body and hubs,
White tyres..£90-120
Orange lower body, Light Grey upper body
and hubs, White tyres £100-125
Late issues with spun hubs £110-130

180 1979-80 **Rover 3500**
White body, plastic chassis and wheels.
Made in Hong Kong, scale 1:35......................£25-35

181 1956-70 **Volkswagen Saloon**
Pale Grey body, Mid-Blue hubs £75-95
Blue-Grey body, Mid-Blue hubs £75-95
Dark Blue body, Mid-Blue hubs £120-140
RAF Blue body, Mid-Blue hubs £120-140
Lime Green body, Mid-Green hubs £175-225
Spun hubs issues:
Pale Grey body, spun hubs £75-100
Blue-Grey body, spun hubs £75-100
Pale Blue body, spun hubs, unpainted or
matt or gloss black baseplate............................£75-100
RAF Blue body, spun hubs................................£75-100
Plastic hubs issue:
Pale Blue body, Blue plastic hubs.....................£250-350
NB See also 'Factory samples' listing.
South African issues: English and Afrikaans text on box.
Lime Green or Pale Yellow body,
Red interior, spun hubs....................................£1,200-1,400
Pale Blue or Metallic Blue body,
Red interior, spun hubs....................................£1,200-1,400
Grey body, Red interior, spun hubs..................£1,200-1,400

182 1958-66 **Porsche 356a Coupé**
Pale Blue body, Cream, Mid-Blue or spun hubs........£80-100
Cerise body, Cream or spun hubs......................£80-100
Red body and hubs, in standard Yellow box
(no coloured spot)...£125-150
Off-White body, Mid-Blue, Beige or spun hubs,
with window glazing..£125-150
Red body and hubs. In late issue lighter
Yellow box with Red spot £250-350
Plum Red body, spun hubs. In lighter Yellow box...£250-350

183 1958-60 **Fiat 600**
Red body, smooth or treaded solid
Grey plastic wheels £70-80
Pale Green body, smooth or treaded
solid Grey plastic wheels.................................£70-80

183 1966-74 **Morris Mini Minor (Automatic)**
Metallic Red body, matt or gloss Black roof,
White interior, spun hubs. Box should contain
'Meccano Automatic Transmission' leaflet.............£70-85
Metallic Red body, Black roof,
White interior, Speedwheels.............................£70-85
Metallic Bright Blue body,
White interior, spun hubs ....£100-125.
NB Late issues with 'Austin Cooper S' cast on
boot (model 250 casting) will be found ....NGPP
Various registration numbers will also be
found, e.g., 'UVR 576D', 'MTB 21G', 'HTB 21H'.

184 1961-65 **Volvo 122 S**
Red body, Off-White interior, spun hubs £70-80
Dark Red body, spun hubs £200-250
Off-White body, White interior, spun hubs............£200-250
Cream body, Cream interior, spun hubs..............£200-250
1962 South African issues: English and Afrikaans ton box.
Grey-Blue body, White interior..........................£600-800
Sage Green, White interior................................£600-800
Pale Green, Fawn interior.................................£600-800

185 1961-63 **Alfa Romeo 1900 Sprint**
Yellow body, Red interior, spun hubs £70-90
Red body, Off-White interior, spun hubs............£70-90

Market prices shown here are for guidance only. They refer ONLY to
mint models in pristine boxes (where appropriate) that are complete with
all of their original contents.

186 1961-67 **Mercedes-Benz 220 SE**
Light Blue body, Red or White interior, spun hubs £50-65
Light Blue body, Yellow interior, spun hubs...........£60-75
RAF Blue body, Cream interior, spun hubs £50-65
1963 South African issue: English and Afrikaans text on box.
Sky Blue or Grey body.....................................£400-600

187 1959-64 **VW Karmann Ghia Coupé**
Red body, Black roof, spun hubs,
White tyres, 'plain' box...................................£80-100
Green body, Cream roof, spun hubs,
White tyres, 'plain' box...................................£80-100
As previous issue but in rare late issue picture box.£100-150

187 1968-77 **De Tomaso Mangusta 5000**
Fluorescent Pink body, White panels front/rear,
Black interior, cast wheels, racing number '7' £35-40

188 1968-74 **Jensen FF**
Yellow body, Black interior, cast wheels or
Speedwheels. In rigid plastic case....................£70-90

189 1959-64 **Triumph Herald Saloon**
Pale or Light Blue roof and sides with White centre,
spun aluminium hubs......................................£75-85
Green roof and sides with White centre,
spun aluminium hubs......................................£75-85
Special issues:
(all in plain standard yellow box with colour spot)
Alpine Mauve body, spun hubs.........................£500-750
Magenta body, spun hubs.................................£500-750
Red lower body and roof, White upper body,
spun hubs, Red spot on box £500-750
Greyish-Green, Pale Whitish-Green roof,
spun hubs, plain box with correct colour spot.........£500-750
Pinkish-Brown body, Pale Grey roof, spun hubs.....£500-750
Dark Grey body and roof, Pale Grey bonnet and
boot, spun hubs, standard box £500-750
All Red, spun hubs, box with Red spot...............£500-750
Very Dark Blue body, Pale Blue hubs..................£500-750
Very Dark Blue lower body and roof,
Pale Blue mid-section, spun hubs £500-750
Deep Grey and White body, spun hubs...............£500-750
Pale Lilac body, Bluish White roof, spun hubs,
in box with Blue and White spot.......................£500-750
Black and Pale Grey body, spun hubs.................£500-750
Monaco Blue body £500-750
Monaco Blue lower body and roof,
Sebring White upper body, spun hubs £500-750
Powder Blue body, blue spot on box £500-750
Powder Blue/Sebring White, Lt. Blue spot on box..£500-750
Lichfield Green body.......................................£500-750
White body, White spot on box £500-750

189 1969-76 **Lamborghini Marzal**
Green/White or Red/White, cast detailed hubs...........£25-45
Yellow/White body, cast detailed hubs £40-45
1976-78 Metallic Blue/White, Speedwheels £35-45
Dark Metallic Green/White, Speedwheels.................£35-45

190 1970-74 **Monteverdi 375 L**
Metallic Maroon body, White interior,
cast wheels or Speedwheels. In rigid plastic case........£35-45
NB See also 'Factory samples' listing.

191 1959-64 **Dodge Royal Sedan**
Cream body with Tan rear flash,
spun hubs, White treaded tyres £125-150
Cream body, Blue rear flash, spun hubs, lighter
Yellow box, late issue – no number on base..........£150-200
Pale Green body with Black flash,
spun hubs, White tyres £125-150
NB Casting used for 258 'USA Police Car'.

192 1959-64 **De Soto Fireflite**
Grey body, Red roof and side flash,
spun aluminium hubs, White tyres...........................**£100-125**
Turquoise body, Light Tan roof and side flash,
spun aluminium hubs, White tyres..........................**£125-175**

192 1970-80 **Range Rover**
May be found with cast detailed or Speedwheels.
Metallic Bronze body, Pale Blue interior....................**£25-35**
Yellow body, Red interior...**£25-35**
Metallic Bronze body, Pale Grey interior **£40-60**
NB See also 'Factory samples' listing.

193 1961-69 **Rambler Station Wagon**
Pale Yellow body, White roof, Red interior,
Black plastic roof-rack, spun hubs, standard box **£70-80**
As previous issue but with White interior.
In Gold 'see-through' US export window-box........**£150-175**
1962 South African issues: English / Afrikaans on box.
Lilac body, Cream or Black roof,
Red interior, spun hubs **£750-1,000**
All-Lilac body, Red interior, spun hubs...........**£750-1,000**
Sage Green body, Red interior, spun hubs **£750-1,000**
Pale Blue body, Cream roof,
Red interior, spun hubs.......................................**£750-1,000**
Dark Blue body, White roof,
Red interior, spun hubs......................................**£750-1,000**
Light Greyish-Green body,
Black roof, Red interior, spun hubs....................**£750-1,000**
All-Cream body, Red interior, spun hubs.............**£750-1,000**

194 1961-67 **Bentley 'S' Coupé**
Grey body, Red interior, Tan hood,
Grey male driver, spun hubs, gloss black baseplate **£70-90**
Metallic Bronze body, Cream interior,
Dark Blue hood, driver, spun hubs.........................**£100-125**
NB Late issues have plated plastic parts.
1962 South African issues: English / Afrikaans on box.
Lime Green body, Red interior,
Black hood, spun hubs **£1,000-1,200**
Cream body, Red interior,
Dark Cream hood, spun hubs **£1,000-1,200**

195 1961-71 **Jaguar 3.4 Mk.II**
Maroon body, White interior, spun hubs.....................**£70-90**
Cream body, Red interior, spun hubs **£70-90**
Light Grey body, Red interior, spun hubs **£70-90**
1962 South African issues: English and Afrikaans on box.
Light or Sky-Blue body, Cream or Red interior **£600-800**
Red or Off-White body, Cream or Red interior **£600-800**

196 1963-70 **Holden Special Sedan**
Metallic Gold body, White roof, spun hubs.
(First Dinky model to have jewelled headlights)........**£65-75**
Turquoise body, White roof, spun hubs,
Grey baseplate, Off-White interior.............................**£65-75**
Turquoise body, White roof, spun hubs,
Silver baseplate, Red interior **£65-75**
Turquoise body, White roof, spun hubs,
Dark Grey baseplate, Red interior.............................**£65-75**
1966 South African issue: English and Afrikaans on box.
White body, Turquoise roof......................................**£600-800**

197 1961-71 **Morris Mini Traveller**
Cream body, Lemon interior, spun hubs **£600-800**
Cream body, Red interior, spun hubs **£90-110**
Cream body, Pale Blue interior, spun hubs.............**£300-400**
Dark Green body, Pale Blue interior, spun hubs......**£300-400**
Dark Green body, Yellow interior, spun hubs **£500-700**
Fluorescent Green body, Red interior, spun hubs,
with or without front number plate **£160-190**
Fluorescent Pink body, Red interior, spun hubs......**£200-250**
NB Unlike 199, there is no 'colour change' label
on the 197 box.

---

198 1962-69 **Rolls-Royce Phantom V**
Metallic Cream lower body, Metallic Light Green
upper body, Blue or Red interior, glossy baseplate,
spun hubs, chauffeur. (First Dinky Toys model
with metallic paint and opening windows) **£75-85**
Metallic Cream upper body, Grey lower body,
Red interior, glossy baseplate, chauffeur, spun hubs ...**£75-85**
Two tone Grey body, Red interior,
matt baseplate, chauffeur, spun hubs...........................**£75-85**
1963 South African issues: English / Afrikaans on box.
Dark Grey over Metallic Cream body,
Red interior **£1,000-1,200**
Sage Green or Two-Tone Grey.........................**£1,000-1,200**
Pale Grey body, Ivory roof, Red interior **£1,000-1,200**
Pale Grey body, Grey roof, Red interior **£1,000-1,200**
Lime Green body, Ivory roof,
Red interior, spun hubs....................................**£1,000-1,200**

199 1961-71 **Austin 7 Countryman**
Blue body with Yellow interior, spun hubs.............**£130-160**
Electric Blue, Powder Blue or Blue-Grey body
with Red interior and 'wood' trim, spun hubs ....**£75-85.**
Fluorescent Orange or Fluorescent Pink body,
Red interior, spun hubs. Box must have bear a small
oblong label stating: 'COLOUR OF MODEL
MAY DIFFER FROM ILLUSTRATION' ....**£150-200.**
Deep Grey body, Red interior,
Brown 'woodwork', spun hubs **£150-200**

200 1954-57 **Midget Racer** (renumbered from 35b)
Silver body, Red grille, Brown driver,
solid Black rubber wheels. **£65-75**

200 1971-78 **Matra 630 Le Mans**
Blue body, RN '5', '9' or '36', Speedwheels...............**£25-30**

201 1979-80 **Plymouth Stock Car**
Blue body, racing number '34', wide plastic wheels...**£35-45**

202 1971-75 **Fiat Abarth 2000**
Fluorescent Red/White body, Speedwheels **£20-30**

202/2 1979-80 **Customised Land Rover**
Yellow body with white crash guard.
White or Black rails/aerials (344 casting)...................**£25-35**

203 1979-80 **Customised Range Rover**
Black body, Yellow/Red design,
White plastic chassis/crash guard...............................**£25-30**

204 1971-74 **Ferrari 312 P**
Metallic Red body and doors, Speedwheels, RN '60' .**£30-35**
Same, but with White doors **£30-35**

205 1962-64 **Talbot Lago Racing Car** (renumbered from 230)
Blue, body Red or Yellow plastic hubs, RN '4',
boxed or blister-packed ('230' on base).................**£250-350**

205 1968-73 **Lotus Cortina Rally**
White body, Blue interior, Red bonnet and side stripe,
'Monte Carlo' logo, RN '7', 2 aerials, cast hubs **£70-80**

206 1962-64 **Maserati Racing Car** (renumbered from 231)
Red/White body, Red or Yellow plastic hubs,
boxed or blister-packed, ('231' on base).................**£250-350**
late issue: As previous model but in lighter Yellow box **£150-200**

206 1978-80 **Customised Corvette**
Red/Yellow or White/Black, plastic chassis
and wide wheels **£20-30**

207 1962-64 **Alfa-Romeo Racing Car** (renumbered from 232)
Red body, Red plastic hubs,
boxed or blister-packed, ('232' on base).................**£250-350**
late issue: As previous model but in lighter Yellow box **£150-200**

207 1977-80 **Triumph TR7 Rally**
White/Red/Blue, RN '8',
plastic chassis and wheels, 'Leyland' **£25-35**

> Market prices shown here are for guidance only. They refer ONLY to
> mint models in pristine boxes (where appropriate) that are complete with
> **all** of their original contents.

208 1962-64 **Cooper-Bristol Racing Car** (renumbered from 233)
Dark Green, White flash, RN '6', Red plastic hubs,
boxed or blister-packed, ('233' on base)..................**£250-350**
late issue: Same, but in lighter Yellow box.............................**£150-200**

208 1971-75 **VW Porsche 914**
Yellow body, Black interior, cast detailed hubs..........**£25-30**
Promotional version in Yellow/Red promotional box..**£70-80**
1976-80 Metallic Blue/Black body, Speedwheels.....................**£25-30**

209 1962-64 **Ferrari Racing Car** (renumbered from 234)
Blue, Yellow triangle, angled '5', Yellow plastic
hubs, boxed or blister-packed, ('234' on base).......**£250-350**
late issue: As previous model but in lighter Yellow box.........**£175-225**

210 1962-65 **Vanwall Racing Car** (renumbered from 239)
Green, Yellow plastic hubs,
boxed or blister-packed, ('239' on base).................**£250-350**

210 1971-73 **Alfa-Romeo 33 Tipo**
Red body, Black doors, White interior,
racing number '36', cast wheels, leaflet in box..........**£30-35**

211 1975 **Triumph TR7 Sports Car**
Metallic Blue body, Union Jack badge.....................**£90-100**
Yellow body, Black bumpers and interior.................**£90-100**
Yellow body, Grey bumpers and interior..................**£90-100**
Red body, Black bumpers and interior......................**£50-60**
Red body, Grey bumpers and interior.......................**£50-60**

212 1965-70 **Ford Cortina Rally**
White body, Black bonnet, 'EAST AFRICAN SAFARI'
and 'CASTROL' logos, Black or Red RN '8',
spotlight, Red interior, spun hubs. In picture box......**£80-100**

213 1970-73 **Ford Capri Rally**
Metallic Red body, Black bonnet, Yellow interior,
racing number '20', rigid plastic case.........................**£55-65**
1973-75 Bronze body, Black bonnet, spotlights, wing mirrors,
Speedwheels, rigid plastic case **£55-65**

214 1966-69 **Hillman Imp Rally**
Dark Blue body, Red interior, 'MONTE CARLO
RALLY' logo, RN '35', spun hubs, picture box..........**£70-80**

215 1965-66 **Ford GT Racing Car**
White body, Red interior, RN '7', spun hubs.............**£55-65**
1966-70 Same, but with Silver spoked wheels..........................**£35-45**
1970-74 Metallic Green body, Orange/Black stripe,
Yellow interior, RN '7', Silver spoked wheels **£45-55**
Metallic Green body, Silver engine,
Red or Black interior ....**£35-45**.
Metallic Green body, Dark Blue/White stripe,
White interior **£35-45**
Yellow or Metallic Blue, Silver or Gold wheels.........**£35-45**

216 1967-69 **Dino Ferrari**
Red body, Light Blue interior.....................................**£40-50**
1969-75 Metallic Blue/Black, Silver or brass spoked
wheels or Speedwheels..**£30-40**

217 1968-70 **Alfa Romeo Scarabeo OSI**
Pink body, cast spoked wheels **£30-35**
1969-74 Red, Orange or Green body, Speedwheels..................**£25-30**

218 1969-73 **Lotus Europa**
Yellow body, Blue panels/roof, chequered flags,
Gold engine **£35-45**
1973-75 Yellow/Black body or Metallic Blue body,
Silver engine, Speedwheels...**£30-35**

219 1977-79 **Leyland Jaguar XJ-5.3**
White body, 'Leyland' decal. (Made in Hong Kong) ..**£35-45**

219 1978-79 **'Big Cat' Jaguar**
White/Red, Black 'Big Cat' decal, (unboxed) **£35-45**
Boxed version with 'The Big Cat' logo **£50-75**

220 1954-56 **Small Open Racing Car** (renumbered from 23a)
Silver (Red hubs), or Red (Silver hubs), RN '4'. **£40-50**

220 1970-73 **Ferrari P5**
Metallic Red body, Yellow interior, cast hubs **£25-30**
1973-75 Metallic Red body, Yellow interior, Speedwheels **£25-30**

221 1954-56 **'Speed Of The Wind' Racing Car**
(renumbered from 23e)
Silver diecast body with plain baseplate....................**£40-45**

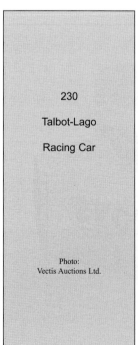

230

Talbot-Lago

Racing Car

Photo:
Vectis Auctions Ltd.

221	1969-76	**Corvette Stingray**	
		Metallic Gold body, Silver or Gold spoked wheels £25-35	
	1976-78	Red or White body, Black bonnet, Speedwheels £25-35	

222 1954-56 **Streamlined Racing Car** (renumbered from 22s)
Silver body with Red, Blue or Green trim **£60-70**

222 1978-80 **Hesketh 308 E**
Dark Blue or Bronze, RN '2',
cast-detailed or Speedwheels......................................**£20-30**
Promotional issue:
As previous model but in
'OLYMPUS CAMERAS' box, (Swiss) **£50-75**

223 1970-75 **McLaren M8A Can-Am**
White body, Metallic Blue engine cover,
cast detailed wheels......................................**£25-35**
1976-78 Metallic Green body, Black engine cover,
White interior, Speedwheels......................................**£25-35**

224 1970-74 **Mercedes-Benz C111**
White body, Blue interior, cast hubs **£25-35**
Metallic Dark Red body, White interior, cast hubs **£25-35**

225 1971-76 **Lotus F1 Racing Car**
Metallic Red body with racing number '7',
inner pictorial box and stand **£25-35**
1976-77 Lime-Green or Metallic Blue body with RN '7' **£25-35**

226 1972-75 **Ferrari 312 B2**
Red body with racing number '5' **£25-35**
1976-80 Bronze or Gold body, Black, White or
Yellow rear wing, racing number '5' **£25-35**

227 1975-77 **Beach Buggy**
Yellow/Grey or Yellow/White body **£25-35**
Green/Grey or Pink/Black body **£25-35**
NB See also 'Factory samples' listing.

228 1970-72 **Super Sprinter**
Blue/Silver or Blue/Orange body, Speedwheels **£25-35**

230 1954-60 **Talbot Lago Racing Car** (renumbered from 23k)
Blue body, Yellow RN '4', Blue diecast hubs..........**£150-175**
1960-62 Blue body, Yellow RN '4', spun aluminium hubs ...**£150-175.**
(Renumbered to 205)

231 1954-60 **Maserati Racing Car** (renumbered from 23n)
Red body, White flash / RN '9', Red diecast hubs ..**£150-175**
Red body, White flash / '9',Yellow plastic hubs......**£200-250**
1960-62 Red body, White flash and RN '9', spun hubs.........**£150-175**
(Renumbered to 206)

232 1954-60 **Alfa-Romeo Racing Car** (renumbered from 23f)
Red body, White RN '8', Red diecast hubs **£150-175**
Red body, White RN '8', Red plastic hubs **£200-250**
1960-62 Red body, White RN '8', spun hubs **£150-175**
(Renumbered to 207)

233 1954-60 **Cooper-Bristol Racing Car** (renumbered from 23g)
Green body and cast hubs, White flash, RN '6' **£150-175**
1960-62 Green body, White flash, RN '6', spun hubs **£145-165**
Green body, White flash / '6', Red plastic hubs **£200-250**
(Renumbered to 208)

234 1954-60 **Ferrari Racing Car** (renumbered from 23h)
Blue body, Yellow nose-cone, cast hubs & RN '5'..**£200-250**
1960-62 Blue body, Yellow nose-cone, RN '5', spun hubs ...**£200-250**
1962-62 Blue body, Yellow triangle on nose, RN '5',
spun hubs, boxed **£300-400**
Blue body, White triangle on nose, RN '8',
Blue plastic hubs **£300-400**
South African issue: South African box.
Red body (dimpled rivets), RN '36', spun hubs **£300-400**
(Renumbered to 209)

235 1954-60 **H.W.M. Racing Car** (renumbered from 23j)
Pale Green body, Yellow RN '7', Green cast hubs. ..**£80-100**

236 1956-59 **Connaught Racing Car**
Pale Green body, Red interior, Mid-Green hubs,
RN '32', White driver **£80-100**

237 1957-60 **Mercedes-Benz Racing Car**
Gloss White body, Red interior, Red plastic hubs
or spun hubs, Red RN '30', Yellow driver...............**£100-125**
1960-62 Matt White body, Red plastic hubs or spun hubs,
RN '30', Blue driver..**£90-110**
1962-64 Matt White body, plastic hubs, RN '30', Tan driver ..**£90-110**
Late issue:
Matt White body, Red plastic hubs, RN '30', Blue
or Yellow driver. Late issue Yellow window box **£100-130**

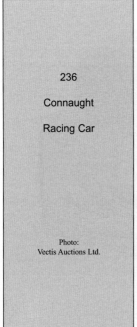

236

Connaught

Racing Car

Photo:
Vectis Auctions Ltd.

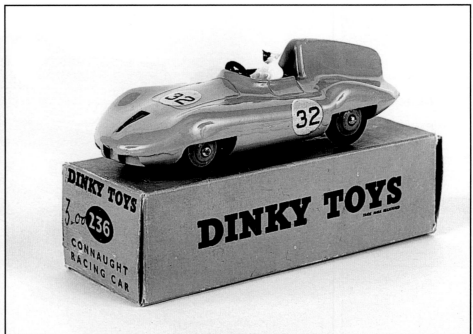

238 1957-60 **Jaguar 'D' type**
Turquoise body, Blue interior, White driver,
with or without RN '4', Blue diecast hubs **£100-125**
NB Boxes for 238 that have a descriptive adhesive
label stating 'Le Mans 1955/56/57' may attract a premium.
1960-62 Turquoise body, Blue interior, White driver,
RN '4', spun aluminium hubs **£120-150**
1962-65 Turquoise body, Blue interior or Turquoise interior,
White or Yellow driver, RN '4', Blue or Yellow
plastic hubs, in plain lighter Yellow box.................**£250-300**

239 1958-60 **Vanwall Racing Car**
Green body, Green hubs, White or Yellow driver,
RN '25', '26' or '35', 'VANWALL' logo................**£125-150**
1960-62 Green body, Yellow driver, RN '35' or '26',
spun aluminium hubs...**£120-150**
1962-65 Green body, White or Tan driver, RN '35',
Yellow plastic hubs. In lighter Yellow box **£150-175**
1962-65 Green body, Yellow driver, RN '35',
Yellow plastic hubs. In lighter Yellow box **£150-175**

240 1963-70 **Cooper Racing Car**
Blue body, White design, Black RN '20', spun hubs,
White driver (Silver or Yellow helmet).......................**£40-50**

241 1963-70 **Lotus Racing Car**
Green body with racing number '7' or '36',
spun hubs, White driver, Silver helmet **£60-80**
Green body with racing number '24', spun hubs,
driver with Red helmet...**£60-80**
South African issue: Green body with RN '24',
cast wheels, White driver with Red helmet.............**£400-600**

242 1963-71 **Ferrari Racing Car**
Red body, RN '36', spun hubs, driver, Silver helmet ..**£60-80**

243 1963-71 **B.R.M. Racing Car**
Green, Yellow cowl, RN '7', spun hubs, Red helmet ..**£60-80**
1963-71 Metallic Green (shades exist), Yellow cowl,
racing number '7', spun hubs...................................**£60-80**
NB Gold, US export issue 'see-through' window
boxes. Model nos. 237 - 243 housed in these boxes
may attract a premium of 50%.

254 1956-59 **Austin Taxi** (FX3)
Two-tone: Yellow upper body and hubs,
Dark Green lower body, Black chassis ('254'),
interior and driver..**£90-120**
Black body, Gloss Grey base ('254'),
spun hubs, interior and driver.................................**£150-200**
Blue body, Light Blue hubs......................................**£500-750**

260 1971-72 **VW 'Deutsche Bundespost'**
Yellow body (129 casting, 100mm),
German export model..**£100-150**

262 1959-60 **Volkswagen 'PTT' Car**
(181 casting, 90mm, fixed doors), Yellow/Black,
'PTT', Yellow cast hubs, Swiss Post export model .**£500-750**
1960-62 As previous issue but with spun aluminium hubs,
Swiss export...**£500-750**
1962-66 Same, but with plastic hubs, Swiss export.............**£500-750**
NOTE 262 models listed above should be in the
correct French / German box with 'Auto Suisse VW'
and 'Schweizer Postauto VW' on the end flap.
1966-68 129 casting (100mm): Yellow/Black, opening doors,
spun aluminium hubs, hard plastic case.................**£150-200**
1968-72 Yellow/Black, opening doors, plastic hubs,
Swiss export...**£100-125**
1972-76 Yellow/Black, opening doors, Speedwheels,
Swiss export...**£100-125**

268 **Renault Dauphine Mini-cab**
See 'Public Transport' section.

281 1968-70 **'PATHE NEWS' Camera Car**
See 'Novelty, Film and TV' section.

340 1954-66 **Land Rover** (renumbered from 27d)
Mid-Green body, Light Brown interior,
Green cast hubs, Tan cast driver **£75-85**
1966-69 Orange body, Green interior, Red cast hubs,
Tan cast driver **£75-85**
Orange body, Deep Blue interior, Red cast hubs,
Tan cast driver **£75-85**
1969-71 Dark Red body, Red cast hubs, Yellow interior,
Blue plastic driver...**£110-140**
1971 Red body, Yellow interior, Blue plastic driver,
Green or Yellow plastic hubs...............................**£110-140**
Orange body, Dark Green interior,
Blue plastic driver, Red plastic hubs.....................**£110-140**

341 1954-66 **Land-Rover Trailer** (renumbered from 27m)
Orange body, Red hubs **£20-30**
Green body, Green hubs **£20-30**
Red body, Black plastic hubs **£150-200**
Olive-Drab body...**£150-200**

342 1966-72 **Austin Mini-Moke**
Metallic Green, Grey canopy with 1 or 2 windows,
bubble-packed or boxed **£45-55**
1972-75 Metallic Greenish-Blue, 1 canopy window,
bubble-packed or boxed **£45-55**

344 1954-61 **Estate Car** See 'Farm and Garden Models'.
344 1970-72 **Land Rover Pick-Up** See 'Farm and Garden Models'.

370 1969-76 **Dragster Set**
Yellow/Red, driver, 'FIREBALL',
'INCH-PINCHER', starter unit................................**£40-50**

405 1954-66 **Universal Jeep** (renumbered from 25y)
Red body and hubs or Green body and hubs **£80-100**
1966-67 Red body, red plastic hubs, boxed in late
lighter yellow box..**£100-130**
1963 South African issues: English / Afrikaans on box.
Green body with Red hubs....................................**£400-600**
Off-White body with Red hubs **£400-600**

448 / 449 **Chevrolet El Camino Pick-up**
See 'Commercial Vehicles' section.

475 1964-66 **Model 'T' Ford**
Blue body, Yellow panels and wheels,
driver/female passenger..**£45-55**

476 1967-69 **Morris Oxford** ('Bullnose')
Yellow body, Blue chassis, Fawn hood, driver **£45-55**

516 1965-66 **Mercedes-Benz 230 SL**
Metallic Red, Cream roof, windows. (French issue) ...**£75-95**

675 1954-59 **Ford US Army Staff Car** See 'Military Vehicles' section.

2162 1973-76 **Ford Capri**
(1:25 scale, vacufrom packed on card base, 17mm long)
Metallic Blue, Black roof, Black or Blue interior........**£70-90**
2214 1974-76 **Ford Capri Rally Car** (1:25 scale)
Red, Black roof and bonnet, RN '12',
Black or Blue interior...**£80-100**
2253 1974-76 **Ford Capri Police Car** (1:25 scale)
White/Orange, 'POLICE', Blue light.......................**£80-100**

Market Price Range
Please note that the prices shown refer to pristine models and boxes.
Items failing to match this standard will sell for less.
Note also that boxes must still contain all their original packing pieces
and additional contents where appropriate.

Dinky Toys cars made by Meccano, Paris, France and sold in Britain (see French Dinky Toys listings)

24kz	1939-40	**Peugeot Car**, Red or Blue, (rubber tyres for UK)	
516		**Mercedes-Benz 230sl**, Bronze body, Cream interior.................	
518	1962-65	**Renault 4L**, Brown or Grey body, steering, windows................	
524	1965-67	**Panhard 24c** Dark Metallic Grey body	
532		**Lincoln Premiere**, Metallic Light Green body, Dk. Green roof.	
530	1965-66	**Citroën DS19**, Light Green body, Light Grey roof..................	

535	1962-65	**Citroën 2cv**, Blue body, steering, windows	
550	1962-65	**Chrysler Saratoga**, Pink/White body, windows.......................	
551	1959-64	**Rolls-Royce Silver Wraith**	
		Same as UK issue 150 'Made in France'.................................	
553	1962-65	**Peugeot 404**, Green or White, windows.................................	
555	1962-65	**Ford Thunderbird**, White, driver, steering.............................	

Dinky Toys cars made in Hong Kong

Models **57-001 to 57-006** all have spun hubs, detailed end-flap picture boxes, and are in a scale of 1:42. Hong Kong made models were issued in tab-ended alternative pictorial card boxes or rare yellow 'see-through' cellophane window boxes.

57-001	1965-67	**Buick Riviera**	Light Blue body with Cream roof and Red interior, cast wheels	**£150-200**
57-002	1965-67	**Chevrolet Corvair Monza**....	Red body, Black roof, White interior, cast wheels	**£150-200**
57-003	1965-67	**Chevrolet Impala**.................	Yellow body with White roof and Red interior, cast wheels	**£150-200**
	US / Canadian issue:		Yellow body with Yellow roof, cast wheels.............................	**£150-200**
57-004	1965-67	**Oldsmobile Dynamic '88'** ...	White body, Blue roof, Red interior, cast wheels	**£200-250**
57-005	1965-67	**Ford Thunderbird**	Blue body with White roof, Red interior, cast wheels	**£200-250**
57-006	1965-67	**Nash Rambler Classic**	Light Green body with Silver roof trim, Cream interior, cast wheels	**£200-250**
180	1979-80	**Rover 3500**..........................	White body with opening doors, plastic wheels	**£20-25**
219	1978-79	**'Big Cat' Jaguar**..................	White/Red, Black 'Big Cat' decal. (This model was bubble-packed or sold unboxed)...	**£40-50**

Dinky Toys made in Italy by Polistil under licence to Dinky Tri-ang

122	1979-80	**Volvo Estate Car**	Orange body, Brown interior, plastic wheels, Brown card box	**£20-30**
			Cream body, Red interior, cast wheels	**£20-30**
243	1979-80	**Volvo 'Police' Car**	White body, Brown card box	**£15-20**

'Mini-Dinky' models

Models 10 – 61 inclusive were made in a scale of 1:65.
Models 94 – 99 inclusive were made in a scale of 1:130.

Mini-Dinky models were issued in 1968 and were made in Hong Kong and Holland. Each model was sold with a free red plastic garage. The cars are fitted with Flexomatic Independent Suspension. Racing cars 60 and 61 were made by Best Box of Holland (now EFSI). The models listed are illustrated in the 1968 US issued 3-page fold-out leaflet which advertised them as 'Swinging Value' at 59 cents and 69 cents. Models 94-99 Construction Vehicles are illustrated in a US issued 'Mini-Dinky' fold-out launch leaflet '1'.

10	**Ford Corsair**, Yellow or Metallic Gold .**£40-50**	20	**Cadillac Coupé de Ville**,	32	**Vauxhall Cresta**, Silver or Dark Green. **£40-50**
11	**Jaguar 'E' type**, Red or Met. Maroon ...**£50-75**		Silver or White **£50-60**	33	**Jaguar**, Red................................**£50-75**
12	**Corvette Stingray**, Blue or	21	**Fiat 2300 Station Wagon**,	57	**Chevrolet Corvair Monza**, Red/Black. **£40-50**
	Metallic Dark Blue **£50-60**		Blue or Yellow/White **£40-50**	60	**Cooper**, Blue '10' **£50-75**
13	**Ferrari 250 LM**, Red or Met. Maroon . **£40-50**	22	**Oldsmobile Toronado**, Met. Pale Blue. **£40-50**	61	**Lotus Racing Car**, Green, '4' **£50-75**
14	**Chevrolet Chevy II**, Yellow or	23	**Rover 2000**, Blue............................. **£40-50**	94	**International Bulldozer**, Yellow **£70-90**
	Metallic Maroon **£40-50**	24	**Ferrari Superfast**, Red **£40-50**	95	**International Skid Shovel**, Yellow **£100-150**
15	**Rolls-Royce Silver Shadow**, Blue **£60-80**	25	**Ford Zephyr 6**, Silver **£40-50**	96	**Payloader Shovel**, White.....................**£70-90**
16	**Ford Mustang**, White, Cream or	26	**Mercedes 250 SE**, White or Bronze **£40-50**	97	**Euclid R40**, Yellow, 10 wheels.................**£70-90**
	Metallic Blue **£40-50**	27	**Buick Riviera**, Blue **£40-50**	98	**Michigan Scraper**, Yellow....................**£100-125**
17	**Aston Martin DB6**, White **£50-75**	28	**Ferrari F 1**, Red, '7' **£40-50**	99	**Caterpillar Grader**, Orange.................**£70-90**
18	**Mercedes Benz 230 SL**, White/Black... **£40-50**	29	**Ford F 1**, White **£40-50**	-	**'Mini-Dinky' 12-Car Collector Case**,
19	**MGB Roadster**, Blue **£50-75**	30	**Volvo 1800s**, Blue............................ **£40-50**		with models **£400-600**
		31	**VW 1600TC**, Blue or Metallic Green.... **£40-50**		

'Dinky Toys' issued by Airfix Products Ltd.

Issued by Airfix as 'DINKY TOYS'; made in France to 1:43 scale. Supplied in the last design of Red/Yellow/Blue 'Dinky Toys' window box with header card. They were all issued circa 1980 and all are in the Market Price Range of **£10-15**.

500	**Citroën 2cv** ......Red/Orange or Green body, 'duck' motif, open roof	504	**Citroën Visa** .....Red body, no decals	
500	**Citroën 2cv** ......Red/Orange or Green body, 'duck' motif, closed roof...	505	**Peugeot 504** .....Blue body with 'flame' decal on doors.......................	
501	**Fiat Strada** ....Blue or Metallic Bronze body, no decals	505	**Peugeot 504** .....Greenish-Gold with Black 'cougar' decal on doors.......	
502	**BMW 530** ....Purple body with 'flame' decal on doors......................	506	**Alfa-Sud** ......Not seen ....NPP	
502	**BMW 530** ....Metallic Green with Black 'cougar' decal....................	507	**Renault 14** ......Not seen ....NPP	
503	**Alfetta GTV** .....Red or Yellow body, Green 'clover leaf' on bonnet.......	508	**Ford Fiesta** .....Not seen ....NPP	

COUGAR Model Toys

Many of the 'Airfix Dinky Toys' appeared erratically in the early 1980s (in France, then in the UK), under the name 'Cougar Model Toys'. For information on this small range of 'budget' toys, please see the 'French Meccano Dinky Toys' chapter where they are listed at the end of the 'Cars' section.

AIRFIX – matchbox sized miniatures made in Hong Kong

Although announced in 1980, only a few seem to have appeared in the UK. Market Price Range **£10-15**.

101	**'56 Corvette** ....White body with Red flash, bubble-packed..............	116	**'63 Corvette** ....Metallic Blue body	
103	**Chevette** ....Yellow, 'Turbo' decal, Silver base, bubble-packed....	117	**'71 Corvette** ....Yellow body with 'Vette' decal	
104	**Honda Accord**........Lilac body, Orange flash, Silver base, bubble-pack ..	119	**Ford Van** ....Blue body with Orange flash	
105	**Toyota Celica** ....Red body, '3', Silver base, Orange bubble-pack	120	**Renegade Jeep** ....Yellow/Green body, Silver base, Green packaging....	
106	**Datsun 280Z**...........Brown body, bubble-packed............................	121	**Chevy Blazer** ....Red body	
107	**BMW Turbo**...........Orange body, Black/Yellow flash, bubble-packed....	122	**Sun Van** ....Orange body with 'Sun Van' decal, Blue packaging .	
108	**Alfa Romeo** ....Purple body with Yellow flash, bubble-packed ...	123	**Yamaha 250 MX**......Blue body with 'Yamaha' decal	
110	**Stepside Pick-up** ....Blue and Brown body, bubble-packed................	124	**Honda MT 250** ....Orange body with 'Honda' decal	
110	**Camper**..................Yellow and Two-tone Brown body	125	**Kawasaki Fll 250**....Red body with 'Kawasaki' decal	
113	**Pick-up** ....Red and Black body, '4 x 4' decal	126	**Suzuki TM 400** ....Yellow/Black body with 'CCI' and 'Suzuki' decals ..	
114	**Firebird** ....Black body..	129	**T-Bird Convertible**. Red and White body......................................	
115	**Camaro** ....Red body with racing-number 'Z28'	130	**Chevy Convertible** . Metallic Blue and White body	

Wooden prototypes, first castings and factory colour samples

These are unique items, produced as samples within the factory to aid the design and development process. Some were made for publicity and catalogue illustration purposes prior to actual volume production. Price guidance is usually not possible since they so rarely come to market in significant quantities. However, the sale in 2001 by Christie's of the Remy-Meeus Collection has enabled us to list the following:

Pre-war items

38a Frazer-Nash BMW, Blue with Grey interior, Turquoise hubs **£400-500**
38a Frazer-Nash BMW, (first casting), Green with Dark Green
    seats, fabricated, painted tinplate baseplate.........................**£300-400**
38d Alvis, (first casting), Blue with Tan seats, 'ALVIS' in
    Indian ink on base **£300-400**
38e Armstrong-Siddeley Coupé, (colour sample), plain Brown
    dashboard, production baseplate painted Khaki..................**£200-300**
38f Jaguar Sports Car, (wooden prototype),
    Dark Green body, 'JAGUAR' in Indian ink on base **£1,200-1,500**
38f Jaguar Sports Car, (1st casting), Green body, Grey seats........**£800-1,000**
39a Packard Sedan, (wooden prototype),
    Dark Blue with Silver windows, 'PACKARD' on base.......**£600-800**
39b Oldsmobile Six Sedan, (wooden prototype), Dark Green with Silver
    windows, 'Oldsmobile Six Sedan' in Indian ink on base **£500-800**
39c Lincoln Zephyr, (wooden prototype of saloon version, not coupé),
    unpainted, with 'Lincoln Zephyr' in pencil on base **£500-600**
39d Buick Viceroy, (wooden prototype), Maroon with Silver
    windows, 'BUICK' in pencil on base..................................**£600-800**
39e Chrysler Royal Sedan, (wooden prototype), Red with Silver
    windows, 'CHRYSLER' in Indian ink on base.............**£1,400-1,700**
39f Studebaker State Commander Coupé, (wooden prototype),
    Yellow Ochre with Silver windows, 'STUDEBAKER' in
    Indian ink on base..**£1,500-1,750**
39 Series Hupmobile, (wooden prototype), Green with Silver
    windows, 'HUPMOBILE' in Indian ink on base.
    Not issued as a production model **£1,200-1,500**
39 Series Luxicab, (wooden prototype), Black and Pale Yellow
    with Silver windows, 'LUXICAB' in pencil on rear spare wheel
    cover and '1st sample not approved' in pencil on base.
    Not issued as a production model **£1,100-1,400**
39 Series Luxicab, (wooden prototype), Black and Canary Yellow
    with Silver windows, 'LUXICAB' in pencil on rear spare
    wheel cover. Not issued as a production model **£1,100-1,400**

Post-war paint colour samples

38b Sunbeam-Talbot, Red body, hubs and tonneau. Tie-on label stating:
    'Approved 22 Oct 1948', plus paint code details................**£200-300**
38e Armstrong-Siddeley Coupé, Green body, Light Grey interior,
    Green hubs. Tie-on label stating:
    'Approved 22 Oct 1948', plus paint code details................**£200-300**
39b Oldsmobile Sedan, Beige body, Fawn hubs. Tie-on label stating:
    '1 Oct 1948', plus paint code details.................................**£300-500**
39e Chrysler Royal Sedan, Cream body, Light Green hubs.
    Tie-on label stating: '1 Oct 1948', plus paint code details ..**£300-500**
40b Triumph 1800, Black body, Silver hubs, rear window pillars.
    Two tie-on labels stating: '30/9/48', + paint code details....**£500-600**
40d Austin Devon, Red body, Maroon hubs. Tie-on label stamped:
    '6 Jan 1950', plus paint code details **£400-600**
40e Standard Vanguard, Fawn body, Fawn hubs, axle clip,
    open rear wheel arches. Tie-on label stating:
    '18 Oct 1948', plus paint code details.................................**£400-600**

(right) **Pre-war Dinky Toys wooden prototype**:

39 Series Luxicab

Black and Canary Yellow
with Silver windows,
'LUXICAB' in pencil on
rear spare wheel cover.
Not issued as a production model

Photograph: Christie's, South Kensington

Other prototypes and designs

We are also aware of the following (these were not in Christie's sale)

107 Sunbeam Alpine in Maroon with Grey interior (unfinished casting)..NPP
107 Sunbeam Alpine in Light Blue with Cream interior (unfinished casting)..
110 Aston-Martin in Grey with Blue interior (unfinished casting) ....NPP
111 Triumph TR2 in Pink with Blue interior...NPP
122 Volvo 256DL Estate in White...NPP
122 Volvo 256DL Estate in Red..NPP
122 Volvo 256DL Estate in Green...NPP
170 Ford Granada Ghia in Metallic Silver..NPP
181 Volkswagen Saloon in Pale Blue (with baseplate, 1970s) ....NPP
181 Volkswagen Saloon in Pale Blue (with spun hubs, 1970s).................NPP
181 Volkswagen Saloon in Metallic Blue ....NPP
181 Volkswagen Saloon in Turquoise...NPP
190 Monteverdi 375L in Metallic Gold (Copper), White interior, cast wheels.
190 Monteverdi 375L in Metallic Black, Red interior, cast wheels...........NPP
211 Triumph TR7. Metallic Green body, Red, Grey or Green interior......NPP
227 Beach Buggy. Copper body, Grey hood, 'fire' design ....NPP
507 Albion Tanker. Green, 'MILK MARKETING BOARD' **£2,000-2,500**
57-001 Buick Riviera with Slate Grey body (Hong Kong made model) ...NPP

**ALL WOODEN PROTOTYPES found in Liverpool Charity Shop and
sold by Bonhams in 2004:**

29h Duple Roadmaster Coach, light blue/grey **£680**
25y Universal Jeep, dark green, tin windscreen **£650**
30w Hindle Smart Helecs, maroon 'BR' logo on front **£600**
40g Morris Oxford, cream/blue, '17/64 Morris' on base....................**£2,000**
132 Packard Convertible, cream, red interior **£880**
472 Austin Van, green, light green hubs **£720**
480 series Bedford Van, cream, green hubs **£850**
Unreleased Austin Wagon prototype, red cab, blue back **£1,500**
522 Big Bedford Lorry, orange cab, green back..................................**£1,500**
Unreleased Leyland Fire Engine prototype **£600**
641 Army 1 ton Lorry, military green, grey windows............................**£600**
673 Army Scout Car, military green **£360**
674 Army Champ, military green...**£300**

A recent Vectis sale produced these prototype items:

Motorised Tram 'LYNDAS COMPOUND', Blue, Cream, Grey roof,
2" long, complete with photos of model on layout **£240**
Wooden mock-up Tram with plastic wheels, Cream and Red with
roof pole **£280**

Dinky Toys Commercial Vehicles Box Types

Commercial Vehicles Box Types Introduction

A mint condition commercial vehicle without its correct box is worth a fraction of the value of its boxed equivalent. Furthermore, as model boxes made from card do not survive as well as their die-cast contents, pristine box examples are scarce and becoming scarcer. The condition of a box is of paramount importance and attention is drawn to the section in the main catalogue introduction, namely: 'Classifying the Condition of Models and Boxes'.

The following listing provides collectors with a working knowledge of the range of box types issued. In addition details are given of their dates of issue, their design and of the models which used them. See also the colour sections for examples of many types of boxes.
Whilst every care has been taken in preparing the listing other variations no doubt exist and information on these is welcomed.
Similarly with no 'dates of birth' available the dates of issue shown are approximate and again any further information is welcomed.

Commercial Vehicles Box Identification

(See also 'Dinky Toys Trade Boxes' section).

Model Colour Identification Marks
These are shown on the box lid and label and take the form of either a circular colour spot or a capital letter, e.g. 'R' for red. A colour spot may be a single colour or in the case of the later two-tone colours models a two-tone colour spot.

'Lead-free' labels 'LF'
In the l950s the government introduced new regulations concerning the lead content of die-cast models. Consequently, to indicate that a model complied with the new regulations, a round white label with 'LF' in blue was added to box end labels for a short time. Alternatively, an 'LF' coloured ink stamp was used. (See example in the colour section.)

Model Reference Numbers
These are always shown on the box lid and label.

Dual numbered boxes c. l953 – 1954
A new numbering system was introduced which resulted in models being issued displaying both the old and new reference numbers. The information was shown in one of two ways:
    (a) A black new number stamped alongside the old number
    (b) A small old model number shown in red on either side of a larger black new number, e.g. 511 911 511". (See examples in the colour section). Dual numbered boxes (issued for a relatively short period) may attract a premium.

Quality Control Box Markings. 1947 – 1957
    (a) Factory Checkers' Marks
A quality control mark may be found on the base of the buff coloured boxes. This takes the form of a coloured ink stamp of a reference number within a circle, e.g. 'M42' or 'M19'. Stamped on the underside of the blue covered box lid may be found a similar ink stamp e.g. 'ZQ Z8'.
    (b) Date Stamps
Ink stamped on the base of boxes or box lids may be found a purple date stamp relating to the date of the model's issue. Recorded examples include: 'GR950' on a (25x) orange coloured box; '10 KR 55' on a (933) blue/white stripe box; 'H656' on a (902) blue/white stripe box; 'KB956' on a (433) yellow covered box lid; '01057' on a (689) military blue/white box.
The Editor would welcome any further information on this subject.

Pre-war issues 1933 – 1939
Apart from sets (see the Gift Sets listing) commercial vehicles were sold unboxed. They were usually packaged in half-dozen retailers trade packs such as Nos. 28/1, 28/2 and 28/3 Delivery Vans.

Post-war Issues 1947 – 1979
In 1947 the first individual boxes were introduced to house the exciting new range of 'Supertoys' models. However, the small commercial vehicles continued to be sold unboxed from trade packs until 1953/54.
The boxes have been catalogued into four types as follows:
    Type 1 1947-75 - Boxes with lift-off lids
    Type 2 1953-75 - All card boxes with tuck-in end flaps
    Type 3 1963-79 - Display boxes
    Type 4 l964-64 - Export only boxes

TYPE I   1947 - 69   BOXES WITH LIFT-OFF LIDS

A 1947-49
(A-a) Brown card box with wrap around all-white label with red lettering 'DINKY SUPERTOYS' and model number shown in black. Model shown as a black/white photographic illustration, e.g., 563 Heavy Tractor.

(A-b) Brown card box with separate labels on the box top and one box end. The half red and white box labels show 'DINKY SUPERTOYS' in red. Model number is white on a black oval background. In addition the main label displays an illustration of the model and whilst the main design of the label remains constant, the position of the model does vary as follows:

(i) Facing inwards on the right side of the label.
 Models recorded using this box: 25x, 501 (1st type), 521 and 563.

(ii) Facing outwards on the left side of the label.
Models recorded using this box: 502, 503, 511, 512, 513 (all 1st types). The small separate label attached to the right side of the box lid is white with red model information text. Some labels include a line drawing of the model eg. 503 and 513.

(iii) Buff plain card box with a single 'wrap round' red and white label which covers the box lid from end to end with 'DINKY SUPERTOYS' in red on the larger Foden type box, one end of the label contains information about the model in German, French and Spanish. In addition, the model number on the top and ends is now white on a circular black background. The model picture is facing inwards from the right and the models recorded in this box to date are: 504 Tanker 1st type and 531.

(iv) As previous issue but the model picture is facing outwards from the left. Models recorded: 511, 512, 521 and 533.

B c.1950
(i) Green covered box with red and white wrap-around label. Models recorded in this box: 25x, 501, 502, 503, 504 (lst and 2nd types), 504 'MOBILGAS', 511, 512, 513 and 521. Model picture facing inwards from the right. 'DINKY SUPERTOYS' in red letters.
(ii) Orange card box with black printing, e.g., 25x Breakdown Lorry.
(iii) Orange card box with orange/white label, e.g., 25x Breakdown Lorry.

C c.1951
(i) Pale or dark blue covered box with wrap-around red and white label. Model picture facing inwards from the right with 'DINKY SUPERTOYS' logo. Models recorded: 25x, 501, 502, 503, 504 (1st and 2nd types), 505, 511, 512, 513, 514 (all issues except 'Spratts'), 521, 531/931, 532/932 and 533/933.

(ii) Pale or dark blue box with wrap-around orange and white label with 'DINKY SUPERTOYS'. Model picture facing inwards from the right front. Beneath the model picture is a black factory code, e.g. on the 522 Big Bedford lorry issue the code is '50522'. Models recorded: 25x, 504 (1st / 2nd), 511, 514 'LYONS' and 'SLUMBERLAND', 531 and 571.

(iii) Same as C(ii) but with model picture facing outwards from the left. Models recorded: 502(1st), 503 (2nd) and 512.

(iv) Same as C(ii) but with model picture facing inwards from the right front but with 'DINKY TOYS'. Models recorded: 501(1st type), 504 Tanker (1st and 2nd types), 504 'MOBILGAS', 514 'WEETABIX', 514 'SLUMBERLAND', 514'SPRATTS', 521, 522, 564, 591/991, and 917.

(v) Same as C (iv) but with model picture facing outwards from the left front. Models recorded: 502, 503 (1st types), 512, 513 (1st types).

(vi) Same as C (iv) but with model picture facing inwards from the left front. Models 505 (1st type), 532 and 581 US issue.

D c1953
(i) Blue and white striped box lid with dark blue bottom section. Box lid is white with dark blue parallel stripes. 'DINKY TOYS' logo is shown in red plus a colour picture of the model facing inwards from the right. The model number is on the left of the picture. Colour identification spots shown as appropriate on box ends. Models recorded:
409, 418, 430, 582, 511, 511/911, 512, 512/912, 513, 513/913, 521/921, 901/2/3 (2nd type), 911/12/13. 917, 921, 923 ('ketchup bottle'), 923 ('baked beans can'), 930, 931, 932/33, 941/42, 963, 980, 982, 991.

NB The 417 Leyland Comet Lorry yellow/green issue was housed in a box with a blue/yellow picture.

(ii) As D (i), but with 'DINKY SUPERTOYS' logo and with the model picture facing inwards from the right. Models recorded:
901/2/3, 905, 913, 918/9, 923, 930, 934/5/6, 942/3, 948, 954, 958, 960, 963/4, 966/7/8/9, 973, 977, 982/3/4, 986, 991, 994.
On the box side is a note stating the colour of the model which may vary from the one illustrated on the box front. This only happened when a model was issued for a short while and hence some of the rarest models were issued in this manner (e.g. 902 Foden Flat Truck in yellow/green livery was issued in box with red/green model picture; 913 Guy Flat Truck with tailboard in yellow/green livery issued in box with all-green model picture; 934 Leyland Octopus Wagon in blue and yellow livery was issued on the standard box with a yellow/green model picture but displaying a dark blue colour spot).
The Editor would welcome any further examples.

(iii) As D (ii), but with model picture facing outwards from the left. 'DINKY SUPERTOYS' logo. Model recorded No.982.

(iv) As D (ii), but with model picture facing inwards from the left. 'DINKY SUPERTOYS' logo. Model recorded No. 979.

(v) Plain blue and white striped box with no model picture on lid. A white end label 'DINKY SUPERTOYS' and the model details in blue letters. Models recorded: 920 and 923.

E Yellow covered box lid with blue bottom section.
(i) c.1956 - 1959
On two of the box sides is a picture of the model set against a white shadow background. The top of the box lid has a 'DINKY TOYS' logo in red. Colour spots shown as appropriate. In addition white circular 'LF' (lead free) labels may be found. Models recorded: 408/9, 417, 419, 430/1/2/3, 437.
NB. The rare 408 Big Bedford Lorry in pink and cream livery was issued in this box but with the standard maroon and fawn model box picture.

(ii) Yellow covered box lid but with red side panels with pictorial scene with 'DINKY TOYS' logo in red. The box lid shows the model picture facing inwards from the right with a pictorial scene in an end panel on the left. Models recorded: 401, 408, 417, 419, 425, 430, 434, 448, 450, 925, 960, 964, 972 and 978.

(iii) Same as previous issue but with 'DINKY SUPERTOYS' logo. Models recorded: 908, 934, 935, 944, 958/9, 962, 964, 972 and 978.
NB. No. 935 Leyland Octopus with chains in the rare dark blue and grey livery was issued in the standard box with the green and grey version illustrated but with a dark blue spot displayed.

(iv) All yellow covered lid with a pictorial scene in the middle of the box lid top. 'DINKY SUPERTOYS' in red. Models recorded: 959, 987/8/9.

F 'One off' box issues with lift-off lids.

(i) Plain dark blue covered box with no picture. White label on box lid end with dark blue text. Model recorded: 982 Pullman Car Transporter in rare mid-blue livery with brownish-grey decks.

(ii) Orange covered box (c.1950) with white/orange wrap-around lid label. Models recorded: 25x Breakdown Truck and 14c Coventry Climax Fork Lift Truck.

**TYPE 2   1953 - 1975
ALL CARD BOXES WITH TUCK-IN END FLAPS**

A 1953 - 1964
(i) Deep yellow box with 'DINKY TOYS' in red plus the model's name and type in black. A white reference number on a black or red oval background is on the box end flaps but no reference is shown on the box face. The model is pictured on the box sides with or without a white shadow background. Colour spots shown as applicable. Foreign language information is shown on one of the box end flaps. Box used for small and medium size models, e.g., 431/432. Box in general use during the model renumbering period. Consequently dual numbered boxes will be found.
Very few boxes were issued displaying just the old type of reference number. Recorded models to date: 25d, e, f, g and 30e. In addition, 29c Bus and 29e Coach have been identified. Please send details if you have any other examples. Later issues display 'WITH WINDOWS' captions.

(ii) Plain light yellow box with two red sides and no model picture. The 'DINKY TOYS' logo, the model type and its reference number are shown in yellow and white. Colour spots are shown as appropriate. Models recorded: 252, 413, 414 and 428 plus 070 and 071 Dublo Dinky.

(iii) 1963 - 1970
Yellow box with red end features panel around the front right side, with or without an upward pointing white arrow. Models recorded: 273, 274, 435.
(iv) 1966 - 1969
A detailed full colour picture box with 'DINKY TOYS' in red plus a pictorial scene on two sides. A yellow laurel leaf design on a black background incorporates the model number Models recorded: 280, 402, 407 'KENWOOD', 914, 923, 944/5, 959/60, 965, 970, 972 and 978.

(v) 1968 - 1974
White fronted box with a narrow yellow band across the face. The box front displays 'DINKY TOYS' in red plus the model number and type in black and white letters. A colour picture of the model is shown on two sides. Models recorded: 407, 438/9/40, 91, 917, 974, 978 and 980.

(vi) 1966 - 1970
Picture box used for large commercials with two full pictorial sides with 'DINKY TOYS' in red. The other sides are yellow and red. Models recorded: 434 'AUTO SERVICES', 914 and 945.

(vii) 1970 - 1975
Heavy card box used for heavy models e.g. 924 Centaur Dump Truck. Box has white face with a colour picture of model combined with a black band across the face and sides.

(viii) Promotional Box Types
(a) No. 274 'JOSEPH MASON PAINTS' Minivan. Dark red box with white letters plus an enclosed leaflet.
(b) No. 491 Plain yellow box with red letters. 'JOBS DAIRY'.
(c) No. 917 Mercedes-Benz LP1920 Truck with 'HENRY JOHNSON' logo. Plain white card box with no lettering.
(d) No. 940 Mercedes-Benz, 'FISONS', plain white box

TYPE 3   1963 - 1979   DISPLAY BOXES

A 1970 - 1976 Vacuform packs
Models displayed on a black card plinth with a blue surface with 'DINKY TOYS' in red and white. The model is covered by a close-fitting see-through protective plastic cover. Known examples include: 407,416, 438/9, 915, 944, 945 'ESSO' and 'LUCAS' issues.

B 1976 - 1979 Window boxes
Cellophane fronted window boxes with a dark blue and red header card giving the model's name and 'DINKY DIECAST TOYS' in yellow and white letters. Known examples include: 275, 432, 440, 451, 940, 950 and 980.
C   1963 - 1966 Fold-back lid display box
224 Commer Convertible Truck and 975 Ruston Bucyrus Excavator which also had a coloured outer box display wrapper issued for a while.

TYPE 4   1964 - 1966   EXPORT ONLY BOXES

A 1964 - 1966
An all-yellow card and cellophane 'see-through' display box.
'DINKY' plus the model type and number is shown across the box front in red letters plus 'A MECCANO PRODUCT MADE IN ENGLAND'. Box issued with a card protection strip. Known models include: 275, 434, 492, 914. A version of this box was used for the 944 'SHELL BP' tanker - see picture in the colour section, Also used for the U.S. Export Series: 'MARVELS IN MINIATURE' which is shown on the sides of the box front in red capital letters, e.g. 275, 434, 437, 448 and 965. Later issues display the range on the base of the box.

B c.1965
Same as previous issue but all-gold box with two black and red diagonal stripes. A rare box type. Known issues include 434 and 989.

INNER BOX LININGS and MODEL SUPPORTS

To be complete a box should contain all its original model supports. The following issues all had supports or linings. In some instances top and bottom linings were included (2).
14c, 400, 561, 581, 908(2), 924, 930(3), 958, 964, 965, 967, 968, 969(2), 972, 974, 976, 977(2), 979(2), 980, 982, 983(2), 984(2), 985(2), 986, 989(2).

Dinky Toys Commercial Vehicles Identification

The 25 Series Lorries 1934 - 1950

Type 1: **(1934-36)**, 'open' chassis (usually black), tinplate radiator, no headlamps,
no front bumper, 'smooth' cast hubs (various colours) with large white tyres. 105 mm.

Type 2: **(1936-46)**, 'open' chassis (usually black), diecast radiator with headlamps but
no front bumper, 'smooth' cast hubs (various colours), with large white tyres. 105 mm.

Type 3: **(1947-48)**, 'closed' chassis (only in black), diecast radiator with headlamps but
no front bumper, 'smooth' or 'ridged' wheel hubs (only in black) ,with black tyres. 105 mm.

Type 4: **(1948-50)**, detailed moulded chassis (only in black), diecast radiator with headlamps and
with bumper, 'ridged' coloured wheel hubs with black tyres. 110 mm.

1st type	2nd type	3rd type	4th type
1934 - 1936	1936 - 1946	1947 - 1948	1948 - 1950
Tinplate radiator without headlights No bumpers Open chassis	Diecast radiator with headlights No bumpers Open chassis	Diecast radiator with headlights No bumpers Plain (closed) chassis	Diecast radiator with headlights and front bumper Moulded chassis

25 Series Trucks 1934-50 Wheel types The first pre-war issues have cast metal wheels followed by chrome (rare) or diecast hubs with large white tyres. The early post-war issues c.1946 have smooth hubs and large black tyres. **1947-48** issues have ridged black hubs with large black tyres. The last issues **c.1949-50** have coloured ridged hubs and attract a premium. Similarly early cast or chrome hubs also attract a premium.

Guy cab types

Guy 1st type cab 1947 - 1954
Exposed radiator
No gusset at either
side of number plate

Guy 2nd type cab 1954 - 1958
Exposed radiator
With gusset at each
side of number plate

Guy Warrior cab 1958 - 1964
Radiator behind grille
Restyled front with
sidelights in wings

Foden cab types

1947 - 1952
Foden 'DG'
(1st type) cab
Exposed radiator
Colour flashes on sides

1952 - 1964
Foden 'FG'
(2nd type) cab
Radiator behind grille
No colour flashes on sides

Identification of
Ford Transit Van
castings
(not illustrated)

Type 1: **(1966-74)**, has sliding driver's door, opening hinged side door, and twin rear doors.

Type 2: **(1974-78)**, non-sliding driver's door, one side-hinged door, one top-hinged rear door.

Type 3: **(1978-80)**, as Type 2 but with a slightly longer bonnet (18 mm.)

Dinky Toys 505 Foden Flat Truck with Chains
'DG' (1st type) cab
Exposed radiator
Colour flashes on sides

Dinky Toys Commercial Vehicles

Market Price Range (MPR) for pre-1954 unboxed commercial vehicle models: Prior to 1954, virtually all smaller, non-Supertoy commercial vehicle models were sold unboxed from retailer's trade boxes of either 6, 4 or 3 models. Consequently, all pre-1954 issues have been priced as being unboxed. Post-1954 models were all boxed and have been priced accordingly. As a consequence, models which have been renumbered will be found to have two differing prices – one for the pre-1954 unboxed version and another for its boxed and renumbered successor.

See also the Trade Box section for details of individual boxes and packs that were used to supply shops.

Ref	Year(s)	Model name	Colours, features, details	Market Price Range
14a	1948-54	B.E.V. Truck	Mid-Blue body with Blue hubs, Fawn driver, hook, (renumbered 400)	£30-35
			Grey body (with Blue, Grey or Red hubs), Fawn driver, hook	£30-35
14c	1949-54	Coventry Climax Fork Lift	Orange, Brown or Dark Red body, Green forks, Fawn driver, 1 packing piece, (renumbered 401)	£25-30
14z	1938-40	Three-wheel Delivery Van	'Triporteur' with Green, Red, Grey, Blue or Yellow body, Black hubs,	
			White tyres, driver is always a different colour from van, French model	NGPP

22 Series

22c	1933-35	Motor Truck	Two-piece lead body with 'HORNBY SERIES' cast-in, tinplate radiator,	
			diecast wheels that may be plain or may have an applied colour wash.	
			Blue cab, Red truck body	£500-600
			Blue cab, Cream or Yellow truck body, Blue wash wheels	£500-600
			Red cab, Green, Blue or Cream truck body	£300-400
			Yellow cab, Blue truck body	£300-400
22c	1935-40	Motor Truck	Orange-Red, Maroon, Green or Blue (diecast one-piece) body, open rear window,	
			coloured diecast hubs	£125-150
			Dark Blue body, chrome hubs	£125-150
			Off-white body, Mid-Blue hubs	£125-150
	1945-47		Red, Green or Brown body, open rear window, Black diecast hubs	£60-70
	1948-50		Red, Green or Brown body, closed rear window, Black diecast hubs	£60-70
22d	1933-34	Delivery Van	Lead body, tinplate radiator, 'HORNBY SERIES' cast-in.	
			Green cab, Blue van body, Blue wash wheels, Type 1	£2,500-3,000
			Orange/Blue body or Blue/Yellow body, Red wheels, no advertising, Type 1	£2,500-3,000
	1934-34		As previous models but with 'DINKY TOYS' cast-in	£400-500
	1934	Delivery Van 'MECCANO'	Orange cab and chassis, Blue van with Red/Black 'Meccano Engineering For Boys'	£3,000-5,000
22d	1934-35		Yellow body (lead), 'Meccano Engineering For Boys' in Red and Black,	
			Type 1. Model number was 22d until April 1935, then it was renumbered 28n	£900-1,200

25 Series

25a	1934-36	Wagon	Maroon, Green, Red or Blue body, Black chassis, Type 1	£300-400
	1936-40		Maroon, Green, Red or Blue body, Black or Red chassis, Type 2	£125-150
	1936-40		Blue body with Orange chassis, Type 2	£150-200
	1946		Grey, Green, Maroon or Blue, Type 2, smooth hubs	£80-100
	1947-48		Grey, Green, Red, Orange, Stone or Blue body, Black chassis, Type 3	£70-80
	1948-50		Grey, Green, Light Blue or Orange body, Black chassis, Type 4	£70-80
			Cream or Red body, Black chassis, Type 4	£70-80
25b	1934-36	Covered Wagon	Blue body, Cream tilt, Black chassis, Type 1	£300-400
	1936-40		Green body, Green, Cream or Yellow tilt, Black chassis, Type 2	£140-180
			Cream/Yellow or Fawn/Cream, Black chassis, Type 2	£140-180
			Orange body, Cream tilt, Green chassis, Type 2	£150-200
	1936-40	Covered Wagon		
		'CARTER PATERSON'	Green body, Blue hubs, Green tilt, Black chassis, Type 2, 'Express Carriers London'	£300-350
		'CARTER PATERSON'	Green body, Blue hubs, Type 2, 'Special Service To The Seaside'	£400-500
		'MECCANO'	Green body, Cream tilt, Black chassis, Type 2, 'Engineering For Boys'	£300-400
			Variation with chrome hubs	£500-600
		'HORNBY TRAINS'	Fawn body, Cream tilt, Black chassis, Type 2, Gold lettering	£300-400
	1945-47	Covered Wagon	Green/Green, Grey/Light or Dark Grey, Blue/Grey, Black chassis, Type 3	£100-140
	1947-50		Green/Green, Grey/Grey, Cream/Red, Cream/Blue, Black chassis, Type 4	£100-140
			Yellow body, Blue tinplate tilt, Black ridged hubs	£300-400
25c	1934-36	Flat Truck	Dark Blue body, Black chassis, Type 1	£150-200
	1936-40		Green or Stone body, Black chassis, Type 2	£125-150
	1946		Fawn, Green or Grey body, smooth hubs, Type 2	£70-80
	1947-48		Green, Blue, Stone or Grey body, Black chassis, Type 3	£70-80
	1948-50		Green, Blue, Orange or Stone body, Type 4	£70-80
	NB		Some pre-war (1934-40) Truck issues will be found with a '20 mph' disc on the rear.	
25d	1934-35	Petrol Tank Wagon	Same chassis casting as other 25 series lorries but with hook removed.	
		(plain, unlettered)	Red body, no advertising, Black chassis, Type 1, open windows to back of cab	£500-750
		'SHELL BP'	Red body, Black chassis, Type 1	£500-750
		'SHELL'	Red body, Blue hubs, Type 1, 'SHELL LUBRICATING OIL' in Gold serif lettering	£500-750
		'ESSO'	Green body, Black chassis, Type 1	£500-750
		'POWER'	Green body, Black chassis, Type 1	£500-750
		'PRATTS'	Green body, Black chassis, Type 1	£500-750
		'CASTROL'	Green body, Black chassis, Blue hubs, Red logo, Type 1	£500-750
		'TEXACO'	Red body, Black chassis/hubs, White logo 'PETROLEUM & PRODUCTS', Type 1	£500-750
	1936-46	'PETROL'	Red body, Black chassis, Black or White lettering, Type 2	£500-750

25d		**Petrol Tank Wagon (continued)**		
		'SHELL BP'	Red body, Black chassis, Blue or chrome hubs, Type 2	£500-750
		'MOBILOIL'	Red body, Black chassis, Type 2	£500-750
		'TEXACO'	Red body, Black chassis, Type 2	£500-750
		'PETROL'	Green body, Black chassis, Type 2	£500-750
		'ESSO'	Green body, Black chassis, Black or Blue hubs, Gold lettering, Type 2	£500-750
		'POWER'	Green body, Black chassis, Type 2	£500-750
		'CASTROL'	Green body, Black chassis, Black or Blue hubs, Red lettering, Type 2	£500-750
		'REDLINE GLICO'	Blue body, Black chassis, Red panel, Gold lettering, Type 2	£500-750
	1945	'POOL' (Wartime)	Grey body, White chassis, Black hubs, Black lettering, Type 2	£500-750
	1945-46	'POOL' (Wartime)	Grey body, Black chassis, Type 2	£500-750
	1945-46	'PETROL' (Wartime)	Grey body, Type 2	£500-750
	1946-47	'PETROL'	Red, Orange, Mid-Green or Dark Green body, Black chassis, Type 3	£200-250
	1947-48	'PETROL'	Orange body, Type 4	£300-400
	1948-50	'PETROL'	Red, Light Green or Mid-Green body, Black chassis, Type 4	£150-200
	1948-?	'PETROL'	Yellow body, Black chassis, Type 4	£200-300
25e	1934-35	**Tipping Wagon**	Maroon/Yellow body, Black chassis, Type 1	£150-200
	1936-40		Maroon/Yellow, Brown/Turquoise or Fawn/Fawn body, Black chassis, Type 2	£100-125
			Fawn/Fawn body, Black chassis, Type 2	£100-125
	1946		Grey, Green or Fawn, Type 2	£70-80
	1947-48		Grey, Stone, Green or Yellow body, Black chassis, Type 3	£70-80
	1948-50		Grey, Stone or Brown body, Black chassis, Type 4	£70-80
	1948-50		Blue/Pink body, Black chassis, Type 4	£70-80
		NB	Some early post-war 25 series Trucks variations exist with smooth hubs.	
25f	1934-35	**Market Gardeners Lorry**	Green body, Black chassis or Yellow body, Green chassis, Type 1	£150-200
	1936-40		Green or Yellow body, Black chassis, Type 2	£70-80
			Green body, Yellow chassis, Type 2	£150-200
	1945-47		Green, Grey, Stone or Yellow body, Black chassis and hubs, Type 3	£70-80
	1947-50		Green, Grey, Yellow or Red body, Black chassis and hubs, Type 4	£70-80
			Orange body, Black chassis and hubs, Type 4	£140-160
			Orange body, Green hubs, Type 4	£300-400
			Green or Yellow body, Black chassis, Yellow hubs, Type 4	£70-80
25g	1935-40	**Trailer**	Dark Blue or Green body with cast-in hook, tinplate drawbar	£35-40
	1946-47		Green, Grey, Stone, Pale Blue or Orange body, cast-in hook, tinplate drawbar	£15-20
	1947-48		Green, Stone, Pale Blue or Orange body, cast-in hook, wire drawbar	£15-20
	1948-49		Green, Stone, Pale Blue or Orange body, tinplate hook, wire drawbar	£15-20
25g	1950-54		Green or Red body with tinplate hook and wire drawbar, (renumbered 429)	£15-20
		NB	Most 25g Trailers have a white 'T' on a square black background, located at the rear.	
25m	1948-52	**Bedford End Tipper**	Dark Green cab and truck body, Black hubs, crank-handle operates tipper	£60-75
	1948-54		Orange cab and truck body, Black hubs	£60-75
			Orange cab and truck body, Light Green hubs	£500-750
			Cream cab and truck body, Red hubs	£500-750
			Dark Green cab and truck body, Light Green hubs	£300-400
			Red cab, Cream back, Red cast hubs	£60-75
			Yellow cab, Mid-Blue back, Yellow cast hubs	£90-120
		NB	25m was renumbered 410 in 1954. All 25m models were sold from trade packs of six.	
25p	1948-54	**Aveling Barford Road Roller**	Mid or Pale Green body with driver and hook, Red wheels, (renumbered 251)	£30-40
			All-Orange body, Tan driver	£150-200
25r	1948-54	**Forward Control Lorry**	Orange body, Black hubs	£100-150
		(renumbered 420)	Orange body, Green hubs	£100-150
			Cream body, Black hubs	£100-150
			Cream body, Blue hubs	£100-150
			Cream body, Black hubs	£100-150
			Dark Brown body, Green hubs	£100-150
			Green body, Cream hubs	£100-150
			Green body, Red hubs	£100-150
			Grey body, Red hubs	£100-150
25s	1937-40	**Six-wheeled Wagon**	Reddish-Brown body, Cream, Brown or Grey tilt, holes in seat (but no figures)	£100-125
			Royal Blue body	£200-250
	1945-48		Brown (various shades), Green or Dark Blue body, Grey or Light Blue tilt, with or without holes for figures (but no figures)	£100-125
			Brick Red body, Grey tinplate tilt, Black hubs	£125-150
25t	1945-47	**Flat Truck and Trailer**	(25c Flat Truck (Type 3), and matching 25g Trailer), Green, Blue, Orange or Stone	£140-160
	1947-50		(25c Flat Truck (Type 4), and matching 25g Trailer), Green or Orange	£120-140
25v	1948-54	**Bedford Refuse Wagon**	Fawn body, Green opening shutters and rear door, (renumbered 252). (Trade box contains 4)	£75-85
25w	1948-54	**Bedford Truck**	Light Green cab, truck body and hubs. (Shades of Pale Green exist)	£60-75
		(renumbered 411)	Same as previous model, but with 'straight across' Black front mudguards	£250-350
			Dark Green cab, Light Green truck body, Light Green hubs	£300-400
			Light Green cab and truck body, Red hubs	£500-750
25x	1949-54	**Commer Breakdown Lorry**	'DINKY SERVICE' logo. First issues in Trade Boxes of 4, then individually in Orange card boxes.	
		(renumbered 430)	Tan cab and chassis (various shades), Light Green back, Red hubs, Black logo	£100-120
			Dark Grey cab, Violet Blue back, Red hubs, White logo	£130-150
			Dark Grey cab, Royal Blue back, Red hubs, White logo	£115-135

28a   **'HORNBY TRAINS'**
1934-34   Type 1, Orange body, 'Hornby Trains' logo **£3,000-5,000**
1934-35   Type 1, Yellow body, 'Hornby Trains British &
      Guaranteed' in Gold. Blue wash wheels **£3,000-4,000**
1935-36   Type 2, smooth cast hubs **£400-500**

28a   **'GOLDEN SHRED'**
      Cream body, 'Golden Shred Marmalade' on left hand
      side, 'Silver Shred Marmalade' on right hand side.
1936-39   Type 2 ....**£3,000-4,000**
1939-41   Type 3 ....**£750-1,000**

28b   **'PICKFORDS'**
      Royal Blue, 'Pickfords Removals & Storage,
      Over 100 Branches' in Gold.
1934-35   Type 1, Purple wash wheels **£3,000-4,000**
1935   Type 1, Dark Blue. Diecast hubs, White tyres **£3,000-4,000**
1935-35   Type 2 ....**£750-1,000**

28b   **'SECCOTINE'**
      Blue body, 'Seccotine Sticks Everything' in Gold.
1935-39   Type 2 ....**£750-1,000**
1939-41   Type 3 ....**£300-400**

28c   **'MANCHESTER GUARDIAN'**
      'The Manchester Guardian' in Gold.
1934-35   Type 1, Black/Red body, Yellow wash wheels **£3,000-4,000**
1935-39   Type 2, Red body, smooth cast hubs **£400-500**
1939-41   Type 3, Red body...**£400-500**

28d   **'OXO'**
      Blue body, 'Beef In Brief' and 'Beef At Its Best' in Gold.
1934-35   Type 1, Green wash wheels...............................**£3,000-4,000**
1935-39   Type 2, smooth cast hubs **£750-1,000**
1939-41   Type 3 ....**£700-900**

28e   **'ENSIGN CAMERAS'**
      Orange body, 'ENSIGN CAMERAS' (on n/s) and
      'ENSIGN LUKOS FILMS' (on o/s) in Gold.
1934-35   Type 1, Blue wash wheels **£3,000-4,000**

28e   **'FIRESTONE TYRES'**
      'Firestone Tyres' in Gold.
1935-35   White body, Type 1..**£3,000-4,000**
1935-39   Blue or White body, Type 2..................................**£750-1,000**
1939-41   Blue or White body, Type 3....................................**£400-500**

28f   **'PALETHORPES'**
      Pale Grey-Blue body, Pink sausage decal, 'Palethorpes
      Royal Cambridge' on van sides, 'Palethorpes Model
      Factory' on rear (Red and Navy Blue transfers).
1934-35   Type 1, Blue wash wheels **£3,000-4,000**
1935-38   Type 2, smooth cast hubs **£750-1,000**

28f   **'VIROL'**
      Yellow body, 'Give Your Child A Virol
      Constitution' in Black.
1938-39   Type 2, Blue wash wheels **£750-1,000**
1939-41   Type 3, smooth cast hubs **£400-500**

28g   **'KODAK'**
      Yellow body, 'Use Kodak Film To Be Sure' in Red.
1934-35   Type 1, Blue wash wheels **£3,000-4,000**
1935-39   Type 2, smooth cast hubs **£750-1,000**
1939-41   Type 3 ....**£400-500**

28h   **'SHARPS TOFFEES'**
      'Sharps Toffee, Maidstone' in Gold.
1934-35   Type 1, Black/Red body, Yellow wash wheels **£1,500-2,000**
1935-35   Type 2, Red body, smooth cast hubs **£500-700**

28h   **'DUNLOP'**
      Red body, 'Dunlop Tyres' in Gold.
1935-39   Type 2 ....**£750-1,000**
1939-41   Type 3 ....**£400-500**

28k   **'MARSH & BAXTER'**
      Dark Green body, 'Marsh's Sausages' and pig logo in Gold.
1934-35   Type 1, Purple or Green wash wheels.................**£3,000-4,000**
1935-39   Type 2, smooth cast hubs **£750-1,000**
1939-41   Type 3 ....**£500-700**

28L   **'CRAWFORDS'**
      Red body, 'Crawfords Biscuits' in Gold.
1934-35   Type 1 only, Yellow or Green wash wheels **£2,500-3,500**

28m   **'WAKEFIELD'S CASTROL'**
      Green body, 'Wakefield Castrol Motor Oil' in Red.
1934-35   Type 1, Yellow wash wheels **£3,000-4,000**
1935-39   Type 2, smooth cast hubs **£400-500**
1939-41   Type 3 ....**£1,500-2,000**

28n   **'MECCANO'**
      Lemon Yellow body, 'Meccano Engineering For
      Boys' in Red and Black.
1934-35   Type 1. Renumbered from 22d........................**£4,000-5,000**
1935-35   Type 2, smooth cast hubs **£400-500**

28n   **'ATCO'**
      Green body, 'Atco Lawn Mowers Sales and
      Service' in Gold/Red.
1935-39   Type 2 ....**£750-1,000**
1939-41   Type 3 ....**£500-700**

28p   **'CRAWFORDS'**
      Red body, 'Crawfords Biscuits' in Gold.
1935-39   Type 2 ....**£750-1,000**
1939-41   Type 3 ....**£750-1,000**

28r   **'SWAN'**
      Black body, 'Swan Pens' and logo in Gold.
1936-39   Type 2 ....**£750-1,000**
1939-41   Type 3 ....**£400-500**

28s   **'FRYS'**
      Brown or Cream body, 'Frys Chocolate' in Gold.
1936-39   Type 2 ....**£750-1,000**
1939-41   Type 3 ....**£300-400**

28t   **'OVALTINE'**
      Red body, 'Drink Ovaltine For Health' in Gold/Black.
1936-39   Type 2 ....**£2,000-3,000**
1939-41   Type 3 ....**£400-500**

28w   **'OSRAM'**
      Yellow body, 'Osram Lamps - a G.E.C. Product'.
      in Gold/Black.
1936-39   Type 2 ....**£750-1,000**
1940-41   Type 3 ....**£500-700**

28x   **'HOVIS'**
      White body, 'Hovis For Tea' in Gold/Black.
1936-39   Type 2 ....**£750-1,000**
1939-41   Type 3 ....**£400-500**

28y   **'EXIDE / DRYDEX'**
      Red body, 'Exide Batteries' and 'Drydex Batteries'
      in Gold/Black.
1936-39   Type 2 ....**£400-500**
1939-41   Type 3 ....**£400-500**

NB   **Further issues in this series were numbered 280, as follows**:

280   1945-47   **Delivery Van (no advertising)**
                Red or Blue body, Type 3, open rear windows **£50-60**
     1948-54   As previous model, but with filled-in rear windows......**£50-60**
                Green body, Type 3, filled-in rear windows...................**NGPP**
                NB The 280 casting provided the basis
                for 34c Loudspeaker Van.

280a   **'VIYELLA'**
      Blue body,'Viyella for the Nursery' in White and Black.
1937-39   Type 2 ....**£2,000-2,500**
1939-41   Type 3 ....**£700-950**

280b   **'LYONS TEA'**
1937-39   Dark Blue body, 'Lyons Tea Always the Best' in
      Red and White. Only issued as Type 2 ....**£750-1,000**

280b   **'HARTLEYS JAM'**
      Cream body, 'Hartleys is Real Jam' in Red/Green.
1939-39   Type 2 ....**£800-1,000**
1939-40   Type 3 ....**£400-500**

280c   **'SHREDDED WHEAT'**
Cream body, Red stripe, 'Welwyn Garden City, Herts'
in Black.
1937-39 Type 2 ....**£750-1,000**
1939-40 Type 3 ....**£400-500**

280d   **'BISTO'**
1937-40 Yellow body, 'Ah! Bisto' with logo, Type 2 ....**£350-500**
1938-39 Type 2, with large Bisto Kids transfer **£750-1,000**
         Type 2, small Bisto Kids transfer, with pie on table..**£600-800**
1939-40 Type 3, small Bisto Kids transfer with pie on table...**£400-500**
1940   Yellow body, wording altered to 'Bisto' with logo.

280e 1937-39 **'ECKO'**
Type 2, Dark Green body, 'ECKO Radio' in Gold **£500-750**

280e   **'YORKSHIRE EVENING POST'**
Cream body, 'Yorkshire Evening Post - The Original Buff'.
1938-39 Type 2 ....**£750-1,000**
1939-39 Type 3 ....**£600-800**

280f   **'MACKINTOSHS'**
Red body, 'Mackintosh's Toffee' in Gold.
1937-39 Type 2 ....**£750-1,000**
1939-40 Type 3 ....**£400-500**

<u>**NB**</u>   <u>**Nos. 280g – 280m were made as promotional models.**</u>

280g 1939 **'BENTALLS'**
Green body, Yellow upper side panels, White roof,
'Bentalls Kingston on Thames' and
'Phone Kin: 1001' in Yellow.
Type 2. Two examples known **£5,000-7,500**

280h 1939 **'MAISON de BONNETERIE'**
Dark Red, Type 2,
Maison de Bonneterie, Leverancier' **£3,000-5,000**

280i 1939 **'LIVERPOOL ECHO'**
Type 2, no other details available.........................**£3,000-5,000**

280j 1939 **'FENWICK'**
Apple Green body, White roof, Type 2,
'Newcastle on Tyne'. Two examples known........**£2,000-3,000**

280k 1939 **'H. G. LOOSE'**
Dark Green body, 'H. G. LOOSE' on Cream panel,
'Looe' and 'Phone 125'.
Type 2. One example known **£2,000-3,000**

280L 1939 **'DE BIJENKORF'**
Type 2, 'Amsterdam Den Haag Rotterdam'....................NGPP

280m 1939 **'LAND'S FOR BAGS'**
Green body, 'Land's for Bags' in Gold.
Type 2. One example known (in poor condition) ....NGPP

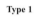

28 / 280 Series Delivery Van Identification

Type 1: **(1933-35)**, two-piece lead body with *'HORNBY SERIES'* (early issues) or *'DINKY TOYS'* cast-in under cab roof, tinplate radiator, no headlamps, thinly-painted coloured solid wheel/tyre castings (some bright plated), 84 mm. (Coloured wheels tend to attract a premium to the price of the model.)

Type 2: **(1935-39)**, one-piece diecast body, cast-in shield-shaped radiator, rear wheel spats, cast smooth wheel hubs with rubber tyres (usually white), 81 mm. All carried advertising.

Type 3: **(1939-41)**, one-piece diecast body with rear wheel spats, cast smooth wheel hubs (various colours) with black tyres, open rear windows, 83 mm. All carried advertising.

Type 3: **(1947-54)**, one-piece diecast body with rear wheel spats, cast ridged wheel hubs (usually black) with black tyres, filled-in rear windows, cast boss under roof , 83 mm. No advertising.

Type 1

Type 2

Type 3

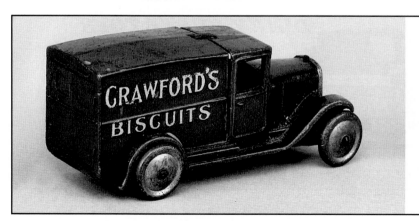

Rear view of

28p

'Crawford's' Delivery Van
(1st type)

Photo: Vectis Auctions Ltd.

Commercial vehicles

30 Series

30e	1935-40	**Breakdown Car** (Crane Lorry) ..	Red, Yellow, Green, Brown or Grey body, Black wings, Black or Blue smooth hubs, open rear window	£100-120
			Blue body, Dark Blue wings, Blue hubs, open rear window	£100-120
	1946-46		Red or Grey body, Black wings, open rear window, ridged hubs	£60-70
	1947-48		Red, Grey or Green body and wings, no rear window, ridged hubs	£40-50
30j	1950-54	**Austin Wagon**	Blue body with hook, Mid-Blue hubs	£100-120
		(renumbered 412)	Light, Medium or Dark Maroon body, Maroon or Red hubs	£100-150
			Brown body, Tan hubs	£400-500
			Dark Blue body, Mid-Blue hubs	NGPP
			Red body, Red hubs	NGPP
30m	1950-54	**Rear Tipping Wagon**	Maroon or Orange cab, Pale Green rear, 'Dodge' on baseplate	£60-70
		(renumbered 414)	Blue or Dark Blue cab, Grey rear	£60-70
30n	1950-54	**Farm Produce Wagon**	See 'Farm and Garden Models'.	
30p	1950-54	**Petrol Tanker**	Based on a Studebaker vehicle.	
30p	1950-51	**'PETROL'**	Red or Green body, cast in aluminium	£80-90
	1951-52	**'PETROL'**	Red or Green body, cast in mazak	£80-90
30p	1952-54	**'MOBILGAS'**	Red body, Blue lettering on White background, (renumbered 440)	£80-90
30pa	1952-54	**'CASTROL'**	Green body and hubs, some cast in aluminium, most in mazak, (renumbered 441)	£80-90
30pb	1952-54	**'ESSO'**	Red body and hubs, 'MOTOR OIL - ESSO - PETROL', (renumbered 442)	£80-90
30r	1951-54	**Fordson Thames Flat Truck**	Red or Green body with hook	£60-70
		(renumbered 422)	Brown body, Brown hubs	£60-70
			Brown body, Maroon hubs	NGPP
30s	1950-54	**Austin Covered Wagon**	Maroon body, Cream cover, Cream hubs, sold unboxed	£100-150
		(renumbered 413)	Dark Blue body, Light Blue cover, Light Blue hubs, sold unboxed	£300-400
			Mid-Blue body, Light Blue cover, Light Blue hubs, sold unboxed	£100-150
30v	1949-54	**Electric Dairy Van 'EXPRESS DAIRY'**	Cream body, Red chassis, hubs and logo, (renumbered 490)	£75-90
			Grey body, Blue chassis, hubs and logo	£75-90
30v	1949-54	**Electric Dairy Van 'N.C.B.'**	Cream body, Red chassis, hubs and logo, (renumbered 491)	£75-90
			Grey body, Blue chassis, hubs and logo	£75-90
30w	1952-54	**Hindle-Smart Helecs**	Maroon body, Maroon or Red hubs, 'British Railways', hook, trailer uncouples, (renumbered 421)	£60-70

DINKY SUPERTOYS

935

LEYLAND OCTOPUS
FLAT TRUCK WITH CHAINS

Photo: Christie's

31 Series

31	1935-35	**Holland Coachcraft Van**	Red, Green, Blue or Orange, 'Holland Coachcraft Registered Design', lead body	£2,000-3,000
	1935-36		Red, Blue or Orange, 'Holland Coachcraft Registered Design', diecast body	£2,000-3,000
	1935		Mid-Green body, Gold stripe, Silver advert., Chrome hubs	£2,000-3,000
	1935		Cream body with Red coachline	£2,000-3,000
	NB		A Red variant from 1935/6 was sold by Christie's in 2001 for £2,350.	
31a	1951-54	**Trojan 15 cwt Van 'ESSO'**	Red body, Maroon or Red hubs, (renumbered 450)	£80-100
31b	1952-54	**Trojan 15 cwt Van 'DUNLOP'** ..	Red body, Maroon or Red hubs, 'The Worlds Master Tyre', (renumbered 451)	£80-100
31c	1953-54	**Trojan 15 cwt Van 'CHIVERS'**.	Green body and hubs, 'CHIVERS JELLIES' and design, (renumbered 452)	£80-100
31d	1953-54	**Trojan 15 cwt Van 'OXO'**	Mid-Blue or Violet-Blue body, Mid-Blue hubs, 'BEEFY OXO', (renumbered 453)	£300-400

33 Series

33a	1935-36	**Mechanical Horse**	Red, Green, Blue or Yellow body, 2.5 mm. trailer step. **NB** 1st type have long slot and chrome hubs.	£150-175
	1936-40		As previous model but trailer step is 9.5 mm. long.	£125-150
	1946-?		As previous model but also in Brown, Grey or Khaki	£125-150
33b	1935-40	**Flat Truck Trailer**	Red, Green, Blue or Yellow body, no sides	£45-55
33c	1935-40	**Open Truck Trailer**	Red, Green, Blue or Yellow body with sides	£45-55
33d	1935-40	**Box Van Trailer**	Green tinplate body on cast chassis, no advertising	£100-125
		'HORNBY TRAINS'	Dark Blue body, 'Hornby Trains British and Guaranteed' in Gold	£300-400
		'HORNBY TRAINS'	Green body, 'Hornby Trains British and Guaranteed' in Gold	£300-400
		'MECCANO'	Green body, 'Meccano Engineering For Boys' in Red and Black	£300-400
	NB		Models 33a and 33d combined and given Ref No 33r	£400-500
33e	1935-40	**Dust Wagon Trailer**	Blue, Yellow Grey or Green 33c (Open Trailer) with Blue, Yellow, Grey or Green tinplate top	£70-90
	1946-47		Grey or Red body with Blue or Yellow tinplate top	£70-90
33f	1935-40	**Petrol Tank Trailer**	Green (33b) chassis/Red tank, or Red chassis/Green tank, no logo	£70-90
		'ESSO'	Green chassis/Red tank with 'ESSO' in Gold	£80-120
		'CASTROL'	Red chassis/Green tank, 'Wakefield Castrol'	£80-120
33r	1935-40	**Railway Mechanical Horse and Trailer Van**	33a Mechanical Horse and 33d Box Van Trailer in railway liveries. These were also available separately as 33ra and 33rd (see below).	
33r		'L.N.E.R.'	Blue and Black, 'L.N.E.R. Express Parcels Traffic'	£250-350
33r		'L.M.S.'	Maroon and Black, 'L.M.S. Express Parcels Traffic'	£250-350
33r		'G.W.R.'	Brown and Cream, 'G.W.R. Express Cartage Services'	£250-350
33r		'S.R.'	Green (Cream cab roof) and Black, 'Southern Railway'	£250-350
33ra	1935-40	**Mechanical Horse 'L.N.E.R.'**	Blue and Black, 'L.N.E.R. 901'	£250-350
33ra		'L.M.S.'	Maroon and Black, 'L.M.S. 2246'	£250-350
33ra		'G.W.R.'	Brown and Cream, 'G.W.R. 2742'	£250-350
33ra		'S.R.'	Green (Cream roof) and Black, '3016 M'	£250-350
33rd		Railway Trailer 'L.N.E.R.'	Blue and Black, 'L.N.E.R. Express Parcels Traffic'	£250-350
33rd		'L.M.S.'	Maroon and Black, 'L.M.S. Express Parcels Traffic'	£250-350
33rd		'G.W.R.'	Brown and Cream, 'G.W.R. Express Cartage Services'	£250-350
33rd		'S.R.'	Green and Black, 'Southern Railway'	£250-350
33w	1947-54	**Mechanical Horse and Open Wagon**	Cab colours: Grey, Fawn, Dark or Mid-Green, Olive, Red, Brown, Blue or Yellow. Trailer colours: Grey, Fawn, Maroon, Brown, Dark or Mid-Green, Olive or Cream. (renumbered 415)	£75-95

34 Series

34a	1935-40	**'ROYAL AIR MAIL SERVICE'**	Blue car body with Silver lettering and Gold crest	£300-400
34b	1938-47	**'ROYAL MAIL' Van**	Red body, Black bonnet/wings/roof/hubs, open rear windows	£150-175
	1948-51		Red body, Black bonnet/wings/roof, Black or Red hubs, filled-in rear windows	£100-125
	1952-52		Red body/roof/hubs, Black bonnet/front wings, filled-in rear windows	£125-150
34c	1948-54	**Loudspeaker Van**	Fawn, Grey, Green, Brown or Blue body (280 casting) Black loudspeakers	£70-80
		(renumbered 492)	Brown, Blue or Green body (280 casting) Silver loudspeakers	£70-80
60y	1938-40	**Thompson Aircraft Tender**	Red with 'Shell Aviation Services' in Gold; Black or White solid rubber wheels	£300-400
151b	1937-40	**6-wheel Covered Wagon**	Gloss Green body, tinplate canopy, seat holes, spare wheel, (renumbered 25s)	£125-150
	1947-54		Matt-Green or Greenish-Brown body, (export only from 1950), (renumbered 620)	£60-70
251	1954-63	**Aveling Barford Road Roller**	Mid or Dark Green body, Red rollers, (renumbered from 25p)	£45-55
			Lime Green or Apple Green body, Red rollers	£70-90
252	1954-60	**Bedford Refuse Wagon**	Fawn body, Green tinplate shutters, Red hubs, window glazing in some, (renumbered from 25v)	£125-150
	1960-63		Lime Green body, Black tinplate shutters, Cream hubs, with or without window glazing...........	£125-150
	1963-63		Orange cab, Light Grey back, Green tinplate shutters and diecast hubs, window glazing, Black grille	£300-350
	1964-64		Orange cab, Light Grey back and diecast hubs, Green plastic shutters, window glazing...........	£250-350
	1964-65		Bright Orange cab, Light Grey back, Green plastic shutters, Red plastic hubs, window glazing	£250-350
			As previous model but with matt-Black base	£250-350
260	1955-61	**'ROYAL MAIL' Van**	(Morris 'J') Red body, Black roof, Gold 'E II R' crest	£125-150
260	1971-72	**Volkswagen 'DEUTSCHE BUNDESPOST'**.	Yellow body (129 casting, 100mm), made for German Market	£100-150
261	1955-61	**Telephone Service Van**	(Morris 'Z') Olive-Green/Black, 'POST OFFICE TELEPHONES', ladder	£100-125
273	1965-70	**Mini Minor Van 'R.A.C.'**	Blue body, White roof, Black base, Red interior, 'ROAD SERVICE' on sides	£175-200
			As previous model but with Blue interior	£175-200
			With Red interior, Silver baseplate and redesigned rear doors	£150-175
	NB		Factory errors have resulted in some rear door logos reading 'ROAD ROAD' instead of 'ROAD SERVICE' as normal.	NGPP

274	1964-73	**Mini Minor Van 'A.A.'**	Yellow body, White roof, 'PATROL SERVICE', original 'entwined' logo	£125-150
			Same, but with Yellow roof, Blue interior	£125-150
			Yellow body, White roof, Red interior, 'AA SERVICE', modern 'simple' logo, Silver or Black base	£75-85
			As previous model but with Blue interior	£75-85
			With Yellow roof and Blue interior	£75-85

Note: 'AA' logo designs a) Embossed paint 'AA', b) Waterslide transfer in square recess, c) Waterslide transfer on raised panel
Rear door casting variations: a) Rear door hinge pins extend directly into chassis holes, b) Rear door hinge pins located into slots
Central base colour variations: a) Red, b) Blue, c) White

274	1970-70	**'JOSEPH MASON PAINTS'**	(Mini Minor Van). Promotional in special Red box with advert card. 650 issued.	
			Maroon body, Red seats and rear van body base, roof sign, 'PAINTS' labels, spun hubs.	£700-800
275	1964-66	**Brinks Armoured Car**	Grey/Blue, 'Brinks Security Since 1859', 2 figures, 2 crates, plastic hubs	£300-400
	1966-70		Same as previous model but no driver or crates, US packaging	£150-200
			Grey body White roof, Blue base, metal hubs, assembled in USA	NGPP
		Mexican issue:	Blue body with Grey doors and Red/White/Blue crests, plastic hubs	£750-1,000
279	1965-71	**Aveling Barford Diesel Roller**	Orange body, Grey engine covers, Blue or Green rollers, Blue driver	£100-125
	1971-80		Yellow cab, Black roof, Silver rollers	£35-45
			Yellow cab, Black roof, Black rollers	£35-45
			Yellow cab, Blue roof, Yellow square engine covers, Silver rollers	£35-45
			Yellow cab, Black roof, Yellow square engine covers, Silver rollers	£35-45
			Yellow cab, Grey Roof, Yellow square engine covers, Silver rollers	£35-45

280 Series Delivery Vans			See '28 Series Delivery Vans'.	
280	1966-68	**Mobile 'MIDLAND BANK'**	White/Silver, Blue stripe, Gold crest, opening doors, figure	£100-125
343	1954-64	**Farm Produce Wagon**	See 'Farm and Garden Models'.	

'Convoy' Series (380-387)

Budget-priced models, having the same generic cab but with different rear body types.

380	1977-79	**Skip Truck**	Yellow and Orange body	£10-20
381	1977-80	**Farm Wagon**	Yellow and Brown body	£10-20
382	1978-80	**Dumper Truck**	Red body/Grey back, Red body/Black back or Yellow body/Grey back	£10-20
383	1978-80	**'N.C.L.' Truck**	Yellow body, 'NATIONAL CARRIERS Ltd'	£10-20
384	1977-79	**Fire Rescue Wagon**	Red body, White fire escape	£10-20
385	1977-79	**'ROYAL MAIL' Truck**	Red body	£10-20
386	1979	**'AVIS' Truck**	Red body. Catalogued but not issued	NPP
387	1979	**'PICKFORDS' Truck**	Red and Blue body. Catalogued but not issued	NPP
?	1979	**'HARRODS' Truck**	Khaki body	NGPP
?	1979	**'POST OFFICE TELEPHONES'**	Khaki body	NGPP
?	1979	**'A.A.' Truck**	Yellow body	NGPP
?	1979	**'AMERICAN FIRE BRIGADE'**	No details	NGPP

NB See also 687 Convoy Army Truck in the Military Vehicles section.

390	1978	**Customised Transit Van**	Metallic Blue body with 'VAMPIRE' and 'flame' design, Transit van Type 3	NGPP
400	1954-60	**B.E.V. Truck**	Dark Blue or Mid-Blue or Grey with Blue, Grey or Red hubs, 1 packing piece, (renumbered from 14a)	£30-35
401	1954-64	**Coventry Climax Fork Lift**	Orange body, Green forks, Tan driver, (renumbered from 14c)	£30-35
			Red body, Green forks	£300-400
402	1966-69	**Bedford 'COCA-COLA' Truck**	Red cab and back, White roof, Blue interior, 'COCA-COLA', six trays of crates, Red plastic hubs	£120-150
404	1967-72	**Climax Fork Lift**	Red/Yellow body with 'CG4' rear logo	£25-35
			Red/Yellow front with all Red rear, plus stick-on 'CG4' label	£20-25
	1978		Yellow body with 'Climax' on fork guide and 'TC4' on engine cover	£20-25
406	1963-66	**Commer Articulated Truck**	Yellow/Grey, Blue plastic hubs, Supertoy, (424 without accessories)	£90-110
407		**Ford Transit Vans**	See 'Commercial Vehicles Identification' pages for an explanation of casting Types 1, 2 and 3.	
	1966-69	**'KENWOOD'**	Blue/White, 'KENWOOD', promotional. Type 1	£100-125
	1970-71	**'TELEFUSION'**	White body, 'Colour TV, Telefusion'. Intended promotional not issued	NPP
	1970-75	**'HERTZ'**	Yellow body, 'Hertz Truck Rentals', promotional. Type 1	£80-100
	1970-73	**'AVIS'**	Red body, 'Avis Truck Rentals'. Kit only but not issued	NPP
		'PELTZ BADKEREI'	Blue lower body, Yellow upper half, promotional	£50-60
408	1956-63	**Big Bedford Lorry** (renumbered from 522 / 922)	Maroon cab, Light Tan back, Fawn or Cream hubs, (with window glazing from 1961)	£125-150
			Dark Blue cab, Yellow back, Yellow or Cream hubs	£175-225
			Pink cab, Cream back, Cream hubs	£1.500-2.000
409	1956-63	**Bedford Articulated Lorry** (renumbered from 521 / 921)	Deep Yellow cab and back, Black wings, Red hubs, Yellow box	£125-150
			As previous model but with window glazing. Lighter Yellow box	£150-200
410	1954-61	**Bedford End Tipper Truck** (renumbered from 25m)	Red cab, chassis and diecast hubs, Cream back	£175-200
			Yellow cab, chassis and diecast hubs, Mid-Blue back, window glazing	£150-175
	1962-63		Red cab, chassis and plastic hubs, Cream back, window glazing	£175-200
			Yellow cab, chassis and plastic hubs, Dark or Mid-Blue back, window glazing	£175-200

Market prices shown here are for guidance only. They refer ONLY to mint models in pristine boxes (where appropriate) that are complete with all of their original contents.

410		**Bedford CF Vans**		
	1972-72	**'SIMPSONS'**	Red/Black, 'Simpsons' and logos, Canadian promotional	£75-100
	1974	**'DANISH POST'**	Yellow body, 'Danish Post' emblem, Danish promotional	£75-100
	1974-75	**'JOHN MENZIES'**	Dark Blue body with 'John Menzies' logo, promotional	£100-125
	1974-74	**'BELACO'**	Brown/Black, 'Belaco Brake and Clutch Parts', promotional	£75-100
	1975-76	**'M.J. HIRE'**	White body, 'M.J. Hire Service', promotional	£25-30
	1975-77	**'MODELLERS WORLD'**	White body, 'Modellers World'. This is a Code 2 model	£25-30
	1975-75	**'MARLEY TILES'**	Red body with 'Marley Building' logo	£25-30
	1979	**'COLLECTORS GAZETTE'**	White body, 'Collectors Gazette' logo. A Code 2 model	£25-30
	1972-74	**'ROYAL MAIL'**	Red body with 'ROYAL MAIL' and 'E II R' crest	£15-20
	1974-80	**'ROYAL MAIL'**	As previous model but with raised rectangle on roof	£15-20
	NB		Many Code-2 issues exist (produced by John Gay) and include the following liveries: 'MOBIL', 'BN', 'HERTZ TRUCK RENTAL', 'JIMMY CARTER', 'MATRA', 'ELF', 'SILVER JUBILEE 1952-1977', 'KLG', 'PORTAKABIN', 'WIMPEY'.	
411	1954-59	**Bedford Truck**	Mid-Green cab, chassis, back and hubs, (renumbered from 25w)	£100-125
	1959-60		Mid-Green cab and body, Pale Green hubs, gloss base, block-tread tyres	£100-125
412	1954-60	**Austin Wagon**	Powder Blue body, Lemon or Dark Blue hubs, (renumbered from 30j)	£350-450
			Maroon body, Red hubs	£120-140
			Dark Blue body, Mid-Blue hubs	£140-160
			Lemon Yellow body, Mid-Green or Blue hubs	£350-450
412	1974-80	**Bedford CF Van 'AA'**	Yellow or Lemon-Yellow body, 'AA SERVICE', headboard, plastic hubs	£15-20
413	1954-60	**Austin Covered Wagon**	Maroon body, Cream tinplate tilt, Cream hubs, (renumbered from 30s)	£100-150
			Maroon body and hubs, Tan tinplate tilt	£100-150
			Dark Blue body, Mid-Blue tinplate tilt, Light Blue hubs	£150-200
			Mid-Blue body, Mid-Blue tinplate tilt, Light Blue hubs	£100-150
			Red body, Light Grey tinplate tilt, Cream or Grey hubs	£200-300
			Red body, Beige tinplate tilt, Red hubs	£200-300
			Light or Mid-Blue body, Cream tinplate tilt, Lemon-Yellow hubs. Plain box	£200-300
			Red body, Grey or Beige tinplate tilt, Grey hubs	£200-300
			Maroon body, Beige tinplate tilt, Red hubs	£150-200
			Olive-drab body, (Royal Army Volunteer Reserve)	NGPP
414	1954-64	**Dodge Rear Tipping Wagon**	Red cab and hubs, Green back	£90-120
		(renumbered from 30s)	Orange cab and hubs, Green back; or Orange cab with Mid-Green back and hubs	£90-120
			Greyish-Blue cab, Grey back, Mid-Blue hubs	£90-120
			Mid-Blue cab and hubs, Grey back	£90-120
			Mid-Blue cab, Cream hubs, Grey back. In late issue lighter Yellow box	£100-125
			Violet-Blue cab, Grey back and hubs	£100-125
			Royal Blue cab, Grey back and hubs	£125-150
	NB		Early issues with or without bonnet louvres.	
415	1954-59	**Mechanical Horse and Wagon**	(Models 33a + 33c), Blue horse/Cream trailer or Red horse/Brown trailer, (renumbered from 33w)	£125-175
		Ford Transit Vans	See 'Commercial Vehicles Identification' pages for an explanation of casting Types 1, 2 and 3.	
416	1975-78	**Ford Transit Van, 'FORD'**	Orange-Yellow body, cast hubs, '1,000,000 TRANSITS', Type 2, promotional	NGPP
416	1975-78	**Ford Transit 'MOTORWAY'**	Yellow body, 'MOTORWAY SERVICES', special lights, Type 2, with two warning boards and cones	£45-55
417	1978-79	**Ford Transit 'MOTORWAY'**	As previous model but Type 3 casting	£30-40
417	1956-58	**Leyland Comet Lorry with Stake Body**	(Stake body secured by a rivet. Yellow box. Renumbered from 531 / 931).	
			Violet Blue cab and chassis, Dark Yellow back, Mid-Blue hubs	£140-160
			Dark Blue cab and chassis, Brown back, Mid-Blue hubs	£200-300
	1958-59		Yellow cab and chassis, Pale Green back, Mid-Green hubs, Grey tyres	£200-300
418	1956-59	**Leyland Comet with Hinged Tailboard**	(Back of model secured by a rivet. Yellow box. Renumbered from 532 / 932).	
			Dark Green cab and chassis, Orange back, Mid-Green hubs	£175-225
			Dark Blue cab and chassis, Mid-Blue back, Blue, Cream or Red hubs	£175-225
419	1956-59	**Leyland Comet Cement Lorry**	Yellow body and hubs, 'Portland Blue-Circle Cement', 1 packing piece, (was 533 / 933)	£110-130
420	1954-61	**Forward Control Lorry**	Cream body, Mid-Blue hubs	£75-100
		(renumbered from 25r)	Red body, Cream hubs	£75-100
			Red body, Mid-Green hubs	£75-100
			Pale Green body, Cream hubs	£75-100
			Pale Green body, Red hubs	£75-100
421	1955-59	**Hindle Smart Helecs**	Maroon body, Red hubs 'British Railways', hook, (renumbered from 30w)	£90-110
422	1954-60	**Fordson Thames Flat Truck**	Red body and hubs, (renumbered from 30r)	£125-150
			Bright Green body and hubs	£125-150
			Dark Green body, Mid-Green hubs. In dual-numbered box	£125-150
424	1963-66	**Commer Convertible Articulated Vehicle**	Primrose-Yellow cab, Silver-Grey back with Blue plastic tilt, Blue plastic hubs, plus detachable White plastic 'stake' body	£150-200
425	1964-69	**Bedford TK Coal Wagon**	Red body and interior, Silver chassis, Red plastic hubs, roof board 'HALL & Co.', 6 bags, scales	£125-150
428	1955-66	**Large Trailer**	Grey body, Red hubs, Black front axle mount, hook, (renumbered 951)	£80-100
			Grey body, Cream hubs. In late issue lighter Yellow box	£75-100
			Grey body, Mid-Blue hubs. In late issue lighter Yellow box	£75-100
	1967-71		Red body, Silver hubs, Silver front axle mount	£60-75
			Yellow body, Red hubs	£60-75
429	1954-64	**Trailer**	Dark Green body, Light Green hubs, wire drawbar, Black treaded tyres, hook, axle pivot is part of main casting, (renumbered from 25g)	£80-100
			As previous model, but with Red body, Black or Red hubs	£80-100

430	1954-64	**Commer Breakdown Truck**	'DINKY SERVICE' logo, operable crane, late issues have window glazing, (renumbered from 25x).	
			Tan cab, Mid-Green back with Black logo, Red hubs. Yellow or Blue/White striped box	**£125-150**
			Cream cab, Mid-Blue back with Black logo, Red hubs. Yellow box	**£450-550**
			Dark Stone cab, Blue back with Black logo, Red hubs. Yellow box	**£450-550**
			Red cab, Light Grey back with Blue logo, Mid-Blue or Red metal hubs. Yellow box	**£450-550**
			Red cab with glazing, Light Grey back with Blue logo, Blue plastic hubs. Yellow box	**£450-550**
			Red cab with glazing, Light Grey back with Blue logo, Red plastic hubs. Yellow box	**£500-750**
430	1977-80	**Johnson 2 ton Dumper**	Orange/Red or Orange/Yellow body with Blue and Red driver, Black or Orange engine	**£20-25**
431	1956-58	**Guy 4 ton Lorry** (2nd type)	Red cab/chassis, Fawn back, Red hubs, unpainted hook, (renumbered from 511 / 911)	**£200-250**
			Violet Blue cab/chassis, Mid-Blue back, Mid-Blue hubs	**£200-250**
			Mid-Blue cab, chassis and back, Supertoys hubs. Later yellow/blue card box with lift-off lid	**£1,000-1,400**
431	1958-60	**Guy Warrior 4 ton Lorry**	Light Tan cab (no window glazing), Dark Green back, Mid-Green hubs	**£300-400**
			Light Tan cab (with window glazing), Dark Green back, Mid-Green hubs	**£300-400**
	1960-64		Red cab (with window glazing), Red chassis, Dark Green back, Red hubs	**£300-400**
432	1956-57	**Guy Flat Truck** (2nd type)	Mid-Blue cab/chassis/hook, Red flatbed, Mid-Blue hubs, (renumbered from 512 / 912)	**£200-300**
	1956-57		Red cab/chassis/hook, Mid-Blue flatbed and hubs	**£300-350**
432	1958-60	**Guy Warrior Flat Truck**	Green cab (no window glazing), Red flatbed, Red hubs	**£200-300**
	1960-64		Green cab (with window glazing), Red flatbed, Red hubs	**£200-300**
432	1976-79	**Foden Tipping Lorry**	White cab, Red chassis, Yellow rear body, (same casting as 668)	**£35-45**
433	1956-57	**Guy Flat Truck with Tailboard** (2nd type)	Dark Green cab/chassis/hook, Mid-Green flatbed and hubs, (renumbered from 513 / 913)	**£200-250**
			Violet Blue cab/chassis/hook, Orange flatbed, Mid-Blue hubs, one packing piece in box	**£200-250**
433	1958	**Guy Warrior Flat Truck with Tailboard**	Listed in the 1958 catalogue but not issued	**NPP**
434	1964-66	**Bedford TK Crash Truck**	White body with Green flash, Dark Green hubs, 'TOP RANK Motorway Services', Red interior	**£100-125**
	1966-70		Red or Metallic Red cab, Pale Grey back, 'AUTO SERVICES', Red metal or plastic hubs	**£90-120**
	NB		Add 15% to price if in detailed picture box or with Green hubs.	
435	1964-66	**Bedford TK Tipper**	Grey cab with Blue roof, Orange back	**£90-120**
	1966-68		Yellow cab with Yellow or Black roof, Silver back, Yellow drop sides	**£90-120**
	1968-71		White cab and roof, Silver back with Blue sides	**£60-80**
			Blue cab, Orange and Grey back	**£75-100**
			Red cab, Black roof, Silver back, Red sides	**£60-80**
436	1963-69	**'ATLAS COPCO' Lorry**	Yellow body, Pale Grey interior, matt baseplate	**£50-60**
			Yellow body, Dark Blue interior, gloss baseplate	**£50-60**
			Yellow body, Black roof, Red interior, Silver/Yellow back, Blue plastic hubs	**£80-100**
437	1962-70	**Muir Hill 2WL Loader**	Red body with hook, no grille detail	**£20-25**
			Yellow body with Red or Silver hubs	**£20-25**
	1970-78		Yellow with Red arms with hook, with or without grille detail	**£20-25**
			Orange body with Orange or Black arms	**£30-40**
438	1970-77	**Ford D800 Tipper Truck** (with opening doors)	Metallic Red cab, Yellow tipper, Yellow or Silver hubs	**£40-45**
			Metallic Red cab, Metallic Blue tipper, Yellow plastic hubs, White interior	**£100-125**
			Orange cab, Orange or Yellow tipper, Silver hubs	**£40-45**
			Bright Red cab, Orange tipper, Silver hubs	**£40-45**
			Bright Red cab, Bright Red tipper, Silver hubs	**£40-45**
	promotional issue:		White cab, Blue back, Silver chassis, with cardboard load 'POLCARB'.	
			Packed in plain White box with folded leaflet	**£200-250**
439	1970-76	**Ford D800 Snow Plough**	Dark Metallic Blue cab, Orange tipper, Yellow plough, White hubs	**£50-70**
	1976-78		Dark Metallic Blue cab, Pale Blue tipper, Yellow plough, Silver hubs	**£50-70**
			Light Metallic Blue cab, Orange tipper, Dark Yellow plough, Silver hubs	**£50-70**
			Light Metallic Blue cab, Pale Blue tipper, Red plough	**£100-125**
			Medium Blue cab, Yellow plough, Powder Blue tipper, Silver hubs	**£50-70**
			Medium Blue cab, Yellow plough, Powder Blue tipper, Lemon hubs	**£50-60**
			Orange cab and tipper, Dark Yellow plough, Silver hubs	**£50-60**
			Orange cab, Dark Yellow tipper and plough, Silver hubs	**£50-60**
			All-Orange body, cast Silver hubs	**£50-60**
440	1977-78	**Ford D800 Tipper Truck** (non-opening doors)	Orange cab, Yellow tipper, Silver or Black chassis	**£35-40**
			Orange cab, Orange tipper, Black chassis	**£35-40**
			Orange cab, Light Blue tipper, Black chassis	**£35-40**
			Red cab, Red Tipper, Black chassis, Silver hubs	**£35-40**
			Red cab, Orange Tipper, Silver chassis, Silver hubs	**£35-40**
			Red cab, Light Blue Tipper, Black chassis, Silver hubs	**£35-40**
			Red cab with Black roof, Red Tipper, Red hubs	**£35-40**
440	1954-58	**Petrol Tanker 'MOBILGAS'**	Red body and hubs, 'MOBILGAS' in White letters with Blue borders, (renumbered from 30p)	**£110-140**
	1958-61		Red body and hubs, 'MOBILGAS' in Blue letters on White background	**£110-140**
441	1954-60	**Petrol Tanker 'CASTROL'**	Mid-Green body and hubs, (renumbered from 30pa)	**£110-140**
442	1954-60	**Petrol Tanker 'ESSO'**	Red body and hubs, Dark Blue decal: 'ESSO MOTOR OIL - PETROL', (renumbered from 30pb)	**£110-140**
			As previous model but with Pale Blue outline decal	**£125-150**
442	1973-79	**Land Rover Breakdown Crane**	White and Red body, 'Motorway Rescue', operable winch	**£25-30**
	1975-78		White body, Red bonnet and door panels, Blue interior, 2 Orange rooflights, Black jib, 'FALCK'	**£40-50**
			All Red body, Blue interior, Light Blue header board, Black jib, Speedwheels, 'FALCK'	**£50-60**
			All Red body, Black interior, deeper Blue header board, Black jib, Speedwheels, 'FALCK'	**£50-60**
443	1957-58	**Petrol Tanker 'NATIONAL'**	Yellow body and hubs, 'NATIONAL BENZOLE MIXTURE'	**£200-250**

448	1963-68	**Chevrolet El Camino Pick-Up with Trailers**	Turquoise/Cream/Red Pick-up and 2 trailers, 'Acme Trailer Hire'	£200-250
449	1961-69	**Chevrolet El Camino Pick-up**	Off-White lower body, Turquoise upper body and roof, Red interior, spun hubs	£100-125
			Off-White lower body, Turquoise upper body and roof, Yellow interior, spun hubs	£175-225
			Off-White lower body, Turquoise upper body and roof, Turquoise interior, spun hubs	£175-225
		NB	Various shades of Turquoise are known to exist.	
		South African issue:	All-Turquoise body, Red interior, spun hubs	£1,000-1,200
		South African issue:	Cream over Caramel lower body, Red interior, spun hubs	£1,000-1,200
		South African issue:	Turquoise over Cream lower body, Red interior, spun hubs	£1,000-1,200
		South African issue:	All-Cream lower body, Red interior, spun hubs	£1,000-1,200
449	1977-79	**Johnston Road Sweeper**	Later version of model 451 but with cast-in (non-opening) cab doors.	
			Yellow or Lime-Green body	£30-35
			All Yellow body, promotional with 'JOHNSTON' stickers, normal box	£40-50
			All Yellow body, promotional with 'JOHNSTON' stickers, special box	£70-80
			Orange or Metallic Red cab, Metallic Green rear	£40-50
450	1954-57	**Trojan Van 'ESSO'**	Red body, White stripe, Red or Maroon hubs, 'Esso' logo, (renumbered from 31a)	£175-225
			Maroon hub version issued in U.S.A. trade packs.	NGPP
450	1965-70	**Bedford TK Van 'CASTROL'**	Green/White body, Red interior, Red plastic hubs, 'CASTROL - The Masterpiece In Oils'	£125-145
451	1954-57	**Trojan Van 'DUNLOP'**	Red body and hubs, 'Dunlop The Worlds Master Tyre', (renumbered from 31b)	£140-180
451	1971-77	**Johnston Road Sweeper**	Orange cab (opening doors), White interior, Metallic Green tank	£40-50
			Yellow cab and tank, White interior	£125-150
			Light Metallic Blue cab, White interior, Metallic Green tank	£110-130
			Metallic Green cab, White interior, Orange tank	£40-50
452	1954-57	**Trojan Van 'CHIVERS'**	Dark Green body, Mid-Green hubs, 'CHIVERS JELLIES' logo, (renumbered from 31c)	£160-190
453	1954-54	**Trojan Van 'OXO'**	Mid-Blue or Violet-Blue body, Mid-Blue hubs, White 'BEEFY OXO', (not boxed), (was 31c)	£300-400
454	1957-59	**Trojan Van 'CYDRAX'**	Light Green body and hubs, 'DRINK CYDRAX' logo	£175-200
455	1957-60	**Trojan Van 'BROOKE BOND'**	Dark Red body, Red hubs, 'BROOKE BOND TEA' logo	£160-190
		promotional issue:	As previous issue with White label on roof. The Red logo states: 'Since 1924 more than 5,700 Trojan 'Little Red Vans' supplied. Replaced on a long life basis'. A similar label is attached to its (normal) box	£400-600
465	1959-59	**Morris 10 cwt Van 'CAPSTAN'**	Light Blue and Dark Blue body, Mid-Blue hubs, 'Have A CAPSTAN'	£200-250
470	1954-56	**Austin A40 Van 'SHELL-BP'**	Red and Green body with 'SHELL' and 'BP' decals	£150-200
470	1954	**Austin A40 Van 'OMNISPORT'**	Factory drawing exists but model not issued	NPP
471	1955-60	**Austin A40 Van 'NESTLES'**	Red body, Yellow hubs, 'NESTLES' logo	£125-150
472	1956-60	**Austin A40 Van 'RALEIGH'**	Dark Green body, Yellow hubs, 'RALEIGH CYCLES' decals	£125-150
480	1954-56	**Bedford CA Van 'KODAK'**	Yellow body, 'Kodak CAMERAS & FILMS' in Red and Black	£125-150
481	1955-60	**Bedford CA Van 'OVALTINE'**	Blue body with 'Ovaltine' and 'Ovaltine Biscuits' logo on Cream panel and sides	£125-150
482	1956-60	**Bedford Van 'DINKY TOYS'**	Orange-Yellow lower body, Lemon upper body and hubs, 'Dinky Toys' in Red	£150-200
490	1954-60	**Electric Dairy Van 'EXPRESS DAIRY'**	Cream body with Red chassis, hubs and logo, (renumbered from 30v)	£90-110
			Light Grey body with Blue chassis, hubs and logo	£90-110
491	1954-60	**Electric Dairy Van 'N.C.B.'**	Cream body with Red chassis, hubs and logo, export model, (renumbered from 30v)	£90-110
			Grey body, Blue chassis, hubs and logo, export model	£90-110
491	1960	**Electric Dairy Van 'JOB'S DAIRY'**	Cream/Red. 1176 made for promotional purposes (Code-2)	£175-225
492	1954-57	**Loudspeaker Van**	Violet-Blue, Fawn or Green body, Silver, Mid-Blue or Black hubs, Silver or Black loudspeakers, (280 casting, Type 3), (renumbered from 34c)	£125-150
492	1964-64	**Election Mini-Van**	White body (as 273), Red interior, Orange loudspeakers, 'Vote for Somebody', figure, microphone and cable. Yellow 'see-through' box	£150-200
501	1947-48	**Foden Diesel 8-Wheel Wagon**	**1st type cab** with flash, spare wheel, hook on some, no tank slits in chassis, no chain-post bosses, Black 'herringbone' tyres, Supertoy.	
			Pale Grey cab and back, Red flash and hubs, Black chassis, no hook	£500-600
			Dark Blue cab, Mid-Blue back and hubs, Silver flash, Black chassis, no hook	£400-500
			Chocolate Brown cab and back, Silver flash, Brown hubs, Black chassis, no hook	£300-400
			Red cab and back, Silver flash, Red hubs, Black chassis, no hook, (US only issue)	£2,000-3,000
			Dark Grey cab and back, Red flash, chassis and hubs, small unpainted hook on some	£400-600
	1948-52		Hook and tank-slits in chassis (introduced 1948), Black 'radial tread' tyres.	
			Violet-Blue cab/chassis, Mid-Blue flash/back/hubs, small unpainted hook	£1,250-1,500
			Red cab/chassis/hubs, Silver flash, Fawn back, unpainted hook, slits on some	£300-400
	1952-54	(renumbered 901)	**2nd cab**, no flash, large painted hook, Supertoy hubs, (renumbered 901).	
			Violet-Blue cab/chassis, Mid-Blue back and hubs, Grey tyres	£300-400
			Red cab/chassis, Fawn back, Red hubs, Grey tyres	£250-350
502	1947-48	**Foden Flat Truck**	**1st type cab** with flash, spare wheel, hook on some, no tank slits in chassis, no chain-post bosses, Black 'herringbone' tyres, Supertoy.	
			Dark Green cab and back, Silver flash, Black chassis, Dark Green hubs, no hook	£700-900
			Mid-Blue cab and back, Dark Blue flash/chassis/hubs, no hook	£1,000-1,250
	1948-52		Hook and tank-slits in chassis introduced in 1948, Black 'radial' tyres.	
			Dark Blue cab/wings/chassis, Red flash and back, Mid-Blue hubs, slits on some, small hook	£1,200-1,500
			Burnt Orange cab/chassis, Mid-Green flash and back, Green hubs, slits on some. In Dark Blue box showing 2nd cab model	£250-350
	1952-52		**2nd cab**, no flash, large painted hook, Supertoy hubs.	
			Dark Blue cab/chassis, Red back, Mid-Blue hubs, chain-post bosses	£1,500-2,000
	1952-54	(renumbered 902)	Dull Orange cab/chassis, Mid-Green back and hubs, chain-post bosses	£300-400
			Red cab/chassis, Green back and hubs	£300-400
			Yellow cab/chassis, Green back and hubs	£1,000-1,250

503 1947-48 **Foden Flat Truck with Tailboard. 1st type cab** with flash, spare wheel, hook on some, no tank slits in
chassis, no chain-post bosses, Black 'herringbone' tyres, Supertoy.
Red cab and flatbed, Black flash and chassis, Red hubs, no hook..£1,000-1,250
Pale Grey cab and flatbed, Dark Blue flash and chassis, Blue hubs, no hook.............................£1,000-1,250
Mid-Grey cab and flatbed, Mid-Blue flash, chassis and hubs..£1,000-1,250

      1948-52 .... Hook and tank-slits in chassis introduced in 1948, Black 'radial' tyres.
Dark Green cab/chassis, Mid-Green flash/flatbed/hubs, small hook...£650-850
Deep Blue cab/chassis, Dull Orange flatbed, Light Blue hubs, hook, slits.................................£600-800
Violet-Blue cab/chassis, Orange back and side flash, Mid-Blue hubs, hook, slits £600-800

      1952-52 .... **2nd cab**, no flash, large painted hook, Supertoy hubs.
Dark Green cab/chassis, Light Green flatbed and hubs, Grey tyres, bosses £1,500-2,000

      1952-56 (renumbered 903) .... Violet-Blue cab/chassis, Orange flatbed, Mid-Blue hubs, chain-post bosses £250-350
      1952-53 .... Dark Orange cab/chassis, Yellow flatbed and hubs, Grey tyres, bosses £1,500-1,700
      1953-54 (renumbered 903) .... Violet-Blue cab/chassis, Yellow flatbed, Mid-Blue hubs, chain-post bosses £400-500

504 1948-52 **Foden 14 ton Tanker** .... **1st type cab** with flash, spare wheel, tinplate tank, small hook,
no advertising, Black 'fine radial tread' tyres, Supertoy.
Dark Blue cab/chassis, Silver flash, Light Blue tank and hubs..£300-400
Violet Blue cab/chassis, Mid-Blue flash, tank and hubs £300-400

      1948-52 .... Red cab/chassis, Silver flash, Fawn tank, Red hubs..£450-550
      1952-57 .... **2nd cab**, no flash, large painted hook, Supertoy hubs.
      1952-52 .... Violet-Blue cab/chassis, Mid-Blue tank and hubs, Grey tyres.
Model housed in 2nd type picture box...£1,500-2,000
      1952-53 .... Red cab/chassis, Fawn tank, Red hubs, Grey tyres £450-550

504 1953-54 **Foden 14 ton Tanker**
'MOBILGAS' (renumbered 941) Red cab/chassis/tank/filler caps/hubs, 'MOBILGAS', Grey tyres.
With Red 'Pegasus' logo at cab end of tank facing the cab £350-450
Same, but with Red 'Pegasus' logo at rear of tank facing away from cab............................£1,500-2,000

505 1952-52 **Foden Flat Truck with Chains** .. **1st type cab** with flash, spare wheel, large hook, slits in chassis, 'dimpled' post bosses,
Black 'fine radial tread' tyres, Supertoy. Blue covered box showing 1st type cab.
Dark Green cab/chassis/flatbed, Mid-Green flash and hubs..£2,500-3,500
Maroon cab/chassis, Silver flash, Maroon flatbed and hubs £7,500-10,000

      1952-54 .... **2nd cab**, no flash, large painted hook, Supertoy hubs.
Dark Green cab/chassis/flatbed, Mid-Green hubs, 'dimpled' chain-post bosses £250-350
Maroon cab/chassis/flatbed/hubs, 'dimpled' chain-post bosses £250-350
      1954-56 (renumbered 905) .... Green cab/chassis/body, Mid-Green hubs, 'rounded' chain-post bosses £250-350
Maroon cab/chassis/body/hubs, 'rounded' chain-post bosses...£250-350

511 1947-48 **Guy 4 ton Lorry** .... **1st type cab** casting, Supertoy, spare wheel, small unpainted hook.
Green cab, back and hubs, Black chassis and wings..£350-450
Brown cab, back and hubs, Black chassis and wings...£350-450
Fawn cab and back, Red chassis, wings and hubs...£350-450
Maroon cab and back, Black chassis and wings..£350-450
Grey cab, back and hubs, Red chassis and wings..£350-450

      1948-52 .... **1st type cab** casting, Supertoy, large painted or unpainted hook.
Red cab/chassis/wings/ 'ridged' hubs, Fawn back..£300-350
Violet-Blue cab/chassis/wings, Mid-Blue back and 'ridged' hubs...................................£300-350
      1952-54 (renumbered 911, 431) .... Red cab/chassis/wings/ 'grooved' hubs, Fawn back £300-350
Violet-Blue cab/chassis/wings, Mid-Blue back and 'grooved' hubs £300-350
      1954 .... **2nd type cab**, Violet-Blue cab and chassis, Mid-Blue back and hubs..................................£300-350

512 1947-48 **Guy Flat Truck** .... **1st type cab** casting, Supertoy, spare wheel, small unpainted hook.
Maroon cab, flatbed and hubs, Black chassis and wings...£400-600
Dark Brown cab, Mid-Green flatbed and hubs, Black chassis and wings £400-600
Yellow cab and flatbed, Black chassis and wings, Red hubs £400-600
Khaki cab and flatbed, Black chassis and wings, Green hubs...£400-600
Grey cab and flatbed, Red chassis and wings, Red hubs..£400-600
Grey cab and flatbed, Black chassis, Black hubs £400-600
Red cab and flatbed, Black chassis, Black hubs..£400-600

      1948-48 .... Brown cab/chassis/wings, Green flatbed, Mid-Green 'ridged' hubs..................................£400-600
      1948-54 (renumbered 912, 432) .... **1st type cab** casting, Supertoy, small or large unpainted hook.
Dark Blue cab/chassis/wings, Red flatbed, Mid-Blue 'ridged' hubs..................................£300-350
      1949-54 .... Orange cab/chassis/wings, Green flatbed, Green 'ridged' hubs..£300-400
      1952-54 .... Mid-Blue cab/chassis/wings, Red flatbed, Mid-Blue 'grooved' hubs.................................£300-350
      1954 .... **2nd type cab**, Red cab and chassis, Mid-Blue back and hubs..£300-350
Mid-Blue cab, chassis and hubs, Red back...£300-350

513 1947-48 **Guy Flat Truck with Tailboard** . **1st type cab** casting, Supertoy, spare wheel, small unpainted hook.
Green cab and flatbed, Black chassis, wings and hubs £200-250
Dark Yellow cab and flatbed, Black chassis, wings and hubs..£300-400
Dark Yellow cab and flatbed, Dark Blue chassis, wings and hubs....................................£300-400
Grey cab and flatbed, Black chassis, wings and hubs £200-250
Grey cab and flatbed, Dark Blue chassis, wings and hubs £500-750

      1948-52 .... **1st type cab**, 'ridged' hubs, Supertoy, small or large unpainted hook.
Dark Green cab/chassis/wings, Mid-Green back and hubs, small hook £250-350
Violet-Blue cab/chassis/wings, Orange back, Mid-Blue hubs, large hook £200-250
      1952-54 (renumbered 913, 433) .... **1st type cab**, Supertoy, 'grooved' hubs, large unpainted hook.
Dark Green cab/chassis/wings, Mid-Green body and hubs £250-350
Deep Blue cab/chassis/wings, Orange body, Mid-Blue hubs £200-250
Yellow cab/chassis/wings, Green hubs £750-950
      1954 .... **2nd type cab**, Violet-Blue cab and chassis, Orange back, Mid-Blue hubs............................£200-250

514 Guy Vans

514	1950-52	Guy Van 'SLUMBERLAND'	Red **1st type cab**/chassis/body and 'ridged' hubs, 'Slumberland Spring Interior Mattresses', spare wheel, Supertoy	**£300-400**
514	1952-52	Guy Van 'LYONS'	Dark Blue **1st type cab**/body, Mid-Blue 'ridged' hubs, 'Lyons Swiss Rolls', spare wheel, Supertoy	**£700-900**
			Same model but rear axle in cast mounts	**£700-900**
514	1952-52	Guy Van 'WEETABIX'	Yellow **1st type cab**/body, Yellow 'ridged' hubs, 'More Than a Breakfast Food', spare wheel, Supertoy	**£2,000-3,000**
	1952-54		As previous model but with Yellow 'grooved' hubs	**£2,000-3,000**
514	1953-54	Guy Van 'SPRATTS' .... (renumbered 917)	Red/Cream **1st type cab**/body, Red 'grooved' hubs, 'Bonio Ovals & Dog Cakes', spare wheel, Supertoy	**£300-400**
521	1948-48	Bedford Articulated Lorry	Red body, Black wings, Black or Red hubs, '20' transfer, 'Supertoys' on base, Brown box	**£250-350**
	1949-50	....	Yellow body, Black wings, Black hubs, '20' transfer, 'Supertoys' on base. Brown box with Red/White label.	**£250-350**
	1950-54	(renumbered 921, 409)	Yellow or Yellowish-Orange body, Black wings, Red hubs, '20' transfer, 'Supertoys' or 'Dinky Toys' on base. Blue box, Orange or White label	**£150-200**
522	1952-54	Big Bedford Lorry .... (renumbered 922, 408)	Maroon cab, Fawn truck body, Fawn hubs, Supertoy	**£130-160**
			Dark Blue cab, Yellow truck body, Yellow hubs, Supertoy	**£175-200**
531	1949-54	Leyland Comet Lorry with Stake Body .... (renumbered 931, 417)	Red cab and chassis, Yellow back and hubs, Blue box	**£150-200**
			Blue cab and chassis, Brown back, Red or Blue hubs, Blue box	**£150-200**
			Violet-Blue cab and chassis, Orange-Yellow back, Red hubs, Blue box	**£150-200**
			Yellow cab and chassis, Pale Green back, Mid-Green hubs, Grey tyres	**£300-400**
		NB Odd colours:	Be wary of colour combinations not listed. The screw fitting makes it easy to interchange the chassis and body components.	
532	1952-54	Leyland Comet Lorry with Hinged Tailboard .... (renumbered 932, 418)	Dark Green cab and chassis, Orange back, Cream hubs, Blue box	**£300-350**
			Dark Green cab and chassis, Orange back, Green hubs, Blue box	**£150-175**
			Mid-Green cab and chassis, Cherry-Red back, Cream hubs, Blue box	**£200-250**
			Dark Blue cab and chassis, Mid-Blue back, Cream hubs, Blue box	**£150-175**
			Dark Blue cab and chassis, Mid-Blue back, Red hubs, Blue/White box	**£150-175**
		NB Odd colours:	Be wary of colour combinations not listed. The screw fitting makes it easy to interchange the chassis and body components.	
533	1953-54	Leyland Comet Cement Wagon	Yellow body and hubs, 'PORTLAND BLUE-CIRCLE CEMENT', Supertoy, (renumbered 933, 419)	**£130-150**
551	1948-54	Trailer .... (renumbered 951)	Grey body, Black hubs, hook, Supertoy	**£30-40**
			Yellow body, Black hubs, hook, Supertoy	**£90-110**
			Green body, Black hubs, hook, Supertoy	**£90-110**
	1969-73	...............................Gift Set issue:	Red body, Grey front chassis, protruding chromed hubs. Only in Gift Set 399	GSP
561	1949-54	Blaw Knox Bulldozer .... (renumbered 961)	Red body, Green or Black rubber tracks, driver, lifting blade, Supertoy. Blue box with Orange/White label, or 'natural' card box with Red/White label, 1 packing piece	**£40-50**
561	1962-64	Citroën Delivery Van	Light Blue body, Red/Yellow 'CIBIE' logo, sliding door. French issue	**£60-70**
562	1948-54	Muir Hill Dump Truck	Yellow body, metal wheels/tyres, hook, (renumbered 962)	**£15-20**
563	1948-54	Blaw Knox Heavy Tractor .... (renumbered 963)	Red, Orange or Blue 561 without the dozer blade. Buff cardboard box has Red/White label, 1 packing piece	**£70-90**
			Dark Blue body, Mid-Blue rollers, Green rubber tracks, Beige driver. Buff box with Red/White picture label	**£200-250**
564	1952-54	Elevator Loader	Renumbered 964 – see that entry for details.	
571	1949-54	Coles Mobile Crane	Yellow and Black, operable crane, 1 driver, Supertoy, 3 packing pieces + instructions, (renumbered 971)	**£30-40**
579	1961-63	Simca Glazier's Lorry	Yellow and Green body, mirror/glass load, 'MIROITIER'. French-made model for issue in the UK	**£90-110**
581	1953-54	Horsebox	Maroon body (cast in aluminium) 'British Railways', 2 packing pieces, (renumbered 981)	**£80-100**
581	1953-54	...............................US issue:	Maroon, 'Hire Service', 'Express Horse Van', 'Express'. Blue box has Orange/White labels with picture of US model, 2 packing pieces, (renumbered 980)	**£500-700**

581	1962-64	**Berliet Flat Truck**	Red and Grey body, 6 wheels plus spare, hook. French issue..	**£70-80**
		NB	The French issues listed above have been included because they were sold in the U.K.	

582 1953-54 **Pullmore Car Transporter** .... Bedford cab/chassis, aluminium trailer with 'DINKY TOYS DELIVERY SERVICE' logo on sides.
(renumbered 982) Same logo on rear ramp plus '20' sign. No window glazing, 'DINKY TOYS' on baseplate,
Black grille/bumper, Silver trim.

1953-53	....	Light Blue cab, trailer and hubs, Fawn decks, six lower deck retaining rivets. Model only issued for very short period	**£400-600**
1953-54	....	As previous model but decks may be Fawn or Grey. Four lower deck retaining rivets	**£110-140**
1954-54	....	Dark Blue cab, trailer and hubs, Fawn decks, four lower deck retaining rivets.	
		Model supplied in 582/982 all Dark Blue box with White end label..............................	**£500-750**
		Model supplied in 582/982 Blue/White striped box	**£200-300**

591	1952-54	**A.E.C. Tanker**	Red/Yellow, 'SHELL CHEMICALS LIMITED', Supertoy, (renumbered 991)	**£140-175**
620	1950-54	**6-wheel Covered Wagon**........	Matt-Green or Greenish-Brown body, 'Export only' (to USA), (renumbered from 151b)...........	**£60-70**
752	1953-54	**Goods Yard Crane**	Yellow operable crane on Blue (or Dark Blue) base (steps in some). Dark Blue box, (renumbered 973)......	**£50-75**
893	1962-64	**Unic Pipe Line Transporter**......	Beige articulated body, spare wheel, 6 pipes. French-made model for issue in the UK	**£90-110**
894	1962-64	**Unic Boilot Car Transporter**	Grey body, 'Dinky Toys Service Livraison'. French-made model for issue in the UK	**£100-120**

901 1954-57 **Foden 8-wheel Diesel Wagon** ..... **2nd type cab**, Supertoy, spare wheel, large hook.
(renumbered from 501)

Red cab and chassis, Fawn truck body, Red hubs.		**£230-350**
Violet-Blue cab and chassis, Mid-Blue truck body and hubs...............................		**£500-700**
Dark Green cab and chassis, Light Green truck body and hubs.		
'LF' sticker on Blue/White striped box lid, '1956' stamped inside bottom of box..............		**£5,000-7,500**

902 1954-56 **Foden Flat Truck** .... **2nd type cab**, Supertoy, spare wheel, large hook.
(renumbered from 502)

		Yellow cab and chassis, Mid-Green flatbed body, Green hubs	**£700-900**
1954-57	....	Burnt-Orange cab and chassis, Mid-Green flatbed body and hubs	**£300-400**
1957-59	....	Dark Red cab and chassis, Green flatbed, Green hubs	
		(NB Red similar to colour of 919 Guy 'GOLDEN SHRED' van)......................................	**£1,000-1,500**
		Cherry-Red cab, wings and chassis, Green flatbed body and hubs................................	**£400-500**
		Orange cab and chassis, Fawn flatbed body, Mid-Green hubs	**£300-400**

903 1954-55 **Foden Flat Truck with Tailboard**. **2nd type cab**, Supertoy, spare wheel, large hook.
(renumbered from 503)

		Violet-Blue cab and chassis, Yellow flatbed, Mid-Blue hubs....................................	**£350-450**
		Yellow cab, chassis and flatbed, Mid-Green hubs. In box with correct colour spot	**£2,000-2,500**
1954-57	....	Violet-Blue cab and chassis, Orange flatbed, Mid-Blue hubs	**£250-350**
1957-60	....	Mid-Blue cab and chassis, Fawn flatbed, Mid-Blue hubs, spare wheel rivetted on	**£500-600**

**Market prices shown here are for guidance only. They refer ONLY to mint models in pristine
boxes (where appropriate) that are complete with <u>all</u> of their original contents.**

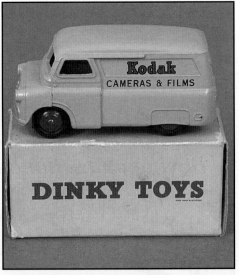

514 Guy Van 'Weetabix' (left)
480 Bedford Van 'Kodak' (above)
Photos: Vectis Auctions

905	1954-56	**Foden Flat Truck with Chains** ..	**2nd type cab**, Supertoy, spare wheel, large hook.	
		(renumbered from 505)	Maroon cab, chassis and flatbed, Maroon hubs, 'rounded' chain-post bosses	**£250-350**
	1954-58	....	Dark Green cab, chassis and flatbed, Mid-Green hubs, 'rounded' chain-post bosses	**£200-300**
	1956-57	....	Maroon cab, chassis and flatbed, Maroon hubs, 'rounded' chain-post bosses	**£250-350**
			As previous issue but with Red hubs	**£350-450**
	1957-64		Red cab and chassis, Grey flatbed, Red metal hubs, 'rounded' chain-post bosses	**£350-450**
	19??-64		Red cab and chassis, Grey flatbed, Red plastic hubs	**£400-500**
	NB		A version with Light Blue cab/chassis and hubs, and Grey flatbed sold for **$3,700** on Ebay in 2004.	
908	1962-66	**Mighty Antar and Transformer**	Yellow tractor unit, Light Grey trailer, Red ramp and hubs, transformer, 3 packing pieces	**£500-600**
911	1954-56	**Guy 4 ton Lorry**	**2nd type cab** casting, Supertoy, 'grooved' hubs, large hook.	
		(was 511, renumbered 431)	Red cab and chassis, Fawn back, Red hubs	**£250-350**
			Violet-Blue cab and chassis, Mid-Blue back and hubs	**£250-350**
			Mid-Blue cab and chassis, Mid-Blue back and hubs	**£400-600**
912	1954-56	**Guy Flat Truck**	**2nd type cab** casting, Supertoy, 'grooved' hubs, large hook.	
		(was 512, renumbered 432)	Orange cab and chassis, Green flatbed body and hubs	**£300-400**
			Mid-Blue cab and chassis, Red flatbed body, Mid-Blue hubs	**£200-250**
			Dark Green cab and chassis, Light Green flatbed body and hubs	**£300-400**
913	1954-54	**Guy Flat Truck with Tailboard** .	**2nd type cab** casting, Supertoy, 'grooved' hubs, large hook.	
		(was 513, renumbered 433)	Yellow cab and chassis, Green body, Green hubs	**£750-950**
	1954-56		Dark Green cab and chassis, Mid-Green flatbed body and hubs.	**£250-300**
			Deep Blue cab and chassis, Orange flatbed body, Light Blue hubs.	
			Usually in Blue/White striped box with picture of Green lorry	**£200-250**
			Deep Blue/Orange model in box with correct colours	**£750-950**
914	1965-70	**A.E.C. Articulated Lorry**	Red cab ('CIA 7392' on doors), White interior, Light Grey trailer, Red plastic hubs,	
			Green tilt 'BRITISH ROAD SERVICES'	**£140-160**
915	1973-74	**A.E.C. with Flat Trailer**	Orange cab, White trailer, 'Truck Hire Co Liverpool'	**£55-65**
			Orange cab, White trailer, 'Thames Board Paper Mills', bubble-packed. Truck carries load	
			of four Brown card tubes with 'UNILINER' logos in Black	**£2,000-2,500**
			Bright Metallic Blue cab, White interior, Orange chassis, Yellow trailer	**£140-160**
917	1954-56	**Guy Van 'SPRATTS'**	Red **2nd type cab**, chassis and Supertoy hubs, Cream/Red van body with	
		(renumbered from 514)	'Bonio Ovals & Dog Cakes' design	**£350-450**
917	1968-74	**Mercedes Truck and Trailer**	Blue cab/chassis (White roof), Yellow trailers, White tilts, pictorial stand and tray	**£100-125**
			Blue cab/chassis (White roof), Yellow trailers, Yellow tilts, pictorial stand and tray	**£100-125**
			Dark Blue cab/chassis, Yellow trailers, Dark Blue tilts, pictorial stand and tray	**£100-125**
		'MUNSTERLAND'	Dark Green cab and trailers, White tilts, Green logo, pictorial stand and tray, promotional	**£350-450**
		'HENRY JOHNSON'	Dark Green body, White tilts, plain White box, promotional	**£350-450**
918	1955-58	**Guy Van 'EVER READY'**	Blue **1st type cab** with small square sides to front number plate	**£400-500**
			Blue **2nd type cab**/body, Red 'grooved' hubs, 'Ever Ready Batteries For Life', spare wheel, Supertoy	**£300-400**
919	1957-58	**Guy Van 'GOLDEN SHRED'** ...	All Red **2nd type cab** and body, Yellow Supertoy hubs,	
			'Robertsons Golden Shred' and 'golly' design, spare wheel	**£700-900**
920	1960-61	**Guy Warrior Van 'HEINZ'**	Red cab and chassis, window glazing, Yellow van body and Supertoy hubs,	
			spare wheel, 'HEINZ 57 VARIETIES' and 'Tomato Ketchup' bottle design	**£1,500-1,750**
921	1954-56	**Bedford Articulated Vehicle**	Yellowish-Orange body, Black wings, Red hubs, Supertoy, (was 521, renumbered 409)	**£120-140**
922	1954-56	**Big Bedford Lorry**	Maroon cab, Fawn back, Fawn hubs, Supertoy, (was 522, renumbered 408)	**£110-130**
			Dark Blue cab, Yellow back, Yellow hubs.	**£200-250**
923	1955-58	**Big Bedford Van 'HEINZ'**	Red cab and chassis, Yellow back and hubs, 'HEINZ 57 VARIETIES' plus Baked Beans can, Supertoy	**£300-400**
	1958-59		As previous model but with 'Tomato Ketchup' bottle advertising	**£1,750-2,250**
924	1972-76	**Aveling Barford 'CENTAUR'** ...	Red/Yellow body, tipping dump truck	**£30-40**
925	1965-69	**Leyland Dump Truck**	8-wheeled Supertoy with 'SAND BALLAST GRAVEL' on tailgate.	
			White (tilting) cab and chassis, Blue cab roof, Orange diecast tipper, Mid-Blue plastic hubs	**£145-165**
			As previous model but with tinplate tipper in Orange, Pale Grey or Red	**£145-165**
930	1960-64	**Bedford Pallet-Jekta Van**	Orange and Yellow body, 'Dinky Toys' and 'Meccano', 3 pallets, 1 packing piece, Supertoy	**£225-275**
931	1954-56	**Leyland Comet Lorry**		
		with Stake Body	Violet-Blue cab and chassis, Orange-Yellow back, Red hubs, Supertoy, (was 531, renumbered 417)	**£175-225**
932	1954-56	**Leyland Comet**		
		with Hinged Tailboard	Dark Green cab and chassis, Orange back, Mid-Green hubs	**£120-140**
		(was 532, renumbered 418)	Dark Green cab and chassis, Red back, Cream hubs	**£120-140**
			Dark Blue cab and chassis, Mid-Blue back and hubs	**£120-140**
			Dark Blue cab, chassis and back, Red hubs	**£120-140**
			Dark Blue cab and chassis, Light (Powder) Blue back, Cream hubs	**£250-350**
			Red cab and chassis, Mid-Blue back and hubs	**£250-350**
	NB	Odd colours:	Be wary of colour combinations not listed. The screw fitting makes it easy to	
			interchange body and body components.	
933	1954-56	**Leyland Comet Cement Wagon**	Yellow body and hubs, 'Portland Blue-Circle Cement', Supertoy, (was 533, renumbered 419)	**£110-130**
934	1956-58	**Leyland Octopus Wagon**	Yellow cab and chassis, Green truck body secured to chassis by a screw, Green band	
			around cab (but without Yellow band above radiator), Red diecast Supertoy hubs, 1 packing piece	**£150-175**
	1958-59	....	As previous model but with Green diecast hubs. Body secured by rivet	**£150-175**
	1958-63	....	As previous model but with Yellow band immediately above radiator,	
			Red diecast hubs, body secured by rivet	**£250-300**
	1963-64	....	Dark Blue cab/chassis, Pale Yellow cab band and rivetted back, Red diecast hubs. In picture box	**£1,750-2,000**
	1963-64	....	Dark Blue cab/chassis, Pale Yellow cab band and rivetted back, Grey plastic hubs. In picture box	**£1,750-2,000**
	1964-64	....	Dark Blue cab/chassis, Pale Yellow cab band and rivetted back, Red plastic hubs. In picture box	**£1,750-2,000**

935	1964-66	**Leyland Octopus Flat Truck with Chains**	6 chain-posts, 8 wheels, flatbed held by rivet, Supertoy, 1 packing piece, picture box.	
			Mid-Green cab/chassis, Pale Grey cab band and flatbed body, Red plastic hubs	£1,250-1,500
			Mid-Green cab/chassis, Pale Grey cab band and flatbed body, Grey plastic hubs	£1,250-1,500
			Blue cab/chassis, Yellow cab flash, Pale Grey flatbed and hubs	£4,000-5,000
936	1964-69	**Leyland 8-wheel Chassis**	Red/Silver, 'Another Leyland on Test', three '5-ton' weights	£120-140
940	1977-80	**Mercedes-Benz LP.1920 Truck**	White cab, Pale Grey cover, Red chassis, hubs and interior	£35-45
			As above but with Black interior and White hubs	£40-50
		'HALB UND HALB'	'MAMPE' & 'BOSCH' on Blue cab, Elephant design. Promotional	£300-400
		'FISON'S'	White body, Red interior, chassis and hubs, Grey plastic cover,	
			'FISON'S THE GARDEN PEOPLE' labels, 2 peat samples. Promotional	£300-400
		'HENRY JOHNSON'	Green body, White cover. Promotional	£400-500
941	1956-56	**Foden 14 ton Tanker**		
		'MOBILGAS'	2nd type cab. Red body and hubs, Black filler caps, Black tyres, Supertoy, (renumbered from 504)	£400-500
942	1955-57	**Foden 14 ton Tanker**		
		'REGENT'	2nd type cab. Dark Blue cab/chassis, Red/White/Blue tank, Black tyres, Supertoy	£400-500
943	1958-64	**Leyland Octopus Tanker**		
		'ESSO'	Dark Red body and diecast hubs, Red tinplate tank with waterslide transfers,	
			'ESSO PETROLEUM', spare wheel, hook, Supertoy, 1 packing piece	£300-400
			As previous model but with Red plastic hubs	£300-400
			With Red plastic hubs, logos on self-adhesive labels	£350-450
944	1963-70	**Leyland Octopus Tanker**		
		'SHELL-BP'	White/Yellow cab and body, Grey chassis and plastic hubs	£200-300
			White/Yellow cab and body, Grey chassis, Black plastic hubs	£300-400
			White/Yellow cab and body, Grey chassis, Red plastic hubs	£300-400
			White/Yellow cab and body, White chassis, Grey or Black plastic hubs	£200-300
	Export issue:		Yellow cab, White chassis, White plastic tank, Red plastic hubs. 'See-through' export box	NGPP
	NB		Each issue has 'SHELL' and 'BP' sticky labels on the front half of the plastic tank.	
944	1963-64	**Leyland Octopus Tanker**		
		'CORN PRODUCTS'	Only 500 of these promotionals issued.	
			White body and plastic tank, 'Sweeteners For Industry' in White on Black labels. In 944	
			'ESSO' box with 'CORN PRODUCTS' sticker, wrapped in Green/Grey striped gift paper	£10,000-15,000
945	1966-75	**A.E.C. Fuel Tanker 'ESSO'**	White cab/chassis, White tank, 'ESSO PETROLEUM', 'Tiger in Your Tank' logo on rear, 1 PP	£90-110
	1975-77		As previous model but without logo at rear, card boxed or bubble-packed	£75-95
	1977-77	**'LUCAS OIL' Tanker**	Green cab and tank, White design on labels, promotional, bubble-packed	£100-125
948	1961-67	**Tractor-Trailer 'McLEAN'** ...(i):	Red cab, Light Grey trailer, Red plastic hubs, Supertoy, 2 packing pieces	£175-225
		(ii):	As previous model but with Black plastic hubs	£175-225
	19??	**'ROADWAY DOVER'** (iii):	As model (i) but with extra graphics on the front of the trailer and on the rear of	
			the cab: 'Roadway Dover Del Express Inc.'. Black plastic hubs	£300-500
	1964 ?	**'BROWN SHOE Co.'** ....(iv):	As 'McLean' model but with 'Brown Shoe Co.' adhesive labels. US Promotional (75 only made)	NGPP
	NB		The trailer moulding is light-sensitive and varies in shade from Pale Grey to Light Grey with a	
			Greenish tinge, through to very Pale Brown. The 'McLean' logo can be Red or Light Orange.	
950	1978-79	**Foden S20 Tanker 'BURMAH'**	Red cab, Red/White trailer, Black or Grey hatches, Red or Cream hubs	£50-75
950	1978	**Foden Tanker 'SHELL'**	Red cab, Red/White trailer, Cream hubs	£75-100
951	1954-56	**Trailer**	Grey body with hook, Red hubs, (was 551, renumbered 428)	£30-40
			Dark Grey body with hook, Lemon Yellow hubs	£50-75
958	1961-66	**Guy Warrior Snow Plough**	Yellow/Black body and plough blade, spare wheel, 1 packing piece, Supertoy	£150-175
			Yellow/Black body, Silver plough blade	£150-175
			Silver blade version in box with picture showing Silver blade	£250-300
959	1961-68	**Foden Dump Truck & Bulldozer**	Red or Deep Red body, Silver chassis and blade, Red hubs (plastic front; metal rear)	£120-140
			As previous model but with Pale Yellow plastic front hubs and Yellow metal rear hubs	£150-175
			All-Red body version	£150-175
960	1960-68	**Albion Lorry Concrete Mixer**	Orange body, Blue rotating drum with 2 Yellow triangles, Black plastic hubs, Grey tyres. Supertoy	£125-150
			Orange body, Grey rotating drum, Black plastic hubs, Grey tyres. Supertoy	£125-150
961	1954-62	**Blaw-Knox Bulldozer**	Red or Yellow body, rubber tracks, Tan driver, Supertoy, (renumbered from 561)	£40-50
	1962-64		Blue body, rubber tracks, Tan driver	£40-50
	1963-64		Red or Yellow body, rubber tracks, Blue driver	£40-50
	1964-64		Orange plastic body with Silver engine detail, Black diecast lifting gear, Green plastic	
			blade and exhaust pipe, Blue driver, Light Green or Olive-Green roller wheels	£200-250
962	1954-66	**Muir Hill Dumper**	Yellow body, hook, Supertoy, 1 packing piece, (renumbered from 562)	£15-20
963	1954-58	**Blaw Knox Heavy Tractor**	Red or Orange body, Green or Black tracks. Blue/White striped box, 1 packing piece, (was 563)	£50-60
	1958-59		Yellow body, Green or Black tracks. Blue/White striped box, 1 packing piece	£60-75
963	1973-75	**Road Grader**	Yellow/Red articulated body, Silver blade, Red lower arm	£20-30
			White or Yellow lower arm.	£30-40
964	1954-68	**Elevator Loader**	Yellow with Mid-Blue or Dark Blue chutes, Blue or Yellow hubs, 1 packing piece	£45-55
	(renumbered from 564)	Boxes:	Early Blue boxes were replaced by Blue/White boxes, then by Yellow 'Supertoys' boxes.	
	Late issue:		Mid-Blue with Yellow chutes, as shown on late picture box design	£100-150
965	1955-61	**'EUCLID' Dump Truck**	Pale Yellow body, Yellow hubs, 'STONE - ORE - EARTH', no windows, operable tipper, 1 PP	£150-175
	NB		1955-56 Grey backed logo; 1959-61 Red backed logo.	
	1961-69		As previous model but with window glazing	£150-175
			Pale Yellow body, Red or Dark Green hubs, window glazing. In detailed picture box	£200-250

| 965 | 1969-70 | 'TEREX' Rear Dump Truck ..... | Yellow body (as previous model but 'TEREX' cast under cab), 1 packing piece ....£300-350 |
| 966 | 1960-64 | Marrel Multi-Bucket Unit .... | Pale Yellow body, Grey skip and tyres, Black hubs, Supertoy, 1 packing piece......................................£140-160 |

967	1959-64	BBC TV Control Room.............	Dark Green, 'BBC Television Service', Supertoy, 1 packing piece £175-200
967	1973-78	Muir-Hill Loader/Trencher	Yellow/Red or Orange/Black body, with driver...£25-35
968	1959-64	BBC TV Roving-Eye Vehicle	Dark Green body, BBC crest, camera, Supertoy, 1 packing piece £150-175
969	1959-64	BBC TV Extending Mast	Dark Green body, BBC crest, dish aerial, mast, Supertoy, 2 packing pieces......................................£150-175

970	1967-71	Jones Fleetmaster Crane...........	(Bedford TK) Red cab, White roof, Red interior, Red plastic hubs, White jib, 2 packing pieces £80-100
	1971-77	......	Metallic Red cab, White interior, and jib, chrome domed hubs, 2 packing pieces £80-100
	1971-77	......	Pale Yellow cab, White interior, and jib, chrome domed hubs, 2 packing pieces £80-100
971	1954-62	Coles Mobile Crane	Yellow and Black, operable crane, 1 driver, Supertoy, (renumbered from 571)..£30-40
972	1955-62	Coles 20 ton	
		Lorry-Mounted Crane	Yellow/Orange (no 'Long Vehicle' signs), 2 drivers, Supertoy, 1 packing piece £40-50
	1962-69	.....	Yellow/Orange (with 'Long Vehicle' signs), 2 drivers, Supertoy £40-50
	1967-69	.....	Yellow/Black, Blue metal driver in lorry cab only, Yellow plastic hubs, Black tyres,
			Black/White diagonal stripes around jib, Yellow 'COLES CRANE" at rear £100-150
			Variation with Black hubs. (In end-flap box) £100-150
973	1954-59	Goods Yard Crane	Yellow operable crane on Blue base. Blue/White striped box with 1 packing piece, (was 752)............£30-40

973	1971-75	Eaton 'YALE' Tractor Shovel ...	Red/Yellow body with Yellow or Silver bucket exterior, cast hubs £20-30
			Yellow/Red body, Silver wheels, no engine covers, cast hubs £25-35
			All Yellow body, Blue wheels, engine covers, cast hubs......................................£25-35
		Factory special:	Window in cab roof, yellow plastic hubs, 'Trojan 6000' tampo prints, 'Eaton' underneath.
			This unique model was presented to the man who designed the actual vehicle. ....NGPP
974	1968-75	A.E.C. Hoynor Car Transporter	Bright Metallic Blue cab, Pale Orange/Dark Orange back, Grey plastic hubs, 3 PP......£125-150
			Dark Metallic Blue cab, Pale Orange/Dark Orange back, Grey plastic hubs, 3 PP £125-150
			Dark Metallic Blue cab, Yellow and Bright Orange back, chrome domed hubs, 3 PP......................£125-150
975	1963-67	'RUSTON-BUCYRUS'	
		Excavator.....................	Pale Yellow plastic body, Red jib and bucket, Black rubber tracks, with instructions £300-350
976	1968-76	'MICHIGAN' Tractor Dozer.....	Yellow/Red body, driver, engine covers, Red hubs, 1 packing piece £30-35
		Promotional:	All Yellow with Blue hubs. (100 / 200 made for Michigan Co.) £100-150
977	1960-64	Servicing Platform Vehicle	Red and Cream body, operable platform, spare wheel, 2 packing pieces £140-160
	NB		Version seen using 667 Missile Servicing Platform Vehicle chassis in the Red/Cream 977 livery ....NGPP
977	1973-78	Shovel Dozer............................	Yellow/Red/Silver, Black or Silver plastic tracks, bubble-packed.. ....£20-25
978	1964-72	Bedford TK Refuse Wagon........	Diecast cab, plastic tipping body, 2 plastic dustbins.
			Green cab, Grey tipping body, Red hubs, White (later Grey) plastic roof rack £40-45
	1973-74	....	Dark Metallic Green cab, Grey tipping body, Red plastic hubs, White (later Grey) plastic roof rack £60-70
	1975-77	....	Lime-Green cab, White interior, Black or Brown chassis, plastic or cast roof rack £60-70
	1978-80	....	Yellow cab with Brown chassis, cast roof rack £35-45
	NB		Over its 16-year production run, 978 came in five different types of packaging:
			lidded box, pictorial and non-pictorial end-flap boxes, bubble-pack, and window box.

979	1961-64	Racehorse Transport	Grey lower body and roof, Lemon-Yellow upper body sides, 2 horses,
			'Newmarket Racehorse Transport Service Ltd', Supertoy, 2 packing pieces £350-450
980	1954-60	Horsebox (US issue)...................	Maroon body (cast in aluminium), 'Hire Service', 'Express Horse Van', 'Express'.
		(renumbered from 581)	In Blue/White striped box with picture of model and 'Hudson Dobson', 2 packing pieces......£500-600
980	1972-79	Coles Hydra Truck 150T	Lemon-Yellow body, triple extension crane, handle at side and rear £30-40
			Yellow or Orange body, 2 side handles, no rear handle £50-60
		'SPARROWS'	Red body, 'SPARROWS CRANE HIRE', (promotional model) £200-300
981	1954-60	Horsebox...................................	Maroon body (cast in aluminium), 'British Railways', 2 packing pieces, (renumbered from 581) £100-125

982	1955-63	Pullmore Car Transporter	Bedford 'O' series cab and chassis plus aluminium trailer with 'DINKY TOYS DELIVERY SERVICE'
		(renumbered from 582)	on sides. Same logo on rear ramp but without '20' sign. Black grille/bumper, Silver trim, 1 packing piece.
	1955-61		Blue cab and back, Mid-Blue hubs, Fawn decks £400-500
			Dark Blue cab, Mid-Blue hubs, Light Blue back and decks, no window glazing.
			Blue/White striped box has picture of 994 Loading Ramp introduced in 1955 ....£125-150
	1961-63		As previous issue but cab has window glazing £140-170

983	1958-63	Car Carrier and Trailer	Red/Grey, 'Dinky Auto Service', 5 packing pieces, (Supertoys 984 and 985) £200-250
984	1958-63	Car Carrier	Red/Grey body, Grey hubs, 'Dinky Auto Service', 2 packing pieces, Supertoy......................................£250-350
984	1974-79	Atlas Digger................................	Red/Yellow body, Yellow arm/cylinders, Silver or Yellow bucket......................................£30-40
			Red/Yellow body, Black plastic arm, Black or Yellow cylinders, Silver bucket......................................£30-40

985	1958-63	Trailer for Car Carrier	Red/Grey body, 'Dinky Auto Service', 2 packing pieces, Supertoy £50-60
986	1959-61	Mighty Antar with Propeller	Red cab (window glazing on some), Grey low-loader, Bronze propeller, 3 packing pieces £200-300
987	1962-69	'ABC TV' Control Room	Blue/Grey/Red, 'ABC TELEVISION', camera/operator/cable......................................£250-300
988	1962-69	TV Transmitter Van 'ABC-TV'	Blue/Grey body, Red stripe, revolving aerial dish, Supertoy £250-300
989	1963-65	Car Transporter	
		'AUTO TRANSPORTERS'.......	Lemon Yellow cab, Pale Grey back, Metallic Light Blue ramps, Red plastic hubs, Supertoy
			boxed in all-card picture box or export-only Gold 'see through' window box, 2 packing pieces.........£1,000-1,500
990		Pullmore Car transporter	
		with Four Cars	See Gift Sets section.
991	1954-70	Large Trailer	Renumbered from 551 – see that entry for details.

| 991 | 1954-55 | A.E.C. Tanker ...... | Red/Yellow 'SHELL CHEMICALS LIMITED', Supertoy, (renumbered from 591) ....£130-160 |
| | 1955-58 | | Red/Yellow, 'SHELL CHEMICALS', Supertoy......................................£120-140 |

Photos: Vectis Auctions Ltd.

Ford Transit casting types:	Type 1: (1966-74), has sliding driver's door, opening hinged side door, and twin rear doors. Type 2: (1974-78), non-sliding driver's door, one side-hinged door, one top-hinged rear door. Type 3: (1978-80), as Type 2 but with a slightly longer bonnet (18 mm.)

Ref	Year(s)	Model name	Colours, features, details	Market Price Range
24a	1934-38	Ambulance	Types 1 or 2 criss-cross chassis, types 1, 2 or 3 grille, plated chrome or Black hubs, open windows.	
			Cream body (Red chassis), Cream body (Grey chassis)	£250-350
			Grey body (Dark Grey chassis), Grey body (Maroon chassis)	£200-250

> **Notable Auction Result**: A pre-production (lead) example of 24a was sold by Christie's in 2001 for **£470**.

Ref	Year(s)	Model name	Colours, features, details	Market Price Range
	1938-40	Ambulance	Type 2 criss-cross chassis, open windows, type 3 grille. See 30f.	
			Cream body (Red chassis), Cream body (Grey chassis)	£200-250
			Grey body (Dark Grey chassis), Grey body (Maroon chassis)	£250-300
			Black body, Black chassis (thought to be for export only)	£500-750
25h	1936-37	Streamlined Fire Engine	Red body, no tinplate chassis, tinplate ladder and bell, White tyres	£175-225
	1937-40		Red body, tinplate baseplate, ladder and bell, Black or White tyres	£125-150
25h	1948-54	(renumbered 250)	Red body and ladder, tinplate baseplate, brass bell, Black tyres	£80-100
25k	1937-39	Streamline Fire Engine	Red body, tinplate base, 6 firemen, ladder, bell, White tyres	£400-500
30f	1935-38	Ambulance	Grey body, Red wings/criss-cross chassis, plain radiator, open windows	£150-200
	1938-40		Grey body, Black moulded chassis, radiator badge, open windows	£90-110
	1938-40	South-African issue:	Grey body, Red cross, 'Bentley type' radiator	£750-950
	1946-47		Grey body, Black moulded chassis, open windows	£80-100
	1947-48		Cream body, Black moulded chassis, filled-in or open windows	£80-100
30h	1950-54	Daimler Ambulance	Cream body, Red crosses and wheels, no window glazing, (renumbered 253)	£80-90
30hm	1950-54	Daimler Military Ambulance	Military-Green body, Red crosses on White backgrounds, (US issue), (renumbered 624)	£200-300
123-P	1977	Austin Princess 'POLICE' Car	All-White, Bronze/Blue or White/Blue. (Model has not yet been seen)	NPP
195	1971-78	Fire-Chief's Range Rover	Red or Metallic Red, 'Fire Service', Speedwheels, bubble-packed	£35-40
243	1979-81	Volvo 'POLICE' Car	White body, plastic chassis. (Some made in Italy by Polistil)	£35-40
244	1977-81	Plymouth Fury Police Car	Black/White, 'POLICE', warning lights, plastic chassis and wheels	£25-30
250	1954-62	Fire Engine	Red body and hubs, Silver tinplate ladder, bell and trim, (renumbered from 25h)	£100-120
250	1967-71	Police Mini Cooper 'S'	White body, Austin Cooper 'S' boot lid transfer, roof sign and aerial, 'POLICE' on doors	£55-65
	1971-73		As previous model but cast boot detail, no aerial	£45-55
	1973-75		As previous model but with Speedwheels	£35-45
		NB	Boot casting variations: (1) 'Morris Mini-Minor' cast-in, (2) 'Austin Mini-Cooper S' cast-in.	
251	1971-72	U.S.A. 'POLICE' Car	(Pontiac Parisienne), White body, Black textured roof, Off-White interior, twin aerials, siren, rooflight	£60-75
252	1969-74	R.C.M.P. Police Car	(Pontiac Parisienne), Dark Blue body, White door panels, White interior, driver, twin aerials, Red light	£60-75
253	1954-58	Daimler Ambulance	Cream body, Red crosses and cast hubs, no window glazing, (renumbered from 30h)	£75-85
	1958-60		White body, Red crosses and cast hubs, no window glazing	£100-125
	1960-62		White body, Red crosses and cast hubs, with window glazing	£80-100
	1962-64		White body, Red plastic hubs, with window glazing	£90-110
254	1971-81	Police Range Rover	White body, Orange side stripes, 'POLICE', twin aerials on some, Speedwheels	£30-35
255	1955-61	Mersey Tunnel Police Van	(Land Rover), Gloss or Matt Red body, smooth or treaded Black tyres, hook, 'MERSEY TUNNEL' and 'POLICE'	£125-150
255	1967-71	Ford Zodiac 'POLICE' Car	White body, driver, 'POLICE' on doors and roof sign, aerial	£55-65
			As previous model but with paper labels on door and blue base	£45-55
255	1977-79	Police Mini Clubman	Blue/White body, 'POLICE', opening doors and bonnet, plastic wheels	£30-35
256	1960-64	Humber Hawk 'POLICE' Car	Black body, Cream interior, White 'POLICE' sign on roof, 'PC 49' licence plates, driver and observer, spun hubs	£80-100
257	1960-69	Canadian 'FIRE CHIEF' Car	(Nash Rambler), flashing light, suspension, window glazing	£55-65
258		**U.S.A. POLICE CAR**		
	1960-61	De Soto Fireflite	(192), Black body, White front doors, 'POLICE' on doors, roof and bonnet, Red roof-light	£100-125
			Same, but with Red interior	£100-125
	1961-62	Dodge Royal Sedan	(191), Black body, White front doors, 'POLICE' on doors, roof and bonnet, Red roof-light	£100-125
	1962-66	Ford Fairlane	(149), Black body, White front doors, 'POLICE' on doors, roof and bonnet, Red light, open window	£80-90
			Same but Dark Blue/White, with closed windows	£80-90
	1966-68	Cadillac 62	(147), Black/White, suspension/steering	£100-125
259	1961-69	Fire Engine (Bedford Miles)	Red body and hubs, 'FIRE BRIGADE' and crest, Red tinplate ladder and bell, Yellow box	£125-150
			As previous model but with 'AIRPORT FIRE TENDER' (from 276)	£125-150
			Red body, spun aluminium hubs	£125-150
261	1967-77	Ford Taunus 'POLIZEI'	White and Green body, (German issue), box has card packing ring and label: 'Special contract run for Meccano Agent in W. Germany'	£200-300
263	1962-68	Superior Criterion Ambulance	Cream, 'AMBULANCE' on windows, stretcher, roof beacon. Red, Pale Blue or Yellow interior	£50-60
263	1978-81	E.R.F. Fire Tender	Yellow body, 'Airport Rescue', flashing light	£40-50
264	1962-65	R.C.M.P. Ford Fairlane	Dark Blue body, White doors, aerial, red beacon, 2 Mounties	£100-125
264	1965-68	R.C.M.P. Cadillac	Dark Blue body, White doors, aerial, red beacon, 2 Mounties	£90-110
264	1978-80	Rover 3500 Police Car	White body, Yellow stripe with 'POLICE' and crest. (Some made in Hong Kong)	£20-30
266	1976-79	E.R.F. Fire Tender	Red body, 'Fire Service', White wheeled escape ladder	£50-60
	1979-80		As previous model but with Metallic Red body	£50-60
	1976-79	Danish issue:	Red body, 'FALCK'	£70-85
267	1967-71	Superior Cadillac Ambulance	Cream and Red body, 'AMBULANCE' on roof, flashing light, stretcher, patient	£50-65
267	1978-79	Paramedic Truck	Red, Yellow cylinders, 2 figures, lapel badge, (TV Series 'Emergency')	£20-30

268	1973-77	**Range Rover Ambulance**	White, 'AMBULANCE', stretcher, bubble-packed	£20-30
269	1962-66	**Jaguar Motorway**		
		'POLICE' Car	White or matt-White body, aerial, roof-light, 2 figures	£100-125
269	1978-79	**Ford Transit 'POLICE' Van**	White/Red/Blue, figures/lights/signs/cones, Type 3 casting	£35-45
270	1969-72	**Ford 'POLICE' Panda Car**	Turquoise body, White doors, Blue/White roof sign, cast hubs	£45-55
	1972-77		As previous model but fitted with Speedwheels	£40-50
271	1975-76	**Ford Transit 'FIRE'**	Red body, hose/axe/bells/plastic ladder, bubble-packed, Type 2	£55-65
		........................Danish issue:	As previous model but with 'FALCK' logo	£65-75
272	1975-78	**'POLICE' Accident Unit**	White, radar gun/beacon/aerial/cones/signs, Type 2 casting	£35-45
274	1978-79	**Ford Transit Ambulance**	White, 'AMBULANCE', Red crosses, beacon, Type 3 casting	£35-45
276	1962-69	**Airport Fire Tender**	Red body, 'AIRPORT FIRE CONTROL', bell, packing ring in box	£75-100
			As previous model but 'FIRE BRIGADE' logo (from 259), no crest	£75-100
276	1976-78	**Ford Transit Ambulance**	White, 'AMBULANCE', Type 2 casting, packing ring in box	£30-40
277	1962-68	**Superior Criterion Ambulance** ..	Metallic Blue, White roof and tyres, flashing light, box has lift-off lid and 1 packing piece	£60-80
			As previous model but in Gold 'see-through' box	£80-90
277	1977-80	**'POLICE' Land Rover**	Black body, White tilt, Blue beacon	£20-30
278	1964-69	**Vauxhall Victor Ambulance**	White, 'AMBULANCE', stretcher and patient, roof-box and light	£60-75
282	1973-79	**Land Rover Fire Appliance**	Red, 'Fire Service', metal ladder, bubble-packed	£30-40
	1974-78	........................Danish issue:	As previous model but with 'FALCK' logo	£35-45
285	1969-79	**Merryweather Marquis**	Metallic Dark Red body, escape ladder, working pump, 'FIRE SERVICE'	£55-65
			As previous model but (non-Metallic), Red body	£55-65
		Danish issue:	As previous model but Red or Metallic Dark Red body, 'FALCK' logo	£85-95
286	1968-74	**Ford Transit 'FIRE'**	Red, 'Fire Service', hose Type 1 casting, bubble-packed	£75-90
			As previous model but Metallic Red body	£75-90
		Danish issue:	As previous model but with 'FALCK ZONEN' logo	£85-95
287	1967-71	**Police Accident Unit**	White body, Orange panels, roof rack and sign, radar gun, aerial, Type 1 casting	£100-125
	1971-74	....	White body, Red panels, roof rack and sign, radar gun, aerial, Type 1 casting	£65-75
		NB	Accessories with 287 include traffic cones and two blue 'POLICE' warning boards.	
288	1971-79	**Superior Cadillac**	White body with Red lower panels, 'AMBULANCE', stretcher and patient, no flashing light	£40-45
		Danish issue:	Black body/White roof, Blue interior and roof bar, 'FALCK' on roof bar and tailgate	£100-125
555	1952-54	**Fire Engine** (Commer)	Red body with Silver trim and ladder, no windows, (renumbered 955)	£75-85
624	1954-?	**Daimler Military Ambulance**	Military-Green body, Red crosses on White backgrounds, (US issue), (renumbered from 30hm)	£200-300
954	1961-64	**Fire Station**	Red, Yellow and 'brick' plastic, base 252 mm. x 203 mm	£200-250
955	1954-64	**Fire Engine** (Commer)	Red body and diecast Supertoy hubs, no window glazing, (renumbered from 555) ...	£90-110
	1964-70		Red body, Red diecast or plastic hubs, window glazing, Black or Grey tyres, housed in Yellow box with drawing or scene, card packing	£150-175
956	1958-60	**Turntable Fire Escape Lorry**	(Bedford cab). Red body and diecast hubs, no windows, Silver deck and ladder	£80-100
	1960-70		Red body, diecast then plastic hubs, window glazing, instructions, 'Tested' label, card packing	£80-100
		NB	A version of 956 has been discovered (in Norway) that has 3 ladders instead of 2.	
956	1970-74	**Turntable Fire Escape Lorry**	(Berliet cab). Metallic Red body and hubs, windows, 'ECHELLE INCENDIE', Silver platform	£175-225
			As previous model but with Black platform	£150-200
	1974-?	.... Danish issue:	Metallic Red body and hubs, windows, 'FALCK'	£175-225
2253	1974-76	**Ford Capri Police Car**	White/Orange, 'POLICE', Blue light, suspension. (1/25 scale)	£80-100

Photo: Vectis Auctions Ltd.

Dinky Toys Farm and Garden models

Ref	Year(s)	Model name and details	Market Price Range
22e	1933-40	**Farm Tractor** 'Modelled Miniature' with 'HORNBY SERIES' cast-in, no hook, Yellow/Dark Blue (lead) body, Red or Yellow (lead) wheels	**£300-400**
		'DINKY TOYS' cast-in, with hook, Red or Yellow wheels are lead, diecast or both, Green/Yellow, Yellow/Blue/Red, Red/Blue, Red/Red	**£300-400**
		Cream/Blue, Cream/Red, Blue/Cream/Red	**£300-400**
27a	1948-54	**'MASSEY-HARRIS' Tractor** (renumbered to 300) Red body, Yellow cast wheels, driver, hook	**£80-100**
27ak	1952-54	**Tractor and Hay Rake** (renumbered to 310) 27a Tractor and 27k Hay Rake	**£150-200**
27b	1949-54	**Halesowen Harvest Trailer** (renumbered to 320) Brown body, Red racks, Yellow metal wheels	**£25-35**
27c	1949-54	**M.H. Manure Spreader** (renumbered to 321) Red body with drawbar, hook, working shredders	**£30-35**
27d	1950-54	**Land Rover** (renumbered to 340) Orange body, Dark Blue interior, Tan driver, Red hubs	**£85-95**
		Orange body, Dk. Green interior, Tan driver, Red hubs	**£75-85**
		Mid-Green body, Light Brown interior, Tan driver, Green hubs	**£75-85**
		Promotional: Very Dark Green body. (Ministry of Food promotional)	**£1,000-1,500**
	1952-53	Gift Set model: Dark Brown body. Only in Gift Set No.2, Commercial Vehicles Set	**GSP**
27f	1950-54	**Estate Car** (renumbered to 344) Pale Brown body with Dark Brown panels, rear axle pillars, Fawn hubs, small lettering on matt or gloss baseplate	**£60-80**
		Grey body with Red side panels	**£100-125**
27g	1949-54	**Moto-Cart** (renumbered to 342) Brown and Green body, driver, 3 metal wheels/tyres	**£40-50**
27h	1951-54	**Disc Harrow** (renumbered to 322) Red/Yellow body, Silver disc blades, tinplate hook	**£20-25**
27j	1952-54	**Triple Gang Mower** (renumbered to 323) Red frame, Yellow tines, Green wheels, cast-in hook	**£20-25**
27k	1953-54	**Hay Rake** (renumbered to 324) Red frame, Yellow wheels, wire tines, operating lever	**£20-25**
27m	1952-54	**Land Rover Trailer** (renumbered to 341) Green body and hubs	**£25-35**
		Blue body and hubs	**£25-35**
		Red body and hubs	**£25-35**
		Orange body, Red, Cream or Beige hubs	**£25-35**
		Militarised version: see 'Military Vehicles' section.	
27n	1953-54	**'FIELD MARSHALL' Tractor** (renumbered to 301) Burnt Orange body and exhaust stack, Silver metal wheels, Tan driver, hook	**£100-130**
		As previous model but with Green metal wheels	**£150-200**
30n	1950-54	**Farm Produce Wagon** (renumbered to 343) Model has stake sides to rear body; Black cast base and hook; hubs same colour as rear body. Yellow cab with Green back	**£60-70**
		Green cab with Yellow back	**£60-70**
		Red cab with Blue back	**£60-70**
105a	1948-54	**Garden Roller** (renumbered to 381) Green handle and Red roller sides	**£15-25**
105b	1948-54	**Wheelbarrow** (renumbered to 382) Brown or Tan and Red body, single metal wheel	**£15-25**
105c	1948-54	**4 wheeled Hand Truck** (renumbered to 383) Green/Yellow or Blue/Yellow	**£10-15**
105e	1948-54	**Grass Cutter** (renumbered to 384) Yellow handle, Green metal wheels, Red blades	**£25-30**
		Yellow handle, unpainted metal wheels, Green blades	**£50-75**
107a	1948-54	**Sack Truck** (renumbered to 385) Blue or Pale Green body, two Black metal wheels	**£10-15**

Ref	Year(s)	Model name and details	Market Price Range
192	1970-74	**Range Rover** Bronze body, various interior colours, cast detailed or Speedwheels	**£25-35**
	1973-79	Black or Yellow body, Speedwheels	**£25-35**
300	1954-62	**'MASSEY-HARRIS' Tractor** (renumbered from 27a) Red body, cast wheels (Yellow centre, unpainted 'tyres'), Tan cast driver	**£100-125**
	1962-64	Red body, Yellow hubs (cast rear, plastic front, rubber tyres), Blue plastic driver, no decals	**£200-300**
	1964-66	Cherry Red body, Yellow/Black plastic hubs, Yellow exhaust, Blue driver, Yellow/White box	**£125-150**
300	1966-71	**'MASSEY-FERGUSON' Tractor** As before, but renamed 'MASSEY-FERGUSON', Yellow plastic hubs and exhaust	**£300-400**
301	1954-61	**'FIELD MARSHALL' Tractor** (renumbered from 27n) Orange body, cast wheels (Green or Silver centres, unpainted 'tyres'), Tan driver, hook	**£150-200**
		Same, but with Yellow or unpainted wheel centres	**£150-180**
	1962-66	Orange body, Green hubs (plastic front, cast rear, rubber tyres), Blue driver	**£300-400**
		Same, but with Green plastic hubs (front and rear)	**£300-400**
	1964-66	Red body, Green plastic hubs	**£200-250**
305	1964-67	**'DAVID BROWN' 900 Tractor** Yellow cab and hubs, Red cowl, Black engine, stickers: 'David Brown 990'. Detailed picture box	**£150-200**
	1967-73	White cab, hubs and cowl, Brown engine, stickers: 'David Brown Selectamatic 990'	**£100-130**
	1974-75	White cab and cowl, Red hubs and engine, stickers: 'Case David Brown 995'. Bubble-packed	**£130-160**
308	1971-72	**'LEYLAND' 384 Tractor** Metallic Red body, Cream hubs, no driver, plastic dome box	**£100-150**
	1973-74	Metallic Red body, White hubs, with driver, Yellow/Red box	**£100-150**
	1975-77	Dark Blue body, White exhaust stack and hubs, Blue plastic driver, Yellow/Red box	**£100-150**
	1978	Orange body, White exhaust stack and hubs, Blue plastic driver, Red/Blue 'hanging' box	**£100-150**
	1978-79	Metallic Red body, White exhaust stack and hubs, Blue plastic driver, Red/Blue 'hanging' box	**£100-150**
		Factory error: Blue body and plastic driver, Red hubs, White exhaust stack. Bubble-packed	**£200-250**
310	1954-60	**Tractor and Hay Rake** (renumbered from 27ak) 300 Tractor and 324 Hay Rake in Blue/White box	**£150-200**
		Same, but late issue in Yellow box with single PP	**£200-250**
319	1961-71	**Weeks Tipping Trailer** Red/Yellow body, cast or Brown plastic wheels, plain or planked trailer bed. One packing piece	**£25-30**
320	1954-60	**Halesowen Harvest Trailer** (renumbered from 27b) Red/Brown body, Red or Brown racks, drawbar, hook, cast or plastic wheels	**£25-35**
		Same, but Red body, Yellow racks	**£25-35**
321	1954-62	**M.H. Manure Spreader** (renumbered from 27c) Red body, Yellow cast wheels, 'MASSEY-HARRIS'	**£25-35**
321	1962-73	Red body, Red or Yellow plastic hubs, no logo	**£25-35**
322	1954-67	**Disc Harrow** (renumbered from 27h) Red/Yellow body, Silver disc blades, tinplate hook	**£25-35**
322	1967-73	White/Red body, Silver disc blades, no hook	**£25-35**
		All White version	**£40-50**
323	1954-63	**Triple Gang Mower** (renumbered from 27j) Red frame, Yellow tines, Green wheels, cast-in hook	**£35-45**
324	1954-64	**Hayrake** (renumbered from 27k) Red frame, Yellow wheels, Black or Silver lever	**£25-35**
325	1967-73	**'DAVID BROWN' Tractor and Disc Harrow** 305 and 322 in White and Red. Box has inner PP	**£100-125**
		305 and 322 in Yellow and Red. Box has inner PP	**£130-150**

340 1954-66 **Land Rover** (renumbered from 27d)
Green body, Pale Brown interior and cast driver,
Green cast hubs **£80-100**

1966-69 Orange body, Dark Green interior,
Red or Green cast hubs, Tan driver.............................**£80-100**
With Red plastic hubs, Blue cast or plastic driver **£110-130**

1969-71 Red body, Yellow interior, Red plastic hubs,
Blue plastic driver, Light Yellow box **£125-150**
Red body, Yellow interior, Yellow plastic hubs,
Blue plastic driver, Light Yellow box **£125-150**

1971 Red body, Yellow interior, Green plastic hubs,
Blue plastic driver, Light Yellow box **£125-150**

341 1954-66 **Land Rover Trailer** (renumbered from 27m)
Orange, Green or Red, drawbar and hook,
cast or plastic hubs **£25-30**
Militarised version: see 'Military Vehicles' section.

342 1954-61 **Moto-Cart** (renumbered from 27g)
Light Green with Tan back and driver, Red hubs **£65-75**
Dark Green with Tan back and driver, Red hubs **£65-75**

343 1954-64 **Farm Produce Wagon** (renumbered from 30n)
Mid-Green cab and chassis, Yellow back and hubs **£80-100**
Yellow cab with Green back and hubs..........................**£80-100**
Dark Red cab with Mid-Blue back and hubs..............**£100-125**
Cherry Red cab with Mid-Blue back and hubs **£100-125**
Late issues with plastic hubs and boxed in the
late lighter Yellow box **£125-150**

344 1954-61 **Estate Car** (renumbered from 27f)
Fawn with Brown or Red panels, Cream diecast
hubs, treaded tyres, large print on base......................**£130-160**
Fawn with Brown panels, spun hubs **£130-160**

344 1970-72 **Land Rover Pick-Up**
Metallic Blue body, White back, bubble-packed.............**£20-30**
1973-78 Metallic Red body, White back, bubble-packed **£20-30**

381 1954-58 **Garden Roller** (renumbered from 105a)
Green and Red..**£15-25**
381 1977-80 **Convoy Farm Truck**
Yellow cab, Brown plastic high-sided truck body **£15-20**
382 1954-58 **Wheelbarrow** (renumbered from 105b)
Brown and Red body, single metal wheel **£15-25**
383 1954-58 **4 wheeled Hand Truck** (renumbered from 105c)
Green or Blue body **£10-15**
384 1954-58 **Grass Cutter** (renumbered from 105e)
Yellow handle, Green metal wheels, Red blades............**£25-30**
Yellow handle, unpainted metal wheels, Green blades ...**£50-75**

385 1954-58 **Sack Truck** (renumbered from 107a)
Blue with two small metal wheels **£10-15**

386 1954-58 **Lawn Mower** (renumbered from 751)
Green/Red, separate grassbox, 'Dinky Toys' cast-in **£80-90**

399 1969-75 **Tractor and Trailer**
300 combined with 428...**£200-250**

428 1955-71 **Large Trailer**
See 'Commercial Vehicles' section for variations.

561 1949-54 **Blaw Knox Bulldozer** (renumbered 961)
Red body, Green or Black rubber tracks, driver,
lifting blade, Supertoy. Blue box with Orange/White
label, or 'natural' card box with Red/White label, 1 PP ..**£40-50**

563 1948-54 **Blaw Knox Heavy Tractor** (renumbered 963)
Red, Orange or Blue 561 without the dozer blade.
Brown cardboard box has Red/White label, 1 PP **£60-70**
Dark Blue body, Mid-Blue rollers, Green rubber
tracks, driver. Brown box, Black/White picture label .**£175-200**

564 1952-54 **Elevator Loader** (renumbered 964)
See 964 (below) for details.

751 1949-54 **Lawn Mower** (renumbered 386)
Green/Red, 'Dinky Supertoys' cast-in **£80-90**

961 1954-62 **Blaw-Knox Bulldozer** (renumbered from 561)
Red or Yellow body, rubber tracks,
Tan driver, Supertoy **£40-50**
1962-64 Blue body, rubber tracks, Tan driver............................**£40-50**
1963-64 Red or Yellow body, rubber tracks, Blue driver **£40-50**
1964-64 Orange plastic body, Silver engine detail, Black diecast
lifting gear, Green plastic blade and exhaust, Blue
driver, Light Green or Olive-Green roller wheels **£200-250**
963 1954-58 **Blaw Knox Heavy Tractor** (renumbered from 563)
Red or Orange body, Green or Black tracks.
Blue/White striped box, 1 PP...................................**£40-50**
1958-59 Yellow body, Green or Black tracks.
Blue/White striped box, 1 PP...................................**£40-50**

964 1954-68 **Elevator Loader** (renumbered from 564)
Yellow with Mid-Blue or Dark Blue chutes,
Blue or Yellow hubs, 1 PP.....................................**£45-55.**
Boxes: Early Blue boxes were replaced by
Blue/White boxes, then by Yellow 'Supertoys' boxes.
Late issue: Mid-Blue with Yellow chutes, as shown
on late picture box design **£100-150**

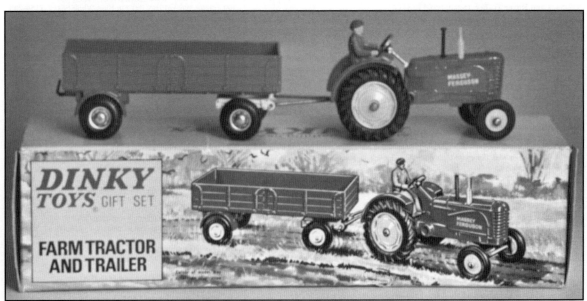

Dinky Toys Motor Cycles

SWRW = solid White rubber wheels, SBRW = solid Black rubber wheels (both are of a larger diameter than those used on the small cars). SGPW = solid Grey plastic wheels.   See also Military, Accessories and Gift Sets sections.

Ref	Year(s)	Model name and details	Market Price Range

041 1952-54 **Police Motor Cyclist**
Post-war reissue for US market of 37a ....NGPP

042 1952-54 **Civilian Motor Cyclist**
Post-war reissue for US market of 37b ....NGPP

043 1952-54 **Police Motorcycle Patrol**
Post-war reissue for US market of 42b ....NGPP

044 1952-54 **'R.A.C.' Motorcycle Patrol**
Post-war reissue for US market of 43b ....NGPP

045 1952-54 **'A.A.' Motorcycle Patrol**
Post-war reissue for US market of 44b ....NGPP

14z 1938-40 **'Triporteur'**
Three-wheel delivery van with Green, Red, Grey, Blue or
Yellow body, Black hubs, White tyres, rider is always a
different colour from van. French model, imported
into England in very small numbers **£200-300**

37a 1937-40 **Civilian Motor Cyclist**
Black motor cycle, Silver engine/exhaust detail; Blue,
Maroon, Green or Black rider, SWRW or thick SBRW ..**£40-50**
1946-49 Black motor cycle without Silver detail,
Green or Grey rider, thin SBRW....................................**£40-50**
1950-54 As previous version, but export only (renumbered 041) .**£40-50**

37b 1937-40 **Police Motor Cyclist**
Black motor cycle with Silver engine/exhaust detail,
Dark Blue rider, SWRW or thick SBRW........................**£75-85**
1946-49 Black motor cycle without Silver engine/exhaust detail,
Dark Blue rider, thick SBRW **£40-50**
1950-54 As previous model, but export only (renumbered 042)...**£40-50**

37c 1937-41 **Royal Signals Dispatch Rider**
Green body, Khaki rider, White or Black rubber wheels.
Sold unboxed...**£150-175**
Boxed version: It is believed that only 1,000 were
sold boxed. Blue box/lid with insert, 'A2237' ....NGPP

42b 1935-40 **Police Motorcycle Patrol**
Black motor cycle, Silver engine/exhaust detail,
Dark Green/Black sidecar, Dark Blue figures,
SWRW or thick SBRW **£75-95**
1946-49 As previous model but without Silver detailing
and with thin SBRW **£45-55**
1950-55 Blue/Green, Blue figures, little detailing,
SBRW, export only (renumbered 043)............................**£40-50**

43b 1935-40 **'R.A.C.' Motorcycle Patrol**
Blue/Black motor cycle/sidecar, Silver engine/exhaust
detail, Blue/Black rider with Red sash,
SWRW or thick SBRW **£75-95**
1946-49 As previous model but no Silver detailing,
thin SBRW. **NB** - two shades of Blue used post-war **£45-55**

44b 1935-40 **'A.A.' Motorcycle Patrol**
Black/Yellow, Brown rider, more detailing,
5mm 'AA' badge, SWRW...**£100-125**
1946-50 Black/Yellow, Tan rider, little detailing,
7mm 'AA' badge, SBRW (renumbered 270) **£50-60**
1950-55 As previous model but export only (renumbered 045)....**£50-60**

270 1959-62 **'A.A.' Motorcycle Patrol**   (renumbered from 44b)
Black/Yellow, Tan rider, 'AA' sign, SGPW **£40-50**
Black/Yellow, Tan rider, 'AA' sign,
solid knobbly Black plastic wheels..............................**£100-150**

271 1959-62 **'T.S.' Motorcycle Patrol**
Yellow motorcycle combination,
Belgian equivalent of the A.A.....................................**£150-200**

272 1959-62 **'A.N.W.B.' Motorcycle Patrol**
Yellow motorcycle combination,
Dutch equivalent of the A.A **£250-300**

Photo: Vectis Auctions Ltd.

See also Action Kits, Aircraft, Ships, Gift Sets and Factory Samples sections.

Since the publication of the 10th Edition, much new information on Dinky Toys military has been gathered. We are indebted to Kevin Barwick for providing the bulk of the updating material for both the English and French Military Vehicles sections.

Colour finish of Dinky Toys Military models.
Military colours tend to be described by collectors, dealers and observers variously as 'Olive Drab' or 'Military Green' or 'Khaki' or 'Matt Green'. This is a less than satisfactory method of describing the colour finish of these models, especially when there are also shades of colour and depth of gloss (or lack of it). We are of the opinion that they fundamentally relate to the same finish anyway, so for the sake of simplicity, this listing contains colour information ONLY where it is clearly specific (sand, camouflage or German

grey, for example). Assume that all the models in this listing are finished in one form or another of this 'Military Green' unless specifically stated otherwise. For all other descriptions of single colour finishes, the following **general** comments may be applied:
Pre-war issues have variations in shade, depth (green/brown), gloss and matt.
1950's Military Vehicles finish is generally regarded as Khaki.
Mike and Sue Richardson prefer to regard pre-war military finish to be Matt Green and post-war to be Olive Drab.
US issues are generally considered to be Olive Drab (a term that seems to have originated in a 1950's US Army recruitment poster).
Late Lines Bros issues are in various green shades, often quite light green.
French issues are more Olive Drab than British Khaki but all generally appear consistent in their groups.

Ref	Year(s)	Model name and details	Market Price Range
1	1954-55	**Military Vehicles (1) Set** See 'Gift Sets' section.	
22f	1933-34	**Army Tank**	
		'Modelled Miniature' with 'HORNBY SERIES' cast-in. Green lead body, Orange revolving turret, Red, White or Green rubber tracks	**£250-350**
	1934-39	Green/Orange lead body, 'DINKY TOYS' cast-in, Red or Green tracks	**£250-300**
		Khaki lead body, 'DINKY TOYS' cast-in, Red or Green tracks	**£250-300**
		Grey lead body, 'DINKY TOYS' cast-in, Red or Green tracks	**£100-150**
22s	1939-41	**Searchlight Lorry**	
		Green body, (22c casting, open cab rear window), smooth hubs. Not boxed	**£100-150**
		Same, but in yellow lidded box 'A2309'	NGPP
25b	1948-50	**Army Covered Wagon**	
		Military-Green body and hubs.	
		South-African issue	**£750-1,000**
25wm	1952-54	**Bedford Military Truck** (renumbered to 640)	
		Made for export to the USA only	**£200-250**
27m	1952-54	**Land Rover Trailer** (renumbered to 341)	
		Made to accompany 669, unpainted hook and drawbar clip	**£300-400**
28	19??-??	**Army Delivery Van**	
		Military-Green body and hubs, Type 3.	
		South-African issue	**£750-1,000**
30hm	1952-54	**Daimler Military Ambulance** (renumbered to 624)	
		Red crosses on White backgrounds, (US issue)	**£200-250**
30sm	1952-54	**Austin Covered Wagon** (renumbered to 625)	
		Made for export to USA only	**£200-250**
37c	1937-41	**Royal Signals Dispatch Rider**	
		Green body, Khaki rider, White or Black rubber wheels. Sold unboxed	**£150-175**
		Boxed version: It is believed that only 1,000 were sold individually boxed. Blue lidded box with insert and number 'A2237'	NGPP
139am	1952-54	**US Army Staff Car** (renumbered to 170m)	
		Ford Fordor with White stars on roof and doors	**£175-250**
		Canadian issue: As previous model but without stars	NGPP
150	1937-41	**Royal Tank Corps Set** See Gift Sets section.	
	1952-55	**Royal Tank Corps Set** See Gift Sets section.	
150a	1937-41	**Royal Tank Corps Officer**	
		Khaki, Black beret, binoculars in hand	**£25-30**
	1952-54	Khaki figure. In box of 12	**£100-120**
	1954	Renumbered 600	
150b	1938-41	**Royal Tank Corps Private**	
		Black overalls, seated	**£25-30**
	1952-54	Khaki, seated. In box of 12	**£100-120**
	1954	Renumbered 604	
150c	1937-41	**Royal Tank Corps Private**	
		Diecast figure in Black overalls, standing	**£25-30**

Ref	Year(s)	Model name and details	Market Price Range
150d	1937-41	**Royal Tank Corps Driver**	
		Die-cast figure in Black overalls, sitting	**£25-30**
150e	1937-41	**Royal Tank Corps NCO**	
		Die-cast figure in Black uniform, walking	**£10-15**
151	1937-41	**Medium Tank Set** See Gift Sets section.	
151a	1937-41	**Medium Tank**	
		White markings, bright chain tracks, aerial, round jockey wheels locating tracks	**£125-150**
		Version with 'flatted' jockey wheels	**£125-150**
		Version with 'spray hole' cast in	**£125-150**
		Version with Black rubber wheels instead of tracks	NGPP
	1947-49	USA export version, no markings, Bright tracks	**£150-200**
		USA export version, no markings, Black tracks	**£150-200**
151b	1937-41	**6-wheel Covered Wagon**	
		Lead body, tinplate canopy, seat holes	**£150-200**
	1937-41	Diecast body, tinplate canopy, seat holes	**£150-200**
	1946	With smooth hubs and early tyres	**£150-200**
	1947-54	With ridged hubs, no seat holes	**£150-200**
	1950-54	USA export model with fixed driver, no other seat holes. (Renumbered 620)	**£200-250**
151c	1937-48	**Cooker Trailer**	
		Wire stand, hole in seat but no figure	**£50-70**
		NB Two styles of baseplate lettering are known for 151c.	
151d	1937-48	**Water Tank Trailer**	
		Gloss Green, sold unboxed	**£50-70**
152	1937-41	**Light Tank Set** See Gift Sets section.	
152a	1937-41	**Light Tank**	
		White markings, chain tracks, aerial	**£100-150**
		With Black rubber wheels instead of tracks	**£125-175**
	1947-50	Without markings, chain tracks, aerial	**£150-200**
	1950-54	US export model, no markings, bright or black tracks, (renumbered to 650)	**£150-200**
		Mid (Chocolate) Brown variation	NGPP
152b	1937-41	**Reconnaissance Car**	
		Six wheels (smooth hubs). Earliest versions had additional front axle support from baseplate	**£150-200**
		Later pre-war versions with normal base	**£100-150**
	1946	With smooth hubs, early tyres	**£150-200**
	1947-49	With ridged hubs	**£125-175**
	1950-54	USA export model (renumbered to 671)	**£125-175**
152c	1937-41	**Austin Seven**	
		Wire windscreen frame, hole in seat, no baseplate	**£100-150**
	1940-41	Same, but cast in lead, hole in seat, no baseplate	**£100-150**
153a	1946-47	**Jeep**	
		US White star on flat bonnet and left rear side, smooth hubs, solid steering wheel, no round hole in base	**£150-200**
	1947	As previous but open spoked steering wheel	**£60-75**
		With Brown body, open spoked steering wheel	**£150-200**
	1948-52	With raised 'domed' bonnet, round hole in base	**£60-75**
	1952-54	US export model, some have rounded axle ends, (renumbered to 672)	**£150-200**

| 160 | 1939-41 | **Royal Artillery Personnel Set** See Gift Sets section. |

160a 1939-41 **Royal Artillery NCO**
Khaki uniform; part of 160 Set **£20-30**

160b 1939-54 **Royal Artillery Gunner**
Khaki, seated, hands on knees; part of 160 Set **£20-30**
1952-55 US export issue: Same, but in green box of 12,
(renumbered to 608) **£150-200**

160c 1939-41 **Royal Artillery Gunlayer**
Khaki, seated, hands held out; part of 160 Set **£20-30**
1952-55 US export issue: Same, but in green box of 12 ....**£150-200**

160d 1939-41 **Royal Artillery Gunner**
Khaki uniform, standing; part of 160 Set **£20-30**
1952-55 US export issue: Same, but in green box of 12 ....**£150-200**

161 1939-41 **Mobile Anti-Aircraft Set** See Gift Sets section.
161a 1939-41 **Searchlight on Lorry**
151b casting plus diecast or lead searchlight...........**£200-250**

161b 1939-41 **Anti-Aircraft Gun on Trailer**
Gloss Green, gun elevates, figure holes,
cast drawbar and hook..**£200-250**
1946-50 Matt Green or Dark Brown **£80-100**
1950-54 US export issue (renumbered to 690) **£125-175**

162 1939-54 **18-pounder Field Gun Set** See Gift Sets section.

162a 1939-41 **Light Dragon Tractor**
Gloss Green, holes in seats, chain tracks **£100-125**
With Black rubber wheels instead of tracks **£250-350**
1946-55 Matt Green, holes in some, chain tracks.................**£100-150**

162b 1939-41 **Ammunition Trailer**
Gloss Green body/baseplate/drawbar/hook..................**£20-25**
1946-55 Matt Green body, Black baseplate **£20-25**
1948-55 US export issue: Matt Green body, Black baseplate.....**£20-25**

162c 1939-41 **18 pounder Gun**
Gloss Green, drawbar cast-in, tinplate shield **£20-25**
1946-55 Matt Green body and shield **£20-25**

170m 1954-54 **Ford US Army Staff Car** (renumbered from 139am)
Ford Fordor Sedan in Matt Olive,
US export issue (renumbered to 675) **£200-250**

281 1973-76 **Military Hovercraft**
Olive-Drab body, Gunner, aerial, 'ARMY' **£25-35**

341 1960 **Land Rover Trailer** (renumbered from 27m)
Olive-Drab body with drawbar and hook **£300-400**

600 1952-55 **Royal Tank Corps Officer**
US only re-issue (renumbered from 150) **£8-12**

601 1966-76 **Austin Paramoke**
Khaki, Grey top, spun hubs, parachute,
in flap-end box, instructions.......................................**£50-60**
1976-78 Dark Grey, Grey top, Speedwheels, parachute,
in bubble-pack with card base, instructions.................**£40-50**

602 1976-77 **Armoured Command Car** See 'Novelty', section.

603 1957-68 **Army Private (seated)**
Diecast, Khaki, Black beret, seated, box of 12............**£40-50**
1968-71 Plastic, Khaki, Black beret, seated, box of 12 ....**£40-50**
603a 1957-68 **Army Personnel Set**
6 cast figures (Khaki, Black berets, seated)..................**£20-30**
1968-71 6 plastic figures (Khaki, Black berets, seated)............**£20-30**

604 1954-60 **Royal Tank Corps Private**
Diecast, Khaki uniform, sitting, export only
(to USA), box of 12 (renumbered from 150b).............**£50-70**
604 1960-72 **Army Personnel**
Six army driver figures (Khaki uniforms) **£20-30**

604 1976-77 **Land Rover Bomb Disposal**
Olive-Drab/Orange, 'Explosive Disposal', Speedwheels,
robot de-fuser kit on sprue. In 'hanging' box **£55-65**

608 1954-55 **Royal Artillery Gunner**
Khaki uniform, seated, hands on knees.
US export issue (renumbered from 160b)....................**£10-15**

609 1974-77 **105 mm. Howitzer and Crew**
Olive-Drab body, three soldiers, Green metal
wheels or Grey plastic wheels, bubble-packed............**£30-40**

612 1973-80 **Commando Jeep**
Driver (green helmet), solid axles, plastic gearstick,
two guns, jerricans, aerial. In 'hanging' box...............**£25-35**
Driver (brown helmet), split axles, metal gearstick.
In bubble-pack with card base **£25-35**

615 1968-77 **US Jeep and 105 mm. Howitzer**
Based on 612, US Army markings, driver (brown
helmet), display box with pull-out tray.......................**£65-85**

616 1968-77 **AEC with Chieftain Tank**
AEC articulated Transporter 'ARMY' with 683
Tank. Instructions printed on pictorial box **£90-110**

617 1967-77 **VW KDF and 50 mm. Gun**
Grey, German markings, Green metal or Grey
plastic wheels, long display box or bubble-pack.........**£75-85**

618 1976-80 **AEC with Helicopter**
AEC articulated Transporter 'RESCUE',
724 Helicopter and net. Flap-end box........................**£90-110**

619 1976-77 **Bren Gun Carrier and Anti-Tank Gun**
Khaki, plastic tracks, 2 figures, gun, 2 sprues each
with 6 shells, White '57' on red shield. Bubble-pack...**£35-40**
NB Two variations exist:
(i) '2035703 4', (ii) 'T2272616' plus star.

620 1954-55 **6-wheel Covered Wagon** (renumbered from 151b)
US export model, blued axles **£200-250**

620 1971-73 **Berliet Missile Launcher**
UK issue of French 816. 'NORD R20' missile.
Yellow flap-end box **£120-150**

621 1954-60 **3 ton Army Wagon**
(Bedford 'RL') tin tilt, no windows, driver in some.
In yellow flap-end box **£60-70**
1960-63 Same but with window glazing..................................**£60-70**

622 1954-64 **10 ton Army Truck**
(Foden) driver, tin tilt, Supertoys box.........................**£70-80**
1954-64 Same, but in Dinky Toys striped box...........................**£70-80**
Late issue: Same, but in yellow lidded picture box..**£200-300**

622 1975-78 **Bren Gun Carrier**
White star, driver, passenger, plastic tracks.
Bubble-pack also contains decal sheet.........................**£25-35**

623 1954-63 **Army Covered Wagon**
(Bedford 'QL') driver in some,
no window glazing, flap-end box.................................**£35-45**

624 1954-? **Daimler Military Ambulance** (renumbered from 30hm)
Red crosses, White backgrounds, US export issue...**£400-500**

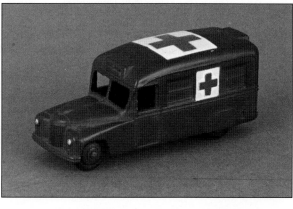

624 US issue Daimler Military Ambulance

Note: Prices shown in the 'Market Price Range' column are applicable ONLY to models in the finest condition in pristine boxes (complete with any additional contents or packing) where appropriate.

625 1952-54 **Austin Covered Wagon** (renumbered from 30sm)
US export issue **£400-500**

625 1975-77 **Six-pounder Gun**
Anti-tank gun, 2 plastic sprues each with 6 shells,
bubble-pack with flat card base **£15-20**

626 1956-61 **Military Ambulance**
(Fordson) Red crosses cast-in, no windows,
deep yellow non-picture end-flap box **£60-75**
1961-62 With window glazing, pictorial end-flap box **£80-100**
1962-62 In non-pictorial end-flap export box with red side ..**£100-125**

630 1973-78 **Ferret Armoured Car**
Plastic wheels, spare wheel...........................**£15-20**

640 1954-? **Bedford Military Truck**
US export issue, (renumbered from 25wm).............**£250-350**

641 1954-61 **Army 1 ton Cargo Truck**
Tin tilt, driver in some, no windows, flap-end box **£35-40**
1961-62 Same, but with window glazing.................................**£40-50**

642 1957-62 **R.A.F. Pressure Refueller**
RAF Blue, French roundel, with or without
driver, blue/white striped Supertoys box **£100-130**
1957-62 Same, but in Dinky Toys box **£110-140**

643 1958-61 **Army Water Tanker**
No window glazing, driver in some, yellow box..........**£30-35**
1961-64 With window glazing, yellow box with red side **£30-35**

650 1954-55 **Light Tank** (renumbered from 152a)
US export issue. Black base, no markings...............**£100-125**

651 1954-70 **Centurion Tank**
Matt or Gloss Olive-Drab body, metal rollers,
rubber tracks, Supertoys Blue/White box, PP..............**£80-90**
US export issue: In U.S. Gold 'see through' box **£150-175**
US export issue: In Yellow/Blue Dinky Toys lidded
box with PP and 'H.Hudson Dobson' sticker **£150-175**
In Blue/White Dinky Toys lidded box, PP.................**£90-120**
Late issue: plastic rollers, screws (not rivets), in
Yellow/Blue lidded box or Yellow end-flap
picture box, PP **£130-160**

654 1973-79 **155 mm. Mobile Gun**
Operable gun, 4 plastic shells, bubble-packed............**£15-20**

656 1975-79 **88 mm. Gun**
German Grey, 6 plastic shells. Bubble-packed **£15-20**

660 1956-61 **Tank Transporter** (Thornycroft Mighty Antar)
Matt Olive-Green, no windows, driver in some **£70-80**
Early issue: 'DINKY TOYS' marked on base.
In Yellow box overprinted 'Dinky Supertoys' **£100-150**
1961-64 Late issue: With window glazing,
Yellow box with 2 packing pieces **£100-125**
1961-64 US export issue: In Yellow/Blue lidded box with
2 packing pieces and 'H.Hudson Dobson' sticker **£150-200**
1964-66 Late issue with 908 detachable trailer (with
transformer locating tabs on upper deck) **£150-200**

660a 1978-80 **Anti-Aircraft Gun with Crew**
Olive-Drab, 3 soldiers. Bubble-packed........................**£15-20**

661 1957-65 **Recovery Tractor**
Six wheels, driver, operable crane, with windows
from 1960, Blue/White Supertoys box, 1 PP.............**£80-100**
With plastic wheels, in Yellow 'picture' box **£150-200**

662 1975-77 **88 mm. Gun with Crew**
German Grey (656 without wheels), 3 crew,
bubble-packed...**£15-20**

665 1964-75 **Honest John Missile Launcher**
Green platform, White missile.
Yellow Dinky Toys end-flap box **£70-90**
Black platform, White missile.
Yellow Dinky Toys end-flap box **£140-160**
Green platform, Grey missile.
Yellow scenic Supertoys lidded box **£90-120**
Green platform, White missile. Bubble-packed...........**£70-90**

666 1959-64 **Missile Erector Vehicle and Corporal Missile Launcher**
Metal erector gears, White missile with Black fins,
Blue/White Supertoys box with 1 packing piece......**£200-250**
Black plastic erector gears, all-White missile,
Blue/White Supertoys box with 1 packing piece......**£175-200**

667 1960-64 **Missile Servicing Platform**
Windows, Blue/White Supertoys box, 1 PP **£175-200**

667 1976-78 **Armoured Patrol Car**
680 body with 676 turret, in 'hanging' box **£15-20**

668 1976-79 **Foden Army Truck**
Windows, plastic tilt and wheels, in 'hanging' box **£25-35**

669 1955-57 **U.S.A. Army Jeep**
White star, (US issue in 'plain' box)........................**£200-300**

670 1954-64 **Armoured Car**
Olive-Drab body, diecast hubs, yellow flap-end box....**£20-25**
1964-70 Olive-Drab body, plastic hubs, yellow flap-end box **£20-25**
Late issue in red-sided yellow flap-end box **£25-35**

671 1954-55 **Reconnaissance Car** (renumbered from 152b)
(Matt) Green body, made for export only **£125-175**

667 Missile Servicing Platform

674 'UN' Austin Champ

669 US issue
Army Jeep (unboxed)

672	1954-55	**US Army Jeep** (<u>renumbered from 153a</u>) US export issue. Some have rounded axle-ends.......**£150-200**	
673	1953-61	**Scout Car** (Daimler) Driver fixed in position, passenger seat hole in some ..**£20-30**	
674	1954-66	**Austin Champ** Cast driver fixed in position, cast steering wheel, seat holes for personnel, deep yellow end-flap box......**£35-45** No driver, plastic steering wheel, yellow end-flap box...**£35-45**	
	1966-71	Plastic driver, plastic steering wheel, plastic hubs, yellow end-flap box...**£35-45**	
674	1958-70	**'U.N.' Austin Champ** White body, no holes for personnel, yellow end-flap box. Made for export only **£300-400**	
675	1954-59	**Ford US Army Staff Car** (<u>renumbered from 170m</u>) Matt Olive body with cross-hatching cast inside roof, sheer-cut star transfers on doors, White circled star on roof. US issue in 'plain' printed box. **£200-250**	
676	1955-62	**Armoured Personnel Carrier** 6 wheels, revolving turret, yellow end-flap box ....**£25-30** Late issue in red-sided yellow end-flap box **£30-35**	
676a	1973-76	**Daimler Armoured Car** Speedwheels, (new version of 670) **£15-20**	
	1973-74	French made version: With camouflage net, ('Made in England' on base)..NGPP	
677	1957-62	**Armoured Command Vehicle** 6 wheels, yellow end-flap box **£60-70**	
680	1972-78	**Ferret Armoured Car** Sand or Khaki, Speedwheels, bubble-packed **£10-15**	
681	1972-78	**DUKW Amphibious Vehicle** RAF Blue or Army-Green body, Speedwheels, bubble-packed **£10-15**	
682	1972-78	**Stalwart Load Carrier** 6 Speedwheels, bubble-packed **£10-15**	
683	1972-80	**Chieftain Tank** Black plastic tracks, fires shells. End-flap 'window' box with polystyrene inner or bubble-packed..............**£25-35**	
686	1957-71	**25-pounder Field Gun** Cast drawbar, (cast hubs, plastic from 1968)...............**£10-15**	
687	1957-67	**25-pounder Trailer** Cast hubs, plastic from 1968. Not individually boxed .**£10-15**	
687	1978-79	**Convoy Army Truck** Khaki tilt 'ARMY'. In 'hanging' box **£10-15**	
688	1957-61	**Field Artillery Tractor** Driver in some, no windows, cast hubs, end-flap box..**£30-40**	
	1961-70	Driver in some, windows, (plastic hubs from 1968) **£30-40**	

689	1957-65	**Medium Artillery Tractor** Driver in some, holes, 6 wheels, tin tilt, in Blue/White Supertoys box with lift-off lid............**£80-100** In Yellow picture box, plastic driver, windows **£150-200**	
690	1954-55	**Anti-Aircraft Gun on Trailer** (<u>renumbered from 161b</u>) Matt Green, made for export only **£80-100**	
690	1974-80	**Scorpion Tank** Brown or Green camouflage net. Decal sheet, spare shells. End-flap 'hanging' box or bubble-packed **£15-20**	
691	1974-80	**Striker Anti-Tank** Plastic tracks, 6 spare missiles. Bubble-packed...........**£15-20**	
692	1955-62	**5.5 Medium Gun** Twin cast drawbar, elevating barrel. In yellow end-flap box or later red-sided yellow end-flap box **£15-20**	
692	1974-80	**Leopard Tank** Grey with German markings, plastic tracks, 6 shells on sprue, decal sheet, bubble-packed **£40-50**	
693	1958-67	**7.2 inch Howitzer Gun** Cast drawbar, yellow end-flap box, packing piece **£30-40**	
694	1975-80	**Hanomag Tank Destroyer** Grey, German markings, plastic tracks/wheels, bubble-packed **£40-50**	
696	1975-80	**Leopard Anti-Aircraft Tank** Grey-Green, German markings, plastic tracks, 2 plastic sprues each with 6 shells, bubble-packed.......**£40-50**	
697	1957-71	**25 pounder Field Gun Set** See Gift Sets section.	
698	1957-64	**Tank Transporter Set** See Gift Sets section.	
699	1955-58	**Military Vehicles (1) Set** See Gift Sets section.	
699	1975-77	**Leopard Recovery Tank** Grey-Green, German markings, dozer blade/jib, aerial, tow-rope, bubble-packed...................................**£40-50**	
815	1962-64	**Panhard Armoured Tank** Military-Green with French flag, (French issue)........**£75-100**	
816	1969-71	**Berliet Missile Launcher** Military-Green body, (French issue).........................**£150-200**	
817	1962-64	**AMX 13-ton Tank** Green body with French flag, (French issue) **£75-100**	
822	1962-64	**Half-Track M3** Green body, rubber tracks, (French issue) **£75-100**	
884	1962-64	**Brockway Bridge Truck** Military-Green, 10 wheels, bridge parts, inflatables. French issue **£200-250**	

675 US issue
Army Staff Car

Pre-war 161 Mobile Anti-Aircraft Unit
plus 603 12 Army Personnel (seated)

651 Centurion Tank and
689 Medium Artillery Tractor

See also Gift Sets section.

Ref	Year(s)	Model name	Colours, features, details	Market Price Range

60a 1934-36 **Imperial Airways Liner**............. Cast body, tinplate wings, 4 x 2-blade propellers. Various colours, in three different patterns:
(Armstrong-Whitworth Atalanta) 1: 'Sunray' main colour with contrasting radial stripes on wings: Silver/Blue, Gold/Blue, Yellow/Blue, Blue/Yellow, Red/Cream, Cream/Red, Cream/Green, White/Blue, White/Blue/Green.
2: 'Two-tone' main colour with contrasting tail and wingtips: Gold/Blue, Yellow/Blue, Cream/Green, Gold/Blue, Yellow/Blue, Cream/Green, Cream/Red.
3: 'Striped' main colour with contrasting chordwise stripes and tail: Cream/Green, White/Blue.
Other variations on these themes may exist, all without registration marks.................................**£500-600**

1936-39 .... Blue, Pale Blue, Cream, Gold, Red, Silver or White; all with Black 'G-ABTI' marking **£500-600**

1939-41 .... Gold, Green or Silver, 'G-ABTI', 'Imperial Airways Liner' under wing, (reissued as 66a).....................**£500-600**

60b 1934-36 **De Havilland 'Leopard Moth'**... Cast fuselage, tinplate wings, single 2-blade propeller.
Green with Yellow tail and wingtips or Dark Blue/Orange, Silver/Green, Blue/Yellow, Blue/Red, Gold/Red, no markings, open windows **£500-600**

1936-39 .... All-over Light Green, Dark Green, Gold, Silver, Beige, Blue, Pale Blue or Red, 'G-ACPT', open windows **£300-500**

1939-39 .... As previous model, but with 'DH Leopard Moth' under wing. Green, Gold or Silver, 'G-ACPT' **£200-300**

1939-41 .... As previous model, but blank side windows. Green, Gold or Silver, 'G-ACPT', (reissued as 66b)......**£200-300**

60c 1934-36 **Percival 'Gull' Monoplane**........ Cast fuselage, tinplate wings, large 2-blade propeller. Reissued as 60k.
Blue with Red tail and wingtips, Red/Blue, Buff/White, Buff/Blue, Buff/Red, Gold/Green, Red/White, Silver/Green, White/Green, White/Blue, open windows, no registration markings **£100-150**

1936-39 .... White, Red, Yellow, Light Blue, Blue, Silver, Buff, 'G-ADZO' in Black, open windows, (Silver version renumbered as 60k) **£100-150**

1939-39 .... As 1936-39 version above, but with underwing stamped 'PERCIVAL GULL'. White, Red, Yellow, Blue, 'G-ADZO' in Black...**£200-300**

1939-41 .... Same but blank or open side windows, 'Percival Gull' under wing, (reissued as 66c) **£200-300**

60c 1936-36 **'Lewis's' 'Amy Mollinson'**
Souvenir Issue .... Mid-Blue with Silver wings and a Blue 'G-ADZO' marking. Sold at Lewis's of Liverpool department store in special 'LEWIS' yellow box. (Renumbered 60k when sold in normal yellow box) **£400-500**

60d 1934-36 **Low Wing Monoplane**.............. Cast body, tinplate wings, 2-blade propeller. Red with Cream tail and wingtips, Orange/Cream, (Vickers Jockey) Blue/Yellow, Silver/Red or Gold/Blue, no markings, no pilot **£100-150**

1936-41 .... Red, Orange, Blue, Gold, Silver, Black or Yellow, 'G-AVYP', pilot's head cast-in, (reissued as 66d) **£100-150**

Red with cream tail and wingtips, no pilot, with 'G-AVYP' marking ....NGPP

As previous but with pilot ....NGPP

60e 1934-36 **General 'Monospar'**.................. Two-piece diecasting, 2 x 2-blade propellers.
Pale Blue with White tail and wingtips, Cream/Red, Gold/Red, Red/Cream, Salmon/Blue or Silver/Blue, no markings **£100-150**

1936-41 .... Silver, Lilac or Gold, 'G-ABVP' in Black, (reissued as 66e)..**£100-150**

Same but with 'General Monospar', Cream, Gold, Lilac, Silver or Blue **£100-150**

60f 1934-36 **Cierva 'Autogiro'**...................... Gold body with Blue rotors and trim, no pilot **£200-300**

1936-41 .... Gold body with Blue trim, unpainted rotors, pilot cast-in, (reissued as 66f) **£150-200**

1936-41 .... Red body with Cream trim, Cream or Silver rotors, pilot cast-in **£150-200**

60g 1935-36 **De Havilland 'Comet'** .... Cast fuselage and wings, enclosed wheels, 2 x 2-blade propellers.
Silver, Red or Gold with Black registration 'G-ACSR' (no underwing description)......................**£100-125**

1936-41 .... Silver, Red or Gold with Black registration 'G-ACSR' ('DH COMET' underwing) **£100-125**

60g 1945-49 **Light Racer (DH 'Comet')**.......... Yellow, Red or Silver, 'G-RACE', 'Light Racer' under wing, 2 x 3-blade propellers.....................**£175-225**

60h 1936-36 **'Singapore' Flying Boat** .... Cast fuselage (126 mm.), tinplate wings, 4 x 2-blade propellers (early hulls lead).
Fully-moulded bow, no roller, Silver with painted RAF roundels......................................**£250-350**

1936-37 .... As previous model but with Red or Green plastic roller...**£250-350**

1937-39 .... As previous model (with Red or Green plastic roller) and with 'Gliding Game' hole **£250-350**

1939-40 .... With Red or Green plastic roller, 'Gliding Game' hole and waterslide transfer RAF roundels **£250-350**

1940-40 .... Hollowed bow, wooden roller, no 'Gliding Game' hole, painted or transfer roundels **£250-350**

1940-41 .... As previous model, but in Pale Grey with transfer roundels..**£250-350**

1941 ? .... As previous model but with name under wing **£250-350**

60k 1936-41 **Percival 'Gull' (Amy Mollison)** . Blue/Silver version of 60c, 'G-ADZO' in Blue, special box..**£300-400**

60k 1936-41 **Percival 'Gull' (H. L. Brook)**..... Blue/Silver version of 60c, 'G-ADZO' in Black, special box..**£300-400**

60k 1945-48 **Light Tourer (Percival 'Gull')** ... Red, Silver or Dark or Light Green, 'Light Tourer' or 'Percival Tourer' under wing, no markings, small or large 2-blade propeller, (renumbered from 60c) **£150-200**

60m 1936-41 **Four Engined Flying Boat** .... Red, Pale Blue, Light Blue, Mid Blue, Dark Blue, Light Green, Mid-Green, Dark Green, Gold, Cream or Silver. 'Civilian' version of 60h with 'G-EUTC', 'G-EUTG', 'G-EVCU', 'G-EXCF', 'G-EXGF', 'G-EXFE', 'G-EYCE' or 'G-EYTV' **£175-225**
NB With or without bow hollow, wood or plastic roller or gliding hole.

60n 1937-40 **Fairey 'Battle' Bomber**.............. Silver or Grey, RAF roundels, 1 x 3-blade propeller, undercarriage....................................**£90-120**

1938-41 .... Silver or Grey, RAF roundels, 1 x 3-blade propeller, without undercarriage, (reissued as 60s) **£120-150**
NB Early issues did not have name of plane cast in.

60p 1936-39 **Gloster 'Gladiator'** .... Silver, stencilled roundels, Red 1 x 2-blade propeller, no name under wing **£100-140**

1939-41 .... Silver or Grey, transfer roundels, 'Gloster Gladiator' under wing **£100-140**

60r 1937-40 **Empire Flying Boat** .... Silver, 4 x 3-blade propellers, Red plastic roller, hole, own box. Liveries:
'CALEDONIA' ('G-ADHM'), 'CANOPUS' ('G-ADHL'), 'CORSAIR' ('G-ADVB'),
'CHALLENGER' ('G-ADVD'), 'CLIO' ('G-AETY'), 'CALYPSO' ('G-AEUA'),
'CENTURION' ('G-ADVE'), 'CAPELLA' ('G-ADUY'), 'CERES' ('G-AETX'),
'CALPURNIA' ('G-AETW'), 'CAMILLA' ('G-AEUB'), 'CORINNA' ('G-AEUC'),
'CAMBRIA' ('G-ADUV'), 'CHEVIOT' ('G-AEUG'), 'CORDELIA' ('G-AEUD')..............**£250-350**

1940-49 .... As previous models but plastic, wood or brass roller, no hole.
'CALEDONIA', ('G-ADHM'), or 'CAMBRIA', ('G-ADUV'), (reissued as 60x)................**£200-250**
NB Camouflage issues: Early issues have Red/White/Blue roundels with a Yellow outer ring. The later (rarer) issues have a darker camouflage with just Blue/Red roundels.

60s	1938-40	**Medium Bomber**	Camouflaged 60n with undercarriage, single roundel has Yellow ring, (reissue of 60n)	**£100-150**
60s	1940-41	**Fairy 'Battle' Bomber**	Camouflaged body, two Blue/Red roundels, no undercarriage, 1 x 3 PB	**£150-200**
	NB		Early issues did not have name of plane cast in.	
60t	1938-41	**Douglas DC3 Air Liner**	Silver, 'PH-ALI' 2 x 3-blade propellers, 'Gliding Game' hole, tail wheel on some, own box	**£200-300**
60v	1937-41	**Armstrong Whitworth Bomber.**	Silver body, 'Gliding Game' hole in some, RAF roundels, 2 x 3-blade propellers, (reissued as 62t)	**£200-300**
60w	1938-40	**Flying Boat 'Clipper III'**	Silver body, 'USA NC16736', 4 x 3-blade propellers, plastic roller, 'Gliding Game' hole	**£150-200**
		(Sikorsky S32) US issue:	Silver body, 'NC 16736' markings, 'gliding' hole, Red plastic roller, leaflet	**£250-350**
60w	1945-48	**Flying Boat**	Silver, Blue or Green, no markings, 4 x 3 PB, brass roller	**£150-200**
60x	1937-41	**Atlantic Flying Boat**	Blue/Cream, 'DAUNTLESS' ('G-AZBP'), 4 x 3 PB, name under wing	**£500-750**
		(reissue of 60r)	Green/Cream, 'WHIRLWIND' ('G-AZBT')	**£500-750**
			Black/White, 'DREADNOUGHT' ('G-AZBV')	**£500-750**
			Orange/Cream 'SWIFTSURE' ('G-AZBU') and Blue/Cream 'ENTERPRISE' ('G-AZBR') and	
			Black/Cream 'ENDEAVOUR' ('G-AZBQ'), Red/Cream 'VALORIUS' ('G-AZBS')	**£500-750**
62a	1939-41	**Vickers-Supermarine 'Spitfire'.**	Silver body (short nose), RAF roundels, 1 x 3-blade propeller	**£100-130**
	1940-41	**'Meccano Spitfire Fund'**	Model 62a in special souvenir box (at 2/6 each). Brass ring through fin allows use as badge or pendant. Proceeds went to Spitfire Fund.	
			Blue, Green, Grey, Magenta, Red, Yellow, or Camouflage	**£500-750**
			Chromium plated version (originally 10/6)	**£1,000-1,200**
62a	1945-49	**'Spitfire'**	Silver, (long nose, bubble cockpit) RAF roundels, 1 x 3-blade propeller	**£35-45**
62b	1939-41	**Bristol 'Blenheim' Bomber**	Silver body, RAF roundels, Red 2 x 3-blade propellers, name under wing	**£100-150**
62b	1945-49	**Medium Bomber**	Silver body, RAF roundels, Red 2 x 3-blade propellers, name under wing	**£60-80**
62d	1940-41	**Bristol 'Blenheim' Bomber**	62b in Camouflage/Black/White, RAF roundels, 2 x 3-blade propellers	**£100-150**
62e	1940-41	**Vickers-Supermarine 'Spitfire'.**	62a in Camouflage/Black/White, RAF roundels, 1 x 3-blade propeller	**£100-150**
62f	1939 ?	**D.H. Flamingo Airliner**	Not issued (some unofficial non-Meccano 'Flamingos' cast in white-metal may be found)	NPP
62g	1939-41	**Boeing 'Flying Fortress'**	Silver, 4 x 3-blade propellers, 'Gliding Game' hole, name under wing, 'U.S.A.A.C.'/stars, own box	**£200-300**
			Pale Grey version without 'Gliding Game' hole	NGPP
62g	1945-48	**Long Range Bomber**	Silver body, Red 4 x 3-blade propellers, no 'Gliding Game' hole, not boxed	**£90-120**
62h	1938-41	**Hawker Hurricane Fighter**	Camouflaged body, RAF roundels, 1 x 2-blade propeller, undercarriage on some	**£100-130**
62k	1938-41	**The King's Aeroplane**	Airspeed 'Envoy', Silver/Red/Blue, 'G-AEXX', 2 x 2-blade propellers, own box	**£300-400**
62m	1938-41	**Airspeed 'Envoy' Monoplane**	Red ('G-ABDA' or 'G-ACVJ'), Silver ('G-ACVI' or 'G-ADCB'), Blue ('G-ADAZ' or 'G-ADCA'),	
			Pale Green ('GADCA' or 'G-AENA'), Mid-Green ('G-AENA'), Gold ('G-AMTC'),	
			Yellow ('G-ACMJ', 'G-ACMT' or 'G-ACVJ')	**£300-400**
62m	1945-48	**Light Transport Plane**	Red, Yellow, Silver or Blue, 'G-ATMH', 2 x 2-blade propellers, name under wing	**£100-125**
62n	1938-41	**Junkers 'Ju90' Air Liner**	Silver, ('D-AALU', 'D-AIVI', 'D-AURE', or 'D-ADLH'), 4 x 3-blade propellers, own box	**£250-350**
62p	1938-41	**'Ensign' Air Liner**	Silver, Red 4 x 3-blade propellers, gliding hole in some, own box. Liveries:	
			'ENSIGN' ('G-ADSR'), 'ELSINORE' ('G-ADST'), 'EXPLORER' ('G-ADSV'),	
			'ECHO' ('G-ADTB'), 'ETTRICK' ('G-ADSX'), 'ELYSIAN' ('G-ADSZ')	**£150-200**
62p	1945-49	**Armstrong Whitworth Air Liner**	As previous casting but no 'Gliding Game' hole, name under wing, no box, Silver, Blue or Green, with Silver or Grey/Green trim, 'EXPLORER' ('G-ADSV') or 'ECHO' ('G-ADTB')	**£300-400**
62r	1939-41	**D.H. 'Albatross' Mail Liner**	Silver, 'G-AEVV', 4 x 3-blade Red propellers, 'Gliding Game' hole, name under wing, own box	**£300-400**
62r	1945-49	**Four Engined Liner**	Grey, Light Blue (Red trim) or Silver (Red trim), no markings, no hole, not boxed	**£100-130**

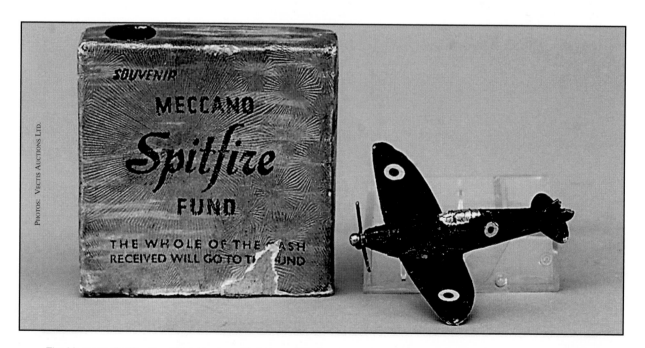

PHOTOS: VECTIS AUCTIONS LTD.

The Meccano 'Spitfire Fund' lapel badge with its box. This item was not given an official reference number by Meccano.

			Grey, Fawn, Light Blue or Silver, 'G-ATPV', 4 x 3-blade Red propellers	£100-130
62s	1939-41	**Hawker 'Hurricane' Fighter**	Silver body, RAF roundels, with or without undercarriage, 1 x 2 or 3-blade propeller	£90-120
	1945-49		Silver body, RAF roundels, no undercarriage, 1 x 3-blade propeller	£60-70
62t	1939-41	**Armstrong Whitley Bomber**	Light Green/Brown camouflage, Yellow ring roundels, 2 x 3-blade propellers, box	£200-300
		(reissue of 60v)	Dark camouflage version, Yellow roundels	£200-300
			Dark camouflage, Red and Blue roundels	£200-300
62w	1939-41	**'Frobisher' Class Air Liner**	Silver (casting as 62r), 4 x 3-blade propellers, 'Gliding Game' hole, own box, 3 liveries: 'FROBISHER' ('G-AFDI'), 'FALCON' ('G-AFDJ'), 'FORTUNA' ('G-AFDK'), (renumbered 68b)	£250-350
62x	1939-41	**British 40 Seat Airliner**	Grey/Green, Red/Maroon, Two-tone Green, Two-tone Blue, Blue/Silver, Yellow/Maroon, 'G-AZCA', not boxed, with or without 'Gliding Game' hole, (renumbered 68a)	£200-250
62y	1939-40	**Giant High Speed Monoplane** ...	Blue/Brown, Blue/Silver, Olive/Green, Blue/Cream, Yellow/Maroon, Red/Maroon, Two-tone Blue or Two-tone Green, 'D-AZBK', 'Gliding Game' hole, not boxed	£300-400
	1945-49		Light/Dark Green, Grey/Green or Silver, no hole or box, 'G-ATBK'	£100-125
63	1939-41	**Mayo Composite Aircraft**	Models 63a (fitted with special tinplate clip) and 63b together in special box (see below)	£700-800
63a	1939-41	**Flying Boat 'MAIA'**	Silver, 'G-ADHK', 'Mayo Composite' under wing, own box	£100-150
63b	1939-41	**Seaplane 'MERCURY'**	Silver, 'G-ADHJ', 'Mercury Seaplane' under wing, 'Gliding Game' hole in some	£75-100
63b	1945-49	**Seaplane**	Silver, 'G-AVKW', no 'Gliding Game' hole, 'Seaplane' under wing	£90-120
	1952-57		Reissue of 63b Seaplane, same as previous model, (renumbered 700)	£90-120
66a	1940-41	**Heavy Bomber**	Camouflaged, RAF roundels, 4 x 2-blade propellers, no name under wing, (reissue of 60a)	£250-300
66b	1940-41	**Dive Bomber Fighter**	Camouflaged, RAF roundels, 1 x 2-blade propeller, (reissue of 60b)	£150-200
66c	1940-41	**Two Seater Fighter**	Camouflaged, RAF roundels, 1 x 2-blade propeller, (reissue of 60c)	£150-200
66d	1940-41	**Torpedo Dive Bomber**	Camouflaged, RAF roundels, 1 x 2-blade propeller, (reissue of 60d)	£150-200
66e	1940-41	**Medium Bomber**	Camouflaged, RAF roundels, 2 x 2-blade propellers, 'General Monospar' under, (reissue of 60e)	£150-200
66f	1940-41	**Army Co-operation Autogiro**	Silver body and blades, Red/White/Blue roundels, (reissue of 60f)	£150-200
67a	1940-41	**Junkers Ju89 Heavy Bomber** ...	Matt-Black with Light Blue underside, Red propellers, Silver cockpit area, Luftwaffe insignia, with or without 'Gliding Game' hole	£750-1,000
68a	1940-41	**'Ensign' Air Liner**	Camouflaged, RAF roundels, no 'Gliding Game' hole, 4 x 3-blade propellers	£300-400
68b	1940-41	**'Frobisher' Class Air Liner**	Light or Dark Camouflage, RAF roundels, 4 x 3-blade propellers, 'Gliding Game' hole in some, (renumbered from 62w)	£150-200
70a	1946-49	**Avro 'York' Airliner**	Silver body, 'G-AGJC', Red 4 x 3-blade propellers. Early version has Silver propeller pins, tinplate base and blued cockpit, (renumbered 704)	£125-150
70b	1946-49	**Tempest II Fighter**	Silver with blued canopy, Yellow band on fuselage roundels, pointed spinner, (renumbered 730)	£35-45
70c	1947-49	**Viking Air Liner**	Silver or Grey body, 'G-AGOL', Red 2 x 4-blade propellers, large pointed spinners, (reissued as 705)	£55-65
70d	1946-49	**Twin-Engined Fighter**	Silver body with blued canopy, (reissued as 731)	£35-45
		variation:	As previous model but 'N' in 'MECCANO' is reversed	£35-45
70e	1946-49	**Gloster 'Meteor'**	Silver body with blued canopy, large roundels, (renumbered 732)	£35-45
70f	1947-49	**Lockheed 'Shooting Star'**	Silver body with blued canopy, Black air intakes, USAF star on port wing, (renumbered 733)	£35-45
700	1954-57	**Seaplane**	Silver body with 'G-AVKW' marking, (renumbered from 63b)	£75-100
			Silver body, 'G-AVKW', no 'Gliding Game' hole, 'Seaplane' under wing	£75-100

Dinky Toys Avro 'York' Air Liner. Note its dual-numbered box.

700	1979	Spitfire Mark II ('Jubilee')	Plated model on plinth, 1 x 3-blade propeller, 'Diamond Jubilee of the RAF', Blue card display box	£150-175
701	1947-49	Short 'Shetland' Flying Boat	Silver, 'G-AGVD', 4 x 4-blade Black propellers, first Supertoys aircraft, own box	£600-800
702	1954-55	DH 'Comet' Jet Airliner 'BOAC'	White/Blue body, Silver wings and tail, 'G-ALYV', Gold wheels, (renumbered 999). Blue/white box	£110-130
704	1954-59	Avro 'York' Airliner	Silver body, 'G-AGJC', 4 x 3-blade Red propellers, ('704' beneath wing), (renumbered from 70a)	£125-150
705	1952-62	'Viking' Air Liner	Silver body with 'G-AGOL' marking, flat head spinners, (renumbered 70c)	£60-75
			Silver or Grey body, 'G-AGOL', 2 x 4-blade Red propellers	£60-75
706	1956-57	Vickers 'Viscount' Airliner	Silver/Blue/White, 'AIR FRANCE', 'F-BGNL', 4 x 4-blade Red propellers	£100-125
708	1957-65	Vickers 'Viscount' Airliner	Silver/White or Metallic Grey/White, 'B.E.A.', 'G-AOJA'	£100-125
710	1965-76	Beechcraft S35 'Bonanza'	Red/White, Bronze/Yellow, or Red/Blue/White body, 1 x 2-blade propeller	£40-50
	German Promotional:		Green/White, 'GLUCK MIT WICKULER' on towing pennant and box	£400-500
712	1972-77	US Army T.42A	Military Green (715), Beechcraft plus wing-tip tanks, 2 x 2-blade propellers	£60-75
715	1956-62	Bristol 173 Helicopter	Turquoise body with Red stripe and Red rotors, 'G-AUXR'	£40-50
715	1968-76	Beechcraft C55 'Baron'	White/Yellow or Red/Yellow body, Yellow 2 x 2-blade propellers	£40-50
716	1957-62	Westland Sikorsky S-51	Red and Cream helicopter body, 2 x 3-blade rotors	£40-50
717	1970-75	Boeing '737'	White/Blue body, White or Blue engine pods, 'LUFTHANSA'	£65-75
718	1972-75	Hawker 'Hurricane' Mk.IIc	Camouflaged body, RAF roundels, Black 1 x 3-blade propeller, guns	£65-75
719	1969-77	Spitfire Mk.II	Camouflaged, RAF roundels, Black 1 x 3-blade propeller (battery-operated), (renumbered 741)	£70-90
			Early issues in 'Battle of Britain' pictorial card box	£60-75
721	1969-80	Junkers Ju87b Stuka	Camouflage/Yellow, German markings, 1 x 3-blade propeller, cap-firing bomb	£90-110
			Early issues in 'Battle of Britain' pictorial card box	£90-110
722	1970-80	Hawker 'Harrier'	Metallic Blue/Olive Camouflage, RAF markings, pilot, aerial	£80-100
723	1970-73	Hawker Siddeley HS 125	Yellow/White/Blue or Metallic Blue/White, drop-down door/steps	£35-45
	1973-73	Hawker Executive Jet	Yellow/White/Blue. In bubble-pack with English and French text. Possibly a promotional sample	£400-600
724	1971-79	'Sea King' Helicopter	Metallic Blue/White, 5-blade rotors, pilot, 'Apollo' space capsule	£50-60
			Early issues in card picture box with pictorial inner stand	£40-50
725	1972-77	Royal Navy 'Phantom II'	Dark Blue body, Black nose, roundels, decals in bubble-pack	£80-90
726	1972-74	Messerschmitt Bf-109E	Desert camouflage, 1 x 3 PB, decals in bubble-pack	£200-250
	1974-76		Grey/Green camouflage, Yellow wing-tips/nose, decals in bubble-pack	£200-250
727	1976-77	U.S.A.F. Phantom F4 Mark II	Brown/Olive camouflage, 2 missiles, 2 figures, (no transfers issued), US market	£500-750
728	1972-75	R.A.F. 'Dominie'	Metallic Blue and camouflage, roundels, retractable wheels, bubble-pack	£40-50
729	1974-76	Multi-Role Combat Aircraft	Grey/Camouflage, swing-wings, decals in bubble-pack	£40-50
730	1952-55	Tempest II Fighter	Same as 70b but without blued canopy and with flat spinner, (renumbered from 70b)	£40-50
730	1972-76	US Navy 'Phantom II'	Grey/Red, 'NAVY', 'USS Saratoga', fires missiles, retractable wheels	£80-90
731	1952-55	Twin-Engined Fighter	Silver body, no blued canopy, (reissue of 70d)	£25-35
731	1973-76	S.E.P.E.C.A.T. 'Jaguar'	Metallic Blue and camouflage body, Orange pilot, opening cockpit	£40-50
732	1952-62	Gloster 'Meteor'	Silver body without blued canopy, small roundels, (reissue of 70e)	£25-35
			Shiny Silver body finish with large roundels	NGPP
732	1974-80	Bell 'POLICE' Helicopter	Orange/Blue/White or Red body, sign boards and cones	£35-45
732	1979	'M.A.S.H.' Helicopter	Green body with 'M.A.S.H.' stickers	NGPP
733	1952-62	Lockheed 'Shooting Star'	Silver body with blued canopy, (reissue of 70f)	£25-35
			Variant with 'in' of 'Made in England by Meccano Ltd' missing	NGPP
733	1973-76	German 'Phantom II'	Grey/Green camouflage body, 'Bundesluftwaffe', two white missiles, instructions and transfers, (German/Austrian market)	£200-300
733	1976-77	US F-4K 'Phantom II'	Brown camouflage, retractable wheels, fires missiles, (US market only)	£80-90
734	1955-62	Supermarine 'Swift'	Grey/Green camouflaged body, RAF markings	£30-40
734	1975-78	P47 'Thunderbolt'	Metallic Silver/Black, Red 1 x 4-blade propeller, retractable wheels, 'U.S.A.A.F.'	£200-250
735	1956-66	Gloster 'Javelin'	Camouflaged 'delta-wing' body, RAF markings, smooth (later treaded) wheels	£40-60
736	1955-63	Hawker 'Hunter'	Camouflaged body, RAF markings	£30-40
736	1973-78	Bundesmarine 'Sea King'	Grey/Orange helicopter, German markings, decals in bubble-pack	£45-55
737	1959-68	P.1B 'Lightning' Fighter	Silver (metal wheels) or Metallic Grey (Black plastic wheels)	£60-80
738	1960-65	DH 110 'Sea Vixen' Fighter	Grey/White body, Black nose, RAF roundels, 'ROYAL NAVY'	£60-80
739	1975-78	A6M5 'Zero Sen'	Metallic Blue/Black, Japanese markings, decals in bubble-pack	£60-80
			Metallic Green/Black, Japanese markings, decals in bubble-pack	£250-350
741	1978-80	Spitfire Mk.II	Camouflaged body, (non-motorised version of 719)	£60-80
749	1955-56	RAF Avro 'Vulcan' Bomber	Silver body (aluminium), only 500 models were made (for Canadian market).	
(992)			992 is the catalogue (and box) number, '749' is cast into the model, (renumbered 992)	
			Two castings exist; one has pointed wingtips, the other more rounded	£1,500-2,000
997	1962-65	Caravelle SE 210 Airliner	Silver/White/Blue, 'AIR FRANCE', 'F-BGNY', metal or plastic wheels, Yellow lidded picture box with card support	£100-150
998	1959-64	Bristol 'Britannia'	Silver with 'CANADIAN PACIFIC' livery in Blue/White, 'CF-CZA' in Blue on wing, striped picture box with card support	£250-275
	1964-65		As previous but with Silver-Grey wings. Yellow lidded picture box with card support	£200-250
999	1955-65	DH 'Comet' Jet Airliner	White body, Blue fin, Silver wings, 'G-ALYV', 'No. 999' cast in underwing, (reissue of 702). Early issues came in Blue/White striped box with an oval '999' sticker over the '702' print.	
			Later boxes were Yellow/Red with printed '999'	£100-125
			As above, but registration 'G-ALYX'	£100-125
			As previous model but with Silver-Grey wings	£100-125

BOX TYPES: Many 1970-79 issues were 'vacuform' packed and these include model nos: 710,712, 715, 717, 718, 721 to 734 inclusive, plus 736 and 739.

Recommended reading:

'**Dinky Toys Aeroplanes - A Collectors Guide and Checklist**'. Contact D.C. Barratt, 230 Earlham Road, Norwich, Norfolk, NR2 3RH. (Tel: 01603-453650).

29c Double Decker Bus identification

1st Type 1938-47
AEC/STL grille, large 'V' shape. Cutaway wings, smooth hubs. No model number on base.

2nd Type 1949-53 and 1957-59
AEC/Regent grille, small 'V' shape. Straight across wings, ridged hubs. '29c' cast into base of <u>some</u> issues.

3rd Type 1948-49 and 1954-63
Leyland grille, undivided shape. Straight across wings, ridged hubs. '29c', '290' or '291' on base.

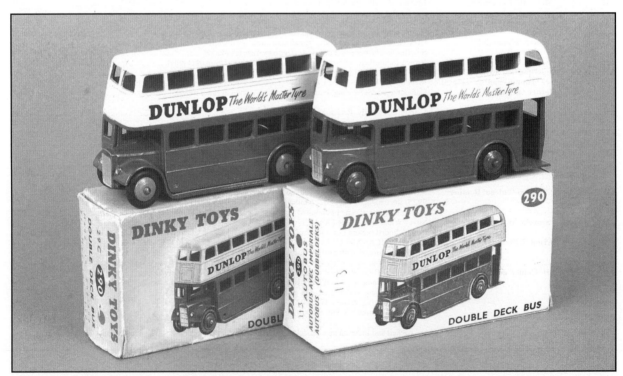

Photo: Vectis Auctions Ltd.

Ref	Year(s)	Model name and details	Market Price Range

16 1936-37 **Silver Jubilee Set**
Locomotive and two interlocking coaches, 'LNER' and
'2590' cast-in, open windows, smooth hubs with
White tyres, special box. Silver loco and coaches,
Grey, Mid-Blue, Dark Blue, Red or Orange trim **£200-250**
Silver loco and coaches with Dark Blue trim **£200-250**
Cream loco and coaches with Red trim **£250-275**
Blue loco and coaches with Dark Blue trim **£250-275**
Green loco and coaches with Dark Green trim **£250-275**

16 1937-40 **Streamlined Train Set**
As previous models but changed name and box **£200-250**
1946-52 Blue/Black loco, 'LNER', Brown/Grey coaches,
filled windows, Black tyres. Individually boxed in
buff box with divisions, yellow label on end of lid. **£125-150**
1952-54 As previous model but with 'BR' crest on tender........**£100-125**
1954 Model renumbered to 798

16z 1935-40 **Articulated Train**
Two-tone Blue, or Gold/Red, or Cream with Red,
Blue or Orange. French issue sold in UK **£200-250**

17 1935-40 **Passenger Train Set**
Black/Maroon loco 17a, Maroon tender 17b,
Maroon/Cream coaches 20a/20b **£200-300**
Black/Green loco 17a, Green tender 17b,
2 Green/Cream coaches 20a/20b **£200-300**
Lead and mazak set in 2nd type box with
correct colour spot...**£400-500**

17a 1934-40 **Locomotive**
Black/Maroon or Black/Green, diecast cab/boiler,
lead chassis **£100-125**
17b 1934-40 **Tender**
Maroon or Green diecast body **£40-50**

18 1935-40 **Tank Goods Train Set**
Green/Black loco (21a), and 3 Green/Black
open wagons (21b) **£200-300**

19 1935-40 **Mixed Goods Train**
Maroon/Black loco (21a), Green/Red open wagon (21b),
Red/Blue 'SHELL' tanker wagon (21d),
Yellow/Red/Green lumber wagon (21e).......................**£400-500**
Set in 3rd type pictorial landscape box (rare) **£800-1,000**

20 1935-40 **Tank Passenger Set**
Green/Black loco (21a), 2 Brown/Green coaches (20a),
Guard's van (20b)..**£300-400**
20a 1935-40 **Coach**
Brown/Cream or Green/White roof,
diecast body, lead chassis **£60-75**

20b 1935-40 **Guard's Van**
Brown/Cream or Green/White roof,
diecast body, lead chassis **£60-75**

21 1932-33 **Hornby Train Set**
Blue/Red loco (21a), Green open wagon (21b),
Green/Blue crane wagon (21c),
Red/Blue 'SHELL' tank wagon (21d),
Yellow/Red/Green lumber wagon (21e),
'HORNBY SERIES' cast into lead body.
Red card box **£500-600**
1934-35 **Modelled Miniatures Train Set**
Contents as previous set, in Red card box **£400-500**

21a 1932-34 **Tank Locomotive**
Red/Blue 0-6-0 tank loco,
'HORNBY SERIES' cast into lead body **£75-100**
1934-41 Maroon/Black or Green/Black,
'DINKY TOYS' cast into lead body **£75-100**
21b 1932-34 **Open Wagon**
Green/Red, Green/Blue, Green/Black, Maroon/Black,
'HORNBY SERIES' cast into lead body **£50-70**
1934-41 Colours as previous model,
'DINKY TOYS' cast into lead body **£50-70**

21c 1932-34 **Crane Wagon**
Green body, Blue chassis,
'HORNBY SERIES' cast-in, lead **£50-70**
21d 1932-34 **Tanker Wagon**
Red tank, Blue or Black chassis,
'HORNBY SERIES' cast-in, lead **£50-70**
1934-41 Red tank, Blue or Black chassis,
'DINKY TOYS' cast-in, lead **£50-70**
21e 1932-34 **Lumber Wagon**
Brown/Blue, Yellow/Red or Yellow/Black,
'HORNBY SERIES' in lead..**£50-70**
1934-41 Brown/Blue, Yellow/Red or Yellow/Black,
'DINKY TOYS', lead..**£50-70**

26 1934-40 **G.W.R. Rail Car**
Early issues are lead, later issues mazak, plastic rollers.
Cream roof, Brown, Green, Yellow or Red body........**£125-150**
Green body with Red roof..**£125-150**

26z 1937-40 **Diesel Road Car**
Cream roof, Red, Green, Orange,
Yellow or Blue body. (French) **£100-125**

27 1934-38 **Tram Car**
Plastic or metal wheels, Red 'OVALTINE' or
'LIPTONS TEA' or no logo. Red, Orange, Green,
Yellow or Light or Dark Blue body,
Cream upper windows and roof **£200-250**
Light Blue or Dark Blue body,
Cream lower/upper windows and roof.........................**£200-250**

29 1934-38 **Motor Bus** (renumbered to 29a)
Plastic or metal wheels, no logo, or Silver or Red
'MARMITE'. Blue, Green, Maroon, Yellow or
Red body, Cream or Silver roof **£200-250**

29b 1936-46 **Streamlined Bus**
Green, Orange or Red coach body, all with Cream
wheel covers, Black or White tyres, smooth hubs **£100-125**
Two-tone Blue, Yellow/Orange, Red/Maroon,
Two-tone Green, or Turquoise/Red,
smooth Black hubs, open rear window **£100-125**
1946-47 Cream and Dark Blue, smooth hubs, open windows ...**£100-125**
1947-50 Grass Green/Light Green, Light Green/Dark Green,
Grey/Blue or Two-tone Blue body,
Black tyres on ridged hubs, filled-in rear window.......**£100-125**

29c **Double Decker Bus**
The different casting types are shown in
the diagrams on the opposite page.
1938-40 **'DUNLOP TYRES'**
1st Type AEC/STL, cutaway wings, stairs cast-in,
smooth hubs, White tyres, crimped axle ends.
Advertisement in Black on Yellow rectangle.
Regular issues:
Cream upper deck and roof with Red, Light Blue,
Maroon, Green or Orange lower deck........................**£300-400**
1938 Early Grey roof issues:
As previous but with Grey roof..................................**£300-400**
Cream upper body, Grey roof, Mid-Green lower body,
Black smooth hubs **£600-800**
Late issue: Dark Blue lower deck,
Cream upper deck and roof..**£300-400**
1938-40 Without advertisements:
As above but without advertisements **£200-300**
Baseplates:
1st issue 'Made in England', 29 mm x 2 mm.
2nd issue 'Made in England', 28 mm x 1.5 mm.
1946 Without advertisements:
1st type AEC/STL grille, cutaway wings, no staircase,
six vertical inside body ribs, smooth Black hubs.
Colours: Green lower deck with Cream or
Grey upper-deck, Green hubs..............................**£150-200**
Red lower deck with Cream or Grey upper deck,
Red hubs...**£150-200**
1947-48 Without advertisements:
As previous model but with post-war
Black ridged hubs..**£100-125**
As previous model but with Two-tone Green body **£160-190**

| | 1948-49 | Without advertisements:
3rd type, Leyland or AEC grille, straight-across wings,
Black ridged hubs. Early issues had 6 vertical inside
body ribs, later issues had 5 (3 on n/s, 2 on o/s).
Red or Green lower deck, Cream upper deck ....£100-125 |
| | 1949-53 | Without advertisements:
2nd type, AEC/Regent grille, straight-across wings,
lengthwise chassis strengthener with hole in chassis
centre, or (1952) eight vertical inside body ribs,
ridged hubs, plus in (1953) '29c' cast in chassis.
Red or Green lower deck, Cream or White upper
deck, hubs match the lower deck colour....................£100-125 |

29c 1954-54 **'DUNLOP'** (renumbered to 290)
3rd type Leyland Titan grille and straight across wings,
early issues have recessed stop lights, late issues (1959)
protrude. Logo 'DUNLOP -The World's Master Tyre'
in Black and Red. Sloping and upright designs exist.
Red or Green lower deck, Cream upper deck,
hubs match lower deck colour....................................**£200-250**

29dz 1939-40 **Autobus**
Green or White body, metal wheels,
(French issue sold in UK) **£80-90**

29e 1948-52 **Single Deck Bus**
Mid-Blue body, Dark Blue flashes, Black hubs..............**£80-90**
Mid-Blue body and hubs, Dark Blue flashes **£90-110**
Cream body and hubs, Red flashes **£60-80**
Cream body, Blue flashes, Blue or Black hubs..............**£60-80**
Light Green body, Dark Green flashes, Black hubs........**£80-90**
Light Green body and hubs, Dark Green flashes........**£140-160**

29f 1950-54 **Observation Coach** (renumbered to 280)
Grey body and hubs, Red flashes and hubs **£70-80**
Cream body and hubs, Red flashes, Red hubs **£80-90**
Cream body and hubs, Red flashes, Maroon hubs..........**£80-90**

29g 1951-54 **Luxury Coach** (renumbered to 281)
Maroon, Cream flashes and hubs....................................**£65-75**
Orange body with Cream flashes and hubs...................**£80-100**
Fawn body with Orange flashes, Cream or Green hubs **£80-100**
Fawn body with Cream flashes and hubs.....................**£100-130**
Blue body with Cream flashes, Yellow hubs **£130-160**
Cream body with Blue flashes and hubs.......................**£80-100**
Cream body with Red flashes and hubs **£100-130**
Cream body, Orange flashes, Green hubs **£100-130**

NB Market Price Ranges for models 29f, g and h are
based on their being unboxed, as compared to prices
for the boxed renumbered issues 280, 281 and 282.

29h 1952-54 **Duple Roadmaster Coach** (renumbered to 282)
Dark Blue body, Light Blue hubs, Silver coachlines.....**£80-100**
Red body and hubs, Silver coachlines...........................**£80-100**
Green lower body, Cream upper body and hubs.........**£150-200**

NB Early issue had a flat roof underside.
Later issues have a rib front to back.

36g **Taxi with Driver**
'TAXI' cast into Black roof, driver cast into chassis.
| | 1936-46 | Grey, Dark Blue, Green, Maroon or Red body,
Black roof, open rear window **£200-250**
Yellow body, Black roof, open rear window...............**£700-900** |
| | 1947-50 | Dark Blue, Green, Light Green, Red,
Maroon or Brown body, Black roof on all,
some open rear windows (usually filled-in).................**£80-100** |

40h 1952-54 **Austin Taxi (FX3)** (renumbered to 254)
Diecast chassis with cast-in driver and model number.
All-Yellow body and hubs,
Black chassis, interior and driver **£100-125**
All-Yellow body and hubs,
Brown chassis, interior and driver **£150-250**
Dark Blue body, Light Blue hubs,
Black chassis, interior and driver **£250-350**
Mid-Blue body and hubs,
Black chassis, interior and driver **£400-600**

067 1959-64 **Austin Taxi (FX3)**
See ref. 067 in the 'Dublo Dinky' section.

115 1979-79 **United Biscuits Taxi**
Yellow/Blue/Black, casting as 120, promotional **£45-55**

120 1979-80 **Happy Cab**
White/Yellow/Blue, solid wheels,
'flower-power' stickers...**£45-55**

241 1977-77 **'SILVER JUBILEE TAXI'**
Silver body and hubs, Union Jack on bootlid,
284 casting...**£30-35**

254 1956-59 **Austin Taxi (FX3)** (renumbered from 40h)
Blue body, Light Blue hubs..**£500-750**
Black body, spun hubs, Grey chassis ('254'),
interior and driver **£110-130**
Two-tone issue:
Yellow upper body and hubs, Dark Green lower body,
Black chassis ('254'), interior and driver...................**£90-120**

265 1960-64 **Plymouth U.S.A. Taxi**
Yellow/Red, '25c First 1/5 Mile, 5c Additional',
windows, White treaded tyres **£100-125**

266 1960-66 **Plymouth Canadian Taxi**
Yellow/Red body with 'Taxi' and '450 Metro Cab' **£100-125**

268 1962-67 **Renault Dauphine Mini Cab**
Red body with 'Meccano', 'Kenwood', and
'Britax Safety Belts' adverts **£120-140**

278 1978-80 **Plymouth Yellow Cab**
Yellow body, 'Yellow Cab Co',
plastic chassis and wheels **£20-30**

280 1954-60 **Observation Coach** (renumbered from 29f)
Grey body, Red flashes and hubs **£125-150**
Cream body and hubs, Red flashes **£125-150**
Cream body, Red flashes, Red or Maroon hubs..........**£130-160**

281 1954-59 **Luxury Coach** (renumbered from 29g)
Cream body, Blue flashes and hubs **£125-150**
Cream body, Red flashes and hubs **£175-225**
Cream body, Orange flashes, Green hubs **£200-250**
Cream body, Orange flashes, Cream hubs **£150-175**
Maroon body, Cream flashes and hubs **£90-120**
Mid-Blue body, Cream flashes, Yellow hubs.............**£200-250**
Fawn body, Orange flashes, Green hubs **£125-150**
Fawn body, Cream flashes and hubs **£125-150**

NB Prices shown assume that models are in boxes
with correct colour spot.

282 1954-60 **Duple Roadmaster Coach** (renumbered from 29h)
Dark Blue body, Light Blue hubs, Silver coachlines **£90-110**
Red body and hubs, Silver coachlines **£90-110**
Light Blue body and hubs, Silver coachlines................**£90-110**
Yellow body, Red coachlines and hubs **£125-150**
US issues:
Dark Green lower body, Cream upper body,
Pale Green hubs **£300-350**
As previous model but with Red hubs **£300-350**

282 1967-69 **Austin 1800 Taxi**
Blue/White body, Red/White 'TAXI' labels on
doors and roof..**£65-75**

283 1956-63 **B.O.A.C. Coach**
Dark Blue/White, '*British Overseas Airways
Corporation*', White tyres after 1960.........................**£125-150**

283 1971-77 **Single Deck Bus**
Metallic Red body, Blue interior, 'RED ARROW'.
Card box with instructions and packing.........................**£40-50**
Same, but in bubble pack with unused decal sheet.........**£35-45**
Metallic Red body, Yellow interior. Bubble pack **£45-55**

NB Also available in kit form with 'GREEN LINE' decals.
See 1023 in the Dinky Action Kits section.

284 1972-79 **London Taxi (FX4)**
Black (or very Dark Blue) body,
detailed boot on some, Speedwheels, driver, 'TAXI' **£30-40**

289 **Routemaster Bus**
'London Transport', Route '221', 'KINGS CROSS',
driver/conductor, cast hubs, spun hubs or Speedwheels.
	1964-65	'TERN SHIRTS', Red body, 'FOR 8am CRISPNESS' transfers..............**£80-100**
	1966-69	'SSSCHWEPPES' Red body, Blue-Green logo on White transfers **£80-100**
	1969-80	'ESSO' Red body, 'ESSO SAFETY-GRIP TYRES' White label .**£60-75** Same as previous issue but with transfers...................**£100-150** Deep Purple body, 'London Transport' and 'ESSO SAFETY-GRIP TYRES' logos, Blue driver and clippie **£300-400**

1968-68	**'LONDON STORES'**	
	Red body, Black/Gold logo,	
	'Festival of London Stores', promotional **£100-150**	
1970	**'INGERSOLL RAND'**	
	Red body, promotional **£100-125**	
1974-74	**'MECCANO'**	
	Gold body, 'MECCANO - DINKY TOYS'.	
	(Very few issued to Press only).........................NGPP	
1977-79	**'MADAME TUSSAUDS'**	
	Red body, driver/conductor, White lower deck seating,	
	Blue on White advert., cast wheels **£80-100**	
	Red body, driver/conductor, Dark Blue lower deck	
	seating, White on Blue ad., plastic wheels...................**£80-100**	
	Red body, with figures,	
	packed in 'SCHWEPPES' picture box **£100-120**	
1977-77	**'WOOLWORTHS'**	
	Silver body, (Silver Jubilee limited issue),	
	figures in some **£25-30**	
1977-77	**'EVER READY'**	
	Silver body, (New Zealand Silver Jubilee issue),	
	no figures ....NGPP	
1979	**'THOLLEMBEEK & FILS'**	
	Gold body, Pale Blue upper interior, Darker Blue lower	
	interior, 'Thollembeek 1929-79', Belgian promo **£80-90**	
	'FORDATH'	
	Red body, Light Blue upper deck seating, Deep Blue lower	
	deck seating. Issued in plain White box with	
	'WITH THE COMPLIMENTS OF FORDATH	
	LIMITED' labels to box ends. Promotional.................**£175-225**	
1979	**'GREENLINE JUBILEE'**	
	All-Green body, 'GREENLINE GOLDEN JUBILEE'	
	promotional...**£70-80**	
	'VISIT BLACKPOOL ZOO'	
	Cream body, plastic wheels,	
	'BLACKPOOL TRANSPORT' promotional **£90-110**	
19??	**'NEW ZEALAND CLUB'**	
	Red body, Blue/White interior,	
	'CAR CLUB'S 10th ANNIVERSARY' **£90-110**

290		**Double Decker Bus** (renumbered from 29c)
		Type 2 (AEC grille), 'DUNLOP - The World's Master Tyre'
		advert may be upright or sloping, '290' cast on base,
		diecast hubs match lower deck.
1954-59		**'DUNLOP'**
		Green lower deck, Cream upper deck **£90-110**
		Red lower deck, Cream upper deck..............................**£90-110**
1959-61		**'DUNLOP'**
		Type 3 (Leyland grille), diecast hubs match lower deck
		colour, roof route box added, Mid Green or
		Dark Green lower deck, Cream upper deck................**£100-125**
		Red lower deck, Cream upper deck **£100-125**
1961-63		Same colours as previous with sloping lettering but
		with spun hubs..**£125-150**
1963		Same body colours but Green or Red plastic hubs......**£175-200**
1963		**'EXIDE BATTERIES'**
		Red or Green lower deck, Cream upper deck with
		'290' cast into base ....NGPP

291		**London Bus**
		Type 3 (Leyland grille) with route '73' on destination board.
1961-62		**'EXIDE BATTERIES'**
		Red body with Red diecast hubs,
		logo in Black and Yellow **£125-150**
		Factory error:
		As previous model, but with 'CORPORATION
		TRANSPORT' transfers on sides, crimped axles..............NGPP
		Promotional:
		Red body and ridged hubs, White treaded tyres,
		no route number, Exide dealer promotional leaflet...........NGPP
1962-63		Same body colours as previous model but with
		spun aluminium hubs. Plain Yellow box....................**£150-175**
1963		Same body colours as previous but with Red plastic
		hubs. Box has alternating Red and Yellow panels **£175-225**

291 - 293		**Atlantean City Bus**
		A Leyland double-decker bus available in several versions:
291	1974-77	**'KENNINGS'**
		Orange body, White engine cover and interior,
		'VAN & TRUCK HIRE' **£45-55**
		As previous model but with Pale Blue engine cover
		and interior..**£45-55**

		As previous model but with 'Yellow Pages' stickers........NGPP
		White body and lower deck interior,
		Pale Blue upper deck interior. Bubble pack...................**£40-50**
		Light Blue body and interior. Bubble pack **£40-50**
	1977	**'LONDON & MANCHESTER ASSURANCE'**
		White model on plinth. 'Your Best Man For Life'.
		(500 issued to agents)..**£400-500**
292	1962-65	**'RIBBLE'**
		Red and White body, 'REGENT' advert. on some **£80-100**
		Red and Cream body with
		'CORPORATION TRANSPORT' fleetname................**£80-100**
		As previous model but no fleetname or logo **£80-100**
292	1977	**'LONDON COUNTRY'**
		Green body, shown in 1977 catalogue, but never issued.
293	1963-65	**'BP'**
		Green/Cream body, Yellow logo and smooth roof,
		'BP IS THE KEY' **£80-100**
		As previous model but with ribbed roof **£100-120**
293	1973-78	**Swiss Postal Bus 'PTT'**
		Yellow body with Cream roof,
		clear or tinted windows, (296 casting) **£25-35**
295	1963-69	**Atlas Kenebrake Bus**
		Light Blue/Grey body, suspension, windows..................**£50-70**
		As previous model but all Blue body, Red interior.....**£125-150**
2		
95	1973-74	**Atlantean Bus**
		'YELLOW PAGES'
		Yellow body, 'Let Your Fingers Do The Walking' **£40-50**
295	1974-76	As previous model but deeper shade of Yellow **£40-50**
		As previous model but finished in Silver,
		no front or rear destination blinds ....NGPP
296	1972-75	**Duple Viceroy 37 Coach**
		Metallic Blue body, clear or tinted windows,
		bubble-packed **£25-35**
		As previous model but Yellow and Cream body
		(see also 293)..**£30-40**
297	1977-77	**Silver Jubilee Bus**
		Leyland Atlantean (291) Silver/Black body, 'National' ..**£30-35**
		'WOOLWORTHS' Silver Jubilee Bus, promotional **£30-35**
784	1972-74	**Dinky Goods Train Set**
		Blue loco 'GER', one Red Truck, one Yellow Truck **£30-40**
798	1954-59	**Express Passenger Train Set** (renumbered from 16)
		Green/Black loco, BR crest, Cream/Maroon
		coaches (Grey roofs), Black hubs/tyres.......................**£125-150**
		Green/Black loco, BR crest, Cream/Maroon
		coaches/roofs/hubs, Black tyres **£125-150**
		Green/Black loco, BR crest, Cream/Maroon
		coaches/roofs, Red hubs, White tyres **£125-150**
949	1961-66	**Wayne 'SCHOOL BUS'**
		Deep Yellow body, Red body lines and interior,
		windows, Red plastic hubs. Supertoy **£160-190**
		As previous model but with Black lines on sides **£200-300**
952	1964-71	**Vega Major Luxury Coach**
		Pale Grey body, Cream interior, Maroon side flash,
		cast hubs, flashing indicators **£80-100**
		Off-White body, Deep Blue interior,
		Maroon side flash, flashing indicators **£80-100**
		Late issues with Red interior, clear indicators **£70-90**
953	1963-65	**Continental Touring Coach**
		Pale Blue body, White roof,
		'Dinky Continental Tours', Supertoy **£300-350**
954	1972-77	**Vega Major Luxury Coach**
		White body, Mid-Blue interior,
		Lemon-Yellow base, cast hubs.................................**£70-90**
		White body, Yellow interior, Black base, cast hubs **£90-110**
		White body, Red interior, Black base, later cast hubs....**£90-110**
961	1973-77	**Vega Major Coach 'PTT'**
		Yellow body, Cream roof, Blue interior, 'P.T.T.' and
		emblem, Swiss model (in normal box) **£100-125**
		Swiss Postal Bus variant:
		Swiss box (Red/White/Yellow, 'Autocar Postal',
		'Postauto', etc), plus label: 'Special contract run 1973
		Swiss Post Office Bus'; also 'Specially boxed for
		Swiss Meccano Agent for sale under their name'........**£250-300**

'Dublo Dinky' models

'Dublo Dinky' models were made in a scale of 1:76. All their wheels are plastic: smooth wheels are fairly soft and treaded wheels are hard.

The late issues with black treaded wheels are rarer and may attract a premium. These versions should all be housed in the later issue lighter yellow boxes.

Ref	Year(s)	Model name	Colours, features, details	Market Price Range
061	1958-59	Ford Prefect	Fawn or Grey body, Silver trim, Grey smooth wheels	£50-60
			As previous but with Grey wheels	£65-75
062	1958-60	Singer Roadster	Orange or Fawn body, Red interior, Grey smooth or knobbly wheels	£65-75
			Yellow body, Grey knobbly wheels	£75-85
063	1958-60	Commer Van	Blue body, Silver trim, Grey smooth or knobbly wheels	£100-125
064	1957-62	Austin Lorry	Green body, Black or Grey smooth or knobbly wheels	£60-70
065	1957-60	Morris Pick-up	Red body, Silver trim, Grey smooth or knobbly wheels	£60-80
066	1959-66	Bedford Flat Truck	Grey body, Silver trim, Grey smooth or knobbly wheels, hook on some	£50-60
067	1959-64	Austin 'TAXI'	Blue lower body, Cream upper body, Black or Grey knobbly wheels	£70-80
068	1959-64	'ROYAL MAIL' Morris Van	Red body, 'E II R' crest, Grey knobbly wheels	£120-150
			Red body, 'E II R' crest, Black knobbly wheels	£100-120
069	1959-64	Massey Harris Tractor	Blue body, Silver trim, Grey knobbly wheels, hole for driver	£90-110
			With Grey knobbly wheels on front and very Light Tan rear wheels	£100-120
070	1959-64	A.E.C. Mercury Tanker	Green cab (glazing in some), Red tank, Black or Grey knobbly wheels, 'SHELL-BP'	£100-125
071	1960-64	Volkswagen Delivery Van	Yellow body with Red 'HORNBY DUBLO' logo, Black or Grey knobbly wheels	£70-90
072	1959-64	Bedford Articulated Truck	Yellow cab, Red semi-trailer, Black or Grey smooth or knobbly wheels	£70-90
073	1960-64	Land Rover/Trailer/Horse	Green car (Grey or Black knobbly wheels), Tan or White horse. Trailers:	
			with Bright Green trailer (Green ramp, smooth Grey wheels)	£120-135
			with Green trailer (Brown ramp, knobbly Grey wheels)	£120-135
			with Bright Green trailer (Black ramp, knobbly Black wheels)	£120-135
			with Orange trailer (Black or Grey plastic wheels and ramp)	£120-135
076	1960-64	Lansing Bagnall Tractor & Trailer	Maroon tractor/trailer, Blue driver/seat, Black smooth or knobbly wheels	£70-90
078	1960-64	Lansing Bagnall Trailer	Maroon body, Black smooth or knobbly wheels, hook, wire drawbar	£40-50
-	c1959	Shop Display Stand	Pale Yellow with Red logo and wording 'NEW SERIES / DUBLO DINKY', etc. 28 x 19cm overall	£300-400

Photo: Vectis Auctions Ltd.

Dinky Toys Ships, Boats and Hovercraft

Ref	Year(s)	Model name	Colours, features, details	Market Price Range
50a	1934-41	Battle Cruiser 'HMS Hood'	Battleship Grey, (without name cast underneath 1939-41) 146 mm	£30-35
50b	1934-41	Battleship 'Nelson' Class	Battleship Grey, 'HMS Nelson' underneath (no name 1939-41) 117 mm	£30-35
50b	1934-41	Battleship 'Nelson' Class	Battleship Grey, 'HMS Rodney' underneath (no name 1939-41) 117 mm	£30-35
50c	1934-41	Cruiser 'HMS Effingham'	Battleship Grey, (without name cast underneath 1939-41) 100 mm	£30-35
50d	1934-41	Cruiser 'HMS York'	Battleship Grey, (without name cast underneath 1939-41) 98 mm	£30-35
50e	1934-41	Cruiser 'HMS Delhi'	Battleship Grey, (without name cast underneath 1939-41) 81 mm	£30-35
50f	1934-41	Destroyer 'Broke' Class	Battleship Grey, no wording underneath, 57 mm	£15-20
50g	1935-41	Submarine 'K' Class	Battleship Grey, wire mast, no wording underneath, 57 mm	£15-20
50h	1935-41	Destroyer 'Amazon' Class	Battleship Grey, no wording underneath, 52 mm	£15-20
50k	1935-41	Submarine 'X' Class	Battleship Grey, wire mast, no wording underneath, 61 mm	£15-20
51b	1934-40	Norddeutscher-Lloyd 'Europa'	Black hull, White superstructure, Brown funnels, name under, 165 mm	£35-45
51c	1934-40	Italia Line 'Rex'	Black hull, White decks, Red/White/Green funnels, name under, 152 mm	£35-45
51d	1934-40	CPR 'Empress of Britain'	Canadian Pacific Railway colours – White hull, Cream funnels, 130 mm	£30-35
51e	1935-40	P & O 'Strathaird'	White hull, Cream funnels, name underneath, 114 mm	£30-35
51f	1934-40	'Queen of Bermuda'	Furness-Withy Line, Grey/White hull, Red/Black funnels, 99 mm	£30-35
51g	1934-40	Cunard 'Britannic'	'White-Star' Liner, Black/White/Brown hull, Black/Tan funnels, 121 mm	£30-35
52	1934-35	Cunard White-Star Liner 'No. 534'	Black/White/Red, '534' cast underneath, boxed, no rollers, 175 mm	£70-80
			Same model but '534 Queen Mary' cast underneath	£70-80
52	1935-35	(renumbered 52b)	As previous model with 'Queen Mary' cast underneath, but without '534'	£70-80
52a	1935-41	Cunard White-Star Liner 'Queen Mary'	Black/White/Red, boxed, with plastic rollers, 175 mm	£70-80
	1946-49		Black/White/Red, boxed, with brass rollers	£70-80
52b	1935-36	Cunard 'Queen Mary'	Black/White/Red, boxed, without rollers, (renumbered from 52)	£70-80
52c	1935-40	'La Normandie'	Black/White, Red/Black funnels, boxed, made in France, pictorial insert	£70-80
52c	1939	Cunard 'Queen Elizabeth'	Announced in 1939 catalogue but never produced	NPP
52m	1936-40	Cunard 'Queen Mary'	Renumbered from 52b, without rollers, supplied unboxed	£40-50
53az	1938-39	Battleship 'Dunkerque'	Battleship Grey, with or without plastic rollers, boxed French issue	£40-60
281	1973-76	Military Hovercraft	See 'Military Vehicles' section.	
290	1970-76	SRN-6 Hovercraft	Red or Metallic Red body, Blue or Black skirt	£20-25
671	1976-78	Mk.1 Corvette	White/Grey/Brown/Black plastic body, fires missiles	£20-25
672	1976-77	OSA-2 Missile Boat	Grey/Whit/Black, fires missiles	£20-25
673	1977-78	Submarine Chaser	Grey/White/Black, fires depth charges	£20-25
674	1977-78	Coastguard Missile Launch	White/Blue/Red/Yellow, 'Coastguard', fires missiles	£20-25
675	1973-77	Motor Patrol Boat	Grey hull with Cream/Black/Red	£20-25
678	1974-77	Air-Sea Rescue Launch	Grey/Black/Yellow, Orange dinghy, pilot/launch	£20-25
796	1960-62	Healey Sports Boat on Trailer	Mid-Green body, Cream hull, Orange cast trailer	£50-75
			Dark Green body, Deep Cream hull, Orange cast trailer	£50-75
			Red body, Deep Cream hull, Orange cast trailer	£150-175
			Yellow body, Cream hull, Orange cast trailer	£150-175
797	1966	Healey Sports Boat	Sold without trailer from trade box of 6. See entry above (796).	

Photo: Swapmeet Publications

Novelty, Space, Film and TV-related models

353 SHADO-2 Mobile ('window' box), 351 UFO Interceptor, 109 Gabriel's Ford, 350 Tiny's Mini-Moke, 353 SHADO-2 (card box)
108 Sam's Car (x2), 106 'The Prisoner' Mini-Moke, 103 Spectrum Patrol Car (x2 - on card base and in card box)
360 Eagle Freighter, 352 Ed Straker's Car (in card box), 106 Thunderbirds 2 & 4 (on card base with perspex cover)
104 Spectrum Pursuit Vehicle (on card base), 353 SHADO-2 Mobile (card base / perspex cover), 100 Lady Penelope's 'FAB 1'

352 Ed Straker's Car (in card box), 109 Gabriel's Model 'T' Ford, 103 Spectrum Patrol Car (in card box)
103 Spectrum Patrol Car (on card base), 350 Tiny's Mini-Moke, 352 Ed Straker's Car (on card base)

Models shown above were sold by Vectis Auctions Ltd. Pictures reproduced by their kind permission.

Dinky Toys Novelty, Space, Film and TV-related models

Market prices shown here are for guidance only.
They refer ONLY to mint models in pristine boxes (where appropriate) that are complete with all of their original contents.

Ref	Year(s)	Model name	Colours, features, details	Market Price Range

100 1967-75 **Lady Penelope's 'FAB 1'**............ (non-fluorescent) Pink body, clear or tinted sliding roof (Pink stripes on early issues), rockets/harpoons, Lady Penelope and Parker figures (TV series 'Thunderbirds').
With ridged cast wheels. Card picture box with pictorial inner stand..**£300-350**
With ridged cast wheels. Supplied in a bubble pack **£200-250**
With Fluorescent Pink body..**£350-450**
NB Rare White version reported (but not seen) sold at auction. Details welcomed, please.

101 1967-73 **Thunderbirds II and IV** .... Metallic Green (including loading door), Red thrusters, Yellow legs. Separate plastic Yellow/Red Thunderbird IV model inside. Card box with pictorial inner stand...**£400-600**
Metallic Green body, Black door, Red thrusters, Yellow legs. Bubble-packed...**£175-225**
Metallic Sea-Blue body, Red thrusters, Yellow legs. Bubble-packed **£175-225**
Metallic Blue body and base, Red thrusters, Yellow legs. Bubble-packed **£125-150**
Metallic Blue body, Black base, Red thrusters, Yellow legs. Bubble-packed..**£175-225**
Metallic Blue body, Yellow base, Red thrusters and legs. Bubble-packed..**£175-225**
Metallic Blue body, White base, Red thrusters and legs. Bubble-packed..**£125-150**
Bubble-packed issues: have card bases with Dark Blue sides and (usually) a Light Blue top. Rarer issues have a Yellow top.

102 1969-75 **Joe's Car**..................................... Metallic Green, White driver, Red engine thruster, battery powered. (TV series 'Joe 90').
Card picture box, pictorial inner stand...**£250-300**
Same model, but in bubble-pack..**£175-225**
NB Blue, Silver, Grey version reported (but not seen) sold at auction. Details welcomed, please.

103 1968-75 **Spectrum Patrol Car** .... TV series 'Captain Scarlet', shaped hubs, 'screaming motor', Red body with Yellow base, Yellow or Cream plastic interior. Card picture box with pictorial inner stand...**£175-200**
Metallic Red body with White base, Yellow or Cream plastic interior...**£160-180**
Metallic Gold body, Blue tinted windows, Yellow or Cream interior..**£175-200**
Pre-production prototype: Yellow body, Lemon interior, aerial, cast wheels, (resin body).................................**£400-500**
NB Metallic Blue and Silver versions reported (but not seen) sold at auction. Details welcomed, please.

104 1968-75 **Spectrum Pursuit Vehicle** .... Metallic Blue, Black base, Black or White front bumper, 'SPV'. Card box has inner pictorial stand........**£300-350**
Metallic Blue body, Black base, White front bumper. Bubble-packed...**£175-200**
Blue body, Light Green base, White front bumper. Bubble-packed..**£110-140**
Blue body and base, White front bumper. Bubble-packed...**£100-125**

105 1968-75 **Maximum Security Vehicle**....... White body, Red base & side stripes, Red or Blue interior, 'RADIOACTIVE' crate, ('Captain Scarlet') ..**£200-250**
Late issue without Red body stripes **£200-250**
NB All issues should include a complete and unused decal sheet.
NB Grey version reported (but not seen) sold at auction. Details welcomed, please.

106 1967-70 **'The Prisoner' Mini-Moke**........ White body, Red/White canopy, 'bicycle' decal on bonnet, card box.
With Black windscreen frame **£250-300**
With Silver windscreen frame and Brown side panels **£200-250**

106 1974-77 **Thunderbirds II and IV** .... Metallic Blue body, Black metal base, Yellow legs. Vacuum-packed **£150-200**
Metallic Blue body, White plastic base, Yellow legs...**£150-200**
1977-79 Metallic Blue body, Black plastic base, Red legs...**£250-300**

107 1967-68 **'Stripey the Magic Mini'**........... White/Red/Yellow/Blue stripes, with Candy, Andy and the Bearandas.
Card picture box with pictorial inner stand **£250-350**

108 1969-71 **Sam's Car** ('Joe 90') .... Card box with tray, pictorial backing, 'WIN' badge, instructions.
Chrome body, Lemon interior...**£120-140**
Gold body, Lemon interior..**£120-140**
1971-75 Pale (Powder) Blue body, Lemon interior, Red engine cover **£140-160**
Metallic Red body, Red or Silver trim, Lemon interior...**£140-160**
Wine Red body, Lemon interior...**£150-175**

109 1969-71 **Gabriel's Model 'T' Ford**........... Yellow/Black, (TV series 'The Secret Service'). Card picture box with pictorial inner stand **£75-85**

111 1976-78 **Cinderella's Coach**..................... Pink/Gold, plastic figures and horses. ('The Slipper & The Rose')...**£20-25**

112 1978-80 **Purdey's TR7** .... Yellow body, Black 'P' logo, Speedwheels. ('The New Avengers') **£55-65**
As previous model but with Yellow 'P' in Black logo on bonnet **£100-125**
As previous model but with Silver 'P' logo on bonnet...**£35-45**

113 **John Steed's Jaguar XJC**........... Metallic Dark Blue, Gold pinstripes, rubbery 'Steed' inside. Approx. 36 issued unofficially...............**£1,000-1,500**
? **John Steed's Ford Granada**....... Approximately 6 pre-production samples issued unofficially. No other details at present...............................NGPP

115 1979-79 **United Biscuits Taxi**................... Yellow/Blue/Black, casting as 120, promotional..**£50-60**
120 1979-80 **Happy Cab** .... White/Yellow/Blue, solid wheels, 'flower-power' stickers **£50-60**

281 1968-70 **'PATHE NEWS' Camera Car** ... Black body, Red interior, cast wheels, cameraman with Brown trousers, camera and stand, (Fiat 2300) ...**£150-175**
As previous model but cameraman has Dark Grey trousers **£175-225**

350 1970-71 **Tiny's Mini Moke** .... Red body, White/Yellow striped top. ('The Enchanted House') **£150-175**

185

351	1971-79	**U.F.O. Interceptor**	From Gerry Anderson's TV series 'U.F.O'. 'S.H.A.D.O.' labels on Light Metallic Green body. Initially packed in card box with pictorial inner mount (prices 20% higher), later bubble-packed.
			with Black missile holder, White/Black missile, clear canopy, Red legs/skids...........£175-200
			with Black missile holder, White/Black missile, Blue canopy, Red legs/skids...........£175-200
			with Red missile holder, Yellow/Black missile, clear canopy, Orange legs/skids. Bubble packed only £175-200
			with Red missile holder, Yellow/Black missile, Blue canopy, Orange legs/skids. Bubble packed only £175-200
352	1971-75	**Ed Straker's Car**	Gold plated body, Blue interior, keyless motor, (TV series 'U.F.O.')...........£100-120
			Yellow body, Pale Grey interior, Black engine covers £250-350
			Red body, Silver trim £70-80
353	1971-79	**'SHADO 2 Mobile'** (TV series 'U.F.O.')	Green body, Red interior, Brown rollers, Silver tracks. Light Green base. All card box...........£100-125
			Green body, Black roof, Pale Grey interior, Dark Green rollers, Black tracks. Bubble-packed...........£250-300
			Green body, Yellow interior, Light Green rollers and base, Silver tracks £100-125
			Metallic Blue body, Pale Grey interior, Black base, rollers, tracks and roof. Window box, internal card base...........£300-350
354	1972-77	**Pink Panther**	Pink car and Panther, flywheel drive, card endflap box...........£35-45
	1977-79		Similar to previous model but without flywheel, bubble-packed...........£35-45
			N.B. A single experimental Green diecast version exists (Christie's sale 4/95).
355	1972-75	**Lunar Roving Vehicle**	Metallic Blue, White astronauts, front/rear steering...........£35-45
357	1977-80	**Klingon Battle Cruiser**	Metallic Blue, fires 'photon torpedoes', (from 'Star Trek')...........£45-55
358	1976-80	**'USS Enterprise'** ('NCC 1701')	White body, Yellow or White 'photon torpedoes', shuttlecraft...........£70-90
359	1975-79	**Eagle Transporter**	White/Green body, Red rear and side thrusters, clear windows. (From 'Space 1999')...........£100-125
			White/Green body, Chrome rear thrusters, Yellow side thrusters, Orange windows...........£100-125
			White/Green body, Chrome rear thrusters, Yellow side thrusters, Red windows...........£100-125
			White/Green body, Red rear thrusters, side thrusters and windows...........£100-125
		NB	All issues should include a complete and unused decal sheet.
360	1975-79	**Eagle Freighter**	White/Red, including rear and side thrusters, 'RADIOACTIVE' drums..(From 'Space 1999')...........£100-125
			White/blue, Red rear and side thrusters...........£100-125
		NB	All issues should include a complete and unused decal sheet.
361	1978-80	**Zygon War Chariot**	Mid-Green body, two Red spacemen and rocket motor...........£35-45
361	1978-80	**Galactic War Chariot**	Metallic Green body, two White/Yellow spacemen, Silver rocket motor...........£35-45
		NB	Light Yellow-Green version reported (but not seen) sold at auction. Details welcomed, please.
361	1978-80	**Missile-firing War Chariot**	Metallic Blue body, two Red spacemen/rocket motor, blister card...........£35-45
362	1978-79	**Trident Star Fighter**	Black/Orange, fires rockets, drop-down stairway...........£35-45
			Metallic Gold body. 500 only issued to guests at a special Meccano Dinner in 1979...........£100-150
363	1979-79	**Cosmic Interceptor**	Metallic Silver/Blue, 2 pilots, Marks & Spencer model ('St.Michael' box)...........£45-55
363	1979-80	**Zygon Patroller**	Metallic Silver/Blue, 2 pilots, ('368' in some catalogues, '363' on box)...........£35-45
			Yellow/Red/Blue version in 'U.S.S. Enterprise' box...........NGPP
364	1979	**NASA Space Shuttle**	White booster and shuttle, decals, instructions, plastic Orange satellite. Pictorial window box £100-150
366	1979	**Space Shuttle**	unboxed version of 364 without booster, with plastic or cardboard load...........£35-45
367	1979-80	**Space Battle Cruiser**	White/Red body, pilot, plastic weapons...........£35-45
368	1979-79	**Cosmic Cruiser**	Blue body, Marks & Spencer model (in 'St.Michael' box)...........£35-45
368	1979-80	**Zygon Marauder**	Red/White, 4 spacemen, ('363' in some catalogues, '368' on box)...........£30-35
371	1980	**Pocket-size 'USS Enterprise'**	Small version of 358, bubble-packed, released after factory closure, (renumbered 801)...........£45-55
372	1980	**Pocket-size Klingon Cruiser**	Small version of 357, bubble-packed, released after factory closure, (renumbered 802)...........£45-55
477	1970-72	**Parsley's Car**	Green/Black/Yellow, head swivels, ('The Adventures of Parsley'). Card picture box with pictorial inner stand...........£100-120
485	1964-67	**Santa Special Model 'T' Ford**	Red/White body, Santa Claus, Xmas tree/toys/decals...........£100-120
486	1965-69	**'Dinky Beats' Morris Oxford**	Pink/Green, 'Da gear', 3 beat-group figures...........£100-150
602	1976-77	**Armoured Command Car**	Green or later Blue-Green body, White star, driver, scanner, fires sparks, (TV series 'The Investigator').....£35-45
802	1980	**Pocket-size Klingon Cruiser**	Small version of 357, bubble-packed, released after factory closure, (renumbered from 372)...........£45-55
803	1980	**Pocket-size 'USS Enterprise'**	Small version of 358, bubble-packed, released after factory closure, (renumbered from 371)...........£45-55

Dinky Toys 'Action Kits'

These Action Kits were issued in the 1970s. Screws were usually included to attach their bases (which have no model numbers). Paint supplied with the kit is not always the same colour or shade as on the relative model when supplied built and finished.

Ref	Year(s)	Model name and details	Market Price Range
1001	1971-77	**Rolls-Royce Phantom V** Various colours (usually Blue), casting as 152	**£30-35**
1002	1971-75	**Volvo 1800s Coupé** Yellow paint, 116 casting	**£30-35**
1003	1971-75	**Volkswagen 1300** Red and White paint supplied, casting as 129	**£30-35**
1004	1971-77	**Ford Escort Police Car** Blue & White paint, 'POLICE' transfers, 270 casting	**£30-35**
1006	1973-77	**Ford Escort Mexico** Red paint and 'MEXICO' transfers, 168 casting	**£30-35**
1007	1971-75	**Jensen FF** Various colours of paint (usually Blue), casting as 188	**£30-35**
1008	1973-77	**Mercedes-Benz 600** Red, Yellow or Green paint supplied, 128 casting	**£30-35**
1009	1971-75	**Lotus F1 Racing Car** Green paint and 'gold leaf" transfers, casting as 225	**£30-35**
1012	1973-75	**Ferrari 312-B2** Red paint and 'SHELL' transfers supplied, 226 casting	**£30-35**
1013		**Matra Sports M530** Not issued	**NPP**
1014	1975-77	**Beach Buggy** Blue paint, casting as 227	**£20-30**
1017	1971-77	**Routemaster Bus** Red paint and 'ESSO Safety-Grip Tyres' transfers, 289 casting	**£30-40**
1018	1974-77	**Leyland Atlantean Bus** Various (mostly White) paint, usually 'NATIONAL' transfers, as 295	**£30-40**
?		**Leyland Atlantean Bus** 'YELLOW PAGES'. There are three variations of this: 1) Mid-Blue interior, reversed front 'Yellow Pages'	**£40-50**
		2) White interior, reversed front 'Yellow Pages' sign	**£40-50**
		3) White interior, correct reading front 'Yellow Pages'	**£40-50**
1023	1972-77	**A.E.C. Single Decker Bus** Green paint, 'GREEN LINE' transfers, casting as 283	**£30-35**
1025	1971-75	**Ford Transit Van** Red paint, 'Avis Truck Rental' transfers, 407 casting	**£30-35**
1027	1972-75	**Lunar Roving Vehicle** Blue/White paint, casting as model 355	**£30-35**
1029	1971-77	**Ford D800 Tipper Truck** Green or Yellow paint supplied, casting as model 438	**£30-35**
1030	1974-77	**Land Rover Breakdown Truck** Red or White paint in kit, casting as 442	**£30-35**
1032	1975-77	**Army Land Rover** Military-Green paint and various 'ARMY' transfers in kit, casting as 344	**£30-35**
1033	1971-77	**U.S.A. Army Jeep** Military-Green paint and military transfers supplied, casting as 615	**£30-35**
1034	1975-77	**Mobile Gun** Military-Green paint, 654 casting	**£30-35**
1035	1975-77	**Striker Anti-Tank Vehicle** Military-Green paint, transfer supplied, casting as 691	**£30-35**
1036	1975-77	**Leopard Tank** Military-Green paint, transfers supplied, 692 casting	**£30-35**
1037	1974-77	**Chieftain Tank** Military-Green paint and transfers, casting as 683	**£30-35**
1038	1975-77	**Scorpion Tank** Military-Green paint and transfers, casting as 690	**£30-35**
1039		**Leopard Recovery Tank** Not issued	**NPP**
1040	1971-77	**Sea King Helicopter** White with Blue or Orange paint plus 'USAF' transfers, casting as 724	**£30-35**
1041	1973-76	**Hawker Hurricane Mk.IIc** Camouflage paints and RAF roundels in kit, casting as 718	**£50-75**
1042	1971-77	**Spitfire Mk.II** Camouflage paints and RAF roundels in kit, casting as 719	**£50-75**
1043	1974-76	**S.E.P.E.C.A.T. Plane** Blue and Green paints, transfers, casting as 731	**£40-60**
1044	1972-75	**Messerschmitt BF-109e** Brown paint, Luftwaffe transfers, casting as 726	**£80-100**
1045	1975-76	**Multi-Role Combat Aircraft** Camouflage paints, transfers, casting as 729	**£40-60**
1050	1975-77	**Motor Patrol Boat** Black/Blue/White paints and stickers, 675 casting	**£20-30**

Dinky Toys Collector Information

Collectors of Dinky Toys may like to know of the following sources of further information.

DTCA – Dinky Toys Collectors Association

President David Cooke. Contact address: D.T.C.A., PO Box 60, Norwich, NR4 7WB, England.

Dinky News – Australia

Editor: Bruce Hoy. Contact address: PO Box 249 Aspley, Queensland 4034, Australia. Tel/Fax: +61-7-3264-4227. E-mail: dinkynews@yahoo.com.au

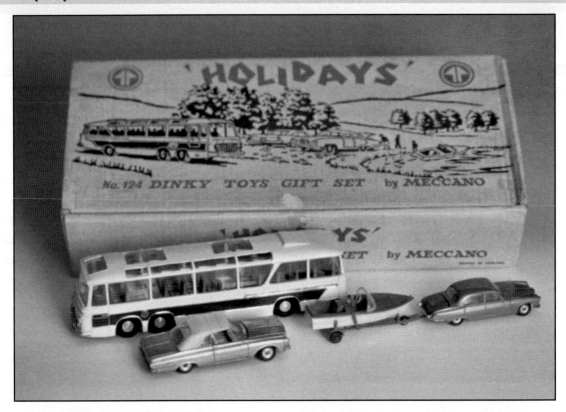

Dinky Toys 124 'Holidays' Gift Set (1964-66), containing 952 Vega Luxury Coach, 137 Plymouth, 142 Jaguar and 796 Healey Sports Boat. A stepped insert holds the models in the closed box and helps to display them when open.

Dinky Toys Gift Set No.149 Sports Cars (Produced between 1958 and 1961).

Photographs: Swapmeet Publications

BOX TYPES

Sets 001-006: Housed in Green card boxes with plain Yellow inserts.
Sets 1, 2, 3, 4, 5, 6: Oblong boxes with Yellow insert card and train picture on lid.

c 1932	Purple marbled 'Modelled Miniatures' box
c 1936	Blue patterned 'MECCANO DINKY TOYS' box, pictorial insert card
c 1939	Green box with plain insert, 'DINKY TOYS' label
1952-56	Green box with Yellow insert, stripe lid label

Train sets 17, 18, 19 and 20 box sequence:
'Modelled Miniatures' : 'Meccano Dinky Toys' : 'Dinky Toys'.

Sets 24, 25 and 30 series:

c 1934	Purple marbled 'Modelled Miniatures' box.
c 1935	Purple marbled 'MECCANO DINKY TOYS' box with Yellow/Red label picturing eight assorted cars and lorries. Purple insert with Gold script on two central lines 'MECCANO DINKY TOYS No '24', '25' or '30'.

NB The 24 Series and 30 series sets also contained a purple packing card stating 'PLEASE REMOVE THIS PACKING CARD TO DISPLAY CONTENTS'.

c 1936	Blue patterned box lid with Yellow/Red label picturing eight assorted cars and lorries. Purple insert with no Gold Script on 25 series (no details available on 24 and 30 series).

Sets 12, 42, 43, 44 and 49 (Pre-war issue):
Blue landscape boxes with inner Blue/Green pictorial inserts.

Sets 151, 152, 156, 161, 162:
Grey/Blue or Blue (152) display boxes with inner pictorial scenic backdrop and packing boards.

Early Post-war USA Special Sets: Sets for the US market were distributed by H. Hudson Dobson of New York. They are housed in flat boxes with a mottled greenish-blue lid. The picture label on the lid depicts a boy's face plus line drawings of various models. The lid often still retains a red 'H. Hudson Dobson' label. The Set number and type are shown on the main label, e.g. 'No. 6 Commercial Vehicles'. Sets 1, 2, 3 and 6 are listed – the Editor would welcome any new information on the contents of these, and of Sets 4 and 5.

> Market prices shown here are for guidance only.
> They refer ONLY to mint models in pristine boxes (where appropriate)
> that are complete with all of their original contents.

Ref	Year(s)	Set name	Contents	Market Price Range

Pre-war sets without 'fatigue' and with pristine boxes attract a premium, as do early Accessory Sets in 'Modelled Miniatures' boxes.

Ref	Year(s)	Set name	Contents	Market Price Range
001	1954-56	**Station Staff ('0' gauge)** (renumbered from 1)	(35mm). 1b Guard (flag in right hand), 1c Ticket Collector (right arm extended), 1d Driver, 1e Porter (with oblong bags), 1f Porter (standing)	£90-120
002	1954-56	**Farmyard Animals (6)**	2 x 2a horses, 2 x 2b cows, 1 x 2c pig, 1 x 2d sheep, simplified painting, (renumbered 2)	£200-300
003	1954-56	**Passengers ('0' gauge)** (renumbered from 3)	(35mm). 3a Woman (with child on left), 3b Businessman (Brown suit and case), 3c Male hiker (no stick), 3d Female hiker (Blue shirt), 3e Newsboy (Grey tray), 3f Woman (Light Red coat, round case)	£90-120
004	1954-56	**Engineering Staff ('0' gauge)** (renumbered 4)	(35mm). 2 x 4b Fitter (all-Blue and all-Brown), 4c Storekeeper (all-Brown), 4d Greaser, 4e Engine-Room attendant	£80-100
005	1954-56	**Train and Hotel Staff ('0' gauge)**	(35mm). 5a Conductor, 2 x 5b waiters, 2 x 5c Porter (both Brown or Blue), (renumbered from 5)	£90-120
006	1954-56	**Shepherd Set**	6a Shepherd (Green hat), 6b sheepdog (all-Black), 4 x 2b sheep, (renumbered from 6)	£200-300
007	1960-67	**Petrol Pump Attendants**	1 male (White overalls), 1 female (White coat)	£30-40
008	1961-67	**Fire Station Personnel**	Set of 6 fire-fighters in Blue uniforms plus hose, plastic, 35 mm. tall	£30-40
009	1962-66	**Service Station Personnel**	Set of 8 plastic figures in various colours and stances, 35 mm. tall	£30-40
010	1962-66	**Road Maintenance Personnel**	Set of 6 workmen using pick, barrow, shovels, drill etc, plus hut, brazier, barrier, and 4 lamps. Plastic, figures are 35 mm. tall	£60-70
050	1961-68	**Railway Staff ('00' gauge)**	12 Blue plastic figures in a clear plastic box. Early issues contained a Policeman, later ones a Shunter	£40-50
051	1954-59	**Station Staff ('00' gauge)**	6 plastic figures in a green card box (re-issue of pre-war Hornby-Dublo Set D1), (renumbered 1001)	£35-45
052	1961-69	**Railway Passengers ('00')**	11 plastic figures plus a seat, in a clear plastic box	£35-45
053	1954-59	**Passengers ('00' gauge)**	6 coloured plastic figures (re-issue of pre-war Hornby-Dublo Set D2), (renumbered 1003)	£35-45
054	1962-70	**Railway Station Personnel**	4 plastic figures plus 8 pieces of furniture in a clear plastic box, ('OO' gauge)	£35-45
1	1931-39	**Station Staff (6) (large)**	(40mm). 1a Station Master, 1b Guard (flag in left hand), 1c Ticket Collector (with open arms), 1d Driver, 1e Porter (round/oblong bags), 1f Porter (walking). 'HORNBY SERIES' (early issues), 'DINKY TOYS' (later)	£150-200
1	1939-41	**Station Staff (6) (small)**	(35mm). As previous set but smaller figures	£100-125
1	1939-41	**Station Staff (6)**	(35mm). 1a and 1d as above, 1b Guard (flag in right hand), 1c Ticket Collector (right arm extended), 1e Porter (oblong bags), 1f Porter (standing)	£150-200
1	1946-54	**Station Staff (5)** (renumbered 001)	(35mm). 1b Guard (flag in right hand), 1c Ticket Collector (right arm extended), 1d Driver, 1e Porter (with oblong bags), 1f Porter (standing)	£90-120
1	1954-55	**Military Vehicles (1) Set** (renumbered 699)	621 3-ton Wagon, 641 1-ton Truck, 674 Austin Champ, 676 Armoured Car. Blue/White box with Blue cut-out base plus packing piece on top	£300-400
No.1	1934-39	**Railway Accessories Set**	'Miniature Luggage and Truck'. A Porter's truck and 4 pieces of luggage (tinplate and cast), items not available separately	£100-125
No.1	1946-48	**Commercial Vehicles Set**	29c Bus, 25b Wagon, 25d Tanker, 25e Tipper and 25f Market Gardeners Lorry. In mottled Green, Blue and Fawn box with inner Green card cut-out base. Box lid has Light Green and Blue silhouette label	£2,000-2,500
No.1	1952-54	**Farm Gear Gift Set** (renumbered 398)	27a Massey-Harris Tractor, 27b Harvest Trailer, 27c Manure Spreader, 27h Disc Harrow, 27k Hay Rake. In Blue/White box with inner cut-out base plus packing piece on top	£2,000-2,500
2	1934-35	**Farmyard Animals**	2 x 2a horses, 2 x 2b cows, 1 x 2c pig, 1 x 2d sheep, in 'Modelled Miniatures' box	£750-1,000
2	1935-40		Six items as previous set but displayed in 'Dinky Toys' box	£600-800
2	1946-54		Six items as previous set but simplified (less detailed) painting, (renumbered 002)	£200-300
		NB	Boxes with a 'H. Hudson Dobson' (of New York) label may sell at a premium of 30% to 35% more.	
No.2	1934-?	**Railway Accessories Set**	'Milk Cans and Truck'. A 4-wheel barrow and 6 milk churns, not available separately	NGPP
No.2	1946-48	**Private Automobiles Set**	39a Packard, 39b Oldsmobile, 39c Lincoln, 39d Buick, 39e Chrysler. Inner Green card base in Green, Blue and Orange mottled box, Green and Blue silhouette lid label (export only issue)	£2,000-2,500
No.2	1952-53	**Commercials Vehicles Set**	25m Bedford End Tipper, 27d Land Rover (Dark Brown), 30n Farm Produce Wagon, 30p 'Mobilgas' Tanker, 30s Austin Covered Wagon. In Blue/White box with inner cut-out base plus packing piece on top	£2,000-2,500
3	1932-39	**Railway Passengers (large)**	(40mm). 3a Woman (with child on right), 3b Businessman (left hand on chest), 3c Male hiker (with stick), 3d Female hiker (White shirt), 3e Newsboy (running), 3f Woman (Red jacket, oblong case). 'HORNBY SERIES' (early issues), 'DINKY TOYS' (later)	£225-275
3	1932-39	**Railway Passengers (small)**	(35mm). As previous set but smaller figures. Oblong Green box with scenic background	£150-175
3	1939-41	**Railway Passengers**	3a Woman (with child on left), 3b Businessman (case in left hand), 3c Male hiker (no stick), 3d Female hiker (White shirt), 3e Newsboy (standing), 3f Woman (Red coat, round case)	£125-175

3	1946-54	**Railway Passengers** .... (renumbered 003)	3a Woman (with child on left), 3b Businessman (Brown suit and case), 3c Male hiker (no stick), 3d Female hiker (with Blue shirt), 3e Newsboy (Grey tray), 3f Woman (Light Red coat, round case)	£90-120
No.3	1934-?	**Railway Accessories Set**	'Platform Machines Etc'. A posting box, ticket machine, label machine and two benches, not available separately	NGPP
No.3	1947-52	**Private Automobiles Set** .... (i) (export only issue)	30d Vauxhall, 36a Armstrong, 36b Bentley, 38a Frazer-Nash, 39b Oldsmobile. Inner Green card cut-out base in Green, Blue and Orange mottled box, Green and Blue silhouette lid label	£2,000-2,500
No.3	1947-52	**Private Automobiles Set** ....(ii) (export only issue)	30d Vauxhall, 36b Bentley, 36d Rover, 38a Fraser Nash, 38c Lagonda. Inner Green card cut-out base in Green, Blue and Orange mottled box, Green and Blue silhouette lid label	£2,500-3,000
No.3	1952-54	**Passenger Cars Set**	27f Estate Car, 30h Daimler Ambulance, 40e Standard Vanguard, 40g Morris Oxford, 40h Austin Taxi, 140b Rover 75. Blue/White box with cut-out tray plus packing piece on top	£3,000-4,000
4	1932-41	**Engineering Staff (6) (large)**	(40mm). 4a Electrician, 2 x 4b Fitter (Blue/White and Brown/White), 4c Storekeeper (Brown/Black), 4d Greaser, 4e Engine-Room attendant 'HORNBY SERIES' (early issues), 'DINKY TOYS' (later)	£150-200
4	1932-41	**Engineering Staff (6) (small)**	As previous set but smaller figures	£150-175
4	1946-54	**Engineering Staff (5)** .... (renumbered 004)	2 x 4b Fitter (all-Blue and all-Brown), 4c Storekeeper (all-Brown), 4d Greaser, 4e Engine-Room attendant	£125-175
No.4	1934-?	**Railway Accessories Set**	A combination of No.1 ('Miniature Luggage & Truck'), No.2 ('Milk Cans & Truck'), and No.3 ('Platform Machines Etc.'). Individual items were not available separately	NGPP
No.4	1953-54	**Racing Cars Set** .... (renumbered 249)	23f Alfa-Romeo, 23g Cooper-Bristol, 23h Ferrari, 23j HWM and 23n Maserati. Blue/White striped box with one packing piece	£1,500-2,000
No.4	1948-48	**Commercial Vehicles Set**	Contains 25d, 25f, 25w, 29c and 30e. Brown/Green box with silhouette lid label. (US export)	£2,000-2,500
5	1932-39	**Train and Hotel Staff (large)**	(40mm). 5a Conductor, 2 x 5b waiters, 2 x 5c Porter (1 Red, 1 Green), 'HORNBY SERIES' (early issues), 'DINKY TOYS' (later)	£300-350
	NB		Also sold in USA – boxes often display 'H. Hudson Dobson' label.	
5	1932-39	**Train and Hotel Staff (small)**	As previous set but smaller figures	£150-175
5	1939-41	**Train and Hotel Staff**	5a Conductor, 2 x 5b waiters, 2 x 5c Porter (both Brown or Blue)	£125-175
5	1946-54	**Train and Hotel Staff**	5a Conductor, 2 x 5b Waiter, 2 x 5c Porter (Brown or Blue) less detail, (renumbered 005)	£90-120
5	c1950	**Military Vehicles Set**	153a (672) US Army Jeep, 161b (690) Mobile AA Gun, 151a Medium Tank, 151b (620) Transport Wagon, and 152b (671) Reconnaissance Car. Green box, inner Green card base and card cut-out packing piece,. Blue, Light Green and Red mottled lid has Purple and Yellow label	£2,000-2,500
6	1934-36	**Shepherd Set**	6a Shepherd (Dark Brown smock, hat and leggings, Black boots, lamb under arm), 6b Collie dog (Black/White), 4 x 2b sheep (Beige, 'Hornby Series' cast-in), set presented in 'Modelled Miniatures' box	£500-750
6	1936-40	**Shepherd Set**	As previous set but in 'Dinky Toys' box	£250-350
6	1946-54	**Shepherd Set** .... (renumbered 006)	6a Shepherd (all Brown below neck, Green hat), 6b Collie dog (all Black), 4 x 2b sheep (without 'Hornby Series')	£150-200
No.6	1946-48	**Commercial Vehicles Set** .... (US export issue)	29c Bus, 29b Streamline Bus, 25h Fire Engine, 30e Breakdown Car and 30f Ambulance. Mottled Purple-Blue box with inner Purple cut-out card base, Yellow/Maroon silhouette lid label	£2,000-2,500
12	1937-41	**Postal Set**	12a GPO Pillar Box, 12b Air Mail Pillar Box, 12c Telephone Call Box, 12d Telegraph Messenger, 12e Postman, 34b Royal Mail Van. Blue box with Yellow insert	£500-600
13	1931-40	**'HALL'S DISTEMPER'**	Advertisement board, White figures (one with Green brush, the other with Blue brush). Box (A898)	£300-400
15	1937-41	**Railway Signals Set**	1 x 15a 'Home' and 1 x 15a 'Distant' (single-arm signals), 2 x 15b 'Home/Distant' (double-arm signals), 1 x 15c 'Home' and 1 x 15c 'Distant' (double-arm signals). Yellow box with Purple insert, 'DINKY TOYS' on lid	£150-175
16	1936-37	**Silver Jubilee Train Set**	Locomotive and two interlocking coaches, 'LNER' and '2590' cast-in, open windows, smooth hubs with White tyres, special box, 300 mm.	
		1:	Silver loco / coaches, Grey, Mid-Blue, Dark Blue, Red or Orange trim.	£250-350
		2:	Silver loco and coaches with Dark Blue trim	£250-350
		3:	Cream loco and coaches with Red trim	£250-350
		4:	Blue loco and coaches with Dark Blue trim	£250-350
		5:	Green loco and coaches with Dark Green trim	£250-350
16	1937-40	**Streamlined Train Set**	As previous models but with a change of name and box	£250-350
16	1946-52		Blue/Black loco, 'LNER', Brown/Grey coaches, solid windows, Black tyres	£150-175
16	1952-54		As previous model but with 'BR' crest on tender, (renumbered 798). Long portrait 'ladder' box with train picture	£125-145
17	1934-40	**Passenger Train Set**	Black/Maroon loco 17a, Maroon tender 17b, Maroon/Cream coaches 20a/20b. Long portrait 'ladder' box with train picture	£300-400
			Black/Green loco 17a, Green tender 17b, two Green/Cream coaches 20a/20b Long portrait 'ladder' box with train picture	£300-400
			Lead and Mazak set in 2nd type box with correct colour spot	£400-500
18	1934-40	**Tank Goods Train Set**	Green/Black loco (21a), and 3 Green/Black open wagons (21b). Long portrait 'ladder' box with train picture	£300-400
19	1935-40	**Mixed Goods Train**	Maroon/Black loco (21a), Green/Red open wagon (21b), Red/Blue 'SHELL' tanker wagon (21d), Yellow/Red/Green lumber wagon (21e). Long portrait 'ladder' box with train picture	£400-500
	rare box version:		Set in 3rd type pictorial landscape box	£800-1,000
20	1934-40	**Tank Passenger Set**	Green/Black loco (21a), 2 Brown/Green coaches (20a), Guard's van (20b)	£300-400
21	1932-33	**Hornby Train Set**	Blue/Red loco (21a), Green open wagon (21b), Green/Blue crane wagon (21c), Red/Blue 'SHELL' tank wagon (21d), Blue/Red/Black lumber wagon (21e). Contained in plain Red 'Hornby Series' box	£500-750
21	1934-35	**Modelled Miniatures Train Set** .	As previous set, but in 'Modelled Miniatures' Red card box	£500-750
22	1933-35	**Motor Vehicles Set**	22a and 22b Cars, 22c Motor Truck, 22d Delivery Van, 22e Tractor, 22f Tank, with 'Hornby Series' or 'Dinky Toys' cast-in. 'Modelled Miniatures' box, Purple lid, full-size full-colour label with pictures of models	£3,000-4,000

23	1936-40	**Racing Cars Set**	Three models: 23c Mercedes-Benz, 23d Auto-Union, 23e 'Speed of the Wind'. Blue box (A2144)..........	**£500-750**
24	1934-40	**Motor Cars Set**.............1st issue:	24a Ambulance, 24b Limousine, 24c Town Sedan, 24d Vogue Saloon, 24e Super Streamlined Saloon, 24f Sportsman's Coupé, 24g Sports Tourer (2 seater), 24h Sports Tourer (4 seater). Purple and Gold marbled box, lid has colour top label and Yellow/Red end label with code 'DT24'	**£7,500-10,000**
		later issue:	Blue box lid (with colour label), Purple inner (A2205)	**£6,000-8,000**
25	1934-37	**Commercial Motor Vehicles**	25a Wagon, 25b Covered Wagon, 25c Flat Truck, 25d Tank Wagon, 25e Tipper, 25f Market Gardener's Lorry. Mauve 'grained' box lid (colour label) (A1052).................................	**£2,500-3,500**
		revised set:	Contains 25b, d, e, f, g and h	**£1,700-1,900**
27ak	1952-54	**'MASSEY-HARRIS' Tractor and Hayrake**..............................	27a Tractor and 27k Hayrake. Renumbered 310	**£150-200**
28/1	1934-40	**Delivery Vans Set in Trade Box**.	(1st type) 28a Hornby, 28b Pickfords, 28c Manchester Guardian, 28d Oxo, 28e Ensign Lukos, 28f Palethorpes Sausages (A1008)	**£15,000-20,000**
		revised set:	28a Hornby, 28b Pickfords, 28c Manchester Guardian, 28e Firestone, 28f Palethorpes, 28n Atco Mowers	**£15,000-20,000**
28/2	1934-40	**Delivery Vans Set in Trade Box**.	(1st type) 28g Kodak, 28h Sharps Toffees, 28k Marsh's, 28L Crawfords Biscuits, 28m Wakefield Castrol, 28n Meccano (A1008)	**£15,000-20,000**
		revised set:	28d Oxo, 28g Kodak, 28h Dunlop Tyres, 28k Marsh's, 28m Wakefield Castrol, 28h Crawfords......	**£15,000-20,000**
28/3	1936-40	**Delivery Vans Set in Trade Box**.	(2nd type) 28r Swan Pens, 28s Frys Chocolate, 28t Ovaltine, 28w Osram Lamps, 28x Hovis, 28y Exide Batteries...........................	**£2,500-3,000**
30	1935-37	**Motor Vehicles**...........................	30a Chrysler Airflow, 30b Rolls-Royce, 30c Daimler, 30d Vauxhall, 30e Breakdown Car (22c 2nd casting), 30f Ambulance	**£4,000-6,000**
	1937-41		As previous set but 30g Caravan replaces 30f Ambulance	**£3,500-4,500**
33/1	1935-37	**Mechanical Horse and Five Assorted Trailers**	33a Mechanical Horse, 33b Flat Truck, 33c Open Wagon, 33d Box Van, 33e Dust Wagon, 33f Petrol Tank with 'WAKEFIELD CASTROL' logo. Blue 'grained' box lid, large colour label.......	**£1,000-1,250**
33/2	1935-37	**Mechanical Horse and Four Assorted Trailers**	33a Mechanical Horse, 33b Flat Truck, 33c Open Wagon and 33e Dust Wagon. In Green display box (code A2036) with Yellow inner tray	**£700-900**
35	1935-41	**Small Cars Set**...........................	35a Saloon Car, 35b Racer and 35c MG Sports Car. In display type box (A2222) with tuck in flap and scenic backdrop...........................	**£750-1,000**
36	1936-41	**Motor Cars with Drivers, Passengers and Footmen**...........	36a Armstrong-Siddeley, 36b Bentley, 36c Humber, 36d Rover, 36e British Salmson 2-seater, 36f British Salmson 4-seater, all with figures. Set housed in Blue landscape box with Yellow tray with Purple inner and Brown board top packing piece. Box code A2205, dated 6-38	**£7,500-10,000**
37a	1937-41	**Motor Cycles Set**.......................	Six of 37a civilian Motor Cyclists in various colours, hand-painted detail, solid White rubber tyres. Blue box with Green and White pictorial inner......................	**£400-600**
37	1938-40	**Motor Cycles Set**.......................	Contains 37a (civilian), 37b (Police), 37c (Signals Despatch)...........................	**£400-600**
39	1939-41	**USA Saloon Cars Set**	39a Packard, 39b Oldsmobile, 39c Lincoln, 39d Buick, 39e Chrysler, 39f Studebaker. Mauve box with full colour label on lid......................	**£2,000-3,000**
42	1935-40	**Police Set**...................................	42a Police Box, 42b Motor Cycle Patrol, 42c Point-Duty Policeman (White coat), 42d Point-Duty Policeman (Blue uniform), in Blue box with pictorial inner (A2114)	**£400-500**
43	1935-41	**'R.A.C.' Set**...............................	43a RAC Box, 43b RAC Motor Cycle Patrol, 43c RAC Guide directing traffic, 43d RAC Guide saluting. Blue box, pictorial inner part, (A2064)......................	**£400-600**
44	1935-41	**'A.A.' Set**....................................	44a AA Box, 44b AA Motor Cycle Patrol, 44c AA Guide directing traffic, 44d AA Guide saluting. Blue box, pictorial inner part, (A2065)......................	**£400-600**
46	1937-41	**Pavement Set**	Dark Grey 'stone' effect (cardboard) pavement pieces in a box	**£100-150**
47	1935-41	**Road Signs Set**	12 road signs, 47e to 47t, (White under base, triangles usually filled-in) Yellow box and inner, box code A2073	**£200-250**
47	1948-54	...................................US issue:	12 road signs, 47e to 47t, (Black under base, open triangles), (renumbered 770). Plain card box with Yellow label on end of lift up lid......................	**£100-125**
		US issue:	White under bases, filled-in triangles, in a plain box marked 'Made in England'. Made for sale by H. Hudson Dobson, 200 5th Avenue, New York	NGPP
49	1935-41	**Petrol Pumps Set**...........'Pratts':	49a, 49b, 49c, 49d, 49e. White rubber hoses, Blue box	**£150-200**
49	1946-50	**Petrol Pumps Set** ....plain:	49a, 49b, 49c, 49d, 49e. Yellow plastic hoses, Yellow box	**£90-110**
	(renumbered 780)	'Pratts':	49, 49b, 49c, 49d, 49e. White rubber hoses, Yellow box	**£150-200**
		plain:	49, 49b, 49c, 49d, 49e. White plastic hoses, Yellow box	**£100-140**
50	1934-42	**Ships of the British Navy**	50a 'Hood', 50b 'Nelson', 50b 'Rodney', 50c 'Effingham', 50d 'York', 50e 'Delhi', 3 x 50f 'Broke', 50g 'X'-class Submarine, 3 x 50h 'Amazon', 50k 'K'-class Submarine. Blue box with Green/Blue label on lid	**£250-300**
51	1934-40	**Great Liners Set**.........................	51b 'Europa', 51c 'Rex', 51d 'Empress of Britain', 51e 'Strathaird', 51f 'Queen of Bermuda', 51g 'Britannic'...........................	**£250-300**
60	1934-35	**Aeroplanes Set**........................... (1st issue)	60a Imperial Airways, 60b Leopard Moth, 60c Percival Gull, 60d Low-Wing Monoplane, 60e General Monospar, 60f Autogiro, no registration letters. Dark Blue box with Green, Blue and White 'Atlanta' airliner on lid label, Yellow/Green side label dated '5-34'	**£2,000-2,500**
60	1936-41	**British Aeroplanes Set**............... (2nd issue)	60a Imperial Airways, 60b Leopard Moth, 60c Percival Gull, 60d Low-Wing Monoplane, 60e General Monospar, 60f Autogiro. All the planes in this set (except 60f) have 'GA-' markings	**£1,500-2,000**
	Box Type i)	Blue box with multicoloured label plus '150 varieties' slogan		
	Box Types ii) and iii)	Same as previous but with '200' or '300 varieties' slogans (code A1040).		

60p	1938-41	Gloster Gladiator Set	Six planes in Silver livery with RAF roundels	£400-600
60s	1938-41	'Medium Bomber' Set	Two renumbered 62n Fairey 'Battle' Bombers with camouflage finish. In Stone-colour box	£250-350
60z	1937-41	'Avions' Set	French Aeroplanes Set with 60az 'Arc-en-Ciel', Potez 58, Hanriot 180t, 61az DeWetoine 500, Breguet Corsair, 60f Cierva Autogiro. Blue box	£900-1,200
61	1937-41	R.A.F. Aeroplanes Set	60h 'Singapore' Flying Boat, 2 x 60n Fairey 'Battle' Bombers, 2 x 60p Gloster 'Gladiator' Biplanes. Contained in Blue box with full colour label on lid	£900-1,200
61z	1937-40	'Avions' Set	French Aeroplanes Set with DeWoitine D338, Potez 56, Potez 58, 61az DeWetoine 500d, Farman F360, 60f Cierva Autogiro. Blue box	£900-1,200
62h	1939	Hawker Hurricane Set	Six planes, camouflaged tops, Black undersides, mounted on card base with 'DINKY TOYS No.62h HAWKER HURRICANE SINGLE SEATER FIGHTER'. Green box dated 7-39	£500-750
62d	1939	Bristol Blenheim Bomber Set	Six planes, camouflaged, mounted on card base with 'BRISTOL BLENHEIM BOMBER MARK IV - DINKY TOYS 62d'. Green box	£400-600
62s	1939-41	Hurricane Fighters Set	Six Fighters, Silver fuselages, RAF roundels, undercarriages, Blue box	£300-400
64	1939-41	Aeroplane Set	60g Light Racer, 62h 'Hurricane' (Camouflaged), 62k 'Kings Aeroplane', 62m Light Transport, 62s 'Hurricane' (Silver), 63b Seaplane 'Mercury'. (In 1940 either 62a 'Spitfire' or 62s were substituted for 62h and 62s)	£1,000-1,250
64z	193?-4?	'Avions' Set	French Aeroplanes Set with 61az Dewoitine 'F-ADBF', 64a Amiot 370, 64b Bloch 220 'F-AOHJ', 64c Potez 63, 64d Potez 662 'F-ARAY'. Blue box, Yellow inner	£2,000-2,500
65	1939-41	Aeroplane Set	60r Flying Boat, 60t 'DC3', 60v 'Whitely' Bomber, 60w 'Clipper III', 62n Junkers, 62p 'Ensign', 62r 'Albatross', 62w 'Frobisher'. Blue box, illustrated leaflet enclosed	£1,750-2,000
66	1940-41	Camouflaged Aeroplanes Set	66a Heavy Bomber, 66b Dive Bomber Fighter, 66c Fighter, 66d Torpedo, 66e Medium Bomber, 66f Army Autogiro (Silver). Yellow-Brown box	£2,000-3,000
68	1940-41	Camouflaged Aeroplanes Set	2 x 60s 'Battle' Bombers, 2 x 62d 'Blenheim', 3 x 62h 'Hurricane' (Camouflage), 3 x 62s 'Hurricane' (Silver), 62t 'Whitely', 68a 'Ensign', 68b 'Frobisher'. Blue or Yellow box, light or dark camouflage. Models display two roundels: Red inside Blue on the wings, and White/Blue/Red on the fuselage sides	£2,500-3,500
	1940-41	US issue:	Camouflaged version of 60s, 62d, 62e, 62h, 62t, 68a and 68b. Box picture shows civilian aircraft. Red label states 'Sold by Meccano Company of America Inc., 200 5th Avenue, New York'	£2,500-3,500
101	1936-40	Dining-Room Furniture	101a Table, 101b Sideboard, 2 x 101c Carver Chair, 4 x 101d Chair	£250-350
102	1936-40	Bedroom Furniture	102a Bed, 102b Wardrobe, 102c Dressing Table, 102d Dressing Chest, 102e Dressing Table Stool, 102f Chair. Brown or Pink. Green box	£250-350
103	1936-40	Kitchen Furniture	103a Refrigerator, 103b Kitchen Cabinet, 103c Electric Cooker, 103d Table, 103e Chair. Light Blue/White or Light Green/Cream	£250-350
104	1936-40	Bathroom Furniture	104a Bath, 104b Bath Mat, 104c Pedestal Basin, 104d Stool, 104e Linen Basket, 104f Toilet. Brown or Pink. Green box	£250-350
118	1965-69	Towaway Glider Set	135 Triumph 2000 (White/Blue), Cream/Red trailer, Yellow glider	£150-200
121	1963-66	Goodwood Racing Set	112 Austin-Healey Sprite, 113 MGB, 120 Jaguar, 182 Porsche, 9 Service Station (009) plastic figures plus seated and standing drivers. In Buff/Red display box with stepped insert	£1,250-1,500
122	1963-65	Touring Gift Set	188 Caravan, 193 Station Wagon, 195 Jaguar, 270 'AA' Patrol, 295 Atlas Kenebrake, 796 Healey Sports Boat on Trailer. In Buff/Red display box with stepped insert	£1,250-1,500
123	1963-65	Mayfair Gift Set	142 Jaguar, 150 Rolls-Royce, 186 Mercedes-Benz, 194 Bentley, 198 Rolls-Royce, 199 Austin Mini Countryman, plastic figures (3 male, 1 female). Buff/Red display box with stepped insert	£1,500-1,750
124	1964-66	Holidays Gift Set	952 Vega Luxury Coach, 137 Plymouth, 142 Jaguar, 796 Healey Sports Boat. In Buff/Red display box with stepped insert	£750-1,000
125	1964-66	Fun Ahoy! Set	130 Ford Corsair with driver, 796 Healey Sports Boat with pilot. Window box	£350-450
126	1967-68	Motor Show Set	127 Rolls-Royce, 133 Cortina, 151 Vauxhall Victor, 171 Austin 1800. In Buff/Red display box with stepped insert	£1,250-1,500
	1968-69		127 Rolls-Royce, 159 Cortina, 151 Vauxhall Victor, 171 Austin 1800. In Buff/Red display box with stepped insert	£1,250-1,500
149	1958-61	Sports Cars Set	107 Sunbeam Alpine, 108 MG Midget, 109 Austin-Healey, 110 Aston-Martin, 111 Triumph TR2, all in 'competition finish'. Blue/White striped box	£2,000-2,500
150	1937-41	Royal Tank Corps Personnel	150a Officer, 2 x 150b Private, 2 x 150c Private, 150e N.C.O. Attached by cord to Yellow card in Yellow box or Grey/Blue box with Yellow inner, code A2187	£200-300
	1946-50	US export only Set:	Post-war issue of pre-war figures in original Green box with 'H. Hudson Dobson' label	£200-300
	1952-55	reissue, US only:	Contains 1 x 150a, 2 x 150b, 2 x 150c, 1 x 150e. Green box with one packing piece	£200-300
151	1937-41	Medium Tank Set	151a Tank, 151b 6-wheel Wagon, 151c Cooker Trailer, 151d Water Tank Trailer, 150d Royal Tank Corps Driver. Drop-front Blue box with pictorial inner, one packing piece with cut-outs	£300-400
152	1937-41	Light Tank Set	152a Tank, 152b Reconnaissance Car, 152c Austin 7 Car with 150d Royal Tank Corps Driver. Drop-front Blue box with pictorial inner, one packing piece with cut-outs	£300-400
156	1939-41	Mechanised Army Set	151a Tank, 151b 6-wheel Wagon, 151c Cooker Trailer, 151d Water Tank Trailer, 152a Tank, 152b Reconnaissance Car, 152c Austin 7 Car with 150d Royal Tank Corps Driver, 161a Lorry with Searchlight, 161b AA Gun on Trailer, 162a Light Dragon Tractor, 162b Ammunition Trailer, and 162c 18-pounder Gun. Drop-front Grey-Blue box (codes: '11-39', 'A2308') with contents shown on lid, four packing pieces.	£3,000-4,000
160	1939-41	Royal Artillery Personnel (reissued as 606 in 1954)	160a N.C.O., 2 x 160b Gunner, 160c Gunlayer, 2 x 160d Gunner (standing). Grey-Blue box (code: A2308) dated 11-39, Yellow box (code: A2303) dated 12-39. Production of this set continued post-war but only for export (to USA)	£200-300
	1952-55	reissue, US only:	Contains 1 x 160a, 3 x 160b, 2 x 160d, 1 x 150e. Green box with inner card stand	£200-300
161	1939-41	Mobile Anti-Aircraft Unit	161a Lorry with Searchlight and 161b A.A. Gun on Trailer. Blue or Green box ('A2257' on some), 1 packing piece with cut-outs	£500-750
162	1939-54	18-pounder Field Gun Unit	162a Light Dragon Tractor, 162b Trailer, 162c Gun. Blue box, 1 packing piece with cut-outs	£150-200

201	1965-68	**Racing Cars Set**	240 Cooper, 241 Lotus, 242 Ferrari, 243 B.R.M.	£350-450
237	1978-79	**Dinky Way Set**	Contains: 178 Mini Clubman, 211 Triumph TR7, 382 Convoy Truck, 412 Bedford 'AA' Van. **N.B.** Export only version of Set 240.	£80-100
240	1978-80	**Dinky Way Set**	211 Triumph TR7, 255 Police Mini, 382 Dump Truck, 412 Bedford Van, 20ft of 'roadway', 20 road signs, decal sheet	£60-80
245	1969-73	**Superfast Gift Set**	131 Jaguar 'E'-type, 153 Aston-Martin DB6, 188 Jensen FF	£125-150
246	1969-73	**International Gift Set**	187 De Tomaso Mangusta, 215 Ford GT, 216 Ferrari Dino	£125-150
249	1962-63	**World Famous Racing Cars**	230 Talbot-Lago, 231 Maserati, 232 Alfa-Romeo, 233 Cooper-Bristol, 234 Ferrari, 239 Vanwall. Bubble-packed onto large display card	£1,500-2,000
249	1955-58	**Racing Cars Set**	Contains 231, 232, 233, 234, 235, (renumbered from 4)	£700-900
294	1973-77	**Police Vehicles Gift Set**	250 Mini-Cooper, 254 Range-Rover, 287 Accident Unit. (Replaces Set 297)	£175-200
297	1963-73	**Police Vehicles Gift Set**	250 Mini-Cooper, 255 Ford Zodiac, 287 Accident Unit. (Replaced by Set 294)	£175-200
298	1963-66	**Emergency Services Set**	258 Ford Fairlane, 263 Ambulance, 276 Fire Tender, 277 Ambulance, with Ambulance-man, Ambulance-woman and Policeman	£400-500
299	1957-59	**Post Office Services**	260 'Royal Mail' Morris Van, 261 'GPO Telephones' Van, 750 Call Box, 011 Messenger, 012 Postman (but no Pillar Box!). Blue and White striped box	£350-450
299	1963-66	**Motorway Services Set**	434 Bedford Crash Truck, 269 Motorway Police Car, 257 Fire Chief's Car, 276 Airport Fire Tender, 263 (later 277) Criterion Ambulance	£1,200-1,500
299	1978-79	**'Crash Squad' Action Set**	244 Plymouth Police Car and 732 Bell Helicopter	£45-55
300	1973-77	**London Scene Set**	Contains 289 Routemaster Bus 'ESSO' and 284 London Taxi	£65-75
302	1979-?	**Emergency Squad Gift Pack**	Paramedic Truck and Plymouth Fire Chief Car plus figures of Gage and DeSoto. Not issued	NPP
303	1978-80	**Commando Squad Gift Set**	687 Convoy Army Truck, 667 Armoured Car, 732 Army helicopter	£75-100
304	1978-79	**Fire Rescue Gift Set**	195 Fire Chief Range Rover, 282 Land Rover, 384 Convoy Fire Truck	£70-90
306	1979-?	**'Space' Gift Pack**	358 'USS Enterprise', 357 Klingon Battle Cruiser, plus Galactic War Chariot. Not issued	NPP
307	1979-?	**'New Avengers' Gift Pack**	Purdey's TR7, John Steed's Special Leyland Jaguar, plus a 'fly-off' assailant! Not issued	NPP
309	1978-80	**Star Trek Gift Set**	357 Klingon Battle Cruiser and 358 'USS Enterprise'	£125-150
310	1954-60	**Tractor and Hayrake**	1st issue: Red 300 Tractor and 310 Hayrake. Blue/White striped box	£200-250
			2nd issue: Cherry Red 300 Tractor with Yellow hubs. In late issue Yellow box with lift-off lid	£250-300
325	19??-??	**'DAVID BROWN' Gift Set**	White 305 Tractor and Red 322 Disc Harrow	£125-175
			Yellow 305 Tractor and Red 322 Disc Harrow	£150-200
398	1964-65	**Farm Equipment Gift Set** (reissue of Set No.1)	300 Massey-Harris Tractor, 320 Harvest Trailer, 321 Manure Spreader, 322 Disc Harrow, 324 Hay Rake. Grey box with hinged lid	£1,000-1,250
399	1969-73	**Farm Tractor and Trailer**	300 Massey-Harris Tractor and 428 Large Trailer (Red/Silver). Yellow window box	£225-275
399	1977-79	**'Convoy' Gift Set**	380 Skip Truck, 381 Farm Truck, 382 Dumper Truck. 'Window' box	£35-45
606	1954-55	**Royal Artillery Personnel**	1 x 160a, 2 x 160b, 1 x 160c, 2 x 160d. Export only (to USA), (reissue of 160)	£150-200
607	1957-71	**25-pounder Field Gun Set**	Tractor, Gun and Ammunition Trailer	£125-150
616	1976-78	**AEC Transporter and Tank**	Militarised version of 974 with 683 Chieftain Tank and camouflage net	£65-80
618	1976-79	**Transporter and Helicopter**	Militarised versions of 974 and 724 with camouflage netting	£70-80
619	1976-78	**Bren-Gun Carrier Set**	622 Bren-Gun Carrier and 625 6-pounder Anti-Tank Gun	£35-45
677	1972-75	**Task Force Set**	680 Ferret Armoured Car, 681 D.U.K.W., 682 Stalwart Load Carrier	£35-45
695	1962-66	**Howitzer and Tractor**	689 Medium Artillery Tractor and 693 7.2in. Howitzer	£300-400
697	1957-71	**Field Gun Set**	688 Field Artillery Tractor, 687 Trailer, 686 25-pounder Field Gun	£80-100
698	1957-65	**Tank Transporter Set**	660 Mighty Antar Tank Transporter and 651 Centurion Tank. One packing piece in box	£160-190
699	1955-58	**Military Vehicles (1) Set** (renumbered from No.1)	621 3-ton Wagon, 641 1-ton Truck, 674 Austin Champ, 676 Armoured Car. Blue/White Striped box with inner lining and stand	£350-450
754	1958-62	**Pavement Set**	Twenty various Grey cardboard pieces representing paving	£30-40
766	1959-64	**British Road Signs**	Country Set 'A'. Six signs of the times, mostly 55 mm high. Yellow box	£70-80
767	1959-64	**British Road Signs**	Country Set 'B'. Six signs of the times, mostly 55 mm high. Yellow box	£70-80
768	1959-64	**British Road Signs**	Town Set 'A'. Six signs of the times, mostly 55 mm high. Yellow box	£70-80
769	1959-64	**British Road Signs**	Town Set 'B'. Six signs of the times, mostly 55 mm high. Yellow box	£70-80
770	1950-54	**Road Signs Set**	12 road signs, 47e to 47t, (Black under base, open triangles) US export only, (renumbered 47)	£125-175
771	1953-65	**International Road Signs**	Set of 12 various road signs with Silver posts and bases, in Yellow box with leaflet	£100-125
772	1959-63	**British Road Signs**	(Sets 766, 767, 768 and 769). 24 various road signs in a Red/Yellow box	£150-200
780	1950-54	**Petrol Pumps Set** (renumbered 49)	49a, 49b, 49c, 49d, 49e (plain). Yellow plastic hoses, export only	£90-110
			Version issued in picture box	£100-150
784	1972-74	**Dinky Goods Train Set**	Blue loco 'GER', one Red Truck, one Yellow Truck	£30-40
798	1954-59	**Express Passenger Train Set** (renumbered from 16)	Green/Black loco, 'BR' crest, Cream coaches (Grey roofs), Black tyres	£100-125
			Green/Black loco, 'BR' crest, Cream coaches/roofs/hubs, Black tyres	£100-125
			Green/Black loco, 'BR', Cream coaches/roofs, Red hubs, White tyres	£100-125
851	1961-	**Sets of vehicle 'Loads'**	2 each of 846 Oil Drums, 847 Barrels, 849 Packing Cases and 850 Crates	£30-40
900	1964-70	**'Site Building' Gift Set**	437 Muir-Hill Loader, 960 Albion Concrete Mixer, 961 Blaw-Knox Bulldozer, 962 Muir-Hill Dumper, 965 Euclid Rear Dump Truck. Grey/Red/Yellow box	£700-900
950	1969-70	**Car Transporter Set**	974 AEC Car Transporter with 136 Vauxhall Viva, 138 Hillman Imp, 162 Triumph 1300, 168 Ford Escort, 342 Austin Mini-Moke. Not issued	NPP
957	1959-65	**Fire Services Gift Set**	257 Fire Chief's Car, 955 Fire Engine, 956 Turntable Fire Escape	£250-350
990	1956-58	**Car Transporter Set**	Contains 982 Pullmore Car Transporter, one packing piece, and these cars: 154 Hillman Minx (Light Green/Cream), 156 Rover 75 (Cream/Blue), 161 Austin Somerset (Red/Yellow), 162 Ford Zephyr (Green/White)	£1,500-2,000
1001	1952-54	**Station Staff ('00' gauge)**	Set of 6 Blue figures (re-issue of pre-war Hornby-Dublo Set D1), (renumbered 051). Green card box	£45-55
1003	1952-54	**Passengers ('00' gauge)**	Set of 6 coloured figures (re-issue of pre-war Hornby-Dublo Set D2), (renumbered 053). Green card box	£45-55
49N2269	1965	**'Road Racers' Set**	Contains: 113 MGB, 114 Triumph Spitfire, 120 Jaguar E-type, 237 Mercedes-Benz, 238 Jaguar D-type, 242 Ferrari Racing Car, 243 BRM Racing Car. Special set for US mail-order company Sears-Roebuck	NGPP

TOYS OF QUALITY MADE BY MECCANO LTD.

DINKY TOYS

200 VARIETIES

A FASCINATING COLLECTING HOBBY

Dinky Toys are the most realistic and the most attractive models in miniature ever produced. They are unique in their perfection of finish, and their range is so wide as to appeal to all tastes. Start now to collect these delightful little models.

STREAMLINE SALOON
Dinky Toys No. 22h
Assorted colours. Fitted with rubber tyres.
Price 6d. each

ROYAL AIR MAIL SERVICE CAR
Dinky Toys No. 34
In correct colours. Fitted with rubber tyres.
Price 6d. each

33A   33C   33F

33E   33B   33D

MECHANICAL HORSE AND FIVE ASSORTED TRAILERS
Dinky Toys No. 33
Fitted with rubber tyres

No. 33a	Mechanical Horse	each	6d.
No. 33b	Flat Truck	,,	6d.
No. 33c	Open Wagon	,,	6d.
No. 33d	Box Van	,,	8d.
No. 33e	Dust Wagon	,,	8d.
No. 33f	Petrol Tank	,,	8d.

Price of complete set 3/6

30A   30B   30C
30D   30E   30F

MOTOR VEHICLES
Dinky Toys No. 30
Fitted with rubber tyres and silver-plated radiators.

No. 30a	Chrysler Airflow Saloon	...	each	9d.
No. 30b	Rolls-Royce Car	...	,,	9d.
No. 30c	Daimler Car	...	,,	9d.
No. 30d	Vauxhall Car	...	,,	9d.
No. 30e	Breakdown Car	...	,,	9d.
No. 30f	Ambulance	...	,,	9d.

Price of complete set 4/6

DELIVERY VANS
Dinky Toys No. 28/1

No. 28a	Hornby Train Van	...	each	6d.
No. 28b	Seccotine Van	...	,,	6d.
No. 28c	Manchester Guardian Van	,,		6d.
No. 28e	Firestone Tyres Van	...	,,	6d.
No. 28f	Palethorpe's Sausage Van	...	,,	6d.
No. 28n	Atco Lawn Mowers Van	...	,,	6d.

Price of complete set 3/—

DELIVERY VANS
Dinky Toys No. 28/2

No. 28d	Oxo Van	...	each	6d.
No. 28g	Kodak Cameras Van	...	,,	6d.
No. 28h	Dunlop Tyres Van	...	,,	6d.
No. 28k	Marsh and Baxter's Sausage Van	...	,,	6d.
No. 28m	Wakefield's Castrol Oil Van	,,		6d.
No. 28p	Crawford's Biscuit Van	...	,,	6d.

Price of complete set 3/—

49D   49A   49E   49B   49C

PETROL PUMPS
Dinky Toys No. 49
Scale models fitted with rubber hose pipes. Finished in correct colours.

No. 49a	Bowser Pump	...	...	each 4d.
No. 49b	Wayne Pump	...		,, 4d.
No. 49c	Theo Pump	...		,, 4d.
No. 49d	Shell Pump	...	...	,, 4d.
No. 49e	Oil Bin (Pratts)	...	...	,, 3d.

Price of complete set 1/6

RAILWAY MECHANICAL HORSE AND TRAILER VAN
Dinky Toys No. 33R
Price complete, L.M.S.R., L.N.E.R., G.W.R. or S.R., 1/6

PILLAR LETTER BOX AIR MAIL
Dinky Toys No. 12b
Price 3d. each

PILLAR LETTER BOX G.P.O.
Dinky Toys No. 12a
Price 3d. each

BEACON
Dinky Toys No. 47d
(Realistic models of the Belisha Safety Beacons).
Price 1d. each

ROBOT TRAFFIC SIGNAL
Dinky Toys No. 47a
(Four-face)
Price 3d. each

ROBOT TRAFFIC SIGNAL
Dinky Toys No. 47b
(Three-face)
Price 3d. each

ROBOT TRAFFIC SIGNAL
Dinky Toys No. 47c
(Two-face)
Right-angle or Back-to-back.
Price 3d. each

HOTCHKISS RACING CAR
Dinky Toys No. 23b
Assorted colours. Fitted with rubber tyres.
Price 6d. each

TRAILER
Dinky Toys No. 25g
For use with Dinky Toys (Commercial Motor Vehicles) No. 25. Fitted with rubber tyres.
Price 7d. each

R.A.C. HUT, MOTOR CYCLE PATROL AND GUIDES
Dinky Toys No. 43
This set is representative of the familiar personnel and road hut of the R.A.C. Each item is finished in correct colours.

No. 43a	R.A.C. Hut	... each	6d.
No. 43b	R.A.C. Motor Cycle Patrol	,,	9d.
No. 43c	R.A.C. Guide directing traffic	,,	3d.
No. 43d	R.A.C. Guide at the salute	,,	3d.

Price of complete set 1/9

A.A. HUT, MOTOR CYCLE PATROL AND GUIDES
Dinky Toys No. 44
Every collector of Dinky Toys will find this new addition to the range of particular interest. Each item is finished in correct colours.

No. 44a	A.A. Hut	... each	8d.
No. 44b	A.A. Motor Cycle Patrol	,,	9d.
No. 44c	A.A. Guide directing traffic	,,	3d.
No. 44d	A.A. Guide at the salute	,,	3d.

Price of complete set 1/11

PRODUCT of **MECCANO** LIMITED LIVERPOOL

STREAMLINE TOURER
Dinky Toys No. 23g
Assorted colours. Fitted with rubber tyres.
Price 6d. each

RACING CAR
Dinky Toys No. 23a
Assorted colours. Fitted with rubber tyres. Price 4d. each

Ask your dealer for a complete illustrated list of Dinky Toys

MECCANO LIMITED   —   BINNS ROAD   —   LIVERPOOL 13

A page from the December 1935 'Meccano Magazine'.

See also: Public Transport Models, Ships, Motor Cycles and Gift Sets sections.
Approximate size of figures: large 40mm (scale 1:42); small 35mm (scale 1:48).
Pre-war box title sequence: 'Modelled Miniatures'; 'Meccano Dinky Toys'; 'Dinky Toys'.

Ref	Year(s)	Model name and details	Market Price Range
1	1939-41	Station Staff (large), see Gift Sets section.	
1	1939-41	Station Staff (small), see Gift Sets section.	
1a	1932-41	Station Master (large), Dark Blue uniform with Gold or Silver buttons on long coat.	£30-35
1a	1932-41	Station Master (small), as previous model but smaller	£20-25
1b	1932-39	Guard (large), Dark Blue coat (Gold or Silver buttons), blowing whistle, flag in left hand	£30-35
1b	1932-39	Guard (small), as previous version but smaller	£20-25
1b	1939-41	Guard (large), Dark Blue coat (Gold or Silver buttons), blowing whistle, flag in right hand	£30-35
1b	1939-41	Guard (small), as previous version but smaller	£20-25
1c	1932-41	Ticket Collector (large), Dark Blue uniform (Gold or Silver buttons), slightly open arms	£30-35
1c	1932-41	Ticket Collector (large), as previous model but with only right arm extended	£30-35
1c	1932-41	Ticket Collector (small), as previous version but smaller	£20-25
1d	1932-39	Driver (large), Mid-Blue uniform (Gold or Silver buttons) holding oil-can.	£30-35
1d	1939-41	Driver (small), as previous version but smaller	£20-25
1e	1932-39	Porter with Bags (large), Dark Blue uniform, oblong case in right hand, round hat-box in left	£30-35
1e	1939-41	Porter with Bags (small), Dark Blue, oblong case in each hand (smaller than previous model)	£20-25
1f	1932-39	Porter (large), Dark Blue uniform, walking, no luggage.	£30-35
1f	1939-41	Porter (small), Dark Blue, standing, no luggage. (Smaller than previous model)	£20-25
2a	1932-41	Horses, One Light Brown or Dark Brown horse, one White horse.	£20-30
2b	1932-41	Cow, 3 versions were available; Light Brown, Dark Brown, or Black and White	£20-25
2c	1932-41	Pig. A Pink porker	£15-20
2d	1932-41	Sheep. White sheep with Black hand-painted detail	£15-20
3a	1932-39	Woman and Child (large), Woman in Green coat, child (in Red) is on woman's right	£30-35
3a	1939-41	Woman and Child (small), Woman in Green suit with Grey scarf and Red hat, child on woman's left	£20-25
3b	1932-39	Business Man (large), Dark Blue suit/hat, walking stick in right hand, left hand holds lapels	£30-35
3b	1939-41	Business Man (small), Grey suit, left hand holds attach case	£20-25
3c	1932-39	Male Hiker (large), Brown clothing, Grey, Brown or Khaki rucksack, walking stick in right hand	£30-35
3c	1939-41	Male Hiker (small), Brown clothing, Khaki rucksack, no walking stick	£20-25
3d	1932-39	Female Hiker (large), Blue skirt, White blouse, walking stick in right hand.	£30-35
3d	1939-41	Female Hiker (small), All Blue clothing, or Dark Blue skirt, White blouse.	£20-25
3e	1932-39	Newsboy (large), Brown or Blue clothing, running, papers in right hand and under left arm	£30-35
3e	1939-41	Newsboy (small), Dark Blue clothing, standing, papers in Cream tray	£20-25
3f	1932-39	Woman, Red jacket, White skirt, coat over left arm, oblong case in right hand	£25-30
3f	1939-41	Woman, Dark Red coat, Black collar, round case in right hand	£25-30
4	1932-39	Engineering Staff. See the Gift Sets section.	
4a	1932-39	Electrician (large), Blue overalls, White sleeves, carrying equipment	£30-35
4a	1939-41	Electrician (small), Blue overalls, White sleeves, carrying equipment	£20-25
4b	1932-39	Fitter (large), All-Blue overalls, or Brown overalls /White sleeves, carrying equipment	£30-35
4b	1939-41	Fitter (small), As previous model but smaller	£20-25
4c	1932-39	Storekeeper (large), Brown coat, Black trousers, holding forms in right hand, casting as 1a	£30-35
4c	1939-41	Storekeeper (small), Brown coat, Black trousers, holding forms in right hand, casting as 1a	£20-25
4d	1932-39	Greaser (large), Brown overalls, holding oil-can in right hand, casting based on 1d	£30-35
4d	1939-41	Greaser (small), Brown overalls, holding oil-can in right hand, casting based on 1d	£20-25
4e	1932-39	Engine-Room Attendant (large), Blue overalls, with or without White sleeves	£30-35
4e	1939-41	Engine-Room Attendant (small), Blue overalls, with or without White sleeves	£20-25
5	1932-39	Train and Hotel Staff. See the Gift Sets section.	
5a	1932-39	Pullman Car Conductor (large), White jacket, Blue trousers, slightly open arms, casting as 1c	£30-35
5a	1939-41	Pullman Car Conductor (small), White jacket, Blue trousers, slightly open arms, casting as 1c	£20-25
5b	1932-39	Pullman Car Waiter (large), White jacket, Blue trousers, two slightly different poses were available	£30-35
5b	1939-41	Pullman Car Waiter (small), White jacket, Blue trousers, two slightly different poses were available	£20-25
5c	1932-39	Hotel Porter (large), Red jacket/Brown trousers, or Green jacket/Blue trousers, casting as 1e	£30-35
5c	1939-41	Hotel Porter (small), Red jacket/Brown trousers, or Green jacket/Blue trousers, casting as 1e	£20-25
6	1933-40	Shepherd Set. See the Gift Sets section.	
6a	1932-41	Shepherd, Brown with Dark Brown hat	£50-75
6b	1932-41	Sheep-dog, Black and White sheep-dog	£20-30
12	1937-41	Postal Set. See the Gift Sets section.	
12a	1935-40	GPO Pillar Box 'GR', Red, with or without Red/Yellow 'Post Office' sign on top, White panel	£25-30
12b	1935-40	Air Mail Pillar Box, Blue body, 'Air Mail', White panel, casting as 12a	£35-40
12c	1936-40	Telephone Box, Cream with Silver windows	£20-30
12d	1938-40	Telegraph Messenger, Dark Blue body, picked out detail in darker Blue, Brown pouch, 35 mm	£20-25
12e	1938-40	Postman, Dark Blue body, darker Blue detail, Brown post bag and badge, 35 mm	£20-25
13	1931-40	'HALLS DISTEMPER'. Figures (lead) usually White, Cream (cardboard) panel, Red lettering	£300-400
15	1937-41	Railway Signals Set. See the Gift Sets section.	
15a	1937-41	Single Arm Signal. One Red 'Home' signal, or Yellow 'Distant' signal	£30-40
15b	1937-41	Double Arm Signal. One Red 'Home' signal and one Yellow 'Distant' signal on single pole	£40-50
15c	1937-41	Junction Signal. Two Red 'Home' signals, OR two Yellow 'Distant' signals on single pole	£65-75
30g	1936-39	Caravan Trailer, 2 wheels, drawbar, body length 81 mm. open roof windows, Blue/Cream, Red/Cream, Green/Cream, Orange/Cream, TT-Green, Chocolate and Beige, Blue hubs	£90-120 / £150-175
	1939-40	As previous models but with filled-in roof windows	£80-110
42	1935-41	Police Set. See the Gift Sets section.	
42a	1936-40	Police Box. Dark Blue box, 'POLICE' in Silver	£25-35
42c	1936-40	Point Duty Policeman, (cast in lead), White coat, Black helmet, 42 mm tall	£25-35
42d	1936-40	Point Duty Policeman, (cast in lead), Dark Blue uniform, White gauntlets, 40 mm tall	£25-35
43	1935-41	'RAC' Set. See the Gift Sets section.	
43a	1935-40	'RAC' Box. Blue and White (tinplate) call-box with 'RAC' emblem	£100-125
43c	1935-40	'RAC' Guide. (cast in lead), Blue uniform, Red sash, directing traffic, 37 mm tall	£25-35
43d	1935-40	'RAC' Guide (saluting), (cast in lead), Blue uniform with Red sash, 36 mm tall	£25-35
44	1935-41	'AA' Set. See the Gift Sets section.	
44a	1935-40	'AA' Box. Black/Yellow tinplate box with 'AA' badge and 3 signs	£100-125
44c	1935-40	'AA' Guide, (cast in lead), Tan uniform, Blue sash, directing traffic, 37 mm tall	£20-25
44d	1935-40	'AA' Guide (saluting), (cast in lead), Tan uniform, Blue sash, 36 mm tall	£20-25
45	1935-40	Garage. Cream/Orange (tinplate), Green opening doors, boxed, 127 x 90 mm.	£300-400
46	1937-40	Pavement Set. Dark Grey 'stone' effect (cardboard) pavement pieces in a box	£80-100

47	1935-41	**Road Signs Set**. See the Gift Sets section.	
47a	1935-41	**4-face Traffic Lights**. Black on White post, Yellow beacon, White base, 62 mm high	**£15-20**
47b	1935-41	**3-face Traffic Lights**. Black on White post, Yellow beacon, White base, 62 mm high	**£15-20**
47c	1935-41	**2-face Traffic Lights**. Back-to-back lights, Black on White post, Yellow beacon, White base	**£15-20**
47c	1935-41	**2-face Traffic Lights**. Lights at 90 degrees, Black on White post, Yellow beacon, White base	**£15-20**
47d	1935-41	**Belisha Beacon**. Black on White post, Orange globe, White base, 51 mm high	**£15-20**
47e	1935-41	**'30 MPH' Limit Sign**. Black on White post, Red top '30', 52 mm high	**£15-20**
47f	1935-41	**De-restriction Sign**. Black on White post, diagonal Black bar on White circle, 52 mm high	**£15-20**
47g	1935-41	**'School' Sign**. Black on White post, Red top, Black 'beacon' design, 51 mm high	**£15-20**
47h	1935-41	**'Steep Hill' Sign**. Black on White post, Red top, Black 'incline' design, 51 mm high	**£15-20**
47k	1935-41	**'S-Bend' Sign**. Black on White post, Red top, Black 'S-Bend' design, 51 mm high	**£15-20**
47m	1935-41	**'Left-Hand Bend' Sign**. Black on White post, Red top, Black 'curve' design, 51 mm high	**£15-20**
47n	1935-41	**'Right-Hand Bend' Sign**. Black on White post, Red top, Black 'curve' design, 51 mm high	**£15-20**
47p	1935-41	**'T-Junction' Sign**. Black on White post, Red top, Black 'T' design, 51 mm high	**£15-20**
47q	1935-41	**'No Entry' Sign**. Black on White post, Red 'bar' design, 48 mm high	**£15-20**
47r	1935-41	**'Major Road Ahead' Sign**. Black on White post, Red top, Black lettering, 54 mm high	**£15-20**
47s	1935-41	**'Crossing No Gates' Sign**. Black on White post, Red top, Black 'loco' design, 51 mm high	**£15-20**
47t	1935-41	**'Roundabout' Sign**. Black on White post, Red top, Black 'arrows' design, 51 mm high	**£15-20**
		NB Pre-war issues have filled in triangles.	
48	1935-41	**Filling and Service Station**. Tinplate construction with 'FILLING AND SERVICE STATION' logo. Orange box.	
		Green roof and base	**£350-500**
		Turquoise roof and base	**£350-500**
		Yellow roof, Green base	**£350-500**
49	1935-41	**Petrol Pumps Set**. See the Gift Sets section.	
49a	1935-40	**Bowser Petrol Pump**. Green pump body, White rubber hose, 46 mm	**£35-45**
49b	1935-40	**Wayne Petrol Pump**. Turquoise pump, White rubber hose, 39 mm	**£35-45**
49c	1935-40	**Theo Petrol Pump**. Blue pump, White rubber hose, 58 mm	**£35-45**
49d	1935-40	**'SHELL' Petrol Pump**. Red pump body, White rubber hose, 53 mm	**£35-45**
49e	1935-40	**'Pratts' Oil Bin**. Yellow bin body and opening tinplate lid, 'Pratts Motor Oil', 32 mm	**£40-50**
		Post-war, 49e was only available in Set 49 (without 'Pratts' logo)	**GSP**

101	1935-40	**Dining Room Set**. See the Gift Sets section.	
101a	1935-40	**Dining Table**. 'Wood' effect dining table, 64 mm	**£30-35**
101b	1935-40	**Sideboard**. 'Wood' effect sideboard with opening doors, tinplate back, 63 mm	**£30-35**
101c	1935-40	**Carver Chair**. 'Wood' effect chair with armrests, 33 mm high	**£15-20**
101d	1935-40	**Dining Chair**. 'Wood' effect chair without armrests, raised 'leather' cushion	**£10-15**
102	1935-40	**Bedroom Set**. See the Gift Sets section.	
102a	1935-40	**Bed**. Brown or Pink double bed	**£30-35**
102b	1935-40	**Wardrobe**. Brown or Pink wardrobe with opening door, tinplate back, 63 mm	**£30-35**
102c	1935-40	**Dressing Table**. Brown or Pink, opening drawers, tinplate mirror, 51 mm	**£30-35**
102d	1935-40	**Dressing Chest**. Brown or Pink, opening drawer, tinplate back, 40 mm high	**£30-35**
102e	1935-40	**Dressing Table Stool**. Brown or Pink stool, 13 mm high	**£15-20**
102f	1935-40	**Chair**. Brown or Pink	**£10-15**
103	1935-40	**Kitchen Set**. See the Gift Sets section.	
103a	1935-40	**Refrigerator**. Light Blue/White or Light Green/Cream, door, tinplate back and food tray	**£35-45**
103b	1935-40	**Kitchen Cabinet**. Light Blue/White or Light Green/Cream, opening doors/drawer, tin back	**£35-45**
103c	1935-40	**Electric Cooker**. Light Blue/White or Light Green/Cream, opening door, tinplate back	**£35-45**
103d	1935-40	**Kitchen Table**. Light Blue/White or Light Green/Cream, 34 mm high	**£30-35**
103e	1935-40	**Kitchen Chair**. Light Blue/White or Light Green/Cream, casting as 102f	**£10-15**
104	1935-40	**Bathroom Set**. See the Gift Sets section.	
104a	1935-40	**Bath**. Pink/White or Light Green/White, Gold taps, 69 mm	**£35-45**
104b	1935-40	**Bath Mat**. Mottled Green (rubber) mat, 50 x 37 mm	**£10-15**
104c	1935-40	**Pedestal Hand Basin**. Pink/White or Light Green/White, Gold taps, tinplate mirror, 63 mm	**£30-35**
104d	1935-40	**Bathroom Stool**. Pink/White or Light Green/White, 15 mm high	**£15-20**
104e	1935-40	**Linen Basket**. Pink/White or Light Green/White, hinged lid, 22 mm high	**£15-20**
104f	1935-40	**Toilet**. Pink/White or Light Green/White, hinged lid, 34 mm high	**£35-45**

---	1935-40	**'Dolly Varden' Dolls House**. Not given a reference number, made of 'leather board' (heavy reinforced cardboard), and supplied packed flat. Cream/Brown upper storey, Red brick ground floor, Red roof, 476 x 260 mm base, 476 mm high	**£500-750**

NB It is not really possible to give individual prices for single 'Dolly Varden' items as they are very rarely available in collectable condition.

Boxed sets sell for £200-300, for example.

See also the Gift Sets section.

Post-war Accessories:

No.47 Road Signs Set,
No.3 Railway Passengers,
No.49 Petrol Pumps
and Oil Bin Set

Photo:
Vectis Auctions Ltd.

Dinky Toys Accessories (Post-War)

See also: Public Transport Models, Ships, Motor Cycles and Gift Sets sections.

Ref	Year(s)	Model name and details	Market Price Range
001	1954-56	**Station Staff ('0' gauge).** 1b Guard (flag in right hand), 1c Ticket Collector (right arm extended), 1d Driver, 1e Porter (with oblong bags), 1f Porter (standing), (renumbered from 1)	**£90-120**
001	1979-80	**'Space War Station'.** Dinky Builda card (54001)	**£15-20**
002	1954-56	**Farmyard Animals (6)** 2 x 2a horses, 2 x 2b cows, 1 x 2c pig, 1 x 2d sheep, simplified painting, (renumbered from 2)	**£200-300**
002	1979-80	**'Blazing Inferno'.** Dinky Builda card (54002)	**£15-20**
003	1954-56	**Passengers ('0' gauge).** 3a Woman (with child on left), 3b Businessman (Brown suit and case), 3c Male hiker (no stick), 3d Female hiker (Blue blouse), 3e Newsboy (Grey tray), 3f Woman (Light Red coat, round case), (renumbered from 3)	**£90-120**
004	1946-54	**Engineering Staff ('0' gauge).** 2 x 4b Fitter (all-Blue and all-Brown), 4c Storekeeper (all-Brown), 4d Greaser, 4e Engine-Room attendant, (renumbered from 4)	**£90-120**
005	1954-56	**Train and Hotel Staff.** ('0' gauge), 5a Conductor, 2 x 5b waiters, 2 x 5c Porter (Brown or Blue), (renumbered from 5)	**£90-120**
006	1954-56	**Shepherd Set.** 6a Shepherd (Green hat), 6b sheepdog (all-Black), 4 x 2b sheep, (renumbered from 6)	**£250-350**
007	1960-67	**Petrol Pump Attendants.** 1 male (White overalls), 1 female (White coat), plastic	**£15-20**
008	1961-67	**Fire Station Personnel.** Set of 6 plastic fire-fighters in Blue uniforms plus hose, supplied in a bag. (Also present in GS 298)	**£65-75**
009	1962-66	**Service Station Personnel.** Set of 8 plastic figures in various colours and stances. Supplied in a bag or a Yellow box	**£65-75**
010	1962-66	**Road Maintenance Personnel.** Set of 6 workmen using pick, barrow, shovels, drill etc, plus hut, brazier, barrier, and 4 lamps Plastic, figures are 35 mm tall. Supplied in a bag or a Yellow box	**£65-75**
011	1954-56	**Telegraph Messenger.** Mid-Blue uniform, detailing in darker Blue, Brown pouch, 35 mm, (renumbered from 12d)	**£10-15**
012	1954-56	**Postman.** Mid-Blue body, darker Blue detail, Brown post bag and badge, 35 mm, (renumbered from 12e)	**£15-20**
013	1954-56	**Cook's Man** (Agent for the Thomas Cook travel company), Dark Blue coat, 40 mm high, (renumbered from 13a)	**£20-30**
050	1961-68	**Railway Staff ('00' gauge).** 12 Blue plastic figures in a clear plastic box. Early issues contained a Policeman, later ones a Shunter	**£40-50**
051	1954-59	**Station Staff ('00' gauge).** 6 plastic figures in a clear plastic box (re-issue of pre-war Hornby-Dublo Set D1), (renumbered 1001)	**£35-45**
052	1961-69	**Railway Passengers ('00').** 11 plastic figures plus a seat, in a clear plastic box	**£35-45**
053	1954-59	**Passengers ('00' gauge).** 6 Blue plastic figures (re-issue of pre-war Hornby-Dublo Set D2), (renumbered 1003)	**£35-45**
		US issue: 6 metal figures in 'Dark Red' box marked 'Made in England, For sale in the United States by H.Hudson Dobson, P.O. Box 254 - 26th Street and Jefferson Avenue, Kenilworth, New Jersey.	**NGPP**
054	1962-70	**Railway Station Personnel.** 4 plastic figures plus 8 pieces of furniture in a clear plastic box, ('OO' gauge)	**£35-45**
1	1946-54	**Station Staff.** See the Gift Sets section.	
1a	1946-54	**Station Master.** Dark Blue uniform (cap, long coat), (in Set 001 till 1956)	**£20-25**
1b	1946-54	**Guard.** Dark Blue uniform, blowing whistle, flag in right hand (see Set 001)	**£15-20**
1c	1946-54	**Ticket Collector.** Blue uniform, only right arm is extended (in Set 001 till 1956)	**£15-20**
1e	1946-54	**Porter with Bags.** Blue uniform, oblong case in each hand (in Set 001 till 1956)	**£15-20**
1f	1946-54	**Porter.** Dark Blue uniform, standing, no luggage (in Set 001 till 1956)	**£15-20**
2	1946-54	**Farmyard Animals.** See the Gift Sets section.	
2a	1946-54	**Horses.** 3 versions; Dark Brown horse (Black tail and mane), Light Brown horse (Light Brown tail and mane), White horse (2 in Set 002 till 1956)	**£20-25**

Ref	Year(s)	Model name and details	Market Price Range
2b	1946-54	**Cows.** Light Brown, Dark Brown, or Black/White (2 in Set 002 till 1956)	**£20-25**
2c	1946-54	**Pig.** Cream body (in Set 002 till 1956)	**£15-20**
2d	1946-54	**Sheep.** White body with Black hand-painted detail (in Set 002 till 1956)	**£15-20**
3	1946-54	**Passengers.** See the Gift Sets section.	
3a	1946-54	**Woman and Child.** Woman in Green suit and hat (Brown scarf), child on left (see Set 003)	**£20-25**
3b	1946-54	**Business Man.** Brown suit, left hand holds attache case (in Set 003 till 1956)	**£20-25**
3c	1946-54	**Male Hiker.** Brown clothing, Brown or Khaki rucksack, no stick (in Set 003 till 1956)	**£20-25**
3d	1946-54	**Female Hiker.** Blue or Dark Blue skirt and shirt, stick in right hand (see Set 003)	**£20-25**
3e	1946-54	**Newsboy.** Dark Blue clothing, standing, papers in Grey tray (in Set 003 till 1956)	**£20-25**
3f	1946-54	**Woman.** Light Red coat, round case in right hand (in Set 003 till 1956)	**£20-25**
4	1946-54	**Engineering Staff.** See the Gift Sets section.	
4a	1946-54	**Electrician.** Blue overalls, White sleeves, carrying equipment (in Set 004 till 1956)	**£15-20**
4b	1946-56	**Fitters.** 2 versions; one in Blue, the other Brown, carrying equipment (Set 004)	**£15-20**
4c	1946-56	**Storekeeper.** Brown coat, Black trousers, holding forms in right hand	**£15-20**
4d	1946-56	**Greaser.** Brown overalls, oil-can in right hand	**£15-20**
4e	1946-56	**Engine-Room Attendant.** Blue overalls, Blue sleeves	**£10-15**
5	1946-54	**Train and Hotel Staff.** See the Gift Sets section.	
5a	1946-56	**Pullman Car Conductor.** White jacket, Blue trousers, slightly open arms, casting as 1c	**£20-25**
5b	1946-56	**Pullman Car Waiter.** White jacket, Blue trousers, two slightly different poses are known	**£20-25**
5c	1946-56	**Hotel Porter.** Red jacket/Brown trousers, or Green jacket/Blue trousers, casting as 1e	**£20-25**
6	1946-54	**Shepherd Set.** See the Gift Sets section.	
6a	1946-56	**Shepherd.** Brown with Green hat	**£40-50**
6b	1946-56	**Sheep-dog.** All-Black sheep-dog.	**£20-30**
12c	1946-54	**Telephone Box.** Red call-box with Black window frames, 58 mm high, (renumbered 750)	**£20-30**
12d	1946-54	**Telegraph Messenger.** Dark Blue body, picked out detail in darker Blue, Brown pouch, 35 mm, (renumbered 011)	**£15-20**
12e	1946-54	**Postman.** Mid-Blue body, darker Blue detail, Brown post bag and badge, 35 mm, (renumbered 012)	**£15-20**
13a	1952-56	**Cook's Man.** (An Agent for the Thomas Cook travel company), Blue coat, 40 mm high, (renumbered 013)	**£20-30**
30g	1948-50	**Caravan.** Orange/Cream, 'Caravan Club', drawbar	**£45-55**
42a	1954-60	**Police Hut.** Dark Blue hut, 'POLICE' in Silver, 66 mm high, (renumbered 751)	**£20-30**
47	1946-50	**Road Signs Set.** See the Gift Sets section.	
49	1946-50	**Petrol Pumps Set.** See the Gift Sets section.	
49a	1946-53	**Bowser Petrol Pump.** Green pump body, White rubber hose, 46 mm	**£35-45**
49b	1946-53	**Wayne Petrol Pump.** Pale Blue pump body, Yellow plastic hose, 39 mm	**£25-35**
49c	1946-53	**Theo Petrol Pump.** Brown pump body, Yellow plastic hose, 58 mm	**£25-35**
49d	1946-53	**'SHELL' Petrol Pump.** Red pump body, Yellow plastic hose, 53 mm	**£25-35**
49e	194?-?	**Oil Bin.** As pre-war 'Pratt's' Oil Bin but only available post-war in Set 49 and without 'Pratts' logo	**£25-35**
117	1963-69	**Four Berth Caravan.** Blue/Cream, clear roof, Fawn plastic interior and door	**£35-45**
		Primrose Yellow/Cream, Red plastic interior, Yellow plastic door	**£35-45**
		Primrose Yellow/Cream, Red plastic interior, Grey plastic door	**£35-45**
188	1961-63	**Four Berth Caravan.** Green/Cream or Blue/Cream, windows, detailed interior	**£35-45**
	1963-63	As previous model but larger windows, (this model replaced by 117)	**£35-45**

190	1956-62	**Streamline Caravan**. Mid-Blue lower body, Deep Cream upper body, Cream hubs, drawbar, metal jockey wheel...**£35-45**
		Yellow lower body, Cream upper body, Cream hubs, drawbar, metal jockey wheel..**£35-45**
	1962-64	As previous models but with knobbly Grey or Black plastic jockey wheel. 2 packing rings also in box **£35-45**
386	1954-??	**Lawn Mower**. Green and Red, 140mm. Was ref. 751....**£50-75**
502	1961-63	**Garage**. Blue/Grey plastic garage, opening door, 272 mm (French issue)..**£90-110**
750	1954-62	**Telephone Box**. Red call-box with Red window frames, 58 mm high, (renumbered from 12c)..................**£25-35**
751	1949-54	**Lawn Mower**. Green and Red, 140mm. Was ref. 386....**£50-75**
751	1954-60	**Police Box**. Dark Blue hut, 'POLICE' in Silver, 66 mm high, (renumbered from 42a)............................**£25-35**
752	1953-54	**Goods Yard Crane**. Yellow with Blue or Dark Blue, mazak or cast-iron base, (renumbered 973)................**£40-50**
753	1962-67	**Police Crossing**. Black/White box on traffic island with policeman directing traffic............................**£80-100**
754	1958-62	**Pavement Set**. 20 Grey cardboard paving slabs in box..**£50-60**
755	1960-64	**Lamp Standard (Single)**. Grey/Fawn/Orange, plastic single-arm lamp on metal base...........................**£20-30**
757	1960-??	**Chocks**. Pack of 10 for 974 Car Transporter **£15-20**
756	1960-64	**Lamp Standard (Double)**. Grey/Fawn/Orange, plastic double-arm lamp on metal base **£30-40**
760	1954-60	**Pillar Box**. Red and Black pillar box, 'E II R' cast-in ..**£25-35**
763	1959-64	**Posters for Hoarding**. Six different coloured poster advertisements (on paper)......................................**£25-35**
764	1959-64	**Posters for Hoarding**. Six different coloured poster advertisements (on paper)......................................**£25-35**
765	1959-64	**Road Hoardings (6 Posters)**. Green plastic hoarding, 'David Allen and Sons Ltd' **£50-60**
766-772		**Road Sign Sets**. See the Gift Sets section.
773	1958-63	**4 face Traffic Lights**. Black/White, Black base, similar to 47a but without beacon, 62 mm **£15-20**
777	1958-63	**Belisha Beacon**. Black/White post on Black base, Orange globe, casting as 47d, 51 mm.........................**£10-15**
778	1962-66	**Road Repair Boards**. Green and Red plastic warning signs, 6 different..**£30-40**
780	1950-54	**Petrol Pumps Set**. See the Gift Sets section.
781	1955-62	**'ESSO' Petrol Station**. 'ESSO' sign, no kiosk, 2 pumps ('ESSO' and 'ESSO EXTRA')........................**£75-100**

782	1960-70	**'SHELL' Petrol Station**. 'SHELL' sign, Green/Cream kiosk, 4 Red/Yellow 'SHELL' pumps **£75-100**
783	1960-70	**'BP' Petrol Station**. 'BP' sign, Green/Cream kiosk, 4 Green/White 'BP' pumps **£75-100**
785	1960-64	**'SERVICE STATION'**. Fawn and Red plastic, with 'BP' sign, 335 x 185 mm (unbuilt kit, boxed).....**£175-225**
786	1960-66	**Tyre Rack with tyres**. Green tyre rack with 21 assorted tyres and 'DUNLOP' on board **£35-45**
787	1960-64	**Lighting Kit**. Bulb and wire lighting kit for model buildings...**£20-25**
788	1960-68	**Spare Bucket for 966** Marrel Multi-Bucket Unit..........**£10-15**
790	1960-64	**Granite Chippings** (plastic) in plastic bag (50790) **£15-20**
791	1960-64	**Imitation Coal** in a plastic bag **£15-20**
792	1960-64	**Packing Cases (3)**. White/Cream plastic packing cases, 'Hornby Dublo', 38 x 28 x 19 mm **£15-20**
793	1960-64	**Pallets**. Orange, Black, Pale Green, Yellow, Lemon, Red, Pink or mottled Purple. For 930 Pallet-Jekta Van and 404 Conveyancer **£15-20**
794	1954-64	**Loading Ramp**. Blue loading ramp for use with 582/982 Carrimore Transporter, (previously 994).........**£15-20**
846	1961-	**Oil Drums**. Pack of 6 oil drums. French issue **£15-20**
847	1961-	**Barrels**. Pack of 6 barrels. French issue......................**£15-20**
849	1961-	**Packing Cases**. Pack of 6 packing cases. French issue ..**£15-20**
850	1961-	**Crates of Bottles**. Pack of 6 crates. French issue **£15-20**
851	1961-	**Sets of vehicle 'Loads'**. Two each of 846 Oil Drums, 847 Barrels, 849 Packing Cases and 850 Crates **£50-60**
954		**Fire Station Plastic Kit**. Red doors, Cream roof, Grey floor, clear roof, 'FIRE STATION'. 'DINKY TOYS' in Red..**£200-250**
994	1954-55	**Loading Ramp**. Renumbered from 794 to 994 then back to 794 after only a year! **£15-20**
973	1954-59	**Goods Yard Crane**. Yellow with Blue or Dark Blue mazak or cast-iron base, steps in early issues, (renumbered from 752)...............................**£40-50**
1001	1952-54	**Station Staff**. See the Gift Sets section.
1003	1952-54	**Station Staff**. See the Gift Sets section.

> **Market prices shown here are for guidance only.**
> **They refer ONLY to mint models in pristine boxes (where appropriate)**
> **that are complete with all of their original contents.**

Spare tyres, batteries, bulbs, etc.

020	1968-75	**Spare tyre**... Black tyre, 16 mm. dia. YB (12)........**£15-20**
021	1970-75	**Spare tyre**... Black tyre, 20 mm. dia. YB (12)........**£15-20**
022	1971-76	**Spare tyre**... Black tyre, 16 mm. dia. YB (12)........**£15-20**
023	1971-76	**Spare tyre**... Black tyre, 16 mm. dia. YB (12)........**£15-20**
024	1971-76	**Spare tyre**... Black tyre, 23 mm. dia. YB (12)........**£15-20**
025	1976 only	**Spare tyre**... Black tyre, 17 mm. dia. YB (12)........**£15-20**
026	1976 only	**Spare tyre**... Black tyre, 21 mm. dia. YB (12)........**£15-20**
027	1976 only	**Spare tyre**... Black tyre, 27 mm. dia. YB (12)........**£15-20**
028		**Spare tyre**... Not issued.................................**NPP**
029	1976 only	**Track** .... Black Track. Box of 6 ....**£15-20**
030	1968-76	**Track** .... Black Track. Box of 6 ....**£15-20**
031	1976-78	**Track** .... Black Track. Box of 6 ....**£15-20**
032	1973-76	**Track** .... Black Track. Box of 6 ....**£15-20**
033	1973-76	**Track** .... Black Track. Box of 6 ....**£15-20**
034	1964-76	**Battery**........ 1.5 volt battery...........................**NGPP**
035	1970-76	**Battery**........ 1.5 volt battery...........................**NGPP**
036		**Battery**........ 1.5 volt battery for use with 276 Fire Tender and 277 Ambulance ....**NGPP**
037		**Lamp** .... Red light-bulb for use with 277 ....**NGPP**
038		**Lamp** .... Blue (or Orange) light-bulb for use with model 276 Airport Fire Tender.....**NGPP**
039		**Lamp** .... Clear light-bulb for 952 Vega Coach ...**NGPP**
081		**Spare tyre**... White fine tread tyre, 14 mm. dia. ....**NGPP**
082		**Spare tyre**... Black narrow tread tyre, 20 mm. dia....**NGPP**
083 (as 099)		**Spare tyre**... Grey tyre, 20 mm. in diameter ....**NGPP**
084		**Spare tyre**... Black 'recessed' tyre, 18 mm. dia. ....**NGPP**
085 (as 092)		**Spare tyre**... White tyre, 15 mm. in diameter ....**NGPP**
086		**Spare tyre**... Black fine tread tyre, 16 mm. dia........**NGPP**

087 (as 60687)	**Spare tyre**... Black big 'tractor' tyre, 35 mm. dia.....**NGPP**
089 (as 60689)	**Spare tyre**... Black 'tractor front tyre', 19 mm. dia. .**NGPP**
090 (as 60790)	**Spare tyre**... Black fine tread tyre, 14 mm. dia. ....**NGPP**
090 (as 60791)	**Spare tyre**... White fine tread tyre, 14 mm. dia. ....**NGPP**
091 (as 60036)	**Spare tyre**... Black block tread tyre, 13 mm. dia. .....**NGPP**
092 (as 14094)	**Spare tyre**... Black block tread tyre, 15 mm. dia. .....**NGPP**
092 (as 14095)	**Spare tyre**... White block tread tyre, 15 mm. dia. .....**NGPP**
093 (as 13978)	**Spare tyre**... Black medium tractor tyre, 27mm dia. **NGPP**
094 (as 6676)	**Spare tyre**... Black smooth tyre, 18 mm. diameter ...**NGPP**
095 (as 6677)	**Spare tyre**... Black block tread tyre, 18 mm. dia. .....**NGPP**
096 (as 7067)	**Spare tyre**... Tyre, 15 mm. in diameter ....**NGPP**
097 (as 7383)	**Spare wheel** Solid rubber wheel, 12 mm. dia. ....**NGPP**
098 (as 10118)	**Spare wheel** Solid rubber wheel, 12 mm. dia. ....**NGPP**
099 (as 10253)	**Spare tyre**... Black block tread tyre, 20 mm. dia. .....**NGPP**
099 (as 10253)	**Spare tyre**... Grey block tread tyre, 20 mm. dia. ......**NGPP**
6676 (as 094)	**Spare tyre**... Black smooth tyre, 18 mm. diameter ...**NGPP**
6677 (as 095)	**Spare tyre**... Black block tread tyre, 18 mm. dia. .....**NGPP**
7067 (as 095)	**Spare tyre**... Tyre, 15 mm. in diameter ....**NGPP**
7383 (as 097)	**Spare wheel** Solid rubber wheel, 12 mm. dia. ....**NGPP**
10118 (as 098)	**Spare wheel** Solid rubber wheel, 12 mm. dia. ....**NGPP**
10253 (as 099)	**Spare tyre**... Black block tread tyre, 20 mm. dia. .....**NGPP**
13978 (as 093)	**Spare tyre**... Black medium tractor tyre, 27mm dia. **NGPP**
14094 (as 092)	**Spare tyre**... Black block tread tyre, 15 mm. dia. .....**NGPP**
14095 (as 092)	**Spare tyre**... White block tread tyre, 15 mm. dia. .....**NGPP**
60036 (as 091)	**Spare tyre**... Black block tread tyre, 13 mm. dia. .....**NGPP**
606087 (as 087)	**Spare tyre**... Black big 'tractor' tyre, 35 mm. dia.....**NGPP**
606089 (as 089)	**Spare tyre**... Black 'tractor front tyre', 19 mm. dia. .**NGPP**
607090 (as 090)	**Spare tyre**... Black fine tread tyre, 14 mm. dia. ....**NGPP**
607091 (as 090)	**Spare tyre**... White fine tread tyre, 14 mm. dia. ....**NGPP**

Dinky Toys Catalogues (UK issues)

Ref	Year(s)	Publication	Cover features, details	Market Price Range

Pre-war Catalogues, leaflets and listings

Hornby 'Modelled Miniatures' were introduced in 1931 as model railway accessories. The first catalogue listings appeared in Hornby Train catalogues, Meccano catalogues and in the 'Meccano Magazine'.

Ref	Year(s)	Publication	Cover features, details	Market Price Range
-	1932-33	Hornby 'Book of Trains'	First 'Modelled Miniatures' listed as 'Railway Accessories'	£40-50
-	1932	Meccano trade catalogue	First 'Modelled Miniatures' listed as 'Railway Accessories'	£40-50
-	1933	'Meccano Magazine'	42 Hornby 'Modelled Miniatures' listed in December issue	£20-25
-	1933-34	Hornby 'Book of Trains'	Accessories are depicted in full colour	£40-50
-	1934	Meccano trade catalogue	'Modelled Miniatures' briefly renamed 'Meccano Miniatures'	£70-90
-	1934	'Meccano Magazine'	February issue contained the last published 'Modelled Miniatures' listing	£30-40
-	1934	'Meccano Magazine'	April issue contained the first 'Meccano Dinky Toys' listing	£30-40
-	1934	'Meccano Magazine'	The May, June, July, August, September and November issues each reflected the increasing number of varieties of 'Dinky Toys'	£15-20
-	1934	'Meccano Magazine'	'150 varieties of Dinky Toys' on double pages in October and December issues	£15-20
-	1934-35	Hornby 'Book of Trains'	Catalogue shows 150 'Dinky Toys' in full colour on a double page	£50-75
13/834/900	1934-35	Meccano Catalogue	Boat plane and model plus boy on cover, 3 pages of Dinky Toys	£40-50
13/834/900	1934-35	'Halford's Toys of Interest'	Includes all Dinky, Hornby, Meccano, etc.	£200-300
16/934/100	1934-35	'Hornby Trains/Meccano' Catalogue	Blue cover, full colour design of 'The World', lists 150 models of Dinky Toys	£70-90
-	1934-35	Meccano Book	Cover depicts viaduct over river, complete Dinky Toys range is listed	£70-90
-	1935	'Meccano Magazine'	January to November issues have various Dinky Toys listings	£15-20
-	1935	'Meccano Magazine'	December issue shows 200 varieties of Dinky Toys in Black and White	£15-20
7/835/65	1935-36	Hornby 'Book of Trains'	Catalogue features 200 varieties of Dinky Toys in full colour	£40-50
-	1935-36	Hornby/Meccano	Catalogue with the same cover as the 1934-35 issue	£70-90
-	1936	'Meccano Magazine'	The February and August issues featured a road layout and a competition; the May issue introduced the 'Queen Mary' model	£15-20
-	1936-37	Hornby 'Book of Trains'	The catalogue features full colour pictures of the Dinky Toys range	£40-50
-	1937	Hornby/Meccano	Catalogue with 1934-35 'World' cover again. Seven pages of listings	£50-70
-	1937	'Meccano Magazines'	Details given in the monthly listings of the superb new 'Army' range	£15-20
13/637/25	1937	8-page Leaflet	8 page fold-out buff leaflet. Front page depicts the 1937 Army models	£35-45
13/638/1150	1938	Hornby/Meccano	74 page Catalogue, full Dinky Toys listings. Numerous b/w pictures	£30-40
13/638/1150/UK	1938	'Wonder Book of Toys'	Two boys with Meccano models plus 11 pages with Dinky Toys	£30-40
8/1238/25	1938	'DINKY TOYS' Catalogue	(Booklet). Cover shows boy and 6 models including 29c Bus, 151a Tank, and 63 Mayo Composite Aircraft. Brown print on pale-yellow paper	£100-125
-	1938	'Meccano Magazine'	Details of the full range (with pictures) are published each month	£25-35
1/439/10	1939	'DINKY TOYS' leaflet	'New Products' leaflet detailing items such as the Presentation Aeroplane Sets Nos 64 and 65. Black printing on pinkish paper	£40-50
-	1939	'MECCANO' booklets	with complete Dinky Toys listings, various	NGPP
13/639/1	1939	Hornby/Meccano	74 page Catalogue, full Dinky Toys listings and Black/White pictures	£100-125
13/639/11500 UK	1939	'A Wonder Book of Toys'	Green and Yellow cover depicts two boys with their Meccano models. The booklet includes 13 pages of Dinky Toys information	£100-125
2/739/10 (1P)	1939	'DINKY TOYS' Catalogue	Famous Red/Yellow cover picture of schoolboy with outstretched arm and 17 models. Contains 14 black and white pages	£200-300
			Same catalogue, but a version with only 10 black and white pages	£175-200
-		'Toys Of Quality'	Maroon Express train features on cover plus 'The Hornby Railway Co' logo. 13 pages of Dinky Toys listings are included	£40-50
-	1939	Trade catalogue	Cover depicts boy with Dinky Toys and Hornby pictures with 'MECCANO TOYS OF QUALITY' logo	£40-50
2/939/20	1939	'Halford's Toys of Interest'	Includes all Dinky, Hornby, Meccano, etc.	£300-400
2/1139/20(3P) UK	1939	'DINKY TOYS' Catalogue	Superb Red and Yellow cover picture of schoolboy with outstretched arm and 17 models. Contains 10 Black/White pages of listings and pictures	£300-400
-	1939	'Meccano Magazine'	Each month contained Dinky Toys listings	£15-20
1/440 /100	1940	'Meccano Products'	Four page leaflet, buff paper, brown printing	£20-30
16/1040 /100	1940	'Meccano Products'	Four page leaflet, off-white paper, green printing (no pictures)	£20-30
16/1040 /200	1940	'DINKY TOYS' leaflet	Listing of models with pictures	£20-30
-	1940	'Meccano Magazine'	Wartime Dinky aircraft and the Meccano 'Spitfire Fund' are featured	£20-30
16/541/25 UK	1941	'DINKY TOYS' leaflet	Wartime camouflaged aircraft feature in this leaflet	£20-30
16/641/20 UK	1941	'DINKY TOYS' leaflet	Similar to previous leaflet, military models listed	£20-30
16/1141/20 UK	1941	'DINKY TOYS' leaflet	Listing of models and retail prices	£20-30

Full Dinky Toys listings also appeared in the toy catalogues of major retailers such as Gamages and Bentalls. These catalogues are difficult to find. Each: £30-40

Post-War Catalogues, leaflets and listings
Early Post-War period, 1945 – 1954

There were at least two editions per annum so the following listings are not complete. The 'leaflet' approach reflects the shortage of paper in early post-war years.

16/1145/75 UK	1945	Meccano leaflet	leaflet lists the models to be reintroduced after the War and features pictures of 23e, 29c, 39a, 62s, 62p. Sepia print on cream paper	£15-25
16/546/30 UK	1946	Meccano leaflet	Sepia printed listing on cream paper featuring pictures of models 70a, 38c, 29c, 23e	£15-25
16/1146/65 UK	1946	Meccano leaflet	Blue/Black print on cream paper, featuring models 70a, 38c, 70b, 38e	£15-25
16/347/50 UK	1947	Meccano leaflet	Brown print on light cream paper. Models depicted are 70a, 70b, 70c, 70e, 38c, 38e, 38f, and 153a Jeep	£15-25
16/448/30	1948	Meccano General Products	booklet with green printing on light cream paper	£15-25
16/948/200	1948		Same as previous issue but with mauve print on light cream paper	£15-25
16/1248/5	1948	'Dinky Toys Tyre Sizes'	Simple Leaflet giving information on Dinky Toys spare tyres	£15-25
16/449/100	1949	Meccano General Products	booklet with brown printing on light cream paper	£15-25
13/1049/150	1949	Meccano General Products	8 pp, cover has boys looking at globe circled by Hornby Trains, Meccano and Dinky Toys	£15-25
	1949	Independent shop listings	Full Dinky Toys listings and pictures featured in the catalogues published by the larger toy shops such as Bentalls, Gamages, etc	£15-25
16/250/100	1950	Meccano Leaflet	A leaflet of two pages, printed in purple with drawings of 22 models	£15-25
16/450/150	1950	Meccano General Products	booklet with pale Blue/Black printing on light cream paper	£15-25
16/550/75	1950	Meccano Leaflet	A leaflet folded into three 'pages', with listings all Meccano items including Dinky Builder	£15-25
13/1050/80 UK	1950	Dinky Toys Leaflet	A 12-page catalogue, printed on cream paper with sepia pictures, 5"x3" approximately	£25-35
-	1950	Independent shop listings	Full Dinky Toys listings and pictures featured in the catalogues of larger toy shops such as Gamages, Bentalls, etc	£15-25
16/251/33	1951	Meccano General Products	booklet with brown printing on light cream paper	£10-15
-	1951	Independent shop listings	Full Dinky Toys listings and pictures featured in the catalogues of larger toy shops such as Bentalls, Gamages, etc	£15-20
16/352/120	1952	Price List	A single sheet printed both sides in dark blue, listing 66 models with 23 model drawings	£10-15
13/952/250	1952	Price List	Beige leaflet with pictures and prices	£10-15
13/953/678	1953	Meccano Catalogue	Includes Dinky Toys, Meccano and Hornby Dublo	£15-20
16/453/500	1953	4-page Leaflet	Buff leaflet; front page shows date '15th April 1953' and boy shouting 'DINKY TOYS'	£15-25
16/753/75 (2P)	1953	4-page Leaflet	Printed in dark brown, with numerous illustrations	£15-20
16/853/25	1953	Price List	Beige leaflet with pictures and prices	£15-20
16/953/200	1953	Price List	no details at present	£10-15
16/454/50 (7P)	1954	4-page Leaflet	Printed in dark brown, with numerous illustrations	£10-15
16/854/25	1954	Price List	Beige leaflet with pictures and prices	£10-15
16/854/25				
16/255/100 (1P)	1955	4-page Leaflet	Dinky Toys and Dinky Supertoys listed; sepia printing	£10-15

UK Catalogue editions, 1952 – 1965

The series included fourteen editions although not all issues were given an edition number. More than one catalogue was issued in some years. It was common for catalogues to be overprinted with the name and address of the toy retailer. Original retail prices can be found under each model reference, or on a stapled-in price list in the centre of the catalogue (except for 1956 and 1957 which have separate loose-leaf price lists). In addition to issuing Dinky Toys catalogues, Meccano Ltd continued to issue 'Meccano Toys Of Quality' leaflets which provided a full listing of Dinky Toys with their retail prices plus details of their 'Hornby', 'Hornby-Dublo' and 'Meccano' products. As many as five printings per annum were produced using green, pink, blue or buff paper. When in perfect condition these leaflets sell for £5-8 each.

16/152/50	1952	(February) 16 pages	Cover features unknown 'C6321'	£55-65
16/452/50	1952	(April) 16 pages	As previous issue	£55-65
15/852/165	1952	(September) 16 pages	Cover shows hands holding 27f Estate Car, 'Dinky Toys' logo	£55-65
?	1953	24 page catalogue	Cover shows boy wearing green sweater, 'Dinky Toys' and 'Price 3d'	£55-65
7/953/150	1953	24 page catalogue	As next item: 7/953/360.	
7/953/360	1953	(1st October) 24 pages	(1) Cover features 555 Fire Engine, 522 Big Bedford Lorry and 25x Breakdown Lorry, price '2d'	£55-65
13/953/678	1953	(1st October)	(2) Cover shows 'Meccano Magic Carpet', two boys plus globe with flag	£55-65
7/754/600	1954	(1st September) 24 pages	Cover features 157 Jaguar, 480 'Kodak' Van, 641 Army Truck, 'Dinky Toys' logo, price '2d'	£40-50
7/755/515	1955	24 page catalogue	'Dinky Toys','Supertoys', 481 'Ovaltine' Van on cover, ('2d')	£40-50
7/456/800	1956	(June) 32 pages	Cover has 942 'REGENT' Tanker, 255 Mersey Tunnel 'Police' Land Rover, 157 Jaguar XK120, 'Dinky Toys' & 'Dinky Supertoys', '2d'	£40-50
7/1056/125 (2P)	1956	(October) 32 pages	Same as previous issue, 2nd printing	£30-40
7/657/820	1957	(August) 28 pages	Cover shows 290 'DUNLOP' Double Decker Bus etc, 'Dinky Toys', and 'Dinky Supertoys', price '2d UK'	£40-50
7/458/856	1958	28 page catalogue	Houses of Parliament shown on front cover with 'Dinky Toys' and 'Dinky Supertoys', price '2d UK'	£40-50
7/559/900	1959	28 page catalogue	Red Jaguar XK120 Coupe (157) on front cover with 'Dinky Toys' and 'UK Seventh Edition', price '3d'	£40-50
7/3/800	1960	32 page catalogue	Motorway bridge on cover, 'Dinky Toys' and 'UK Eighth Edition'	£40-50
7/561/700	1961	32 page catalogue	Black/Yellow cover with 6 models, 'Dinky Toys', 'UK 9th Edition'	£40-50
7/562/600	1962	32 page catalogue	Cover features 120 Jaguar 'E' type, 'Dinky Toys', price '2d'	£40-50
7/263/400	1963	?	No details available for this reference number	£25-35
13/163/200	1963	32 page catalogue	Motor Show stands featured on cover, '11th Edition', 'UK', '2d'	£25-35
13/763/400	1963	32 page catalogue	11th Edition, 2nd impression	£25-35
7/164/450	1964	8 page catalogue	'Widest Range & Best Value In The World' and 'Dinky Toys' logos Price '3d'	£25-35
7/764/450 (2nd.Ptg.)	1964	8 page catalogue	(2nd printing). As 7/164/450 except that page 8 shows Bedford TK instead of accessories	£25-35
7/265/200	1965	16 page catalogue	Rolls-Royce (127) on cover with 'Dinky Toys by Meccano' Price '3d'	£25-35
7/865/135 (2 ptg)	1965	16 page catalogue	(2nd printing). Cover features cars 127, 128, 133, 151 and 178	£25-35

UK Catalogue editions, 1966 – 1978

Up to 1972, original retail prices were on a refence listing stapled-in to the centre of the catalogue or bound-in at the back. However, no retail prices are shown on the lists for 1972 to 1978. For 1978, this list is found on the last three pages of the catalogue.

72561/2	1966	106 page catalogue ....'1st Edition', '6d', 'Always Something New From Dinky' on the cover. Bound-in (pink) price list	£25-30
72561/2	1966	(2nd edition, after 21st July) .....Same cover as 1st, 104 pages plus bound-in (buff) price list	£20-25
72571	1967	104 page catalogue ....'No.3', '6d' 12 models on cover, same logo as 72561/2. Bound-in (pale-green) price list	£20-25
		Same as previous entry, but '2nd Printing' appears on the first page of the price list	£20-25
72580	1968	104 page catalogue ....'No.4', '6d', Spectrum Pursuit Vehicle (104) on cover. Logo as 72561/2. Buff price list	£20-25
72585	1969	(May) 24 pages ....'No.5', '3d'. 102 'Joe's Car', and same logo as 72561/2. '1st Printing 1st May 1969'	£15-20
		(Sept) 24 pages ....2nd printing of 72585	£15-20
165000	1970	(May) 24 page catalogue ....'No.6', '3d', many models on cover. Same logo as 72561/2.	£15-20
	1971	(Feb) 24 page catalogue ....'2nd Printing, 1st February 1971' of 165000	£15-20
100103	1971	24 page catalogue ....'No.7', '2p', '1971 Meccano Tri-ang Ltd' on rear cover. Same logo as on 72561/2. (Note the change to Decimal Currency in 1971)	£10-15
100107	1972	(June) 28 pages ....'No.8', '2p', 683 Chieftain Tank. '1st Printing, June 1972'	£10-15
		2nd printing of 100107	£15-20
100108	1972	28 pages ....'No.8', 725 Phantom, 784 Goods Train etc. on cover, but no date or price. No price list	£10-15
100109	1973	40 pages ....'No.9', '3p', '1st Printing'. Shows 924 'Centaur', 'Dinky Toys'	£10-15
		(October) 40 pages ....2nd printing of 100109	£15-20
100113	1974	(May) 48 pages ....'No.10', '4p', cover shows 731 S.E.P.E.C.A.T. and 'Dinky Toys'	£10-15
100115 UK	1975	(June) 48 pages ....'No.11', '5p', 'Dinky Toys' and 675 Motor Patrol Boat on cover	£10-15
100118 UK	1976	48 page catalogue ....'No.12', '5p', 'Dinky Toys' and 358 'USS Enterprise' on cover	£10-15
100122 (UK)	1977	44 page catalogue ....'No.13' and '5p'. Cover features 357 Klingon Battle Cruiser	£5-10
100100	1978	44 page catalogue ....'No.14', '5p', 180 Rover 3500 on front cover. 'Airfix Group' logo on rear	£5-10

Leaflets and Price Lists, 1954 – 1978

Further information. It is known that other leaflets, literature and price lists were published. The Editor would welcome more information to add to these listings.

16/854/25	1954	Price List	no details	£30-40
16/155/100	1955	Leaflet / Price List	no details	£30-40
7/455/250	1955	(May) 8 page leaflet	251, 641, 170 and 401 on cover, 'Dinky Toys' and 'Dinky Supertoys'	£20-30
16/655/25	1955	'Hamley's' Leaflet	no details	£30-40
16/156/225	1956	Leaflet	no details	£30-40
16/556/500	1956	Leaflet / Price List	no details	£30-40
16/656/525	1956	Leaflet / Price List	no details	£30-40
no ref	1957	Booklet	Yellow cover, 'A NEW SERIES' and 'DUBLO DINKY TOYS' in red	£30-40
DT/CF/3 16/257/250 (1P)	1957	Leaflet and Price List	Yellow front leaflet '1st January 1957', pictures of 716, 162, 626, and 250 Fire Engine, 'Dinky Toys' and 'Dinky Supertoys' in Red	£30-40
DT/CF/4 UK 16/757/250 (2P)	1957	Leaflet and Price List	Yellow front folding leaflet. 'July 1957'. Pictures of 418 Leyland Comet, 923 'Heinz' Van, and 164 Vauxhall + 190 Caravan. 'Dinky Toys' and 'Dinky Supertoys' in Red	£30-40
16/857/500	1957	Leaflet / Price List	no details	£30-40
DT/CL/20 16/1157/100 UK	1957	Two-sided Leaflet	'Dublo Dinky Toys' in Red on Yellow. Pictures of first 3 issues: 064, 065, 066	£30-40
16/958/100	1958	Leaflet	Car Carrier and Trailer leaflet	£30-40
10/758/450	1958	Leaflet / Price List	no details	£30-40
DT/CF/5 16/159/100	1959	Illustrated Price List	Colour cover showing 983 Transporter and cars, etc.	£30-40
DT/CF/6 16/759/100 2ndP	1959	Price List with colour pictures	Leaflet cover shows nos. 998, 967, 968 and 986. Dated '1959/UK' on front	£30-40
10/1259/50	1959	Price List	no details	£30-40
DT/CF/7 16/160/100 (3P)	1960	Illustrated Price List	Colour cover with 666 Missile Vehicle and 785 Service Station, etc.	£30-40
DT/CF/8 16/160/100 (4P)	1960	Illustrated Price List	Colour cover with 930 Pallet-Jekta plus GS 951 Fire Service, etc.	£30-40
DT/CF/11 8/561/100	1961	Illustrated Price List	(72535/02) Colour cover with 4 cars and 'Purchase Tax Surcharges 26th July 1961'	£30-40
72557/02	1965	Leaflet	Cover with 133, 127, 128, 151 and 171, with price list	£30-40
16/766/50M	1966	Leaflet / Price List	no details	£30-40
72579	1967	Leaflet	Trade Fair leaflet, 'THUNDERBIRDS'	£30-40
72939	1967	Leaflet / Price List	no details	£30-40
72569	1968	Leaflet	Features 103-105 'Captain Scarlet' vehicles	£30-40
100217	1971	Leaflet	Four page 'Action Kits' leaflet	£20-30
100261	1971	Single sheet	Full-colour flyer featuring 'All Action Fighting Vehicles'	£20-30
no ref.	72-75	Dinky Driver's Diary	6 models shown on the cover; descriptions and diagrams of 1970s models inside	£20-30
no ref.	1979	Trade Catalogue 1979	'Fifty New Models', 11½ x 8¼ inches	£20-30

Meccano Trade Catalogues listing Dinky Toys

These were issued for many years but little information has been recorded (please send any information that you may have). For example:
Ref. 100126 – **1978 Trade Catalogue** with 'Todays World', 'Todays Meccano', Todays Dinky Toys' on the cover plus colour design of late 1970s models on Motorway with 'Meccano' buildings in background.
Ref. 100102 – **1979 Trade Catalogue** 'Today's Meccano & Dinky'.

Meccano Catalogues 1954 - 1958

with colour **'Dinky Toys'** and **'Hornby-Dublo'** listing. Details known to the compiler relate solely to issues in the mid-1950's period. 'MECCANO TOYS OF QUALITY' logo on each cover.

13/654/995UK	1954-55	**24 pages, price '2d'** ....Cover depicts 4 boys on a desert island. Black/White pictures....................................	**£20-25**
13/655/797UK	1955-56	**28 pages, price '2d'** ....Cover shows boys looking in toyshop window Black/White pictures	**£20-25**
13/756/525UK	1956	**32 pages, price '4d'** ....Cover depicts Dinky Toys, Hornby-Dublo, and a Meccano helicopter. This is a large catalogue with colour printing...	**£30-35**
13/757/500UK	1957	**32 pages, price '4d'** ....Famous cover showing Meccano Tower, Hornby-Dublo train crossing a viaduct and Dinky Toys passing beneath. Large, with colour pictures	**£50-75**
13/758/450UK	1958	**20 pages, price '4d'** ....Cover depicts boy, Hornby-Dublo train, 8 Dinky Toys and a Meccano model. Includes some superb engine pictures...	**£30-35**

Meccano Magazines, 1942 - 1952

During the latter part of the war and especially during the early post-war years when Dinky Toys catalogues were not issued, the Meccano Magazine was the main source of new information for collectors. It advised on the reintroduction of models after the war and of the forthcoming new releases. Consequently the Magazines of this period are highly collectable in their own right.
1942 - September 1943. No Dinky Toys adverts or listings appeared.
September 1943 - December 1944. Back page adverts for Meccano incorporated listing and pictures of De Havilland Flamingo Aircraft and Buick 'Viceroy' Saloon.
January - November 1945. Back page adverts said 'Sorry, not available but will be ready after the war'.
December 1945. Advert on back page announced 'Ready during December'.
1946. Virtually every month a new model was added to the listing printed on the inside front cover. A picture of each model was shown.
January - September 1947. New models added regularly each month.
October 1947. First advert appears of Dinky Supertoys with pictures of 501 Foden Diesel Wagon, 502 Foden Flat Truck, 503 Foden Flat Truck with Tailboard, 511 Guy 4 ton Lorry, 512 Guy Flat Truck, 513 Guy Flat Truck with Tailboard, and 701 Short 'Shetland' Flying Boat.
1948. Single page advert every month, new models continually introduced.
1949, 1950, 1951. Double page advert each month listing new models.
1952. Double page adverts each month. The December issue shows Gift Sets No.1 Farm Gear and No.2 Commercial Vehicles.
Prices for Meccano Magazines of this period range between **£10-15** each.

Meccano Magazines 1952 - 1975

With the introduction of yearly Dinky Toys catalogues from 1952 the Meccano Magazine lost its somewhat unique role as a combined magazine/catalogue. However, with the help of 'The Toyman' and his monthly articles plus superb colour advertising of new models, the Magazine continued to provide a valuable service for collectors. Meccano Magazines of this period are in the price range of **£5-10**.

Dinky Toys Club Licences, Newsletters, etc.

no ref.	19??-??	**Dinky Toys Club Certificate**............(unused) **£100-125**	
no ref	1955-??	**Dinky Toys Club Enamel Badge** **£35-45**	
no ref	1955-??	**Dinky Toys Club 'Welcome' Letter** ....NGPP	

Dinky Toys Club Newsletters

?	195?	**Dinky Toys Club Newsletter No.1**, '3d', 'Greetings from Australia' on cover **£60-80**	
19/759/35	1959?	**Newsletter No.2**, '3d'. Stirling Moss on cover, 150 Rolls-Royce featured in centre-fold.............**£60-80**	
?	19??	**Newsletter No.3**, 'M1' on cover.........................**£60-80**	
DTC/L/1	1958-59	**Collector's Licence**, Brown cover, 16 pages ...**£125-150**	
DTC/L/2	1959-60	**Collector's Licence**, Red cover, 16 pages **£100-125**	
DTC/L/3	1960-61	**Collector's Licence**, Green cover, 16 pages **£60-80**	
DTC/L/4	1961-62	**Collector's Licence**, Yellow cover, 16 pages.......**£60-80**	

Factory drawings

UNISSUED MODELS
A number of models were planned but not actually produced by Meccano. This is list of known factory drawings and plans for such models.
Austin A40 Van 'OMNISPORT' drawing dated 31-8-57. **Guy Warrior Van** 'GOLDEN SHRED' drawing dated 26-3-57, Job No. 14794. **Leyland Fuel Tanker** drawing dated 30-9-65, Job No. 62520. **Single-Deck Bus** drawing dated 14-5-34, Job No. 6763. **Jowett Javelin Saloon** drawing dated 10-10-47, Job No. 12886. **Renault Fregate** drawing dated 4-7-57, Job No. 20106. **Triumph Dolomite** (intended 38e) drawing dated 1939. **Vampire Jet** drawing dated 27-11-45, Job No. 12157. **Firebrand Aircraft** drawing dated 18-12-45, Job No. 12159.

PRODUCTION MODELS
In October 2000, Christie's South Kensington sold part of the Mike and Sue Richardson collection of Meccano General Assembly Drawings for the Dinky Toys range. The following is a small selection of items from that sale. The reference numbers are 'Job Numbers'.

Drawings – English Saloon Cars. 13866/7 **Jaguar XK120 and Base**, 20335 **Base XK150**, 20329 **Spring XK150**, 13381/3 **Austin Atlantic Body and** Base, 20121/2 and 20118/9 **Rolls-Royce Silver Wraith** (various parts), 62035/6/7 **Chauffuer and Passengers**, 13360/1/2 **Rover 75**, 14844/5 **Spring and Base for Humber Hawk**, 14982/4 **Singer Gazelle Body and Base**, 14088/9 **Austin A30 Body and Base**, 14721/3 **Sunbeam Rapier Body and Base**, 14721/3 **Sunbeam Rapier Body and Base**, 14745/7 **Hillman Minx Body and Base**, 7889 **Ford Zephyr Body**, 14097/8 **Vauxhall Cresta Body and Base**, 14937/8 **Fiat 600 Body and Base**, 14847/8 **Austin A105 Body and Base**. (*All 1950s*). In all, 33 items sold in one lot for.......................**£750**

Drawings – Buses. 10897/8 **Double Deck Omnibus Body and Base** (both with dyeline copies), **Memo** 15954 about 17693 **'Dunlop' Transfers**, 13480/2 **Luxury Coach and Base**, 13750/2 **Duple Roadmaster Coach and Base**, 13424/6 **Observation Coach and Base**. 12 items in one lot sold for........**£420**

Drawings – Fodens. 12163/6 and 12822 **Cab and Chassis, Body and Tanker Body**, 12164/5/9 **Bogie, Clip and Washer for Spare Wheel** + 7 drawings for **Chains, Stanchions, Tank parts**, etc. 13 items sold for.......**£550**

Drawings – Leyland Octopus. 7874 **Cab and Chassis**, 7875 **Front Bogie**, and **Memo** 20649 **Label for 'ESSO'**. 3 items sold as one lot for.............**£120**

Overseas Catalogues

Catalogues were often adapted so that they could be switched for use in most countries in the world irrespective of the language or the currency used. An example of this is the 1965 catalogue:

72257/02UK 1965   **UK catalogue** ....16 pages. Cover depicts 5 cars namely Nos.127, 128, 133 and 171 plus a description of various model features **£25-35**

72557 1965   **Overseas edition** ....16 pages. The cover is the same but replacing the features listing is a panel with 'Precision Diecast Scale Models' printed in English, German, French, Spanish, Italian and Swedish. The catalogue pages contain only the basic English model name and number - all the English text having been removed. The models are the same as 72257/02 ....**£25-35**

72559 1965   **Overseas edition** ....24 pages. Whilst the cover is the same as 72557, the listings are entirely different for they feature both English and French Dinky Toys, including the French issues sold in the UK........**£40-50**

Price lists. Prior to the overseas editions being despatched, price lists in the correct language and currency would be inserted.
The Editor would like to express his thanks to the many collectors around the world who have contributed to this listing. New information would be welcomed.

For French Dinky Toys Catalogues, please see the Catalogues listing at the end of the French Meccano Dinky Toys section.

Africa   (Distributor unknown)

KENYA
1961 **Illustrated List** **£75-100**
RHODESIA
1953 **Illustrated Price List** **£75-100**
1954 **Illustrated Price List** **£75-100**
SOUTH AFRICA
1955 **Catalogue '7/655/20'**, Ovaltine Van + 7 others, 24 pages **£50-75**
TANGANYIKA & UGANDA, Combined Catalogue (year unknown) ...**£75-100**

Australia

Agents (in 1952): E. G. Page & Co. (Sales) Pty., Ltd., Danks Building, 324 Pitt Street, Sydney, Australia.

1950 **Meccano General Products Catalogue '13/550/68'**, as 1949 UK Catalogue, 'Meccano World-Famous Toys' **£80-100**
1952 **Catalogue '5/352/37.5'**, Cover has sepia drawings of hands holding 27f, with 139b, 25x and 532 ....**£50-75**
1952 **Catalogue '13/852/12'**, Cover shows boy with green sweater. An example sold at auction in 1998 for **£250**
1955 **Catalogue '7/655/30'**, 282, 591, 290, 961, 430, 251, 962 and 481 on cover **£40-60**
1956 **Leaflet '16/456/15'**, 8 page folded leaflet with coloured drawings and price list. Cover has 132, 255 and 781 ....**£25-35**
1957 **Leaflet '16/357/7.5 (1P)'**, folded colour leaflet with 716, 162, 626 and 955 on the front **£25-35**
1957 **Leaflet '16/757/15 (2P)'**, folded colour leaflet with 932, 923, 164, 190 and 'Dinky Toys and Dinky Supertoys' on billboard ...**£25-35**
1957 **Catalogue '7/757/30'**, Piccadilly Circus, colour, vertical, no prices, 28 pages **£75-100**
1958 **Catalogue '7/658/40'**, Cover as UK issue **£30-45**
1959 **Catalogue '7/559/40'**, Cover as UK issue **£30-45**
1960 **Catalogue '23/560/40'**, Cover as UK issue **£30-45**
1961 **Catalogue '7/61/40'**, Cover as UK issue **£30-45**
1962 **Catalogue '7/662/40'**, Cover as UK issue **£30-45**
1963 **Catalogue '13/163/100'**, Cover as UK issue **£25-35**
1964 **Catalogue '7/364/100'**, Cover as UK issue **£25-35**
1969 **Catalogue '72585'**, Cover as UK issue **£25-35**
1971 **Catalogue '100103'**, Cover as UK issue **£20-25**
1978 **Catalogue '100100'** ('No.14'), '20c' on cover, 44 pages. 'Liberty Trading Pty Ltd, Surrey Hills, Marshall St. NSW' on checklist........**£20-25**

Belgium and Luxembourg (French printing)

Agents: P FREMINEUR et Fils, Rue des Bogards 1, Bruxelles 1

1936 **Meccano Catalogue '13/736/265'** **£200-300**
1954 **Catalogue '16/1053 /10'**, Same cover as 1953 UK issue **£40-50**
1954 **Catalogue '16/1054 /2'**, Same cover as 1954 UK issue **£40-50**
1956 **Catalogue '16/656/156'** (DT/CL/5). Cover as 1956 UK issue **£40-50**
1958 **Leaflet '16/1258/12.5 Belgium'** ('DT/CL/32' on cover). Printed in England. 168 Singer and 178 Plymouth on cover. Text in French and Flemish **£40-50**
1959 **Catalogue '7/539/-'**, Red Jaguar XK140 on cover **£30-40**
1960 **Catalogue** (no ref.). English and French models in one catalogue, 48 pages. Printed and issued only in Belgium and Luxembourg. Cover depicts Land Rover plus two French Dinky Toys cars. 'Frs 3-'. **£75-100**

Belgium (Flemish printing)

1954 **Illustrated price list '16/1054 /2'** **£40-50**
1966 **1st Edition price list '72551'**, in French and Flemish, 164 pages ...**£40-50**

Canada

Agents: Meccano Limited, 675 King Street West, Toronto and 187 - 189 Church Street, Toronto.

1934 **Leaflet '10/34'**, Yellow leaflet with 'LOCKE BROS. OF MONTREAL' stamp **£150-200**
1937 **Leaflet '13/637/5'**, Eight page leaflet **£150-200**
1938 **Leaflet '7/38'**, Ten page fold-out leaflet with full range **£150-200**
1940 **Leaflet '13/840/5'**, 12 black and white pages, 8.75" x 5.875". Cover shows boy with outstretched arms plus 62h, 151a, 36g, 43a, and 33r. 'The Fascinating Collecting Hobby' ...**£150-200**
1941 **Leaflet '6/41'**, 12 page fold-out leaflet showing full range **£150-200**
1951 **Catalogue '16/351/25'**, 16 pages, boy + 3 models, blue pictures **£60-70**
1953 **Catalogue '7/953/150'**, 555 Fire Engine, 522 Big Bedford, 25x Breakdown Truck, 28 pages **£50-60**
1955 **Illustrated price list: '16/355/90'**, Off-White leaflet **£30-35**
1955 **Catalogue '7/655/90'**, Illustration of Bedford 'Ovaltine' Van plus seven other models **£50-60**
1956 **Catalogue '7/556/90'**, Regent Tanker/Tunnel, 1st June 1956 in colour, 32 pages **£50-60**
1956 **Illustrated price leaflet '16/656/18c'**, (DT/CL/4) in colour, featuring 131 Cadillac and 660 Tank Transporter **£20-30**
1956 **Illustrated price leaflet '16/756/18'**, in colour, featuring 706 Vickers 'Air France' Airliner **£20-30**
1957 **Catalogue '7/757/90'**, Piccadilly Circus, vertical, in colour, with prices, 28 pages **£50-60**
1959 **Catalogue '7/559/90'**, Red Jaguar + 6 models on cover, 28 pages .**£50-60**
1960 **Catalogue '7/560/90'**, cover as UK issue **£40-50**
1961 **Catalogue '3/41/25 7252 3/42'**, Black with 7 models and '9th' on cover, Canada/English, 32 pages **£40-50**
1963 **Catalogue '13/163/100 7254 2/42'**, Motor Show 11th, Canada/English, 32 pages **£40-50**
1963 **Catalogue '13/1063 /50 7254 8/42'**, Flyer 8in x 10¼in. 10 models on cover, 'Canada 1963', 8 pages **£30-40**
1964 **Trade Catalogue '7/364/150'**, 8 page catalogue plus 4 page trade price list (half catalogue width, in centre) **£30-40**
1964 **Catalogue '7/464/150 72550/42'**, '12th', 8in x 11in, Canada/English, 8 pages **£20-30**
1964 **Catalogue** (no ref.), Flyer, 5½ x 3½, shows 6 Hong Kong models, 12 pages **£10-15**
1965 **Catalogue** (no ref.) 1st Ed. 8½ x 5½, 5 models on cover, 16 pp...**£20-25**
1966 **Catalogue '72561'**, 1st Edition, 108 pages **£30-40**
1966 **Catalogue '72561'**, 2nd Edition, 106 pages **£30-40**
1967 **Catalogue '72571'**, 3rd edition, 106 pages **£30-40**
1968 **Catalogue '72580'**, 4th Edition, 106 pages **£30-40**
1969 **Catalogue '72585'**, 5th Edition, 24 pages **£20-30**
1970 **Catalogue '165000'**, cover as UK issue **£15-25**
1971 **Catalogue '100103'**, cover as UK issue **£15-25**

Cyprus
1969 **Catalogue** (no ref.), Same as UK issue **£50-75**

Egypt
1952 **Catalogue '5/652/2'**, Different p.9 from UK issue with pictures of US 39 Series cars and British cars **£100-150**

Eire and Channel Islands

Agents: S.J. Gearey, 1 St Stephens Green, Dublin. (Ceased trading 1968).
Agents from 1969: Kilroy Bros Ltd, Shanowen Road, Whitehall, Dublin 9.

1953 **Catalogue '7/953/9'**. 'Eire' and 'C.I.' on cover **£40-50**
1955 **Catalogue '7/755/20'**. 'Eire' and 'C.I.' on cover **£40-50**
1959 **Catalogue '7/659/75'**, 'Eire' on cover. **£40-50**
1964 **Catalogue '7/364/7'**, 'Eire' on cover. **£30-40**
1969 **Catalogue 'No.5'**, 'Irish' on cover, (agents: Kilroy Bros Ltd). **£30-40**

Catalogues

Hong Kong

Representatives: W.R.Loxley & Co. Ltd., Jardine House, 11th Floor, 20 Pedder Street, Hong Kong.

1959 **Illustrated price list 'DT/CF/5'**, same cover as UK issue **£50-75**

Italy

Agents: Alfredo Parodi, Piazza 8, Marcellino 6, Genova.

1957 **Leaflet '16/657/5'**, with 101-105 ....**£30-35**
1957 **Leaflet '16/3/57/5'**, showing 677 and 472 'Raleigh' **£30-35**
1957 **Leaflet '16/357/5'**, 642 and 455 'Brooke Bond Tea' **£30-35**
1957 **Leaflet '16/857/5'**, 237 Mercedes front, 136, 236, 238 back **£30-35**
1957 **Leaflet '16/457/5'**, 697 Military Set...**£30-35**
1957 **Leaflet '16/457/5'**, 661 and 919 'Golden Shred' **£30-35**
1957 **Leaflet** (no ref.), with 163, 236 and 238 on racing circuit...............**£30-35**
1957 **Leaflet** (no ref.), with 237, 661, and 919 'Golden Shred'................**£30-35**
1957 **Illustrated Leaflet '16/357/5'**, 'Italy' printed after the ref. no......**£30-35**
1957 **Leaflet '12/757/50'** (DT/CL/15) 642 and 455 'Brooke Bond'..........**£30-35**
1957 **Catalogue '7/857/50'**, Same cover as UK issue 7/657/820 ....**£40-50**
1957 **Leaflet 'DT/CL/12'**, with 677 and 472 on cover..........................**£30-35**
1958 **Catalogue '7/758/50'**, Same cover as UK issue 7/458/856 ....**£40-50**
1964 **Catalogue '7/364/40 7225 0/37'**, 12th, 8in x 11in, includes
       four pages of French Dinky, 12 pages in total **£30-35**

Malaya and Singapore

Agents: King & Co, Singapore.

1957 **Catalogue '16/557/25 (1P)'** (DT/CF/3), 8 pages, cover depicts 170,
       626, 716, 955, other pictures within, price list in $ **£40-50**
1958 **Catalogue '7/958/10'**, cover as UK, 4 pages with prices in $ **£40-50**

Netherlands/Holland

Agents: Hausemann & Hotte NV, Kromboomsloot 57-61, Amsterdam.

Pre-War Editions
1936 **'1/736/5'** Yellow paper with Black printing **£175-200**
1937 **'13/637/75'** Yellow paper with Black printing **£175-200**
1938 **'13/738/22'** Yellow paper with Black printing **£175-200**

Post-War Editions - Some black/white, later coloured as per UK issues.
1954 **Illustrated price list '16/954/108'**, Printed in French **£15-20**
1955 **'8/1255/50** (DT/L/7)', no details....................................**£40-50**
1956 **'16/256/30n** (DT/CL/2)', no details.................................**£30-40**
1956 **'16/256/30n** (DT/L/9)', no details..................................**£30-40**
1958 **'16/1158 /20'**, 'Nederland Frs 3-'. Cover same as 1958 UK issue ..**£30-35**
1962 **'16/256/30** (72538/29)', no details.................................**£20-25**
1967 **Catalogue '72571'**, 3rd Ed., price list in Dutch florins, 162 pages..**£40-50**
1970 **Catalogue** (no ref.), 6th Edition includes 8 pages of French Dinky,
       32 pages in total **£20-30**

Portugal

1956 **Illustrated Catalogue** (no ref.), no details........................**£40-50**
1957 **Illustrated Leaflet, 'DT/CF/4'**, no details.........................**£50-70**
1958 **Illustrated Catalogue '7/858/5'**, Houses of Parliament on cover..**£50-60**
1959 **Illustrated Catalogue** (no ref.), no details.......................**£40-50**
1961 **Illustrated Catalogue '5/261/25'**, 9th edition **£40-50**
1963 **Illustrated Catalogue** (no ref.), no details.......................**£30-40**
1960s **Illustrated Catalogue '7255049'**, group of 1960s cars on cover..**£30-40**
1969 **'No.5' Catalogue '72585'**, cover features 'Joe 90's Car' **£30-40**

Spain

1957 **Illustrated Leaflet 'DT/CL15 SP 16/457/5'**, Similar to Italian leaflet with 697 on colour front of single sheet, unpriced list on reverse **£10-15**

Sweden

Agents: Ludvig Wigart & Cos, AB Helsingborg.

1954 **'7/654/14'**, 4 pages, 3 pages colour pictures plus price list
       in Kroner with Swedish text....................................**£40-50**
1957 **Leaflet '16/357/15'**, Leaflet depicts 455 'Brooke Bond' Trojan
       plus 642 RAF Tanker. Price list in Kroner; Swedish text.....**£15-20**
1957 **Catalogue**, 28 pages **£70-90**
1961 **Catalogue '14/561/60'**, as 1961 UK issue, text in Swedish **£30-40**
1968 **Catalogue '72580'**, 162 pp, as UK 1968 edition, but in Swedish **£20-30**

Switzerland

Agents: Riva & Kunzmann SA Basel 2, Switzerland. From 1965 address changed to Prattela, Switzerland.

1956 **Catalogue '7/356/20'**, Ovaltine + 7 others, prices in francs, 24 pp..**£40-50**
1958 **Catalogue '7/858/80'**, cover as UK version...........................**£40-50**
1962 **Catalogue '72537/25'**, 10th Edition, 48 pages, same as
       UK issue 72537/02 plus French Dinky **£40-50**
1963 **Catalogue '13/163/175'**, 11th Edition, 48 pages, same as
       UK issue 13/163/20 plus French Dinky.........................**£40-50**
1965 **Catalogue '72559'**, 24 pp, cover as UK 72557 + French Dinky......**£40-50**

United States of America

Agents: H. Hudson Dobson, PO Box 254, 26th St and Jefferson Avenue, Kenilworth, NJ.
In 1952 the address was: PO Box 254, 906 Westfield Avenue, Elizabeth, NJ.

From 1957 the address changed to 627 Boulevard, Kenilworth. New York showroom: 200, Fifth Avenue, PO Box 255. Models sold by this distributor will often be found with an 'H.Hudson Dobson' label
From 1963: Lines Bros Inc, 1107 Broadway, New York. From ?: AVA International, Box 7611, Waco, Texas 76710.

War-Time Issue
1941 **Large leaflet** (no ref.), no details available ....NGPP

Post-War Editions
1951 **Catalogue** (no ref.), boy's side face, 5 models, black and white,
       green printing, 16 pages **£100-125**
1952 **Catalogue** (no ref.), hands holding 27f (139b and 25x in picture).
       Unlike the UK edition, 39b, 39c and 39e are shown in
       two-tone colours **£100-125**
1953 **Catalogue '7/753/150'**, same cover as 1953 UK issue 7/953/360....**£50-75**
1954 **Catalogue '7/954/150'**, same cover as 1954 UK issue 7/754/600....**£50-75**
1954 **Catalogue '7/753/150'**, 157 Jaguar, 480 Kodak, 641 Army,
       separate price list, 28 pages.................................**£50-75**
1955 **Catalogue** (no ref.), 20 models on cover, 5 French, black and
       white, prices in $, 32 pages **£50-75**
1956 **Catalogue** (no ref.), ...'Ever-Ready' + 11 others, Feb 57,
       black/white, prices in $, 32 pages **£50-75**
1957 **Catalogue** (no ref.), Yellow/Red cover shows model 697 plus Red
       lined sections displaying English and French models. Red
       panel with US address of H.Hudson Dobson. 36 black/white
       pages of English and French models **£100-125**
1957 **Catalogue** (no ref.), Yellow, Red lines, black/white, 9-30-57,
       prices in $, 36 pages **£50-75**
1958 **Catalogue '7/958/250'**, Houses of Parliament, prices in $, 32pp..**£50-75**
1959 **Leaflet '7/7/125'**, Colour, English and French, prices in $...........**£20-30**
1959 **USA Catalogue '7/559/250'**, Cover depicts Red Jaguar XK140 etc
       26 pages English models, 6 pages French **£50-75**
1959 **Leaflet '7/8/125'**, 3 pp of colour pictures + price list. English and
       French items on cover, (195 Jaguar 3.4, 265 Taxi)..............**£45-55**

1960 **Leaflet** (no ref.), 6 pages introducing 'Mini-Dinky' **£40-45**
1960 **Catalogue '7/3/30 NP'**, no details **£45-55**
1961 **Leaflet '16/161/100 72529/22'**, 4 pages...........................**£20-30**
1961 **Catalogue '14/561/200'**, Black with 7 models, USA 1961, 48 pp..**£50-75**
1962 **Leaflet '9/762/50'**, '72542/22' and 'D.T./CL.12'.....................**£10-15**
1962 **Catalogue '725377/22'**, 10th Ed., 48 pp, UK 7253702 + French **£20-30**
1962 **Catalogue '72537/22'**, 120 Jaguar 'E'-type, 10th Ed. '5c',
       16 pages of French Dinky, 48 pages in total **£50-75**
1963 **Catalogue '13/763/60'**, 11th Ed., 48 pp, UK 13/763/400 + French ..NGPP
1963 **Leaflet '16/163/50 7254 7/22'**, illustrated flyer price list, b/w.......**£20-30**
1963 **Catalogue '13/763/10 7254 5/22'**, Motor Show 11th USA,
       16 pages of French Dinky, 48 pages in total.................**£25-35**
1965 **Leaflet** (no ref. no.) Lines Bros flyer 8½in x 11in,
       Hong Kong on cover **£20-30**
1965 **'Lines Bros' leaflet** (no ref. no.), 4 pages, Yellow/Red cover
       with 113 MGB..**£30-35**
1967 **Leaflet '72577/3'**, 10in x 12¼in includes 5 Hong Kong Dinky......**£15-20**

1971 **Catalogue '100103'**, 7th Edition, same as UK, 24 pages **£10-15**
1972 **Catalogue '100108'**, 8th Edition, same as UK, 28 pages **£10-15**
1973 **Catalogue '100110'**, 9th Edition, same as UK, 40 pages **£10-15**
1973 **Leaflet '100265'**, 4 pages Dinky Action Kits Catalogue **£10-15**
1974 **Catalogue '100114'**, 10th Edition, same as UK, 48 pages **£10-15**
1975 **Catalogue '100/117'**, 11th Ed., 40 pages, same as UK 100115 ....**£10-15**
1976 **Catalogue '100/120'**, 12th Ed., 40 pages, same as UK 100118 ......**£10-15**
1977 **Catalogue '100/135'**, 13th Ed., 40 pages, same as UK 100122,
       but background on cover is Blue not Red.....................**£10-15**
1978 **Catalogue '100/101'**, 14th Ed., 64 pages, same as UK 100/100 ....**£10-15**

West Germany

Agents: Biengngraeber of Hamburg.

1969 **Catalogue '72585'**, 32 pages, No.5 features 'Joe's Car' on cover,
       Catalogue in English, price list in German **£40-50**

Dinky Toys Trade Boxes

Virtually all Dinky Toys models were supplied in their own individual boxes from around 1954. Before then, most small models were supplied to shopkeepers in 'Trade Boxes' containing 3, 4, 6 or 12 identical models separated by strips of card. (Some aircraft and ship models were an exception to this general rule). A single item would be sold without further packaging except perhaps for a paper bag.

These Trade Boxes have become collectors items in their own right whether full or empty (the latter selling for between £20 and £50 depending on its rarity and that of its original contents. Most of these boxes that come to auction are full and the listing below derives mostly from surveys of such items undertaken for the 8th, 9th and 10th Editions. We are grateful to David Cooke and Tony Murphy for updating and enhancing the listing for this Edition. The boxes listed here are only those observed or reported. It is known that other trade packaging of this type exists and the Editor would welcome any additional information on the subject.

Expect Trade Boxes containing rare colour variations to attract a corresponding premium. **NB** See also Gift Sets for 62h and 62d pre-war Aeroplane Trade Box items. **NGPP = No guide price at present.**

Ref	Models, number in box, details	Market Price Range

Type 1 Pre-Second World War. Card boxes that have a four-digit reference code number preceded by the letter 'A'. Most have a covering of yellow paper. (The few exceptions that have orange-brown, blue or green paper coverings are noted in the list). Wording: 'Dinky Toys Made in England by Meccano Limited'. Printed information consists of model name and number, often with a date and quantity. The date code is usually a month number and year number separated by a full stop thus: '3.40', in this case indicating March 1940.

Ref	Models, number in box, details		Market Price Range
22e	Tractor	6 ... A966B	£400-500
22g	Streamline Tourer	6 ...A2018	£1,500-1,750
23	Racing Car	6 ...A1002	£1,500-2,000
24g	Sports Tourer	6 ...A1017	£1,500-2,000
24h	Sports Tourer	6 ...A1018	NGPP
25d	Petrol Wagon	6 ...A1022	NGPP
25e	Tipping Wagon	6 ...A1023	NGPP
25f	Market Gardener's Lorry	6 ...A1024	NGPP
26	Rail Autocar	6 ...A1001	NGPP
27	Tram Car		£900-1,200
28/1	Delivery Vans, 1st Type	6 ...A1008	£5,000-7,500
29a	('Q' type) Motor Bus	6	£1,000-1,500
29c	Double-Decker Bus	6 ...A2226	£1,200-1,600
30e	Breakdown Car	6 ...A2060	£150-200
30g	Caravan	6 ...A2106	£100-150
32	Chrysler Airflow, orange-brown	6 ...A2032	£2,000-3,000
33a	Mechanical Horse, orange-brown	6 ...A2037	NGPP
36f	British Salmson 4-str with Driver	6 ...A2211	NGPP
37c	RCS Dispatch Rider, green	6 ...A2237	£150-200
37c	RCS Dispatch Rider, blue	6 ...A2237	£150-200
39e	Chrysler Royal Sedan	6 ...A2290	£1,000-1,500
47d	Beacon, orange-brown	12 .A2058	NGPP
50a	Battle Cruiser HMS 'Hood'	12 .A1030	NGPP
50f/50h	Destroyers 'Broke' and 'Amazon' Class, 12, A1035		NGPP
50g/50k	Submarines 'K' and 'X' Class	12 .A1036	NGPP
62d	Bristol Blenheim Bombers, green	6	£400-600
62h	Hawker Hurricane Fighters, green	6 ...'7-39'	£400-600
62m	Airspeed Envoy Monoplane	6 ...A2234	NGPP
62s	Hurricane Fighters, blue	6	£300-400
63b	Seaplane 'Mercury'	6 ...A2253	NGPP
151a	Medium Tank	6 ...A2190	£3,000-4,000
152c	RTC Austin Seven	6 ...A2196	£400-500
160b	Royal Artillery Gunners	12	£200-250
160g	R.A. Personnel, (quantity not stated)	A2303	NGPP

Type 2 The first of the post-war trade boxes. Brown card box with yellow contents label affixed to one end (occasionally both ends) No box reference code in the main, but exceptions are noted below.

Ref	Models, number in box, details		Market Price Range
14a	B.E.V. Electric Truck	6	£150-200
23a	Racing Car	6	£500-750
23d	Racing Car	6	£175-225
25b	Covered Wagon	6	£500-750
25d	Petrol Wagon	6	£200-300
25e	Tipping Wagon	6	£250-350
25f	Market Gardeners Lorry, 6, 'VK29' / 'AS39'		£250-350
25g	Trailer	6	NGPP
25h	Fire Engine	6	£300-400
25j	Jeep	6 ...'M26'	£250-350
25p	Aveling Barford Diesel Roller	4 ...'M__'	£150-200
25r	Forward Control Lorry	6 ...'M23'	£300-350
25t	Flat Truck and Trailer	3	£300-350
25v	Bedford Refuse Wagon	4	£200-300
27a	Massey-Harris Tractor	3	£150-200
29b	Streamlined Bus	6 ...'M24'	NGPP
29c	Double Deck Bus (packed vertically)	6	£400-500
29c	Double Deck Bus (laid flat)	6	£200-300
29e	Single Deck Bus	6	£300-350

Ref	Models, number in box, details		Market Price Range
30b	Rolls-Royce	6	£300-400
30d	Vauxhall	6	£300-400
30f	Ambulance, 'M28' / 'M35'	6	£300-400
33w	Mechanical Horse and Open Wagon	3	£200-250
34b	Royal Mail Van	6	£300-400
34c	Loudspeaker Van	6 ...'VK49'	£150-180
36a	Armstrong-Siddeley Limousine	6	£350-400
38c	Lagonda Sports Coupé	6	£250-300
39a	Packard Super 8 Touring Sedan	6	£400-500
39d	Buick Viceroy Sedan	6 ...'M24'	£400-500
40a	Riley	6 ...'M__'	£350-450
40b	Triumph 1800	6	£350-450
40e	Standard Vanguard	6	£350-450
40e	Standard Vanguard	6 ...'M50'	£350-450
105a	Garden Roller	6	£100-125
152b	Reconnaissance Car	6	£400-500
161b	Mobile Anti-Aircraft Gun	6	£300-400

Type 3 Second design of post-war box. All-yellow with direct printing (no label). All are pre-1953/1954 renumbering. No box reference code.

Ref	Models, number in box, details		Market Price Range
23b	Small Closed Racing Car	6	£200-300
23c	Large Open Racing Car	6	£200-300
23e	'Speed of the Wind' Racing Car	6	£200-300
25h	Fire Engine	6	NGPP
25m	Bedford End Tipper	4	£250-300
25t	Flat Truck and Trailer	3	£300-325
25v	Bedford Refuse Wagon	4	£350-400
25w	Bedford Truck	4	£200-300
25y	Universal Jeep	4	£150-225
27a	Massey-Harris Tractor	3	£150-200
27b	Harvest Trailer	3	£75-85
27c	MH Manure Spreader	3	£85-100
27d	Land Rover	4	£150-200
27f	Estate Car	4	£200-300
27g	Motocart	3	£100-150
27h	Disc Harrow	4	£60-80
29f	Observation Coach	6	£350-450
30h	Daimler Ambulance	6	£200-300
30j	Austin Wagon	6	£400-500
30m	Rear Tipping Wagon	6	£150-200
30r	Thames Flat Truck	6	£130-160
30s	Austin Covered Wagon	6	£200-250
30v	Electric Dairy Van	6	£250-300
30v	Electric Dairy Van 'NCB'	6	£250-300
31a	Trojan 'Esso' Van	6	£600-700
31b	Trojan 'Dunlop' Van	6	£600-700
35c	MG Sports Car	6	£250-300
36a	Armstrong-Siddeley Limousine	6	£400-500
37b	Police Motor Cyclist	6	£150-200
38b	Sunbeam-Talbot	6	£400-500
38e	Armstrong-Siddeley	6	£450-550
39e	Chrysler Royal Sedan	6	NGPP
40b	Triumph 1800 Saloon	6	£350-450
40d	Austin Devon	6	£350-450
40f	Hillman Minx Saloon	6	£350-450
40g	Morris Oxford Saloon	6	£350-450
40j	Austin Somerset	6	£350-450
42a	Police Box	6	£140-170
47c	Two-face Traffic Lights	12	£40-70
70d	Twin Engined Fighter	6	£100-130
70e	Gloster Meteor	6	£40-60
70f	Shooting Star	6	£100-150
105a	Garden Roller	6	£80-90
105b	Wheelbarrow	6	£80-90
105c	4-wheeled Hand Truck	6	£40-60
105e	Grass Cutter	6	£90-110

107a	Sack Truck	6		£90-110
139a	Ford Fordor	6		£250-300
139b	Hudson Commodore	6		£500-700
140a	Austin Atlantic	6		£400-500
152b	Reconnaissance Car	6		£400-500
161b	Mobile AA Gun	6		£300-400
603a	Army Personnel (metal). NB early boxes long, later issues are square	12		£80-110
603a	Army Personnel (plastic)	12		£40-50

Type 4 As Type 3 but with the addition of a five-digit box reference code.

23f	Alfa Romeo Racing Car	6	50189	£400-500
23s	Streamlined Racing Car	4	50012	£300-400
25h	Fire Engine	6	50019	£300-400
25m	Bedford Truck	4	50021	£200-250
25p	Aveling-Barford Diesel Roller	4	50022	£150-200
25y	Universal Jeep	6	50159	£150-225
27a	Massey-Harris Tractor	3	50029	£150-200
27h	Disc Harrow	4	50035	£60-80
27j	Triple-Gang Mower	3	50156	£150-200
27m	Land-Rover Trailer	4	50161	£90-110
29g	Luxury Coach	6	50042	£400-500
29h	Duple Roadmaster Coach	6	50163	£300-400
30h	Daimler Ambulance	4	50049	£200-300
30j	Austin Wagon	6	50050	£400-500
30m	Rear Tipping Wagon	6	50052	£200-250
30p	Mobilgas Tanker	6	50051	£500-600
30pa	Castrol Tanker	6	50146	£500-700
30pb	Esso Tanker	6	50147	£500-700
30w	Electric Articulated Lorry	3	50059	£300-400
31a	Trojan Esso Van	6	50149	£500-600
31c	Trojan Chivers Van	6	50151	£600-800
33w	Mechanical Horse and Open Wagon	3	50060	£200-250
34c	Loudspeaker Van	6	50062	£200-250
35a	Saloon Car ('Slide-tray' type box)	6	50063	£300-400
35b	Racer ('Slide-tray' type box)	6	'CZ35'	£280-330
40f	Hillman Minx	6		£350-450
40g	Morris Oxford	6		£350-450
40h	Austin Taxi	6	50097	£350-450
70a	Avro York Air-Liner	1	50123	NGPP
70b	Hawker Tempest Fighter	6	50124	NGPP
70c	Viking Air-Liner	6	50125	NGPP
70f	Shooting Star Jet Fighter	6	50128	NGPP
105e	Grass Cutter	6	50132	£90-110
139b	Hudson Commodore	6	50135	£500-700
140a	Austin Atlantic	6	50136	£500-700
140b	Rover 75	6	50137	£350-450

Type 5 As Type 3 (all-yellow, direct printed, no reference code), but these display the 'dual numbering' of the models contained. They generally date from around 1954 when Meccano renumbered most of the Dinky Toys. They are listed here in the order of the earlier model numbering system.

12c/750	Telephone Call Box	6	£80-120
23a/220	Racing Car	6	£400-500
23e/221	'Speed of the Wind' Racing Car	6	£200-250

23s/222	Streamlined Racing Car	4	£200-300
25g/429	Trailer	6	£80-120
25h/250	Fire Engine	6	NGPP
25r/420	Forward Control Lorry	6	£200-250
25w/411	Bedford Truck	4	£200-250
25y/405	Universal Jeep	4	£200-250
27a/300	Massey-Harris Tractor	3	£150-200
27d/340	Land-Rover	4	£200-250
27g/342	Motocart	3	£80-120
27m/341	Land-Rover Trailer	4	£80-120
29g/281	Luxury Coach	6	£300-350
30r/422	Fordson Thames Flat Truck	6	£70-100
30s/413	Austin Covered Wagon	6	£250-300
30v/490	Electric Dairy Van 'Express Dairy'	6	£250-300
30v/491	Electric Dairy Van 'N.C.B.'	6	£120-160
30w/421	Electric Articulated Lorry	3	£125-150
31b/451	Trojan Van 'Dunlop'	6	£400-500
31c/452	Trojan Van 'Chivers'	6	£400-500
35b/200	Midget Racer	6	'CZ35'	NGPP
40b/151	Triumph 1800 Saloon	6	£250-350
40j/161	Austin Somerset Saloon	6	£350-450
42a/751	Police Hut	6	£50-80
63b/700	Seaplane	6	£250-350
70c/705	Viking Airliner	6	NGPP
70d/731	Twin Engined Fighter	6	NGPP
70e/732	Meteor Jet Fighter	6	NGPP
70f/733	Shooting Star Jet Fighter	6	£80-100
105a/381	Garden Roller	6	£80-120
105b/382	Wheelbarrow	6	£60-80
105c/383	4-wheeled Hand Truck	6	£80-120
105e/384	Grass Cutter	6	£120-150
107a/385	Sack Truck	6	£50-70
140a/106	Austin Atlantic Convertible	6	NGPP
140b/156	Rover 75	6	£200-250

Type 6 Post 1953-54, all-yellow printed box. These contain the newly-introduced (or re-introduced) models having just a single three-digit reference number.

270	'AA' Motor Cycle	6	£200-300
272	'ANWB' Motor Cycle	6	£250-350
603	Army Personnel - Private (seated)	12	NGPP
673	Scout Car	6	£65-85
687	Field Gun Trailer	6	£65-85
705	Viking Airliner	6	£200-300
750	Telephone Call Box	6	£200-300
751	Police Hut	6	£150-180
755	Lamp Standard, single-arm	6	£30-40
756	Lamp Standard, double-arm	6	£30-40
760	Pillar Box	6	£150-200
768	Racks with Tyres	6	£75-100
773	Robot Traffic Signal	12	£150-175
777	Belisha Beacon	12	£65-90
786	Tyre Rack	6	£120-160
788	Spare Bucket for 966	6	£175-225
797	Healey Sports Boat	6	£150-200

Type 7 (Post-war). Small boxes, covered in green paper; with 'flap' ends.

12d	Telegraph Messenger	6	'50175' on some	£100-125
12e	Postman	6	'50176' on some	£100-125
13a	Cook's Man	6	'50174' on some	£100-125
43b	'RAC' Motorcycle Patrol	6		£300-400
44b	'AA' Motorcycle Patrol	6		£300-400
760	Pillar Box	2		NGPP

Type 8 (Post-war). A box specially designed for 551 Large Trailer.

551	Large Trailer, 3. 'Dinky Toys', brown, yellow label		£80-120
551	Large Trailer, 3. 'Dinky Toys', blue card, '50551'		£80-120
551	Large Trailer, 3. 'Supertoys', brown	'50551'	£80-120
551	Large Trailer, 3. 'Supertoys', green	'(M49)'	£80-120
551	Large Trailer, 3. 'Supertoys', green	'(IH89)'	£80-120
551	Large Trailer, 3. 'Supertoys', blue card	'50551'	£80-120
551	Large Trailer, 3. 'Supertoys' yellow card	'(M44)'	£80-120

Type 9 These began appearing from the mid-1950s. They are 'trade packs' rather than trade boxes as they contain quantities of individually boxed models. Thin grey (or brownish-grey) card construction with flap ends or tuck-in ends; direct printing mostly in black. The printing on outer boxes for Dublo Dinkys 067 and 069 is in red. The major exception here is 078 which has an outer box of similar design to the individual Dublo boxes inside.

067	Austin Taxi	6	NGPP
069	Massey-Harris Tractor	6	£150-200
078	Lansing-Bagnall Trailers	6	£140-170
106	'The Prisoner' Mini-Moke	6	£600-800

159	Morris Oxford	6	£350-450
161	Austin Somerset	6	£600-800
188	Jensen FF	6	£150-200
188	4-berth Caravan	6	£175-200
195	Jaguar 3.4 Saloon	6	£400-500
292	Leyland Atlantean Bus	6	£350-450
471	Austin Van 'NESTLE'	6	£300-400
491	Electric Dairy Van 'N.C.B.'	6	£300-400
252/25v	Refuse Wagon	4	£350-400
260	Royal Mail Van	6	NGPP
260	VW 'Deutsche Bundespost'	6	£150-200
344/27f	Estate Car	4	£200-250
492/34c	Loudspeaker Van	6	£200-250
675	Ford US Army Staff Car	6	NGPP
677	Armoured Command Vehicle	6	£200-250
755/6	Lamp Standards, yellow/red box	6	NGPP
994	Loading Ramp (for 982)	3	£55-80

Type 10 Later 1970s trade packs without printing. A small yellow label is attached that shows the model number only. 432 is an exception, being shrink-wrapped with no label.

305	David Brown Tractor	6	NGPP
308	Leyland 384 Tractor	6	NGPP
432	Foden Tipping Lorry, factory shrink-wrapped pack, 6		£80-100

The 'A' List. Before the War, most trade boxes (and some Set boxes) carried a box reference number preceded by the letter 'A'. Those that have been observed (or reported or confirmed) are listed here, in numerical order, along with the month/year (where known) of introduction and description of contents. Our thanks go to Tony Murphy for this listing.

Box no.	Date	Model ref. and name
A 830	-	7 Set, 'Hornby Series' Watchman's Hut
A 873	-	MM 1, Station Staff
A 898	-	13 Set, Halls Distemper Set
A 899	-	21 Set, Train Set
A 930	-	1 Set, Station Staff
A 953	-	4 Set, Engineering Staff
A 966	12-33	22c, Motor Truck
A 966B	12-33	22e, Tractor
A 1001	5-34	26, Rail Autocar
A 1002	5-34	23, Racing Car
A 1005	5-34	6 Set, Shepherd Set
A 1008	5-34	28/1, Delivery Vans
A 1009	5-34	28/2, Delivery Vans
A 1017	5-34	24g, Sports Tourer (4 seater)
A 1018	5-34	24h, Sports Tourer (2 seater)
A 1019	5-34	25a, Wagon
A 1020	5-34	25b, Covered Van
A 1021	5-34	25c, Flat Truck
A 1022	5-34	25d, Petrol Tank Wagon
A 1023	5-34	25e, Tipping Wagon
A 1024	5-34	25f, Market Gardeners Van
A 1025	12-34	29a, Motor Bus
A 1026	12-34	27, Tram Car
A 1029	12-34	50, Ships of British Navy Set
A 1030	12-34	50a, Battle Cruiser 'Hood'
A 1032	12-34	50c, Cruiser 'Effingham'
A 1034	12-34	50e, Cruiser 'Delhi'
A 1035	12-34	50f/50h, Torpedo-Boat Destroyer
A 1036	12-34	50g/50k, Submarine 'K' Class
A 1037	12-34	51, Famous Liners Set
A 1040	12-34	60, Aeroplanes Set
A 1043	12-34	17, Passenger Train Set
A 1044	5-34	18, Goods Train Set
A 1045	5-34	19, Mixed Goods Train Set
A 1046	5-34	20, Passenger Train Set
A 1051	-	24, Motor Cars Gift Set (blue box, 2nd chassis)

Box no.	Date	Model ref. and name
A 1052	-	25, Commercial Motors Gift Set (blue box, type 2)
A 1053	-	2, Farmyard Animals Set
A 1054	-	3, Railway Passengers Set
A 2009	11-35	28/1, Delivery Vans (type 2)
A 2013	12-35	60f, Aeroplane Cierva 'Autogiro'
A 2018	4-35	22, Streamline Tourer
A 2032	-	23c, Mercedes Benz Racing Car
A 2032	6-35	30a/32, Airflow (see previous ref.)
A2034	6-35	49, Petrol Pumps Set
A 2035	12-34	52a, 'Queen Mary' (with rollers)
A 2036	6-37	33, Mechanical Horse and 4 Trailers Set
A 2037	6-35	33a, Mechanical Horse
A 2041	6-35	25g, Trailer
A 2042	6-35	48, Petrol Station
A 2047	6-35	D.H. 'Comet' Aeroplane
A 2052	6-35	12, Pillar Letter Box Airmail
A 2058	11-35	47d, Beacon
A 2060	11-35	30e, Breakdown Car
A 2061	11-35	30, Motor Vehicles Set
A 2062	2-36	45, Garage
A 2064	11-35	43, 'RAC' Hut, Motorcycle Patrol and Guides
A 2065	11-35	44, 'AA' Hut, Motorcycle Patrol and Guides
A 2073	-	47, Road Signs Set (12)
A 2099	-	28/3, Delivery Vans
A 2106	5-36	30g, Caravan Trailer
A 2108	-	16, Streamline Train Set
A 2110	5-36	23c, Mercedes-Benz Racing Car
A 2111	5-36	23d, Auto-Union Racing Car
A 2113	12-38	60h, Singapore Flying Boat
A 2114	10-37	42, Police Hut, Motorcycle Patrol and Policemen
A 2144	12-36	23, Racing Cars Set
A2146	12-37	60n, Fairey Battle Bomber
A 2149	12-37	60k, Percival 'Gull' Monoplane
A 2172	10-37	15, Railway Signals Set
A 2177	12-37	60p, Gloster Gladiator
A 2185	10-37	61, RAF Aeroplanes Set
A 2187	10-37	150, Royal Tank Corps Pers'l. Set
A 2188	10-37	151, RTC Medium Tank Set
A 2189	10-37	152, RTC Light Tank Set
A 2190	12-37	151a, Medium Tank
A 2194	10-37	152a, Light Tank
A 2196	10-37	152c, Austin Seven Car
A 2205	10-37	Motor Cars w. Drivers/Passengers

Box no.	Date	Model ref. and name
A 2211	?	36f, British Salmson 4-str with Driver
A 2216	12-37	12, Postal Set
A 2220	12-38	60r, Empire Flying Boats
A 2222	5-36	35, Small Cars Set
A 2223	12-38	60s, Medium Bomber
A 2225	12-38	60t, Douglas DC3 Air Liner
A 2226	12-38	29c, Double Deck Bus
A 2227	12-38	60v, Armstrong Whitworth 'Whitley'
A 2229	12-37	37a, Civilian Motor Cyclist
A 2230	12-37	37b, Police Motor Cyclist
A 2231	12-38	60w, Flying Boat 'Clipper III'
A 2233	12-38	62k, Airspeed 'Envoy' King's Aeroplane
A 2234	12-38	62m, Airspeed 'Envoy' Monoplane
A 2235	7-40	66d, Torpedo Dive Bomber
A 2237	12-37	37c, Royal Corps of Signals Despatch
A 2245	12-38	25s, Six Wheel Wagon
A 2246	12-38	62n, Junkers Ju90 Air liner
A 2247	12-38	23m, 'Thunderbolt' Speed Car
A 2250	12-38	62p, Armstrong Whitworth 'Ensign' Liner
A 2251	4-39	63, Mayo Composite Aircraft
A 2252	4-39	63a, Flying Boat 'Maia'
A 2253	4-39	63b, Seaplane 'Mercury'
A 2257	3-39	161, Mobile Anti-Aircraft Unit Set
A 2260	3-39	162, 18-lb Quick-Firing Gun Unit
A 2265	4-39	62r, DH 'Albatross' Mail Liner
A 2268	6-39	62s, Hawker 'Hurricane'
A 2269	12-40	60t, A-W 'Whitley' (Camouflaged)
A 2276	4-39	62w, Imp. Airways 'Frobisher' Liner
A 2277	4-39	62x, 40-Seat Airliner
A 2281	7-40	66, Camouflaged Aeroplanes Set
A 2284	4-39	62h, H. 'Hurricane' Camouflaged
A 2285	-	62g, Boeing Flying Fortress
A 2288	5-39	64, Presentation Aeroplane Set
A 2289	5-39	65, Presentation Aeroplane Set
A 2290	6-39	39e, Chrysler 'Royal' Sedan
A 2291	6-39	39f, Studebaker
A 2298	9-39	23p, Gardner's MG Record Car
A 2303	9-39	160, Royal Artillery Personnel
A 2303	7-40	160, Royal Artillery Personnel
A 2308	7-40	156, Mechanised Army Set
A 2327	-	62e, Spitfire (Camouflaged)
A 2328	-	62d, Blenheim Bomber (Camouflaged)
A 2343	7-40	67a, Junkers Ju89 Heavy Bomber
A 2349	7-40	68, Camouflaged Aeroplanes Set

Black wooden Trade Display Unit in plain cardboard box. 'Property of Meccano Ltd Liverpool' in black on gold; 3 shelves in light blue/white/yellow; 4 gold supports with 2 yellow and 2 red supports; 4 red tin flags 'DINKY TOYS'; 3 tin flags 'ASK FOR BOOKLET', 'OVER 200 MODELS', and 'ALWAYS SOMETHING NEW'; plus 2 red and 2 yellow balls **£400-500**
Glass Display Case. Oak frame with three glass shelves. Size approximately 32" (80 cm.) wide, 24" (60 cm.) high, 9" (22 cm.) deep. With 'DINKY TOYS' in green lettering on glass front. **£300-400**
Large wooden Display Unit 'DINKY SHOWROOM',
50" x 22" x 38" **£1,000-1,200**
Trade Display Stand Large yellow folding cardboard stand which non-erected measures approximately 28" (70 cm.) x 14" (35 cm.); three display levels with 'DINKY TOYS' logo in green plus 'MECCANO PRODUCT' in red on top header board. Outer corrugated cardboard packing has green printed instruction leaflet. **£200-300**
Trade Display Stand Small yellow and red folding cardboard stand which non-erected measures approximately 12" (31 cm.) x 7" (15 cm.); with one 'DINKY TOYS' and two 'DINKY SUPERTOYS' logos in red plus yellow 'MASTERPIECES IN MINIATURE' logo on red background. **£100-125**

Display Stand (circa 1950 - 1960) Large metal stand which measures approximately 36" x 21" x 22" (91.5 x 53 x 56 cm.); with nine display shelves covered in black plastic track. Metal advertisement affixed to top states in yellow/red/black 'A MOTOR SHOW FOR GIRLS AND BOYS', 'PRECISION DIE-CAST MODELS BY MECCANO', 'BEST RANGE', and 'BEST VALUE IN THE WORLD'. Lower large transfer also in yellow/red/black repeats the message. **£400-500**

Window Sign (plastic), Top half is dark blue with white 'MECCANO' logo, bottom half is yellow with red 'Dinky Toys' logo. Approx. 18"x6" **£100-125**

Counter Display (cardboard), Small display stand suitable for a single new model, 'ALWAYS NEW MODELS' logo in white on red background, header states 'DINKY TOYS' in red on yellow. **£100-125**
Counter Display (cardboard) 'BATTLE OF BRITAIN' Blue/yellow displaying 719 Spitfire MkII and 721 Junkens JU 87b Stuka. **£100-150**

Shop Display Carousel with tripod base supporting four stacks of clear plastic. **£200-300**
Illuminated Shop Display Sign with 'DINKY TOYS' in large wooden letters above a glass panel lettered either 'Made by Meccano Ltd' or 'British and Guaranteed'. **£300-400**

Shelf Display Card in 'landscape' format, featuring the Hesketh 308E Racing Car with 'OLYMPUS' advertising **£100-150**
Illuminated Counter or Window display unit 13" x 9"" with perspex front 'DINKY TOYS' and 'NEW MODELS EVERY MONTH' logo. **£100-1500**

Counter Carousel Unit with 'Always Something New from Dinky' around its edge. Red/Yellow 'DINKY TOYS BY MECCANO' sign on top, 26" high overall. **£200-250**
Metal Counter Display Sign, triangular in shape with red 'DINKY TOYS' on yellow background, approximately 8" x 1" x 1". **£30-40**

Electric Revolving 'Meccano' Wooden Display Stand
'DINKY TOYS - LOOK FOR THE NAME ON THE BASE' logo,
(28" square and 10" high). **£250-350**

Pre-War 'Meccano Dinky Toys' Advertising Sign. An example of this double-sided hanging sign was sold by Christie's, South Kensington for £632. It shows pictures and details of 22, 24, 25 and 28 series models available in 'Season 1934'. Date code: '16/734/1'. Size: 11in x 9in (28cm x 23cm). **£500-600**

- c.1959 **'Dublo Dinky' Shop Display Stand.** Pale Yellow with Red logo and wording 'NEW SERIES / DUBLO DINKY', etc.
Stand dimensions: 28cm x 19cm overall. **£300-500**

Dinky Toys Price Tickets. Aluminium tags to place on toys plus sheet of 200 self-adhesive labels showing model number and price **£200-250**
Wall Chart. 1963 Dinky Toys and Dinky Superotys Wall Chart listing all tyre sizes for vehicles. **£100-125**
c1960 Electric 'Dinky Toys' Perspex Hanging Sign. Yellow sides with red letters, 1,300mm long **£250-350**
c1970s Electric 'Dinky Toys' Perspex Hanging Sign. Yellow sides with red letters, 1,270mm long **£175-225**
c1960 'Dinky Toys' Counter-top Stand for the Italian market. Steel tubular and metal sheet construction approx. 30cm high, triangular back, two shelves, 'Novita', 'Meccano'. Dark cream and white. **£90-120**
Note: This section is far from complete and the Editor would welcome details of other trade stands, posters, display cards, promotional material and advertising signs.

1960s Window leaflets / posters / stickers

72569	Lady Penelope's 'FAB 1'	£50-60
72579	Captain Scarlett and Thunderbirds	£50-60
?	486 'Dinky Beats' Morris Oxford	£30-40
?	107 'Stripey, the Magic Mini'	£30-40
?	101 Thunderbirds	£30-40
?	153 Aston-Martin DB6	£30-40
?	970 Jones Fleetmaster Crane	£20-30
?	281 Pathe News Camera Car	£30-40
?	158 Rolls-Royce Silver Shadow	£20-30
?	131 Ford 40-RV	£20-30
?	282 Austin 1800	£20-30
?	280 Midland Mobile Bank	£20-30
?	129 Volkswagen Beetle	£20-30
?	163 Volkswagen 1600TL	£20-30
?	166 Renault R16	£20-30
?	135 Triumph 2000 and 240 Cooper Racing Car	£20-30
?	141 Vauxhall Victor Estate Car	£20-30

1970s Shop window self-adhesive posters

100362	1972 Double-sided poster featuring 'All Action Fighting Vehicles' and '10 Great Fighting Vehicles'	£20-30
100367	1973 Double-sided poster featuring 'Highway Action Models'	£20-30
100482	1971 Single-sided poster advertising '451 Road Sweeper'	£20-30
100524	Single-sided poster advertising 'No 410 Bedford Van'	£20-30
100537	Single-sided poster with 'No 654 155mm Mobile Gun'	£20-30
100595	Single-sided poster advertising 'No 694 Hanomag Tank Destroyer'	£20-30
100602	Single-sided poster advertising 'No 293 Swiss PTT Bus'	£20-30
100604	Single-sided poster advertising 'No 656 88mm Gun'	£20-30
100734	Single-sided poster advertising 'No 668 Foden Army Truck'	£20-30
100741	Single-sided poster advertising 'No 432 Foden Tipper Truck'	£20-30
100742	Single-sided, advertising 'No 430 Johnson 2-ton Dumper'	£20-30
100523	Single-sided, advertising 'No 682 Stalwart Load Carrier'	£20-30
100531	Single-sided poster advertising 'No 683 Chieftain Tank'	£20-30
100496	Single-sided poster advertising 'No 725 F-4K Phantom II'	£20-30
?	Poster advertising '442 Land-Rover Breakdown Crane'	£20-30
?	Poster advertising '967 Muir-Hill Loader and Trencher'	£20-30
?	Poster advertising '915 AEC with Flat Trailer'	£20-30
?	Poster advertising 1/25th scale Ford Capri and Police Car	£30-40
?	Poster advertising 1/25th scale Saloon Cars	£30-40
?	Poster advertising 724 Sea King Helicopter	£20-25
?	Poster advertising 984 Atlas Digger	£20-25
?	Poster advertising 977 Shovel Dozer	£20-25
?	Poster advertising 963 Road Grader	£20-25
?	Poster advertising 726 Messerschmitt BF109E	£20-25
?	Poster advertising 730 US Navy Phantom	£20-25
?	Poster advertising 731 S.E.P.E.C.A.T. Jaguar and 728 RAF Dominie	£20-25
?	Poster advertising 734 P47 Thunderbolt	£20-25
?	Poster advertising 739 Zero Sen	£20-25

All other late issued leaflets not lisred. ....each: **£20-25**

Retailer's aluminuim price tickets for attachment
to Dinky Toys boxes. Photo: Vectis Auctions Ltd.

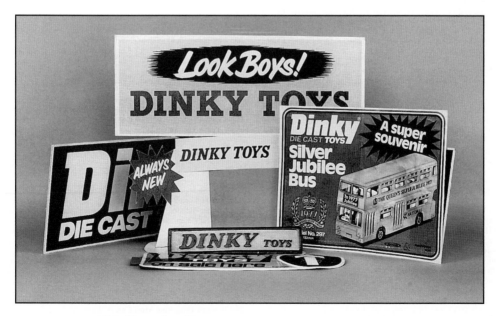

Dinky Toys sales aids

Photo: Vectis Auctions Ltd.

These Auction Results are provided to support the Market Price Range guidance throughout the Catalogue.

Vectis Auctions Ltd.
Fleck Way, Thornaby, Stockton -on-Tees TS17 9JZ

Abbreviations: M = Mint, **NM** = Near Mint, **EP** = Excellent Plus,
E = Excellent, **GP** = Good Plus, **G** = Good, **F** = Fair.

DUBLO DINKY TOYS
062 Singer Roadster, EP in G box £60
064 Austin Lorry, green NM in E box £60
067 Austin Taxi, black knobbly tyres, M in GP box £70
069 Massey Tractor, grey knobby wheels, M in GP box £100
070 Mercury Tanker, grey knobbly wheels E in GP box £60
073 Land Rover & Trailer, maroon etc, NM in F box £130

UNBOXED CARS
36b Bentley, green/black, ridged £220
38f Jaguar, light grey, red interior/ridged hubs, GP- E £360
38c Lagonda, green/dark green interior, black R/hubs E £90
39a Packard, olive green, black ridged hubs, EP £110

BOXED CARS
35d Yellow Trade box for 6, models GP - E in GP box....................£320
102 MG Midget, deep yellow, red interior/hubs, GP in F box £120
104 Aston-Martin, light blue/dark blue, EP in F box £190
105 Triumph TR2, light grey, red interior, spun hubs, EP in G box £320
108 MG, red body/hubs, brown interior, GP - E in G box £140
114 Triumph Spitfire, metallic grey, red interior, E in E box £120
120 Jaguar 'E'-type, metallic blue, white seats, spun hubs,
  boxed in gold export type box, E in E box £250
135 Triumph, bluish grey, black roof, red interior, GP in G box £360
135 Triumph, black, cactus green roof, promotional, E in E box £480
136 Vauxhall Viva, metallic blue, red interior, NM in E box £70
138 Hillman Imp, metallic blue, blue interior, EP in GP box £190
151 Triumph 1800, dark blue, mid-blue hubs, E in F box £90
141 Vauxhall Victor Estate, 'Lightning Fasteners' promo, G in G box...£750
152 Austin A40 Devon, greyish green, beige hubs, EP in GP box £200
153 Standard, closed arches, cream, blue hubs, EP in GP box £160
154 Hillman Minx, light brown, cream hubs, EP in F box £150
154 Hillman Minx, TT cream/lime green, NM in GP box £260
156 Rover 75, TT violet blue/cream, GP in G box £220
157 Jaguar XK 120, red body/hubs, E in GP box £120
157 Jaguar XK, greyish green, beige hubs, NM in GP box £170
157 Jaguar XK 120, TT yellow/grey, NM in GP box.......................£280
158 Riley, light green, mid green hubs, NM in GP box £150
159 Morris, TT cerise/cream, cream hubs, EP in E box £120
160 Austin A30, turquoise, grey plastic wheels, NM in E box £100
161 Somerset, TT black/cream, cream hubs, EP in G box £150
167 AC Aceca, cream, deep red roof, cast hubs, E in GP box £130
169 Ford Corsair, silver, black vinyl roof, red interior, E in GP box £120
170 Ford Fordor, 'lowline' TT cream/red, NM in G box £160
171 Hudson, 'highline', TT blue/red, EP in EP box £150
172 Studebaker, 'lowline' TT cream/cerise, NM in E box £160
174 Hudson Hornet, yellow/grey stripe NM in E box £150
184 Volvo122s, off-white version, spun hubs, EP in GP box £280
197 Morris Traveller, cream, blue interior, EP in E box £420
233 Cooper Racing Car with spun hubs £155
234 Ferrari, yellow triangle on nose, yellow hubs, NM in F box £260
238 Jaguar 'D'-type, turquoise, yellow driver/hubs, EP in E box ...£305
239 Vanwall Racing Car, green, black knobbly tyres, E in GP box £200
268 Renault Dauphine Mini Cab, EP in GP box............................£120

COMMERCIAL VEHICLES
28n 'MECCCANO' Delivery Van, Poor £635
33a Mechanical Horse 'MECCANO', VG, no box.........................£420
286 Bedford Fire Tender, E in E box £130
343 Farm Produce Wagon, yellow/green, EP in G box £130
410 Bedford End Tipper, red/cream, EP in G box £150
418 Leyland with Tailboard, green, mid green hubs, EP in G £200
431 Guy - rare mid blue body, 2nd type, EP overall £1,300
431 Guy Warrior, dark green, mid green hubs, E in E box £260
450 Trojan Van 'ESSO', E in GP box £190
452/31c Trojan Van 'CHIVERS', M in F dual numbered box.........£170
501 Foden Wagon, 1st type, red/fawn, E in GP box £240
503 Foden Flat Truck with Tailboard 1st type,
  TT green, GP-E in E buff box £750

511 Guy Lorry, 1st type, fawn/red, E in GP box £360
905 Foden Flat Truck with Chains, 2nd type, maroon, E in E box..........£320
917 Guy Van 'SPRATTS', E in F box...£300
918 Guy Van 'GOLDEN SHRED', E in G box £700
923 Big Bedford 'HEINZ', Ketchup logo, E in E box...................£1,410
965 Euclid Dump Truck 'TEREX', E in G box £360
979 Racehorse Transport, E in GP box £280
982 Pullmore Car Transporter, dark blue cab/trailer, E in F box............£460

AIRCRAFT
60 Aeroplane Set, E in E box £800
60b Leopard Moth, dark blue/orange, VG unboxed £590
60b Leopard Moth, violet blue/orange tips/tail, GP.....................£500
60c Amy Mollinson's, blue/silver..£280
60d Low Wing Monoplane, red 'AVYP', G..................................£240
60e General Monospar, violet, blue wing tips/tail, G-GP £420
60f Cierva Autogiro, yellow, green tips, silver blade, G £160
60s Fairey Battle Bomber, camouflage, E £280
60t Douglas DC3 Airliner, E in GP box £280
62g Flying Fortress, silver E in E box £260
62k The King's Aeroplane, 'G-AEXX', E in GP box £440
62t Whitworth Bomber, camouflage, E in E box £200
62w Imperial 'Frobisher' Airliner, 'G-AFD', M in GP box £320
67a Junkers Heavy Bomber, E in G box £220
702 DH Comet Airliner, 'ALYV', M in GP box £160
749 Avro Vulcan Bomber, G unboxed...£500

NICKY TOYS
735 Gloster Javelin, E in G box...£120
738 DH 110 Sea Vixen, NM in G box £110

GIFT SETS
No 1 Farm Gear, all items GP - E in G box £1,200
No 4 Racing Cars, all GP - E in GP box £2,100
44 AA Hut/Motor-cycle/Guide Set, GP inG box £190
51 Famous Liners, GP in GP box £320
64 Aeroplane Set, fatigued - GP in F box £1,000
118 Towaway Glider Set, E in G box £80
149 Sports Car Set, E in E box £2,479
161 Mobile Anti-Aircraft Unit, G boxed £775
245 Superfast Set, contents NM - M, in GP box £150
299 Post Office Services, GP - E in GP box.................................£320
399 Massey Tractor, yellow hubs, blue driver NM in E £280
990 Tractor Set, Tractor (white/brown), E in GP box £470

TRADE BOXES
38g Taxi x 6, F - GP in F - GP in 'buff' box £280
38c Lagonda x 6, G - GP in G buff box £300
39a Packard x 6, G - EP in F - G buff box £380
40d Austin Devon x 6, GP - E in GP - E buff box.......................£360
154/40f Hillman Minx x 6, GP - E in G - E yellow box £360
40g Morris Oxford x 6, G - E in F yellow box £280
170/139a Ford Fordor x 6, GP - E in GP - F yellow box £300

Wallis & Wallis
West Street Auction Galleries, Lewes, Sussex, BN7 2NJ

Abbreviations: M = Mint, **E** = Excellent, **VG** = Very Good,
G = Good, **F** = Fair.

CARS
22b Sports Coupé, yellow/green, E £410
23g Cooper-Bristol, green body and diecast hubs, E in E box £280
28h Delivery Van 'SHARPES TOFFEE', F £730
23j HWM Racing Car, E in E box £95
30c Daimler, grey/black, post-war, E £100
38c Lagonda Sports Car, grey, red seats £225
38e Armstrong Siddeley, green, grey seats, post war, VG £95
102 Joe's Car, M in M box £260
103 Spectrum Patrol Car, metallic red, M in M box £175
157 Jaguar XK 120, TT yellow/grey, VG in G box £130
258 DeSoto Fireflite 'POLICE', E in VG box £118
268 Renault Dauphine Mini Cab, VG, boxed £130
GIFT SETS
42 Police Set, contents complete, G in G original box £400
49 Petrol Pumps Set, (missing hoses) VG in VG box £165

COMMERCIAL VEHICLES
408 Big Bedford Lorry, maroon/brown VG, box G £150
413 Austin Covered Wagon, red, grey cover, VG unboxed.....................£235
450 Trojan Van 'ESSO', VG - M in box with wear....................................£120
451 Trojan Van 'DUNLOP', VG in damaged box.....................................£100
430 Commer Breakdown, dark stone/blue, G in G box £170
492 Loudspeaker Van, dark blue, mid-blue hubs, M boxed £70
512 Guy Flat Truck, dark blue/red, VG in worn box...............................£120
513 Guy Truck/Tailboard, TT green, E in E box.....................................£152
661 Recovery Tractor, matt olive green, G in G box.................................£380
749 Avro Vulcan Bomber, playworn £300
901 Foden Diesel Wagon, red/fawn, boxed VG - M £300
902 Foden Flat Truck, 2nd type, red/green, E in E box...........................£270
914 AEC Lorry, M in E box £165
917 Mercedes-Benz Truck, VGC including box £120
917 Guy Van 'SPRATT'S', M in G box £410
923 Big Bedford Van 'HEINZ BEANS', VG - M, box F £190
941 Foden 'MOBILGAS' Tanker, GC, box shows wear............................£200
986 Mighty Antar/Propeller, VGC minor chips in F box £160

Christie's South Kensington
85 Old Brompton Road, London SW7 3LD.

Abbreviations: M = Mint, E = Excellent, VG = Very Good,
G = Good, F = Fair.

28L 'CRAWFORDS BISCUITS' Van, 1st type, VG.............................£3,750
503 Foden Flat Truck with Tailboard, first type, red body,
     black flash, E in VG box £900
502 Foden Flat Truck, first type, green, VG in G box.............................£1,200
514 Guy Van 'LYONS', VG in VG box...£1,195
502 Foden Flat Truck, first type, dark blue cab, red flash and back,
     mid-blue hubs, VG in G box £1,075
514 Guy 'WEEETABIX' Van, F-G in G-VG box £418
512 Guy Flat Truck (yellow, red hubs) plus brown
511 Guy 4-ton Lorry, and red/yellow 531 Leyland Comet plus
942 'REGENT' Tanker, VG-E in G-VG box £1,434
Foden Tankers - 1st type TT blue 504 Tanker plus
942 'REGENT' Tanker, VG-E in G-VG boxes £776
25d Petrol Tank Wagon half-dozen box, various contents:
25d 'REDLINE GLICO' Tank Wagon F-G ,
25f Market Gardener's Van VG, plus 25b, 25e, 25h and 25g, all F-G......£896
157 Jaguar XK120 (grey-green with tan hubs), 238 'D' type Jaguar
(turquoise), 187 VW Karmann Ghia (red) and a
Porsche 356A (blue with cream hubs), VG in G-VG boxes £573
No. 4 Racing Cars Set, VG in VG box £1,150
No. 44 'AA' Gift Set, models VG in G box £420

George Kidner
The Old School, The Square, Lymington, Hampshire SO41 8GN

Abbreviations: M = Mint, E = Excellent, VG = Very Good,
G = Good, F = Fair.

106 Austin Atlantic, black, red hubs, VG in VG box £140
132 Trade Box, six Packard Convertibles, E in E box................................£765
156 Rover 75, TT blue/cream, Mint boxed £225
159 Morris Oxford, dark green, mid-green hubs, G boxed.......................£170
161 Austin Somerset, TT black/cream, G in G box...................................£400
167 AC Aceca, grey/red, cast hubs, E in E box £110
189 Triumph Herald, (special) Monaco Blue, Mint in Good box £1,500
189 Triumph Herald, (special) Monaco Blue/Sebring White, G/G £900
189 Triumph Herald, (special) Alpine Mauve, VG in G box £900
189 Triumph Herald, (special) TT red and white G-M in G box £900
189 Triumph Herald, (special) all red, G-M in G box £950
189 Triumph Herald, (special) Powder Blue, M in G box £1,500
189 Triumph Herald, (special) Powder Blue/Sebring White, M, G box ...£950
189 Triumph Herald, (special) Lichfield Green, M in G box...................£1,400
189 Triumph Herald – red/white, E, boxed..£1,115
901 Foden Diesel Wagon, red/fawn, 2nd type £300
903 Foden Flat Truck, 2nd type, mid-blue/fawn, G in G box £705
923 Big Bedford 'HEINZ BEANS', good boxed.......................................£360
942 Foden 'REGENT' Tanker, good boxed £190
956 Turntable Fire Escape, E in E box £150
Trade Pack, 6 metalllic red, No.103 Spectrum Patrol Cars, Mint........£1,120
Trade Pack of six 105 Maximum Security Vehicles, Mint boxed............£825
161 Austin Somerset – Black and cream, Good boxed £340

Bonhams
Montpelier Street, Knightsbridge, London SW7 1HH

ALL WOODEN PROTOTYPES found in Liverpool Charity Shop:
29h Duple Roadmaster Coach, light blue/grey...£680
25y Universal Jeep, dark green, tin windscreen...£650
30w Hindle Smart Helecs, maroon 'BR' logo on front...............................£600
40g Morris Oxford, cream/blue, '17/64 Morris' on base £2,000
132 Packard Convertible, cream, red interior..£880
472 Austin Van, green, light green hubs £720
480 series Bedford Van, cream, green hubs £850
Unreleased Austin Wagon prototype, red cab, blue back........................£1,500
522 Big Bedford Lorry, orange cab, green back.....................................£1,500
Unreleased Leyland Fire Engine prototype...£600
641 Army 1 ton Lorry, military green, grey windows...............................£600
673 Army Scout Car, military green £360
674 Army Champ, military green £300

PRE-WAR ISSUES
4 Engineering Staff, G-E in G-E box..£75
14z Delivery Van, green with blue/black driver, F.....................................£65
24a Ambulance, 2nd type, cream/red, F-G £200
25b Covered Wagon, 2nd type, blue with cream tilt, G £320
25f Market Gardeners Lorry, 1st type, green/black, G £140
25 Series Commercial Vehicles Set, all VGC in F-G box £1,350
30a Chrysler Airflow Saloon, blue, silver hubs, G £360
30d Vauxhall, black, egg box grill, G..£200
30 Series Motor Cars empty box, F - G £700
30 Series Motor Vehicles Set, F - G £820
31 'HOLLAND COACHCRAFT' Van, mid-green, F - G £700
48 Petrol Station, turquoise roof, G £120
49 Petrol Pumps Set, FG - E in G box £180
No. 60 Camouflaged Aeroplanes Set, F - E, box good £1,550
60a Imperial Airways Liner, gold 'G-ABTI', G-E £380
62k The King's Aeroplane, silver, red and blue, E in E box £280
161 Mobile Anti-Aircraft Unit, slight fatigue, G boxed £220
162 18-pounder Field Gun Unit Set, G-E in G-E box £180

POST WAR COMMERCIAL VEHICLES
465 Morris 'CAPSTAN' Van, E boxed..£125
501 Foden Wagon, 1st type, grey, red flash, G in F-G box £500
503 Foden Flat Truck, 1st type, violet blue cab, orange back,
     mid-blue hubs, E in G box £700
514 Guy Van 'WEEETABIX', G in F-G box £1,050
514 Guy Van 'SPRATT'S', G in G box £380
941 Foden 'Mobilgas' Tanker, VG in G box £470
984/985 Car Carrier/Trailer, both E in G-F boxes £280

Special Auction Services
Kennetholme, Midgham, Near Reading, Berkshire RG7 5UX.
Abbreviations: M = Mint, E = Excellent, VG = Very Good,
G = Good, F = Fair.

CARS
100 Lady Penelope's 'FAB1', E in G box £180
106 Thunderbirds 2 and 4, black base, M in E bubble pack.....................£150
102 Joe's Car, E-M in VG-E box...£1,701
107 'Stripey, the Magic Mini', E - M in G box £260
107 Sunbeam Alpine, light blue, E - M in G box £130
108 MG Midget Sports, red, E in G box £190
111 Triumph TR2 Sports, turquoise, E - M in G box £200
118 Tow Away Glider Set, E-M in G-VG box...£180
132 Packard Convertible, green, E - M in G Box £110
133 Cunningham 5R Road Racer, E in VG box £90
136 Vauxhall Viva, metallic blue, E in G-VG box £80
156 Rover 75 Saloon, maroon, E in F box..£100
172 Studebaker Land Cruiser, blue, E - M in G box £120
178 Plymouth Plaza, TT blue, E - M in G box..£130
180 Packard Clipper Sedan, cream/ pink, E in G box...............................£110
197 Morris Mini Traveller, fluorescent green, E in F box £160
350 Tiny's Mini Moke, E in VG-E box..£140

COMMERCIAL VEHICLES
33R Mechanical Horse/Trailer 'LNER', F-G £130
260 Morris 'Royal Mail' Van, E in G box (grubby)...................................£75
440 'Mobilgas' Tanker, E-M in VG box £130

471 Austin 'Nestles' Van, E-M in F-G box......£120
482 Bedford 'DINKY TOYS' Van, E-M in G-VG box......£150
505 Foden Flat/Chains, 2nd type, maroon, E in VG box......£320
533 Leyland Cement Wagon, VG - E in G box......£80
903 Foden Truck/Tailboard, 2nd, blue/orange, E in G box......£280
913 Guy Flat Truck/Tailboard, blue/orange......£240
915 AEC with Trailer, orange/white, E in VG box......£50
921 Bedford Articulated Lorry, yellow/black, VG-E in G box......£120
934 Leyland Octopus Lorry, E-M in F-G box......£150
965 Euclid Rear Dump Truck, E-M in VG-E box......£80
968 BBC Roving Eye Vehicle, E in E box......£110
969 BBC Extending Mast Vehicle, E in G (grubby) box......£120
982 Pullmore Transporter, light blue, E-M in VG box......£150
Gift Set 229 Post Office Services, VG in F-G original box......£260

AIRCRAFT

Set 61 RAF Aeroplanes, F-G in F original blue box......£320
701 Shetland Flying Boat, G unboxed......£210
704 Avro York Airliner, E - M in G yellow box......£100

Collectoys
BP 22 - 18001 Bourges Cedex, France

Condition Grading System: Models shown as A. B. C. & D.
Boxes - a. b. c. d. Unboxed o.

CARS

23d Auto Union Racing Car, Red, B..o......£620
30a Chrysler Airflow, green, B.o......£270
104 Aston-Martin DB3, green, red interior and hubs A.b......£165
105 Triumph TR2, grey, red interior and hubs A.b......£130
106 Mini Moke 'Prisoner', A.a......£170
112 Austin-Healey Sprite, lilac, cream interior, A.c......£1,650
118 Triumph 2000/Glider Set, A.d......£180
VW 1500, metallic bronze, A.b......£120
152 Austin Devon, grey-green, beige hubs, A.b......£330
152 Austin Devon, maroon (prune), B.b......£220
156 Rover 75, green, A.b......£262
157 Jaguar XK 120, TT turquoise/cerise, A.d......£200
160 Austin A30, turquoise, A.c......£135
162 Ford Zephyr, TT blue, B.b......£110
169 Studebaker Golden Hawk, green/cream, A.a......£180
170 Ford Fordor Sedan, TT cream/red, A.b......£300
170 Ford Fordor Sedan, TT blue/pink, A.b......£140
181 Volkswagen Saloon, lime green, mid-green hubs, A.b......£230
182 Porsche, red body, spun hubs, A.a......£150
190 Caravan, blue/cream. A.c......£55
193 Rambler Cross Country - South African issue,
  greyish green, red interior. A.d......£975
193 Rambler Cross Country - South African issue,
  lilac body, red interior. A.b......£750
197 Morris Mini Traveller, cream/woody, A.b......£135
198 Rolls-Royce Phantom, grey/cream, A.b......£100
207 Alfa Romeo in a bubble pack, A.b......£450
254 Taxi, black, A.b......£130
245 Superfast Gift Set, 131/153/188, All A. box c......£130
246 International Gift Set, 187/215/216, All A box b......£130
261 Ford Taunus 'POLIZEI', green/white, A.b......£300
268 Renault, empty Trade Box (6) and 1 boxed model, A.c......£260
262 VW 'PTT SUISSE', yellow/black, spun hubs,A.b......£450
262 VW 'PTT SUISSE', 1972 issue - plastic hubs A.b......£150
266 Plymouth Canadian 'TAXI', yellow/red, A.b......£350
281 Fiat 2300 'PATHE NEWS' Car, A.a......£220
57/004 Oldsmobile Dynamic 88, white/blue, red interior, A.b......£310
57/005 Ford Thunderbird, blue, white roof, A.a......£350

COMMERCIAL VEHICLES

28c 1st Type Van 'MANCHESTER GUARDIAN', C......£1,790
28e 1st Type Van 'FIRESTONE TYRES', E......£1,930
28f 1st Type Van 'PALETHORPES', C......£2,890
28g 1st Type Van 'KODAK', C......£4,135
273 Austin Mini 'RAC', C.c......£125
274 Austin Mini 'AA', A.c......£150
274 Mini 'Joseph Mason Paints' promotional A.b......£825
299 Post Office Services Set, B.b......£520
300 Massey-Harris Tractor, A.b......£140
301 Field Marshall Tractor, B.b......£130
28k 1st Type Van 'MARSHES SAUSAGES', C......£4,480
408 Big Bedford Lorry, maroon/fawn, M in E box......£450
412 Austin Covered Wagon, maroon, red hubs, A.b......£100

Austin Covered Wagon, TT blue, A.b......£125
409 Bedford Articulated Lorry, yellow/black, A.b......£340
420 Forward Control Lorry, red, green hubs, A.b......£100
414 Dodge Tipper Lorry, blue/grey, A.b......£130
424 Commer Articulated Vehicle, A.b......£180
443 'National Benzole' Tanker, A.b......£245
454 Trojan 'CYDRAX' , A.c......£260
492 Loud Speaker Van, Blue/silver, A.b......£195
506 Prototype Albion Milk Tanker, green body,
  'MILK MARKETING BOARD', C......£2,620
514 Guy Van 'WEETABIX', B.c......£1,880
514 Guy Van 'LYONS', C.b......£965
908 Mighty Antar with Transformer, A.b......£820
913 Guy Flat Truck with Tailboard, TT green, A.b......£310
918 Guy Van 'EVER READY', A.b......£575
919 Guy Van 'GOLDEN SHRED', B.b......£330
936 Leyland Chassis, B.b......£140
940 Mercedes 'HENRY JOHNSON', green, A.d......£350
942 Foden 'REGENT' Tanker, A.b......£550
977 Platform Servicing Vehicle, cream/red, B.c......£165
979 Racehorse Transport 'NEWMARKET', A.b......£345
980 Horse Box 'EXPRESS', export issue, B.b......£520
987 ABC TV Control Room, A.b......£420
988 TV Transmitter Van, A.a......£300

28 Series Set - 28A, 28B, 28D, 28H, 28M, 28N. C. - D......£7,585
070 Dublo Dinky AEC Mercury Tanker, A.a......£120

MILITARY

660 Thorneycroft Mighty Antar, A.b......£135
666 Corporal Missile, A.c......£130
674 Austin Champ 'UN' issue, A.b......£260
675 Ford Fordor US Army Staff Car, A.c......£345

BUSES

283 B.O.A.C. Coach. A.a......£150
295 Atlas Kenebrake, sky blue, red interior, A.b......£165
290 Double Deck Bus 'EXIDE', C.b......£165
949 Wayne School Bus, deep yellow/black lines B.b......£330
953 'Dinky Continental Tours' Coach, A.b......£1,030
63a Armstrong Whitworth, camouflage, E, no box......£350
Set 60 British Aeroplanes Set, 6 models, F-M in G box......£1,640

Lacy, Scott & Knight
The Auction Centre, 10 Risbygate Street,
Bury St Edmunds, Suffolk IP33 3AA.
Abbreviations: M = Mint, NM = Near Mint, E = Excellent,
VG = Very Good, G = Good, F = Fair.

CARS

30A Chrysler Airflow, c1946, no chassis, cream body, G......£80
30b Rolls-Royce, c1947, fawn/black, G......£75
30c Daimler, c1947, dark green/black, G......£45
30d Vauxhall, c1947, 'shield' radiator, olive green/black, G......£65
36a Armstrong Siddeley, c1947, mid-blue/black, G......£55
36b Bentley, c1947, blue/black, smooth hubs, G......£65
36b Bentley, c1947, green/black, ridged hubs, G......£55
36c Humber Vogue, c1947, grey/black, G - NM......£80
38a Frazer Nash, c1947, blue, grey interior - G......£85
38f Jaguar SS100, c1947, mid-blue, grey interior, G......£55
36d Rover, c1947, grey/black, G......£65
39a Packard Super 8 Tourer, c1947, dark brown, NM......£65
39b Oldsmobile 6 Sedan, c1947, grey, some chips, G......£32
39c Lincoln Zephyr Coupe, c1947, brown, F - G......£28
39d Buick Viceroy Saloon, c1947, grey, G - NM......£50
39e Chrysler Royal, c1947, mid-green, G......£38
40e Standard Vanguard, c1948, open rear arches, G - NM......£65
40b Triumph 1800 Saloon, c1947, grey, NM......£52
100 Lady Penelope's 'Fab 1', NM in G box......£160
103 Spectrum Patrol Car, metallic red, NM in G box......£150
Spectrum Pursuit Car, NM in NM box......£125
105 Maximum Security Vehicle, M in NM box......£130
152 Austin Devon, TT pink/green, G - NM, unboxed......£150

164 Vauxhall Cresta, grey/green, NM in G box......£80
166 Sunbeam Rapier, yellow/cream, NM in NM box......£75
170 Lincoln Continental, metallic bronze, M in G box......£70
445 Chevrolet El Camino, turquoise/cream, NM in G box......£75
149 Sports Cars Set, 6 models, F - G in G box......£920

COMMERCIAL VEHICLES
Dinky Toys – **25a Wagon** (1936-40) – blue/orange, VGC £360
28m Delivery Van 'WAKEFIELDS CASTROL', 1st, G.....................£1,200
430 Commer Breakdown Truck, tan/green, M in NM box £95
431 Guy Warrior Lorry, tan/green, G in P box £68
454 Trojan Van 'CYDRAX', NM - M unboxed £75
504 Foden Tanker, 1st type, dark blue, F - G in F box £105
514 Guy 'SLUMBERLAND' Van, G in G box £150
533 Leyland Comet Cement Lorry, NM in NM box £130
902 Foden Flat Truck, 2nd, orange/green, F - G unboxed..........£75
903 Foden Flat Truck, violet blue/orange/mid-blue, G /VG £115
905 Foden Chain Lorry, 2nd type, red/grey, G unboxed............£95
918 Guy 'EVER READY' Van, G in G box £170
919 Guy 'GOLDEN SHRED' Van, NM in G box £440
930 Pallet-Jekta Van, G in M box £160
942 Foden 'REGENT' Tanker, G - E in G box £290
953 Continental Coach, NM unboxed...£70
958 Snowplough, yellow/black, M in G box £105
960 Cement Lorry, orange, blue drum, NM in M box £160
984 Mighty Antar with Propeller, NM in NM box £180
991 A.E.C. Tanker, G, 591 in G 991 box £70
AIRCRAFT
No 60 Aeroplanes Set - 1st issue in 2nd box, 60a Atlanta with
'sunray' wings, blue/gold autogiro etc, G - E in G - E box................£1,200
62k Airspeed Envoy 'The Kings Aeroplane', NM in NM box £350
739 A6MS Zero-Sen, green/black, M in G box £55
Avro Vulcan Bomber, VGC £2,700

Internet Auction Results

The following results have been selected from a survey of 'online' auction sales in 2005. Readers should be aware that, unlike traditional 'bricks and mortar' auction houses, descriptions of items for sale (and the condition thereof) are the vendors' own and not that of an established valuations specialist.

No.4 Racing Car Set. Usual models, Mint, boxed, all packing £2,600
61 RAF Aeroplanes Gift Set, Excellent, boxed.......................£680
28 Series Type 1 Delivery Van, orange/blue, Slightly chipped £460
28a Delivery Van 'Hornby Trains', yellow,
Slightly chipped to chipped £875
28c Delivery Van 'Manchester Guardian',
Slightly chipped to chipped £450
28h Delivery Van 'Sharp's Toffee',
Slightly chipped to chipped £550
101 Sunbeam Alpine Tourer, blue, Mint, boxed £296
102 MG Midget, Touring Finish, orange, red hubs, Mint, boxed .£335
104 SPV Captain Scarlet, metallic light blue, Mint, boxed £155
107a Sack Trucks, blue, x 6, Mint, boxed, complete.................£100
108 Sam's Car, Mint, boxed..£170
109 Austin-Healey 100 Sports, dark yellow, Mint, boxed £120
114 Triumph Spitfire, gold, Mint, boxed £205
114 Triumph Spitfire, gold, Mint, boxed £126
130 Ford Corsair, red, off-white interior, Mint, boxed...............£52
131 Jaguar E Type, bronze, Mint, bubble pack £43
134 Triumph Vitesse, green, white sideline, Mint, boxed £102
134 Triumph Vitesse, green, white sideline, Mint, boxed £86
143 Ford Capri, turquoise, white roof, Mint, boxed £102
146 Jaguar Mk X, metallic silver-green, Mint, boxed £180
147 Cadillac 62, metallic green, red interior, Mint, boxed........£105
149 Sports Cars Gift Set, Very near mint, boxed..................£1,926
152 Austin Devon, sage green, Mint, boxed £90
154 Hillman Minx, Light green/green hubs, V. near mint, boxed ..£186
156 SAAB 96, metallic deep red, Mint, box one inner tab missing ..£42
161 Ford Mustang 2+2, white, Mint, plastic case £40
161 Ford Mustang 2+2, white, Mint, plastic case £33
163 Bristol 450, dark green, Mint, boxed £98
168 Singer Gazelle, green, grey, spun hubs, Mint, boxed.........£60
169 Ford Capri, metallic silver, black, Mint, boxed £89
174 Hudson Hornet, red, yellow roof and side flash,
Very near mint, boxed £176
180 Rover 3500, white, Mint, window box £26
181 Volkswagen, light grey, spun hubs, Very near mint, boxed....£130
183 Fiat 600 Saloon, red, Mint, boxed £135
183 Fiat 600 Saloon, red, Mint, boxed £68
183 Morris Mini Minor, red, black roof, Mint, boxed £108
183 Morris Mini Minor, red, black roof, Mint, boxed £58

184 Volvo 122S, red, Very near mint, boxed £123
184 Volvo 122S, red, Very near mint, boxed £71
185 Alfa Romeo 1900 Super Sprint, red, Very near mint, boxed...£96
187 VW Karmann Ghia, green, cream roof, Mint, boxed £165
189 Triumph Herald, pinkish-lilac, Chipped £105
194 Bentley S Coupe, grey, maroon seats, Mint, boxed £181
198 Rolls-Royce Phantom V, mid grey, light grey, Mint, boxed £98
199 Austin Seven Countryman, blue, red interior, Mint, boxed ...£156
205 Lotus Cortina Rally Car, white, RN 7, Mint, boxed £175
208 Porsche 914, yellow, Mint, plastic case £25
211 Triumph TR7, red, black interior, Mint, window box £20
212 Ford Cortina Rally Car, white, black RN '8', Mint, boxed ...£102
221 Corvette Stingray, white, black bonnet, Mint, window box £10
225 Lotus F1 Racing Car, red, Mint, boxed...............................£25
230 Talbot Lago Racing Car, blue, blue metal wheels,
Mint, dual numbered box £255
230 Talbot Lago Racing Car, blue, spun hubs, Mint, boxed £290
231 Maserati Racing Car, red, yellow PW, Mint, boxed £425
231 Maserati Racing Car, red, red PW, Mint, boxed £330
231 Maserati Racing Car, red, red metal wheels,
Mint, dual numbered box £170
231 Maserati Racing Car, red, spun hubs, Mint, boxed £310
232 Alfa Romeo Racing Car, red, red PW, Mint, boxed..........£250
232 Alfa Romeo Racing Car, red, red RW, Mint,
plain red/yellow box £210
233 Cooper-Bristol Racing Car, green, spun hubs, Mint/boxed ..£220
233 Cooper-Bristol Racing Car, green, red PW, Mint, boxed ...£265
234 Ferrari Racing Car, blue, yellow nose and PW, Mint, boxed .£345
234 Ferrari Racing Car, blue, yellow nose, spun hubs,
Mint, incorrect dual numbered box £275
236 Connaught Racing Car, green, RN '32', Mint, boxed £83
239 Vanwall Racing Car, green RN '35', Mint, box sl.damage £85
255 Police Mini Clubman, Mint, window box £38
258 USA Police Car Dodge, Near Mint, boxed £75
266 Plymouth Canadian Taxi, Very near mint, boxed £155
309 Star Trek Gift Set, Mint, window box £185
350 Tiny's Mini Moke, red, Near mint, boxed £135
351 U.F.O. Interceptor, Mint, boxed with packing £160
352 Ed Straker's Car, gold, blue int., Mint, boxed with packing......£77
353 Shado 2 Mobile, Mint, boxed with packing........................£215
353 Shado 2 Mobile, Mint, window box £90
358 USS Enterprise, Mint, window box £51
407 Ford Transit 'Hertz Rentals' van, Mint, boxed £45
410 Bedford Van, 'John Menzies', Mint, high bubble pack £53
425 Bedford TK Coal Truck, Mint, yellow export box £103
502 Foden Flat Truck, 1st cab, green, silver flash, Mint, boxed ...£275
502 Garage, Mint, boxed ....£xx
591 AEC Tanker 'Shell Chemicals Limited', V.near mint, box £155
617 VW KDF with 50mm P.A.K. Anti-Tank Gun, Mint, card box ...£75
620 Berliet Missile Launcher, Mint, bubble pack £103
622 10-Ton Army Truck, Mint, boxed £52
622 10.Ton Army Truck, Very near mint, boxed £37
622 10-Ton Army Truck, Mint, window picture box £282
617 VW KDF with 50mm PAK Gun, Mint, card box with pack £82
654 155mm Mobile Gun, Mint, bubble pack £51
656 88mm Anti-aircraft Gun, Mint, bubble pack £67
660 Tank Transporter, Mint, boxed £70
661 Recovery Tractor, Mint, boxed with packing £65
662 Static 88mm Gun with crew, Mint, bubble pack £91
665 Honest John Missile Launcher, Mint, full scene box £80
690 Scorpion Tank, Mint, window box £40
694 Hannomog Tank Destroyer, Mint, bubble pack £90
696 Leopard Anti-Aircraft Tank, Mint, bubble pack £97
697 25-Pounder Field Gun Set, Mint, boxed £75
702 DH Comet Airliner, G-ALYV, Mint, boxed, packing £87
715 Beechcraft C55 Baron, red, yellow engine cowlings
Mint, boxed £34
726 Messerschmit bf109E, Mint, bubble pack £54
902 Foden Flat Truck, orange/green, Very near mint, boxed ...£195
903 Foden Flat Truck with Tailboard, blue, fawn back,
Very Near Mint, boxed £340
903 Foden Flat Truck with Tailboard, blue, fawn back,
Near Mint, boxed...£206
930 Bedford Pallet Jetka Van, with pallets, Near mint, boxed ...£211
972 20-Ton Lorry Mounted Crane, French example,
Mint, boxed, with packing £206
977 Commercial Servicing Platform Vehicle, V.near mint, box ..£240
978 Refuse Wagon, light met. green, grey, red hubs, Mint, boxed ..£23
979 Racehorse Transport, Mint, split damage to box £175
980 Express Horse Box, maroon, Mint, boxed £135
982 Pullmore Car Transporter, with boxed ramp,
Very Near Mint, boxed £124

Nicky Toys, 1968 - 1975

In the late 1960s Meccano shipped out to India obsolete model dies and tools. The objective was to overcome exporting difficulties by manufacturing toys in India itself. The Indian manufacturing company was S. Kumar & Co who traded as Atamco Private Ltd. For trade mark reasons the toys were sold as 'Nicky Toys' and the arrangement was that the words 'Meccano' and 'Dinky Toys' would be obliterated from the dies. Similarly an arrangement was agreed in respect of deleting 'Dinky Toys' from the original model boxes.

However, the removal process was not diligently implemented which resulted in Nicky Toys occasionally being sold with 'Dinky Toys' being displayed both on their baseplates and on their boxes. These models are sought after by collectors and attract a premium at auctions.

After S.Kumar & Co. had manufactured the models from the original dies, they were finished by various firms of outworkers and as a result many different paint, decal and wheel versions exist. The details of the models listed are taken from various recent auction listings so their existence is confirmed. The figures shown in the 'Market Price Range' column are based on recent auction results and reflect the prices achieved by mint models in good boxes.

Types of Nicky Toys Boxes

i) Original yellow box with 'Dinky Toys' on the front and end flaps of the box and with a single model picture on front of box. This is the type of box which should have had all references to 'Dinky Toys' removed or overstamped.

ii) A plain yellow card box with 'Nicky Toys' stamped on the box end flaps and with 'Manufactured by: ATAMCO PRIVATE LTD. CALCUTTA' printed on the box sides.

iii) A yellow box with a full colour picture on the side. 'Nicky Toys' is clearly printed on all sides of the box and on the end flaps.

Ref.	Model name	Details	MPR
050	Jaguar 'Police' Car	Metallic Red or Red/White body	£80-100
05	VW 'Police' Car	Blue body, white doors	£80-100
051	Mercedes 220E 'Taxi'	Black/Yellow, Grey or Orange body, all with a 'Taxi' headboard	£80-100
054	Standard Herald Mk.II	Metallic Green, Red, Blue, Lemon-Yellow or White/Red body	£80-100
094	Rolls-Royce	Gold body	£80-100
113	MGB Sports	Light Blue, Navy Blue, Metallic Red or Light Green body, with driver	£100-125
115	Plymouth Fury	Metallic Green, Silver or Blue body	£80-100
120	Jaguar 'E'-type	Metallic Green, Red or Grey-Green	£100-125
		Apple-Green, Blue, Silver or Yellow	£100-125
134	Standard Herald Mk.II (Triumph Vitesse)	Red or Turquoise, both with White body stripe	£80-100
		Green or Blue, both with Red body stripe	£80-100
137	Plymouth Fury Conv.	Red with Yellow interior or Yellow with Black interior	£80-100
		Apple-Green or Metallic Green	£80-100
		Red or Cream	£80-100
137	Plymouth Fury Sports	Silver with Blue interior	£80-100
		Yellow or Blue body	£80-100
		Apple-Green, Red or Turquoise body	£80-100
142	Jaguar Mk.X	Metallic Green with White interior	£80-100
		Green with White interior	£80-100
		Metallic Red or Metallic Turquoise	£80-100
		Silver or Pale Yellow body	£80-100
144	Volkswagen 1500	Red, White, Blue or Metallic Green	£80-100
	'Police' version	Blue and White body	£80-100
146	Daimler V8 Saloon	(Jaguar 3.4 litre). No colour details	NGPP
	'Police' version	Red and White body	£80-100
170	Lincoln Continental	Blue or Silver, both with White roof	£100-150
		Pale Yellow or Cream, Black roof	£100-150
		Metallic Red with White roof	£100-150
		Metallic Turquoise with White roof	£100-150
186	Mercedes Benz 220SE	Metallic Red or Grey, both with Light Grey interiors	£80-100
		Metallic Light Green or Metallic Blue	£80-100
		Silver body, White interior	£100-120
194	Bentley 'S' Coupé	Metallic Red, White tonneau, Black interior	£80-100
		Metallic Green, Black tonneau, Red or Yellow interior	£80-100
		Cream or Blue with Red interiors	£80-100
		Silver or Gold body	£80-100
195	Jaguar 3.4 litre	Silver body, Light Grey interior	£80-100
		Cream or Blue with Red interiors	£80-100
238	Jaguar 'D'-type (RN '35' on some)	Light Blue body, Yellow plastic hubs	£70-90
		Racing Green, Red or Silver body	£70-90
		Metallic Red or Metallic Green body	£70-90
239	Vanwall Racing Car	Dark Metallic Blue, Red or Green	£70-90
		Light Blue, Grey or Yellow body (NB All issues have a blue plastic driver)	£70-90
295	Standard '20' Minibus	Metallic Red, Green or Silver body	£60-80
		Pale Blue, Red or Grey body	£60-80
	'Ambulance' version	White body, Blue rooflight, red crosses on roof/doors	£60-80
405	Universal Jeep	Gloss Brick Red body	£100-125
		Light Grey or Blue body	£100-125
	Army versions	Olive Green or Drab Green (All have black windscreen frame)	£100-125
626	Military Ambulance	Gloss Green body	£80-100
660	Mighty Antar Tank Transporter	Gloss Green body	NGPP
693	Howitzer 7.2	Dark Military Green body	NGPP
705	Viscount Airliner	Red, White and Blue 'BEA' livery	NGPP
735	Gloucester Javelin	RAF and camouflage liveries	£90-110
738	Sea Vixen	RAF and camouflage liveries	£80-100
949	Wayne School Bus	No details available	NGPP
962	Dumper Truck	No details available	NGPP
999	Comet Airliner	No details available	NGPP

Nicky Toys Catalogue Cover depicts Jaguar Mk.10 at Motor Show.
Range of models shown in two-tone colour £40-60

The Editor would welcome any further information to help complete this section.

Nicky Toys 194 Bentley 'S' Coupé. Note the type iii) box, the simple tinplate baseplate, the plastic wheels and the variable spreading of the spigot heads.

French Meccano Dinky Toys

The history of French Meccano Dinky Toys mirrors that of the Liverpool parent company. The Meccano France subsidiary was set up by Frank Hornby at Rue Ambroise Thomas in Paris in 1912, primarily to import British-made Meccano outfits and components. Having successfully marketed Meccano in France the obvious next step was to manufacture it there and in 1921 a factory was duly established at Rue Rébéval in Paris. This was initially used as offices and warehousing until 1924 when French-made Meccano became available, the Meccano Guild having been created a year before.

Production on French soil proved even more successful and a major new factory was soon required. Building of the famous plant at Bobigny was started in 1929. In 1931, the year in which Frank Hornby became MP for Everton, French Hornby 'Lead Models' nos. 1, 2 and 3 were introduced, followed by 'Miniature Models' nos. 4 and 10 in 1932. 'Modelled Miniatures' made their appearance in England in these years. Early in 1934 'Hornby Modelled Miniatures' were announced in France. Originally intended to extend the growing range of Hornby railway accessories, they were very briefly renamed 'Meccano Miniatures'. Before the year was out they had acquired the name 'Dinky Toys' in both countries. In the same year the Bobigny factory took over all French Meccano production while the Rue Rébéval premises reverted to offices and warehousing.

In 1935, 'Dolly Varden' dolls house furniture was introduced in England and the following year in France. Military vehicles became part of the Dinky range in Britain in 1937 but plans to introduce models of this type in France came to nothing before the War. Some of the English model tanks and guns were sent there between 1938 and 1940 along with some aircraft and ships. A very small part of French production was imported into the Britain in the late 1930s and most of their references were given a 'z' suffix.

During the late pre-war period the names were removed from aircraft dies and the models were given vague generic titles such as 'Long Range Bomber' and 'Medium Bomber'. Some planes like the Gloster Gladiator had no name at all and models of ships were given similar anonymity. It has been said that this was done for the cause of national security – to prevent Nazi intelligence from identifying the actual planes and ships by looking at the toys!

Among resources eagerly seized by the occupying German forces was naturally any factory that could turn instantly to the production of armaments. The French Meccano factory was thus commandeered in 1940 and required to produce various industrial items to satisfy the German war effort and even some toys to be sold under the Märklin name in German-occupied parts of the Continent. Production of conventional Meccano products was of course prohibited. There were very many shortages by the time peace was declared, rubber being a particular problem in France from 1940 since Nazi activities had completely cut off supplies.

When Meccano haltingly returned to production in 1946, Dinky Toys tyres were noticeable by their absence. The metal wheel castings first used in 1940 continued to be fitted right up to the beginning of 1950. Even the 49 series Petrol Pumps had to be sold without hoses for a while!

One of the most common vehicles on British and Continental roads during and after the War was the US Army Jeep. Thus in 1946 the 153a Jeep was introduced in England and the 24-M in France.

Any study of the history of Dinky Toys needs documentation from contemporary Meccano sources. Much of the required information is to be found in various catalogues and Meccano Magazines of the period but is not always reliable as an indicator of the date of introduction of models. Advertising did not always coincide with supply of models and distribution was not always even across the country. Most catalogues were generally accurate but occasionally announcements of forthcoming additions to the range could be just wishful thinking or proclamation of intent rather than actual production. Illustrations in early catalogues sometimes present problems with inaccurate line drawings and heavily retouched photographs. French catalogues suffered additional problems in having photos or drawings of English prototypes.

Many French catalogues were printed in England and some were actually English catalogues with a small amount of additional text in French plus a French currency price list. There is a marked similarity between French and English numbering systems and between actual castings, particularly before the War. However, it is important to remember that French castings are different from similar English ones, and come from French dies. All French Dinky Toys carry specific information either cast-in or stamped on a tinplate base as to the country of manufacture or assembly of the item.

In 1951, the Rue Rébéval factory closed and all French production was centralised at Bobigny. The French Meccano Magazine re-appeared in 1953 and 24-U Simca and 25-B Peugeot Van were introduced in their own individual yellow boxes. The first French Dinky Supertoy was issued in 1955.

Promotional opportunities were always being sought by Meccano and the idea of a society for young drivers of toy vehicles was welcomed by Roland Hornby who initiated the French Dinky Toys Club in 1957. 1960 saw the introduction of the French version of 'Dublo' trains ('Hornby ACHO'), production of which continued until 1974. French Hornby 'O' gauge train manufacture came to an end in 1963.

The early 1960s was a time of diversification for Meccano in both England and France with Scalextric and other toys being added to the range of products. In a decade of changing fortunes they continued to design and manufacture an interesting range of Dinky Toys. In 1970 production was moved to a factory at Calais, partly to help relieve the industrial pressure in the Paris area and also to benefit from access to a major port. To cut costs in an increasingly difficult economic climate, manufacture of French Dinky cars was undertaken by Auto-Pilen of Spain in 1975. Other production continued at Calais until 1978 when all remaining French Dinky Toys manufacturing rights were signed over to the Spanish company.

Over the years, French and English Dinkies have had remarkable similarities and some quite paradoxical differences, reflecting the independence of the two companies. 'Speedwheels', for instance, were deemed essential in England to compete with Corgi's WhizzWheels and Lesney Superfast, while in France the need seems not to have been at all apparent. The range of ship models was quite extensive in England but very limited in France. The understandable dominance of French cars in the range resulted in a stream of taxi models in France while motorcycles were completely ignored after the Triporteur was withdrawn. The excellent French idea of a diamond shaped 'viewport' in the famous yellow boxes was restricted to that country and not tried in England. We have no 'Novelty' section in the French Dinky listings since the only Dinkys that would come under that heading would be imported British ones! Indeed, the only film or television-related item to have originated in France is 1406 Michel Tanguy's Renault 4L Sinpar from the French TV series 'Les Chevaliers du Ciel'.

Some interesting models exist as accessories, particularly among the railway items. All the French castings of figures differ from English ones and have distinctly French characteristics, the 'Normandy' farmer and his French countrywoman spouse, the female railway crossing keeper, and the railway Cook with his poultry dish are particularly pleasing. Road signs provide another area of interest, some of the later French versions being only available as a free addition with certain models and not sold individually.

Cars - identification and casting differences

Although French and English reference numbers (particularly pre-war) are strikingly similar, it is very important to treat them as completely different systems in order to avoid confusion. The majority of French castings are different, as are the tyres. Surprisingly, small detail differences occur, as with steering wheels for instance. Post-war French-made open sports cars such as 22-A Maserati and 546 Austin-Healey have cast steering wheels with three spokes while those fitted to English made sports cars have four spokes. Many pre-war French made tyres have 'DUNLOP' moulded into the side-wall; post-war Spanish produced tyres similarly display the name 'PIRELLI'.

The 23b Streamlined Racing Car as made and sold in England from 1935 was based on a French Hotchkiss racing car. Unlike the English version, there were two French castings with the 23b reference. One is obviously the Hotchkiss (introduced in France in 1940). The other (pre-war) one is said by some to be modelled on a Renault Nervasport or possibly a Delahaye record car.

The 23 Racing Car is generally considered to have been inspired by the MG Magic Midget though it was never actually named as such by Meccano. Many modifications were made to the actual car in the 1930s in attempts to break

various endurance and speed records, and both English and French models mirrored these changes during their production. Racing numbers on the French 23 and 23a models were never contained within a circle and were initially stencilled, later mask-sprayed. All the French 23 series castings have either 'Made in France' or 'Fab. en France' cast underneath and also have a number of other differences from the English castings.

The first French Dinky Toys car model to be sold in its own box was the 24-U Simca Aronde in 1953. Many of the French boxes had a 'viewport' or aperture (usually diamond shaped) to allow a glimpse of the model. This enabled dealers and potential buyers to establish the colour of the model without the need to open the box. At the same time it saved the cost of printing a matching colour spot on the outside.

From 1969 a free 595 Traffic Sign was included as an additional attraction with certain models and these are noted in the listings that follow. More than twenty different plastic signs were made (see the 'Accessories' listing for details). They were not sold individually, but selections were available in Gift Sets 592 and 593.

24R (533)

Peugeot 203

Photo:
Collectoys, France

Cars

Ref	Year(s)	Model name and details	Market Price Range

22a 1933-37 **Sports Roadster**
Lead two-seater open body, lead wheels, scale 1:53.
Grey body / Blue wings; Blue body / Yellow wings;
Silver body / Red wings **£500-750**
Green body / Yellow wings; Cream body / Red wings,
Yellow body / Black wings......................................**£500-750**

22-A 1958-58 **Maserati Sport 2000**
Dark red body, Tan seats, plated convex hubs, 1:43.
white driver. Early bases are matt; later ones shiny....**£300-350**
1958-59 (Renumbered as 505)
Dark red body, dark red seats, plated convex hubs,
white driver **£90-110**
Same, but bright red body and seats...........................**£90-110**

22b 1934-37 **Sports Coupé**
Lead two-seater closed body, lead wheels, scale 1:53.
Cream body with black wings; Blue body with red
wings; Red body with blue wings **£500-750**
Green body with yellow wings **£500-750**
Grey body with green wings **£500-750**
Buff body with Black wings and hubs **£500-750**

22c 1934-37 **Sports Roadster**
As 22a, but with white rubber tyres on smooth
silvered lead hubs **£500-750**

22d 1934-37 **Sports Coupé**
As 22b, but with white rubber tyres on smooth
silvered lead hubs **£500-750**

23 1933-35 **Racing Car**
Lead body with contrasting colour flash over main colour,
smooth lead hubs, 'DUNLOP' tyres coloured to match
body flash. Indication of driver, 4 exhaust stubs,
no exhaust pipe, scale 1:53.
Orange (with white, blue or green flash) **£150-200**
Cream (with blue, green or red flash) **£150-200**
Blue (with silver or white flash)................................**£150-200**
Yellow (with blue flash) **£150-200**
1934-36 Lead body with contrasting colour flash, smooth lead
hubs, black or white or coloured tyres matching
colour flash. Helmet detail, 4 exhaust stubs, no pipe.
Blue (white flash); green (orange flash)....................**£150-200**
White (blue flash); silver (blue or red flash)..............**£150-200**
Cream (with blue, cream, green or red flash)............**£150-200**

23a 1936-37 **Racing Car**
Diecast body and smooth hubs; black, white or coloured
'DUNLOP' tyres that match colour flash. No driver,
4 exhaust stubs, no exhaust pipe.
Blue (white flash), green (orange flash)
White (blue flash); Silver (with blue or red flash)......**£200-250**
Cream (with blue, cream, green or red flash)............**£200-250**
1937-39 Diecast body and smooth hubs; black, white or
coloured 'DUNLOP' tyres that match colour flash.
Six branch exhaust pipe, driver helmet detail, scale 1:53,
90mm. Racing numbers '1' or '12'.
Blue (with silver or white flash)................................**£200-250**
Orange (with green or blue flash) **£200-250**
Yellow (with blue flash) **£200-250**
Cream (with blue, green or red flash) **£200-250**
1939-40 As previous model but smooth diecast hubs in
assorted colours, black or white tyres, RNs '1' or '12'.
Blue (silver or white flash).......................................**£200-250**
Orange (green or blue flash)......................................**£200-250**
Yellow (blue flash)
Cream (blue, green or red flash)................................**£200-250**
1940-40 As 1937-39 model but with unpainted diecast wheels.
Blue (silver or white flash).......................................**£200-250**
Orange (green or blue flash)......................................**£200-250**
Yellow (blue flash)...**£200-250**
Cream (blue, green or red flash)................................**£200-250**

23b 1935-37 **Streamlined Racing Car**
Diecast body, plated smooth hubs, 'DUNLOP' tyres in
the colour of the body flash, 1:53.
Blue (red flash, '1'), Yellow (red flash, '2'),
Orange (blue flash, '3'), Cream (blue flash '4'),
White (green flash '5'), Red (green flash, '6')...........**£200-250**
1937-40 Diecast body, plated or black smooth hubs,
white 'DUNLOP' tyres, 1:53.
Blue (red flash, '1'), Blue (white flash, '11' or '12')..**£200-250**
Red (green flash, '6'), Red (silver flash, '2').............**£200-250**
Yellow (red flash, '2'), Cream (blue flash, '4') **£200-250**
White (green flash, '5') **£200-250**
Green (white or silver flash, '7' or '8') **£200-250**
Orange (green flash, '9' or '10') **£200-250**
Orange (blue flash, '3') **£200-250**
1940-40 As previous model but with cast metal wheels
(black or unpainted)..**£200-250**
NB Many of the pre-war 23b models listed left the factory
without having the racing numbers applied. The rarity
levels for these is much the same as the numbered ones,
consequently prices are similar.
1949-49 Re-issue of 1940 model with cast metal wheels
(black or unpainted)..**£130-180**
1949-49 As 1939 issue but cream painted smooth hubs, black tyres.
Red body, silver flash, racing numbers '1' to '6' on
cream background **£110-140**
1952-52 Brief re-issue of previous model **£110-140**

23b 1940-40 **Hotchkiss Racing Car**
Red (silver flash, RNs '1' to '6'),
unpainted mazak wheels, 1:53....................................**£200-250**
1948-49 As previous model but with painted mazak wheels....**£200-250**
1950-51 Same, but cream painted convex hubs, black tyres.....**£100-150**

23c 1949-49 **Mercedes-Benz W154**
Silver, (RNs '1' to '6'), driver, painted or
unpainted metal wheels (2 sizes known), 1:43.............**£90-120**
1949-51 As previous model but black or red painted
convex hubs, black tyres..**£350-450**

23d 1950-? **Auto-Union Record Car**
Light green, filler cap on some, RNs '1' to '6',
red convex hubs, black tyres, 1:43. ....**£90-120**
As previous model but with bright green
convex hubs, black tyres, racing number '2' **£3,000-4,000**
NB Unlike the UK version, the rear axle ends are not visible.

23-H 1953-54 **Talbot-Lago GP Car**
Blue body, (RN's '1' to '6' in white paint), driver
cast in, blue convex hubs, ribbed tyres, 1:43. ....**£100-125**
1954-55 Same but numbers '1' to '6' on yellow transfers **£100-125**
1955-59 (Renumbered in 1959 as 510)
Blue, (RNs '1' to '6' and '22' to '27' on yellow
transfers), plated convex hubs **£100-125**

23-J 1956-56 **Ferrari GP Car**
Red body, (RN's '1' to '6'), smooth grille, driver,
plated convex hubs, 1:43. ....**£120-150**
1957-59 (Renumbered in 1959 as 511)
Dark red body (RNs '1' to '6' and '33' to '38'),
squared grille, plated convex hubs **£150-200**

24-A 1956-57 **Chrysler New Yorker**
'CHRYSLER NEW YORKER' on base and on box.
Scale 1:48. All have plated convex hubs.
Lemon yellow body, green seats **£120-150**
Red body, ivory seats..**£100-120**
1957-60 (Renumbered in 1960 as 520)
'CHRYSLER NEW YORKER 1955' on base and
on box. Scale 1:48. All have plated convex hubs.
Lemon Yellow or Mustard Yellow body, green seats..**£300-400**
Red (or orange-red) body, ivory seats **£300-400**
Light metallic blue body, ivory or pale grey seats **£300-400**

24b 1934-35 **Limousine**
4 doors cast-in, horizontal bonnet louvres (aligned),
large headlights, no sidelights, black or white
'DUNLOP' tyres on smooth hubs, scale 1:53.
Yellow body (with black or red wings) **£300-400**
Green body (with blue wings) **£300-400**

1936-39 4 doors cast-in, horizontal bonnet louvres (stepped),
medium or small headlights, sidelights on wings,
black or white 'DUNLOP' tyres on smooth hubs.
Green body (with red wings) **£300-400**
Grey body (with blue wings) **£300-400**

1940-48 As previous model but unpainted mazak wheels.
Grey body (red wings); Yellow body (red wings)......**£300-400.**
Red body (black wings)..**£300-400**
Blue body (black wings); Green body (black wings)..**£300-400**

24-B 1956-58 **Peugeot 403 8cv**
No window glazing, base without towing notch,
plated convex hubs, smooth white tyres, 1:43.
Blue or Black body **£80-100**

1958-59 (Renumbered in 1959 as 521)
Base has towing notch, plated convex hubs,
smooth white tyres.
Blue or Light grey body **£100-120**
Pale Yellow body **£150-200**

24-C 1956-58 **Citroën DS19**
No window glazing, plated convex hubs,
smooth white tyres, scale 1:43.
Green body with white or pale grey roof **£110-130**
Ivory body (with very dark purple roof) **£110-130**

24-CP 1958-59 **Citroën DS19**   (renumbered in 1959 as 522)
As 24-C but with window glazing. In 24-C box with
'24CP' sticker, later in own box.
Green body (with white or pale grey roof)..............**£150-170**
Ivory body (with very dark purple roof) **£150-170**
Dark orange body (cream roof) **£150-170**
Brown body (cream roof) **£150-170**
Yellow body, grey roof **£200-250**

24d 1934-35 **Vogue Saloon**
Spare wheel in wing, large headlights, no sidelights, smooth
mazak hubs, black or white 'DUNLOP' tyres, 1:53.
Blue body (with black wings) **£300-400**
Green body (with red wings) **£300-400**

1936-37 Spare wheel in wing, medium headlights, sidelights
on wings, smooth mazak hubs, black or white
'DUNLOP' tyres.
Red body (black wings)...**£300-400**
Blue body (yellow or black wings) **£300-400**
Green body (yellow wings) **£300-400**

1938-39 No spare wheel, small headlights, sidelights on wings,
smooth mazak hubs, black or white 'DUNLOP' tyres.
Grey body (with black wings)...................................**£300-400**
Green body (with maroon wings)...............................**£300-400**

1940-48 No spare wheel, medium or small headlights,
sidelights on wings, painted mazak wheels.
Yellow body (red wings), Grey body (red wings)......**£300-400**
Red body (black wings), Blue body (black wings).....**£300-400**

24-D 1957-59 **Plymouth Belvedere** (renumbered in 1959 as 523)
Plated convex hubs, 1:48. Model picture on some boxes.
Green body, black roof and side flash **£100-120**
Tan body, brown roof and side flash **£200-250**
Grey body, Red roof and side flash **£80-100**
White body, blue roof and side flash, convex hubs **£275-325**
White body, blue roof and side flash, concave hubs...**£350-400**
Pink body, Pale Maroon roof and side flash **£375-450**

24e 1934-35 **Aerodynamic Saloon Car**
Large headlights, no sidelights, smooth mazak hubs,
black or white 'DUNLOP' tyres, 1:53.
Green body, blue or red wings...................................**£200-250**

1936-39 Medium or small headlamps, sidelights in wings,
smooth mazak hubs, black or white 'DUNLOP' tyres.
Blue body (with black wings) **£200-250**
Red body (with black or yellow wings) **£200-250**

1940-48 Medium or small headlamps, sidelights in wings,
cast metal wheels.
Blue body (black wings), Green body (black wings)..**£200-250**
Red body (black wings), Yellow body (red wings).....**£200-250**

24-E 1957-59 **Renault Dauphine** (renumbered in 1959 as 524)
No window glazing, plated convex hubs,
smooth black tyres, scale 1:43.
Olive-green or Brick-red body **£150-200**
Raspberry-red body **£120-150**
Bright Blue body **£400-500**
Turqoise body **£200-250**

24f 1934-35 **Sportsman's Coupé**
Two-door body with spare wheel in wing,
large headlights, no sidelights, smooth mazak hubs,
black or white 'DUNLOP' tyres, scale 1:53.
Green body (with yellow wings) **£300-400**
Blue body (with black wings) **£300-400**

1936-37 Two-door body with spare wheel in wing,
medium headlights, sidelights on wings, smooth mazak
hubs, black or white 'DUNLOP' tyres.
Blue body (black or yellow wings) **£300-400**
Green body (yellow wings) **£300-400**
Red body (black wings)...**£300-400**

1938-39 Two-door body, no spare wheel, small headlights,
sidelights on wings, smooth mazak hubs,
black or white 'DUNLOP' tyres.
Red body (black wings) **£300-400**
Yellow body (black or red wings) **£300-400**
Blue body (maroon wings) **£300-400**
Cream body (blue wings) **£300-400**

1940-40 Two-door body, no spare wheel, medium or small
headlights, sidelights on wings, painted mazak wheels.
Red body (black wings), Blue (black wings).............**£300-400**
Green (black wings), Yellow body (red wings)..........**£300-400**

1947-48 Re-issue of 1940 versions (with cast metal wheels):
Red, blue, green or yellow body, black wings **£300-400**

24-F 1958-59 **Peugeot 403-U Familiale** (renumbered in 1959 as 525)
Sky blue, no windows, plated convex hubs, 1:43 ....**£100-120**

1958 Dark red body (no windows). Only a few made as
gifts for 1958 visitors to Meccano factory **£2,000-3,000**

22A

Maserati Sport 2000

Photo: Vectis Auctions Ltd.

24g 1934-35 **4-seat Sports Car**
Spare wheel, open windscreen, large headlights,
no sidelights, black or white 'DUNLOP' tyres, 1:53.
Blue body (with black wings) **£300-400**
Green body (with red wings).....................................**£300-400**
1936-37 Spare wheel, solid windscreen, medium headlights,
sidelights in wings, black or white 'DUNLOP' tyres.
Yellow body (with red wings) **£300-400**
Grey body (with blue wings) **£300-400**
1938-39 Spare cast-in, solid windscreen, small headlights,
sidelights in wings, black or white 'DUNLOP' tyres.
Green or cream body, red wings...........................**£300-400**
1940-40 Spare wheel cast-in, solid windscreen, medium or
small headlights, sidelights in wings,
unpainted mazak wheels, 1:53.
Grey body (red wings); yellow body (red wings).......**£200-300**
Red body (black wings)...**£200-300**
1947-48 Re-issue of 1940 versions (unpainted mazak wheels).
Grey body (red wings)..**£200-300**
Yellow body (red wings)..**£200-300**
Red body (black wings)..**£200-300**

24h 1934-35 **2-seat Sports Car**
Spare wheel, open windscreen, large headlights,
no sidelights, black or white 'DUNLOP' tyres, 1:53.
Green body (blue wings) **£300-400**
Black body (blue or red wings) **£300-400**
Red body (black wings)...**£300-400**
1936-37 Spare wheel, solid windscreen, medium headlights,
sidelights in wings, black or white 'DUNLOP' tyres.
Yellow body (black wings)......................................**£300-400**
Blue or green body (red wings)..............................**£300-400**
1938-39 Spare cast-in, solid windscreen, small headlights,
sidelights in wings, black or white 'DUNLOP' tyres.
Green body (red wings) **£300-400**
Red or yellow body(black wings) **£300-400**
1940-40 Spare cast-in, solid windscreen, medium or small
headlights, sidelights in wings, unpainted mazak wheels.
Cream or yellow body (red wings)
Green or red body (black wings)...........................**£200-300**
1947-48 Re-issue of 1940 versions with unpainted
mazak wheels, 1:53.
Cream or yellow body (with red wings) **£200-300**
Green or red body (with black wings).......................**£200-300**

24-H 1958-59 **Mercedes-Benz 190sl** (renumbered in 1959 as 526)
Cream body (various shades), black hard-top, 1:43.
Picture on some boxes...**£100-120**
Silver body, black roof, plated convex hubs **£140-160**
24-J 1959-59 **Alfa-Romeo 1900 Sprint** (renumbered in 1959 as 527)
Red or Blue body, windows, plated convex hubs,
smooth black tyres, scale 1:43....................................**£80-100**

24k 1939-40 **Peugeot 402**
No baseplate (and no base retainers cast inside body),
black or white 'DUNLOP' tyres on smooth painted
mazak hubs, scale 1:53.
Maroon, Blue, Light blue, Red or Yellow body.........**£300-400**
1947-48 No baseplate (and no retainers cast inside),
unpainted mazak wheels.
Maroon, Blue, Light blue, Red or Yellow body.........**£500-750**
1948-48 With tinplate base/front bumper (and with base
retainers cast inside body), unpainted mazak wheels.
Maroon, Blue, Light blue, Red or Yellow body.........**£500-750**

24-K 1959-59 **Simca Vedette Chambord** (renumbered in 1959 as 528)
Ivory/red body, plated convex hubs, scale 1:43. ....**£80-100**
Light green/dark green body....................................**£90-110**

24 l 1939-40 **Peugeot 402 Taxi** (all have a tinplate taxi-meter)
Royal blue/yellow, smooth cast hubs, no base............**£500-700**
Maroon/cream, smooth cast hubs, no base **£500-700**
1947-47 Royal blue/yellow or maroon/cream, metal wheels,
tinplate meter, no base **£500-700**
Maroon/cream, metal wheels, no base **£500-700**
1948-48 Royal blue/yellow, metal wheels, with base..............**£500-700**
Maroon/cream, metal wheels, with base **£500-700**

24-L 1959-59 **Vespa 400 2cv** (renumbered in 1959 as 529)
Blue/grey, plated convex hubs, 1:43, '24L' on box........**£65-75**
Orange/grey, plated convex hubs. '24L' on box..........**£300-400**
24m 1946-48 **Military Jeep**
US Military olive-drab body and khaki painted mazak
wheels (mounted inside-out for effect), white star on
bonnet, cast star at rear, tinplate windscreen frame
(bonnet castings exist with and without frame
supports), wire steering wheel, scale 1:43..................**£700-900**
NB: 24m was the first new French made Dinky Toys model
to appear after the war. They were supplied to shops in
trade boxes of twelve units. A trailer was designed to
complement the Military Jeep but was never produced,
nor did 24m ever acquire a towing hook.
24m 1948-49 **Civilian Jeep**
Castings as military version, usually unpainted wheels
(a few painted).
Red body...**£400-500**
Green body..**£400-500**
Blue, orange, sand, yellow, metallic grey or
metallic gold body...**£400-500**

24-M 1959-59 **VW Karmann-Ghia** (renumbered in 1959 as 530)
Black/red body, plated convex hubs, scale 1:43...........**£90-120**

24-N 1949-58 **Citroën 11BL**
1st version: Small rear window, small lettering on base,
widely spaced grille bars, spare wheel cover, tinplate
front bumper, no direction indicators,
smooth roof interior. scale 1:43.
2nd version: With 16mm wide rear window, small
lettering on base, boot replaces spare wheel cover,
shallow rear axle supports, with direction indicators,
smooth roof interior.
3rd version: With 17mm wide rear window,
large lettering on base, boot replaces spare wheel cover,
deep rear axle supports, cast front bumper,
with direction indicators, hatched roof interior.
1949-49 Navy blue body, black mazak wheels **£750-900**
1950-51 As first version but the front wheel arch casting
extends below the baseplate.
Metallic gold body, black convex hubs, black tyres ...**£500-700**
Metallic grey body and red convex hubs, black tyres.**£450-650**
Black body and yellow convex hubs, black tyres **£300-400**
1951-52 As first version but with large rear window.
Black body, yellow or cream hubs, black tyres..........**£300-400**
1953-55 Integral front bumper, big or small rear window,
rounded boot, narrow grooves on grille, small print
on base, straight windscreen base, smooth inside roof.
Black body, cream convex hubs, black tyres **£130-160**
1955-57 As 1953-55 model but large print and '24N' on base.
Inside of roof is cross-hatched.
Black body, cream convex hubs **£100-125**
Light grey body, yellow convex hubs **£120-160**
1957-58 As 1953-55 model but large print and '24N' on base,
arched base to windscreen.
Black body (cream convex hubs) **£100-125**
Light Grey body (Light Grey convex hubs)...............**£100-125**
1958-58 As previous but with plated convex hubs, white tyres.
Black body **£100-125**
Light grey body, grey hubs....................................**£120-140**
NB: 24-N Citroën models were all supplied to shops in
grey trade boxes each containing six models.

24-N 1959-59 **Fiat 1200 Grand Vue**
Announced only in the 1959 Swiss catalogue but not
made as 24-N. Renumbered and produced as 531.

24-O 1949-49 **Studebaker State Commander**
Casting as the English 39f model but the black tinplate
base is marked 'Fabriqué en France'. Scale 1:48.
Cream body, painted mazak wheels **£400-500**
Red body, painted mazak wheels............................**£400-500**
Metallic blue-green body, painted mazak wheels **£400-500**
1950-50 Cream body, red convex hubs, black tyres...............**£300-400**
Metallic blue-green, red convex hubs, black tyres......**£300-400**
Cream or Red body, Black hubs..............................**£150-175**
NB: 24-O Studebaker was supplied to shops in
trade boxes of six units.

24-P 1949-49 **Packard Super 8 Limousine**
Casting as English 39a but with black tinplate base
marked 'Fabriqué en France', scale 1:48.
Blue body, painted convex hubs...............................**£750-850**
Turqoise body, painted convex hubs **£750-850**
Metallic Gold body, painted convex hubs.................**£750-850**
NB: 24-P Packard was supplied to shops in
trade boxes of six units.

24-Q 1950-51 **Ford Vedette**
Navy blue body and convex hubs,
small baseprint, scale 1:43.....................................**£900-1,000**
Metallic blue body (red hubs) **£200-250**
Grey body and hubs...**£200-250**
Turquoise body and hubs..**£200-250**
Sand body and hubs..**£200-250**
1952-55 Metallic blue, red convex hubs, large base print........**£150-175**
Turquoise body and hubs, or Grey body and hubs.....**£150-175**
Sand body and hubs..**£150-175**
NB: 24-Q was supplied to shops in trade boxes of six units.

24-R 1951-52 **Peugeot 203**
Small rear window, smooth inside roof,
round filler cap on right rear wing, scale 1:43.
Maroon body, cream convex hubs.............................**£150-200**
Metallic gold body, cream or red convex hubs **£450-600**
Iridescent Violet body, cream convex hubs.............**£750-1,000**
Grey body, grey convex hubs **£2,000-3,000**
Metallic blue body, cream convex hubs **£150-175**
Metallic green body, creamy-yellow convex hubs.....**£150-200**
1953-55 Small rear window, cross-hatching inside roof, no filler cap.
Grey body, grey convex hubs **£90-120**
Metallic blue-green body, cream convex hubs...........**£120-140**
Grey-blue body, cream convex hubs **£100-130**
1955-56 Grey or grey-blue body, spun hubs,
white tyres, small rear window, no filler cap **£100-130**
1956-57 Grey-blue body, spun hubs, white tyres,
big rear window, square filler cap **£100-130**
Pale grey-green body, spun hubs, white tyres,
big rear window, square filler cap **£100-130**
1957-59 As previous model but with lime green body **£800-1,000**
1959 (Renumbered in 1959 as 533)
Promotional: Lime green body, 'Club Dinky Toys'.**£750-1,250**
NB: 24-R was supplied to shops in trade boxes of six units.

24-S **Simca 8 Sport**
1952-54 1st type: thin windscreen frame,
unpainted convex hubs, white tyres, scale 1:43.
Grey body, red seats, ...**£90-120**
Black body, fawn seats **£300-400**
Black body, red seats **£100-130**
1954-56 Grey body, red seats, spun hubs, white tyres **£90-120**
Black body, red seats **£90-120**
1956-59 2nd type: thick windscreen frame, spun hubs, white tyres.
Grey body, red seats **£150-200**
Black body, red seats **£200-300**
Ivory body, red seats **£100-120**
Duck-egg Green or Duck-egg Blue body, Red seats...**£125-150**
NB: 24-S was supplied to shops in trade boxes of six units.
1959 (Renumbered in 1959 as 534)

24-T **Citroën 2cv** (1951-53)
1952-52 Mid-grey or metallic grey (grey hood), grey-gold hubs,
one rear lamp, rear axle ends not rounded, scale 1:43.
Sold unboxed (supplied to shops in trade boxes
of six units) **£90-120**
1953-54 Mid-grey or metallic grey (gloss or matt grey hood),
grey-gold hubs, one rear lamp, rounded rear axle ends.
In individual box with '24T' and 'MECCANO' in
large print on ends...**£80-90**
Dark grey body, matt grey hood, cream convex hubs.....**£80-90**
Light grey body, matt grey hood, cream convex hubs....**£80-90**
1955-59 Light grey body, gloss or matt grey hood, cream hubs,
three red rear lamps, rounded rear axle ends. In own box
with '24T' and 'MECCANO' in small print on ends......**£75-85**
Maroon body, matt-grey hood, cream convex hubs.......**£75-85**
Grey-blue body, dark grey-blue hood,
grey concave or convex hubs......................................**£100-120**
1959 (Renumbered in 1959 as 535)

24-U 1953-55 **Simca 9 Aronde**
1st type: 'stepped' grille, painted convex hubs, 1:43.
Olive green body **£100-150**
Light grey-green body **£90-120**
Mid grey or light grey body **£150-200**
24-U 1956-57 **Simca Aronde Elysée**
2nd type: 'wide' grille, spun hubs.
Light grey or Light Grey-Green body **£150-200**
Sky blue body **£100-150**
1958-59 Light grey-green body, dark green roof.....................**£100-150**
Blue or Sky-Blue body, White roof............................**£100-150**
NB: 24-U Simca was the first French Dinky Toy to be
supplied in its own individual box (in 1953).
1959 (Renumbered in 1959 as 535)

24UT 1956-58 **Simca Aronde Elysée Taxi**
Red/blue body, meter and roof sign,
painted convex hubs, second grille, scale 1:43 ....**£110-130**
1958-59 As previous model but with plated convex hubs........**£110-130**
NB: 24-UT was supplied to shops in trade boxes of six units.
1959 (Renumbered in 1959 as 537)

24-V 1954-56 **Buick Roadmaster**
1st type: smooth inside roof, unpainted convex hubs,
white tyres, scale 1:48.
Blue body, dark blue roof **£160-200**
Yellow body, green roof **£160-200**
1956-59 2nd type: cross-hatched inside roof,
plated convex hubs, white tyres.
Blue body, dark blue or cream roof............................**£160-200**
Yellow body, green roof **£160-200**
Lemon-yellow body, green roof ....* **£750-1,000**
Salmon-Pink body, black roof **£500-700**
Ivory body, Blue roof **£400-600**
Ivory/metallic blue body...**£500-600**
Red/yellow with blue roof..**£1,000-1,250**
1959 (Renumbered in 1959 as 538)

24-X 1954-56 **Ford Vedette**
With or without 'Made in France, Imprimé en France'
on individual boxes. Scale 1:43.
Dark blue body and convex hubs **£120-140**
Pale grey-blue body and convex hubs........................**£100-125**

24XT 1956-59 **Ford Vedette Taxi**
Black body, beige or cream roof, meter,
taxi sign, spun hubs **£125-150**
1959 (Renumbered in 1959 as 539)
NB: 24-XT was supplied to shops in trade boxes of six units.
It was never individually boxed.

24-Y 1955-57 **Studebaker Commander Coupé**
1st type: Base has no towing eye, plated convex hubs,
smooth tyres, scale 1:48. '24Y' on box but no illustration.
Red body, Dark Cream roof **£150-200**
Light Green body, Dark Green roof **£150-200**
Ivory body, Maroon roof **£200-250**
Orange body, Tan roof..**£200-250**
1957-58 2nd type: Base has a towing eye, plated convex hubs,
smooth tyres. '24Y' and picture of model on box.
Red body, Cream roof...**£150-200**
Light Green body, Dark Green roof **£150-200**
Ivory body, Dark Red roof **£300-350**
1958-59 3rd type: Base has towing eye, front wing panels
match the roof colour, plated convex hubs, smooth tyres.
'540-24Y' and picture of model on box.
Red body, Cream roof and wing panels **£200-250**
Ivory body with Maroon roof and wing panels..........**£200-250**
Pale grey body, maroon roof and wing panels **£200-250**
1959 (Renumbered in 1959 as 537)
NB: The 1959 catalogue shows a two-tone blue version of
24-Y/540 but it has not been seen. Also, a photo
exists showing a 24-Y prototype of the 1953-54
Studebaker, but only the 1955 car was actually modelled.

24-Z 1956-58 **Simca Vedette 'Versailles'**
1st type: Base has no towing eye, plated convex hubs,
white tyres, picture on some boxes. Scale 1:43.
Yellow body, black roof..**£100-120**
Light blue body, White roof **£100-120**

* An example of this version of 24-V Buick was sold by Collectoys in June 2004 for **£3,520.**

24-Z 1958-59 2nd type: Base has towing eye, plated convex hubs, white tyres, picture on box.
Yellow body, black roof...**£100-120**
Light blue body, White roof.............................**£100-120**
1959 (Renumbered in 1959 as 541)

24ZT 1959-59 **Simca Ariane Taxi**
Black body, red roof, plated concave hubs.
'542-24ZT' on box..**£100-125**
1959 (Renumbered in 1959 as 542)

30a 1935-39 **Chrysler Airflow**
English castings painted and assembled in France.
Smooth hubs, black or white 'DUNLOP' tyres, 1:48.
Green, Blue or Red body...............................**£200-250**

35a 1939-40 **Simca 5**
No base, black rubber wheels, scale 1:50.
Red, dark red, maroon, light blue, mid-blue, royal blue, grey, grey-blue, green, light green, brown, silver, yellow, gold, cream.....................................**£250-300**
1939-40 Export version of 35-A with white rubber wheels.
Red, dark red, maroon, light blue, mid-blue, royal blue, grey, grey-blue, green, light green, brown, silver, yellow, gold, cream.....................................**£250-300**
1940-40 No base, black painted mazak wheels.
Red, dark red, maroon, light blue, mid-blue, royal blue, grey, grey-blue, green, light green, brown, silver, yellow, gold, cream.....................................**£250-300**
1948-50 No base, black rubber wheels.
Red, dark red, maroon, light blue, mid-blue, royal blue, grey, grey-blue, light green, mid-brown, silver, yellow, gold, cream.....................................**£100-125**
Green, dark brown..**£150-200**

Numbers 100 to 106 were produced as 'Dinky Juniors'
- a pocket-money budget series. Most fitted with spun steel hubs or Silver hubs with 'DUNLOP'tyres. 1:43.
100 1963-68 **Renault 4L**
Pale-green body..**£400-500**
101 1963-66 **Peugeot 404** (553 casting)
Orange body, no frame to rear number plate........**£400-500**
1966-69 Orange or red-orange, rear number plate has frame ...**£400-500**
102 1963-68 **Panhard PL17**
Grey-blue or Bright blue body.........................**£400-500**
103 1964-68 **Renault R8**
Red body..**£400-500**
103 1969-69 **Renault R8S Gordini**
Red body, painted headlights..........................**£450-600**
104 1964-68 **Simca 1000**
Pale yellow or lime-green body........................**£300-400**
105 1964-68 **Citroën 2cv**
Grey body, Light Grey concave hubs.................**£400-500**
106 1965-69 **Opel Kadett**
Yellow body...**£500-700**

500 1967-71 **Citroën 2cv**
Beige (dark grey open top), painted concave hubs.
'Made in France' on aperture box.....................**£80-90**
Blue-Grey body (dark blue open top)................**£80-90**
Pale grey body (mid-grey open top)..................**£80-90**
1974-? Spanish issues:
1974-75 Beige (dark grey open top), painted hubs. 'Made in Spain' over-stamped on box, own box printed later........**£80-90**
1975-76 Beige (dark grey open top), painted hubs. 'Made in Spain' and 'Meccano' on large non-aperture box...........**£80-90**
1976-78 Orange body, 'square' headlamps, rivetted base, plated concave hubs. 'Made in Spain, imprimée en France, ref 500' on box.............................**£70-80**
1978-? Orange body, 'square' headlamps, screwed base, plated concave hubs. 'Made in Spain, imprimée en Espagne, ref 011500' on box............................**£70-80**

501 1967-70 **Citroën DS19 'POLICE' Car**
Very dark blue/white, roof beacon, concave hubs, scale 1:43..**£200-300**
503 1967-69 **Porsche Carrera 6**
White/red body, 'Carrera' in black, 1:43. Box has 'moteur...280km/h' outside of yellow lines................**£100-120**
1969-71 Same model but box has 'moteur...280km/h' within yellow lines...**£100-120**

505 1959-60 **Maserati Sport 2000** (renumbered from 22a)
Dark or bright red, shiny baseplate, convex chromed hubs, white driver, scale 1:43 ....**£100-125**
1960-61 Dark or bright red, shiny baseplate, concave chromed hubs, white driver.....................**£125-150**

506 1960-61 **Aston-Martin DB3S**
Emerald green, concave hubs, driver, racing numbers '1' to '17', scale 1:43...........................**£100-150**
NB: 506 used the English 104 body casting with 'Made in France' base and a French three-spoke steering wheel.

506 1967-72 **Ferrari 275 GTB**
Cast base, cast detailed wheels, nylon tyres, scale 1:43.
Red body...**£90-110**
Yellow body...**£110-130**
Yellow body, 'hybrid' with Red doors/bonnet/boot **£80-90**

507 1967-71 **Simca 1500 Estate Car**
White, Metallic Dark Grey or Silver-Grey body, camping table,concave hubs, black tyres, 1:43 ....**£100-120**
507-P 1967-71 **Simca 1500 'POLICE' Car**
White and Dark Blue body, Red interior, aerial at one side of roof....................................**£5,000-6,500**

508 1966-71 **Daf 33**
Dark red body, cast base, concave hubs, black tyres, female driver, 1:43...**£80-100**
Metallic bronze, concave chromed hubs, black tyres..**£110-130**
Beige body, concave chromed hubs, black tyres..........**£90-110**

509 1966-68 **Fiat 850**
Red body, white tilting seats, concave hubs, 1:43..........**£70-90**
Yellow body, red tilt seats, concave hubs....................**£100-125**
White body, red tilt seats, concave hubs.....................**£80-100**
1968-71 Spanish issues:
Red, yellow or white body, 'PIRELLI' tyres, Barcelona number plate. 'DINKY-POCH' on box......**£400-500**
Turquoise-green body, white interior, 'PIRELLI' tyres, Barcelona number plate. 'DINKY-POCH' on box......**£450-600**

510 1959-59 **Talbot-Lago GP Car** (renumbered from 23-H)
Blue body, (RN's '1' to '6' and '22' to '27' on yellow transfers), driver cast in, plated convex hubs.............**£100-150**

510 1965-68 **Peugeot 204**
Two-part rear bumper, rivetted floor, concave hubs, 1:43.
Metallic dark red body. 'Par autorisation des automobiles PEUGEOT' on box. **£100-125**
Greenish-beige body. 'Par autorisation des automobiles PEUGEOT' on box. **£100-125**
1968-68 Spanish issues: Two-part rear bumper, rivetted floor, concave hubs, 'PIRELLI' tyres.
Bright Red body, 'DINKY-POCH' on box.
Assembled in Spain **£500-750**
1968-71 Same, but White body. Made for export to Spain.......**£400-450**
1977-78 One-piece rear bumper, screwed floor, Beige-pink body. Made in Spain, box printed in Spain ..**£50-75**
1981 Promotional issue: Off-White body with 'VGE' in Blue/White/Red with Presidential Election decor.......**£400-500**

511 1959-63 **Ferrari Racing Car** (renumbered from 23-J)
Red body, 'cross-hatched' grille, racing numbers '1' or '22' to '27', driver, concave hubs, radial or block tread tyres, scale 1:43 ....**£100-125**

511 1968-71 **Peugeot 204 Cabriolet**
Cast base, aluminium concave hubs, tilting seats, 1:43.
Sky-blue open body, black interior............................**£140-170**
Red open body, black interior..................................**£170-200**

512 1962-66 **Leskokart Midjet Kart**
Blue body, Black plastic wheels. Plastic driver (white with yellow or blue jacket). Scale 1:43.......................**£80-100**
Same but driver with red jacket.................................**£200-250**

513 1966-68 **Opel Admiral**
Metallic blue or metallic red, detailed hubs, luggage, scale 1:43 ....**£90-120**
1968-69 Spanish issue: Same but with 'PIRELLI' tyres. 'DINKY-POCH' on box **£250-300**

514 1966-71 **Alfa-Romeo Giulia 1600ti**
Plated concave hubs, working windows,
head and rear lights, scale 1:43.
Beige or White or Metallic Grey body, Red interior...**£100-130**
Pale Green body, Red interior **£125-150**
Spanish export issue: Metallic Grey body,
'PIRELLI' tyres, Barcelona number plate.................**£200-300**

515 1963-70 **Ferrari 250GT 2+2**
Red body, White interior, concave hubs, black tyres,
scale 1:43 ....**£100-125**
Metallic blue body, concave hubs, black tyres.............**£90-110**

516 1964-65 **Mercedes-Benz 230SL**
Removable hard-top, concave hubs,
'MERCEDES 230SL' on base, French box.
Metallic silver/cream body **£130-160**
Metallic red-orange/cream body...............................**£100-120**
Metallic red/cream body **£120-140**
1965-66 Same as previous model but with
'MERCEDES-BENZ 230SL' on base. French box **£100-125**
1966-70 Metallic red-orange/cream as 1965-66 version but
in British box for export to UK and USA **£70-90**

517 1962-64 **Renault R8**
Blue or Primrose-Yellow body, concave hubs, 1:43 ...**£100-125**
1964 (Renumbered in 1964 as 1517)
NB: Model was introduced on the same day as the actual car.
1968-70 Spanish issues:
Cream body, concave hubs, 'PIRELLI' tyres,
Silver rear number plate. 'DINKY-POCH' on box **£400-600**
Dark blue body, concave hubs, 'PIRELLI' tyres,
Silver rear number plate. 'DINKY-POCH' on box **£400-600**

517-P 1969 **Renault R8 Police Car**
Dark blue/white, 'POLICE'.
Commissioned for use by Police **£600-700**

518 1961-64 **Renault R4L**
Pale blue or light blue body, first grille,
concave hubs, scale 1:43 ....**£50-60**
1964 Brick-red or brown body **£50-60**
1964 Grey-green body **£95-125**
1964 (Renumbered in 1964 as 1518)
1964-64 Red body, 'POMPIERS de PARIS'.
Commissioned for use by Fire Service.....................**£1,200-1,600**
1964-64 Yellow/blue 'PTT' livery.
Commissioned for use by Postal Service **£500-600**
1968-70 Spanish issues:
As standard 1964 French model but Violet body,
'PIRELLI' tyres. 'DINKY-POCH' on box **£400-600**
1975-77 Dark blue, second grille, concave hubs.
'Made in Spain' and pink '4L' on box...........................**£55-65**
1977-? Sky blue, second grille, concave hubs.
'Made in Spain' and blue '4L' on box...........................**£55-65**

518-A 1970-71 **Renault 4L, 'AUTOROUTES'**
Orange body, first grille, plated concave hubs.
Box also contains 595r Traffic Sign 'Road Works' **£200-250**

519 1961 **Facel Vega Facellia**
Announced in the 1961-62 catalogue but not produced......**NPP**

519 1962-70 **Simca 1000**
1962-63 Red or Light blue-grey body, Cream interior,
Black base. '519' in black oval on box **£70-90**
Lime-Green or Light yellow body, Cream interior **£220-260**
Sky-blue body, white interior......................................**£80-90**
1962-64 Light blue-grey body, Red interior, Black base,
concave hubs, rubber tyres. '519' in black oval on box..**£55-65**
1963-64 Metallic grey body, black or green interior.
Existence not confirmed ....**NPP**
NB: The 1962-64 version of 519 was renumbered in 1964 as 1519.
Production of 519 continued as follows:
1964-66 Light blue-grey body, white interior. Anodised base,
concave hubs, nylon tyres. '519' in black band on box..**£70-90**
1966-68 South-African issues:
Turquoise body, red interior, concave hubs.
Assembled and painted in South Africa **£600-800**
Dark red body, white interior, concave hubs.
Assembled and painted in South Africa **£600-800**

1968-70 Spanish issues:
Metallic blue body, Cream interior, concave hubs,
'PIRELLI' tyres. 'DINKY-POCH' on box **£500-700**
Red body, Cream interior, concave hubs,
'PIRELLI' tyres. 'DINKY-POCH' on box **£250-300**

520 1960-61 **Chrysler New Yorker** (renumbered from 24-A)
'CHRYSLER NEW YORKER 1955' on base and on box.
Concave hubs, scale 1:48.
Yellow body, green seats **£200-250**
Red body, ivory seats **£100-120**
Light metallic blue body, ivory seats.........................**£275-350**

520 1963-64 **Fiat 600D**
White body, Red interior, concave hubs.........................**£65-75**
1964-64 Red or Cream body, concave hubs, scale 1:43...............**£75-85**
1964 (Renumbered in 1964 as 1520)
1968 Spanish export issues:
Pale yellow body, concave hubs,
'PIRELLI' tyres. 'DINKY-POCH' on box **£200-250**
Light blue body, concave hubs,
'PIRELLI' tyres. 'DINKY-POCH' on box **£300-400**
Off-White body, concave hubs, 'PIRELLI' tyres,
Silver number plate. 'DINKY-POCH' on box.............**£250-300**

521 1959-60 **Peugeot 403 8cv** (renumbered from 24-B)
Light grey body, no windows, base has towing notch,
plated convex hubs, smooth white tyres.......................**£90-110**
Cream body, no windows, base has towing notch,
plated convex hubs, smooth white tyres.......................**£150-200**
1960-62 With windows and towing notch, plated concave hubs,
smooth or treaded white tyres.
Light grey body. (Light blue-grey picture and
black picture on box)...**£100-125**
Cream body. (Light blue-grey picture and
black picture on box)...**£150-200**
1962-64 521 became individually unavailable in 1962 but
was included in Gift Set 503 up to 1964.

522 1959-60 **Citroën DS19** (renumbered from 24-CP)
With windows, convex hubs, smooth white tyres,
scale 1:43. '24CP' on box.
Green/white, or Ivory/very dark purple. **£150-175**
Yellow/grey, or Orange/cream.................................**£150-175**
1960-63 With concave hubs, smooth white tyres. '522' on box.
Orange/cream body..**£110-140**
Yellow/grey body **£100-130**
1963-68 With concave hubs, treaded white tyres. '522' on box.
Orange body, cream roof **£100-130**
Yellowish-beige body, pale grey roof.........................**£150-200**
Pale yellow body, grey roof.......................................**£100-130**

523 1962 **Simca Driving School Car**
Announced (but not illustrated) in the 1962 price list.
Not produced..**NPP**

523 1959-60 **Plymouth Belvedere** (renumbered from 24-D)
Convex hubs, scale1:48. Picture on some boxes.
Green body, black roof and panel................................**£90-110**
Tan body, metallic brown roof and panel....................**£150-200**
Grey body, orange-red roof and panel.........................**£85-100**
White body, blue roof and panel, convex hubs **£300-350**
1960-61 With concave hubs.
Tobacco-brown body, maroon roof and panel.............**£200-300**
White body, blue roof and panel **£375-450**

523 1963-64 **Simca 1500**
Light-blue body, concave hubs, scale 1:43....................**£60-80**
1964 (Renumbered in 1964 as 1523)
Light blue or Metallic grey body, concave hubs............**£60-80**
1968-69 Spanish issue: Bright Blue body, plated concave
hubs, 'PIRELLI' tyres. 'DINKY-POCH' on box........**£400-600**

524 1959-60 **Renault Dauphine**
With windows (some without), convex hubs,
smooth black tyres, scale 1:43. '524 - 24E' on box.
Turquoise, Brick-red or Raspberry-red body **£120-150**
Ivory-White body...**£150-200**
1960-60 As previous models but box has 'DINKY TOYS' in
upright lettering plus '524'.
Turquoise body **£150-175**
Brick-red body **£120-150**

Raspberry-red body **£150-175**
Ivory-White body...**£150-200**

1960-61 Bright Blue-Green body. Box has 'DINKY TOYS'
in upright lettering plus '524'.
Special limited edition for Paris Dinky Toys Club **£500-750**

1960-61 With windows, concave chromed hubs.
Box has 'DINKY TOYS' in oblique lettering plus '524'.
Turquoise body, smooth or treaded black tyres..........**£100-140**
Brick-red body, smooth or treaded black tyres **£100-140**
Raspberry-red body, smooth or treaded black tyres....**£100-140**

1961-64 524 became individually unavailable in 1961 but
remained in Gift Set 503 up till 1964.

524 1964-66 **Panhard 24CT**
Metallic grey body, concave chromed hubs,
'DUNLOP' tyres, scale 1:43. In French box **£80-100**
Pale yellow-green body, concave chromed hubs,
'DUNLOP' tyres. In French box **£70-90**

1966-69 Metallic grey body; steel hubs, in English box
(model made for export to UK and USA)....................**£80-100**

525 1959-60 **Peugeot 403 Estate Car** (renumbered from 24-F)
Sky blue, no windows, convex hubs,
rear bumper over-riders **£80-100**
1960-62 Sky blue, concave hubs, no rear bumper over-riders ..**£120-140**
NB: Model was originally shown in catalogues as being
available in black. It was never produced in that colour.

525 1964-70 **Peugeot 404 Commercial Traveller's Car**
With yellow or black rear number plate, spun hubs,
windows, scale 1:43.
Ocean blue body **£100-125**
Cream body **£100-125**

525 1964-64 **Peugeot 404 Fire Car**
Red body, 'Pompiers de Paris', concave chromed
hubs, 'DUNLOP' plastic tyres, aerial....................**£1,500-2,000**

526 1959-60 **Mercedes-Benz 190sl** (renumbered from 24-H)
No windows, convex hubs, scale1:43. Picture on some
boxes. All have 526 models have a black hard-top.
Cream body (various shades) **£75-100**
Silver body..**£100-120**
1960-62 With windows, convex hubs. '526' and picture on box.
Cream body (various shades) **£75-100**
Silver body..**£80-100**

526 1961-63 **Mercedes-Benz 190sl Hard-Top**
With windows, concave hubs. '526' and picture on box.
Cream body (various shades) **£80-100**
Silver body..**£90-120**

527 1959-63 **Alfa-Romeo 1900 Sprint** (renumbered from 24-J)
Red or Blue body, cream interior, windows, concave
hubs, smooth (later treaded) black tyres, scale 1:43 .....**£80-100**
Red body with red interior..**£150-200**
Turquoise body **£4,000-5,000**

528 1959-61 **Simca Vedette Chambord** (renumbered from 24-K/2)
1959-60 Ivory and Red body, convex hubs, scale 1:43 ....**£150-200**
Light and Dark Green body, convex hubs....................**£75-90**
1960-61 Ivory and Red body, concave hubs, scale 1:43 ....**£150-200**
Light and Dark Green body, concave hubs **£75-90**

528 1966-71 **Peugeot 404 Cabriolet**
With female driver, steel hubs, scale 1:43.
White or Metallic blue open body, red interior **£140-180**
Pale grey or Light Beige open body, red interior **£170-200**

529 1959-63 **Vespa 400 2cv** (renumbered from 24-L)
1959-60 Blue/grey, plated hubs, scale 1:43. '24L' on box **£70-80**
1960-63 Blue/grey body, convex hubs, '529' on box...................**£70-80**
Orange/grey body, convex hubs, '529' on box...........**£300-400**

530 1959-59 **VW Karmann-Ghia** (renumbered from 24-M)
Black/red ('pointed' bonnet), convex hubs, 1:43 ....**£80-100**
1960-61 Black/red body ('rounded' bonnet), convex hubs **£100-120**
1961-62 Same, but with concave hubs **£150-200**

530 1964-70 **Citroën DS19**
Steel hubs. French '522' box with '530' labels,
later in own '530' box.
1964-64 Metallic Grey body...**£1,500-2,000**
1964-66 Red/Cream body, Ivory interior, Silver base **£150-175**
Lime green/grey body, pale grey interior, Silver base **£150-175**
1966-68 Steel hubs. British box. Model made for export to
UK and USA.
Red/Cream body, Ivory interior, Silver base **£90-110**
Lime green/grey body, pale grey interior, silver base ...**£90-110**
1968-70 Spanish issues:
Spun hubs, 'PIRELLI' tyres. 'DINKY-POCH' on box.
Red/Cream body, Ivory interior, Black base **£500-600**
Lime green/grey body, pale grey interior, black base .**£500-600**
Bright Blue body **£700-900**
Silver-Grey body...**£700-900**

530 1976-78 **Citroën DS23**
Metallic red/black body, concave hubs, scale 1:43.
Made in Spain **£120-140**
NB: 530 Citroën DS23 was shown in the 1974 catalogue
but production did not start until Auto-Pilen took
over the dies in 1976. The plastic base on this model
(and some other Spanish models) was made in
different colours and some are held in place by screws
rather than rivets. Consequently, beware the 'rare
combination' of base and body colours as they are
easily interchanged.

531 1959-60 **Fiat 1200 Grande Vue** (renumbered from 24-N)
With convex hubs, smooth tyres, scale 1:43.
Metallic Bronze/Cream body...**£80-90**
Cream/metallic blue body...**£120-140**
NB: 531 was shown in the 1959 Swiss catalogue with
the reference '24N'.
1960-62 With concave hubs, smooth or treaded tyres.
Metallic Bronze/Cream body...**£90-100**
Cream/metallic blue body...**£130-160**

532 1959-60 **Lincoln Premiere**
Silver body, dark red roof, convex hubs, scale 1:43.
Box has no view window **£225-275**
Light blue body, silver roof..**£100-125**
Metallic green body, dark green roof **£100-125**
1960-65 Bright blue body, silver roof, concave hubs,
white smooth or treaded tyres. View window in box..**£500-650**
Light blue body, silver roof..**£90-100**
Metallic green body, dark green roof **£90-100**
196?-? Export model: Dark blue body, silver roof.
In gold card and cellophane box **£300-400**
NB: A dark green wooden prototype of 532 exists...................NPP

533 1959-59 **Peugeot 203** (renumbered from 24-R)
Grey-blue or Pale grey-green body, convex hubs,
white tyres, big rear window, square filler cap **£90-120**

533 1963-70 **Mercedes-Benz 300 SE**
With plated concave hubs, scale 1:43.
Metallic blue body..**£150-175**
Metallic orange-red body..**£150-175**
Metallic red body..**£150-175**

534 1959-59 **Simca 8 Sport** (renumbered from 24-S)
Grey, back or Pale greenish-blue body, red seats,
thick windscreen, convex hubs, scale 1:43 ....**£100-125**
Cream body, red seats **£100-125**

534 1963-68 **BMW 1500**
Red body, steel hubs, scale 1:43..................................**£90-100**
Lime green body, plated concave hubs **£100-120**
1968-? Spanish issue:
Metallic blue, plated concave hubs, 'PIRELLI' tyres,
'DINKY-POCH' on box **£500-750**

535 1959-60 **Citroën 2cv**
Red or Brighter Red body, painted steel hubs,
glossy baseplate. Box has '535-24T' printing **£90-110**
Blue body with Brighter Blue roof...............................**£150-175**
1960-63 Red or Blue body, chromed steel hubs,
blued-steel baseplate. Box has '535' printing...............**£90-110**

536 1959-59 **Simca Aronde Elysée** (renumbered from 24-U)
Light grey-green/dark green, or pale green/dark
green, second grille, convex hubs, scale 1:43 ....**£100-125**
Blue body, ivory roof....................................**£100-125**
Sky blue body, ivory roof............................**£300-400**
NB: Though renumbered from 24-U to 536, no boxes
have yet been seen bearing the new number.

536 1965-70 **Peugeot 404 and Trailer**
Red car, ivory interior, concave hubs, black skis on
yellow rack (or yellow skis on black rack), cream plastic
single-wheel trailer (no. 812), luggage, scale 1:43 .....**£160-200**

537 1959-60 **Simca Aronde Elysée Taxi** (renumbered from 24-UT)
Red/blue body, convex plated hubs, 2nd grille, 1:43 ......**£80-90**

537 1965-67 **Renault R16**
Concave hubs, black treaded rubber tyres, scale 1:43.
Box has single viewport, R16 leaflet in early issues.
Sky-Blue body, gloss black base with '537' **£70-90**
Metallic Grey body, gloss black base with '537' **£60-80**
1967-70 Concave hubs, 'DUNLOP' nylon tyres. Box has single
viewport, R16 leaflet discontinued in 1967.
Light Blue body, matt black base with '537' **£50-65**
Metallic Grey body, matt black base with '537' **£50-65**
1968-69 Spanish issue: Bright Blue, '537' on base, concave
hubs, 'PIRELLI' tyres, 'DINKY-POCH' box..............**£250-350**
1969-70 Sky-Blue body, matt black base without '537' reference,
concave hubs, 'DUNLOP' plastic tyres.
Box has single viewport **£60-75**
1974-78 Spanish issue: Metallic grey body, base without '537',
concave hubs, 'DUNLOP' plastic tyres. 'MECCANO'
and 'Made in Spain' on box (no viewport) **£60-75**

538 1959-59 **Buick Roadmaster** (renumbered from 24-V)
All have convex hubs. Scale 1:48.
Blue/dark blue body....................................**£130-170**
Yellow/green body......................................**£100-150**
Blue/cream body...**£100-150**
Ivory/metallic blue body..............................**£500-600**
Salmon-pink/black body...............................**£500-600**

538 1963-70 **Ford Taunus 12M**
Turquoise body, steel or spun hubs, 1:43 ....**£90-110**
Brick red body, steel or spun hubs **£80-95**

538 1976-78 **Renault R16 TX**
Metallic plum, concave hubs, rear number plate on
sticker. Made in Spain **£70-90**
NB: 538 Renault R16 was shown in the 1974 French
catalogue, but production was delayed until 1976.

539 1959-59 **Ford Vedette Taxi** (renumbered from 24-XT)
Black/beige (various shades), meter, taxi sign,
plated convex hubs, white tyres **£75-85**
NB: 539 was never individually boxed (supplied to
shops in trade boxes of six).

539 1963-66 **Citroën ID19 Estate**
Gold/Cream body, red or white seats, black or white
steering wheel, steel hubs, black or white tyres, 1:43.**£100-125**
Green-Gold body, darker Cream roof, spun hubs **£125-150**

540 1959-60 **Studebaker Commander** (renumbered from 24-Y)
With convex hubs, smooth tyres. Tinplate base has
towing notch. '540-24Y' and picture of model on box.
Ivory body, Maroon roof and wing panels, ...**£120-150**
Orange body, Dark Cream roof and wing panels........**£140-180**
1960-61 With concave hubs, treaded tyres. Towing notch in
base. '540-24Y' and picture on box.
Ivory body, Maroon roof and wing panels **£150-200**
Orange body, Dark Cream roof and wing panels.
Existence not confirmed ....NPP

540 1963-64 **Opel Kadett**
Red or Pale Green body, steel hubs..............................**£85-95**
1964 Bright Blue body, plated steel hubs...........................**£200-300**
1964 (Renumbered in 1964 as 1540)
NB: 540 Opel was available with either the standard size hubs
or smaller hubs. Both types were concave and were
steel or spun aluminium with black tyres.

541 1959-60 **Simca Vedette Versailles** (renumbered from 24-Z)
With convex hubs, white tyres, towing notch.
Picture on box.
Yellow/black body **£100-125**
Light blue/ivory body **£90-110**

542 1959-62 **Simca Ariane Taxi** (renumbered from 24-ZT)
'Ariane' on base, '542-24ZT' on box, window glazing, 1:43.
Black body, Red (later Orange-Red) roof, meter,
taxi sign, convex hubs (concave from 1961) **£125-150**
Reversed colours: Red body, Black roof....................**£300-400**

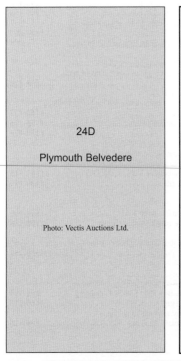

24D

Plymouth Belvedere

Photo: Vectis Auctions Ltd.

542 1964-69 **Opel Rekord**
With concave hubs. Scale 1:43.
Metallic blue two door body **£80-100**
Metallic gold-cream two door body **£80-100**
Metallic grey two door body **£80-100**

543 1960-63 **Renault Floride**
Concave hubs, smooth or treaded white tyres, scale 1:43.
Metallic green body **£70-80**
Metallic green-gold body...**£70-80**
Metallic bronze body **£70-80**
White body, aluminium hubs, smooth white tyres ...**£750-1,000**
NB: A wooden prototype of 543 is known to exist.
It was painted pink..**NPP**

544 1959-60 **Simca Aronde P60**
Convex hubs, scale 1:43. Box without (later with) viewport.
Two-tone Grey body (with Silver flash)..............**£90-110**
Brick red body (with Cream or Pinkish-Cream roof)....**£90-110**
1960-63 Concave hubs. Box with one viewport.
Two-tone Grey body **£90-110**
Brown body (with Off-White roof and Silver flash)....**£90-110**
Cream body, Red roof, smooth white tyres..........**£4,000-5,000**

545 1960-63 **De Soto Diplomat**
Concave hubs and (usually) treaded white tyres, 1:43.
Salmon-pink/black body, Silver flash.......................**£100-125**
Metallic green body, ivory roof.................................**£200-250**

546 1960-61 **Austin-Healey 100-6**
White body (different shades of white reported),
driver, 3-spoke steering wheel, concave hubs, 1:43....**£120-150**

546 1964-67 **Opel Rekord Taxi**
Black body, aluminium or steel concave hubs, white tyres,
1:43. Box has German text as this model was made only
for export to Germany for this period. The taxi sign
lettering may be in white or yellow.............................**£350-500**

547 1960-64 **Panhard PL17**
1st type: Sidelights to front and rear of centre-hinged
doors, black painted baseplate, steel hubs, rubber tyres.
2nd type: As 1st type but without rear sidelights.
3rd type: Front-hinged doors, sidelights under headlamps,
black painted baseplate, steel hubs, rubber tyres.
4th type: As 3rd type but with blued-steel baseplate,
steel or aluminium hubs.
5th type: Aluminium hubs with plastic 'DUNLOP' tyres.
1960-60 1st type, Violet body....................................**£90-100**
1st type, Brick red body **£90-110**
1960-61 2nd type, Violet body....................................**£90-100**
2nd type, Brick red or Orange body **£90-110**
1962-63 3rd type, Violet body.....................................**£70-85**
3rd type, Orange body **£60-80**
1963-64 4th type, Violet or Brick-Red body **£100-120**
1964-64 5th type, Blue-grey body **£120-150**
5th type, Blue body..**£300-350**
1964 (Renumbered in 1964 as 1547)

548 1960-63 **Fiat 1800 Familiale Estate Car**
Lilac body with Black roof, concave hubs, scale 1:43..**£90-120**
Lavender body, Black or Blue roof, concave hubs **£90-120**
Yellow body, metallic brown roof, concave hubs **£100-125**
Yellow body, black roof, concave hubs......................**£100-125**
Two-tone Blue body, Black roof, concave hubs.........**£100-125**
1962 South African issues:
Ivory body (with Red interior), concave hubs **£600-800**
Lime Green body, concave hubs **£500-600**
Green-Bronze body, concave hubs **£500-600**
Yellow body, metallic maroon roof **£400-500**

549 1961-61 **Borgward Isabella TS**
Concave hubs, black or white tyres, scale 1:43.
Turquoise body, ...**£110-140**
Light Green body **£110-140**
Metallic grey body **£110-140**

550 1961-65 **Chrysler Saratoga**
Plated concave hubs, smooth or treaded white tyres.
Pale Pink with White flash **£90-100**
Deep Pink with White flash **£90-100**
Violet with black flash...**£200-250**

551 1959-61 **Rolls-Royce Silver Wraith**
Light grey/dark grey body, concave hubs, 1:43. ....**£90-100**

551 1965-67 **Ford Taunus 17M Police Car**
Dark Green/white, 'POLIZEI', concave hubs,
scale 1:43, German text on box................................**£500-700**

552 1961-64 **Chevrolet Corvair**
Concave hubs, indication of filler cap on some, 1:43.
Turquoise body, Cream interior...............................**£60-70**
Blue-Grey body, Cream interior.................................**£70-80**
Red body **£75-100**
1963 South African issues:
Silver body (with Off-White interior) **£500-700**
Light Grey-Blue body (with Off-White interior) **£500-700**
Smokey-Green body, Off-White interior.............**£1,000-1,500**
1964 (Renumbered in 1964 as 1552)

553 1961-68 **Peugeot 404**
1st type: Round 'O' on bonnet, steel hubs,
smooth black or white tyres, painted baseplate.
2nd type: Squared 'O' on bonnet, steel hubs,
treaded black tyres, painted baseplate.
3rd type: As 2nd type with reinforcement behind
front number plate, revised glazing moulding common
to 536 with opening roof, blued-steel baseplate.
Aluminium hubs and plastic 'DUNLOP' tyres.
1961-62 1st type, Cream body, dark red interior....................**£100-120**
Cream body, dark brown interior...............................**£125-150**
Pale blue body, bright red interior **£100-120**
1962-64 2nd type, Cream body, dark (later bright) red interior**£100-125**
Cream body, dark brown interior...............................**£110-150**
1963-66 3rd type, Pale blue body, bright red interior..............**£100-120**
1963 South African issues:
Pale green body, bright red interior......................**£1,000-1,250**
Metallic charcoal grey body, bright red interior....**£1,000-1,250**
Cream body, dark red interior.............................**£800-1,000**
1964 (Renumbered in 1964 as 1553)
1968-68 Spanish assembled model:
3rd type, but with 'PIRELLI' tyres, 'DINKY-POCH' on box.
Bright Blue body, bright red interior,
Barcelona number plate.....................................**£900-1,100**

554 1961-63 **Opel Rekord**
Concave hubs, (usually) white tyres, scale 1:43.
Coral-pink/ivory body...**£90-110**
Mustard-yellow/ivory body **£110-130**
Beige body, white roof..**NGPP**
Turquoise/ivory body...**£500-600**
1962 South African issues:
Pale Blue body with Light Grey interior.................**£800-1,000**
Bright Blue body with Light Grey interior **£800-1,000**
Dark Blue body with Light Grey interior...............**£800-1,000**
Metallic Dark Green body, Grey interior **£1,000-1,250**

555 1961-69 **Ford Thunderbird**
1st type: Black painted baseplate, steel hubs,
smooth white tyres.
2nd type: Blued-steel baseplate, steel hubs,
treaded white tyres.
3rd type: Blued-steel baseplate, aluminium hubs,
treaded white tyres.
NB: Driver may wear bright or dark suit,
steering wheel may be cream or black.
White body, Red interior...**£110-130**
Red body, Sky-Blue interior **£110-130**
Dark Brown body, Sky-Blue interior..........................**£110-130**
Dark Brown body, Pale Green interior.......................**£100-150**
1966-? South African issues:
Bright Blue open body, Red interior **£900-1,200**
Metallic Blue open body, Red interior **£900-1,200**
Sand open body, Red interior................................**£900-1,200**
Red open body, Red interior..................................**£900-1,200**

556 1962-70 **Citroën ID19 Ambulance**
1st type: Steel hubs, metal steering wheel,
centred transfer lettering.
2nd type: As 1st type, but with plastic steering wheel.
3rd type: As 2nd type, but with aluminium hubs.
4th type: Aluminium hubs, plastic 'DUNLOP' tyres,
plastic steering wheel, transfer lettering aligned to left.
1962-67 1st/2nd/3rd type: Grey/cream body. In standard box
until 1964, then in 'Super detail' box **£100-125**
1967-70 4th type: Grey/cream body. In 'Super detail' box **£100-125**

554

Opel Rekord

Photo:
Collectoys, France

557 1962-70 **Citroën Ami 6**
1st type: Steel hubs, spare wheel under bonnet,
black painted base.
2nd type: Steel hubs, engine detail under bonnet,
black painted base.
3rd type: As 2nd type, but with blued-steel baseplate.
4th type: As 3rd type, but with aluminium hubs and
plastic 'DUNLOP' tyres.
1962-62 1st type, Pale green body, white or pale grey roof........£90-110
Light blue body, with white or pale grey roof..............£90-110
Light blue body, pale blue roof.......................................£90-110
1963-64 2nd type. Pale green body, white or pale grey roof......£90-110
Light blue body, with pale blue roof £90-110
Bright Blue body, white or pale grey roof..................£90-110
1964 (Renumbered in 1964 as 1557)
1964-70 3rd/4th types. Pale green; white or pale grey roof £90-110
Light blue body, white or pale grey roof.......................£90-110

558 1962-64 **Citroën 2cv Azam**
Yellow body, brown roof £100-125
Beige body, brown roof £150-175
Green body, dark green roof..£75-85
Greyish-green body, black roof...................................£75-85
1964 (Renumbered in 1964 as 1558)

558 1968-70 **Citroën 2cv**
Spanish issue:
Yellow/maroon or Green/dark green body, concave
hubs, 'PIRELLI' tyres, 'DINKY-POCH' on box........£300-400

559 1962-64 **Ford Taunus 17M**
Steel or aluminium hubs, smooth or treaded
black or white tyres, 1:43.
Ivory body..£80-100
Pale Grey body £80-100
Metallic Brown or Metallic Grey-Brown body............£80-100
1964 (Renumbered in 1964 as 1559)
1968-69 Spanish issue: Yellow body, concave hubs,
'PIRELLI' tyres, 'DINKY-POCH' on box £1,400-1,600

1400 1967-71 **Peugeot 404 G7 Taxi** (536 casting)
Black body, red top with sunroof, taxi sign and aerial,
'Ampere 28.30' and 'G7' shield on doors, concave
hubs, black 'DUNLOP' tyres, 1:43, yellow box £250-350

1401 1967-70 **Alfa-Romeo Guilia 1600Ti** (514 casting)
Dark red body in 'rally' finish with Yellow stripe,
spotlights, concave hubs. Yellow box.........................£150-200

1402 1968-71 **Ford Galaxie Sedan**
Detailed wheels, scale 1:43. Perspex box.
Dark Red (Cream interior)...£90-110
Metallic Gold body (Red interior) £90-110

1402 1968-68 **Ford Galaxie Police Car**
Black/white body, 'POLICE'.
Commissioned for use by Police £2,000-3,000

1403 1967-71 **Matra M530**
White or Orange body, concave hubs,
two-part roof can be stowed in boot. Perspex box........£80-100

1404 1968-69 **Citroën ID19 Estate Car**
Grey/red, 'RADIO TELE LUXEMBOURG',
camera/operator, concave hubs. Yellow box £500-750
1969-71 Grey/red, 'RTL LUXEMBOURG', ('RTL' in black),
concave hubs. Yellow box £500-750
1971-71 Grey/red, 'RTL LUXEMBOURG' ('T' of 'RTL' in
black/white check). Yellow picture box £3,500-4,500
Same model but with Grey/orange-red body.
Yellow box...£2,000-2,500

1405 1968-70 **Opel Rekord 1900s**
Metallic blue body, scale 1:43. In perspex box..............£70-80
1405E 1970-71 **Opel Rekord 1900s**
Metallic blue body, 1:43. Export model in card box...£150-250
1405P 1968-68 **Opel Rekord 1900s**
Prototypes using the 1405 casting were prepared for
the 1420 Opel Commodore. '1405' on the base.
Silver or Red body, black 'vinyl' roof, Black interior,
paper number plate £85-95

1406 1968-71 **Renault 4L Sinpar 'Tanguy'**
Khaki-green camouflage body, driver (Michel Tanguy),
passenger, painted concave hubs. Featured in TV serial
'Les Chevaliers du Ciel' ('Knights of the Sky') £250-350

1407 1968-71 **Simca 1100**
Metallic grey body, concave hubs.
'Made in France' yellow viewport box £80-100
Dark red body. This was the intended colour when
1407 was introduced but its existence is doubtful ....NPP
1974-78 Spanish issue: Metallic green body, concave hubs.
'Made in Spain' overprinted on French box (later in
Spanish box also printed 'Made in Spain')....................£60-70

1408 1969-70 **Honda S800**
Yellow body, concave hubs, scale 1:43. Yellow box.....£90-110

1409 1970 **Simca 1800**
A prototype for the 1409 Chrysler 180 but with
'Simca 1800' on the base. Just a few were sold - they
were finished in the same metallic blue-grey paint
as the production version...**£200-250**

1409 1970-71 **Chrysler 180**
Metallic blue-grey body, 'Chrysler' on base,
'DUNLOP' tyres, scale 1:43. Yellow box **£75-90**
NB: 595w Traffic Sign 'Danger - Cyclists' included with 1409.

1410 1968-71 **Moskvitch 408**
Red body, plated concave hubs, 1:43. Yellow box.........**£50-60**

1411 1971-72 **Renault Alpine A310**
Bright red body, plastic hubs, scale 1:43. Yellow box **£70-90**

1413 1968-70 **Citroën Dyane**
Off-white body, luggage, concave hubs, 1:43. Box has
'DYANE CITROËN' in white on yellow.......................**£60-70**
1969-71 Same model but box has 'DYANE CITROËN' in
white on green...**£60-70**
1977-78 Spanish issue: Off-white body, concave hubs...............**£50-60**

1414 1969-70 **Renault R8 Gordini**
Blue body, white stripes, driver, RN '36',
jewelled lights, alumimium concave hubs **£200-300**

1414 1969-70 **Renault R8-S**
Promotional model: Yellow or Mustard-Yellow body,
driver in some **£1,500-2,000**

1415 1969-71 **Peugeot 504**
Pale Blue body, concave hubs, scale 1:43.
Clear plastic box **£90-110**
Dark blue body **£500-600**
1974-76 Spanish issue: Pale yellow body, concave hubs or
special wheels. Card box **£60-80**

1416 1969-70 **Renault R6**
Bright red body, first grille (round headlamps),
concave hubs. Side view of white model on box...........**£60-70**
1970-74 As previous model but with rear view of
dark grey model on box **£60-70**
1974-76 Spanish issue:
Red or yellow body, second grille (square headlamps),
concave hubs. Side view of white model on box.........**£80-100**

1416 1974-75 **Renault Postal Car**
Code 2 model based on Spanish-made components,
commissioned by the Postal Service.
Yellow, second grille (square headlamps), plated
concave hubs. Side view of white model on box...........**£70-90**

1416P 1970-70 **Renault R6 Fire Car**
Code 2 model based on Spanish-made components,
commissioned by the Fire Service.
Red body and hubs, 'POMPIERS de PARIS',
second grille, side view of white model on box.........**£100-125**

1417 1969-71 **Matra V12 F1**
Blue body, driver (J.P.Beltoise), RN '17' (transfer,
later on label), special wheels, 1:43. Yellow box...........**£60-70**
NB: 595c Traffic Sign 'Dangerous Bend To Right'
included with 1417.

1419 1969-71 **Ford Thunderbird**
Battery in base for rear lights, special wheels,
scale 1:43. Perspex box.
Metallic green body (black 'vinyl' roof on some) **£75-85**
NB: A prototype exists with a Metallic Red body and
Black 'vinyl' roof. (Not issued)........................NPP
Metallic grey body, dark metallic grey roof............**£800-1,100**
NB: 595g Traffic Sign 'Caution - Animals Crossing'
included with 1419.

1420 1970-71 **Opel Commodore GS**
Red body, black 'vinyl' roof, special wheels,
1:43. Some boxes have a printed design in a panel **£90-100**
NB: The Opel Commodore had a 6-cylinder engine, but as
1420 was produced using the 1405 casting, the model
retains a 4-cylinder engine and the 'Rekord' badges.
595o Traffic Sign 'Customs' included with 1420.

1421 1969-71 **Opel GT 1900**
Dark blue body, detailed chromed wheels, luggage rack,
scale 1:43. Yellow box...................................**£100-140**
NB: 595f Traffic Sign 'Speed Limit' included with 1421.

1422 1969-71 **Ferrari 3L V12 F1**
Red body, driver (Jacky Ickx), RN '26',
detailed chromed wheels, scale 1:43 ....**£90-110**
NB: 595e Traffic Sign 'Road Narrows' included with 1422.

1423 1969-71 **Peugeot 504 Convertible**
Dark Blue, plastic base, plated concave hubs,
scale 1:43. Yellow box...................................**£200-300**
NB: 595i Traffic Sign 'Two Way Traffic' included with 1423.

1424 1969-70 **Renault R12**
Mustard-Yellow body, opening doors, Red interior,
reversed 'V' shape on grille, aluminium concave hubs,
sidelights. Yellow box...................................**£70-80**
NB: 595h Traffic Sign 'Danger - End of Quay'
included with French-made 1424.

1424 1977-78 **Renault R12-TL**
Spanish issue:
Yellow body, fixed doors, alminium concave hubs,
second (corrected) grille, no sidelights. Yellow box **£70-80**

1424G 1971-71 **Renault R12 Gordini Rally Car**
Blue, white stripes, RN '5', silver headlights, fixed doors,
aluminium concave hubs, second grille, sidelights.
Yellow box...**£150-200**
1974-78 Spanish issue: Blue (slightly darker than 1971 model),
white stripes, yellow headlights, fixed doors,
aluminium concave hubs, second grille, sidelights.
Yellow box...**£100-125**

1425 1969-71 **Matra 630 Le Mans**
French blue body, driver (Pescarolo), RN '5',
scale1:43. Plastic box **£60-70**

1425E 1971-71 **Matra 630 Le Mans**
French blue body, driver (Pescarolo), RN '5',
scale 1:43. Yellow card box................................**£80-100**
NB: 595k Traffic Sign 'Road Narrows from Left'
included with 1425.

1426 1969-71 **Alfa-Romeo Carabo P33**
Metallic green/plain green/black/orange, special wheels,
scale 1:43. Yellow box....................................**£70-80**
Orange-yellow/green/black/orange-red, special wheels.
Yellow box...**£100-125**
NB: 595m Traffic Sign 'Danger - Loose Chippings'
included with 1426.

1428 1970-74 **Peugeot 304**
White body, concave hubs, scale 1:43. Yellow box **£80-100**
NB: 595p Traffic Sign 'Humpback Bridge' included
with French made 1428.
1974-78 Spanish issue: Met. green, concave hubs. Yellow box....**£70-90**

1429 1970-71 **Peugeot 404 Police Car**
Blue/white body, 'POLICE', plastic base, concave hubs,
scale 1:43. Yellow box...................................**£250-350**
NB: 595n Traffic Sign 'Cycling Prohibited' included
with 1429.

1430 1970-71 **Fiat Abarth 2000**
Orange body, special wheels, scale 1:43. Plastic box also
contains a 595u Traffic Sign 'Dangerous Bends'...........**£30-40**

1431 1970 **Porsche 917**
A model planned but not actually issued............................NPP

1432 1970-71 **Ferrari 312P**
Red body, no driver, RN '60', special wheels, 1:43.
Plastic box also has a 595v Traffic Sign
'All Vehicles Prohibited' **£60-75**

1432E 1971-? **Ferrari 312P**
Red body, no driver, '60', special wheels. Card box **£60-75**

1433 1971-74 **Surtees TS5 V8 F1**
Red body, white driver, yellow helmet, RN '5' or '14',
scale 1:43. Yellow card box..............................**£40-50**

1435 1970-71 **Citroën Présidentielle**
Metallic grey and plain charcoal grey body, chauffeur,
felt carpet, flag, electric interior light,
scale 1:43. Special plastic and rigid card box **£450-600**

1435E 1971 **Citroën Présidentielle**
As 1435 but in blue presentation box (200 made) **£2,000-2,500**

1450 1977-78 **Simca 1100 Police Car**
Spanish issue: Blue/white or black/white body,
'POLICE', plated concave hubs **£50-60**

Cars

1451 1978-? **Renault R17-TS**
Spanish issue:
Orange-yellow body, plated concave hubs, scale 1:43....**£50-60**
NB: 1451 was announced in the 1976 French catalogue but production only took place in Spain from 1978.

1452 1977-78 **Peugeot 504**
1977-78 Spanish issues:
Metallic copper body, fixed doors, special wheels.
'réf. 1452' on box. **£50-60**
1978-78 Metallic bronze body, fixed doors, special wheels.
Box has: 'réf. 011452' and 'conformité du produit aux normes francaises' ....**£50-60**.
NB: Different registration numbers (on labels) may be found on 1452.

1453 1977-78 **Renault R6**
Spanish issue:
Blue-grey, fixed bonnet, square headlamps, concave hubs..**£75-85**
NB: Although only available in blue-grey, 1453 continued to be shown in yellow in contemporary catalogues.

1454 1978-78 **Matra Simca Bagheera S**
Spanish issue: Green body, concave hubs, 1:43.............**£35-45**

1455 1978-78 **Citroën CX Pallas**
Spanish issue: Metallic blue body, concave hubs, 1:43 ..**£50-60**
NB: 1455 was announced (but not illustrated) in the 1977 catalogue but was not available before May 1978.

1517 1964-65 **Renault R8** (renumbered from 517)
Blue body, concave hubs, 1:43. In blister pack............**£80-100**
Yellow body, concave hubs, 1:43. In blister pack........**£80-100**

1518 1964-65 **Renault R4L** (renumbered from 518)
Pale blue body, first grille. In blister pack **£80-100**
Light blue body, first grille. In blister pack.................**£80-100**
Brick-red body, first grille. In blister pack **£80-100**
Maroon body, first grille. In blister pack.....................**£80-100**
Grey-green body. In blister pack ....NGPP

1519 1964-65 **Simca 1000** (renumbered from 519)
Light blue-grey, red interior, black painted base.
Blister pack **£80-100**

1520 1964-65 **Fiat 600 D** (renumbered from 520)
Red body, concave hubs. Bister pack **£70-90**
Pale yellow body, concave hubs. Bister pack................**£70-90**

1523 1964-65 **Simca 1500** (renumbered from 523)
Mid-blue body, concave hubs, 1:43. In blister pack **£70-90**
Light Blue body, concave hubs. In blister pack **£70-90**
Metallic Grey body, concave hubs. In blister pack **£70-90**

1539 1980? **VW Scirocco**
Spanish issue: Metallic light green body, special wheels, scale 1:43................................**£60-70**

1540 1964-65 **Opel Kadett** (renumbered from 540)
Red body, concave hubs, sliding windows. Blister pack **£70-80**
Pale Green body, concave hubs. Blister pack.................**£70-80**
Blue body, concave hubs. Blister pack........................**£130-170**

1540 1980? **Renault R14**
Spanish issue: Metallic bright green body, special wheels, 1:43 ....**£60-70**

1541 1981? **Ford Fiesta**
Spanish issue: Metallic light blue body, special wheels, scale 1:43................................**£50-60**

1542 1980? **Chrysler 1308 GT**
Spanish issue: Metallic green, special wheels, 1:43 ....**£35-45**

1543 1980? **Opel Ascona**
Spanish issue: Orange-yellow, special wheels, 1:43 ....**£60-70**

1547 1964-66 **Panhard PL17** (renumbered from 547)
Violet body, anodised base, concave hubs, sidelights under headlights, 1:43.. In blister pack **£80-100**
Brick red body, anodised base, concave hubs, sidelights under headlights. In blister pack **£80-100**

1552 1964-66 **Chevrolet Corvair** (renumbered from 552)
Raised filler cap on some. Blister pack.
Turquoise blue body **£65-75**
Orange-red body **£65-75**

1553 1964-66 **Peugeot 404** (renumbered from 553)
Ivory body, dark red interior. Blister pack....................**£90-110**

1557 1964-66 **Citroën Ami 6** (renumbered from 557)
Green/white, no spare wheel. Blister pack.....................**£60-70**
Blue/white, no spare wheel. Blister pack **£60-70**

1558 1964-66 **Citroën 2cv Azam** (renumbered from 558)
Yellow/maroon body, Grey concave hubs (black tyres), scale 1:43. In blister pack **£45-60**
Light yellow/maroon body, Grey concave hubs (black tyres). In blister pack **£60-70**
Green/dark green body, Grey concave hubs (black tyres). In blister pack **£60-70**

1559 1964-69 **Ford Taunus 17M** (renumbered from 559)
Metallic gold body, concave hubs, 1:43. Blister pack.....**£70-90**
Metallic grey-gold body, concave hubs. Blister pack **£70-90**
Ivory body, concave hubs. Blister pack.........................**£70-90**

512

Kart

Photo:
Vectis Auctions Ltd.

517

Renault R8

Photo:
Vectis Auctions Ltd.

SOLIDO-COUGAR Models. Cast by Solido in France, all the models are in 1:43 scale, all have plastic wheels and 'Dinky Toys France' on the plastic base, and all were supplied in a 'Dinky Toys GB' box. Compare this list with the 'COUGAR Model Toys' list that follows it.

1401	1981	**Citroën 2cv6**
		Orange-red body (beige open top) with 'ducks' decal **£25-35**
		Green body (grey open top) with 'ducks' decal **£25-35**
1402	1981	**Citroën 2cv6**
		Orange-red body (beige closed top) with 'ducks' decal..**£25-35**
		Green body (grey closed top) with 'ducks' decal..........**£25-35**
1402	1981	**Citroën Visa**
		Metallic jade green (white base, tinted windows),
		no decals **£25-35**
		Metallic red, (grey base, clear windows), no decals **£25-35**
1403	1981	**Fiat Ritmo/Strada**
		Metallic orange body (dark cream base), no decals........**£25-35**
		Metallic blue body (yellow base), no decals **£25-35**
1404	1981	**BMW 530**
		Metallic green with 'Cougar' decal **£25-35**
		Metallic purple with 'flames' decal **£25-35**
1405	1981	**Alfa-Romeo Alfetta GTV**
		Red body, 'shamrock' decal...**£25-35**
		Yellow body, 'shamrock' decal.....................................**£25-35**
1406	1981	**Peugeot 504**
		Metallic yellow with 'cougar' decal **£25-35**
		Metallic blue with 'flames' decal **£25-35**
	1983	Black body, 'Dinky France' decal, plastic wheels.
		(Lyons 1983 promotional) **£35-45**

COUGAR Model Toys. Many of the 'Airfix Dinky Toys' appeared erratically in the early 1980s (in France then in the UK) under the name of 'Cougar Model Toys'. Every one had a plastic base marked 'Dinky Toys made in France' and the code '1/43 07 80'. They were presented in card backed blister-packs with 'Metal Cougar' and 'Fabriqué par Solido' printing. Numbers printed on card are 100 less than numbers moulded on base.

1301-1401	**Citroën 2cv6**
	Orange-red body with 'ducks' decal,
	Grey base/interior/open top **£15-25**
	Green body, 'ducks' decal, grey base, orange interior,
	tan open top **£15-25**
1302-1402	**Citroën Visa**
	Metallic jade green, no decal, white base,
	dark cream interior..**£15-25**
	Metallic red body, no decal, grey base and interior **£15-25**
1303-1403	**Fiat Ritmo**
	Metallic orange (dark cream base/interior), no decal....**£15-25**
	Metallic blue (yellow base/interior), no decal................**£15-25**
1304-1404	**BMW 530**
	Metallic green, 'cougar' decal, grey base,
	black/grey interior, green tinted windows **£15-25**
	Metallic purple, 'flames' decal, grey base,
	black/grey interior, yellow tinted windows **£15-25**
1305-1405	**Alfetta GTV**
	Red body, 'shamrock' decal, tan base,
	black/tan interior, yellow tinted windows **£15-25**
	Yellow body, 'shamrock' decal, tan base,
	black/tan interior, blue tinted windows **£15-25**
1306-1406	**Peugeot 504 Berline**
	Metallic yellow, 'cougar' decal, brown base and tinted
	windows, black/brown interior **£15-25**
	Metallic blue body, 'flames' decal, blue base and
	interior, clear windows **£15-25**

Commercial Vehicles

French Dinky commercial vehicles (in keeping with other ranges) have very similar series numbering to their English counterparts. But, like the cars, the French castings are different in many ways from the Liverpool produced versions and of course are marked 'Made in France' or 'Fab en France'.

An interesting point about the 25 Series is that although there was a range of body styles on offer at any one time, there was only one chassis casting for a particular period. This meant that the chassis dies wore out at a disproportionate rate to the body dies. Chassis castings are found that come from either a crisp new die or from one that is weary from over-use, and the appearance can be so different that some collectors have thought these to be the result of intentional design changes. The only differences however are the ones noted in this listing.

On the French 25 series the headlights are larger and more pointed than the English equivalent. They were originally silver plated, later silver painted. The size of the headlights was reduced over the years and are best classed as large,

medium and small. Modern replacement parts (radiator/grille/bumper) which are intended for the English lorries are not suitable for use on the French 25 Series. Like the cars, the lorries had 'DUNLOP' tyres, first in the colour of the body, later black or white. The problem of shortage of rubber affected the lorry production in 1940 and for four years after the war ended, so that in those periods the lorries had to be produced with all-metal wheels. Metal failure affects pre-war mazak castings whether they are of French or English origin though the commercial vehicles seem not to be so drastically affected as for instance aircraft or ship models.

The first French Dinky Toys commercial vehicle model to be issued in an individual yellow box was 25-B Peugeot D3a Van in 1953. In England the Supertoys range was introduced in 1947 but it was not till 1955 that a French Supertoys model appeared. The 'Auto-Echelle de Pompiers' (Delahaye Fire Escape) was the first French model to be presented in the famous blue and white striped Supertoys box and was given the number 32-D.

Ref	Year(s)	Model name	Colours, features, details	Market Price Range
14	1935-39	**Triporteur**	Tinplate base, smooth hubs (various colours), black or white 'DUNLOP' tyres, scale 1:40. The driver may be found as a solid casting or hollow-cast. His cap is usually the same colour as his jacket. His trousers and boots were black or very dark brown (hand applied paint that may vary in shade or extent). Vehicle colours: Yellow, Red, Light Blue, Navy Blue. Driver's jacket: Blue, Grey or Green	£750-1,000
		note:	The 1935 catalogue illustration (a drawing) shows 14 with a front bumper but the existence of this version is very much in doubt.	
14	1940-49	**Triporteur**	Plain cast wheels (black or unpainted), tinplate base, scale 1:40. Vehicle colours: Yellow, Red, Light Blue, Navy Blue. Driver's jacket: Blue, Grey or Green	£500-750
14	1950-52	**Triporteur**	Painted ridged hubs with black rubber tyres, no base. Vehicle colours: Yellow, Red, Light Blue, Navy Blue. Driver's jacket: Blue, Grey or Green	£250-500
14-C	1950-59	**Coventry Climax Fork Lift Truck**	Orange/green/black, painted ridged hubs, grey tyres, made in England. French box (orange-red outer, yellow inner), 1:43	£40-50
		note:	14-C was renumbered in 1959, then assembled in France and issued as 597.	
25a	1935-39	**Open Lorry**	Open chassis, grille/headlights casting, front bumper, cast-in tow hook, painted smooth hubs, black or white 'DUNLOP' tyres, 1:65. Green/black, blue/black, yellow/brown	£250-350
25a	1940-48	**Open Lorry**	Same, but with unpainted cast wheels. Green/black, red/black, red/grey, brown/grey	£250-350
25-A	1950-52	**Ford Livestock Truck**	Metallic grey or metallic light blue body, painted ridged hubs, 1:65	£150-200
			Silver body, red ridged hubs	£250-350
			Yellow cab, Red back and ridged hubs	£3,000-4,000
25b	1935-39	**Covered Lorry**	Open chassis, grille/headlights casting, front bumper, cast-in tow hook, smooth hubs, black or white 'DUNLOP' tyres, removable tilt, 1:65. Green/black (green tilt), blue/black (beige tilt), Red/brown (green tilt), blue/red (beige tilt)	£350-450
25b	1940-48	**Covered Lorry**	Open chassis, grille/headlights casting, front bumper, cast-in hook, unpainted cast (or Cream) wheels, removable tilt. Red/black (green tilt), blue/black (green tilt), Red/black (cream tilt), red/grey (green tilt)	£150-200
25-B	1953-53	**Peugeot D3a Van**	Navy blue body (cross-hatching on inside of roof), no advertising, red ridged hubs, 1:50.	£600-750
			Grey body (cross-hatching on inside of roof), no advertising, red ridged hubs	£600-750
	1953-54		Yellow and green body (smooth inside roof), 'LAMPE MAZDA' logo, painted ridged hubs	£200-300
		note:	This was the first French Dinky Toys commercial vehicle model to be issued in an individual yellow box.	
25BV	1954-59	**Peugeot Post Van**	Dark green body (smooth or cross-hatched inside roof), 'POSTES'	
		(Renumbered in 1959 as 560)	(thin lettering, tampo). Box print: '25BV, marque déposée' only	£130-160
			Same model, but with box print: '25BV, marque déposée, Made in France, Imprimé en France'	£130-160
25c	1935-39	**Flat Truck**	Open chassis, grille/headlights casting, front bumper, cast-in tow hook, smooth hubs, black or white 'DUNLOP' tyres, scale 1:65. Turquoise/black, blue/black, green/black	£225-275
			Red/brown or grey/red	£225-275
	1940-48		Open chassis, grille/headlights casting, front bumper, cast-in tow hook, unpainted mazak wheels. Blue/black, green/black, Cream/red or grey/red	£100-125
25-C	1954-57	**Citroën H Van**	Metallic grey and gold body (official Citroën colours), painted ridged hubs, 1:50. Yellow box (grey model shown)	£100-125
25CG	1957-59	**Citroën H Van**	Cream body, 'FROMAGE CH GERVAIS', in 25-C yellow box but with '25CG' sticker	£160-190
	1959-59	(Renumbered in 1959 as 561)	Turquoise body (various shades), 'CIBIE', ridged or concave hubs, box with '25C' or '25CG' printed	£300-400
25d	1935-35	**Tanker Lorry**	Red body (smooth inside tank), no advertising, maroon open chassis (no hook), grille/headlights casting, front bumper, smooth hubs, red 'DUNLOP' tyres, scale 1:65	£300-400
	1936-37		Red body (smooth or ridged inside tank), 'STANDARD ESSOLUBE', black open chassis, smooth hubs, black or white 'DUNLOP' tyres	£300-400
	1938-39		Red body (ridged inside tank), 'ESSOLUBE - ESSO', black or red open chassis, smooth hubs, black or white 'DUNLOP' tyres	£300-400
25d	1940-49	**Tanker Lorry**	Red body (ridged inside tank), 'ESSOLUBE - ESSO', black open chassis, mazak wheels	£200-300
			Maroon body (ridged inside), 'ESSO' or 'ESSOLUBE', grey or black open chassis, mazak wheels	£200-300
25-D	1959-59	**Citroën 2cv Van 'BÉBÉ LORRAIN'**	Grey body, cream hubs. Only 80 made of this Code-2 promotional (see 562)	£6,000-8,000

25e 1935-39 **Tipping Lorry** .... Tipping rear truck body, open chassis, grille/headlights casting, front bumper, cast-in tow hook, smooth hubs, black or white 'DUNLOP' tyres, scale 1:65

Blue cab, yellow body, black or brown chassis **£240-300**

Green cab, blue body, black or red chassis **£240-300**

Green cab, yellow body, red, black or brown chassis **£240-300**

1940-48 .... As previous version, but with painted mazak wheels.

Cab/body/chassis colours: Blue/yellow/black, Green/yellow/brown, or Cream/green/red **£130-180**

25f 1935-39 **Market Gardener's Lorry** .... Open chassis, grille/headlights casting, front bumper, cast-in tow hook, smooth hubs, black or white 'DUNLOP' tyres, scale 1:65.

Violet body (black chassis), Cream body (black chassis), or Green body (red chassis) **£240-300**

Grey body, Black chassis **£300-400**

1940-48 .... As previous version, but with unpainted mazak wheels.

Body/chassis colours: Cream/Red, Yellow/Red, Turquoise/Black, Light Green/Grey **£240-300**

25g 1935-39 **Flat Trailer with Headboard** ..... Blue, red or green, 4 mazak hubs, black or white tyres, 1:65. ....**£30-40**

1940-48 .... Turquoise, red or green, two axles, unpainted or black mazak wheels. **£30-40**

1949-50 .... Red or green, two axles, painted ridged hubs, black tyres. **£30-40**

25-H 1949-49 **Ford Beverage Truck** .... Flat truck with removable tailboard, cast-in tow hook, spare wheel, scale 1:65.

Blue, cream, turquoise, red, brown, metallic green, bright green body, painted mazak wheels **£250-350**

1950-50 .... Blue, cream, turquoise, red, brown, metallic green or bright green body and ridged hubs **£300-400**

Metallic green body, bright green hubs **£300-400**

Turquoise body **£750-1,000**

25-I 1949-49 **Ford Open Wagon** .... Blue, red, green, dark grey, maroon, or brown body, cast-in towing hook, painted mazak wheels, 1:65 ....**£150-200**

1950-50 .... Beige or metallic grey body, cast-in hook, painted ridged hubs (colour as body) **£300-400**

1951-52 .... Dark red or light blue body, separate rivetted hook and spare wheel, matching ridged hubs **£200-300**

Cream body, separate rivetted hook and spare wheel, matching ridged hubs **£2,000-2,500**

25-J 1949-50 **Ford Covered Wagon** ....(plain) Tinplate tilt (no advertising), cast-in towing hook, spare wheel, painted mazak wheels or ridged hubs.

Metallic gold (green tilt), red (green or red tilt), Light blue (cream tilt), dark blue (brown tilt),

Brown (brown tilt), brown (green tilt), Cream body, brown tilt **£375-475**

25-JB 1949-50 **'SNCF'** .... Blue (dark blue tilt), 'SNCF' round logo, cast-in hook, black mazak wheels or ridged hubs **£1,000-1,500**

1951-52 .... Blue (dark blue tilt), 'SNCF' round logo, separate hook, black ridged hubs **£400-500**

25-JJ 1949-52 **'CALBERSON'** .... Wide spacing to letters, plus map of France, cast-in (later separate) hook, scale 1:65.

Yellow or Yellow Ochre body with black tilt, painted mazak wheels or Red or Black ridged hubs **£600-800**

25-JV 1953-53 **'GRAND MOULINS DE PARIS'** Grey body, black tilt, separate hook, painted ridged hubs **£300-400**

25-K 1949-49 **Studebaker Farm Produce Truck** Short lateral bonnet mouldings, small windows, tool-box, painted mazak wheels (usually black), 1:55.

Red/blue, blue/turquoise, red/yellow, turquoise/red **£350-450**

Blue/greyish-green **£350-450**

1950-50 .... Red/blue, blue/red, blue/turquoise, red/turquoise-green, painted ridged hubs **£200-250**

1951-52 **Studebaker Farm Produce Truck** Long curved bonnet mouldings, large windows, outline of tool-box only, painted ridged hubs.

Red/yellow, blue/maroon, blue/red **£150-200**

Red cab, Blue back **£400-500**

25-L 1949-50 **Studebaker Covered Truck** .... Short lateral bonnet mouldings, small windows, tool-box, painted mazak wheels or ridged hubs.

Red body, yellow tinplate tilt **£750-1,000**

Blue body, yellow or brown tinplate tilt **£750-1,000**

Turquoise body, cream or yellow tinplate tilt, red or cream hubs **£750-1,000**

1951-52 .... Long curved bonnet mouldings, large windows, tool-box outline only, painted ridged hubs

Blue (brown tilt, blue hubs), red (yellow tilt, red hubs) **£300-400**

25-M 1949-50 **Studebaker Tipping Truck** .... Short bonnet mouldings, small windows, tool-box, painted mazak wheels or ridged hubs, 1:55.

Dark green/metallic grey, dark green/plain grey **£100-130**

1951-52 .... Long bonnet curved bonnet mouldings, large windows, tool-box outline only, painted ridged hubs.

Dark green/metallic grey, dark green/plain grey **£70-85**

Khaki/silver (cream hubs) **£700-900**

25-M 1950-55 **Ford Tipping Truck** .... Green cab, metallic or plain grey tipper, black or Green ridged hubs, 1:65 ....**£65-75**

25-O 1949-50 **Studebaker Milk Truck** .... Blue/eggshell Cream or Blue/White, 'NESTLÉ' (transfer), short bonnet mouldings, small windows, tool-box, painted wheels or ridged hubs, ten milk churns, 1:55. Red box with yellow interior **£400-600**

1951-54 .... Blue/white, 'NESTLÉ' advertising on some, long curved bonnet mouldings, large windows, tool-box outline only, painted ridged hubs, ten churns. Red box with yellow inner. **£350-450**

25-O 1950-50 **Ford Milk Truck** .... Blue/white body, 'NESTLÉ' (transfer, thick lettering). Long red box with yellow inner, card spacer **£400-500**

1954-55 .... Blue/white body, 'NESTLÉ' (tampo, plain or open (later) lettering). Shorter (correct length) box **£400-500**

25-P 1949-49 **Studebaker Pick-Up** .... Mustard-yellow and dark red body, painted mazak wheels, short bonnet mouldings, small windows, tool-box, 1:55. ....**£500-600**

1950-55 .... Yellow/Red, ridged hubs, short or long bonnet mouldings, small or large windows, box outline only. **£100-150**

25-Q 1949-49 **Studebaker Covered Pick-Up** .... Green cab and tilt, red body, short bonnet mouldings, small windows, tool-box, painted wheels, 1:55......**£500-750**

Dark grey-green cab and tilt, yellow ochre body, painted wheels **£500-750**

1950-52 .... Green/Yellow, Green hubs, short or long bonnet mouldings, small or large windows, box outline only **£500-700**

25-R 1949-50 **Studebaker Breakdown Truck** .. Red body, 'DINKY SERVICE' on some, short bonnet mouldings, small windows, tool-box, painted mazak wheels or ridged hubs **£400-500**

1951-54 .... Red body, 'DINKY SERVICE', long curved bonnet mouldings, large windows, tool-box outline only, painted ridged hubs **£150-200**

25-R 1954-54 **Ford Breakdown Truck** .... Red body, 'DINKY SERVICE', red ridged hubs, black tyres, 1:65. ....**£300-400**

1954-55 .... Red body, no logo, plated ridged hubs, white tyres. ....NGPP

French Dinky Toys 32AB Panhard Articulated Lorry 'SNCF'

French Dinky Toys Simca Cargo Vans – 33A in green and orange (no advertising) and 33AN 'BAILLY'

Photographs: Vectis Auctions Ltd.

25-S 1949-49 **Single-axle Trailer**...................... Red body, concave rear lamps, painted wheels, scale 1:55. ....£30-35
       1950-50 .... Red (Cream hubs), Yellow (Red hubs), Green (Yellow hubs). Concave or raised rear lamps £30-35
25-T 1949-49 **Single-axle Covered Trailer** .... As 25-S but with tinplate tilt, concave rear lamps, painted mazak wheels.
                         Red body (green tilt), or yellow body (brown tilt) £30-35
       1950-55 **Single-axle Covered Trailer** .... Red (green tilt, green ridged hubs), yellow (brown tilt, yellow ridged hubs). Concave or raised rear lamps..£30-35

25-U 1950-50 **Ford Tanker** .... Red body, 'ESSO', painted ridged hubs, hook and spare wheel support, pierced base, 1:65....................£400-500
       1951-51 .... As previous model but without the support for hook/spare wheel £120-140
       1952-53 .... As 1951 version but with smaller transfers and non-pierced base £100-125
25-V 1950-51 **Ford Refuse Tipper** .... Dark green body, Dark or Mid-green ridged hubs, smooth tailgate interior surface, 1:65 ....£80-100
       1952-55 .... Dark green body, dark-green ridged hubs, cross-braced tailgate interior surface £70-90
27AC 1950-50 **Massey-Harris Tractor**
            and Manure Spreader ...... Red tractor and implement made in England, painted wheels, 1:43. French display box (Red)................£400-600

30e 1936-39 **Breakdown Lorry** .... Fitted with the (lead) crane from 21d Railway Crane Truck. , smooth hubs, 'DUNLOP' tyres. Scale 1:65.
                         Yellow body, green crane, brown or black chassis £300-350
                         Red body, green crane, red or Black chassis; or Blue body, green crane, black chassis............................£300-350
       1938-39 .... Green body, green crane, brown chassis; or Red body, red crane, black chassis £300-350
       1940-40 .... With mazak wheels. Blue body with blue crane, or Yellow body, black chassis £900-1,200

PANHARD ARTICULATED LORRIES:
32-A 1952-52 (plain).......................... Blue body, plain or silver grille, painted ridged hubs, 1:60. Sold unboxed £200-250
32-AB 1952-52 **'SNCF'**.......................... Blue body, 'SNCF' (locomotive in round logo), painted ridged hubs. Sold unboxed (3 to a trade box) £400-500
       1954-59 (Renumbered in 1959 as 575) Blue body, 'SNCF' (pale green French map logo), painted ridged hubs.
                         Sold unboxed (three to a trade box) or later in own yellow box (add £30 to price) £150-200
32-AJ 1952-53 **'KODAK'** .... Yellow body (smooth inside cab roof), 'KODAK', painted ridged hubs,
                         1:60. Sold unboxed (supplied to shops in trade boxes of three)...........................£400-500
       1955-57 .... Yellow body (cross-hatching in cab roof), 'KODAK', painted ridged
                         hubs. Sold unboxed (supplied to shops in trade boxes of three)...........................£450-550
              US issue: Yellow body, (different letter shape from the French issue)...........................£800-1,100
32C 1954-55 **Panhard Titan-Coder Tanker,**
            'ESSO' .... Red body, 'ESSO' (large transfers), painted ridged hubs, '32C TRACTEUR PANHARD' on Yellow box........£160-200
       1956-59 (Renumbered in 1959 as 576) Red body, 'ESSO' (medium transfers), '32C TRACTEUR PANHARD' in 5 languages on Yellow box............£130-160

33A 1955-56 **Simca Cargo Van** .... Indented (early) or raised (later) cab step-plate, no hook mounting, spare wheel held by screw, 1:55.
                         Olive-green/yellow (green/yellow picture on yellow box), painted ridged hubs...........................£140-200
                         Olive-green/orange (green/orange picture on yellow box), painted ridged hubs...........................£140-200
33AN 1956-59 **Simca Cargo Van, 'BAILLY'** .... Indented or raised cab step-plate, with hook and mounting, spare wheel held by screw.
       (Renumbered in 1959 as 577) Yellow/white body, 'BAILLY DEMENAGEMENTS' logo, painted ridged hubs, yellow box £200-250
33-B 1955-59 **Simca Cargo Tipper Truck**........ Indented (later raised) cab step-plate, no hook mounting, smooth or grooved tipper surface,
       (Renumbered in 1959 as 578) indented (later raised) tailgate central reinforcement, painted ridged hubs.
                         Dark green/grey, dark green/grey, metallic dark green/metallic grey. Yellow box...........................£90-110
                         As previous models, but later version with hook and mounting. Yellow box £90-110
33-C 1955-59 **Simca Glazier's Truck**.............. Grey/dark green, indented or raised cab step-plate, hook mounting on later issues, grey ridged hubs, 1:55.
       (Renumbered in 1959 as 579) 'MIROITIER SAINT-GOBAIN'. Yellow box has '33C MIROITIER' in French, later in 5 languages £120-170

34-A 1955-59 **Berliet Quarry Truck** .... No spare wheel support, ridged and concave painted hubs, 1:55.
       (Renumbered in 1959 as 580) Blue/black, orange tipper. Box first without then with picture and '34A'...........................£90-110
       1957-59 ....Promotional: Blue/black, orange tipper. In 'BERLIET' yellow box £500-750
34-B 1956-57 **Berliet Container Truck**............ Spare wheel screwed on, iron container-lifting eye, ridged and concave painted hubs.
       (Renumbered in 1959 as 581) Red/black/light grey, matt grey container. No picture on yellow box...........................£100-120
       1957-59 .... As previous model but with cast-in lifting eye, yellow box has picture + '34B plateau avec container' £100-120
              Promotional: Yellow body, 'BAILLY' on container £120-140

35-A 1955-55 **Citroën U23 Breakdown Truck** . Red body, large tool-box, closed fuel tank, yellow 'DINKY TOYS' logo.1:50. '35A' on box....................£110-140
       1956-59 (Renumbered in 1959 as 582) ...... Dark red body, small tool-box, open fuel tank, Yellow 'DINKY TOYS' logo. '35A' on box £110-140

36-A 1956-59 **Willeme Log Lorry** .... Orange cab, yellow semi-trailer (pierced beam), wooden logs, black painted base,
       (Renumbered in 1959 as 897) ridged and concave hubs, radial tread tyres, 1:55. '36A' on Supertoys box...........................£100-130
36-B 1958-59 **Willeme Tractor & Closed Trailer** Red tractor, orange semi-trailer with removable green plastic tilt, painted ridged and concave hubs,
       (Renumbered in 1959 as 896) 4 rollers on trailer prop, 1:55, '36B' on Supertoys box £150-200

38-A 1957-59 **Unic Marrel Multi-Skip Truck**.. Grey and golden-yellow (or Lemon-Yellow) body (windows in some), fixed skip,
       (Renumbered in 1959 as 895) ridged and concave painted hubs, black radial or block tread tyres, 1:55, '38A' on Supertoys box £130-170
39-A 1957-59 **Unic Boilot Car Transporter** ..... Silver/orange, ridged and concave hubs, black radial tread
       (Renumbered in 1959 as 894) tyres, 1:55, '39A' on Supertoys box £180-200
                         Variation with all-Red trailer and Black hubs...........................£500-750
39-B 1959-60 **Unic Sahara Pipe Transporter** .. Beige body (various shades), white roof, 'open' trailer, painted ridged
       (Renumbered in 1960 as 893) and concave hubs, 6 black tubes, 1:55. '893' on Supertoys box £120-150

50 1957-59 **Salev Mobile Crane** .... Grey body, Red crane, Blue driver, ridged and concave painted hubs, 1:43. (Renumbered in 1959 as 595) £120-150
70 1957-59 **Two-Axle Covered Trailer** .... Red or yellow, green tilt, ridged or concave hubs, 1:60, '70' on yellow box. (Renumbered in 1959 as 810).........£30-40
90-A 1958-59 **Richier Diesel Roller**................ Yellow body, blue driver, red roller wheels, '90A' on Yellow box. Supertoy. (Renumbered in 1959 as 830) £90-110
560 1951-? **Muir-Hill Dumper** .... Yellow body, metal wheels. Imported from England; sold in special blue box, French printing on label £55-65

560 1959-60 **Peugeot D3A Van** .... Dark or Light Grey body, painted ridged hubs, 1:50. (Renumbered from 25-BV).......................£550-625
560 1959-60 **Peugeot Post Van, 'POSTES'** .... Dark green body, 'POSTES' (thick letters, transfer). Box print: '25BV, marque déposée' only £150-200
                         Same model, but box print reads: '25BV, marque déposée, Made in France, Imprimé en France' £150-200
       1960-61 .... Same model, but 'POSTES' transfer has oval or more square letter 'O'. Box reads '25BV/560' £150-200
       1960-61 .... Same model (transfer with oval 'O' of 'POSTES'), concave painted hubs. '560' on box £150-200

French Dinky Toys 563 Renault Estafette Pick-up and 25C Citroën 1200Kg Van

French Dinky Toys 885 Saviem Sinpar Steel Carrier

Photographs: Vectis Auctions Ltd.

560	1960	Peugeot D3a Van ....Promotional:	Turquoise body, 'CIBIE', yellow ridged hubs	£2,500-3,500
560-P	1961	Citroën 2cv Van Promotional:	Yellow cab, Silver back, red 'PHILIPS' logo and design on door	£4,000-5,000
560	1963-70	Citroën 2cv Postal Service Van .	Yellow body and concave hubs, blue 'swallow' logo. Yellow box print reads:	
			'C'est une fabrication MECCANO', or (later): 'C'est une fabrication MECCANO TRI-ANG'	£125-150
560-E	1968-70	Citroën 2cv Azam Van...............	Pale Green body, plated concave hubs, 'PIRELLI' tyres, 'DINKY-POCH' on box. Export to Spain	£1,750-2,250
561	1951-59	Blaw-Knox Bulldozer	Red/black, with driver. Model made in England, Blue box made in France. (Renumbered in 1959 as 885).......	£100-125
561	1959-59	Citroën H Van ......(was 25-CG)	Cream body, 'FROMAGE CH GERVAIS', 1:50. In own box with '25CG GERVAIS' print....................	£200-250
	1959-63	....	Turquoise body (various shades), 'CIBIE', painted ridged hubs (concave from 1961).	
			In 25CG box with '561 CIBIE' sticker over the number	£300-400
	1963-66	....	White/blue body, 'GLACES GERVAIS', blue concave hubs. Picture box	£400-500
	1964-64	.... Promotional:	Blue body, 'BAROCLEM', aluminium concave hubs. Code 2 promotional in special picture box	£4,000-6,000
561	1972-72	Renault 4L Van	Yellow body, 'PTT', first grille, grey security window, plastic base, chromed concave hubs, 1:43.	£2,500-3,000
562	1951-?	Muir-Hill Dumper	Golden yellow, with driver, 1:43. Model made in England, Blue box made in France	£50-60
562H	1965-68	Citroën 2cv Van,		
		'WEGENWACHT'	Yellow body, concave hubs, '25D' on black painted base or anodised base without '25D'.	
			Model made for export to Netherlands. Yellow box marked 'WW' from 1968....................	£500-750
563	1960-62	Renault Estafette Pick-Up	Orange or green body, green tilt, painted concave hubs, 1:43, Yellow box without, later with, illustration	£60-80
564	1963-65	Renault Mirror Truck	Red-orange body, 'SAINT-GOBAIN/MIROITIER', painted concave hubs, 1:43. Yellow box	£150-175
			As previous model but with Brick red body. Yellow box	£150-175
565	1965-71	Renault Estafette Camper	Bluebody, Ivory or White plastic roof, chromed concave hubs, 1:43. Yellow box	£200-250
566	1965-70	Citroën H Currus Van...............	Blue/white body, 'POLICE', painted concave hubs, working warning lights	£200-300
567	1967-70	Unimog Snow Plough	Yellow/black body, brown removable top, painted concave hubs, 1:50. Yellow box	£120-140
569	1967-71	Berliet Stradair Side Tipper	Light green/dark green body, painted hubs, green or black motor, 1:43. Yellow box, instruction leaflet	£250-400

570 PEUGEOT J7 TAXI VANS:

570	1967-67	'ALLO-FRET'	Blue body, blue or white roof, aluminium concave hubs, aerial, 1:43, 108mm. Yellow box	£300-400
570	1968-68	'ICI'	Blue/white body, 'IMPERIAL CHEMICAL INDUSTRIES'. Code 2 promotional....................	£1,000-1,500
570A	1970-71	'AUTOROUTES'	Orange body, two workmen plus equipment, 1:43. On diorama base in yellow box	
			(also containing a 595s Traffic Sign 'Pedestrians Prohibited')	£600-750
571	1951-57	Coles Mobile Crane	Yellow and black, painted hubs, 1:50. Model made in England, Blue box made in France (see 972)............	£70-80
571	1969-71	Saviem Goelette		
		Horse Box and Sulky................	Blue/'wood'/white, painted concave hubs, racehorse, Green two-wheel	
			racing cart (sulky) with driver, 1:43. Yellow picture box	£900-1,200
572	1970-71	Berliet Quarry Truck	Red body, yellow plastic tipper, plastic hubs, 1:43. 595s Traffic Sign 'No Overtaking For	
			Heavy Vehicles' included in yellow box	£400-650
575	1959-63	Panhard Artic. Lorry, 'SNCF' ..	Blue body, 'SNCF' on Pale (later Dark) Green French map logo, painted ridged or concave hubs.	
		(previously 32-AB)	Sold unboxed (three to a trade box), later in own Yellow box (add £30 to price)	£120-150
576	1959-60	Panhard Titan-Coder Tanker,		
		'ESSO'	Red body, 'ESSO' (medium lettering), painted ridged hubs.	
		(previously 32-C)	'32C TRACTEUR PANHARD' in 5 languages on yellow box	£175-200
	1960-61	....	Red or Dark Red body, 'ESSO' (smaller lettering), painted ridged hubs (concave from 1961).	
			Yellow box has 'DINKY TOYS' in italics, '576' and description in 5 languages on flap..........................	£160-200
	1961-61	....	Same, but with concave hubs	£200-250
577	1959-61	Simca Cargo Van, 'BAILLY'	Yellow/white body, 'BAILLY DEMENAGEMENTS'. Indented or raised cab step-plate, with hook	
		(previously 33-AN)	support, spare wheel held by screw (later by rivet), painted ridged hubs (later concave)	£540-200
577	1965-71	Berliet Livestock Truck.............	Yellow and green, two black and white cows, painted concave hubs, 1:43. Yellow box	£150-200
578	1959-70	Simca Cargo Tipper Truck	Dark or Mid-green/Metallic Grey, indented or raised cab step-plate, with hook mounting, spare wheel	
		(previously 33-B)	held by screw (later by rivet), scale 1:55. Yellow box	£80-100
579	1959-61	Simca Mirror Truck,		
		'SAINT-GOBAIN'	Grey/Dark Green, 'MIROITIER SAINT-GOBAIN'. Indented or raised cab step-plate, with hook mounting,	
		(previously 33-C)	spare wheel screwed on, Grey or Yellow ridged hubs, scale 1:55.	
			Yellow box has '33C MIROITIER' in 5 languages	£120-160
	1961-67	....	Yellow/Dark Green, Yellow ridged hubs, spare wheel rivetted. Yellow box changed to read: '579-33C'..	£140-180
	196?-6?	.........................Export model:	Yellow/Dark Green or Grey/Dark Green, Grey ridged hubs or Cream concave hubs	£150-200
			Pale Grey/Pale Green, without 'SAINT-GOBAIN', Cream ridged or concave hubs.	£100-150
580	1959-61	Berliet Quarry Truck	As 34-A but with spare wheel support, ridged and concave painted hubs, block tread tyres.	
		(previously 34-A)	Blue/Black, Orange tipper. Picture on yellow box	£150-175
	1961-70	....	Same model but with cast-in spare wheel location, concave painted hubs and anodised base..............	£150-175
581	1959-60	Berliet Container Truck............	Spare wheel held by screw, ridged and/or concave painted hubs, round (later square) section tyres.	
		(previously 34-B)	Red/Black/Light Grey, Dark Grey container. Picture on yellow box	£100-120
	1960-65	....	Same, but spare wheel rivetted on. Yellow box has picture and '34B plateau avec container' in 7 languages	£120-140
582	1959-69	Citroën Breakdown Truck,		
		'DINKY TOYS'	Painted ridged hubs, smooth black tyres, small tool-box, open fuel tank, 1:50.	
		(previously 34-A)	Dark red body, yellow 'DINKY TOYS' logo. '35A' on box	£100-150
	1969-71	....	Red body and concave hubs, yellow logo, plastic hook, smooth or treaded black tyres. '582' on box	£120-160
584	1961-65	Berliet Covered Lorry...............	Red or Yellow body (either with Green tilt), concave hubs, 1:43. Yellow box (picture on later ones)........	£100-120
585	1961-64	Berliet Builders Lorry...............	Blue/orange/grey, wide (later narrow) boards in tipping body, painted concave hubs, 1:43. Yellow box....	£100-125
586	1961-65	Citroën 55 Milk Lorry	White/blue body, 30 bottle crates, painted concave hubs, 1:43. Yellow box	£500-700
587	1964-70	Citroën H Display Van,		
		'PHILIPS'	Yellow/silver body, red concave hubs, household appliances, 1:43. Yellow picture box	£600-800
588	1964-70	Berliet Beer Lorry	Yellow/red/brown, 'BIERES, LIMONADES, EAUX MINÉRALES',	
			painted concave hubs, crates and barrels, 1:43. Yellow picture box	£250-300
588K	1970-71	.........................Promotional:	Red body, 'KRONENBOURG LE GRAND NOM des BIERES d'ALSACE'. Code 1 promotional	£3,500-4,500
589	1965-69	Berliet Breakdown Lorry..........	Red body, 'DEPANNAGE' in yellow or White, chromed concave hubs, 1:43	£250-300
	1970-71	....	Orange body, 'DEPANNAGE AUTOROUTES', chromed concave	
			hubs, aerial. 595t Traffic Sign 'Maximum Height 3.5 metres' included in box...............................	£250-300
595	1959-61	Salev Mobile Crane	As reference 50 but crane pillar not held by rivet, painted concave hubs.......................................	£80-110

596	1960-63	**LMV Road Sweeper/Washer**	Cream and green body, rotating and pivoting brush mechanism, 1:43. Yellow box	**£80-110**
597	1959-61	**Coventry Climax Fork Lift Truck**......................	(was 14-C) Orange/Yellow (or Green)/Black, ridged or concave hubs, 'assemblé en France' on base	**£60-75**
803	1967-69	**Unic Articulated Lorry, 'SNCF'**	Dark blue body, cream trailer roof, 'SNCF' and 'PAM-PAM', plastic hubs, 1:43. Yellow picture box.......	**£250-350**
805	1966-71	**Unic Multi Skip and Gas Tanker**	Red/black/white, interchangeable skip and 'PROPANE-PRIMAGAZ' gas tank (from Hornby ACHO range), painted concave hubs, 1:55. Yellow picture box	**£300-400**
810	1959-62	**Two-Axle Covered Trailer**	(previously 70) Red or Yellow, Green tilt, ridged or concave hubs, 1:60. '70' (later '810') on Yellow box ...	**£40-50**
	1962-?	**Two-Axle Covered Trailer, 'ESSO'**	Red body and tilt, 'ESSO' transfers, painted concave hubs. Yellow box.......................................	**£55-65**
830	1959-69	**Richier Diesel Roller**.................	(90-A) Yellow body, Blue driver, Red wheels, '90A-830' (later '830') on Yellow box, 1:43. Supertoy	**£90-120**
881	1969-70	**GMC Circus Truck and Animal Trailer**..........................	Red/yellow/black, 'PINDER FAUVES', no hole in seat for driver, plastic animals, card supports, 'SUPER DINKY MECCANO FRANCE' on chassis, painted concave hubs, 1:43. Yellow box	**£1,000-1,500**
	1970-71	....	Same, but with hole in seat for driver, and 'DINKY-TOYS MECCANO TRI-ANG' on chassis	**£1,000-1,500**
882	1969-70	**Peugeot 404 + Circus Caravan** .. **'Le SUPER CIRQUE PINDER'**	Red/Yellow/White Peugeot 404 (536) and Caravelair Armagnac 420 Caravan (564), roof hoardings, chromed concave hubs. Yellow box also contains : a 595L Traffic Sign 'Maximum Width 2 metres', 'Martin' the circus bear and a leaflet	**£1,500-1,800**
885	1959-61	**Blaw-Knox Bulldozer**	Orange/Grey/Black, driver, 1:43. 'assemblé en France' on base (see 561). Blue/White striped picture box	**£150-175**
885	1966-71	**Saviem Sinpar Steel Carrier**......	Red cab, grey chassis, driver, plastic hubs, steel load held by magnets, scale 1:43. Yellow picture box (showing yellow/grey vehicle)	**£300-350**
886	1960-65	**Richier Road Profiler**	Yellow body, driver, plastic hubs, scale 1:43. Supertoys box.......................................	**£200-250**
887	1959-61	**Muir-Hill Dumper**	Yellow-Cream body, driver, painted ridged hubs, 1:43. English components, 'assemblé en France' on base	**£40-50**
887	1963-71	**Unic Articulated Tanker, 'BP'**...	White/green/lemon yellow, 'AIR BP', plastic hubs, hoses for filling tank, electric lights switched by spare wheel, scale 1:43. Supertoys blue/white box with full colour picture on lid...................	**£150-200**
888	1960-66	**Berliet Sahara Pipe-Layer**	Sand body (various shades), White roof, operable crane, most with White or Beige plastic hubs (a few cast metal), most with tow hook (a few without), scale 1:50	**£175-225**
	1968	.....................................Promotional:	As previous model but with 'Société Languedocienne de Forages Pétroliers'	**£1,000-1,200**
889	1959-62	**Coles Mobile Crane**	Orange/yellow, 2 drivers, painted concave hubs, 'assemblé en France' on base. Was 972; reissued as 972	**£60-80**
893	1960-70	**Unic Sahara Pipe Transporter** .. (previously 39-B)	Beige body (various shades), White roof, window glazing, pierced (later solid) trailer painted ridged and concave hubs, 6 tubes, 1:55. Supertoys box without (later with) '893'	**£150-175**
	196?	.....................................Promotional:	Beige body, White roof, window glazing, 'solid' trailer, painted concave hubs. 'DESTINATION: PETROLE DU SAHARA' on box. Code 2 promotional	**NGPP**
894	1959-68	**Unic Boilot Car Transporter** ..... (previously 39-A)	Silver/orange, 'DINKY TOYS SERVICE LIVRAISON', painted concave hubs, black block tread tyres, scale 1:55. '894' on Supertoys box	**£150-180**
895	1959-65	**Unic Marrel Multi-Body Truck** . (previously 38-A)	Grey and golden-yellow body, fixed skip, ridged and concave (or all concave) painted hubs, black block tread tyres, scale 1:55. '895' on Supertoys box	**£120-140**
896	1959-71	**Willeme Tractor and Covered Trailer**........................ (previously 36-B)	Red tractor, inclined (later straight) chassis members, Orange semi-trailer, Green tilt, painted ridged and/or concave hubs, 4 (later 2) rollers on trailer prop. '36B-896' (later just '896') on Supertoys box	**£140-180**
897	1959-71	**Willeme Log Lorry** .... (previously 36-A)	Orange tractor (chassis members on spindle), Yellow semi-trailer (pierced, later solid), black painted base, painted concave hubs, radial or block tread tyres, 1:55. '897-36A' (later just '897') on Supertoys box......	**£125-165**
898	1961-65	**Berliet Transformer Carrier, 'ALSTHOM'**	Orange body, Grey transformer (loose parts within), painted ridged (later concave) hubs. Supertoys box	**£400-500**
972	1957-62	**Coles Mobile Crane** .... (Renumbered in 1959 as 889)	Orange and yellow, two drivers, painted concave hubs, 1:50. English parts, 'assemblé in France' on base....	**£60-80**
1412	1968-71	**Hotchkiss Willys Recovery Jeep**	Red and Yellow body, Orange or Black jib with lamp, painted concave hubs, scale 1:50	**£100-130**

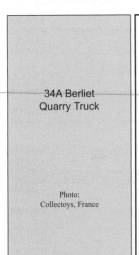

34A Berliet Quarry Truck

Photo: Collectoys, France

Emergency Vehicles

Market prices shown here are for guidance only. They refer ONLY to mint models in pristine boxes (where appropriate) that are complete with <u>all</u> of their original contents. See also 'Gift Sets' section.

Ref	Year(s)	Model name	Colours, features, details	Market Price Range
25BR	1959	Peugeot D3a Fire Service Van	A prototype exists with a light red body (cross-hatching inside roof), dark red ridged hubs and identical transfers to the 25D Citroën van	NPP
25D	1958-59	Citroën 2cv Fire Service Van	Red body and ridged hubs, 'Pompiers Ville de Paris', 1:43. Yellow box. Renumbered 562 in 1959	£130-170
	1959-59		Grey body, 'BÉBÉ LORRAIN', cream hubs. Only 80 were made of this code-2 promotional model	£3,500-5,000
32D	1955-59	Delahaye Fire Escape	Red body, chromed ladder, painted ridged hubs, smooth White tyres (specially made for this model),	
		(Renumbered in 1959 as 899)	scale 1:55. Blue/White striped Supertoys box. (32-D was the first of the French Dinky Supertoys)	£150-200
32E	1957-59	Berliet First-Aid Vehicle	Bright Red (occasionally Brownish-Red) twin-cab body (no markings), detachable hose reel, painted	
		(Renumbered in 1959 as 583)	ridged (concave through 1959) hubs, white tyes, 1:55, '32E' on Supertoys box	£150-200
80F	1959-59	Renault Military Ambulance	Renault Goelette in Gloss or matt finish, painted ridged hubs, 1:55. Yellow box	£60-75
		(Renumbered in 1959 as 820)		
501	1967-70	Citroën DS19 'POLICE' Car	Very dark blue/white, roof beacon, plated concave hubs, 1:43	£160-200
507P	1967-71	Simca 1500 'POLICE' Estate Car	Dark blue/white body. Commissioned for use by Police	£300-350
517P	1969	Renault R8 'POLICE' Car	Dark blue/white. Commissioned for use by Police	£400-450
518	1964-64	Renault 4L	Red body, 'POMPIERS de PARIS'. Commissioned by Fire Service	£375-425
525	1964-64	Peugeot 404 Fire Car	Red body, 'Pompiers de Paris', concave chromed hubs. Commissioned for use by Fire Service	£400-500
551	1965-67	Ford Taunus 17M Police Car	Green/white, 'POLIZEI', plated concave hubs, 1:43, German text on box. Made for export to Germany and Benelux countries	£800-1,000
556	1964-67	Citroën ID19 Ambulance	Same, but 'A' of 'Ambulance' and 'M' of 'Municipale' are not aligned. 'Super detail' box	£80-100
	1967-70		Grey/cream body, plated concave hubs, 'DUNLOP' nylon tyres, plastic steering wheel, without '556' on base, 'A' of 'Ambulance' and 'M' of 'Municipale' are not aligned. 'Super detail' box	£110-140
562	1959-61	Citroën 2cv Van (was 25-D)	Red body and ridged hubs, 'POMPIERS VILLE de PARIS', scale 1:43	£130-170
	1961-63		Red body and concave hubs, 'POMPIERS VILLE de PARIS', smooth or treaded black tyres	£140-180
566	1965-70	Citroën H Currus Van, 'POLICE'	Blue/white body, painted concave hubs, working warning lights	£200-300
568	1968-70	Berliet Gak Fire Escape	Red twin-cab body, extending chromed ladder, painted concave hubs, 1:43. Yellow picture box	£250-300
570P	1971-72	Peugeot J7 VSAB Fire Van	'POMPIERS', Red body, painted hubs, 'MECCANO FRANCE SA' on diecast base. Yellow box	£300-450
	1972-		Later version, with 'MECCANO TRI-ANG' on plastic base. Yellow box	£300-450
583	1959-63	Berliet First-Aid Vehicle	Bright Red twin-cab body (no markings), detachable hose reel, painted	
		(Renumbered from 32-E)	concave painted hubs, white tyes, 1:55, '32E' (later '583-32E') on Supertoys box	£140-180
	1962-63	...Promotional issue:	Red twin-cab body with 'POMPIERS de PARIS' shield, concave hubs. Fire Service promotional	£200-250
820	1959-70	Renault Goelette Ambulance	Gloss or matt finish, painted concave hubs, treaded rubber (later nylon) tyres, 1:55. Yellow box	£60-75
		(Renumbered from 80-F)		
899	1959-65	Delahaye Fire Escape (was 32-D)	Red body, black steering wheel, painted ridged hubs, smooth white tyres, 1:55. '32D' on Supertoys box	£200-250
	1965-70		Red body, white steering wheel, painted concave hubs, treaded white tyres. '899' on Supertoys box	£200-250
1402	1968-68	Ford Galaxie Police Car	Black/white body, 'POLICE'. Commissioned for use by Police	NGPP
1416P	1970-70	Renault R6 Fire Car	Code 2 model based on Spanish-made components, commissioned by the Fire Service.	
		'POMPIERS de PARIS'	Red body, second grille (square headlamps), red concave hubs. Side view of white model on box	£400-500
1429	1970-71	Peugeot 404 Police Car	Blue/white body, 'POLICE', plastic base, plated concave hubs, 1:43. Yellow box	£200-300
		note:	595n Traffic Sign 'Cycling Prohibited' included with 1429.	
1450	1977-78	Simca 1100 Police Car	Blue/white or black/white body, 'POLICE', plated concave hubs. Made in Spain	£25-40

French Dinky Toys 32E
Berliet First Aid Vehicle

Photo: Vectis Auctions Ltd.

Military Vehicles

A number of military vehicle models were designed in the late 1930s and the prototypes were shown in the June 1940 French catalogue. They were never put into production because of the Nazi Occupation. It came as no surprise that, following liberation by the Allies, the first new French Dinky Toy to be introduced was a model of the US Army Jeep so common at the time. The unavailability of rubber meant that all-metal wheels had to be used instead of hubs and tyres. The wheels used on the Jeep were mounted inside-out to give a heavy duty off-road effect.

During the 1960s and 1970s a number of military models from the English range were imported into France. These are listed in the Imports section. 681 DUKW Amphibious

Vehicle was not one of those imported as the French factory produced a much more detailed version (number 825). Note that the letters 'DUKW' are not initials nor are they an abbreviation - they are simply part of the General Motors design reference system of the time.

All the models listed are finished in various shades of military green unless otherwise stated. The paint can be found to be either gloss, semi-gloss or matt but this does not affect the price range.

Some military items are also noted in the Accessories section.

Ref	Year(s)	Model name	Colours, features, details	Market Price Range
24M	1946-48	Military Jeep	US Military olive-drab body and mazak wheels (mounted inside-out for effect), white star on bonnet, tinplate windscreen frame (some bonnet castings have frame supports), wire steering wheel, scale 1:43	£400-600
		note:	24-M was the first French made Dinky Toy to appear after the War. Trade boxes contained twelve units.	
80A	1957-59	Panhard EBR75 FL11 (renumbered in 1959 as 815)	Painted hubs, radial tread tyres, side headlamps or red lights, scale 1:55. '80A' on base and box (picture on some boxes)	£50-70
80-B	1958-59	Hotchkiss Willys Jeep	No driver (but hole in some), no hook, convex or ridged painted hubs, smooth black tyres, scale 1:50. '80B' printed on deep yellow end-flap box (picture on some)	£50-70
80-BP	1959-59	Hotchkiss Willys Jeep (renumbered in 1959 as 816)	With driver, no hook, convex or ridged painted hubs, smooth black tyres. There are two end-flap box types: 1 - '80B' Yellow box (with picture) has '80BP' stickers; 2 - '80BP' printed on Yellow box (with picture)	£50-70
80-C	1958-59	AMX 13 Tank (renumbered in 1959 as 817)	Gloss or matt finish, no aerial, rubber tracks, rear roller treads indented or raised, scale 1:55. '80C' on Yellow end-flap box	£50-70
80-D	1958-59	Berliet 6x6 All-Terrain Truck	Tinplate tilt, black cab floor, painted hubs, 1:55. '80D' but no picture on yellow end-flap box	£50-70
	1959-59	(renumbered in 1959 as 818)	Tinplate tilt, khaki cab floor, painted hubs. '80D' and picture on yellow end-flap box	£50-70
80-E	1958-59	Obusier ABS 155mm Gun (renumbered in 1959 as 819)	Gloss or matt finish, painted concave hubs, 1:55. Yellow end-flap box with or without picture, one PP	£40-50
			Same but with painted ridged hubs	£50-60
80-F	1959-59	Renault Goelette Ambulance (renumbered in 1959 as 820)	Gloss or matt, no roof vent or red crosses, ridged hubs, 1:55. Deep yellow end-flap box (model picture faces left)	£60-75
676	1972-72	Daimler Armoured Car	Painted concave hubs, camouflage net, 1:55. Model first made in France though 'Made in England' wrongly stated on base. 'MECCANO FRANCE' on yellow box	£150-200
		note:	676 was replaced after a short time by the Liverpool-made model with new reference '676L'.	
800	1974-?	Renault 4x4 Sinpar	(Revised and renumbered from 815). Khaki body, grey-green-khaki top, camouflage net, no gear lever, no aerial support, black or white plastic radio, painted concave hubs, 1:43. 'MECCANO' on base and box ('camouflage' effect on yellow end-flap box)	£90-120
801	1973-75	AMX 13 Tank (renumbered from 817)	Matt khaki body, grey nylon tracks, plastic rollers, camouflage net, aerial (a few without), scale 1:55. '801' on yellow, part camouflaged box	£55-75
802	1974-?	Obusier ABS 155mm Gun (renumbered from 819)	Khaki body with camouflage net, 'OBUSIER 155' replaces '80E' on base, painted concave hubs, 1:55. 'Camouflage' effect on yellow box	£40-50
804	1973-?	Mercedes-Benz Unimog	(Revised and renumbered from 821). Khaki body and camouflage net, 'MERCEDES TOUS TERRAINS, 804' on chassis, grey-blue base without '821', painted concave hubs, ridged tyres. 'MECCANO TRI-ANG' on yellow box with 'camouflage' effect (box contains unused transfer sheet)	£110-140
806	1973-?	Berliet Recovery Truck	(Revised and renumbered from 826). Khaki body and base, driver, plastic hook, camouflage net, without 'TOUS TERRAINS BERLIET' on chassis, painted concave hubs. 'Camouflage' effect on yellow box	£200-250
807	1973-?	Renault All-Terrain Ambulance	Khaki body with roof vents and red crosses, plastic concave hubs and base, 1:55. Yellow end-flap box	£150-175
808	1971	Dodge WC56 Command Car	Announced in the 1971 catalogue but made as reference 810 from 1972.	
808	1972-74	GMC US Army Recovery Truck	Sand body (hole for driver), painted concave hubs, black removable top, 1:43. Yellow box with insert	£200-250
	1974-?		Olive-drab body (hole for driver in some), painted concave hubs, black top. Yellow box with insert	£200-250
809	1970-	GMC US Army 6x6 Truck	Olive drab/black body (white stars), driver (white or khaki helmet), painted concave hubs, 1:43. Yellow box has design panel and insert	£125-150
809	197?-?	GMC 6x6 Truck	Khaki/black (white stars), driver (grey helmet), painted concave hubs. 'MECCANO' on box but no design panel, box has insert	£175-225
		note:	595q Traffic Sign 'Automatic Level Crossing' included with 809, plus additional 'white star' transfer sheet.	
810	1972-74	Dodge WC56 Command Car	Removable top, soldier, camouflage net, concave hubs, 1:43. 'Camouflage' effect yellow box, transfers	£150-200
813	1969-71	AMX with 155mm ABS Gun	Gloss or matt finish, nylon tracks, 1:55, 96mm. Yellow end-flap box	£140-190
	1972-?		Gloss or matt finish, nylon tracks, simplified gun, camouflage net. 'Camouflage' effect on yellow box	£140-190
814	1963-71	Panhard Armoured Car	Khaki finish, painted concave hubs, black (later Grey-Blue) base, scale 1:52. 'C'est une fabrication MECCANO' printed on plain side of Yellow end-flap box, insert, aerials in packet	£40-50
815	1959-63	Panhard EBR75 FL11 (renumbered from 80-A)	Gloss or matt finish, '80A' on base, painted hubs, block tread tyres, scale 1:55. Picture and '815' on box	£40-50
815	1969-74	Renault 4 Sinpar Gendarmerie ('revised' in 1974 and issued as 800)	Khaki body, green-khaki top, two military policemen, gear lever, aerial, light grey plastic radio, painted concave hubs, 1:43. 'MECCANO TRI-ANG' on base	£140-170
816	1959-61	Hotchkiss Willys Jeep (80-BP)	Driver, no hook, painted ridged hubs, smooth black tyres, 1:50. Picture and '816-80BP' on yellow box	£50-70
	1962-63		Driver, cast-in hook, concave hubs, smooth or treaded black tyres. Picture and '816' on yellow box	£50-70
816	1969-71	Berliet Rocket Launcher	Khaki/grey body, white/red rocket ('NORD, R-20'), painted concave hubs, 1:55. Yellow end-flap box	£200-250
817	1959-64	AMX 13 Tank (Was 80-C)	Gloss or matt khaki, no aerial, rubber tracks, rear roller treads raised, 1:55. '80C' on yellow box	£50-70
	1965-70		Same but only in gloss khaki and with aerial. With (later without) '80C' on base. '817' on yellow box	£50-70
	1973-75	(renumbered in 1973 as 801)	Same but matt khaki body, grey nylon tracks on plastic rollers, Yellow box with 'camouflage' effect	£50-70

818	1959-65	**Berliet 6x6 All-Terrain Truck**...	(Was 80-D). Tinplate tilt, khaki cab floor, painted concave hubs, 1:55. '80D' and picture on yellow box......**£50-70**
	1965-70	....	Same, but 'TOUS TERRAINS BERLIET' on base (a few without), '818' and picture on yellow box..........**£50-70**
819	1959-65	**Obusier ABS 155mm Gun**	(Was 80-E). Khaki body, painted ridged hubs, '80E' on base, scale 1:55. Fully illustrated yellow box..........**£40-50**
	1965-74	....	Gloss khaki body, painted concave hubs. Fully illustrated yellow box. (Revised in 1974; issued as 802).....**£40-50**
820	1959-70	**Renault Goelette Ambulance**	No roof vents, no red crosses, concave hubs, treaded plastic tyres, Yellow box (picture faces left)...............**£60-75**
		(renumbered from 80-F)	Same but with roof vents. Model picture on later boxes faces right **£60-75**
821	1960-63	**Mercedes-Benz Unimog**	'MERCEDES-UNIMOG' on chassis, '821' on black painted base,
			painted concave hubs, smooth tyres. No picture on yellow end-flap box **£50-70**
	1963-65	....	'MERCEDES-BENZ UNIMOG' on chassis, '821' on black
			painted base, painted concave hubs, smooth tyres. Picture and 'MECCANO' on yellow end-flap box **£45-55**
	1965-66	....	As previous model. but with ridged tyres. Picture and 'MECCANO TRI-ANG' on yellow end-flap box **£45-55**
	1966-70	....	Same model, but with grey-blue base without '821'. Picture and 'MECCANO TRI-ANG' on yellow box ...**£45-55**
	1973	....	Revised in 1973 and issued as 804.
822	1960-63	**White M3 Half-Track**................	Matt finish, no machine gun, black painted chassis, painted concave
			hubs (smooth black tyres), 1:50. Picture of model on yellow end-flap box **£70-80**
	1963-65	....	Matt or gloss finish, with machine gun, anodised chassis, painted concave hubs (treaded black tyres).
			Picture of model plus scene and 'C'est une fabrication MECCANO' on some yellow end-flap boxes..........**£70-80**
	1965-71	....	Same, but with picture of model plus scene and 'C'est une fabrication MECCANO TRI-ANG' on box ...**£70-80**
823	1962-66	**Marion Mobile Kitchen**.............	Khaki body, black or khaki base, painted concave hubs, scale 1:50. 'Cuisine Roulante' on Yellow box **£50-60**
823	1969-70	**GMC Military Tanker**...............	Khaki/black, plastic tank, removable cab canopy, painted concave hubs, scale 1:43.
			Yellow end-flap box has insert and also contains a 595b Traffic Sign 'Maximum Weight 5.5 tonnes' **£200-300**
824	1963-64	**Berliet Gazelle 6x6 Truck**	Removable cab canopy and tilt, painted concave hubs, 1:55.
			'Cabine vitrée' ('cab window glazing') on illustrated yellow end-flap box..**£120-140**
	1964-70	....	Same model, but 'Cabine vitrée aménagée' ('cab window glazing fitted') on yellow end-flap box...........**£120-140**
825	1963-71	**GMC DUKW Amphibian**	Gloss or matt finish, drums and boxes, painted concave hubs, driver
			with later issues, 1:55. Yellow end-flap box (picture on later boxes) **£120-140**
826	1963-70	**Berliet Recovery Truck**	Plastic driver, metal hook, black base, 'TOUS TERRAINS BERLIET' on chassis,
			painted concave hubs, scale 1:55. Deep yellow end-flap box also contains pink instruction leaflet..........**£140-170**
	1973	....	Revised in 1973 and issued as 806.
827	1964-71	**Panhard EBR75 FL10**...............	Khaki body, aerial/aerial point in some, painted concave hubs, 1:55. Yellow scenic end-flap box with PP....**£60-70**
828	1964-71	**Jeep SS10 Missile Launcher**	Driver, missile battery, concave hubs, 1:50. Yellow scenic end-flap box has instructions printed on side **£55-70**
829	1964-71	**Jeep 106SR Gun Carrier**	Driver, plastic gun, painted concave hubs, 1:50. Yellow scenic end-flap box (instructions on side) **£55-70**
834	1963-70	**Mobile Bridge Pack**	Khaki plastic 6 part bridge plus inflatable boats (as supplied with 884), scale 1:55 ....NPP
841	1959-71	**Tank Tracks Pack**	Twelve tracks for AMX tanks ....NPP
843	1962-71	**Military Tyre Pack**	Twelve treaded black tyres (large for 818 and similar) ....NPP
852	1962-71	**Tank Tracks Pack**	Ten replacement tracks for 822 White M3 Military Half-Track...NPP
856	1963-71	**Machine Gun**...........................	Plastic armament for use on 822 White M3 Half-Track..NPP
883	1964-66	**AMX 13 Bridge Layer**..............	Gloss or matt, '13t AMX' on base, scale 1:55. Yellow box reference on black oval, instructions..............**£150-200**
	1966-71	....	Same, but 'Char AMX poseur de pont, réf.883' on base. Yellow box has reference on violet band..........**£150-200**
884	1961-70	**Brockway Bridge Layer**	10 element bridge, 2 inflatable boats, 1:55. Supertoys box ('884' on some) also contains leaflet/map......**£200-250**
890	1959-63	**Berliet T6 Tank Transporter**	Gloss or matt finish, painted ridged hubs, 1:55, Supertoys box has no illustration................................**£160-250**
	1963-70	....	Gloss or matt finish, painted ridged or concave hubs. Illustration on blue/white Supertoys box................**£130-160**

French Dinky Toys
Military Vehicles

80D All-Terrain Truck

829 Jeep 106SR
Gun Carrier

814 Panhard
Armoured Car

828 Jeep SS10
Missile Launcher

Photo: Vectis Auctions Ltd.

Aircraft

In comparison with the English factory, Meccano France produced only a small range of model aircraft. They are nonetheless rather attractive and much sought after. Pre-war planes are especially difficult to find in good stable condition since the metal deterioration problem equally affected production on both sides of the Channel.

Some interesting models were designed at the end of the 1930s in the French 64 series (listed below). These were announced in the 1939 Meccano Magazine but with the advance of the occupying German forces production did not take place. Around this period a few small (normally silver) planes were given a camouflage finish and advertised as 'Reconnaissance' or

'Spotter' planes though it is very unlikely that serious production of these was actually undertaken.

Some of the English 60 series were imported into France before the war, and very few post-war (see the Imports section for details). Of the few new French made aircraft models to appear in the late 1950s, the Caravelle is perhaps the most desirable, particularly in the Swiss, Scandinavian or Algerian liveries with their specially printed Supertoys boxes.

As in England the French factory produced a number of boxed sets of model aircraft in the 1930s. They are fully described in the Gift Sets section.

Ref	Year(s)	Model name	Colours, features, details	Market Price Range
60a	1935-40	DeWoitine D388 Rainbow	(L'Arc en Ciel). Three engines, each with 2-blade propellers and no tinplate surrounds.	
			Silver/red, Gold/red, Cream/red, Cream/green, Gold/green, Gold/blue	£200-300
60A	1957-59	Dassault Mystere IVa Jet	Metallic grey, single jet, blue cockpit. Yellow box. Renumbered in 1959 as 800	£70-80
60b	1935-40	Potez 58	Tinplate main wings, 2-wheel undercarriage, 2-blade propeller, 2-part windscreen.	
			Yellow/grey	£150-250
			Red/silver	£200-300
60B	1957-59	Sud Aviation Vautour 'SNCASO'	Metallic grey, twin jet, blue cockpit. Yellow box. Renumbered in 1959 as 801	£80-100
60c	1935-40	Henriot H180T	Tinplate main wings, 2-wheel undercarriage, 2-blade propeller, 3-part windscreen.	
			Green/silver, Green/red, Blue/white, Red/silver	£150-250
60C	1956-59	Lockheed Super G Constellation (renumbered in 1959 as 892)	Silver, 'AIR FRANCE', 'FB-HBX', 4 x 3-blade propellers, scale 1:190. Supertoys box	£125-150
60d	1935-40	Breguet Corsaire	Open two-seater fuselage with tinplate main wings and 2-blade propeller.	
			Silver/red, Red/green, Red/yellow	£200-300
60D	1957-59	Sikorsky S58 Helicopter (renumbered in 1959 as 802)	White/grey/blue, 'SABENA', black rotors. Yellow box	£100-125
60e	1935-40	DeWoitine 500 Hunter	Open cockpit, tinplate main wings, 2-wheel undercarriage, 2-blade propeller.	
			Cream/red, Light cream/green	£200-300
60E	1957-59	Vickers Viscount (renumbered in 1959 as 803)	White/grey/blue, 'AIR FRANCE', 'FB-GNX', 4 x 4-blade propellers, scale 1:190. Yellow box	£125-175
60f	1935-40	Cierva Autogiro	Cast body, with or without pilot.	
			Gold (Red rotors), Cream (red or Blue rotors), Silver (red or blue rotors), Red (Cream rotors)	£200-300
60F	1959-59	Caravelle SE210, 'AIR FRANCE' (renumbered in 1960 as 891)	Metallic grey/white/blue, 'FB-GNY', operable steps, scale 1:190. Supertoys box	£130-180
61a	1938-40	Dewoitine D338	Basic casting as 60a L'Arc en Ciel but with 3 x 3-blade propellers and tinplate engine surrounds.	
			Green/silver or Red/gold (in a different arrangement from L'Arc en Ciel)	£150-250
	1939-40		Different casting from first version of 61a and also having the reference 64. Three engines, each with 3-blade propellers and tinplate engine surrounds, gliding hole. 'FA-DBF' marking on body.	
			Silver or Light green body	£150-250
61b	1938-40	Potez 56	Blue/silver, Red/silver, Yellow/silver. 2 x 2-blade propellers	£150-250
61c	1938-40	Farman F360	Open two-seater, single 2-blade propeller.	
			Silver/blue, Silver/red, Silver/yellow, Silver with roundels	£150-250
61d	1938-40	Potez 58 Air Ambulance	Silver body with red cross on silver or White ground	£200-300
61e	1938-40	Henriot H180M	Silver wings and fuselage with roundels, 2-blade propeller	£200-300
61f	1938-40	Dewoitine 500 Hunter	Silver wings and fuselage with roundels, 2-blade propeller	£200-300
64	1939-40	Dewoitine D338	Different casting from previous version of Dewoitine with more prominent tailfin and also having the reference 61a. Three engines, each with 2-blade propellers, gliding hole. 'FA-DBF' marking.	
			Silver or Light Green body	£150-200
64a	1939-40	Amiot 370	Twin engine monoplane, 2 or 3-blade propellers, gliding hole.	
			Beige, Pink, Red or Blue; or Pale green with red circles on wings; or Silver with French roundels	£150-250
	1948-49		A small number of pre-war castings were issued in various colours.	£150-250
64b	1939-40	Bloch 220	Twin engine airliner marked 'FA-OHJ', 2 x 3-blade propellers, gliding hole.	
			Silver, Dark red, Pale green or Ivory	£150-250
64c	1939-40	Potez 63	Twin engines, twin tailplanes, 3-blade propellers.	
			Beige, Red, Blue, Silver, Silver with French roundels	£150-250
	1948-49		A small number of pre-war castings were issued in various colours.	£150-250
64d	1939-40	Potez 662	Four engine passenger plane marked 'FA-RAY', 3-blade propellers, twin tailplanes, gliding hole.	
			Silver, Red, Light blue, Yellow	£150-200
800	1959-64	Dassault Mystere IVa Jet	Metallic grey, single jet, blue cockpit. Yellow box. Renumbered from 60-A	£70-80
801	1959-64	Sud Aviation Vautour 'SNCASO'	Metallic grey, twin jet, blue cockpit. Yellow box. Renumbered from 60-B	£80-100
802	1959-61	Sikorsky S58 Helicopter	White/grey/blue, 'SABENA', black rotors. Yellow box. Renumbered from 60-D	£100-125
803	1959-61	Vickers Viscount, 'AIR FRANCE'	White/grey/blue, 'FB-GNX', 4 x 4-blade propellers, scale 1:190. Yellow box. (Renumbered from 60-E)	£125-175
804	1959-63	SNCAN Noratlas	Metallic grey, twin-fuselage French military plane, 2 x 4-blade propellers. Yellow box	£150-250
891		Caravelle SE210	(Renumbered from 60-F). All have 'Escalier escamotable' (operable steps) and Supertoys box. Scale 1:190.	
	1959-59	'AIR FRANCE'	Silver/white/blue, 'FB-GNY'	£200-250
	1959-68	'AIR FRANCE'	Metallic grey/white/blue. '60F' under wing of early issues (later without)	£250-350
	1960-?	'SWISSAIR'	Metallic grey/white/red. 'HB-ICX', 'Swissair' on box	£900-1,200
	1960-?	'SAS'	('SCANDINAVIAN AIRWAYS SYSTEM'), Metallic grey/white/blue. 'SE-DAA'. 'SAS' on box	£900-1,200
	1960-?	'AIR ALGERIE'	Metallic grey/white/red. 'FO-BNH'. Supertoys 'Air Algerie' on box	£900-1,200
892	1959-62	Lockheed Super G Constellation	Silver, 'AIR FRANCE', 'FB-HBX', 4 x 3-blade propellers, scale 1:190. Supertoys box	£200-250

No. 60z 'Avions' Gift Set

Photo: Collectoys, France

Trains (See also Gift Sets and Accessories sections)

16   1935-40   **Northern Sector Railcar**
'Autorail' with 3 articulated coaches in mazak, tinplate base, silvered or black lead hubs, white rubber tyres. Boxed.
Blue-grey/dark blue; Grey/blue; Grey/red;
Gold/red; Cream/red; Cream/green **£100-125**

16a   1940   **Two-Car Railcar**
A two-part version of 16a.
Advertised in the 1940 catalogue but not issued.................NPP

17   1935-38   **Electric Goods Train**   See 'Gift Sets' section.
18   1934-38   **Steam Goods Train**   See 'Gift Sets' section.
19   1935-38   **Electric Passenger Train**   See 'Gift Sets' section.

19a   1935-36   **Electric Locomotive**
Cast in lead. Various basic colours...................................**£60-80**
          1936-40   Cast in mazak. Silver/red; Light green/red;
Green/black; Gold/blue; Two-tone blue **£50-70**

20   1935-38   **Steam Passenger Train**   See 'Gift Sets' section.

20a   1935-40   **Passenger Coach**
Red/blue or Green/blue. Cast in lead **£25-35**

21   1934-38   **Steam Mixed Goods Train**   See 'Gift Sets' section.

21a   1934-40   **Steam Tank Locomotive**
Red/blue; Green/blue; Green/black. Cast in lead **£30-45**

21b   1934-40   **Timber Wagon**
Red/green wagon cast in lead, yellow mazak 'log'........**£30-45**

21c   1934-40   **Coal Wagon**
Green/red or Green/black wagon, cast in lead **£30-45**

21d   1934-38   **Crane Wagon**
Blue and green; Green and blue; Red and blue;
Yellow and red. Cast in lead, crane has 'open' jib **£25-35**

21d   1938-40   **Crane Wagon**
Blue and green; Green and blue; Red and blue;
Yellow and red. Cast in lead, crane has 'solid' jib **£25-35**

26   1934-35   **Bugatti Autorail**
Cast in mazak, smooth sides, small windows. May have silvered metal cast wheels or bakelite moulded rollers in red, green or blue. Cream body with blue, yellow, green, red or orange sides...**£90-120**
          1934-40   Same, but with ridged sides and larger windows.
Yellow body (red or green sides); Green (red sides).....**£90-120**

Caravans and Campers

See also Gift Sets section.

Ref	Year(s)	Model name	Colours, features, details	Market Price Range
564	1969-71	**Caravelair Armagnac 420**	Blue/white, plated concave hubs, 1:43. Yellow box has 595a Traffic Sign 'Danger of Falling Rocks'	**£100-150**
565	1965-71	**Renault Estafette Camping Car**	Light blue body, ivory roof, floral curtains, aluminium concave hubs, scale 1:43. Yellow box	**£140-180**
811	1959-59	**Caravan** ('Henon' style)	Cream/White, smooth roof casting, window glazing in most, tinplate drawbar, plated ridged hubs, 1:43.	**£80-100**
	1960-63		As previous model, but with ribbed body casting	**£70-90**
812	1965-69	**Camping Trailer**	Cream body with luggage, single plated ridged hub and black tyre, 1:43. Sold only in plastic bag	**£40-50**

Ships

Most of the Dinky Toys model ships sold in France were imported English issues (see the Imports section for details). Those of French design and manufacture are listed below. No boxed sets made entirely in France appear to have been produced, though the Liverpool made castings of the British Naval Warships set were imported into France between 1938 and 1940. They were sold in a French version of the presentation box. The 'Locomotion Moderne' set was intended to contain ship models but was another of those proposals which fell victim to the outbreak of war (see the Gift Sets section for details).

Ref	Year(s)	Model name	Colours, features, details	Market Price Range
52c	1937-40	**Steamship 'Normandie'**	Black/white/red, no rollers, 175mm. Blue box has coloured picture of the ship at sea on the lid, and a picture of the ship and the port of Manhattan on the inner part	**£175-250**
	1940-40		Black/white/red, no rollers, 175mm. Blue box has no inner picture	**£120-170**
52d	1937-40	**Steamship 'Normandie'**	Black/white/red, with metal rollers, 175mm. Blue box has coloured picture of the ship at sea on the lid, and a picture of the ship and the port of Manhattan on the inner part	**£175-250**
	1940-40		Black/white/red, with metal rollers, 175mm. Blue box has no inner picture	**£120-170**
	1947-48		Black/white/red, with metal rollers, 175mm. Blue box has no inner picture	**£120-170**
53a	1937-40	**Battleship 'Dunkerque'**	Battleship grey, with metal rollers, 120mm. Light yellow one-piece illustrated box	**£100-150**
53b	1937-40	**Battleship 'Dunkerque'**	Battleship grey, no rollers, 120mm. Light yellow one-piece illustrated box	**£100-150**
870	1962-71	**Steamship 'France'**	White/black/red, scale 1:1200, 263mm.	**£150-200**

'Dolly Varden' Doll's House Furniture

Models of 'Dolly Varden' Dolls House Furniture were available in France and England. They are very similar in range and appearance but are definitely different castings with a different finish. French boxed sets generally appear to have much bigger boxes than the English equivalent. It is thought that the 'Dolly Varden Dolls House' was never advertised in France and is consequently almost impossible to find there.

Ref	Year(s)	Model name and details	Market Price Range
101	1936	**Dining Room Furniture Set** See 'Gift Sets' section.	
101a	1936-40	**Dining Table**, Light or Dark mottled brown	**£10-15**
101b	1936-40	**Sideboard**, Light or Dark mottled brown	**£15-20**
101c	1936-40	**Carver**, Light or Dark mottled brown	**£10-15**
101d	1936-40	**Chair**, Light or Dark mottled brown	**£10-15**
102	1936-40	**Bedroom Furniture Set** See 'Gift Sets' section.	
102a	1936-40	**Bed**, Mottled lilac	**£10-15**
102b	1936-40	**Wardrobe**, Mottled lilac	**£15-20**
102c	1936-40	**Dressing Table**, Mottled lilac, with mirror	**£15-20**
102d	1936-40	**Chest of Drawers**, Mottled lilac	**£15-20**
102e	1936-40	**Stool**, Mottled lilac	**£10-15**
102f	1936-40	**Chair**, Mottled lilac (casting as 101d)	**£10-15**

Ref	Year(s)	Model name and details	Market Price Range
103	1936-40	**Kitchen Furniture Set** See 'Gift Sets' section.	
103a	1936-40	**Refrigerator**, Pale green/cream or Blue/ivory	**£15-20**
103b	1936-40	**Sideboard**, Pale green/cream or Blue/ivory	**£15-20**
103c	1936-40	**Cooker**, Pale green/cream or Blue/ivory	**£15-20**
103d	1936-40	**Table**, Pale green/cream or Blue/ivory	**£10-15**
103e	1936-40	**Chair**, Pale green/cream (casting as 101d), or Blue/ivory (casting as 101d)	**£10-15**
104	1937-40	**Bathroom Furniture Set** See 'Gift Sets' section.	
104a	1937-40	**Bath**, Pink	**£10-15**
104b	1937-40	**Bath Mat**, Pink rubber (prone to deterioration)	**£10-15**
104c	1937-40	**Hand Basin**, Pink, with mirror	**£15-20**
104d	1937-40	**Stool**, Pink	**£10-15**
104e	1937-40	**Linen Basket**, Pink	**£10-15**
104f	1937-40	**Toilet**, Pink	**£10-15**

Collectors notes

Buses

29d 1939-51 **Renault TN4H Paris Bus**
All have Dark Green cast lower body, Cream tinplate top, scale 1:80. Variations as follows:
1939-40 Base on some, cast hubs, black or white 'DUNLOP' tyres...**£300-400**
1940-40 No base, painted mazak wheels......................**£200-250**
1940-49 Base on some (may be black or silver painted), painted mazak wheels...............................**£200-250**
1950-51 Driver set high; with base (may be black or silver painted), yellow ridged hubs....................**£250-300**

29D 1952-54 **Somua-Panhard Paris Bus**
Dark green/cream, smooth inside roof, painted ridged hubs, 1:70. Not boxed individually.................**£150-175**
1954-59 (renumbered in 1959 as 570)
Dark green/cream, cross-hatched inside roof, painted ridged hubs. Yellow box marked '29D'........**£150-175**

29E 1950-50 **Isobloc Autocar** (All have painted ridged hubs, 1:70)
Smooth sides and roof, painted ridged hubs, scale 1:70.
Blue/cream, smooth sides and roof.............................**£250-350**
Dark green/light green, smooth sides and roof..........**£200-250**
Blue/silver, smooth sides and roof..............................**£250-350**
1951-52 Blue/silver, smooth roof, raised side detail...............**£185-225**
1953-55 Red/silver, smooth roof, raised side detail..................**£110-130**
Orange/silver, smooth roof, raised side detail.............**£125-150**
Blue/silver, ridged roof, raised side detail......................**£75-95**

29F 1956-58 **Chausson AP521 Autocar**
Painted ridged hubs, scale 1:65. Box flap reads '29F AUTOCAR CHAUSSON' in French only.
Blue/cream body or Red/cream body.........................**£100-125**
1958-59 (renumbered in 1959 as 571)
As previous models, but concave hubs. Box flap reads '29F AUTOCAR CHAUSSON' in 4 languages..........**£110-135**

541 1963-71 **Mercedes-Benz Autocar**
18 seater body, chromed concave hubs, 1:43. Yellow box.
Mid-red and cream, Orange-red and cream, or Deep Pink (various shades) and cream.........................**£90-110**
1966-? South African issue:
Blue/cream body, chromed concave hubs...............**£800-1,200**
19?? 'PTT SUISSE'
Orange/Silver body, chromed concave hubs........**£3,500-4,500**

570 1959-61 **Somua Paris Bus OP5** (29-D)
Dark green/cream, cross-hatched inside roof, painted ridged hubs. In Yellow box marked '29D'.......**£90-120**

571 1959-60 **Chausson AP521 Autocar** (renumbered from 29-F)
Painted concave hubs, 1:65. Box flap reads '29F AUTOCAR CHAUSSON' in 4 languages.
Blue/cream body..**£130-150**
Red/cream body...**£120-140**

889 1965-70 **Berliet Paris Autobus**
Green/greenish-white, 'DUNLOP', 'PEPSI-COLA', painted concave hubs, scale 1:49.
Supertoys blue/white box, colour picture on lid........**£200-250**

889U 1965-70 **Berliet Urban Bus**
Red/cream or Orange/Cream, 'DUNLOP', 'PEPSI-COLA', painted concave hubs. Supertoys blue/white box with colour illustration of the Place Bellecour in Lyons.....**£225-275**

NB 889 Paris Bus was modelled on a Berliet vehicle though the 1965-66 catalogue attributes it to Saviem.

French Dinky Toys 29F Chausson AP521 Autocar

Photos: Vectis Auctions Ltd.

French Dinky Toys 29E Isobloc Autocar

Accessories

P re-war figures 1 to 10 inclusive were hollow cast in lead and individually hand painted. The colours stated are therefore those observed but any other colours and shades are possible especially with painted detail. The bases are usually brown, beige or grey (some blue ones seen) and are usually marked 'MECCANO DINKY TOYS' though some early ones may be found with 'HORNBY' marked under them. Early boxes were blue-grey (often marked 'Série Hornby'), later ones were red (usually printed 'Dinky Toys' and with various shades and degrees of surface gloss). They vary greatly as far as the printing is concerned. After the War, Meccano-France considered most of the figures to be primarily railway accessories so they reverted to listing them in the 'Hornby Railway Accessories' range. Their boxes generally reflect this thinking after 1948, and between 1950 and 1955 most of models 1 to 10 were issued in plastic as 'Hornby unbreakable figures'.

Ref	Year(s)	Model name and details	Market Price Range
1	1934-40	**Station Staff Set**	See 'Gift Sets' section
1a	1934-40	**Station Master.** Dark blue coat, grey or grey-green trousers	**£30-35**
1b	1934-40	**Porter.** Light blue uniform with red belt, no luggage	**£30-35**
1c	1934-40	**Railway Guard.** Dark blue coat, grey or grey-green trousers	**£30-35**
1d	1934-40	**Policeman.** Dark blue uniform	**£30-35**
1e	1934-40	**Controller.** Dk. blue coat, grey or grey-green trousers	**£30-35**
2	1934-40	**Railway Passengers Set**	See 'Gift Sets' section
2a	1934-40	**Normandy Farmer.** Various rustic colours	**£30-35**
2b	1934-40	**Farmers Wife.** A 'Peasant type Bécassine' with basket and umbrella, red or orange dress (later turquoise)	**£30-35**
2c	1934-40	**Young Woman.** Bag under right arm, various colours	**£30-35**
2d	1934-40	**Boy Scout.** Boy in French scout uniform (all khaki or khaki shorts/green shirt)	**£30-35**
2e	1934-40	**Boy (sitting).** Satchel under right arm, various colours	**£30-35**
2f	1934-40	**Girl (sitting).** Bag under left arm, various colours	**£30-35**
2g	1934-40	**Bench Seat.** Green or brown painted tinplate	**£30-35**
3	1934-40	**Animals Set**	See 'Gift Sets' section
3a	1934-40	**Pig.** Pink (shades may vary)	**£20-30**
3b	1934-40	**Sheep.** Cream, white or dark brown (shades may vary)	**£20-30**
3c	1934-40	**Horse.** Grey or reddish-brown 'mottled' finish (painted using a 'run' technique). Various shades known	**£20-30**
3d	1934-40	**Bull.** White or reddish-brown 'mottled' finish (painted using a 'run' technique). Various shades known	**£20-30**
4	1934-40	**Railway Personnel Set**	See 'Gift Sets' section
4a	1934-40	**Cook.** White cook's outfit, carrying a (usually gold painted) fowl on a dish	**£30-35**
4b	1934-40	**Engine Fireman.** Dark blue overalls, coal shovel	**£30-35**
4c	1934-40	**Greaser.** Dark blue overalls, oilcan	**£30-35**
4d	1934-40	**Wheel Tapper.** Dark blue overalls, sounding mallet	**£30-35**
4e	1934-40	**Gate Keeper.** Female figure (green shirt, black skirt) with red flag	**£30-35**
4f	1934-40	**Porter with Luggage.** Dark blue uniform, carrying case and hat-box (various shades seen)	**£30-35**
5	1934-40	**Railway Passengers Set**	See 'Gift Sets' section
5a	1934-40	**Woman and Child.** Green or brown (various shades). Single hollow casting	**£30-35**
5b	1934-40	**Businessman.** Grey or brown (shades), with briefcase	**£30-35**
5c	1934-40	**Male Tourist.** Brown (various shades), with walking stick and camera	**£30-35**
5d	1934-40	**Clergyman.** Black garb, with umbrella (usually red and grey)	**£30-35**
5e	1934-40	**Newsboy.** Grey or brown (various shades known), papers under left arm	**£30-35**
5f	1934-40	**Woman with Tennis Racket.** Green, grey or beige (various shades), tennis racket in right hand	**£30-35**
6	1934-40	**Shepherd Set**	See 'Gift Sets' section
6a	1934-40	**Shepherd.** Light brown (various shades), with crook in right hand and lamb under left arm	**£30-35**
6b	1934-40	**Sheepdog.** Black, with or without white detail	**£30-35**
10	1934-40	**Assorted Figures Set.** Consists of Sets 1, 2 and 4. Box has two illustrations	**£250-350**
	1938-40	The same set but in box with no illustration	**£220-270**
40	1953-59	**Traffic Signs 'Town' Set**	See 'Gift Sets' section
41	1953-59	**Traffic Signs 'Route' Set**	See 'Gift Sets' section
49	1935-40	**Set of Fuel Pumps**	See 'Gift Sets' section
49	1949-50	**Set of Fuel Pumps**	See 'Gift Sets' section
49a	1935-40	**Pillar type Fuel Pump.** Blue, green, yellow, red, cream, gold or white. White rubber hose, wire crank handle, scale 1:43, 60mm.	**£75-100**
	1948-53	Reissue of pre-war version (sold without the hose between 1948-50)	**£30-35**
49b	1935-40	**'SHELL' Mobile Oil Pump.** Blue, green, yellow, red, cream, gold or white. White rubber hose, 1:43, 47mm.	**£75-100**
	1948-50	Reissue of pre-war version (but sold without hose)	**£30-35**
49c	1935-40	**Double Output Fuel Pump.** Blue, green, yellow, red, cream, gold or white. Two white rubber hoses, scale 1:43, 55mm. high	**£75-100**
	1948-52	Reissue of pre-war version (without hoses 1948-50)	**£30-35**
49D	1954-59	**Pump Island, 'ESSO'.** Two pumps (red/white and blue/white), 'ESSO' sign. Yellow box. Renumbered in 1959 as 592	**£80-100**
502	1959-66	**Garage.** Yellow/grey, sky-blue/grey or all light grey, plastic, with parking numbers '0' to '9'. Yellow box	**£100-120**
590	1959-68	**Traffic Signs 'Town' Set**	See 'Gift Sets' section
591	1959-68	**Traffic Signs 'Route' Set**	See 'Gift Sets' section
592	1959-63	**Pump Island, 'ESSO'.** (49-D) Two pumps (red/white and blue/white), 'ESSO' sign, 1:43. 'DINKY TOYS 592-49D' on box	**£65-75**
592	1969-71	**Traffic Signs 'Town' Set**	See 'Gift Sets' section
593	1969-71	**Traffic Signs 'Route' Set**	See 'Gift Sets' section
594	1969-71	**Traffic Lights (3-colour).** Battery operated grey/black plastic traffic lights, 1:43. Yellow box	**£65-75**

TRAFFIC SIGNS. Since the messages given on road signs are often more graphical than textual, the list that follows contains literal interpretations that reflect the general meaning of the signs rather than attempting accurate translations. **Traffic Signs** 595a to 595w were not available for purchase, they were included free in the box of the model mentioned. Scale 1:43.

Ref	Year(s)	Model name and details	Market Price Range
595a	1969-72	**'Danger of Falling Rocks',** (with model 564 Caravan)	NPP
595b	1969-72	**'Maximum Weight 5.5 tonnes',** (823 GMC Tanker)	NPP
595c	1969-72	**'Dangerous Bend to Right',** (with 1417 Matra F1)	NPP
595d	1969-72	**'No Overtaking for Heavy Vehicles',** (572 Berliet Truck)	NPP
595e	1969-72	**'Road Narrows',** (with model 1422 Ferrari F1)	NPP
595f	1969-72	**'Speed Limit',** (with model 1421 Opel GT)	NPP
595g	1969-72	**'Caution - Animals Crossing',** (1419 Ford Thunderbird)	NPP
595h	1969-72	**'Danger - End of Quay',** (with 1424 Renault R12)	NPP
595i	1969-72	**'Two-Way Traffic',** (with model 1423 Peugeot 504)	NPP
595k	1969-72	**'Road Narrows from Left',** (model 1425 Matra 630)	NPP
595L	1969-72	**'Maximum Width 2 metres',** (882 Peugeot 'Pinder')	NPP
595m	1970-72	**'Danger - Loose Chippings',** (with 1426 Alfa-Romeo)	NPP
595n	1970-72	**'Cycling Prohibited',** (with 1429 Peugeot 'Police')	NPP
595o	1970-72	**'Customs',** (with model 1420 Opel Commodore)	NPP
595p	1970-72	**'Humpback Bridge',** (with model 1428 Peugeot 304)	NPP
595q	1970-72	**'Automatic Level Crossing',** (with 809 GMC Truck)	NPP
595r	1970-72	**'Road Works',** (with model 518 Renault 'Autoroutes')	NPP
595s	1970-72	**'Pedestrians Prohibited',** (570 Peugeot 'Autoroutes')	NPP
595t	1970-72	**'Max. Height 3.5 metres',** (589 Berliet 'Autoroutes')	NPP
595u	1970-72	**'Dangerous Bends',** (with model 1430 Abarth)	NPP
595v	1970-72	**'All Vehicles Prohibited',** (with 1432 Ferrari 312P)	NPP
595w	1970-72	**'Danger - Cyclists',** (with model 1409 Chrysler 180)	NPP
833	1962-	**Transformer.** Grey plastic 'ALSTHOM' transformer (as supplied with 898), scale 1:55. In yellow box	**£30-50**
834	1963-70	**Mobile Bridge Pack.** Khaki plastic six part bridge plus inflatable boats (as with 884)	**£20-30**
835	1959-71	**Tyre Pack.** Twelve large black treaded tyres for racing cars and commercial vehicles (smooth till 1961). Was 6676	**£5-10**
836	1959-71	**Tyre Pack.** Twelve white treaded tyres (smooth till 1960). Previously 6677	**£5-10**
837	1959-71	**Tyre Pack.** Twelve black smooth tyres (small). Previously 7067	**£5-10**
837	1961-71	**Tyre Pack.** Twelve black treaded tyres (small)	**£5-10**
837	1965-71	**Tyre Pack.** 12 black nylon tyres (small). French versions often marked 'DUNLOP', Spanish usually 'PIRELLI'	**£5-10**
838	1961-71	**Tyre Pack.** Twelve white tyres (small). Was 7068. 'DUNLOP' or 'PIRELLI' markings not seen	**£5-10**

839	1959-63	**Tyre Pack**. Twelve tyres, round or square section (treaded version of 11190). Sold in paper (later, plastic) packet ..**£10-15**
839	1971-71	**Rally Pack**. Two sheets of rally transfers, scales 1:32 and 1:24 ....**£15-20**
840	1959-70	**Elastic Cord Pack**. Pack of 6 (later 10) elastic cords for 32D and 899 Delahaye Fire Escape. Was 11146 ....**£5-10**
841	1959-71	**Tank Tracks Pack**. Twelve black rubber tracks for AMX tanks. Was 11924.......................................**£10-15**
842	1959-64	**Tyre Pack**. Twelve tyres for 24-L Vespa. Was 12110 .....**£10-15**
843	1962-71	**Military Tyre Pack**. Twelve treaded black tyres (large square section for 818 and similar) **£10-15**
844	1959-70	**Pipe-Line Pack**. Six black tubes (as with 893 Sahara Pipe Transporter)..**£15-20**
845	1959-70	**Barrier Pack**. Ten grey plastic barriers (Vauban-Samia), scale 1:43 ....**£15-20**
846	1959-70	**Oil Drum Pack**. Ten grey plastic oil drums...................**£15-20**
847	1959-70	**Barrel Pack**. Ten brown plastic barrels.........................**£15-20**
848	1959-70	**Trunk Pack**. Ten brown plastic travelling trunks with hinged lids...**£15-20**
849	1959-70	**Packing Case Pack**. Ten ivory plastic packing cases with lifting lids, in plastic 'Bobigny' bag **£15-20**
850	1959-70	**Bottle Crate Pack**. Ten white or cream plastic crates with transparent or orange bottles...........................**£20-25**
851	1959-70	**Assortment Pack**. Contains ten items - two each of 846 (barrels), 847 (barrels), 848 (trunks), 849 (packing cases) and 850 (bottle crates)..................**£20-25**
852	1962-71	**Half-Track Tracks Pack**. Ten replacement tracks for 822 White M3 Half-Track, (black rubber)....................**£10-15**
853	1962-64	**Tyre Pack**. Twelve extra large black tyres for use on 803 Unic and 888 Berliet.....................................**£10-15**
854	1962-68	**Milk Crates Pack**. Ten grey plastic milk crates with white bottles, as with 586 Citroën P55 Milk Lorry **£20-25**
855	1962-65	**Tyre Pack**. Twelve small black rubber treaded tyres for use on Renault R4, etc..**£10-15**
855	1965-70	**Tyre Pack**. As previous, but made of black nylon **£10-15**
856	1963-71	**Machine Gun**. Black plastic (822 White Half-Track) **£10-15**

857	1970-71	**Racing Tyre Pack**. Two small tyres for use on the front wheels of Formula 1 racing cars **£10-15**
858	1970-71	**Racing Tyre Pack**. Two larger tyres for F1 rear wheels.**£10-15**
859	1970-70	**Tyre Pack**. Four tyres for use on 1419 Ford **£10-15**
860	1963-?	**Battery**. 1.5 volt battery for use with 276L......................**£5-10**
861	1964-?	**Lamp Bulb**. 1.5 volt bulb for use with 887 BP Tanker **£5-10**
862	1965-?	**Lamp Bulb**. 1.5 volt bulb for use with 566 Citroën **£5-10**
863	1964-?	**Battery**. Mazda battery for use with 887 then 952L........**£5-10**
864	1968-?	**Lamp Bulb**. Bulb for use with 276L, 160L and 952L......**£5-10**
6676	1950-59	**Tyre Pack**. Twelve large black smooth or treaded tyres (racing cars, articulated commercials). With letter 'M' on sidewall till 1958. (Renumbered in 1959 as 835)......**£10-15**
6677	1950-59	**Tyre Pack**. Twelve large white treaded tyres (some smooth). 'M' on sidewall till 1958, renumbered 836 in 1959 ....**£10-15**
7067	1950-59	**Tyre Pack**. Twelve smooth black tyres (small) for touring cars 25-BV, 25-CG, 25-D, 29-D and 80-BP. 'M' on sidewall till 1958, renumbered 837 in 1959 ....**£10-15**
7068	1953-59	**Tyre Pack**. Twelve smooth white tyres (small). letter 'M' on sidewall till 1958. (Renumbered in 1959 as 837)......**£10-15**
11146	1958-59	**Elastic Cord Pack**. Six elastic cords for 32-D and 899 Delahaye Fire Escape. (Renumbered in 1959 as 840)......**£5-10**
11190	1953-59	**Tyre Pack**. Twelve large black ribbed tyres originally for racing cars. Design was changed in 1958 to make them suitable for use with military vehicles. Paper packets marked either 'Racing Tyres' or 'Cross Country Tyres'. (Renumbered in 1959 as 839) **£10-15**
11924	1958-59	**Tank Tracks Pack**. Twelve black rubber tracks for AMX Tanks. Renumbered 841 in 1959....................**£10-15**
12110	1959-59	**Tyre Pack**. Twelve tyres for 24-L Vespa. Renumbered 842 in 1959 ....**£10-15**
---	1935-40	**Milk Churn (large)**. 2 fixing holes in base, scale 1:43 ..**£30-40**
---	1948-50	**Milk Churn**. Smaller churn, scale 1:43, as supplied with 25-O Studebaker and Ford 'NESTLE' Trucks.......**£30-40**
---	1969-?	**Driving Test Circuit**. Printed road layout with town and country elements, 1:43, boxed **£25-40**

French Dinky Toys Accessories shown in the 1962 Catalogue

Photograph: Swapmeet Publications

Gift Sets

Ref	Year(s)	Model name	Contents,, details	Market Price Range
1	1934-40	**Station Staff Set**	Six figures: 1 x 1a Station Master, 2 x 1b Porter (no luggage), 1 x 1c Guard, 1 x 1d Policeman, 1 x 1e Inspector. Two pictures on lid of card box	£250-300
1	1938-40	**Station Staff Set**	Same set but in box with no illustration	£225-275
2	1934-40	**Railway Passengers Set**	Contains a tinplate bench (2g) and six figures: 2a Normandy Farmer, 2b Farmer's Wife, 2c Young Girl, 2d Boy Scout (with stick), 2e Boy (sitting), 2f Girl (sitting). Red box has illustrations, yellow inner	£225-275
	1938-40		Same set but in red box (yellow inner) with no illustration	£200-250
3	1934-40	**Animals Set**	Contains six animals: 3a Pig, 3b Sheep (dark brown), 3c Horse (grey), 3c Horse (brown), 3d Bull (mottled White), 3d Bull (mottled reddish-brown). Box has two pictures on lid	£300-350
	1938-40		Same set but in box with no illustrations	£250-300
4	1934-40	**Railway Personnel Set**	Six figures: 4a Cook (with fowl), 4b Engine Fireman, 4c Greaser (with oilcan), 4d Wheel Tapper (with mallet), 4e Female Gate-Keeper (with flag), 4f Porter (with luggage). Box has two illustrations	£225-275
	1938-40		The same set but in box without illustration	£175-225
5	1934-40	**Railway Passengers Set**	Contains six figures: 5a Woman and Child, 5b Businessman, 5c Male Tourist (with camera), 5d Clergyman, 5e Newsboy, 5f Female Tennis Player. Two different pictures on box	£225-275
	1938-40		Same set but in box without illustration	£175-225
6	1934-40	**Shepherd Set**	6a Shepherd (light brown), 6b Sheepdog (black), 4 x 3b Sheep (white or cream). Box has two illustrations	£400-500
	1938-40		Same set but box has no illustration	£300-400
10	1934-40	**Assorted Figures Set**	Consists of Sets 1, 2 and 4. Box has two illustrations	£250-350
	1938-40		The same set but in box with no illustration	£220-270
17	1935-38	**Electric Goods Train**	19a Electric Locomotive, 21b Timber Wagon, 21c Coal Wagon, 21d Crane Wagon. Diorama box	£250-300
	1938-40		As previous model, but box has no diorama.	£175-225
18	1934-38	**Steam Goods Train**	21a Steam Tank Locomotive, 3 x 21c Coal Wagon, Diorama box	£250-300
	1938-40		As previous model, but box has no diorama.	£175-225
19	1935-38	**Electric Passenger Train**	19a Electric Locomotive, 3 x 20a Coach. Diorama box	£250-300
20	1935-38	**Steam Passenger Train**	21a Steam Tank Locomotive, 3 x 20a Coach. Diorama box	£250-300
	1938-40		As previous model, but box has no diorama.	£175-225
21	1934-38	**Steam Mixed Goods Train**	21a Tank Locomotive, 21b Timber Wagon, 21c Coal Wagon, 21d Crane Wagon. Diorama box	£350-450
	1938-40		As previous model, but box has no diorama.	£225-275
24	1935-36	**Passenger Cars Set**	6 cars: 24b Limousine, 24d Vogue Saloon, 24e Aerodynamic Saloon, 24f Sportsman's Coupé, 24g 4-seat Sports Car, 24h 2-seat Sports Car. Yellow box without illustration	£6,000-9,000
	note:		The basic box for this set was adapted to contain the 25 series Commercial Vehicles Set.	
	1936-39		6 cars: 24b Limousine, 24d Vogue Saloon, 24e Aerodynamic Saloon, 24f Sportsman's Coupé, 24g 4-seat Sports Car, 24h 2-seat Sports Car. Purple box with picture (two different designs exist)	£4,000-6,000
	1940-48		The same set, but in Blue box without illustration	£3,000-4,000
24-55	1955-55	**Touring Cars Gift Set**	5 cars: 24-R Peugeot 203, 24-T Citroën 2cv, 24-U Simca Aronde 9, 24-V Buick Roadmaster, 24-X Ford Vedette	£1,500-2,000
24-56	1956-56	**Touring Cars Gift Set**	5 cars: 24-R Peugeot 203, 24-T Citroën 2cv, 24-U Simca Aronde Elysée, 24-Y Studebaker Commander, 24-Z Simca Vedette Versailles	£1.500-2,000
24-57	1957-57	**Touring Cars Gift Set**	5 cars: 24-A Chrysler New Yorker, 24-B Peugeot 403 8cv, 24-E Renault Dauphine, 24-Y Studebaker Commander, 24-Z Simca Vedette Versailles	£1,500-2,000
24-58	1958-58	**Touring Cars Gift Set**	5 cars: 24-B Peugeot 403 8cv, 24-C (or 24-CP) Citroën DS19, 24-D Plymouth Belvedere, 24-E Renault Dauphine, 24-Z Simca Vedette Versailles. Red/yellow/green/black box	£1,500-2,000
	note:		The annual '24 series' of Gift Sets was renumbered in 1959 ; the next issue in the series is 500.	
25	1935-37	**Commercial Vehicles Gift Set**	6 lorries: 25a Open Lorry, 25b Covered Lorry, 25c Flat Lorry, 25d Tanker Lorry, 25e Tipping Lorry, 25f Market Gardeners Lorry. Purple and gold box.	£2,000-2,500
	note:		The basic box for this set was adapted from that used for the 24 series Passenger Cars Set.	
	1938-39		The same set, but in a long Blue box.	£1,500-2,000
	1940-48		Same set, but all wheels are solid metal. Long blue box with printed ends (yellow base, blue inner).	£1,500-2,000
25S	1948-48	**Commercial Vehicles Gift Set**	The same set, all models having solid metal wheels, and in a Light blue box.	£2,500-3,500
25N	1949-49	**Commercial Vehicles Gift Set**	6 lorries: 25-H Ford Beverage Truck, 25-I Ford Open Wagon, 25-J Ford Covered Wagon, 25-K Studebaker Market Gardeners Truck, 25-L Studebaker Covered Delivery Truck, 25-M Studebaker Tipping Truck. Blue or yellow box.	£3,500-5,000
	1950-50		The same set, but in a Red box.	£3,500-5,000
40	1953-59	**Traffic Signs 'Town' Set** (renumbered in 1959 as 590)	Six diecast signs: 'No Entry', 'No Waiting', '30km/hr', 'No Overtaking', 'Maximum Weight 5.5 tonnes', 'Right (or Left) Turn'. Scale 1:43, each 55mm. high, yellow box with 'Code de la Route' leaflet	£65-75
41	1953-59	**Traffic Signs 'Route' Set** (renumbered in 1959 as 591)	Six diecast signs: 'Danger - Crossroads', 'Priority' marker, 'Dangerous Bends', 'Caution - School', 'Level Crossing with Gates'. Small signs 37mm. high; large signs 52mm., scale 1:43,. Yellow box, leaflet..	£65-75
49	1935-40	**Set of Fuel Pumps**	Five pumps: 2 x 49a Pillar type Fuel Pump, 1 x 49b Mobile Oil Pump, 2 x 49c Double Output Pump. Blue box, later yellow	£400-500
49	1949-50	**Set of Fuel Pumps**	Identical to pre-war version and in yellow box	£300-400
50	1938-40	**British Naval Warships Set**	14 English-made models in French printed box: 50a 'Hood', 50b 'Nelson', 50b 'Rodney', 50c 'Effingham', 50d 'York', 50e 'Delhi', 3 x 50f 'Broke', 50g 'X' class Submarine, 3 x 50h 'Amazon', 50k 'K' class Submarine	£200-300
60	1935-37	**Aircraft Presentation Set**	6 models: 60a DeWoitine D338 Rainbow, 60b Potez 58, 60c Henriot H180T, 60d Breguet Corsaire, 60e DeWoitine 500 Hunter, 60f Cierva Autogiro. Purple and gold box (models are set out in a straight formation along the length of the box). Picture on lid	£1,500-1,750
	1937-39		The same 6 models but set out in a diagonal formation within a bright blue box. Picture on box lid	£1,500-1,750
	1939-40		The same 6 models but set out in a diagonal formation within a Dark Green box. Picture on box lid	£1,500-1,750
	1957-59	(renumbered in 1959 as 501)	4 models: 60-A Dassault Mystere IVa, 60-B Sud Aviation Vautour, 60-D Sikorsky S58, 60-E Vickers Viscount. Supertoys box, picture on lid	£300-400

61	1938-39	**Aircraft Presentation Set**	5 models: 61a DeWoitine D338, 61b Potez 56, 61d Potez 58, 61e Henriot H180M, 61f DeWoitine 500 Hunter. Blue box.............................**£900-1,400**
	1939-46		6 models: 61a DeWoitine D338, 61b Potez 56, 61c Farman F360, 61d Potez 58, 61e Henriot H180M, 61f DeWoitine 500. Green box **£750-1,250**
64	1939-48	**Aircraft Presentation Set**	Five models: 61a DeWoitine D338, 64a Amiot 370, 64b Bloch 220, 64c Potez 63, 64d Potez 662. Green box with illustration...................**£750-1,250**
70	1939?	**Modern Travel Set** .... **('Locomotion Moderne')**	Five different forms of travel represented by: 23b Racing Car, 26 Railcar, 52c Steamship 'Normandie', 53a Steamship 'Dunkerque', 60a DeWoitine Rainbow. Advertised in 1939(?) catalogue but no production known...**NPP**
101	1936	**Dining Room Furniture Set**	101a Table, 101b Sideboard, 2 x 101c Carver, 4 x 101d Dining Chair. Light or dark mottled brown........**£300-350**
102	1936-40	**Bedroom Furniture Set**	102a Bed, 102b Wardrobe, 102c Dressing Table, 102d Chest of Drawers, 102e Stool, 102f Chair. Lilac...**£300-350**
103	1936-40	**Kitchen Furniture Set**	103a Refrigerator, 103b Sideboard, 103c Cooker, 103d Table, 103e Chair. Pale Green/Cream or Blue/Ivory.**£300-350**
104	1937-40	**Bathroom Furniture Set**............	104a Bath, 104b Bath Mat, 104c Hand Basin, 104d Stool, 104e Linen Basket, 104f Toilet. Pink veined...**£300-350**
500	1959-59	**Touring Cars Gift Set**	5 models: 521 Peugeot 403 8cv, 522 Citroën DS19, 523 Plymouth Belvedere, 524 Renault Dauphine, 541 Simca Vedette Versailles **£2,000-3,000**
501	1959-62	**Aircraft Presentation Set** .... (renumbered from 60)	4 models: 800 Dassault Mystere IVa, 801 Sud Aviation Vautour, 802 Sikorsky S58, 803 Vickers Viscount **£300-400**
503	1963-64	**Touring Cars Gift Set**	5 models: 521 Peugeot 403 8cv, 522 Citroën DS19, 543 Renault Floride, 544 Simca Aronde P60, 545 DeSoto Diplomat. Blue/yellow/grey box...........................**£2,000-3,000**
536	1965	**Peugeot 404 and Trailer**	Red car, black skis on yellow rack or yellow skis on black rack, cream plastic trailer (no. 812), luggage .**£175-200**
590	1959-68	**Traffic Signs 'Town' Set**	(Was 40). Six diecast signs (1:43, 55mm. high): 'No Entry', 'No Parking', 'Maximum Weight 5.5 tonnes', 'Right (or Left) Turn', '30km/hr', 'No Overtaking'. Yellow box with 'Code de la Route' leaflet **£70-80**
591	1959-68	**Traffic Signs 'Route' Set**	(Was 41). Six diecast signs: 'Danger - Crossroads', 'Priority' marker, 'Dangerous Bends', 'Caution - School', 'Level Crossing with Gates'. Small signs 37mm. high, large signs 52mm. Scale 1:43. Yellow box, leaflet...**£70-80**
592	1969-71	**Traffic Signs 'Town' Set**	Twelve plastic signs on diecast bases: 'Caution - Gyratory System', 'No Entry', 'Parking', 'No Parking', 'Caution - School', 'No U-Turn', 'Taxis', '45km/hr', 'No Overtaking', 'Do Not Use Horn', 'Blue Zone', 'No Left Turn'. Scale 1:43. In 'window' box **£100-125**
593	1969-71	**Traffic Signs 'Route' Set**	Twelve plastic signs on diecast bases: 'Autoroute', 'End of Autoroute', 'Autoroute Toll Point', 'End of Speed Limit', 'Crossroads - Give Way', 'Dangerous Crossing', 'Priority' marker, 'Stop', 'Dangerous Bend', 'Caution', 'Gradient 10%', 'Low Flying Aircraft'. 1:43. In 'window' box...................**£100-125**
1460	1969-70	**Touring Cars Gift Set**	6 models: 501 Citroën DS19 'POLICE' Car, 507 Simca 1500GLS Estate, 508 Daf 33, 509 Fiat 850, 513 Opel Admiral, 514 Alfa-Romeo 1600. Blue/yellow box...........................**£2,500-3,500**
1462	1969-69	**'Three Days' Gift Set**	4 models: 507 Simca 1500GLS Estate, 508 Daf 33, 509 Fiat 850, 514 Alfa-Romeo 1600. Sold in a special 'Sac-cadeau'(plastic Gift-Bag)...**£600-800**
	note:		'Galeries Lafayette' is a Paris department store with branches in several French towns. Annually '3J' sales are held in these shops. Selection 1462 was specially made for the 1969 'Trois Jours' ('Three Days') sale.

French
Dinky Toys

No.25
Commercial Vehicles
Set

Photograph:
Collectoys, France

Catalogues and Magazines

Note that some post-war catalogues have '57B.16273' or '60B.3844' printed at the bottom of the back cover or in some inconspicuous corner. These are not catalogue reference numbers but a form of 'registered design' for publicity material. As they have no other meaning to collectors they are therefore not shown in the following list. French Dinky Toys are also mentioned in catalogues from other countries, notably Spain and Holland. We are in need of details of Meccano advertising in other countries and would welcome any help our readers could provide.

Ref	Year(s)	Publication	Contents, features, details	Market Price Range
---	1949	**Catalogue**	Sepia cover, 'Nouveauties Dinky Toys'	£50-60
---	1950	**Catalogue** (12 page booklet)	Blue on white cover shows 'Dinky Toys Miniatures' issuing from Meccano factory through arched gateway. 'Meccano 78-80 Rue Rébéval Paris (XIX)' on back cover. No price list	£50-60
---	1951	**Catalogue**	Green / sepia, 'Miniatures Dinky Toys' in black	£60-70
175-5-52	1952	**Catalogue** (10 page booklet)	Glossy pages fold out to twice the size of the cover. Cream cover with green and red printing. Black and white photographic illustrations, no prices, 'Imp. HENON PARIS' on last page	£60-70
---	1953	**Catalogue** (20 page booklet)	Pale grey stylized car of the period and trees on cover overprinted with 'Miniatures Dinky Toys' and 'C'est une fabrication Meccano' in red. Black and white inside illustrations; no price list	£40-50
---	1954	**Catalogue** (20 pages)	Cover simulates a Supertoys box with the famous blue/white stripes and shows Buick Roadmaster, Esso Tanker and Citroën 'H' van. Pictures inside are in black and white. No prices	£40-50
---	1954	**Leaflet**	Various, advertising new issues	£10-15
---	1955	**Catalogue** (16 page booklet)	No price list. Blue/white stripes on cover, plus Marrel truck and 32-D Delahaye fire appliance	£40-50
---	1956	**Catalogue** (April, 16 pages)	Colour printing inside, no prices. 'Supertoys look' covers with Berliet Container Truck, Autocar Chausson and Citroën car on front with Willème Log Lorry and rear view of 32-D on back cover	£40-50
---	1956	**Catalogue** (September, 20 pages)	Similar to April catalogue but cover has Log Lorry, Citroën car and Dassault plane. No price list	£40-50
---	1957	**Summer Catalogue** (16 pages)	Driverless vehicles emerging from tunnel on front cover. Printed in France	£40-50
---	1958	**Summer Catalogue** (16 pages)	Maserati and Merceds on front cover. Two to five models per page (drawn). Printed in France	£40-50
DL 1958/3	1958	**Meccano Catalogue** (32 pages)	The colourful cover shows a boy's face, an electric train at speed on a blue/gold Meccano track and three Dinky Toys. 8 pages of Dinky Toys. September price list enclosed. Printed in France	£40-50
---	1959	**Catalogue** (20 pages)	Colour booklet like 1958 issue. Cover shows Simca and lorry at an Esso station. No price list	£40-50
---	1960	**Catalogue** (24 page booklet)	Full colour with Renault Floride and Panhard on the cover. Printed at Mulhouse in France	£40-50
---	1961	**Catalogue** (20 pages)	Full colour booklet printed in Belgium. Pictures of real vehicles plus parts of a road map of France with various Dinky Toys on it. No price list	£30-40
---	1962	**Catalogue**	Includes mention of Hornby boats and Hornby Acho trains	£30-40
---	1962	**Catalogue** (24 pages)	Cover shows Renault R4 parked on quayside next to Steamship 'France'. Printed in Belgium	£30-40
---	1963	**Catalogue** (32 pages)	'First half' catalogue. Cover shows Dinky Mercedes against photo of the actual car. February price list (on very pale green pages) stapled in. Printed in England	£30-40
---	1963	**Catalogue** (32 pages)	'Second half' catalogue (cover as 'first half'). Includes price list dated 'Juillet 1963' in centre	£30-40
---	1964	**Catalogue** (16 pages)	Full colour pages with April price list (on orange paper) stapled in. Five new models pictured and described on the cover which also has photo of car showroom interior. Printed in England	£25-35
---	1964	**Catalogue** (16 pages)	Booklet with October price list	£25-35
---	1965	**Catalogue** (20 pages)	Full colour 'first half' catalogue. Front cover shows 128L Mercedes and 537 Renault. April price list (1965/1, orange paper) stapled in. Printed in England	£25-35
---	1965	**Catalogue** (Winter 1965-66)	28 pages; includes October price list 1965/2 on red paper. Cover depicts 889 Autobuses and 510 Peugeot. The only photo within is of an actual AMX Bridge-Layer in action. Printed in England	£25-35
---	1966	**Catalogue**	'First half' catalogue	£25-35
---	1966	**'Second half' Catalogue**	(122 pages). Simca and Opel on the cover. September price list on blue paper. Printed in England	£25-35
---	1967	**'First half' Catalogue**		£25-35
---	1967	**Catalogue** (128 pages)	Porsche Carrera on cover. September price list (on pink paper) fixed in at rear. Lady Penelope's 'FAB 1' shown as newly introduced. Printed in England. '2e édition' printed inside back cover	£25-35
---	1968	**'First half' Catalogue** (130 pages)	With February price list	£25-35
---	1968	**'Second half' Catalogue**	(122 pages). Simca and fast-cornering Opel on the cover. Printed in England	£15-20
---	1969	**'First half' Catalogue** (24 pages)	Front cover shows hard-braking Ford Thunderbird avoiding errant daschund, yellow Opel GT in foreground. Rear cover advertises 'free' Traffic Signs. Printed in England	£25-35
---	1969	**'Second half' Catalogue**		£20-30
91.761	1970	**Catalogue** (24 pages)	'1970.1' printed on cover which also shows a Porsche and a Ferrari 312P racing round a banking which has 'La Marque du Connaisseur' on it in yellow. Printed in England	£20-30
91.762	1970	**Catalogue**	As previous catalogue but with '1970.2' on front cover. Printed in England	£20-30
91.786	1971	**Catalogue** (24 pages)	Cover depicts a Citroën Présidentielle and a Renault R12. Printed in England	£20-30
91.780	1971	**Meccano Tri-ang leaflet**	(full colour). Nearly A4 size; one side depicts 1971 Dinky Toys. 'Gyro-Jets' and 'Spirofoil' on reverse	£6-10
---	1976	**Meccano Catalogue** (108 pages).	Only 10 pages of Dinky Toys (English and French). Brown cover	£25-35

MAGAZINES

Ref	Year(s)	Publication		Market Price Range
---	1924-38	**Meccano Magazine**	Published monthly from 1924 to 1938, large format	£5-10
---	1953-57	**Meccano Magazine**	Published monthly from October 1953 to October 1957, small format	£5-10
---	1957-59	**Meccano Magazine**	Published monthly from November 1957 to September 1959, large format	£5-10
---	1959-60	**'Actualités Meccano' Journal**	Published between October 1959 to October 1960 (5 issues), each	£5-10

Promotional Material

1957-	**Membership Certificate**. 'Parchment' style 'CLUB DINKY TOYS' certificate	£45-55
1960-	**Membership Certificate**. As above, but amended	£45-55
1960-	**Subscription Reminder**. Reminder form	£10-20
1961-	**Subscription Reminder**. As above, but updated	£10-20
1957-	**Membership Document**. Printed details of Club membership	£10-20
1954-	**Dinky Toys Driver's Licence**	£35-45
1957-	**Button Insignia**. A round metal badge, 'CLUB DINKY TOYS', screw fitting through button-hole	£35-45
1957-	**Brooch Insignia**. As above, but with 'safety pin' lapel fitting	£35-45
1957-	**Key Ring**. Round metal badge within stitched 'leather' surround	£35-45

1957-	**Key Ring**. Round metal badge encapsulated in clear plastic	£35-45
	Display Case. A small display case (no other details)	£150-250
1961-	**ESGE Display Case**. A larger display case (cream/yellow/red) with 5 shelves, 'DINKY-TOYS MECCANO' on glazing	£400-500
	Illuminated Display Case. Large display case with 6 shelves and electric lighting	£450-600
	Illuminated Curved Case. Large curved display case with 6 shelves and electric lighting	£450-600
	Counter Sign. Diecast triangular block painted red/cream, 'DINKY TOYS'	£75-100

English Dinky Toys imported into France

The models in the following list were those manufactured in Liverpool and sent to France for sale over different periods of time. In the main they were complete English made models but some were supplied in component form for assembly in the French factory.

It is understood that the boxes were either made in England and printed "Fabriqué en Angleterre" and "Imprimé en Angleterre", or were made in France and printed "Fabriqué en Angleterre" and "Imprimé en France". In some cases the model and the box were sold just as they came from Binns Road with no modification or overprinting of any kind. It is therefore important when seeking variations to make sure whether the model was only imported fully built, imported as plain castings for assembly in France, or both (at different times). They were also on occasions supplied complete except for the baseplate which was fitted in France. The degree of painting often varied, some items being supplied fully finished while others were still "raw" from the dies.

Some models were supplied with English tyres, some without, so that French tyres could be fitted. Body colours were much the same as the UK versions though could be different shades, unique colours or a different range of colours. The 60h Singapore Flying Boat was for instance painted in a camouflage finish for the French market, and 108L Sam's Car was only available in silver or blue in France. Some renumbering also took place when models previously assembled in France (imported only as components) were later imported ready made. A couple of examples of this practice are 150/551 and 885/961. Virtually every post-war import from England carries the suffix 'L' after its reference number to indicate its Liverpool origin.

Note also that from time to time various factory items were exchanged between Liverpool and Bobigny (this included equipment components and complete or partial dies and tools). This was done either to make up an end of run deficiency, to replace worn or broken dies, to experiment with prototypes or simply to evaluate a new idea. Consequently there may well be oddities still to be found which do not conform to the known output. If you have knowledge of any item or variation not listed, do please communicate it to the Editor so that we may share the information with others in the collecting fraternity. Thank you.

The prices you should expect to see asked for these essentially English productions are likely to be much the same as for the same items sold in British shops or auction houses.

French ref.no.	Years imported	Model
14-C	1950-51	Coventry Climax Fork Lift Truck
23c	1938-39	Mercedes Racing Car
23d	1938-39	Auto-Union Record Car
23e	1938-39	'Speed of the Wind'
23m	1938-39	'Thunderbolt'
25h	1938-39	Streamlined Fire Engine
27-AC	1950-50	Tractor and Manure Spreader
29b	1939-39	Streamlined Bus
30a	1935-39	Chrysler Airflow
30b	1935-37	Rolls-Royce
30g	1938-39	Camping Trailer
50	1937-38	Battleship Gift Set
51b	1937-39	Norddeutscher-Lloyd 'Europa'
51c	1937-39	Italia Line 'Rex'
51d	1937-39	'Empress of Britain'
52a	1936-39	'Queen Mary'
60h	1938-38	Singapore Flying Boat (camouflaged)
60m	1938-39	Singapore Flying Boat (civilian)
60r	1938-39	'Empire' Flying Boat
60w	1938-39	'Clipper III' Flying Boat
62k	1938-39	'King's Aeroplane'
62n	1939-39	Junkers 'Ju90'
62p	1939-39	'Ensign' Air Liner
63	1939-39	Mayo Composite
100L	1968-71	Lady Penelope's 'FAB 1'
101L	1968-69	Thunderbirds II / IV
104L	1969-71	Spectrum Pursuit
106L	1969-70	'The Prisoner' Moke
108L	1970-71	Sam's Car
110L	1965-68	Aston-Martin DB5
114L	1964-66	Triumph Spitfire
116L	1967-71	Volvo P1800
118L	1967-70	Towaway Glider Set
127L	1965-68	R-R Silver Cloud
128L	1965-70	Mercedes 600
129L	1968-68	Volkswagen 1300
131L	1969-71	Jaguar 'E'-type 2+2
132L	1968-71	Ford RV40
142L	1963-67	Jaguar Mark 10
150L	1962-64	R-R Silver Wraith
151a	1938-38	Medium Tank
152a	1938-38	Light Tank
152L	1967-70	R-R Phantom V
153L	1968-70	Aston-Martin DB6
155L	1962-65	Ford Anglia
160L	1968-71	Mercedes-Benz 250
161	1939-40	Mobile A-A Gun
161L	1967-71	Ford Mustang
162	1939-40	Light Dragon Tractor
163L	1967-71	Volkswagen 1600TL
165L	1969-70	Ford Capri 1600
172L	1967-71	Fiat 2300 Estate
173L	1969-71	Pontiac Parisienne
174L	1969-70	Ford Mercury Cougar
175L	1969-71	Cadillac Eldorado
176L	1969-71	NSU Ro80
182L	1962-64	Porsche 356a
186L	1962-63	Mercedes-Benz 220
187L	1969-71	De Tomaso Mangusta
188L	1969-71	Jensen FF 542
189L/1	1962-64	Triumph Herald
189L/2	1969-71	Lamborghini Marzal
190L	1971-?	Monteverdi 375L
192L	1971-?	Range Rover
194L	1962-63	Bentley 'S'
195L	1962-65	Jaguar 3.4
198L	1963-66	R-R Phantom V
199L	1962-67	Austin 7 Countryman
200L	1971-?	Matra 630
202L	1971-?	Fiat Abarth 2000
204L	1971-?	Ferrari 312 P
205L	1969-71	Lotus Cortina
208L	1971-?	VW Porsche 914
210L	1971-?	Alfa-Romeo 33 LM
213L	1970-71	Ford Capri 1600 GT
215L	1965-71	Ford GT Le Mans
216L	1968-71	Ferrari Dino
217L	1969-71	Alfa-Romeo Scarabeo
218L	1970-71	Lotus Europa GT
220L	1970-71	Ferrari P5
221L	1970-71	Chevrolet Corvette
223L	1970-71	McLaren Can-Am
224L	1971-?	Mercedes-Benz C111
225L	1971-?	Lotus 49B F1
238L	1971-?	Ferrari 3L F1 (not issued)
240L	1963-70	Cooper Racing Car
241L	1963-70	Lotus Racing Car
242L	1963-70	Ferrari Racing Car
243L	1964-70	BRM Racing Car
252L	1962-64	Bedford Refuse Truck
253L	1962-62	Daimler Ambulance
258L	1962-63	De Soto USA Police
258L	1963-64	Dodge USA Police
258L	1965-66	Cadillac USA Police
258L	1967-68	Ford Fairlane USA Police Car
263L	1963-68	Super Criterion Ambulance
270L	1969-71	Ford Escort Police
276L	1963-69	Airport Fire Tender
300L	1962-70	Massey-Harris Tractor
308L	1971-?	Leyland Tractor
320L	1962-70	Halesowen Trailer
321L	1962-71	Massey-Harris Manure Spreader
324L	1962-64	Hay Rake
340L	1962-67	Land Rover
341L	1962-67	Land Rover Trailer
344L	1971-?	Land Rover Pick-up
351L	1971-?	'SHADO' Interceptor
370L	1970-71	Dragster / Launcher
401L	1962-64	Coventry Climax Fork Lift Truck
437L	1963-71	JCB Hydraulic Shovel
439L	1971-?	Ford Snow Plough
449L	1962-63	El Camino Pick-up
451L	1971-?	Ford D800 Johnston Road Sweeper
475L	1964-68	Ford Model 'T' 1908
476L	1965-69	Morris Oxford 1913
485L	1964-70	Ford Model 'T' 'Father Christmas'
601L	1967-70	Austin Para-Moke
615L	1968-71	Jeep / Field Gun
617L	1969-71	VW KDF / Field Gun
620L	1971-?	Berliet Gazelle with Missile
651L	1962-70	Centurion Tank
661L	1962-63	Recovery Tractor
665L	1965-71	Honest John Carrier
666L	1961-65	Corporal Missile
667L	1962-64	Servicing Platform
676L	1972-?	Scout Car
697L	1962-70	Artillery Set
719L	1970-71	Spitfire
721L	1970-71	Stuka Ju 87b
722L	1970-71	Hawker Harrier
724L	1971-?	Sea Rescue Helicopter
796L	1962-68	Dinghy on Trailer
930L	1961-64	Bedford 'Pallet-Jekta'
936L	1965-68	Leyland Test Chassis
952L	1964-70	Vega Major Coach
958L	1962-65	Guy Snow Plough
960L	1962-69	Albion Cement Mixer
961L	1962-63	Blaw-Knox Bulldozer
962L	1962-64	Muir-Hill Dumper
964L	1962-63	Elevator Loader
965L	1961-64	Euclid Quarry Truck
971L	1962-63	Coles Mobile Crane
972L	1962-69	Coles Lorry Crane
973L	1971-?	Yale Diesel Shovel
974L	1969-71	AEC Hoynor Car Transporter
976L	1969-71	Michigan Shovel Dozer

French Dinky Toys Numerical Index

These Auction Results are provided to support the Market Price Range guidance throughout the Catalogue.

Collectoys
BP 22 - 18001 Bourges Cedex, France

Condition Grading System: Models shown as A. B. C. & D.
Boxes - a. b. c. d. Unboxed o.

CARS
22A Maserati Sports 2000, red, A.b £95
23c Mercedes, Silver/red, A unboxed £480
23d Auto Union, green body/hubs, No. '2', black tyres....................£4,135
24k Peugeot 402, red, D, unboxed....................£80
24M Civilian Jeep, yellow, R unboxed £165
24N Citroën Traction 11 BL, black, yellow hubs, B, unboxed....................£310
24O Studebaker State Commander, metallic blue, D, unboxed....................£205
24R Peugeot 203, grey, C, unboxed....................£80
24R Peugeot 203, beige, no filler cap, small rear window, unboxed......£3,520
24S Simca 8 Sport, black with beige interior, B, unboxed....................£300
24U Simca 9 Aronde, blue, white roof, A, unboxed £295
24Q Ford Vedette, 1949 issue, blue, A, unboxed....................£225
24Q Ford Vedette, 1949 issue, beige, A, unboxed....................£275
24A Chrysler New Yorker, 1955 issue, red, A.b....................£80
24A/520 Chrysler New Yorker, 1955 issue, blue, C. b....................£275
24B Peugeot 403, mid blue, A.b....................£95
24B Peugeot 403, pale yellow, B.c....................£350
24CP Citroën DS 19, yellow ochre, grey roof, A.b....................£760
522 Citroën DS 19, pale yellow (citron), A.b....................£225
24D Plymouth Belvedere, TT pink and pale maroon, A.c....................£450
24D Plymouth Belvedere, TT blue and white, C.a....................£205
24E Renault Dauphine, olive green, A.a....................£205
24E Renault Dauphine, bright blue, A.b....................£615
24E Renault Dauphine, green-grey, A.d....................£135
527 Alfa Romeo 1900 Super Sprint, turquoise, A.a....................£5,175
24L Vespa 400, orange, A.b....................£410
535 Citroën 2cv, TT blue, A.c....................£295
24U Simca 9 Aronde, pale grey, A.c....................£260
24U Simca 9 Aronde, blue, white roof, A....................£295
24V Buick Roadmaster, 2nd issue, yellow/green, A.b....................£1,035
24V Buick Roadmaster, salmon/black, A.a....................£690
24V Buick Roadmaster, ivory/blue, B.b....................£590
24Y Studebaker Commander, ivory/red, A.b....................£380
511 Peugeot 204 Cabriolet, sky blue, A.b....................£180
518A Renault 4l 'AUTOROUTES', orange, A.b....................£260
530 Citroën DS 19, 1964 issue, metallic grey, B, unboxed....................£2,275
542 Simca Ariane 'Taxi', black/red, A.b....................£135
544 Simca Aronde P60, cream/red, A.b....................£5,000
546 Opel Rekord 'Taxi', black, A.b, export R.F.A. issue....................£225
551 Ford Taunus 'Polizei', black/white, A.a....................£330
559 Ford Taunus 17M, yellow, A.c, (Spanish issue)....................£1,800
1402P Ford Galaxie 500 'POLICE', A, unboxed....................£2,070
1404 Citroën ID 19 Break, 'RADIO TELE LUX', A.c....................£520
1414 Renault 8 Gordini, blue, A.a....................£330

GIFT SETS
24-57 Tourism Set
    Models - 24A, 24B, 24E, 24Y, 24Z, A-C, Box c....................£1,900
24-58 Tourism Set
    Models 24B, 24C, 24D, 24E, 24Z, A-B, Box b....................£3,100

COMMERCIALS
14a Triporteur, yellow, D. o....................£140
14a Triporteur, red, D. o....................£140
25a Open Lorry, turquoise, D. o....................£150
25H Ford Beverage Truck, metallic green, B. o....................£420
25H Ford Beverage Truck, turquoise, B. o....................£1,100
25L Ford Open Wagon, cream, A.o....................£2,750
25JB Ford 'SNCF', 1949 1st type cab, TT blue body, A.o....................£1,500
25JB Ford 'SCNF', 1950 2nd type, blue, A.o....................£490
25JB Ford 'SNCF', 1951 4th type, blue, A.o....................£165
25JJ 'CALBERSON', 1st type, yellow/black/red, B.o....................£590
25JV Ford 'GRAND MOULINS DE PARIS', A.o....................£350
25L Studebaker Truck, turquoise, cream back, A.o....................£1,040
25L Studebaker Truck, red, yellow back, A.o....................£1,300
Studebaker Milk Truck, sky blue/white, A.o....................£450

Studebaker Covered Pick Up, green/yellow, A.o....................£860
Studebaker Breakdown Truck, 'DINKY SERVICE', red, A.o....................£650
25U Ford Tanker 'ESSO', 1st type, red, B.o....................£125
25L Ford Refuse Tipper, dark green, B.o....................£95
29d Somua Panhard Paris Bus, green/cream, A.b....................£180
29e Autocar Isobloc, TT green, B.o....................£140
29e Autocar Isobloc, blue/silver, A.o....................£325
29e Autocar Isobloc, red/silver, C.o....................£140
29F Chausson Autocar, red/cream, C.b....................£75
32AB Panhard 'SNCF', 1st type, (loco logo), dark blue, A.o....................£1,035
32AB Panhard 'SNCF' in green letters, A.b....................£150
32AJ Panhard 'KODAK', yellow, red logo, A.o....................£560
25B Peugeot D3A 'LAMPE MAZDA', A.b....................£150
25BV Peugeot D3A 'POSTES', A.a....................£655
33AN Simca Cargo 'BAILLY', yellow/white, A.a....................£140
561 Citroën 1200 Kg 'CIBIE', turquoise blue/green, A.a....................£310
561 Citroën 1200 Kg 'GERVAIS' Ice Cream Van, A.a....................£520
562H Citroën 2CV, export, 'WEGENWACHT', A.b....................£1,100
565 Renault Estafette Camping, sky blue/cream, A.c....................£230
566 Citroën 'Police Secours', B.b....................£210
571 Saviem Horse Transporter and Sulky, A.a....................£630
572 Berliet Quarry Truck, red/yellow, B.a....................£310
570 Peugeot J7 'ALLO FRET', A.b....................£240
570A Peugeot J7 'Autoroutes', orange, A.b....................£490
577 Berliet Truck 'GAK', green/yellow, B.c....................£140
587 Citroën 1200Kg 'PHILIPS', A.b....................£420
579 Simca Glass Lorry, yellow/green, A.a....................£520
882 Peugeot 404 and 'PINDER' Caravan, A.b....................£770
886 Richier Profiler, yellow/red, A.a....................£260
899 Delahaye Fire Engine, A.b....................£260

MILITARY
806 Berliet 6x6 Recovery Truck, khaki, A.b....................£150
808 Dodge Command Car, A.b....................£240
809 GMC US Army Truck, khaki, A.b....................£140
823 GMC US Army Tanker, khaki, B.b....................£165
824 Berliet Gazelle 6x6 Truck, khaki, A.b....................£130
883 Char AMX 13 Bridge Layer, khaki, A.b....................£165
884 Brockway Bridge Layer, khaki, A.b....................£165
890 Berliet Tank Transporter, khaki, B.b....................£75

Vectis Auctions Ltd.
Fleck Way, Thornaby, Stockton -on-Tees TS17 9JZ

Abbreviations: M = Mint, NM = Near Mint, EP = Excellent Plus,
E = Excellent, GP = Good Plus, G = Good, F = Fair.

CARS
24D Plymouth Belvedere, white/blue, G-GP, unboxed....................£130
24K Simca Chambord, TT green, white tyres, EP, unboxed....................£70
24Q FordVedette, silver-blue, red hubs, NM, unboxed....................£130
24 Q Ford Vedette, green, GP unboxed....................£60
24R Peugeot 203, grey, cross hatched roof, EP....................£90
24R Peugeot, met' blue/cream, smooth roof, E unboxed....................£240
24T Citroën 2cv, maroon/grey, cream hubs, E....................£80
24UT Simca Aronde Taxi, maroon/blue, E - EP, unboxed....................£90
24XT Ford Vedette Taxi, black/tan, EP unboxed....................£70
24V Buick Roadmaster, TT blue, EP....................£90
528 Peugeot 404 Cabriolet, white, red interior, GP unboxed....................£50
553 Peugeot 404, turquoise, red interior, E - EP, unboxed....................£100
24Y Studebaker Commander, TT green, EG in E box....................£100
24Y Studebaker Commander, orange/tan, NM in GP box....................£240
501 Citroën DS 19 Police Car, spun hubs, E in GP box....................£150
509 Fiat 850, yellow, red interior, spun hubs, EP in E box....................£130
511 Peugeot 204, red, black interior, spun hubs, EP in E box....................£100
511 Peugeot 204, blue, dark blue interior, spun hubs, EP in E box....................£100
511 Ferrari Racing Car, red, RN '27', spun hubs, EP in E box....................£100
514 Alfa Romeo Giulia, white, red interior, spun hubs, EP in GP box....................£130
515 Ferrari 250 GT, metallic blue, ivory interior, NM in G box....................£100
516 Mercedes, metallic silver, cream roof/interior, EP in E box....................£160
517 Renault 8, blue, red interior, spun hubs, EP in E box....................£80

517 **Renault 8**, primrose yellow, red interior, spun hubs, E in GP box £120
521 **Peugeot 403**, primrose yellow, spun hubs, E in E box £150
524/24E **Renault Dauphine**, ivory, GP in G box £100
524 **Renault Dauphine**, turquoise, spun hubs, EP in GP box £180
527 **Alfa Romeo 1900**, blue, chrome hubs, NM in NM box £120
528 **Peugeot 404**, metallic blue, red interior, spun hubs, E in F-G box £130
531 **Fiat Grand Vue**, ivory/blue, spun hubs, EP in E box £160
532 **Lincoln Premiere**, TT green, chrome hubs, NM in E box £130
532 **Lincoln Premiere**, dark cerulean blue, silver roof,
    spun hubs, US export issue, E in F box £340
533 **Mercedes Coupé**, metallic blue, cream interior, EP in G box £180
536 **Peugeot 404**, red, ivory interior, plus skis etc, EP in F box............£140
539 **Citroën ID19 Estate**, metallic gold/ivory, EP in NM box £130
542 **24ZT Simca Ariane Taxi**, black/red, EP in G box £100
545 **De Soto Diplomat**, metallic green/ivory, spun hubs, EP in GP box.....£190
546 **Austin-Healey 100**, white, red interior, spun hubs, E in F box £170
546 **Opel Rekord Taxi**, black, spun hubs, E in G box £190
548 **Fiat 1800 Estate**, yellow/black, spun hubs, EP in E box £130
548 **Fiat 800 Estate**, TT blue, spun hubs, EP in E box £100
551 **Ford Taunus Police Car**, dark green, spun hubs, EP in G box £280
556 **Citroën Ambulance**, grey/cream, spun hubs, NM in E box £120
558 **Citroën 2cv**, yellow/tan, EP in GP box £110
1404 **Citroën ID19 Estate**, 'RTL LUXEMBOURG', E in F box............£380
1406 **Renault Sinpar 'Michel Tanguy'**, E in F box £140
1415 **Peugeot 504**, pale blue, E in F box £40
1414 **Renault 8 Gordini**, white, spun hubs, NM in G box £150
1423 **Peugeot 504 Cabriolet**, dark blue, E in G box £120
1424G **Renault 12 Gordini**, blue, E in G box...............................£100
1429 **Peugeot 404 Police Car**, complete, EP in F box £190
1435 **Citroën Presidentielle**, TT grey, E in GP box £220
Gift Set 24 - 57, complete set, models G - E, box F......................£500

COMMERCIAL VEHICLES

25B **Peugeot D3A Van 'LAMPE MAZDA'**, E in F box......................£120
25O **Milk Delivery Truck**, E in G - GP box.................................£240
32AB **Panhard Truck/Trailer 'SNCF'**, E in GP box £140
32C **Panhard Tanker 'ESSO'**, EP in GP box £140
518A **Renault 4 'Autoroutes'**, complete, E-EP in GP box £180
Citroën 2cv Postal Van, GP on GP box £120
561 **Citroën Van 'Glaces Gervais'**, blue/white, E in GP box..............£420
561HC **Citroën Van 'Baroclem'**, blue, NM in F box £3,400
561 **Postal Service Van**, yellow, red interior, EP in E box £340
564 **Renault Estafette Glaziers Van**, E in G crushed box.................£160
566 **Citroën Police Van**, dark indigo blue, E in F box £220
Mercedes Snow Plough, E in F box.....................................£120
Berliet Stradair Side Tipper, EP in G box £240
570 **Peugeot J7 Van 'Allo Fret'**, E in GP box £110
570A **Peugeot J7 Van 'Autoroutes'**, EP in G box £380
570 **J7 Fire Service Van**, E-EP in GP box £350
571 **Saviem Horse Transporter with Sulky**, E in E box £560

572 **Berliet GBO Tipper**, red/yellow, EP in GP box..........................£240
587 **Citroën Van 'Philips'**, yellow/silver, E in F-G box £300
Berliet Brewery Wagon, yellow, red hubs, E in E box £140
803 **Unic Articulated Truck/Trailer 'SNCF'**, E in G-GP box...............£180
881 **GMC 6X6 'PINDER CIRCUS' Truck**, NM in P box £380
882 **Peugeot 404 &Caravan, 'PINDER CIRCUS'**,
    includes rare colour leaflet, EP in F-G box £540
888 **Berliet Sahara Crane Truck**, desert sand, E in GP box................£200
898 **Berliet Low Loader/Transformer**, G in F box £120
889 **Berliet PCM Paris Bus**, TT green, E in GP box £150
889U **Berliet PCM Urban Bus**, red/cream, EP in E box £150

SPANISH PRODUCTION

500 **Citroën 2cv**, orange, ivory interior, EP in GP box......................£80
530 **Citroën DS23**, metallic red/black, E in F box £80
538 **Renault 16TX**, metallic purple, tan interior, E in G box £70
1450 **Simca Police Car**, black/white, NM in GP box..........................£50

Bonhams

Montpelier Street, Knightsbridge, London SW7 1HH

24c **Citroën DS19**, ivory, black roof, Mint, boxed..................................£110
24d **Plymouth Belvedere**, mid green, black roof, side panel,
    Very near mint, boxed...£75
24d **Plymouth Belvedere**, mid green, black roof, side panel,
    Mint, boxed...£102
24k **Simca Vedette Chambord**, red, ivory, Mint, boxed......................£102
24v **Buick Roadmaster**, deep blue, black roof, Mint, boxed £130
24v **Buick Roadmaster**, yellow, dark green roof, Mint, Boxed..............£120
24v **Buick Roadmaster**, deep blue, black roof, Mint, Boxed...............£90
507 **Simca 1500**, metallic silver with picnic table, Mint, boxed £110
519 **Simca 1000**, light blue, Mint, boxed £105
524 **Renault Dauphine**, turquoise, windows, silver ridged hubs,
    Mint, boxed...£140
532 **Lincoln Premiere**, blue, silver roof, Mint, boxed.......................£90
532 **Lincoln Premiere**, met. light green, dark green roof, Mint, boxed £80
542 **Simca Taxi 'Ariane'**, black red roof, Mint, 542/24ZT box £95
545 **De Soto Diplomat**, orange, black roof, Mint, boxed £100
547 **Panhard PL 17**, 4th type, violet, Mint, boxed £77
552 **Chevrolet Corvair**, light blue, Mint, boxed £70
564 **Renault Estafette Miroitier**, Mint, boxed...............................£285
885 **Saviem Pipe Truck**, Mint, full scene box £320
808 **GMC Army Recovery Truck**, Mint, boxed, with packing £186
814 **AML Panhard**, with unused decals, aerials in pack, Mint, boxed £62
823 **GMC Military Tanker**, Near Mint, boxed £110
50 **Grue Salev**, version without rivet, Mint, boxed...........................£200
60c **Lockheed Super G Constellation**, Very near mint, boxed...............£114

French
Dinky Toys

No.882

'Pinder' Circus Set
(Peugeot 404
and Caravan)

Photograph:
Vectis Auctions Ltd.

Lone Star

Robert Newson has provided the following information on Lone Star models.

'Lone Star' was the trade name of Die Casting Machine Tools Ltd (DCMT) who started in 1939 as manufacturers of diecasting machines. They were based at Palmers Green in North London. After the war they started making diecast toys which were distributed by The Crescent Toy Co Ltd. In the Crescent Toys section of this catalogue, the items listed as 'early post-war models' were all made by DCMT with the exception of the Locomotive and the Racing Car. From 1950 DCMT arranged their own distribution direct to wholesalers. Over the next four decades DCMT Lone Star made several ranges of diecast vehicles including

'Slikka Toys' (early 1950s), 'Modern Army Series' (mainly 1960s), 'Roadmaster Majors' (1960s and 1970s), 'Farmer's Boy' (1980s) and the well known 'Lone Star Locos' miniature railway system (later called 'Treble-O-Lectric' or 'Treble-O-Trains'). The four ranges of most interest to collectors are listed here - the original DCMT 'Roadmasters' of 1956, the 1:50 scale 'Roadmasters' (1960s), the 'Impy' and 'Flyers' series made in various forms from 1966 to the mid 1980s, and the miniature 'Tuf-Tots' (1970s). The Editor would welcome any further information on Lone Star products.

NB See the 'Miscellaneous Models' colour section for Lone Star pictures.

DCMT Lone Star Roadmasters

This was a short-lived series introduced in 1956, consisting of three sports cars and four veteran cars, all around 1:35 to 1:40 scale. The models had diecast bodies but all other components were plastic. Plastic drivers and passengers were included with the models.

-	-	**1904 Darracq 'Genevieve'**	Black or Red body, Yellow plastic chassis; Metallic Blue or Silver body, Black plastic chassis	£200-300
-	-	**1904 Daimler 'Windsor' Phaeton**	Red body, Yellow plastic chassis	£60-70
-	-	**1912 Ford Model 'T'**	Silver body, Black plastic chassis	£60-70
-	-	**1912 Morris Oxford 'Bullnose'**	Metallic Blue body, Black plastic chassis	£80-100
-	-	**Daimler Conquest Roadster**	Red, Metallic Light Blue, Pale Yellow, Pale Green or Pale Blue	£80-100
-	-	**Ford Thunderbird**	Red, Metallic Light Blue, Pale Yellow, Pale Green or Pale Blue	£80-100
-	-	**MG Midget TF**	Metallic Light Blue or Red	£80-100

Lone Star Roadmasters - 1:50 scale

In 1960 Lone Star produced four American cars on behalf of the US firm of Tootsietoy. These were the first four models listed below and they had 'Tootsietoy Classic Series' cast underneath. This arrangement only lasted for a couple of years, as by 1962 there were eight models available, all now marked 'Lone Star Roadmasters'. The models featured plated grilles, bumpers and wheels, and had windows but no interior detail. Around 1964 the plated parts were replaced by less attractive painted or self-coloured plastic, and vacuum-formed interiors were fitted. Later issues have yellow interiors, white wheels, plastic grille and bumpers. Five further numbers were added to the range before they were withdrawn around 1966.

1258	-	**Farm King Tractor and Trailer**	Red tractor, 'Farm King' paper label, Blue trailer, 'Farm Estates Co.' paper label. (Roadmaster Major)	£60-70
1470	-	**Chevrolet Corvair**	Red or Orange-Red	£60-70
1471	-	**Rambler Rebel Station Wagon**	Sea-Green, Metallic Blue-Green or Green with Cream roof, Metallic Brown with White roof or all Green	£60-70
1472	-	**Cadillac 62**	Pale Blue, Blue with Cream roof or all Blue	£60-70
1473	-	**Ford Sunliner Convertible**	White or Light Blue; Red interior	£60-70
1474	-	**Chevrolet El Camino Pick-Up**	Yellow or Orange	£60-70
1475	-	**Dodge Dart Phoenix**	Metallic Dark Blue or Mid Blue	£60-70
1476	-	**Rolls-Royce Silver Cloud II**	Grey with Black upper half or Metallic Blue	£70-80
1477	-	**Dodge Dart Police Car**	Black, 'POLICE PATROL' or 'POLIZEI'	£70-80
1478	-	**Rambler Ambulance**	White, Red Cross transfer on bonnet	£70-80
1479	-	**Chevrolet Corvair**	Red body, 'FIRE CHIEF', 'FEUERWEHR' or 'BRANDWEER'	£70-80
1480	-	**Chevrolet Corvair**	Army Staff Car (continued after 1966 as no.1273 in ``Modern Army'' series), Olive Green	£60-70
1481	-	**Rambler Military Ambulance**	(continued after 1966 as no.1274 in 'Modern Army' series), Olive Green	£70-80

Lone Star 'Tuf-Tots'

The first thirteen Tuf-Tots were introduced in 1969, and the next five followed in 1970. The remainder had appeared by 1972. They were available boxed or bubble-packed, and when bubble-packed there was an additional '2' in front of the model number to give a four-digit reference. Later, models were sold in open counter-top trays.

The trucks were based on a common US Ford chassis. Most models exist in numerous colour variations. The series was discontinued after 1980. Market Price Range is **£5** to **£10**.

601	**Ford Petrol Tanker**	'ESSO' labels
		'ESSO' cast into sides
602	**Citroën DS Convertible with Driver**	
603	**Chevrolet Corvette Stingray Convertible with Driver**	
604	**Dodge Dart Convertible with Driver**	
605	**Mercedes-Benz 280SL Convertible with Driver**	
606	**Ford 'TT' Tow Truck**	
607	**Ford 'Big L' Dumper Lorry**	
608	**Jeep and Trailer**	'Herts. Farm', scale 85:1
609	**Ford 'Autos' Flat Truck** with metal petrol pump island	
		with plastic petrol pump island
610	**Ford Tipper Lorry**	'LS Construction Co.' labels
		with ribs cast onto body instead of labels
611	**Ford Luton Van**	with 'Express Freight' labels
		with ribs cast onto body instead of labels
612	**Ford Articulated Low-Loader** 'Apache'	
613	**Chris Craft Capri Speedboat** (plastic) **on Trailer**, scale 86:1	
614	**Ford Refuse Lorry**	with 'City Refuse' labels
		with 'City Refuse' cast lettering

615	**Ford Cement Mixer**	
616	**Ford Milk Float**	'Milk, Milk, Milk' cast on each side
617	**Ford Cattle Transporter**	
618	**Ford Skip Lorry**	
619	**Citroën DS Coupé**	
620	**Chevrolet Corvette Stingray Coupé**	
621	**Dodge Dart Coupé**	
622	**Mercedes-Benz 280SL Coupé**, scale 86:1	
623	**Routemaster Bus**	with 'London Bus' advertisements
624	**ERF Fire Engine**	with ladder, 'Fire Brigade' labels
625	**Caravan**	
626	**Ford Circus Cage Lorry** with plastic lion, 'Circus' cast-in	
627	**Tractor Shovel**	

Gift Sets

2570	**Building Site Playset**	4 models plus sand hopper
2571	**Garage Playset**	4 models plus car ramp
2572	**Highway Playset**	4 models plus street and traffic lights
2573	**Travel Playset**	4 models plus 'Stop' barrier
2574	**Dutch Farm Playset**	4 models plus windmill
2575	**Bridge Playset**	4 models plus girder bridge
579	**Commercial Vehicle Set** 6 models	
580	**Car and Trailer Set**	6 models
581	**12 Vehicle Set**	12 models
582	**Highway Set**	
		3 models plus sand hopper, car ramp, street and traffic lights
583	**Travel Set**	
		3 models plus girder bridge, windmill and 'Stop' barrier

An advertisement for **Lone Star Impy** models as it appeared in the 'Eagle and Boy's World' comic of 24 June 1967.

In the following listing the year shown is the date of introduction. Most models remained in production until 1976. **IW** = Impy wheels, **FW** = Flyers wheels, **HSW** = Hi-Speed wheels, **BPW** = black plastic wheels.

7	1971	**Vauxhall Firenza**, IW / FW, RHD and LHD	£15-25
8	-	**Ford Capri**, not issued	NPP
9	1970	**Maserati Mistral**, IW or FW	£10-20
10	1966	**Jaguar Mk.X**, IW or FW	£10-20
11	1966	**Chevrolet Corvette Stingray GT**, IW or FW	£10-20
12	1966	**Chrysler Imperial**, IW or FW	£10-20
13	-	**Ford Thunderbird**, not issued	NPP
13	1971	**Toyota 2000 GT**, Flyers wheels	£10-20
14	1966	**Ford Zodiac Mk.III Estate**, IW or FW	£10-20
15	1966	**Volkswagen Microbus**, IW or FW	£10-20
16	1966	**Ford Zodiac Mk.III Estate 'POLICE' Car**, IW or FW	£10-20
16	-	**Chrysler Imperia 'POLICE' Car**, IW or FW	£10-20
16m	-	**Mercedes-Benz 220 SE 'POLIZEI' Car**, Impy wheels	£10-20
17	1966	**Mercedes-Benz 220 SE**, IW or FW	£10-20
18	1966	**Ford Corsair**, IW or FW	£10-20
19	1967	**Volvo 1800 S**, IW or FW	£10-20
20	1967	**Volkswagen Ambulance**, IW or FW	£10-20
21	1967	**Fiat 2300 S Coupé**, IW or FW	£10-20
22	1967	**Rolls-Royce Silver Cloud III Convertible**, IW or FW	£10-20
23	1967	**Alfa Romeo Giulia 1600 Spider**, IW or FW	£10-20
24	1967	**Foden Tilt-cab 8w Tipper**, black plastic or HSW	£10-20
25	1967	**International Harvester Tractor Shovel**	£10-20
26	1967	**Foden Tilt-cab Petrol Tanker, 'MOBIL'**, BPW or HSW	£10-20
27	1967	**Ford Taunus 12M**, IW or FW	£10-20
28	1967	**Peugeot 404 Saloon**, IW or FW	£10-20
29	-	**Cement Mixer Lorry**, not issued	NPP
29	1971	**Foden Tilt-cab Box Van, 'LUCAS'**, BPW or HSW	£15-20
29	1972	**Foden Tilt-cab Box Van,** 'EXPRESS FREIGHT' labels, black plastic wheels	£15-25
30	1967	**AEC Merryweather Fire Engine**, black plastic or HSW	£10-20
31	1967	**Ford Transit Breakdown Lorry, 'ESSO'**, BPW or HSW	£10-20
32	1968	**'FIRE CHIEF' Car**, Ford Corsair, red, IW or FW	£10-20
32		**'FEUERWEHR' Car**, Ford Corsair, red, Impy wheels	£10-20
33	1968	**Austin-Western Mobile Crane**, elevating jib	£10-20
34	1968	**Euclid Crawler Tractor**, rubber tracks	£10-20
35	-	**Articulated Flat Truck**, not issued	NPP
36	1969	**Lotus Europa**, Flyers wheels	£10-20
37		**Ford GT**, not issued	NPP
38	1971	**Chevrolet Corvette Stingray**, Flyers wheels	£15-25
39	1971	**Ford Mustang**, Flyers wheels	£15-25
40	1973	**Cadillac Eldorado**, Flyers wheels	£10-20
41	1972	**Leyland Builders Supply Lorry**, 4 girders, 8 HSW	£10-20
41	1973	**Leyland Builders Supply Lorry**, 4 girders, 6 HSW	£10-20
41	1973	**Foden Half-cab Builders Supply Lorry**, 4 girders,6 HSW	£10-20
42	1972	**Foden Half-cab Tipper, 'TILCON' labels**, 8 HSW	£15-25
43	1973	**Leyland Flat Lorry with Pipes**, 6 HSW	£10-20
43	1973	**Foden Half-cab Flat Lorry with Pipes**, 6 HSW	£10-20
44	1972	**Leyland Marine Transport Lorry**, Speedboat, 8 HSW	£10-20
44	1973	**Leyland Marine Transport Lorry**, Speedboat, 6 HSW	£10-20
44	1973	**Foden Half-cab Marine Transport Lorry,** Speedboat, 6 HSW	£10-20
46	1973	**Leyland Dropside Lorry**, 6 Hi-Speed wheels	£10-20
47	1973	**Leyland High-Side Lorry**, 6 Hi-Speed wheels	£10-20
47	1973	**Foden High-Side Lorry**, Half-cab, 6 HSW	£10-20
48	1973	**Leyland Hopper Lorry**, 6 HSW	£10-20
48	1973	**Foden Half-cab Hopper Lorry**, 6 HSW	£10-20
49	1973	**Foden Half-cab Tipper**, 6 HSW	£10-20

IMPY GIFT SETS All are scarce, hence NGPP

301	1967	**Six-piece Gift Set**	NGPP
302	1967	**Six-piece Gift Set**	NGPP
303	1968	**'MOBIL' Gift Set**	NGPP
304	1968	**Five-piece Commercial Vehicle Gift Set**	NGPP
309	1968	**Twelve-piece Gift Set**	NGPP

IMPY ACCESSORIES

401	1967	**Car Lifting Ramp**	£5-10
402	1967	**Lock-Up Garage** (plastic)	£5-10
403	-	**Service Station** (not issued)	NPP
404	1968	**'MOBIL' Petrol Pump Island**, Canopy, Forecourt Sign	£5-10
406	-	**Fire House** (not issued)	NPP

IMPY TWO-PACKS

422	**VW Ambulance** (20) and **Mercedes-Benz 'Polizei'** (16M)	£20-30
423	**Fiat 2300S** (21) and **Breakdown Lorry** (31)	£20-30
424	**Foden Tanker** (26) and **Ford Taunus** (27)	£20-30
425	**Ford Zodiac** (14) and **Tractor** (25)	£20-30
427	**Alfa Romeo** (23) and **'MOBIL' Petrol Pumps** (404)	£20-30
431	**Chevrolet Corvette** (11) and **Fiat 2300S** (21)	£20-30
432	**Fire Engine** (30) and **Ford Corsair 'FEUERWEHR'** (32)	£20-30

IMPY series, post-1976
The Market Price Range is shown as £5 - £10 but as yet there is little collectors' interest in these recent models.

50	**Six-wheel Tipper**	£5-10
51	**Six-wheel High Side Lorry**	£5-10
52	**Six-wheel Flat Lorry with Crane**	£5-10
53	**Six-wheel Flat Lorry with Speedboat**	£5-10
54	**Six-wheel Cement Mixer**	£5-10
55	**Six-wheel Luton Van**	£5-10
56	**Six-wheel Dropside Lorry**	£5-10
57	**Six-wheel Flat Lorry with Water Tank**	£5-10
58	**Six-wheel Hopper Lorry**	£5-10
59	**Six-wheel Flat Lorry with Pipes**	£5-10
60	**Six-wheel Flat Lorry with Planks**	£5-10
61	**Six-wheel Petrol Tanker**	£5-10
71	**Range Rover**	£5-10
72	**Cadillac Eldorado**	£5-10
73	**Chevrolet Corvette Stingray**	£5-10
74	**Toyota 2000 GT**	£5-10
75	**Range Rover Police Car**	£5-10
76	**Chevrolet Corvette Stingray 'GT Rally'**	£5-10
77	**Jaguar Mk.X**	£5-10
78	**Maserati Mistral**	£5-10
79	**Ford Mustang**	£5-10
80	**Lotus Europa**	£5-10
81	**Volvo Coupé**	£5-10
82	**Mercedes-Benz**	£5-10
181	**Articulated Flat Lorry with Crane**	£5-10
182	**Articulated Petrol Tanker**	£5-10
183	**Articulated Low Loader with Tuf-Tots car**	£5-10
184	**Articulated Flat Lorry with Pipes and water tank**	£5-10
185	**Cadillac Eldorado with Tuf-Tots Speedboat on trailer**	£5-10
185	**Range Rover with Tuf-Tots Speedboat on trailer**	£5-10
185	**Range Rover 'RNLI'** with boat on trailer	£5-10
185	**Jaguar Mk.X with Cabin Cruiser on trailer**	£5-10
186	**Crane Lorry** (no.52) with Impy car	£5-10
187	**Luton Van** (no.55) with Trailer	£5-10
188	**Articulated Low Loader with Cabin Cruiser**	£5-10
189	**Articulated Flat Lorry with Planks**	£5-10
190	**Petrol Tanker** (no.61) with Trailer	£5-10
191	**High Side Lorry** (no.51) with Trailer	£5-10
192	**Cement Mixer** (no.54) with Flat Trailer	£5-10
1251	**Articulated Car Transporter**	£5-10
1252	**AEC Merryweather HTTL Fire Engine** (re-packed no.30)	£5-10
1256	**Car Transporter** (no.1251) with four Impy cars	£30-40

Lone Star Sets
'**International Peace Force Vehicles' Set** (made 1974) contains:
1271 Small Tank, 1272 Searchlight on Trailer, 1273 Mortar Launcher, 1274 Radar Detector Unit, 1275 Ack-Ack Gun, 1276 Silver Small Canon, 1277 All Blue Military Jeep..NGPP
'**GULLIVER COUNTY' Series. Boxed set of three Coaches.** White card box with scene depicting a coach, fire engine, articulated lorry and two cars.
i) Mid-Green Coach, Grey wheels, 'SCHOOL BUS' logo on sides
ii) Cream Coach, Grey wheels, 'SCHOOL BUS' logo on sides
iii) Mid-Green Coach, Grey wheels, 'GREENLINE' logo on sides......**£100-150**
'**War in the Desert' Set** includes 3 German and 3 US military vehicles....NGPP

Miscellaneous items
1259 Routemaster Bus. Made 1972-89, paper adverts 'SEE LONDON BY BUS' and 'BUY LONE STAR'. Route is '29 VICTORIA', Plastic wheels .**£5-10**
RAC Land Rover and Caravan ...no details..NGPP

'Aircraft of the World' Series (boxed, spare transfers, 1:250 scale)
'**Scandinavian Airlines' Caravelle**	£40-50
'**Pan American' Boeing 707**	£50-60
'**BOAC' De Havilland Comet 4c**	£50-60
'**BOAC' Bristol Brittania**	£50-60
'**British and Commonwealth' Bristol Brittania**	£50-60
'**Aer Lingus' Vickers Viscount**	£50-60

'Modern Army' Series
'**Lorry', 'Bren Gun Carrier' and 'Jeep'**	each: **£10-15**
'**Small Mobile Fighting Unit'**	NGPP

'**Farm' Series,** '**Jeep'** £10-15

Matchbox Toys

Introduction

The company was founded in 1947 by the unrelated Leslie and Rodney Smith who combined their names to form 'Lesney' Products Ltd. They were soon joined by Jack Odell – a recognised die-casting expert.

The most famous of the various early products was the 'Coronation Coach'. During the 1950s the company developed the highly successful Matchbox '1-75' and 'Models of Yesteryear' ranges. Today, certain models in the '1-75' series are highly sought after and fetch very high prices at auction.

Following a difficult trading period Lesney Products Ltd was bought in 1982 by the Universal Toy Co. of Hong Kong. Models issued subsequently fall outside the scope of this publication. (Collectors requiring information on the later issues should contact MICA whose details appear on the opposite page).

The Models of Yesteryear section has been completely replaced by a unique new listing specially prepared for the Catalogue by Horace Dunkley, the leading authority on Yesteryears. The Editor is indebted to Trevor Bannister and Nigel Cooper who have fully revised the '1-75' Series listings.

The Editor would also like to thank the many collectors who have contributed additional information.

'Moko' Products

'**Moko Products**' was a toy distribution firm founded by Moses Kohnstam who came to Britain from Nuremburg, Germany around 1900.

Moko provided the distribution and storage facilities and, irrespective of the supplier, all toys were marketed as Moko products. The early issues after the Second World War were housed in plain cardboard boxes with 'tuck in' ends. These usually had only single colour printing that did not include a picture of the model. During the early 1950s the packaging became much more attractive with

brightly coloured boxes displaying a picture of the model inside. Moko will best be remembered for their distribution of the early Matchbox '1-75' toys under the name of 'Moko-Lesney'. Moses Kohnstam was succeeded by Richard Kohnstam in 1953.

The following listing of Moko items constitutes all the information available to publish at present. Additional information would be welcomed by the Editor.

---	**Railway Timekeeper's Watch**	
	with slide to house matches inside casing.........................**£250-350**	
c1948-53	**Mechanical Tractor**	
	Probably early Lesney. Orange body, Green rubber tracks, Black wheels, Green/Black driver, (early issue in plain box) **£300-400**	
1950-55	**Mechanical Tractor**	
	As previous model but with Orange wheels, (later issue in picture box)...**£300-400**	
1947-50	**Excavator (with open cab)**	
	Orange body and jib, Black digger and chassis, Green rubber tracks, Orange crank handle. Early card box has 'Moko TOYS OF DISTINCTION' logo..............**£300-400**	
1950-55	**'RUSTON BUCYRUS' Excavator**	
	Yellow over Red body with Black '10 RB' logo. Black or Dark Green chassis, jib, digger, crank wheel and rubber tracks. Later box with full colour picture **£200-250**	
1950-55	**Builder's Crane**	
	All Blue crane base and jib with unpainted metal hook. Later card box with full colour picture **£350-450**	
1947-50	**Crawler Bulldozer**	
	Red body and dozer blade (possibly early Lesney). In card box (plain at first, later with colour picture).........**£250-300**	
1947-50	**Farm Tractor and Wagon**	
	Blue driver **£600-700**	
1950-55	**'Pop-Pop Series' Motor Scooter**	
	Blue or Dark Red scooter with Black seat. Female figure has blonde hair, blue sweater, red or blue trousers. Later box with full colour picture **£450-550**	
1950-55	**Drummer Boy (Mechanical)**	
	Red body, Gold trim, Black busby. Cream/Yellow drum, Gold drumsticks...**£1,000-1,250**	
1947-50	**Hayrake**	
	Yellow/Green body or Orange body.................................**£100-150**	
1947-50	**Merry-go-Round**	
	Blue/Red base and centre column, Maroon/Blue roof, 2 Red and 2 Blue seated figures. Plain card box **£400-500**	
1947-50	**Mechanical Mouse**	
	Grey body with Red eyes plus curling tail. Early plain card box..**£175-200**	
c1950	**Peregrine Puppet**..**NGPP**	
c1950	**'Jumbo, the Walking Elephant'**. Mechanical / tinplate.	
	With diagonal printing **£300-400**	
	With horizontal printing **£400-500**	
c1950	**0-4-0 Tank Engine**	
	Light Metallic Green, bare metal wheels **£125-150**	

Moko 'Farmette' Series

Miniature size models packed in end-flap type boxes with colour picture of the model. The die-cast horses have dark brown bodies and white feet.
NB These are delicate models; check for metal deterioration.

No.1	50-53	**Timber Trailer with two Horses**	
		Green body, four Red wheels, timber load................**£150-200**	
No.2	50-53	**Farm Cart** (4 wheels) **with two Horses**	
		Mid or Dark Blue, Red raves, Red 12-spoke wheels .**£150-200**	
No.3	50-53	**Bull Wagon with two Horses** (in tandem)	
		Green wagon, Brown metal bull, four Red 12-spoke wheels. **£150-200**	

Moko 'Treasure Chest' Series

Packed in Brown 'chests' with yellow 'strapping'.
NB These are delicate models; check for metal deterioration.

No.10	50-53	**Hay Cart**, Orange body,	
		2 Green raves, 2 Green wheels, one horse **£50-75**	
No.11	50-53	**Millers Cart**	
		Blue body, 2 Red wheels, 3 White sacks, one horse....**£50-75**	
No.12	50-53	**Water Cart**	
		Green/Red cart, 2 Red wheels, one horse **£50-75**	

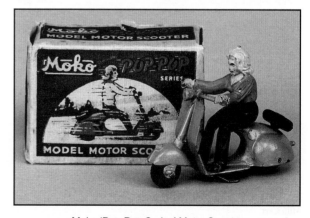

Moko 'Pop-Pop Series' Motor Scooter
Photo: Vectis Auctions Ltd.

Moko mechanical tinplate toys:

'Jumbo, the Walking Elephant'

and

'Merry-go-Round'.

Photo: Vectis Auctions Ltd.

The early 'Lesney' toys

Lesney Products issued their first diecast toys in 1948. Whilst production ceased during the Korean war period (1950-52), the models produced formed the basis from which the 1-75 series was launched in 1953. They were sold in boxes under the name of 'MoKo' who were ultimately to also market all the early 1-75 series models. **NB Models were sold boxed.**

Road Roller
All Green (shades) body and flywheel, unpainted wheels **£350-400**
As previous but with Red roller wheels and Yellow flywheel **£350-400**
With a driver but without a flywheel....................................**£200-250**
Without a driver and without flywheel..................................**£150-200**
Cement Mixer
All Green or All-Blue body, Red wheels.................................**£150-200**
Pale Green body, Red or Yellow drum and wheels **£200-250**
Dark Green body, Red or Yellow drum and wheels **£200-250**
Red body, Green drum and wheels.......................................**£200-300**
Orange engine cover, Black drum, Yellow wheels........................**£250-350**

Caterpillar Tractor
Orange or Yellow body, Red roller wheels, Black rubber tracks **£300-400**
Caterpillar Bulldozer
Green, Orange or Red body, Black rubber tracks.........................**£300-400**
Yellow body, Red dozer blade and wheels **£175-200**
Prime Mover
Orange tractor (Green engine on some), Blue trailer,
Red/Yellow dozer, 'BRITISH ROAD SERVICES' **£1,000-1,500**
As previous but with Beige trailer.......................................**£1,200-1,500**

'MASSEY-HARRIS' 745D Tractor
Red body, Cream hubs, Black rubber tyres **£450-550**
Milk Cart
Orange body, White driver and six crates, Black or Brown horse,
Black or Grey wheels, 'PASTEURISED MILK' cast-in................**£650-750**
As previous model but with Blue body **£800-1,000**

Soap-Box Racer
Brown box, Grey wheels (16 + 9 spokes),
Brown or Dark Blue boy, Pink face...**£2,500-3,500**
Quarry Truck
Yellow body, Black tyres, 'LAING'. Only one known to exist ....NGPP

Covered Wagon with Barrels
Green body, White cover, two Red barrels, six Mid-Brown horses
(with White tails), with postilion rider and wagon driver **£250-300**
Covered Wagon
Same model but with Chocolate Brown horses and **no barrels** **£175-200**

'RAG & BONE MERCHANTS' Cart
Yellow body, Red wheels, Black horse, Brown driver, with
7 pieces of 'junk': mangle-wheel, bike frame, bedhead, bath,
bucket, box, cistern **£1,500-2,000**
Same but Green body, Red wheels **£1,500-2,000**

Coronation Coach (large)
Gold coach with King and Queen, eight White horses, Gold/Red
trappings, four Red riders. 200 issued **£600-800**
Modified version: Gold, Silver or Gilt coach with just the
Queen inside. Horses and riders as for previous model **£175-200**
Coronation Coach (small)
Silver or Gold coach, eight White horses, Red/Gold trappings,
four Red riders, 'A MOKO TOY BY LESNEY' cast into
horsebar (1,000,000 sold) **£120-140**

'Muffin The Mule' ......White body, Red/Gold harness, Black trim ...**£300-400**
Excavator ....Digger and chassis are Dark Brown **£250-300**
Breadbait Press
1st type: Red body, unpainted 'butterfly' press. Boxed..................**£125-150**
2nd type: As 1st type but with Green press **£70-80**
3rd type: As 2nd type but with 'MILBRO' cast onto Red body **£70-80**

Matchbox Model Identification

Model Number is always cast into the base, chassis or body. Obvious exceptions are the early models which were not numbered. 'Lesney' is cast into all issues between 1953 and 1982.

'**Matchbox**' or '**Matchbox Series**' is shown on the base or chassis of all issues after 1965. All issues after 1957 had the model name on the base or chassis. Exceptions include those without a base (e.g., No.24 Excavator).

Suspension and **windows**. Car models were fitted with windows after 1961 and suspension after 1965. **Baseplates** are metal castings until the late 1970s

when plastic bases introduced. From 1983 they are marked 'Made in Macau'.

Wheels were metal castings on early models and were gradually changed to grey, silver or black plastic. **Superfast wheels** introduced in late 1960s and issues from 1968-69 may be found with either type. Novelties such as '**Laser Wheels**' introduced in the late 1980s. '**Rolamatics**' were introduced in the 1970s having working parts that were operated by pushing (see the Superfast section for these).

Model descriptions. This Catalogue tries to give original maker's description of model names and colours but early Matchbox listings are known to be inaccurate graphically. Maker's catalogue photographs are often taken of mock-ups months

before production starts while model designs become changed before release.

Dimensions refer to the greatest overall measurement (usually the length).

Superfast issues are listed separately elsewhere in this Matchbox section.

Abbreviations used in this listing:
BPT = Black plastic tyres
BPW = Black plastic wheels
GPW = Grey plastic wheels
MPR = Market Price Range
MW = metal wheels
RN = racing or rally number
SPW = Silver plastic wheels

Ref.	Intro.	Details	MPR

MB 1

Ref.	Intro.	Details	MPR
1a	53	**Diesel Road Roller** (Aveling Barford). Red metal roller wheels, Tan driver cast-in, no number, crimped axles, 49mm.	
		Type 1: curved lower canopy ends and thin braces above canopy supports, **Type 2**: straight ends and thick braces above supports, brace extension.	
		Dark Green body, Type 1	£250-350
		Dark Green body, Type 2	£60-70
		Light Green body, Type 2	£250-300
1b	56	**Diesel Road Roller** (Aveling Barford) Light Green body, Red metal roller wheels, Lt. or Dk. Tan driver, high peaked canopy, no number, hook, 57 mm	£35-45
1c	58	**Diesel Road Roller** (Aveling Barford) Light Green body and driver, Red metal roller wheels, number cast-in, high peaked canopy, hook, 62 mm	£80-100
		Dark Green body	£40-60
1d	62	**Diesel Road Roller** (Aveling Barford) Green body and driver, Red plastic rollers, 67 mm	£25-30
1e	67	**Mercedes Truck** Turquoise body, Orange canopy, Black plastic wheels, 75 mm	£8-12

MB 2

Ref.	Intro.	Details	MPR
2a	53	**Muir Hill Site Dumper**. Dark Green body, Red dumper, Green painted MW, 42 mm	£200-250
		Same but with unpainted MW	£40-50
2b	57	**Muir Hill Site Dumper**. Same but: Tan driver, metal wheels, 46 mm	£40-50
		Same but GPW, crimped axles	£50-60
		Same but GPW, rounded axles	£50-60
2c	62	**Muir Hill Dumper Truck** Red body, Green dumper, '*LAING*', Black plastic wheels, 54 mm	£20-30
		Same but '*MUIR HILL*' logo and picture-box (72 only known)	£60-80
2d	67	**Mercedes Trailer**. Turquoise body, Orange top, BPW	£8-12

MB 3

Ref.	Intro.	Details	MPR
3a	53	**Cement Mixer** Orange MW, Blue main body	£30-40
		GPW, crimped axles	£80-100
		GPW, rounded axles	£80-100
3b	61	**Bedford Tipper Truck**. (All have Grey body and chassis)	
		Maroon back, GPW, 24 treads	£160-180
		Maroon back, GPW, 45 treads	£160-180
		Maroon back, BPW	£20-30
		Red dump, GPW	£80-100
		Red dump, BPW	£25-35
3c	67	**Mercedes Ambulance**. Cream or Off-White body	£20-30

MB 4

Ref.	Intro.	Details	MPR
4a	54	**Massey Harris Tractor**. (with mudguards over rear wheels), Red body, Gold or Yellow rear hubs, Tan driver	£60-80
4b	57	**Massey Harris Tractor**. (without mudguards over rear wheels), metal wheels, Gold or Yellow rear hubs	£125-150
		Grey plastic wheels	£80-90
4c	60	**Triumph T110 Motor Cycle** Steel Blue bike/sidecar, Silver spoked wheels, BPT	£90-120
		Same but with Copper body (beware fakes)	£2,000-3,000
4d	66	**Stake Truck**, Yellow cab, Blue stake body, BPW	£70-80
		Yellow cab, Green stake body	£12-15

MB 5

Ref.	Intro.	Details	MPR
5a	54	**London Bus** (52 mm).	
		'Buy Matchbox Series' on paper label	£60-70
5b	57	**1957 London Bus** (57 mm).	
		'Buy Matchbox Series' decal, metal wheels	£40-50
		'Buy Matchbox Series' decal, Grey plastic wheels	£60-70
		'Players Please' decal, GPW	£120-150
		'BP Visco-Static' decal, knobbly GPW	£400-500
5c	60	**Routemaster** (66 mm).	
		'Players Please' decal, GPW	£110-130
		'Peardrax', GPW or BPW	£700-800
		'BP Visco-Static' decal, Grey or Black plastic wheels	£25-35
		'Baron of Beef' decal, Grey or Black plastic wheels	£350-450
5d	65	**Routemaster** (70 mm).	
		'BP Longlife' decal	£20-25
		'BP Visco-Static' decal or label	£15-20
		'Baron of Beef' decal	£400-500
		'Pegram' label	£400-500

MB 6

Ref.	Intro.	Details	MPR
6a	54	**Quarry Truck** 55mm.	
		Orange body, Grey tipper with six ribs, metal wheels	£40-50
		Same but Grey plastic wheels, domed/crimped axles	£4,000-5,000
6b	59	**Euclid Quarry Truck**	
		Yellow body, four ribs, decals, six BPW, '*Euclid*'	£40-50
		Knobbly GPW, domed axles	£1,500-2,000
6c	63	**Euclid Dump Truck**	
		Six Black wheels (rear double wheels are one piece)	£15-20
		Ten Black wheels (rear wheels are normal double wheels)	£15-20
6d	68	**Ford Pick Up** Red body, White canopy, chrome grille	£18-20
		Same but White grille	£25-35

MB 7

Ref.	Intro.	Details	MPR
7a	54	**Horse Drawn Milk Float**	
		Dark Orange body, White driver, crates and logo, metal wheels	£70-80
		As previous but with GPW	£110-140
		Pale Orange body, metal wheels	£70-80
		Pale Orange body and logo, White hat and crates, GPW	£110-140
		Pale Orange body, Silver driver and crates, Grey plastic wheels (beware fakes)	£550-650
7b	61	**Ford Anglia** Light Blue, Green windows, GPW	£70-80
		With Silver plastic wheels	£45-55
		With Black plastic wheels	£35-40
7c	67	**Refuse Truck**. Orange-Red body, Grey and Silver dumper	£10-15

MB 8

Ref.	Intro.	Details	MPR
8a	55	**Caterpillar Tractor** (42 mm).	
		Yellow body and rollers, Red driver, Green tracks	£350-450
		Same but with unpainted rollers	£50-65
		Orange body and driver, Gold or Silver grille, Green tracks	£65-80
		Yellow body/driver, Silver or Yellow grille, Green or Grey tracks	£40-50
8b	58	**Caterpillar Tractor** (42 mm).	
		Yellow body and driver, no.'8' cast-in, Green rubber tracks	£70-85
8c	61	**Caterpillar Tractor** (48 mm).	
		Yellow body, metal rollers, Green tracks	£40-55
		Same but with Silver rollers	£90-110
		Same but with Black rollers	£30-35
8d	64	**Caterpillar Tractor** (51 mm).	
		Yellow body, no driver, Green rubber tracks, Black rollers	£20-25

8e 66 **Ford Mustang**
White body, Black wheels with Silver hubcaps **£25-35**
White body, Silver wheels with Black tyres................................**£20-30**
Orange body, Silver wheels **£400-500**

MB 9

9a 55 **Dennis Fire Escape** (57mm).
Red body, no front bumper, metal wheels, crimped axles..............**£45-55**
9b 58 **Dennis Fire Escape** (58mm).
Red body, with front bumper, MW, number cast underneath........**£70-80**
Same but with GPW..**£350-450**
9c 59 **Merryweather Marquis Series III Fire Engine**
Red body with Tan ladder, GPW, crimped axles, 64 mm............**£60-75**
Same but with rounded axles **£40-50**
Same but with Gold ladder **£40-50**
With Gold ladder and BPW...**£30-40**
With Silver ladder, BPW...**£80-90**
With Tan ladder, BPW..**£65-75**
9d 66 **Boat and Trailer** (76mm, 77mm).
Blue/White boat, Blue trailer, Black plastic wheels......................**£15-20**

MB 10

10a 57 **Scammell Mechanical Horse**
Red cab, Gold trim, Grey trailer, crimped axles, MW, 56mm **£70-85**
10b 57 **Scammell Mechanical Horse**
Red Cab, Brown trailer, crimped axles, metal wheels, 75 mm **£50-60**
Red cab, Gold trim, Light Brown trailer, Grey plastic wheels.......**£85-95**
Red cab, Silver trim, Light Brown trailer, Grey plastic wheels **£75-85**
10c 61 **Foden 8-wheel Sugar Container**
Dark Blue body, with crown on rear decal, Grey wheels.............**£90-110**
Without crown, Grey wheels...**£70-80**
Without crown, Silver wheels...**£150-180**
Without crown, Black wheels..**£50-60**
10d 66 **Leyland Pipe Truck**
Red body, 6 or 7 Grey pipes, Silver base and grille......................**£15-20**
Same but White base and grille **£60-75**

MB 11

11a 55 **E.R.F. Road Tanker**. All models with metal wheels.
Green body, Gold trim **£1,400-1,800**
Dark Yellow body, Silver trim..**£150-175**
Light Yellow body, Silver trim...**£85-100**
Red body, Gold trim, small 'ESSO' decal on rear of tank **£120-140**
Same but large 'ESSO' decal...**£75-85**
Same but two small 'ESSO' decals on tank sides **£600-800**
Same but two large 'ESSO' decals on tank sides **£600-700**
11b 58 **'ESSO' Petrol Tanker (E.R.F.)**.
All models with red body and 'ESSO' decal at rear.
Metal wheels, Gold trim **£350-450**
Metal wheels, Silver trim **£75-85**
Grey plastic wheels **£60-70**
Silver plastic wheels...**£1,000-1,100**
Black plastic wheels..**£90-100**
11c 65 **Jumbo Crane**
Yellow body and weight box **£25-30**
Yellow body, Red weight box **£15-20**
11d 69 **Mercedes Scaffolding Truck**
Silver body, Yellow plastic scaffolds, BPW **£15-18**

MB 12

12a 55 **Land Rover**
Green body, Silver trim on some, Tan driver, MW, 43 mm **£40-50**
12b 59 **Land Rover Series II**
Green body, Black plastic wheels, crimped axles............................**£50-60**
BPW, rounded axles..**£35-45**
Grey plastic wheels **£250-350**
12c 65 **Land Rover Safari**
Green body, Brown luggage, BPW...**£25-30**
Blue body, Brown or Red-Brown luggage, BPW............................**£18-20**
Metallic Gold body, BPW, (beware fakes) **£1,200-1,500**

MB 13

13a 55 **Wreck Truck** (51mm).
Tan body, Red crane and hook, MW on crimped axles....................**£40-55**
13b 58 **Wreck Truck** (54mm).
Light Brown body, Red crane and hook, '13' cast-in, MW **£40-60**
Same but with GPW..**£70-85**

13c 60 **Thames Trader Wreck Truck**
All models with Red body and crane.
Yellow side decals, knobbly Grey MW (24 treads), Red hook.......**£70-80**
Fine tread Grey wheels (45 treads), Grey hook.............................**£85-100**
BPW, Silver or Grey hook..**£50-60**
13d 65 **Dodge Wreck Truck**
Green cab, Yellow body, Grey hook, 'BP' decal **£3,500-4,500**
Note: Fakes from 1970 have red hooks, 'BP' labels, crimped
axles and the thick crane casting. Only the original Green cab
version (from the Lesney factory) has a thin crane. But these
fakes (only 24 were produced) are now sought after by some
collectors and thus sell for **£600-800**
Yellow cab, Green body, Grey hook..**£20-30**
Same but with Red hook..**£20-25**

MB 14

14a 55 **Ambulance (Daimler)** (49mm). Cream body, Silver trim,
Red cross on roof, MW on crimped or domed/crimped axles,
no number, 'Ambulance' cast on sides...**£40-50**
14b 58 **Daimler Ambulance** (59 mm). All have a 'Red Cross' on roof.
Cream body, metal wheels **£40-50**
Cream body, Grey plastic wheels **£70-80**
Off-White body, metal wheels **£140-160**
Off-White body, GPW...**£90-110**
Off-White body, SPW..**£200-250**
14c 62 **Bedford Lomas Ambulance**
All models with 'Red Cross' and 'LCC Ambulance' on sides.
White body, Black plastic wheels...**£125-150**
White body, Silver plastic wheels...**£275-300**
Off-White body, Silver plastic wheels **£120-150**
Off-White body, locating marks for Red Cross cast into
roof, Silver grille, Silver plastic wheels...................................**£350-400**
Off-White body, Grey plastic wheels...**£200-240**
Off-White body, Black plastic wheels **£30-35**
14d 68 **Iso Grifo**
Metallic Blue body, Blue interior...**£25-30**
Dark Metallic Blue, Blue interior...**£20-25**

MB 15

15a 55 **Diamond T Prime Mover**
Yellow body, six MW, hook, no number, 55 mm.................**£2,000-2,500**
Orange body, six metal wheels **£30-35**
Same but with ten GPW..**£400-500**
15b 59 **Super Atlantic Tractor**
Orange body, Black base, hook, BPW, 67 mm................................**£50-60**
Orange body, knobbly GPW...**£1,750-2,000**
15c 63 **Tippax Refuse Collector**. All models with Blue body,
Grey container and Black wheels.
With knobbly tread wheels (24 treads), decal................................**£60-70**
With fine tread wheels, *'Cleansing Service'* decal or label...........**£20-25**
15d 68 **Volkswagen 1500 Saloon**
Off-White or Cream body, '137' decals on doors..........................**£35-40**
Same but '137' labels on doors...**£25-35**

MB 16

16a 55 **Transporter Trailer**. Tan body, 6 MW (crimped axles or
domed <u>and</u> crimped axles) **£25-35**
16b 60 **Super Atlantic Trailer**
Beige body, Grey plastic wheels **£90-100**
Orange body, GPW..**£950-1,100**
Orange, BPW, Black or Orange drawbar..**£35-45**
16c 63 **Scammell Snow Plough**. Grey body, Orange tipper,
Red/White or Orange/White decal, GPW **£110-130**
With Black plastic wheels...**£25-30**
16d 69 **Case Bulldozer Tractor**
Red/Yellow body, Green rubber tracks, hook, 64 mm **£12-15**

MB 17

17a 55 **Bedford Removals Van**. All models with
'MATCHBOX REMOVALS SERVICE' decals and MW.
Light Blue body, Silver trim **£200-250**
Maroon body, Silver trim..**£450-500**
Maroon body, Gold trim..**£225-250**
Light or Dark Green body, Silver trim **£200-250**
17b 58 **Bedford Removals Van**
Green body, MW, decal with or without Black outline **£40-50**
Green body, Grey plastic wheels, decal with outline **£70-90**
Dark Green body, GPW, decal with outline.....................................**£175-200**
17c 60 **Austin FX3 Taxi**
Maroon body, Mid-Grey interior, Tan driver, GPW **£45-55**
Same but with SPW, Mid-Grey interior...**£100-120**
With Pale Grey interior and Silver plastic wheels...........................**£120-140**

17d 64 Foden Tipper
Red chassis, Orange tipper, *'HOVERINGHAM'*, Black base..........**£30-40**
Same but with Red base...**£15-20**

17e 69 Horse Box
Red cab, dark green box, grey door,
chrome base, 2 white horses on sprue...**NGPP**

MB 18

18a 55 Caterpillar Bulldozer (46 mm).
Yellow body, Red blade, Green tracks...................................**£40-50**

18b 58 Caterpillar Bulldozer (50 mm).
Yellow body and blade, Green tracks....................................**£60-70**
Same but with Grey tracks...**£70-80**

18c 61 Caterpillar Bulldozer (58 mm).
Yellow body and blade, Green tracks, metal rollers............**£25-30**
Same but Silver plastic rollers **£140-160**
Same but Black plastic rollers..**£25-230**

18d 64 Caterpillar Bulldozer (62 mm). Yellow body and blade,
no driver, Green tracks, Silver plastic rollers....................**£140-160**
Black plastic rollers..**£20-25**

18e 69 Field Car. Yellow body, Red-Brown roof, Red hubs........**£10-15**
Same but unpainted base..**£10-12**
Same but with Green hubs..**£400-500**

MB 19

19a 56 MG Midget TD
Cream body, Brown driver, Red seats, MW, no number, 51 mm..**£80-100**
Off-White body, metal wheels..**£120-140**

19b 58 MG 'MGA' Sports Car. All models with Off-White body,
Red seats and Tan driver.
Metal wheels, Gold trim...**£300-400**
Metal wheels, Silver trim...**£140-160**
Grey plastic wheels, Silver trim..**£140-160**
Silver plastic wheels...**£250-300**

19c 62 Aston Martin DBR5. All models with Metallic Green body,
Yellow wheels, White driver.
Number '19'..**£40-60**
Number '41' or '52'...**£120-140**
Number '3' or '5'..**£80-100**

19d 65 Lotus Racing Car. Dark Green body, Yellow wheels,
White driver, racing number '3' as decal or label.........................**£10-15**
Orange body, RN '3'...**£40-50**

MB 20

20a 56 E.R.F. Stake Truck
Light Green body, Silver trim, metal wheels...................**£2,000-3,000**
Maroon body, Gold trim, MW..**£250-300**
Maroon body, Silver trim, MW...**£35-45**
Maroon body, Silver trim, Grey plastic wheels..................**£200-300**
Dark Red body, metal wheels..**£45-55**
Dark Red body, GPW...**£200-300**

20b 59 E.R.F. 68G Truck. All have Dark Blue body and 'EVER READY'
decals on sides. Early decals with Orange outline, later with Red.
GPW, crimped axles...**£100-125**
GPW, rounded axles...**£100-125**
Silver plastic wheels...**£140-160**
Black plastic wheels...**£60-80**

20c 65 Chevrolet Impala Taxi
Orange-Yellow body, Cream interior, GPW, Taxi decal.......**£1,800-2,000**
Orange-Yellow, Cream interior, BPW, Silver base, Taxi decal **£30-40**
Same but with unpainted base..**£15-20**
Same but with red interior..**£20-30**
Yellow body, Cream interior, Taxi label............................**£120-140**
Same but with Red interior...**£25-30**

MB 21

21a 56 Bedford Coach (57 mm).
Green body and base, *'LONDON-GLASGOW'*, MW **£60-70**

21b 58 Bedford Coach (68 mm).
All have Black base and *'LONDON TO GLASGOW'* decals.
Green body, metal wheels...**£80-100**
Green body, Grey plastic wheels...**£90-110**
Dark Green body, GPW...**£250-300**

21c 61 Commer Bottle Float
All models with Pale Green body and Black base.
On early models the bottles are Cream, later ones are White.
Bottle on door, SPW, clear windows..................................**£100-130**
Bottle on door, SPW, Green windows **£70-80**
Cow on door, SPW..**£50-60**
Cow on door, GPW...**£175-200**
Cow on door, BPW...**£25-30**

21d 68 Foden Concrete Truck
Yellow body, Red chassis, Black wheels..............................**£15-20**

MB 22

22a 56 Vauxhall Cresta. Body colours and shades from Dark
Red to Maroon, roof from White to Cream.......................**£35-45**

22b 58 Vauxhall Cresta
Pale Pink or Cream body, without windows, metal wheels **£600-650**
Same but Grey plastic wheels..**£120-140**
Same but with windows...**£175-200**
Pale Pink body, Blue-Green side panels, GPW **£2,500-3,500**
Light Metallic Brown body, Blue-Green side panels, GPW **£200-250**
Light Grey body, Lilac side panels, Grey or SPW............**£120-125**
Light Gold body, Grey or SPW..**£120-150**
Dark Gold body, Silver wheels..**£120-150**
Metallic Copper body, Grey, Silver or Black wheels **£175-200**

22c 65 Pontiac GP Sports Coupé
Red body, Pale Grey interior, BPW, pattern no. on base..............**£25-35**
Red body, Pale Grey interior, BPW, no pattern no. on base..........**£35-40**

MB 23

23a 56 Berkeley Cavalier Caravan
Pale Blue, *'On Tow MBS 23'*, metal wheels, 65 mm **£40-60**

23b 57 Berkeley Cavalier Caravan. All have *'ON TOW'* rear decal.
Pale Blue, metal wheels..**£30-40**
Lime-Green, metal wheels...**£110-130**
Lime-Green, GPW...**£60-80**
Metallic Lime-Green, GPW...**£1,200-1,500**

23c 60 Bluebird Dauphine Caravan
All models without windows and with *'ON TOW'* rear decal.
Metallic Lime-Green body, Grey plastic wheels **£1,000-1,200**
Metallic Mauve body, Maroon base......................................**£600-800**
Metallic Mauve body and base, Grey plastic wheels **£40-50**
Metallic Mauve body and base, Silver wheels.......................**£30-40**
Metallic Mauve body and base, Black wheels....................**£400-500**
NB A few issues of 23c are known with plastic windows ....**NGPP**

23d 65 Trailer Caravan
Yellow body, knobbly-tread wheels......................................**£12-15**
Yellow body, fine-tread wheels..**£30-40**
Pink body, knobbly-tread wheels...**£30-40**
Pink body, fine-tread wheels..**£12-15**

MB 24

24a 56 'Hydraulic' Excavator
Orange-Yellow body, metal wheels, *'WEATHERILL'*, 58 mm **£30-40**
Same but Yellow body, metal wheels, *'WEATHERILL'*.................**£50-70**

24b 59 'Hydraulic' Excavator
Yellow body, Grey plastic wheels, crimped axles **£35-45**
Yellow body, Grey plastic wheels, rounded axles **£25-30**
Yellow body, Black plastic wheels.......................................**£15-20**

24c 67 Rolls-Royce Silver Shadow
All models with Metallic Red body and Black base.
Black wheels with Silver hubcaps..**£20-25**
Silver wheels with Black tyres...**£15-18**

MB 25

25a 56 Bedford 12 cwt Van
Dark Blue body, Black base, *'DUNLOP'* decals, MW **£40-50**
Grey plastic wheels...**£45-55**
Black plastic wheels...**£1,200-1,500**

25b 60 Volkswagen 1200
Metallic Steel-Blue body, GPW, clear windows.................**£60-70**
As previous model but with Green tinted windows.............**£45-55**
Same but with SPW..**£50-60**

25c 64 Bedford Petrol Tanker
Yellow cab, Green chassis, White tank, *'BP'*, BPW **£20-25**
Same but Grey plastic wheels..**£600-800**

** 64** German issue: Dark Blue cab and chassis,
White tank, *'ARAL'*, Black plastic wheels............................**£150-200**

25d 68 Ford Cortina Mk.II
Metallic Light Brown body, Black plastic wheels...............**£20-25**
Gift Set issue: Same but with Yellow roof rack **£40-60**
Blue body, Silver base, Black plastic wheels **£800-1,100**

MB 26

26a 56 E.R.F. Cement Mixer (45 mm)
Orange body, Gold trim, MW, crimped axles.....................**£275-300**
Same but with Silver trim...**£45-55**
With GPW, Silver trim...**£80-90**
With SPW, Silver trim...**£600-800**

26b 61 Foden Cement Mixer (66 mm)
Orange body, Lt or Dk Grey barrel, small knobbly GPW.......**£800-1,000**

Orange body, Orange barrel, Grey or Black plastic wheels **£20-25**
Orange body, Orange barrel, Silver plastic wheels.....................**£800-900**

26c 68 G.M.C. Tipper Truck
Red cab, Green chassis, Silver tipper, BPW, 67 mm.......................**£10-12**

MB 27

27a 56 Bedford Low Loader (78mm)
Pale Blue cab, Dark Blue trailer, six MW, crimped axles **£700-900**
Pale Green cab, Tan trailer...**£90-110**

27b 58 Bedford Low Loader (95mm)
Pale Green cab, Tan trailer, metal wheels.................................**£80-90**
Same but with GPW..**£120-140**
Dark Green cab, Light Brown trailer, Grey plastic wheels **£140-160**

27c 60 Cadillac Sixty Special
Metallic Pale Green, Cream roof, GG, Crimson base, SPW **£350-400**
Silver-Grey body, Off-White roof, SPW...................................**£110-130**
Metallic Lilac body, Pink roof, Crimson base, GPW or SPW **£125-150**
Same model but with Black base..**£90-110**
Same but Black base and BPW **£120-130**

27d 66 Mercedes 230 SL
White body, Red interior...**£18-20**

MB 28

28a 56 Bedford Compressor
Orange/Yellow body, Silver trim, metal wheels, 47 mm.................**£25-35**
Yellow body, Silver trim, MW, domed/crimped axles....................**£50-60**

28b 59 Ford Thames Compressor Truck
Yellow body, Black wheels, crimped axles **£40-50**
Yellow body, Black wheels, rounded axles **£20-25**
Yellow body, Grey wheels **£900-1,100**

28c 64 Jaguar Mk.10
Pale Metallic Brown, Cream seats, BPW, 74 mm **£30-40**
With 'Matchbox' lapel badge...**£50-60**
With GPW and without 'Matchbox Series' on base **£800-900**

28d 68 Mack Dump Truck
Orange body, Red wheels **£15-20**
Orange body, Yellow wheels..**£20-25**

MB 29

29a 56 Bedford Milk Delivery Van
Light Brown body, White bottle load, metal wheels, 57 mm.........**£35-45**
Same but GPW, White or Cream bottles **£40-50**

29b 61 Austin A55 Cambridge
Two-tone Green body, Green tinted windows, GPW **£35-45**
Same but SPW, clear or tinted windows....................................**£35-45**
Same but with BPW..**£20-25**

29c 66 Fire Pumper Truck
Red body, with or without *'Denver'* decal **£15-20**

MB 30

30a 56 Ford Prefect
Grey-Brown body, Red and Silver trim, MW, 58 mm **£30-35**
Same but with GPW..**£40-50**
Same but Light Blue body, Grey plastic wheels, 58 mm **£220-260**

30b 61 Magirus-Deutz Crane Lorry
Light Brown body, Red or Orange crane, GPW..................**£5,000-7,500**
Silver body, Orange jib and hook, Grey or Silver wheels.............**£60-70**
Silver body, Orange jib, Grey or Silver hook, Grey or BPW.........**£30-35**

30c 65 8 Wheel Crane Truck
Green body, Orange jib **£15-20**
Turquoise body, Orange jib..**£600-700**

MB 31

31a 57 Ford Station Wagon
Yellow body, metal wheels, 66 mm..**£40-45**
Yellow body, Grey plastic wheels...**£45-55**

31b 60 Ford Fairlane Station Wagon
Yellow body, Black base, Grey plastic wheels **£300-350**
Yellow body, Black base, Silver plastic wheels.........................**£250-300**
Yellow body, Crimson base, clear or Green windows, SPW **£200-250**
Metallic Green body, Pink roof, Crimson base, GPW or SPW......**£40-50**
Same but with Black base, SPW..**£60-70**
Same but with Black base, GPW..**£80-90**
Same but with Black base, BPW **£100-120**

31c 64 Lincoln Continental
Metallic Blue body, BPW **£18-20**
Sea Green body **£15-18**
Metallic Lime Green body **£1,400-1,600**

MB 32

32a 57 Jaguar XK-140
Off-White body, Black base, metal wheels, 60 mm **£40-50**
Same but with GPW..**£50-65**
Red body, metal wheels **£80-100**
Bright Orange-Red body, GPW **£175-225**
Dark Red, Black base, GPW **£175-225**

32b 62 Jaguar 'E'-type
Metallic Red body, Green windows, Grey tyres, 66 mm **£180-200**
Metallic Red body, clear windows, grey tyres.............................**£45-55**
Metallic Red body, clear windows, Black tyres **£40-50**

32c 68 Leyland Tanker All have a White tank.
Green chassis, Silver base and grille, 'BP' decal **£40-50**
Green chassis, Silver base and grille, 'BP' label.........................**£15-20**
Green chassis, White base and grille, 'BP' label.........................**£80-100**
Blue chassis, Silver base and grille, 'ARAL' label....................**£150-175**

Matchbox Motor Cycles and Sidecars
66b Harley-Davidson   36b Lambretta Motor Scooter   4c Triumph T110
(See also pages 38 and 39 for colour pictures of early Matchbox models)

MB 33

33a 57 **Ford Zodiac**
Dark Green body, hook, no windows, MW, 68 mm......................**£30-40**
58 Dark Blue body, hook, no windows, metal wheels..................**£700-800**
58 Sea-Green body, hook, no windows, metal wheels...............**£100-120**
Same but with GPW..**£60-75**
59 Metallic Mauve body, Orange panels, no windows, GPW.........**£110-130**
60 Same but with Green tinted windows, GPW or SPW...............**£70-90**
33b 63 **Ford Zephyr 6**. Sea-Green body, GPW, 67 mm..................**£40-50**
same but with SPW..**£25-35**
same but with BPW..**£20-25**
33c 68 **Lamborghini Miura**
Yellow body, White interior, 71 mm. Black plastic wheels.........**£15-20**
Yellow body, White interior, Chrome hubs...........................**£300-400**
Metallic Gold body, White interior, Chrome hubs...................**£300-350**

MB 34

34a 57 **Volkswagen 15cwt Van**. All have Blue body; 'MATCHBOX' decals.
Metal wheels..**£35-45**
Grey plastic wheels...**£35-45**
Silver plastic wheels..**£1,500-2,000**
34b 62 **Volkswagen Caravette**. All have Pale Green body; Green interior.
Silver wheels..**£250-300**
Knobbly-tread Grey wheels (24 treads)..............................**£40-50**
Fine-tread Grey wheels (45 treads)...................................**£50-60**
Black wheels..**£35-45**
34c 67 **Volkswagen Camper**
Silver body, with high roof (7 windows).............................**£25-30**
same but lower roof (1 window)..**£20-25**
Pale Green body, Dark Green base/interior, SPW.............**£1,500-1,750**

MB 35

35a 57 **E.R.F. Marshall Horse Box**
Red cab, Beige back, metal wheels, 52 mm........................**£30-35**
Same but with GPW...**£30-40**
With Silver plastic wheels...**£175-200**
With Black plastic wheels..**£75-90**
35b 64 **Snow-Trac**. Red body, Silver base, White tracks,
'Snow Trac' cast on sides..**£25-30**
same but with 'Snow Trac' decals on sides........................**£15-20**
same but without 'Snow Trac'..**£15-20**

MB 36

36a 57 **Austin A50 Cambridge**
Blue-Green body, Black base, metal wheels, 60 mm.............**£30-35**
Same but with GPW...**£30-40**
Pale Blue body, GPW..**£50-60**
36b 61 **Lambretta and Sidecar**
Pale Metallic Green Scooter and side-car, BPW, 49 mm..........**£60-80**
36c 66 **Opel Diplomat**
Metallic Gold body, Silver engine.....................................**£10-15**
Metallic Gold body, Grey engine......................................**£35-45**

MB 37

37a 57 **Karrier Bantam Lorry** (open base)
All models with 'COCA-COLA' side and rear decals.
Orange-Yellow body, uneven load, metal wheels.................**£180-200**
Yellow body, uneven load, metal wheels...........................**£180-200**
Orange-Yellow body, even load, metal wheels......................**£45-55**
Orange-Yellow body, even load, grey plastic wheels............**£180-220**
Yellow body, even load, metal wheels................................**£60-80**
Yellow body, even load, Grey plastic wheels......................**£220-240**
37b 60 **Karrier Bantam Lorry** (Black baseplate)
All models with 'COCA-COLA' side and rear decals.
GPW, crimped axles..**£100-120**
GPW, rounded axles..**£35-45**
Silver plastic wheels..**£750-850**
Black plastic wheels...**£70-80**
37c 66 **(Dodge) Cattle Truck**. Yellow body, Grey cattle box,
2 White bulls, Silver plastic base....................................**£15-20**
Unpainted metal base...**£10-15**

MB 38

38a 57 **Karrier Refuse Collector**
All models with 'Cleansing Department' side decals.
Grey-Brown body, MW..**£350-400**
Grey body, metal wheels..**£40-50**
Grey body, GPW, crimped axles..**£75-85**
Grey body, GPW, rounded axles..**£50-60**
Silver body, GPW..**£50-60**
Silver body, SPW...**£600-700**

38b 63 **Vauxhall Victor Estate**
Yellow body, Red interior, Grey wheels............................**£200-300**
same but with Silver wheels...**£25-30**
same but with Black wheels..**£20-25**
Yellow body, Green interior, GPW.....................................**£60-70**
same but with Silver wheels...**£30-35**
same but with Black wheels..**£20-25**
38c **Honda Motorcycle and Trailer**
Metallic Green bike, Orange trailer without decals................**£30-40**
Same, but Orange trailer with 'Honda' decals....................**£80-120**
Same, but Yellow trailer with 'Honda' decals or labels.........**£20-25**

MB 39

39a 57 **Ford Zodiac Convertible**
Pale Peach body, Light Brown base/interior/driver, MW..........**£300-400**
Same but with Light Green base and interior, metal wheels......**£70-80**
Same but with Light Green base, Grey plastic wheels............**£60-70**
Pale Peach body, Silver plastic wheels............................**£200-300**
Dark Peach body, Blue-Green base and interior, GPW............**£60-80**
Dark Peach body, Blue-Green base and interior, SPW...........**£120-150**
Dark Peach body with Sea-Green base, Grey plastic wheels.....**£75-85**
39b 62 **Pontiac Convertible**
Metallic Purple body, Crimson base, Red steering wheel, SPW..**£100-120**
Same but with Grey wheels..**£450-500**
Lemon body, Crimson base, Red steering wheel, SPW or GPW....**£65-75**
Same but Cream steering wheel...**£25-35**
Lemon body, Black base, SPW..**£80-90**
Same but with Grey wheels...**£80-100**
Same but with Black wheels..**£30-35**
39c 67 **Ford Tractor**
Blue body, Yellow engine cover, Black plastic tyres, 55 mm.....**£15-20**
Blue body and engine cover..**£20-25**
All-Orange body, Yellow hubs..**£70-80**

MB 40

40a 57 **Bedford 7 Ton Tipper**
Red body, Brown tipper, metal wheels, 53 mm.....................**£35-45**
Same but with Grey plastic wheels, domed crimped axles.......**£35-45**
Same but with Grey plastic wheels on rivetted axles............**£30-35**
40b 61 **Leyland Tiger Coach**
Steel Blue body, GPW...**£90-110**
Silver plastic wheels...**£25-35**
Black plastic wheels...**£20-25**
40c 67 **Hay Trailer**. Blue body, Yellow plastic hay racks
and wheels, Black plastic tyres...**£12-15**
NB No. 40c deleted in 1972 but appeared in Two-Packs between 1976-1981.

MB 41

41a 57 **Jaguar 'D'-Type** (55 mm)
Green body, MW, No '41'..**£70-80**
Green body, MW, No '52'..**£400-500**
Green body, GPW, No '41'..**£90-120**
41b 60 **Jaguar 'D'-Type** (62 mm). All have Green body and Black base.
GPW, crimped axles, No '41'..**£70-80**
same but with rounded axles..**£60-70**
Wire hubs with Black tyres, No '41'...................................**£60-80**
same but with No '5' or '6'..**£150-200**
Red hubs with Black tyres...**£400-500**
41c 65 **Ford GT Racer**. All models with racing number '6'.
White body, Red hubs and interior, BPT............................**£300-400**
White body, Yellow hubs, Black tyres................................**£20-25**
Yellow body, Yellow hubs, black tyres (US set)...................**£175-200**
White body, spoked wheels, Black tyres.........................**£2,000-2,200**

MB 42

42a 57 **Evening News Van**
Yellow body, 'EVENING NEWS' decals, MW, 57 mm...............**£35-40**
GPW with 24 treads..**£35-40**
GPW or BPW with 45 treads...**£150-175**
BPW with 24 treads..**£125-150**
42b 65 **Studebaker Lark Wagonaire** (with hunter and dog figures),
Blue body, sliding rear roof painted as body......................**£100-150**
Same but rear roof painted Light Blue................................**£25-30**
42c 69 **Iron Fairy Crane**. Red body, Yellow boom, BPW.............**£15-18**

MB 43

43a 58 **Hillman Minx**
Apple Green body, Silver/Red trim, metal wheels, hook.........**£500-750**
Blue/Grey body, Pale Grey roof, metal wheels......................**£40-45**
Same but with GPW..**£60-70**
Turquoise body, Cream roof, Grey plastic wheels.................**£50-60**

43b 62 A.B. Tractor Shovel
Yellow body, driver and shovel...£150-200
Yellow body and shovel, Red driver and base..........................£20-25
Yellow body, driver and base, Red shovel...............................£40-45
Yellow body, Red driver, base and shovel...............................£250-300

43c 68 Pony Trailer
Yellow body, Grey ramp, Light Brown base, BPW £15-20
same but with Dark Green base...£10-15

MB 44

44a 58 Rolls-Royce Silver Cloud
Metallic Silver-Blue body, Red trim, metal wheels, 67 mm £30-35
   60 As previous but with GPW £30-40
Same but with SPW £60-70

44b 64 Rolls-Royce Phantom V
Metallic Mauve body, Black plastic wheels.............................£25-30
Same but with Grey plastic wheels...£200-250
Same but with Silver plastic wheels...£250-300
Metallic Silver-Grey body, Black plastic wheels.....................£90-110
Same but with Silver plastic wheels...£400-600

44c 67 GMC Refrigerator Truck
Red body, Sea-Green container, Black wheels, 76 mm...................£10-15

MB 45

45a 58 Vauxhall Victor
Red body, MW, 61 mm £2,000-3,000
Yellow or Lemon body, MW..£35-40
Yellow body, metal wheels, no dashboard casting bar £350-375
Yellow or Lemon body, GPW, no window glazing £40-45
same but with clear windows...£70-80
same but with Green windows...£50-60
Lemon, Green windows, SPW...£80-90
Yellow body, SPW or BPW...£80-90

45b 65 Ford Corsair with Boat
Cream body, Red interior, Black wheels, Silver painted base........£40-45
Same but with unpainted base £25-30
Same but with Grey wheels £80-100
Models with white interior are pre-productions £600-800

MB 46

46a 58 Morris Minor 1000
Pale Brown body, no windows, metal wheels, 53 mm........£2,000-3,000
Dark Green body, Black base, MW, domed crimped axles............£60-70
Dark Blue/Green body, MW...£70-80
Same but with GPW £100-125
Blue body, GPW £150-200

46b 60 'PICKFORDS' Removals Van
Dark Blue body, GPW, three line decal £90-120
Dark Blue body, SPW, three line decal.....................................£140-160
Dark Blue body, GPW, two line decal £150-200
Dark Blue body, SPW, two line decal £250-300
Green body, GPW £80-110
Green body, SPW £140-160
Green body, BPW £60-80
'BEALES BEALESONS' Van. Light Brown body,
'Beales Bealesons' decal, BPW, without box..........................£400-500
Same but in special White box with 'sun' and
'It's A Pleasure' decal..£500-600

46c 68 Mercedes-Benz 300 SE. Green body.............................£20-25
   69 Metallic Blue body...£15-20

MB 47

47a 58 Trojan Van
Red body, *'BROOKE BOND TEA'* decals, MW, 58 mm.................£35-45
Same but with GPW..£50-60

47b 63 Commer Ice Cream Van *'LYONS MAID'*,
Metallic Blue body, BPW...£120-150
Same but with Blue body..£30-40
Blue body, knobbly Grey plastic wheels £350-450
Blue body, Black wheels, White side decals £40-50
Cream body, *'LYONS MAID'*..£200-230
Cream body, White side decals..£60-70
'LORD NIELSENS ICE CREAM',
Cream body, Red/White labels, Black base, BPW.....................£80-90
Blue body, Black plastic wheels £100-130

47c 68 DAF Container Truck
Sea Green body, Grey roof, Yellow container, BPW.................£50-60
Silver body, Grey or Silver roof, Yellow container, BPW £12-15

MB 48

48a 58 Meteor Sports Boat and Trailer
Black trailer, Light Brown boat, Blue hull, metal wheels £30-40
With Grey plastic wheels £50-60
With Silver plastic wheels..£175-200

48b 61 Sports Boat and Trailer. Boat with Cream or White deck and
Red hull or with Red deck and Cream or white hull.
Dark Blue trailer, Black plastic wheels £50-60
Dark Blue trailer, Grey plastic wheels......................................£100-120
Light Blue trailer, Black plastic wheels....................................£40-50

48c 66 (Dodge) Dumper Truck
Red body, Silver trim, wide or narrow BPW, 76 mm £10-15

MB 49

49a 58 M3 Personnel Carrier
Military Green, White bonnet star on some, MW and rollers........£25-30
Grey plastic wheels, metal rollers...£30-35
Grey plastic wheels and Grey plastic rollers £350-400
Grey plastic wheels, Silver rollers £80-100
BPW and rollers, Grey tracks..£30-40
BPW and rollers, Green tracks...£30-40

49b 67 (Mercedes) Unimog
Light Brown body, Sea-Green base, 61 mm..............................£20-25
Light Brown body, Red base (factory error?)............................£700-800
Light Blue body, Red base..£15-20

MB 50

50a 58 Commer Pick-Up
Pale Brown body, MW, 64 mm..£30-40
Pale or Light Brown body, GPW..£35-45
Light Brown body, SPW...£150-180
Red and White body, SPW...£600-800
Red and Grey body, SPW...£180-200
Red and Grey body, GPW...£180-200
Red and Grey body, BPW...£160-180

50b 64 John Deere Lanz Tractor
Green body, Yellow hubs, Grey tyres, 50 mm...........................£20-25
Same but Black tyres..£10-15

50c 69 Ford Kennel Truck
Metallic Green body, White grille, smooth kennel floor............£20-25
Same but textured kennel floor and/or Silver grille £15-20

MB 51

51a 58 Albion Chieftain
All models with Yellow body, Tan or Light Beige load,
'PORTLAND CEMENT' decals, metal wheels £40-55
'BLUE CIRCLE PORTLAND CEMENT' decals, MW..................£50-60
Same but with GPW..£40-55
Same but with SPW..£180-200
Same but with knobbly BPW...£200-250

51b 64 Tipping Trailer
Green body, three Yellow barrels, Yellow hubs, Grey tyres...........£10-15
With Yellow hubs, Black tyres...£12-15

51c 69 AEC Mammoth Major 8 Wheel Tipper
Orange body, Silver tipper, *'DOUGLAS'*, White base grille........£90-110
Same but chrome base £40-50
Yellow body, Silver tipper, *'DOUGLAS'*..................................£60-80
Yellow body, Silver tipper, *'POINTER'*...................................£25-35

MB 52

52a 58 1948 Maserati 4 CLT
Red body, Cream driver, no decal, BPW, 61 mm £40-50
Same with racing number '52'..£35-45
Red body, racing number '52', wire wheels, BPT......................£350-400
Lemon body, wire wheels, '30' or '52'.......................................£40-50
Same but number '3' or '5'...£120-140

52b 65 B.R.M. Racing Car
Blue body, Yellow hubs, BPT, '5'..£15-20
Same but with racing number '3' £60-80
Dark Blue (Ultramarine) body, racing number '5' £75-85
Gift Set model: Red body, Yellow hubs with Black tyres £70-80
Dark Cherry Red body, Yellow hubs, racing number '5' £100-120

MB 53

53a 58 Aston Martin DB2-4 Mk.I
Metallic Green body, MW, 65 mm £30-40
Same but with GPW..£60-80
Metallic Red, knobbly GPW £300-350
Metallic Red, knobbly BPW £200-240

53b 63 Mercedes-Benz 220SE
Maroon body, Silver wheels £25-30
Maroon body, Grey wheels £30-40
Maroon body, Black wheels £60-80
Dark Red body, Grey wheels £60-80
Dark Red body, Black wheels £20-25
53c 68 Ford Zodiac Mk.IV
Light Metallic Blue body, BPW £20-25
Light Metallic Green body, Black plastic wheels.............**£1,000-1,250**

MB 54

54a 58 Saracen Personnel Carrier
Olive Green body, six BPW, crimped axles....................£25-35
Same but with rounded axles...£20-25
54b 65 Cadillac Ambulance
White, Red cross label or decal and roof lights, BPW £20-25

MB 55

55a 58 DUKW Amphibian
Olive Green body, MW £20-25
Same but GPW or BPW £35-40
In box with Green model picture (normally Red picture)..........£180-200
55b 63 Ford Fairlane 'POLICE' Car
Non-metallic Dark Blue body, BPW £280-320
Metallic Blue, knobbly BPW £120-130
Metallic Blue, BPW £70-90
Metallic Blue, GPW £900-1,200
Metallic Blue, SPW £450-500
55c 66 Ford Galaxy 'POLICE' Car
White body, 'Police & Shield' decal, Blue roof light.............£150-200
same but with Red roof light £18-20
55d 68 Mercury 'POLICE' Car
White body, 'Police & Shield' labels, Red roof light...........£350-380
Same but with Blue roof light...£25-35

MB 56

56a 58 London Trolley Bus. All models with Red body,
'DRINK PEARDRAX' and destination decals.
Black poles, metal wheels, (beware fakes) £250-300
Black poles, GPW, (beware fakes) £300-400
Red poles, metal wheels £45-55
Red poles, GPW £300-400
Red poles, BPW £45-55
Red poles, SPW £150-180
56b 65 Fiat 1500 (all have Black plastic wheels)
Sea-Green body, Brown luggage £15-20
Same but with Red-Brown luggage £10-15
Gift Set version: Red body, Red-Brown luggage £70-80

MB 57

57a 58 Wolseley 1500
Pale Green body, GPW, Gold trim, 55 mm £220-250
Same but with Silver trim £35-45
57b 61 Chevrolet Impala
All versions have Metallic Blue body and Pale Blue roof.
Clear windows, Black base, SPW £110-130
Clear windows, Dark Blue base, SPW £70-80
Green windows, Dark Blue base, SPW £25-30
Green windows, Dark Blue base, GPW £50-60
Green windows, Pale or Light Blue base, SPW £120-140
Black base, GPW £75-85
Black base, SPW £70-80
Black base, BPW £60-70
57c 66 Land Rover Fire Truck
Red body, 'KENT FIRE BRIGADE', BPW, 64 mm £25-30
Same but with GPW...£500-750

MB 58

58a 58 AEC 'BEA' Coach
Dark Blue body, White letters, Grey wheels, 65 mm £50-60
Dark Blue body, Black letters on White ground, GPW £40-50
Same but with SPW £175-200
Same but with BPW £200-225
58b 62 Drott Excavator
Red body, Silver base, Black rollers, Green tracks £20-25
Same but with Silver rollers £100-120
Orange body, Silver base, Black rollers £25-30
Orange body and base, Black rollers £15-20
58c 68 DAF Girder Truck
White body, Red base and 12 girders, 6 BPW, 75 mm £10-15

MB 59

59a 58 Ford Thames Van 'SINGER'
Pale Green body, GPW...£60-75
Same but SPW, rivetted axles £200-250
Dark Green body and Grey plastic wheels, rivetted axles £220-250
Dark Green body, Silver plastic wheels, rivetted axles.............£250-300
59b 63 Ford Fairlane Fire Chief
All models with Red body and 'FIRE CHIEF' decals on
doors and bonnet, BPW £40-50
With GPW £200-250
With SPW £250-300
With shield decals on doors (pre-production trial) £200-250
59c 66 Ford Galaxie Fire Chief
Red body, Blue dome light, 'FIRE CHIEF', BPW £20-25
Same but with Red dome light £250-350

MB 60

60a 58 Morris J2 Pick Up
All with Light Blue body and 'BUILDERS SUPPLY COMPANY'
decals. 'Supply Company' in Black, Grey plastic wheels.............£50-60
'SUPPLY COMPANY' in White, with rear window,
GPW or BPW £30-35
Same but with SPW £40-50
Without rear window, GPW £180-200
Without rear window, BPW £30-40
60b 66 Site Hut Truck
Blue body, Yellow and Green plastic building, Black wheels........£12-18

MB 61

61a 59 Ferret Scout Car
Olive Green body, Tan driver, Black plastic wheels, 57 mm £25-30
61b 66 Alvis Stalwart 'BP'
White body, Green wheels with BPT, smooth carrier bed £30-40
Same but with ribbed carrier bed.....................................£15-20
White body, Yellow wheels with Black tyres £60-80
Two-Pack version: Military Olive Green body, Black wheels............£20-30

MB 62

62a 59 AEC General Service Lorry
Olive Green body, tow hook, six BPT, 68 mm.................£30-35
62b 63 Commer TV Service Van
All have Cream body, Red plastic ladder, aerial and 3 TV's.
'RENTASET', knobbly Grey wheels (24 treads)..........£400-500
'RENTASET', Black wheels £40-50
'RENTASET', fine-tread Grey wheels (45 treads) £300-350
'RADIO RENTALS', BPW £50-60
'RADIO RENTALS', fine-tread Grey wheels £450-550
62c 68 Mercury Cougar
Cream body, White interior, Chrome hubs £2,000-2,500
Metallic Lime Green body, Red interior...........................£10-15

MB 63

63a 59 Service Ambulance (Ford)
Olive Green body, Red crosses, BPW, crimped axles £35-40
Same but with rounded axles £25-30
63b 63 Alvis Foamite Crash Tender
Red body, Silver hose nozzle, six BPW, 63 mm £85-100
With Gold hose nozzle £20-30
63c 68 Dodge Crane Truck
Yellow body, Red hook, 76 mm £10-15
Yellow body, Yellow hook £15-18

MB 64

64a 59 Scammell Breakdown Truck
Olive Green body, metal or plastic hook, BPW, 64 mm £35-45
64b 66 MG 1100
Green body, White seats, driver, dog, BPT, 67 mm £15-20

MB 65

65a 59 Jaguar 3.4 litre
Dark Blue body, Silver rear number-plate, GPW, 62 mm..............£80-90
As previous but with Blue rear number plate...................£35-45
Metallic Blue body and number plate, Grey plastic wheels.......£100-130
65b 62 Jaguar 3.8 Sedan
Metallic Red body, Silver base, Silver plastic wheels, 68 mm £80-90
Red body, Silver plastic wheels £150-200
Red body, Grey plastic wheels £50-60
Red body, Black plastic wheels £30-35
65c 67 Claas Combine Harvester
Red body, Yellow blades and front hubs, no hole in base.........£150-250
As previous but with hole in base......................................£10-12

MB 66

66a 59 **Citroën DS 19**
Yellow body, Silver trim, GPW £50-60
Same but with SPW £150-200
66b 62 **Harley-Davidson Motor Cycle**
Metallic Bronze bike and sidecar, spoked wheels, BPT.............£100-120
66c 66 **'GREYHOUND' Coach**
Silver-Grey body, clear windows, Black plastic wheels...............£90-110
Silver-Grey body, Amber windows, Black plastic wheels £10-15

MB 67

67a 59 **Saladin Armoured Car**
Olive Green body, six BPW, crimped axles, 61 mm £30-35
Same but with rounded axles £25-30
67b 67 **Volkswagen 1600 TL**
Red body, Black wheels with Silver hubcaps...............................£25-30
Red body, Silver wheels with black tyres.................................£18-20
Gift Set version: Red body with Maroon plastic roof rack £80-90
Metallic Purple body, Chrome hubs with Black tyres................£300-400

MB 68

68a 59 **Austin Radio Truck Mk.II**
Olive Green body and base, BPW, crimped axles........................£30-35
Same but with rounded axles £25-30
68b 65 **Mercedes Coach** (all have BPW)
Turquoise/White body, US issue...£180-200
Orange/White body, BPW...£15-20

MB 69

69a 59 **Commer Van 'NESTLES'**
Maroon body, driver, Yellow logo, GPW, 56 mm £45-55
Red body, GPW with 20 treads..£60-70
Red body, GPW with 36 treads..£90-100
69b 65 **Hatra Tractor Shovel**
Orange body, Orange wheels, Grey tyres, 78 mm £65-75
With Red hubs, Grey tyres...£30-40
With Red hubs, Black tyres..£25-30
With Yellow hubs, Black tyres...£20-25
Yellow body, Yellow hubs..£20-25
Yellow body, Red hubs...£100-120
Orange body, Yellow shovel £500-600

MB 70

70a 59 **Ford Thames Estate Car**
Turquoise and Yellow body, Grey wheels, no windows..................£40-45
Grey wheels, clear windows..£40-50
Grey wheels, Green windows £25-30
Silver wheels, clear windows..£40-50
Silver or Black wheels, Green windows £35-40
70b 66 **Ford Grit Spreader**
Red body, Pale Lemon container, BPW, 68 mm £15-20
Red body, Dark Yellow container, Black or Grey slide, BPW.......£60-70

MB 71

71a 59 **200 gallon Austin Water Truck (with Badge)**
Olive Green, BPW, with first *'Matchbox Collectors'* badge.........£75-100
Same model, but without badge..£30-40

71b 64 **Jeep Gladiator Pick-Up**
Red body, Green interior, Black plastic wheels, 66 mm £50-60
Red body, White interior £20-25
71c 69 **Ford Heavy Wreck Truck** (all BPW)
Red and White body, Amber windows, smooth loadbed............£500-700
Same but with ribbed loadbed £400-500
Same but with Green windows £20-25
Military Green body..£20-25

MB 72

72a 59 **Fordson Major Tractor**. All models with Blue body.
Grey front wheels, Orange rear hubs with Grey tyres, 50 mm £40-45
Black front wheels, Orange rear hubs with Black tyres £35-40
Orange hubs front and rear, Grey tyres..................................£40-45
Orange hubs front and rear, BPT.......................................£30-35
Yellow hubs front and rear, Grey or Black tyres £900-1,000
72b 66 **Jeep CJ5**
Orange-Yellow body, Yellow hubs, White interior..................£800-1,000
Yellow body, Yellow hubs, Red interior £15-20

MB 73

73a 59 **Leyland R.A.F. 10 ton Refueller**
Airforce-Blue body, roundel, six GPW, 66 mm £50-60
Same but with BPW...£2,500-3,000
73b 62 **Ferrari F1 Racing Car**. Red body, Grey or White driver,
RN '73', 'spoked' metal hubs, Black plastic tyres £30-35
73c 68 **Mercury Commuter Station Wagon**
Metallic Lime Green body, Silver hubs, Black plastic tyres £12-15

MB 74

74a 59 **Mobile 'REFRESHMENTS' Bar**
White body, Pale Blue base, Blue interior, GPW £175-225
Cream body, Light Blue base, Grey plastic wheels...................£200-250
Pinkish Cream body, Light Blue base, Grey plastic wheels........£500-600
Silver body, Light Blue base, Grey plastic wheels....................£30-40
Silver body, Turquoise base, Silver plastic wheels..................£250-300
Silver body, Light Blue base, Black plastic wheels................£800-1,000
Silver body, Sea Green or Dark Blue base £100-120
74b 66 **Daimler Fleetline Bus**
Cream body, 'ESSO' decals £15-20
Cream body, 'ESSO' labels £30-35
Green body, 'ESSO' labels £15-20
Red body, 'ESSO' labels £30-35

MB 75

75a 60 **Ford Thunderbird** All have Cream body and Peach side panels.
Blue base, SPW £50-75
Blue-Green base, SPW £300-400
Black base, SPW £70-80
Black base, GPW £120-150
Black base, BPW £350-400
75b 65 **Ferrari Berlinetta**
Metallic Green body, wire wheels, Silver painted base................£50-60
Metallic Green body, wire wheels, unpainted base £20-25
Metallic Green body, Silver wheels with Black tyres £15-20
Red body, Chrome hubs with Black tyres £280-320
Red body, wire wheels £600-650

'Matchbox Series' Miniature Metal Vehicles by Lincoln Industries, New Zealand. See opposite page for details.

Matchbox '1-75' Series early Accessory Packs

A1a	1957	**'ESSO' Petrol Pump Set**................Red pumps, White figure................	**£30-40**
A1b	1963	**'BP' Petrol Pump Set**................White pumps, Yellow/White decal................	**£25-35**

A2 1957 **Car Transporter**...................Box type 1: Dark Blue/Yellow front and back 'MOKO - LESNEY' line-drawing box.
Box type 2: Yellow front/back, Blue end tabs, 'LESNEY MATCHBOX SERIES' logo.
    1: Pale blue body, Dark Blue logo 'MATCHBOX CAR TRANSPORTER', metal wheels on tractor and trailer, 1st type box...........................**£50-60**
    2: Pale Blue body, Red 'CAR COLLECTION Ltd CAR TRANSPORTER', Black plastic wheels on tractor and trailer, 1st type box...............**£60-70**
    3: Pale blue body, Red 'CAR COLLECTION Ltd CAR TRANSPORTER', Grey plastic wheels on tractor and trailer, 1st type box...............**£40-50**
    4: Red cab and lower deck, Grey upper deck and sides, BPW, Red logo: 'CAR COLLECTION Ltd' on Pale Yellow background, 2nd box...**£220-240**

A3	1957	**Garage** ....Yellow/Green/Red, opening doors, all metal with metal connecting clip........................	**£30-40**
A4	1960	**Road Signs Set**...................Eight Red/White/Black signs 'Lesney' on base...................	**£30-40**
A5	1960	**'HOME STORES' Shop**.................Food shop with window display and opening door..................	**£40-45**
MG1a	1959	**Service Station and Showroom**......'MATCHBOX GARAGE', Red plastic building with Yellow base and roof sign................	**£70-80**
		Same but Yellow plastic building with Red base and roof sign................	**£60-75**
MG1b	1961	**Service Station and Showroom**......'MATCHBOX', Yellow plastic building and ramp, Red sign 'MATCHBOX', 'ESSO'................	**£180-200**
		Same but White plastic building with Green base and Yellow sign 'BP'................	**£120-150**
MG1c	1968	**Service Station**...................Green and Yellow plastic building and card forecourt 'BP'...............	**£65-75**
MF1a	1963	**Fire Station** ....White building with Green roof, 'MATCHBOX FIRE STATION' on a Brown or Red background........	**£200-250**
		White building with Red roof, 'MATCHBOX FIRE STATION' on a Brown or Red background..........	**£160-190**

'Matchbox' Series Painting Books

Four different types of cover and contents numbered 1 to 4.
Mint unused set of books...................**£2,000-3,000**

Major Packs Series

M1 58 Caterpillar Earthmover
Yellow body, MW, crimped or rounded axles, 99mm...........**£40-50**

M1 63 'BP' Petrol Tanker
Green/Yellow/White body, knobbly or fine tread BPW.......**£75-100**

M2 58 Bedford Articulated Truck 'WALLS ICE CREAM'
All versions have a Light Blue tractor cab, 101mm.
Cream trailer, metal wheels **£50-60**
59   Cream trailer, Grey plastic wheels...................**£50-60**
59-61 White trailer, Grey plastic wheels....................**£75-85**

M2 61 Bedford Tractor and York Trailer 'DAVIES TYRES'
Orange cab, Silver trailer, clear windows, knobbly BPW......**£65-75**
With Green tinted windows, knobbly BPW **£55-65**
With Grey knobbly tread wheels...................**£95-110**
With Black fine tread wheels (45 treads) **£60-80**
With Grey fine tread wheels (45 treads)....................**£160-180**
Silver cab, Dark Red trailer, Black base **£200-220**

M2 64 Bedford Tractor and York Trailer 'LEP INTERNATIONAL'
Silver cab, Dark Red trailer, Dark Red base **£130-150**
Silver cab, Dark Red trailer, Black base **£60-70**

M3 59 Mighty Antar Tank Transporter and Centurion Tank
Both models in Military Olive Green, Transporter always
has Black wheels. Tank with metal rollers **£45-55**
Tank with Grey plastic rollers **£220-250**
Tank with Black plastic rollers **£140-160**

M4 59 Ruston Bucyrus Excavator
Maroon cab, Yellow shovel arms, Black base, Green tracks .**£50-70**

M4 65 'FREUHOF' Hopper Train
Maroon tractor, two Silver trailers, Red hubs, BPT **£75-100**
With Red plastic hubs and Grey tyres...................**£175-200**

M5 59 'MASSEY FERGUSON 780' Combine Harvester
Red body, Yellow blades, Silver front hubs, Black rear........**£40-50**
Orange front hubs, Black rear hubs **£400-500**
Yellow front hubs, Black rear hubs,
Silver metal steering wheel...................**£400-500**
Yellow plastic steering wheel and front hubs,
Black rear hubs **£700-900**

Orange front and rear hubs with Black tyres.....................**£120-140**
Yellow front and rear hubs with Black tyres **£175-200**

M6 60 Scammell Transporter 'PICKFORDS'
Dark Blue tractor, Maroon low-loader, BPW, 279mm...........**£75-90**
Blue tractor, Bright Red low-loader, BPW......................**£140-180**

M6 66 Racing Car Transporter 'BP'
Green body, Silver ramp/rear door, Red hubs with BPT,
'Monza/Le Mans/Sebring/Nurburgring' on sides **£300-350**
With 'Le Mans/Sebring/Silverstone/Nurburgring' on sides ...**£40-50**

M7 60 Thames Trader Cattle Truck 'JENNINGS', Dark Red cab,
Light Tan box trailer, knobbly GPW **£60-70**
With Dark Tan rear lamp, knobbly GPW **£70-80**
As previous model but with knobbly BPW **£85-100**
Same but with Grey fine-tread wheels (45 treads) **£130-150**
Same but with Black fine-tread wheels (45 treads)..........**£120-140**
Light Blue cab, base and rear ramp, Metallic Copper back,
Grey plastic wheels...................**£2,000-3,000**

M8 61 'MOBILGAS' Petrol Tanker
Red body, White 'MOBILGAS' logo, knobbly GPW..........**£70-85**
With Black knobbly-tread wheels (24 treads) **£150-200**
With Black fine-tread wheels (45 treads) **£200-250**

M8 64 Guy Warrior Car Transporter Blue-Green cab, Orange trailer,
Orange wheels with Grey tyres, 209 mm.
'FARNBOROUGH-MEASHAM' in Black, White outline ...**£120-140**
'FARNBOROUGH-MEASHAM' in White, Black outline **£50-60**

M9 62 Inter-State Double Freighter 'COOPER-JARRETT'.
All versions have a Dark Blue cab.
Silver trailers, one-piece double wheels, Yellow lettering ...**£80-100**
Same but double wheels are two separate wheels.................**£70-80**
Same but Orange lettering **£150-200**
Grey trailers, Yellow lettering, Red plastic hubs **£120-150**

M10 62 Whitlock Dinkum Dumper
Yellow body, 'DD-70', unpainted metal wheels, 108 mm **£50-60**
Same but Red plastic hubs with Black tyres **£60-70**

Lincoln Industries 'Matchbox Series'

Collectors should be aware that a range of models exists which were made in New Zealand and which at first sight appear to be Matchbox Miniatures. The packaging in particular is strikingly similar to early Lesney Matchbox boxes, even to the extent of having 'MATCHBOX SERIES' printed in a banner as on the Lesney boxes.

It seems that the makers, Lincoln Industries, were so taken with the Lesney idea of 'a model in a matchbox' that they were tempted to capitalise on it by adopting it themselves. 'Lincoln Industries Ltd' and 'Made in New Zealand' are also clearly marked on the boxes so confusion should be avoidable. The

models are a little cruder than genuine Matchbox products and all seem to have metal wheels. They are nevertheless collectable and include: a Utility Truck, Breakdown Truck, Large Parcels Van, Ambulance, and a sports car resembling a Jaguar XK120. See illustration on opposite page.

These auction results were achieved by Vectis Auctions Ltd. in July 2000:
4506 Coach......................Green body......................**£170**
4509 Ambulance ....Red cross on roof..........................**£140**
4510 Jaguar XK120 ....Cream, with driver.........................**£560**
The Editor would welcome more details of these products.

Matchbox Presentation and Gift Sets

Presentation Sets

The first presentation set was sold in the USA in 1957 and consisted of an enlarged normal 'Matchbox' containing eight of the sixty-four models that Lesney manufactured at that time. The first sets were not sold in the UK until 1959.

Ref	Year(s)	Set name	Contents, features, details	Market Price Range
PS 1	1957	Matchbox Presentation Set	Contains models 1 - 8 (only available in USA)	£2,000-3,000
PS 2	1957	Matchbox Presentation Set	Contains models 9 - 16 (only available in USA)	£2,000-3,000
PS 3	1957	Matchbox Presentation Set	Contains models 17 - 24 (only available in USA)	£2,000-3,000
PS 4	1957	Matchbox Presentation Set	Contains models 25 - 32 (only available in USA)	£2,000-3,000
PS 5	1957	Matchbox Presentation Set	Contains models 33 - 40 (only available in USA)	£2,000-3,000
PS 6	1957	Matchbox Presentation Set	Contains models 41 - 48 (only available in USA)	£2,000-3,000
PS 7	1957	Matchbox Presentation Set	Contains models 49 - 56 (only available in USA)	£2,000-3,000
PS 8	1957	Matchbox Presentation Set	Contains models 57 - 64 (only available in USA)	£2,000-3,000
PS 1	1959	Private Owner Set	Contains 19 MGA, 43 Hillman Minx, 45 Vauxhall Victor, A-3 Garage	£600-800
PS 2	1959	Transporter and 4 Cars Set	Contains 30 Ford, 31 Ford Station Wagon, 33 Ford Zodiac, 36 Austin A50, and an A-2 Transporter	£500-600
PS 3	1959	Transporter and 6 Cars Set	Contains 22 Vauxhall Cresta, 32 Jaguar XK, 33 Ford Zodiac, 43 Hillman Minx, 44 Rolls-Royce Silver Cloud, 45 Vauxhall Victor and an A-2 Transporter	£600-800
PS 4	1959	Commercial Vehicle Set	Contains No.5 Bus, 11 Petrol Tanker, 21 Long Distance Coach, 25 'Dunlop' Van, 35 Horse Box, 40 Bedford Tipper, 47 'Brooke Bond' Van and 60 Morris Pickup	£750-1,000
PS 5	1959	Army Personnel Carrier Set	Contains M3 Personnel Carrier, 54 Saracen, 55 DUKW, 61 Ferret, 62 General Service Lorry, 63 Ambulance, M-3 Tank Transporter	£350-400

Gift Sets

The packaging for the first UK issued sets consisted of a frail blue box with a yellow lid panel on which were displayed (in red) the models making up the set. Sets in similar packaging were issued for the German market. Note however that contents may vary within the same type of box (the G4 Farm set listed below is an example). Please advise us of any other different model combinations you may have.

Ref	Year(s)	Set name	Contents, features, details	Market Price Range
GS 1	c1960	Garage Set 'C'	'MATCHBOX' Sales and Service Station (Red/Yellow), Roadway Layout, Accessories Pack No.1 (Esso petrol pumps), Accessory Pack No.2 (Car Transporter, Blue/Red lettering), Major Pack No.6 ('Pickfords' Transporter), 1-75 series models (5c, 29b, 31b, 42a, 45a, 46b, 57b, 74a). All models are individually boxed and housed in larger display box printed with 'MATCHBOX SERIES' and pictures of the garage and models, etc.	£1,800-2,000
G 1	1960-61	Commercial Motor Set	Contains: 5b 'Players Please', 20b, 37a (even load), 47a, 51a, 59a, 60a and 69a. (All models in G 1 had Grey plastic wheels)	£550-600
G 1	1962-63	Commercial Vehicle Set	Contains 5c 'Visco-Static', 10c, 12b, 13c, 14c, 21c, 46b, 74a	£550-600
G 1	1965	Motorway Set	Contains 6, 10, 13, 33, 34, 38, 48, 55, 71 and R-1 layout	£700-900
G 1	1967	Service Station Set	A1 Service Station and 'BP' Pump Set, 31c or 32c, 13d and 64b in pictorial display case	£200-240
G 2	1960-61	Car Transporter Set	A-2 Transporter (metal wheels) and cars 22b, 25b, 33b, 39a, 57b and 75a	£500-700
G 2	1960-61	2nd issue:	A-2 Transporter (with Grey plastic wheels to tractor and Black plastic wheels to trailer), plus cars 7b, 22b, 25c, 27c, 57b and 75a	£500-700
G 2	1962-63	Car Transporter Set	Contains models 25b, 30b, 31b, 39b, 48b, 65b and Accessory Pack No.2	£500-700
G 2	1965	Car Transporter Set	Contains 22c, 28c, 36c, 75b and Major Pack 8b	£300-350
G 2	1967	Transporter Set	Contains K8 Transporter, 14d, 24c, 31c and 53c	£180-200
G 3	1960-61	Building Constructors Set	Contains 2, 6, 15, 16, 18, 24, 28 and M-1	£240-280
G 3	1962-63	Constructional Plant Set	Contains 2, 6, 15, 16, 18, 24, 28 and M-1	£240-280
G 3	1963-64	Farm and Agricultural Set	Contains K8, K11, M5 and M7	£270-300
G 3	1965	Vacation Set	Contains 12c, 23d, 27d, 42b, 45b, 56b, 68b, and Sports Boat on Trailer. Artwork on box	£250-300
			Same contents but in plain white box with red lettering	NGPP
G 3	1968	Farm Set	Contains 4d, 12c, 37d, 40c, 39c, 43c, 65c and 72b	£120-150
G 4	1960-61	Farm Set (1st issue)	M-7 Cattle Truck (GPW), 12b Land Rover (BPW), 23b Berkeley Caravan (Lime Green, GPW), 31b Ford (Met.Green/Pink/Maroon, SPW), 35a Horse Box (MW), 50a Commer (Lt.Brown, SPW), 72a Fordson (Orange rear hubs, GPW)	£800-1,100
		(2nd issue)	M-7 Cattle Truck (GPW), 12b Land Rover (BPW), 23c Bluebird Dauphine Caravan (Metallic Mauve, SPW), 31b Ford (Yellow, Maroon base, clear windows, SPW), 35a Horse Box (SPW), 50a Commer (SPW), 72a Fordson (Orange rear hubs, GPW)	£300-350
G 4	1963	Grand Prix Set	Contains 13c, 14c, 19c, 41b, 47b, 52a, 32b, 73b and Major Pack No.1, R-4 Racetrack, instructions	£650-750
G 4	1965	Racetrack Set	13d, 19d Green, 19d Orange, 41c White, 41c Yellow, 52b Blue, 52b Red, 54b, Major Pack M-6 29c	£500-600
G 4	1968	Race 'n' Rally Set	19d Orange, 19d Green, 52b Blue, 52b Red, 29d, 3c, 41c, 67b, 25d, 8e	£200-250
G 5	1960-61	Military Vehicles	Contains 54, 62, 63, 64, 67, 68 and M-3	£200-250
G 5	1963	Army Gift Set	Contains 54a, 62a, 63a, 67a, 68a, 64a and Major Pack No.3	£220-250
G 5	1965	Army Gift Set	Contains 12, 49, 54, 61, 64, 67 and M-3 (picture box)	£220-250
G 5	1965	Fire Station Set	Contains Fire Station, 29c, 54b and 59c	£250-300
G 6	1965	Commercial Trucks Set	Contains 6, 15, 16, 17, 26, 30, 58 and 62	£250-300
G 6	1966	Truck Set	Contains 16c, 17d, 25c, 26b, 30c, 69b, 70b, 71b	£200-250
G 9	1963	Major Series Set	Contains Major Packs 1, 2, 4 and 6	£250-350
G 9	1965	Service Station Set	Contains 13, 33, 71, A-1, MG-1	£220-250
G 10	1963	Service Station Set	Contains Service Station, 13c, 25b, 31b, and Accessory Pack No.1	£250-300
G 10	1965	Fire Station Set	Contains MF-1, 14, 59, 2 of No.9	£250-300
FB 5	1969	Matchbox Traffic Game	Contains two cars (No.45 Ford Corsair and No.56 Fiat 1500) plus game board, etc	£175-200
?	?	'GAF' Racing Car Game	Belgian game set contains four 24d 'TEAM MATCHBOX' racing cars including the rare Metallic Blue and Yellow variants. Set issued by 'GAF', not by Matchbox	£300-400

272

Matchbox 'King-Size' Series 1960 – 1970

Following successful sales of Major Models, Lesney Products decided to further develop the range by introducing a larger scale toy. The name chosen was 'King-Size'. In 1966 the popular Major Models were discontinued in name but were themselves built into the King-Size range.

Ref	Year(s)	Model name and details	Market Price Range
K1-1	60	**Hydraulic Shovel** All Yellow body, Grey plastic wheels, 'WEATHERILL'	**£40-45**
K1-2	63	**Tipper Truck** Red cab and chassis, Orange tipper, 'HOVERINGHAM'	**£40-50**
	NB	'HOVERINGHAM GRAVELS LTD' issued models in their own outer box to their customers	**£120-150**
K1-3	71	**'O & K' Excavator** Red body, Silver shovel, tinted windows, BPT	**£40-50**
K2-1	60	**Dumper Truck** Red body, 'MUIR HILL 14B', Black or Green MW	**£40-50**
K2-2	64	**Dumper Truck** Yellow body, 'KW DART' logo, 6 Red wheels, BPT	**£40-50**
K2-3	68	**Scammell Wreck Truck** White body, Red jib and wheels, Grey hook, 'ESSO'	**£100-125**
	71	Gold body version	**£50-60**
K3-1	60	**Caterpillar Bulldozer** Yellow body, Red engine, Grey metal rollers	**£50-60**
		As previous model but with Red metal rollers	**£50-60**
		As previous model but with Yellow metal rollers	**£50-60**
		As previous model but with Red plastic rollers	**£70-100**
K3-2	65	**'HATRA' Tractor Shovel** Orange body, Red wheels	**£35-45**
K3-3	70	**'MASSEY FERGUSON' Tractor and Trailer** Red body, Yellow trim	**£60-70**
K4-1	60	**'McCORMICK INTERNATIONAL' Tractor** Red body, Green wheels	**£40-50**
		As previous model with Orange or Red wheel hubs	**£60-80**
K4-2	67	**GMC Tractor and Hoppers** Dark Red cab, 2 Silver hoppers, 'FREUHOF' logo	**£80-100**
K4-3	69	**Leyland Tipper** Dark Red cab and chassis, Silver tipper 'W. WATES'	**£40-50**
		As above but with Yellow/Green body colours	**£750-1,000**
		With Red cab and chassis, Green tipper	**£50-60**
		With Blue cab and chassis, Silver tipper 'Miner' label	**£60-70**
		With Silver tipper and 'LE TRANSPORT' logo	**£30-40**
K5-1	61	**Tipper Truck** Yellow body and tipper, Red wheels, 'FODEN' logo	**£40-50**
K5-2	67	**Racing Car Transporter** Green body, Silver drop down rear door, Red wheels	**£35-40**
K5-3	70	**Tractor and Trailer** Yellow body, Red chassis, 'MUIR HILL'	**£35-40**
K6-1	61	**Earth Scraper** Orange body, Red engine, 'ALLIS CHALMERS'	**£35-45**
K6-2	67	**Mercedes Ambulance** Off-White body, Red badge, ambulance-man, stretcher	**£50-60**
K7-1	61	**Rear Dumper** Yellow body, Red engine, 'CURTISS-WRIGHT'	**£35-40**
K7-2	67	**Refuse Truck** Red body and wheels 'CLEANSING DEPARTMENT'	**£25-30**
	72	Blue body version	**£60-70**
K8-1	62	**Prime Mover and Transporter with Crawler Tractor** Orange bodies, Yellow tractor, 'LAING', unpainted or Red plastic hubs, Green tracks	**£175-200**
K8-2	67	**Guy Warrior Transporter** 'FARNBOROUGH - MEASHAM' Blue cab, Yellow car trailer	**£60-70**
		Orange cab, Orange or Yellow trailer	**£60-80**
		Dark Aqua cab, Yellow trailer	**£600-800**
K8-3	70	**'CATERPILLAR TRAXCAVATOR'** Yellow body and shovel, Blue or White driver	**£30-35**
	72	Silver body	**£50-60**
K9-1		**'AVELING BARFORD' Diesel Road Roller** Green body, Red wheels and driver	**£40-45**
		Same, but with Grey driver	**£200-250**
K9-2	67	**'CLAAS' Combine Harvester** Red body, Yellow blades and wheels,	**£40-50**
		Green body, Red blades and wheels	**£40-50**
K10-1	63	**'AVELING BARFORD' Tractor Shovel** Blue-Green body, Red seat and wheels	**£50-70**
K10-2	66	**Pipe Truck.** Yellow body, Red wheels, 6 Grey pipes	**£45-50**
		('Super-Kings' issue) Purple body, Grey or Yellow pipes	**£25-30**
K11-1	63	**'FORDSON SUPER MAJOR' Tractor and Trailer** Blue tractor, Grey/Blue trailer	**£80-90**
K11-2	69	**DAF Car Transporter** Yellow body, Yellow/Red decks	**£60-70**
		Metallic Blue body, Gold trailer decks	**£60-70**
K12-1	63	**Breakdown Truck** 'MATCHBOX SERVICE STATION', Green body, Yellow jib,	**£40-50**
K12-2	69	**Scammell Crane Truck** Yellow body and chassis, 'LAING' on crane	**£40-50**
	71	Silver body	**£60-70**
K13-1	63	**Concrete Truck** Orange body and barrel, 'READYMIX' logo	**£50-60**
		As previous model but with 'RMC' logo	**£50-60**
K14-1	64	**Jumbo Crane** Yellow body and crane, 'TAYLOR JUMBO CRANE'	**£30-35**
K15-1	64	**Merryweather Fire Engine** Red body, Silver ladder, 'KENT FIRE BRIGADE'	**£35-45**
K16-1	66	**Tractor and Twin Tippers** Green cab, Yellow tippers, 'DODGE TRUCKS' in Red	**£80-90**
		Yellow cab, Blue tippers same logo (Superfast)	**£60-65**
K17-1	67	**Low Loader and Bulldozer** Green cab and loader, Red/Yellow Bulldozer	**£80-90**
	71	Red cab, 'TAYLOR WOODROW'	**£60-70**
K18-1	66	**Articulated Horse Box** 'ASCOT STABLES', Red cab, Brown box, 4 White horses	**£70-80**
K19-1	67	**Scammell Tipper** Red body, Yellow tipper, Silver trim	**£25-30**
K20-1	68	**Tractor Transporter (Ford)** Red body, Yellow rack, 3 Blue/Yellow tractors (MB39c)	**£70-80**
		As previous model but with Orange tractors	**£120-150**
	71	Blue cab	**£180-200**
K21-1	69	**Mercury Cougar** Gold body, Cream or Red seats	**£25-30**
K22-1	69	**Dodge Charger** Blue body, Yellow or Pale Blue seats	**£50-60**
K23-1	69	**Mercury 'POLICE' Car** White body with 'HIGHWAY PATROL' logo	**£35-45**
K24-1	69	**Lamborghini Miura** Red body, Cream seats	**£30-35**

'Battle-Kings' issued 1974

Models packed in 'window' boxes. Each has a 'military' theme and includes three plastic soldiers. Expect to pay **£20-25** for any of these items.

K101 **Sherman Tank**	K111 **Missile Launcher**
K102 **M48 AS Tank**	K112 **DAF Ambulance**
K103 **Chieftain Tank**	K113 **Crane Truck**
K104 **King Tiger Tank**	K114 **Army Aircraft**
K105 **Hover Raider**	**Transporter**
K106 **Tank Transporter**	K115 **Petrol Tanker**
K107 **155mm Gun**	K116 **Troop Carrier**
K108 **Half Track**	**and Howitzer**
K109 **Sheridan Tank**	K117 **Rocket Launcher**
K110 **Recovery Vehicle**	K118 **Army Helicopter**

'Sea-Kings' issued 1976

These models were packed in 'window' boxes. Expect a Market Price of **£12-18** for any of these 'Sea-Kings'.

K301 **Frigate 'F109'**	
K302 **Corvette 'C70'**	
K303 **Battleship '110'**	
K304 **Aircraft Carrier with 4 aircraft '36'**	
K305 **Submarine Chaser 'C17'**	
K306 **Convoy Escort 'F101'**	
K307 **Helicopter Carrier with 2 Helicopters**	
K308 **Guided Missile Destroyer**	
K309 **Submarine '117'**	
K310 **Anti Aircraft Carrier**	

'Big MX' models 1972 - 1974

Special packaging contained models and accessories powered by an 'Activator Gun' which plugged into them and operated the mechanisms.

MX1 **Incinerator Site** + K7 Refuse Truck	**£50-70**
BM2 **Mechanised Tractor Plant** and Winch Transporter (K20-1 Ford), with Blue/Yellow MB39c Tractors	**£70-80**
	with Orange MB39c Tractors	**£120-150**
BM3 **Mechanised** (K12 Scammell) **Crane Truck** and Building Site	**£50-70**
BM4 **Mechanised Coal Delivery Hopper** and (K4 Leyland) Tipper	**£50-70**
BM5 **Mechanised Quarry Site** and (K8, silver/red) Traxcavator	**£40-50**
BM6 **Fire Rescue Scene** with mechanised (K15 Merryweather) Fire Engine plus 4 figures and scenery	**£120-140**

'King-Size' Gift Sets

---	1963	**King-Size Set**	Contains K1-1, K2-1, K3-1, K5-1, K6-1	**£250-300**
---	1965	**Construction Set**	Contains K16-1, K7-1, K10-1, K13-1, K14-1	**£200-300**
---	1966	**King-Size Set**	Contains K16-1, K11-1, K12-1, K15-1	**£200-300**

'Super-Kings' and 'Speed-Kings' 1971 – 1980

After 1970 the 'King Size' range developed into the larger 'Super-Kings' Series. They were fitted with extra wide speed slick tyres.

During the period 1971-79 certain issues were sold as 'SPEED KINGS' and retailed in different coloured packaging. These have been identified in the listings by the abbreviation (SPK).

Market Price Range. In general 'Super-Kings' are not very collectable and most models may be purchased for **under £15**. However, a little more price information on some of the rarer items has been received since the previous Edition and this is shown where appropriate. We regret we are unable to provide more specific price information on the remainder at this time.
Further information on the rare issues and price levels would be welcomed.

K2	77	*'24 HOUR'* Car Recovery	£25-35
K3	74	Mod Tractor and Trailer	£25-35
K3	74	Grain Transporter, Green cab (German)	£60-70
	74	Red, *'KELLOGGS'*	£20-25
K4	74	Big Tipper, blue/silver	£60-70
K5	72	Muir Hill Tractor and Trailer, Yellow	£25-30
		Blue (German)	£60-70
K6	76	Cement Mixer, blue	£20-25
K6	76	Motor Cycle Transporter, *'HONDA'*	£30-35
K7	73	Transporter, *'TEAM MATCHBOX'*	£30-35
	74	With 'Martini' labels	£45-50
K9	73	Fire Tender *'DENVER'*	£30-35
K10	76	Transporter, *'AUTO TRANSPORT'*	£30-35
K11	76	Recovery Truck, *'SHELL RECOVERY'*	£40-50
	76	Recovery Truck in Red	£70-80
K12	75	Hercules *'LAING'* Crane	£40-50
K13	71	Building Transporter, 'DAF'	£30-35
K13	76	Aircraft Transporter	£50-60
K14	71	Scammell Freight *'LEP'*	£40-50
K14	77	Breakdown Truck, *'SHELL'*	£40-50
K15	71	Merryweather Fire Engine, *'KENT'*	£30-40
K15	73	Londoner Bus issues.	
		'HARRODS - ENTER A DIFFERENT WORLD'	£30-40
		'CARNABY STREET'	£30-40
		'SILVER JUBILEE',	£30-40
		'HARRODS - MORE THAN MONEY'	£30-40
		'LONDON DUNGEON'	£30-40
		'HAMLEYS'	£30-40
		'ROYAL WEDDING 1981'	£30-40
		'LONDON WIDE TOUR'	£30-40
		'TELEGRAPH & ARGUS'	£30-40
		'MACLEANS'	£30-40
		'HERITAGE OF ENGLAND'	£30-40
		'BUTTERKIST'	£30-40
		'TOURIST LONDON'	£30-40
		'FIRESTONE'	£30-40
		'CHESTERFIELD 1984'	£30-40
		'LONDON PLANETARIUM'	£30-40
		'PETTICOAT LANE'	£30-40
		'NESTLES MILKY BAR'	£30-40
K16	74	Ford LTS Tanker, *'TEXACO'*, *'CHEMCO'*, *'LEP'*, *'ARAL'* *'SHELL'*, *'EXXON'*, *'TOTAL'* *'U.S. MATCHBOX CLUB'*, *'QUAKER STATE'*	£20-30
	75	With 'BP' labels	£200-300
K16		Dodge Tractor, Yellow/Blue tippers	£80-90
K17		Container Truck *'DBP'*, *'PENGUIN'*, *'7 UP'*, *'GENTRANSCO'*	£30-50
		'TAYLOR WOODROW', Pink/Lime	£60-70
K18	74	Tipper Truck *'TARMAC'*, *'US STEEL'*, *'HOCH & TIEF'*	£30-40
K19	79	Security Truck	

		'GROUP 4', *'FORT KNOX'*	£30-40
K20	73	Cargo Hauler	£30-35
K20	79	Peterbilt *'HEAVY DUTY'*	£30-35
K21	71	Cougar Dragster (SPK)	£20-30
K21	74	Tractor Transporter	£30-40
K21	79	Ford Transcontinental *'CONTINENTAL'*, *'DANZAS'*, *'POLARA'*, *'SUNKIST'*	£30-35
K22	73	Dodge Dragster (SPK)	£20-30
K22	74	Hovercraft, *'SEASPEED'*	£30-40
		'HOVERLLOYD'	£30-40
		All-white	£40-50
K23	71	Mercury *'POLICE'* Car, (SPK)	£20-30
K23	74	Low Loader, *'HOCH & TIEF'*	£30-40
K24	71	Lamborghini Muira	£20-30
K24	77	Scammel Truck *'LONDON TO GENEVA'*	£30-40
		'MICHELIN'	£30-40
		'GENTRANSCO'	£30-40
		'BAUKNECT'	£30-40
K25	77	Powerboat and Trailer *'SEABURST'*	£30-35
		'CHRYSLER'	£30-35
K25	78	Digger, *'MUIRHILL'*	£20-30
K26	71	Mercedes Ambulance (SPK)	£30-40
K26	78	Bedford Cement Truck *'McALPINE'*	
		'HOCH & TIEF'	£30-40
K27	71	Camping Cruiser	£20-30
K27	78	Powerboat Transporter *'EMBASSY'*	£30-40
		'MISS SOLO'	£30-40
K28	71	Drag Pack (SPK)	£25-35
K28	78	Bedford Skip Truck *'HOCH & TIEF'*	£25-35
		'HALES'	£25-35
K29	71	Muira *'SEABURST'* Set, (SPK)	£25-35
K29	77	Ford Delivery Van, *'U-HAUL'*, *'AVIS'*, *'Mr SOFTY'*, *'BASSETTS'*, *'TAA'*	£30-35
K30	72	Mercedes C111	£20-30
K30	78	Unimog/Compressor	£20-30
K31	72	Bertone Runabout (SPK)	£20-30
K31	78	Peterbilt Refrigeration Truck *'CHRISTIAN SALVESON'*, *'PEPSI'*, IGLOO', *'GERVAIS GLACE'*, *'DR KOCH'S TRINK'*, *'DURA PENTA'* (S. African), *'BURGER KING'*	£30-40
K32	71	Shovel Nose	£20-30
K33	78	Cargo Hauler	£20-30
K34	72	Thunderclap (SPK)	£20-30
K34	74	Pallet Truck	£20-30
K35	72	Lightning (SPK)	£20-30
K35	79	Massey Ferguson Tractor & Trailer	£50-75
K36	72	Bandolero (SPK)	£20-30
K36	78	*'LAING'* Transporter	£40-50
K37	73	Sandcat (SPK)	£20-30
K37	79	Leyland Tipper *'LAING'*	£30-40
K38	74	Gus's Gulpher (SPK)	£20-30
K39	73	*'MILLIGANS MILL'* (SPK)	£20-30
K40	73	Blaze Trailer *'FIRE CHIEF'* (SPK)	£25-35
K41	73	Fuzz Buggy *'POLICE'* (SPK)	£25-35
K41	78	Brabham F1 (SPK)	£20-30

K42	73	Nissan 270X (SPK)	£20-30
K42	79	Traxcavator Road Ripper	£20-30
K43	73	*'CAMBUSTER'* (SPK)	£20-30
K44	73	*'BAZOOKA'* (SPK)	£20-30
K44	78	Surtees F1	£20-30
K45	73	Marauder (SPK)	£20-30
K46	74	Racing Car pack with K34 and K35	£35-45
K47	73	Easy Rider Tricycle (SPK)	£30-40
K48	74	Mercedes 350 SLC, (SPK)	£20-30
K49	73	Ambulance (SPK)	£20-30
K49	74	*'MALTESER'* Truck	£20-30
K50	74	Street Rod (SPK)	£20-30
K51	73	Barracuda (SPK)	£20-30
K52	73	Datsun Rally Car (SPK)	£20-30
K53	76	Hot Fire Engine (SPK)	£20-30
K54	76	AMX Javelin (SPK)	£20-30
K55	76	Corvette *'CAPER CART'* (SPK)	£20-30
K56	76	Maserati Bora (SPK)	£20-30
K57	76	Javelin Drag Racing Set, K38 & K39 (SPK)	£30-40
K58	76	Corvette Power Boat Set, K45 etc. (SPK)	£30-40
K59	76	Ford Capri Mk.II (SPK)	£30-40
K60	76	Ford Mustang (SPK)	£20-30
K61	76	Mercedes *'POLICE'* (SPK)	£20-30
	78	Mercedes *'POLIZEI'* (SPK)	£20-30
K62	77	Doctors Car (SPK)	£20-30
K63	77	Mercedes 'Binz' *'AMBULANCE'* (SPK)	£20-30
K64	78	*'FIRE CONTROL'* Range Rover (SPK)	£20-30
K65	78	Plymouth Mountain Rescue *'EMERGENCY RESUCE'*	£50-60
		'BERGRETTUNG WACHT'	£50-60
K66	79	Jaguar XJ12 *'POLICE'* Set	£20-30
K67	78	Dodge Monaco (SPK) i) *'FIRE CHIEF'*	£20-30
		ii) *'HACKENSACK'*	£20-30
K68	78	Dodge Monaco and Trailer (SPK)	£30-40
K69	78	Jaguar XJ12 and Caravan (SPK)	£40-50
K70	79	Porsche Turbo	£20-30
K71	79	Porsche *'POLIZEI'* Set	£20-30
K72	79	Brabham F1, Red or Green	£20-30
K73	79	Surtees F1, White or Tan	£20-30
K74	79	Volvo Estate	£20-30
K75	79	Airport *'FIRE'* Rescue *'AIRPORT FIRE TENDER'*	£20-30
		'FLUGHAFEN-FEUERWEHR'	£20-30
		'SECURITE AEROPORT'	£20-30
K76	79	Volvo Rally Set *'CIBIE'*	£20-30
K77	79	Rescue Vehicle *'STRASSEN SERVICE'*	£20-30
		'SECOURS ROUTIER'	£20-30
		'HIGHWAY RESCUE'	£20-30
K78	79	US Police Car, *'POLICE'*, *'POLIZEI'* or *'CITY POLICE'*	£20-30
K79	79	US Taxi	£20-30

K101-K115 Battle Kings – see separate listing.

'Convoy' Series

The 'Convoy' model range was launched in 1982 and early issues were made in England before manufacture was transferred to Macau. Many variations exist particularly in the USA where they have been used as promotionals linked to NASCAR truck racing. For a listing of the many variations available contact:
Carr Collectables, Central House, High Street, Ongar, Essex, CM5 9AA. Tel: (01277-366144).

Matchbox Catalogues

Year	Publication details	Market Price Range
1957	**Folded Leaflet** .... Yellow cover has Blue edging and depicts No.1 Diesel Roller. Colour pictures of nos. 1 - 42 of '1-75'series **£140-180**	
1957	**Folded Leaflet** .... Blue/Yellow cover featuring MOY No.1 Allchin 7nhp Traction Engine 1st series box. Contents list first nine Yesteryears **£180-200**	
1958	**16-page catalogue** .Cover shows Rolls-Royce (44), emerging from box. Models 1 - 60 in colour inside, early 'Major Packs' and Accessory Packs...**£80-90**	
1959	**Leaflet** .... 'Everyone buys MATCHBOX TOYS by LESNEY'. Blue with line drawings. Gives details of Presentation and Gift Sets **£200-300**	
1959	**Folded Leaflet** .... Features first 14 Yesteryears in colour **£85-100**	
1959	**16-page catalogue** .Same cover as 1958 catalogue with '1959 Edition'. Lists 1-75's, Major Packs and accessories. Colour pictures **£85-100**	
1959	**24-page catalogue** .'UK' and '2d' on cover with MOY No.9, 1-75 series, No.'43', and Accessory No.'2'. Colour contents show MB 1 - 72 and MOY 1 - 14 plus Accessories and Major Packs. **£85-100**	
1960	**32-page catalogue** .'UK' and '3d' on cover featuring logo *'ALL THE MATCHBOX POCKET TOYS BY LESNEY'* plus semi-circle picture of MOY and 1-75's. Contents illustrate all ranges **£75-90**	
1961	**32-page catalogue** . *'International Pocket Catalogue'* on cover with picture of 1-75 model No.5 Bus. New style smaller catalogue listing all issues in colour plus International price list.............**£60-70**	
1962	**20-page catalogue** .'2d', *'International Pocket Catalogue'* and *'1962 Edition'* on cover. All issues listed, European price list included **£40-50**	
1963	**20-page catalogue** .No.53 Mercedes-Benz printed on cover with '2d' and *'1963 Edition'*. Contents include good Gift Set pictures and listings .**£25-35**	
1964	**32-page catalogue** .'3d' on cover depicting Blue Mk.10 Jaguar (No.28). *'1964 Matchbox Prices'* on back cover. Contents include superb Gift Set pictures and listings **£25-35**	
1965	**32-page catalogue** .Cover features Motor Racing Cars. *'1965 Matchbox Prices'* on back cover. Excellent full colour Gift Set pictures. (Price 3d) **£20-25**	
1966	**40-page catalogue** .London scene and *'Price 3d'* on cover. Excellent pictures of mid-sixties Gift Sets plus history of Matchbox..........................**£20-25**	
1967	**40-page catalogue** .Cover shows flags and 1-75 issues, *'Price 3d'*. Contents list and depict Veteran Car Gifts. **£20-25**	
1968	**40-page catalogue** .1968 car picture and *'Price 3d'* on cover. Inc. details of manufacturing processes **£20-25**	
1969	**48-page catalogue** .Cover features Motorway scene. Contents include detailed history of the real cars making up the MOY range **£12-15**	
	2nd edition: ....The 2nd edition of the 1969 catalogue inc. first reference to *'Superfast'* issues **£12-15**	
1970	**64-page catalogue** .Only drawings of models (no photographs) throughout. Superfast track featured. '6d', *'MATCHBOX SUPERFAST'* and a collage of models on cover **£8-10**	

Year	Publication details	Market Price Range
1971	**64-page catalogue** .'24p' on Blue/Red cover with scorpion design. 'Speed Kings' listed plus pictures of first Superfast Gift Sets....................................**£8-10**	
1972	**72-page catalogue** .Yellow *'MATCHBOX'* and '3p' on cover. Contents feature launch of 'Scream'n Demon' bikes and excellent Gift Set pictures.............**£8-10**	
1973	**80-page catalogue** .'5p' and '1973' on cover of the largest Matchbox catalogue produced. Contents include good 'Super Kings' and Aircraft Kit listing ..**£8-10**	
1974	**64-page catalogue** .'2p' and '1974' on cover. Includes first 'SKYBUSTERS' listing **£5-8**	
1975	**64-page catalogue** .'2p' and '1975' on cover. Contents feature 'Rolamatics' and 'Battle Kings' **£5-8**	
1976	**64-page catalogue** .'1976' on cover. Contents feature 'Sea Kings' plus 'Baby Dolls' and 'Disco Girl Dolls'........**£5-8**	
1977	**80-page catalogue** .'1977' on cover. Contents list the 'Two Pack' (TP) range of 1-75's. Good Gift Set pictures and listings of 1-75's...............................**£5-8**	
1978	**64-page catalogue** .'1978' on cover. Includes good 'SKYBUSTERS' and 1-75 Gift Set pictures ..**£5-8**	
79-80	**80-page catalogue** .'5p' and '1979-80' on cover. The contents feature good pictures of Gift Sets G1 - G8. '900' TP series introduced...............................**£5-8**	
80-81	**80-page catalogue** .'5p' on cover. All ranges listed including 'Walt Disney' and 'Power Track' equipment ..**£4-6**	
81-82	**64-page catalogue** .'5p' and '1981-82' on cover. 'Adventure 2000' space models pictured. 'Playtrack', 'Popeye' and 'Streak Sets' listed **£4-6**	
82-83	**64-page catalogue** .'1982-83' on cover. 'Convoy' series introduced, good MOY pictures....................**£2-4**	
1984	**64-page catalogue** .'1984' on cover. 'MATCHBOX SPECIALS' introduced, good Gift Set pictures, 'Burnin' Key Cars', 'Rough Riders' and 'Lock Ups'....**£2-4**	
1985	**48-page catalogue** .'1985' and 'chequered flag' design on cover. All ranges listed plus introduction of 'Trickshifters', 'Power Blasters', 'Matchmates' and 'Carry Cases'. (Printed in Italy).............**£2-4**	
1986	**48-page catalogue** .'1986' on cover. 'High Riders', 'Twin-Pack', 'Action Packs' listed inside. 'Motor City' **£2-4**	
1987	**72-page catalogue** .'1987' on cover. Listing includes 'Superfast Lasers', 'Pocket Rockets', 'Speed Riders', 'Streak Racing', 'Hot Rod Racers', 'Turbo 2', 'Turbo Specials' and 'Demolition Cars'. **£2-4**	
1988	**88-page catalogue** .'1988' on cover. Listing includes Miniatures Gift Sets pictures, 'Lasers', 'Super GT Sport' and 'Super Miniatures', 'Team Convoy', 'Road Blasters', 'Motor City' and 'Action Matchbox'. Also includes 'MICA' and 'Junior Matchbox Club' membership details..............**£2-4**	
1989	**80-page catalogue** .'1989' on cover. Listings include 'Miniatures', 'Twin-Pack', 'Motor City' Gift Sets, 'Dinky Collection', 'World Class', 'Conn-Nect-Ables', 'Flashbacks', 'Super ColourChangers' and 'Skybusters ColourChangers' ....**£2-4£2-4**	

Overseas Catalogue Editions

During the 1960s there were normally six editions of each catalogue: British, International, U.S.A., German, French and French-Canadian. The catalogues were usually of the same format as the UK editions but with the appropriate language and currency. 'INTERNATIONAL CATALOGUE' was shown on the front cover together with the edition, e.g. 'EDITION FRANCAISE', 'INTERNATIONAL' or 'U.S.A. EDITION'.
The 1960 'International Pocket Catalogue' listed the national prices for every product in Australia, Austria, Belgium, Spain, Denmark, Eire, France, Germany, Great Britain, Holland, Hong Kong, Italy, Kenya and East Africa, Singapore and Malaysia, South Africa, Sweden and Switzerland. From 1972 the country-specific editions only listed the model range available in that country.

Market Price Range Prices are equivalent to those asked for UK editions.

Other Matchbox literature

'Mike and The Modelman' (1st edition 1970), was a childrens' book issued by Lesney telling the Matchbox story.
A copy in perfect condition should cost between **£25 - £30**.

Trade Catalogues have been published for many years and occasionally become available for sale. Those before 1970 are scarce and no price information is possible at present. Those from the 1970-80 period tend to be in the region of £10-15 while post-1980 editions sell for £2-5 depending on content and condition.

This listing refers to Superfast models produced between 1969 and 1983. In this period, most models in the range were presented in picture boxes with some variations being sold in Twin Packs and carded 'bubble packs'. The 'cut-off point' for many collectors of these Matchbox Miniatures is 1983 when picture boxes ceased. 'See-through' window boxes sealed at both ends were then introduced.

All the models listed have 'Made in England' bases. Those with 'Macau', 'China', 'Thailand' or elsewhere are too numerous to mention and are outside the scope of this listing. There are also many wheel variations for the models listed, such as 5-spoke, 4-spoke, 'dot-dash' etc., but again, only specific wheel variations such as hub colour are noted. Due to limitations of space, it has been necessary to introduce the use of the following abbreviations into the listing. These have been mainly restricted to indicate colour of bases and window glazing.

Windows	Base colour
AG = amber glass	BB = black base
BG = blue glass	GB = grey base
CG = clear glass	PB = purple base
GG = green glass	SB = silver base
OG = orange glass	UB = unpainted base
PG = purple glass	WB = white base
	YB = yellow base

Wheels	General
BW = black wheels	BE = black engine
NW = narrow wheels	CE = chrome engine
UW = unpainted	LE = limited edition
WW = wide wheels	SE = silver engine
	TP = Twin Pack

MB 1e   Mercedes Truck

70-70	Metallic gold body, yellow or orange canopy, green glass, narrow wheels **£18-20**	
76	Military olive drab green body, tan canopy, purple glass, WW, '4TS702K', (TP) **£35-40**	
76-80	Same but military olive green................**£8-12**	
76-80	Red body, yellow or orange canopy, PG, wide wheels, 'Transcontinental' (TP) **£8-10**	
80-82	Light blue body, light orange canopy, purple glass, WW, 'IMS' (TP) **£12-15**	

MB 1f   Mod Rod

71	Yellow body, OG, SE, red wheels, UB or SB, 'spotted cat's head' label **£20-30**	
71-75	Same but with black wheels **£10-12**	
	Black wheels and silver base...............**£18-20**	
71-75	Same but with 'Wildcat' label **£10-12**	
73	Same but with 'Flower' label **£20-25**	
74	Same but with 'Scorpion' label **£35-40**	
78	Striped silver body, BW, UB. (U.S.A. 'Roman Numeral' LE)..........**£25-30**	

MB 1g   Dodge Challenger

76-79	Red body, white roof, silver interior.......**£6-8**	
76-79	Same but with white interior **£10-15**	
76-79	Same but with red interior **£15-18**	
80-82	Blue body, white roof, red interior **£6-8**	
82-83	Orange body, blue roof, black interior, UB or SB, 'Revin Rebel' **£10-12**	
82	Same but with white roof **£15-20**	

MB 2d   Mercedes Trailer

70	Metallic gold body, yellow or orange canopy, green glass, narrow wheels **£15-18**	
76	Military olive drab green body, tan canopy, WW, '4TS702K' (TP) **£30-35**	
76-80	Same but military olive green.............**£10-12**	
76-80	Red body, WW, yellow or orange canopy, 'Transcontinental' (TP)......**£8-10**	
80-82	Light blue body, light orange canopy, WW 'IMS' (TP)....................**£10-12**	

MB 2e   Jeep Hot Rod

71-75	Pink body, white or cream seats, light or dark green base **£10-15**	
	Same but white base **£45-50**	
75-76	Red body, white or cream seats, WB **£12-18**	
	Same but green base **£45-50**	

MB 2f   Rescue Hovercraft

76-78	Light or dark lime green body, fawn or light brown skirt, red or silver air intakes, amber or red windows, 'Rescue'...........**£6-8**	
76-79	With Metallic light or dark green body ...**£6-8**	
	Same but with red windows **£7-10**	
78	Same but black skirt **£7-10**	
	Black skirt, red or purple windows **£10-12**	
78-80	Pale green body, black skirt, purple or AG, '2000' or 'Rescue'.............**£15-20**	

MB 2g   S-2 Jet

81-82	Black/yellow, yellow or red glass............**£6-8**	
82-83	Metallic light blue and white or grey, clear glass, 'Viper' on some **£7-10**	

MB 3c   Mercedes 'Binz' Ambulance

70-73	Cream or off-white body, light blue glass, NW, opening rear door **£15-20**	
	Same but with dark blue glass..............**£15-20**	
77-80	Cream body, dark blue glass, red cross on doors, rear door cast shut (TP) **£10-12**	
78-80	Military olive-green body, WW with silver hubs, rear door cast shut (TP)....**£15-25**	
	Same but with black hubs..................**£12-15**	

MB 3d   Monteverdi Hai

73-78	Orange body, pale yellow interior, black or UB, '3' on bonnet **£7-10**	
	Same but with '6' on bonnet...............**£12-15**	

MB 3e   Porsche Turbo

78-79	Metallic brown body, cream interior, clear glass, black base ...**£7-10**	
79-80	Metallic brown body, UB **£10-12**	
	Silver body, CG, cream or red interior, black or dark grey base **£5-7**	
	Tan interior, black or dark grey base ..**£12-15**	
	Tan interior, brown base **£18-20**	
	Red interior, brown base **£8-10**	
80-82	Metallic green body, cream interior, clear glass, black or dark grey base....**£6-8**	
	With light or dark yellow interior............**£6-8**	
	Same but with unpainted base **£10-12**	
	Red interior, dark GB or BB.............**£12-15**	
	Red body, tan interior, opaque glass, black base, 'Porsche Turbo 90' **£10-18**	
82-83	Red body, tan or white interior, CG, black or dark grey base, 'Porsche Turbo 90' on some....................**£5-8**	

MB 4d   Stake Truck

70-72	Orange-yellow cab, green stake body, green glass....................**£20-25**	
	Same but bright yellow cab **£80-100**	

MB 4e   Gruesome Twosome

71-75	Gold body, SB or UB, cream interior, purple glass **£7-10**	
	With white or yellow interior **£12-15**	
	Gold body, SB, cream interior, AG **£60-70**	
75	Red body, SB or UB, yellow interior, purple glass **£12-15**	
	Same but with cream interior **£12-15**	
	Orange-red body, SB or UB, cream interior, purple glass **£25-30**	

MB 4f   Pontiac Firebird

75-77	Metallic light blue body, UB, AG.........**£8-10**	
78-80	Same but metallic dark blue **£12-15**	

MB 4g   '57 Chevy

80-81	Purple body, silver interior, UB, CG **£8-10**	
82-83	Red, 'Cherry bomb', SB or UB, CG **£7-10**	
	Same but with black base **£20-25**	

MB 5e   Lotus Europa

69-70	Dark metallic blue body, ivory interior, UB, NW **£12-15**	
	Same, no 'Superfast' cast on base ...**£200-300**	
	Dark metallic blue with '20' and stripe labels from G3 racing set....................**£25-30**	
70-75	Pink body, ivory interior, silver base, NW or WW **£25-30**	
	Same but with unpainted base **£10-12**	
	Same, but with UB, NW, '20', and stripe decals.................................**£25-30**	
77-78	Black body, ivory interior, UB, NW, 'JPS' (Japanese issue)..................**£20-25**	
	Same but without 'JPS' (TP) **£12-15**	

MB 5f   Seafire Boat

75-79	White deck, blue hull, orange-yellow, blue or lemon man, black or red exh'ts ..**£4-6**	
79-82	Red deck, white hull, orange-yellow or lemon man, red exhausts, black trailer (TP)...........................**£7-10**	
81	Red deck, blue hull, lemon man, red exhausts, black trailer (TP)..........**£80-100**	
81	White deck, brown hull, lemon or orange-yellow man, red exhausts **£45-50**	
82	Black deck, yellow hull, red man, red exhausts, black trailer (TP)............**£30-35**	
83	Red deck, yellow hull, red man, red exhausts, black trailer (TP)..........**£35-40**	

MB 5g   US Mail Truck

78-82	Dark or light blue body, white roof (small or large windows), WB, BW, black or silver hubs, 'US Mail' on some **£6-8**	
	Same but with black base **£7-10**	
78	Pale blue body, white roof, 'sleet and snow' base, 'US Mail'. US LE **£10-12**	

MB 5h   4x4 Jeep Off-Road

82-83	Metallic light or dark bronze body, black base, 'Golden eagle' **£7-10**	

MB 6d   Ford Pick-up

70-71	Red body, white roof, white or chrome grille, NW or WW, black base............**£18-20**	
	Metallic green or UB **£30-35**	
	Green or Grey base **£18-20**	

MB 6e   Mercedes 350sl

74-75	Orange body, black roof, UB, ivory or pale yellow interior, amber or CG **£7-10**	
75-79	Yellow body, black roof, UB, pale yellow interior, amber or CG................**£7-10**	
77	Silver body, black roof, UB, pale yellow interior, CG, 'Rennservice' (German issue) **£40-50**	
	Same but without 'Rennservice'........**£25-35**	
79	Metallic bronze body, black roof, UB, pale yellow interior, amber glass **£12-18**	
79-81	Metallic bronze, white roof, AG, UB, pale yellow or cream interior **£7-10**	
81-82	Metallic red body, white roof, UB, pale yellow interior, AG or CG **£6-8**	

MB 6f   Mercedes Convertible

82-83	Metallic blue body, white interior, UB or SB, silver side stripe on some **£8-10**	
83-84	Maroon body, BB, SB or UB **£8-10**	

MB 7c   Ford Refuse Truck

70-72	Orange or orange-red cab, grey back ..**£18-20**	

MB 7d   Hairy Hustler

71-74   Metallic bronze body, AG, '5' on yellow
        side stripe and bonnet, GB or BB.........**£8-10**
        Same but purple glass **£55-60**
        Metallic bronze body, AG, '5' on blue
        side stripe and bonnet, UB or BB.........**£8-10**
        Same but green base **£12-15**
        Same but green base, plain sides **£12-15**
        Same but black base, plain sides **£10-12**
        Metallic bronze body, AG, '3' on
        side labels, '5' on bonnet, BB..............**£25-30**
        Metallic bronze, AG, '3' or '137' on sides,
        'Scorpion' on bonnet, GB or BB **£40-50**
75-77   White 'Streakers' version, AG, red stripes
        with black/white check, GB or BB........**£7-10**
        Same but with black base **£7-10**
78   White body, AG, grey base **£25-35**
78-79   Yellow body, AG, 'flames', BB,
        US 'Roman Numeral' Ltd. Edition......**£18-20**

MB 7e   Volkswagen Golf

76-77   Metallic lime green body, yellow interior,
        AG, BB, roof-rack, black surfboards **£8-10**
77-81   Same but metallic light green body **£8-10**
77-81   Metallic dark green body, yellow or
        lemon interior, AG, BB or GB **£8-10**
        Same but with orange glass **£8-10**
        Red interior, grey base **£20-30**
77   Yellow body and interior, matt black
        base, 'ADAC' , (German issue).........**£25-30**
79-80   Red body, yellow interior, CG or AG,
        BB, roof rack, surfboards, (TP)..........**£12-15**
        Same but red interior, CG, (TP)..........**£35-40**
81-82   Yellow body, red interior, CG, BB or
        GB, roof rack and black surfboards........**£4-6**
82-83   Silver body, red interior, CG, BB or GB,
        green stripes and 'Golf' **£4-6**
        Same but with tan interior **£15-20**

MB 8e   Ford Mustang

70   White body, red interior, BB, CG......**£80-100**
70-71   Red body, red interior, BB, CG **£200-250**
        Same but with ivory interior..........**£120-140**
        Orange-red body, red interior **£200-250**
        Same but with ivory interior...............**£60-80**

MB 8f   Wildcat Dragster

71   Pink body, yellow interior, black
        and orange 'Wildcat' labels, BB.........**£12-15**
71-75   Same but Orange body, BB **£40-50**
        Same but UB or orange base **£20-25**
        With dark or bright yellow base **£20-25**
        Same but with grey base **£18-20**
        Orange body, yellow interior, yellow/
        orange 'Wildcat' labels on some, BB ..**£12-15**
        Same but grey base **£10-12**
        Same but with UB or green base **£30-35**
        Orange body, yellow interior,
        black base, 'Rat Rod' labels **£30-40**
        Same but with 'Sailboat' labels **£50-60**

MB 8g   De Tomaso Pantera

75-81   White body, red interior, blue base,
        '8' and 'Pantera' labels on some..........**£10-12**
        Same but orange interior......................**£6-8**
        With unpainted base..............................**£6-8**
        White body, orange interior, '9' or
        yellow 'Sun' in black or green circle
        bonnet label, blue base.......................**£12-15**
81-82   Blue body, black interior, '8' and
        'Pantera' labels on some, BB, US issue ..**£6-8**
NB   MB8g can be found with the larger rear
        wheels swapped with the smaller front.

MB 8h   Rover 3500

81   Yellow body, red interior, sunroof,
        black base, (G1 Gift set)..................**£225-250**
        Metallic bronze body, white interior,
        sunroof, black base **£15-20**
        Same but dark or light tan interior **£8-10**

MB 9d   Boat and Trailer

70-72   White hull, light turquoise deck,
        dark blue trailer....................................**£15-20**
76-83   White hull, light blue deck,
        light blue trailer (TP) **£15-20**
82   White hull, black deck,
        light or dark blue trailer (TP) **£40-50**
        Same but with black trailer..................**£20-25**

MB 9e   AMX Javelin

72-78   Metallic lime green body, opening doors,
        yellow interior, AG, black air intake,
        UB or SB..**£10-12**
        Same but with silver air intake **£20-25**
        Metallic lime green body, orange interior,
        AG, black air intake, UB or SB **£10-12**
        Same but white interior, UB **£25-30**
        Same but with blue interior **£40-50**
76-78   Metallic light blue body, yellow or
        orange-yellow interior, AG, UB or SB **£4-6**
78-81   Metallic dark blue body, cast-in doors,
        orange-yellow interior, AG, UB
        or SB, (TP)..**£4-6**
80-81   Blue body, cast-in doors, UB or SB,
        orange-yellow interior, AG, black
        air intake, white '1', (US Ltd.Ed.)........**£12-15**
81-83   Metallic dark green body, cast-in
        doors, orange-yellow interior, AG,
        UB or SB, black air intake, (TP) **£4-6**
82   Red body, cast-in doors, UB or SB,
        orange-yellow interior, AG, (TP) **£20-25**

MB 9f   Ford Escort RS2000

78-82   White body, tan interior, BB, CG, '9',
        'Ford', 'Shell', and 'Dunlop' decals....**£10-12**
        Same but with grey base **£10-12**
        Same but red interior, black base **£90-100**
        White body, tan interior, BB, CG,
        'Phantom' decals **£18-20**
80-82   Blue body, tan interior, BB or GB,
        CG, 'Phantom' decals, (TP) **£10-12**
        Same but with blue-grey base............**£20-25**
82-84   Green body, tan interior, BB or GB,
        CG, 'Phantom' decals (TP) **£10-12**
        Green body, white interior, BB, CG,
        'Phantom' decals, (TP) **£20-30**
        Same but with red interior **£90-100**

MB 10d   Pipe Truck

70   Red body, silver base and grille,
        6 grey pipes on sprue **£60-70**
70-73   Same but orange-red body **£20-25**
        Orange base, silver base and grille,
        6 grey or yellow pipes on sprue **£12-15**
        Same but grey base and grille.............**£30-35**

MB 10e   Piston Popper

73-80   Metallic blue body, yellow interior,
        AG, 'Superfast' on UB......................**£80-100**
        Same but 'Rola-Matic' on UB **£8-10**
        Same but with silver base **£18-20**
        With CG, 'Rola-Matic' on UB or SB..**£18-20**
80   White body, yellow interior, AG,
        'Rola-Matic' on UB (German
        multi-pack issue)............................**£200-225**
80-81   Yellow body (red flames) and interior,
        AG, 'Rola-Matic' on UB. US LE........**£15-20**

MB 10f   Plymouth Gran Fury Police Car

79-81   White body, black panels, blue or pale
        or dark yellow glass, UB, 'Police' **£8-10**
82-83   Same but with 'Metro Police Traffic
        Control', shield and '012', UB or SB......**£6-8**
        Same but 'Mercury' base from no 55....**£8-10**

MB 11d   Scaffolding Truck

70-72   Silver body, red base and grille, green
        glass, yellow scaffolding, NW,
        'Builders Supply Company' **£15-20**

MB 11e   Flying Bug

72-77   Red body, SB or UB, grey glass, yellow
        exhausts, silver helmet, square cut or
        heart-shape bonnet decal....................**£12-15**
        Heart-shape decal, UB, blue glass......**£25-30**
78   Orange body, UB, black glass and
        exhausts, flying beetle bonnet decal,
        US Ltd. Ed. **£18-20**

MB 11f   Car Transporter

NB   Usually comes with 1 red, 1 blue and
        1 yellow car. Other combinations are
        common (e.g., 1 blue and 2 yellow)
        but this does not affect the price.
77-80   Orange cab, white or beige back, BB
        or UB, blue, purple or green glass........**£5-8**
80-83   Red (later Dark Orange) cab, beige or
        grey back, BB, SB or UB, blue or
        purple glass..**£5-8**

MB 12c   Safari Land-Rover

70   Metallic blue body, white interior,
        UB, NW, brown luggage **£1,500-2,000**
70   Green body, fine GPW.....................**£150-200**
70-71   Metallic gold body, white interior,
        UB, NW, brown luggage **£20-25**

MB 12d   Setra Coach

71   Metallic gold, grey roof, UB, CG........**£20-25**
        Same but with white roof **£18-20**
72-73   Yellow body, white roof, UB, CG **£18-20**
        Same but with green glass **£150-200**
73-74   Metallic crimson, UB, CG or GG.......**£12-15**
74-75   Met. purple, UB or PB, CG or GG......**£12-15**

MB 12e   Big Bull

75-79   Orange, green shovel, black rollers **£30-40**
        Same but with yellow rollers............**£12-15**
        Same but with orange rollers.................**£5-7**

MB 12f   Citroën CX

79-82   Light or dark metallic blue body, pale
        yellow or cream or ivory interior, SB or
        GB or BB or UB, clear or blue glass.....**£8-10**
        Light metallic blue, tan interior **£10-12**
        Dark metallic blue, red interior **£80-90**
82-83   Yellow body, red interior, black base,
        dark blue glass, (TP).........................**£10-12**
        With clear glass, BB, GB or SB, (TP)....**£8-10**
        Yellow, red interior, BB, CG, 'Team
        Matchbox' in black or blue, (TP) **£12-15**
83   White body, red interior, BB or UB,
        blue glass/lights, 'Ambulance', (TP).....**£8-10**
        Same but 'Police', 'Marine Division'
        and '8' prints, blue stripes, (TP)...........**£8-10**

MB 13d   Dodge Wreck Truck

70-71   Yellow (or lighter yellow) cab, green
        back, yellow crane, red hook 'B.P.'......**£25-30**

MB 13e   Baja Buggy

71-78   Metallic light green body, orange interior,
        UB, black or red exhausts, red or
        orange bonnet flower label **£6-8**
        With red exhausts, no bonnet label.......**£8-10**
        With red exhausts, 'Police' bonnet
        label from 55d....................................**£35-40**
        Same but with red interior **£30-35**
        Metallic light green body, orange interior
        from 47c, UB, red exhausts,
        orange bonnet flower label **£150-200**
78   Metallic dark green body, orange interior,
        UB, red exhausts, orange flower label **£6-8**
        Same but 'Sun' label from 47c **£18-20**

MB 13f   Simon Snorkel

78-80   Light red body, SB or UB, blue glass,
        blue lights, yellow crane and man..........**£6-8**
        Same but amber glass and lights **£25-30**
80-82   Dark red body, SB or UB, blue glass,
        blue lights, yellow crane and man..........**£6-8**
82   Same but white crane and man.............**£8-10**

MB 14d   Iso Grifo

69-71	Metallic dark blue body, pale or dark blue interior, UB, NW **£18-20**
	Same but with white interior **£200-250**
71-75	Lighter metallic blue body, white interior, UB or SB, NW **£18-20**
	Sky blue, white interior, UB, NW **£18-20**
77-78	Lighter powder blue, white interior, UB, WW, (Japanese issue)...................**£25-30**

MB 14e   Mini Ha Ha

75-82	Red body, dark blue glass, UB, 'flesh' coloured man, brown helmet, 4 circle side labels........................**£15-20**
	Same but with purple man..................**£20-25**
	'Flesh' man, light blue glass **£10-12**
	Purple man, light blue glass.................**£12-15**
	Pink man, light blue glass..................**£10-12**
	Red body, light blue glass, 'flesh' or pink man, 2 circle side labels **£10-12**

MB 14f   Leyland Petrol Tanker

82-83	Red cab, white tank, 'ELF' with red/blue stripes or orange/turquoise stripes **£4-6**

MB 15d   Volkswagen 1500

69-70	Off white or cream body, cream interior, '137', 'Monte Carlo'..........................**£25-35**
70-72	Metallic red body, cream interior, '137', 'Monte Carlo' on some **£25-30**
77-78	Off white body, cream interior, '137', no bumper decal (Japanese issue)...........**£25-30**

MB 15e   Forklift Truck

72-77	Red body, yellow hoist, grey forks, UB, black steering wheel, 'horse' and 'Lansing Bagnall' labels.....................**£5-7**
	Same but with green or black base.........**£6-8**
77-82	Red body, unpainted hoist, yellow forks, UB, black steering wheel, 'horse' and 'Lansing Bagnall' labels.....................**£5-7**
	Same but with green or black base.........**£6-8**
	Same but no steering wheel **£5-7**
	Same but with black or grey forks.........**£5-7**
	With red forks, no steering wheel........**£12-15**
82-83	Orange body, unpainted hoist, black forks and roof, UB or SB or BB, no steering wheel, 'Hi-Lift' labels............**£10-12**
NB	Models can be found with 'horse' label facing forwards or backwards and before or after 'Lansing Bagnall'.

MB 16d   Case Bulldozer

69-74	Red body, yellow cab, shovel, engine and base, green rubber tracks **£8-10**
	Same but with black tracks.................**£10-12**
77	Military olive drab green body, black shovel, BB, black tracks (TP)............**£55-60**
	Same but olive green body (TP).........**£20-25**

MB 16e   Badger

74-80	Metallic bronze body, SB, silver radar, green glass (Rola-Matic)...............**£10-12**
	Same but BB or SB, cream radar **£8-10**
	Same but with light or dark grey base...**£8-10**
	Dark grey or black base, black radar....**£8-10**
	Same but with purple glass.................**£10-12**
	Black base, white radar, green glass.....**£8-10**
	Same but with dark grey base.............**£8-10**
76	Military olive drab green body, light grey base, cream radar, green glass(TP)....**£35-40**
76-78	Same but olive green body (TP).........**£18-20**

MB 16f   Pontiac Firebird

80-81	Metallic light brown body, red interior, UB, 'Eagle' bonnet label on most........**£8-10**
81-82	Same but metallic light gold body.........**£8-10**
	Same but metallic dark gold body.........**£8-10**
82-83	White body, red interior.........................**£6-8**

MB 17e   Horse box

70	Red cab, dark green box, grey door, chrome base, 2 white horses on sprue.**£55-60**
70-71	Same but orange-red cab **£20-25**
	Orange-red cab, light grey-white box, mustard door...................................**£20-25**
	Same but orange cab............................**£15-18**
	Mustard-yellow cab, dark green box, grey door.......................................**£15-18**

MB 17f   'Londoner' Buses

Unless otherwise stated all buses have red bodies and white interiors. Most have metal bases in gloss or matt black, grey, brown or unpainted. Before changing to the Titan bus some were fitted with plastic bases. Factory issued models are listed first, then Lesney issued promotional models.

72-74	'Swinging London', 'Carnaby Street' ...**£8-10**
73	Silver plated Gift Ware version **£70-80**
73	Gold plated Gift Ware version............**£70-80**
73-80	'Berger Paints'. ('Brush' logos may be at front or rear of label) **£5-7**
73	Same but silver body **£70-80**
73	Same but gold body **£90-100**
	Same but orange body **£45-50**
73	Same but cream body, brown roof......**£60-65**
75	'Esso Extra Petrol'..............................**£65-70**
77	'Silver Jubilee 1952-77'. Silver body with red interior, special issue box **£12-15**
	Same but red body, white interior **£70-80**
78	'Matchbox 1953-78'..............................**£4-6**
	Same but orange body **£65-70**
	Same but blue body **£45-50**
72	'Preston Guild Merchant' **£75-80**
73	'Impel 73' Trade Fair **£35-40**
	'London and Kensington Hilton'........**£75-80**
	'The Baron of Beef' **£100-120**
	'Sellotape Selbstklebebander' **£250-300**
	'Sellotape Packaging Systems' **£250-300**
	'Sellotape Electrical Tapes' **£250-300**
	'Barclays Bank' **£80-90**
	'Chambourcy Yogurt'........................**£65-70**
	'Interchemicals and Plastics' **£200-250**
74	'Typhoo puts the 'T' in Britain'..........**£80-90**
76	'Impel 76' Trade Fair. Cream body with brown roof, white interior **£25-30**
	'British Airways Busch Gardens' **£60-70**
	'Ilford HP5 Film'..........................**£150-180**
	'A.I.M. Building Fund 1976'............**£35-40**
	'Selfridges'.......................................**£15-20**
	'Santa Claus, Aviemore Centre' **£35-40**
	'Amcel takes you places'....................**£65-75**
	'Eduscho Kaffee' **£140-160**
77	'New! The Museum of London'.........**£18-20**
	'Army and Navy'...............................**£18-20**
	'Jacob's the Biscuit Makers' Red body with white interior...........**£35-40**
	Orange body with white interior.........**£18-20**
78	'Aral-Deutschlands Autopartner' Blue body with white interior.............**£45-50**
	Same but red body **£90-100**
79	'Impel 79' Trade Fair.........................**£25-30**
80	'You can't kid a Bisto kid' **£8-10**
	'Borregaard Paper' **£90-100**

MB 17g   Leyland Titan Bus

82	'Berger Paints' **£3-5**
	'Laker Skytrain'...................................**£3-5**
82	'Chesterfield Transport Centenary' **£3-5**
	'Matchbox No.1, Montepna' Pale blue/white (Greek issue).............**£18-20**
	Same but red body **£20-25**

MB 18e   Field Car

70-75	Light yellow body, light brown roof, white interior, SB, NW or WW **£18-20**
	Same but WW, UB..............................**£15-18**
	Black roof, UB, WW **£30-40**

76	Military olive drab green body, tan roof, black interior, BB, 'A' square door labels, black wide wheels (TP)...........**£35-45**
76-80	Same but olive green body (TP)........**£18-20**
	Same but 'RA391' bonnet label.........**£18-20**
	With circled star bonnet label (TP) **£20-25**
77-78	White body, black roof, black interior, BB, Black/white checked bonnet label, black wide wheels (TP) **£200-300**
	Same but silver wheel hubs (TP)......**£200-300**
	Orange body, black roof, black interior, BB, black/white checked bonnet label, black wide wheels (TP) **£12-15**
	Same but silver wheel hubs (TP) **£12-15**
	Orange body, black roof, black interior, SB, black/white checked bonnet label, black wide wheels (TP) **£20-25**
78-80	Metallic ruby-red body, tan roof, black interior, SB or BB, '44', 'Champion' and 'Goodyear' bonnet label (TP)...............**£8-10**
80	Dark orange body, black roof, black interior, BB or SB, 'AC Filters' and '179 Scout Racing' labels, US Ltd. Ed. **£20-25**
	Same but no labels, US Ltd. Ed. **£20-25**
82-83	Dark yellow body, black or tan roof, black interior, SB, black/white checked bonnet label, (TP) **£25-30**
	Orange, black roof and interior, BB, black/white checked bonnet, (TP) **£18-20**
	Orange body, black or tan roof, white interior, BB, '44', 'Champion' and 'Goodyear' bonnet label, (TP)...........**£25-30**

MB 18f   Hondarora

74-75	Red body, chrome forks, SE, black seat, 'Honda' tank labels, WW **£18-20**
75-80	Same but no labels or with BW.............**£8-10**
	Red body, black forks, SE, white seat, 'Honda' tank labels, WW **£85-95**
	Same but with black seat **£10-12**
76	Orange body, black forks, SE, black seat, 'Honda' labels, (King Size no 6)...**£20-25**
76	Military olive drab green, black forks, BE, black seat, no labels, WW (TP)....**£25-30**
76-78	Same but military olive green (TP).....**£15-18**
81-82	Metallic green body, black forks, BE or SE, black seat, no labels, BW **£6-8**
82-83	Yellow body, black forks, SE, black seat, no tank labels, black wheels.......**£8-10**
	Same but with brown or tan rider.........**£8-10**

MB 19d   Lotus Racing Car

70	Metallic purple body, UB, SE, white driver, round No.'3' side labels **£35-40**

MB 19e   Road Dragster

70-75	Light red body, UB or SB, off-white interior, '8' labels normal or sideways ..**£8-10**
	Same but with 'Scorpion' labels..........**£40-50**
72	Metallic pink body, UB, off-white interior, 'Wynns' labels. Promotional ..**£60-70**
	Same but smaller 'Wynns' labels........**£60-70**
75	Metallic purple body, UB, off-white interior, 'Scorpion' labels....................**£40-50**
	Same but with '8' labels or no labels **£8-10**
	Metallic red body, UB, off-white interior, '8' labels as normal **£200-250**

MB 19f   Cement Truck

76-81	Red body, yellow barrel with red stripes, unpainted base, green glass **£5-7**
	Same but black stripes or no stripes.......**£5-7**
79	Same but grey barrel with red stripes.....**£5-7**
	Same but with purple glass.................**£10-12**
81-82	Red body, lemon barrel with red stripes unpainted base, green glass **£5-7**
	Same but black stripes or no stripes.......**£5-7**
	Same but with purple glass..................**£8-10**

MB 19g   Peterbilt Cement Truck

82-83	Metallic green body, orange barrel, yellow or white 'Big Pete'....................**£7-9**

MB 20d   Lamborghini Marzal

69	Metallic red body, white interior, UB	**£15-18**
70	Same but with 'Avon' and '2' labels from G3 Racing Specials set	**£20-25**
71	Bright pink body, white interior, UB	**£30-40**
	Bright pink, silver base	**£30-40**
	Same but with 'Avon' and '2' labels from G3 Racing Specials set	**£20-25**
71-75	Orange or orange-pink body, white interior, unpainted base	**£10-12**
72	Yellow body, white interior, UB, ('Brroom Stick' blister pack issue)	**£40-50**

MB 20e   Police Patrol

75-80	White, UB, orange or red 'Police' stripe, orange light and interior (Rola-Matic)	**£7-10**
	White body, UB or SB, orange 'Police' stripe, blue or yellow light and interior	**£6-8**
	Same but with black base	**£8-10**
	White body, UB, 'Ambulance' and Red Cross, orange light and interior	**£15-18**
76-78	White body, UB, orange 'Site Engineer' stripes, orange light and interior, (G3 Consruction Set)	**£30-35**
	Same but with orange body	**£25-30**
	Orange body and 'Police' stripe, orange light and interior, UB, (G3 Set)	**£25-30**
76	Military olive drab green body, UB, yellow and red 'Police' arrow, orange light and interior (TP)	**£40-50**
	Same but 'Ambulance' labels	**£40-50**
76-77	Military olive green body, UB, yellow and red 'Police' arrow, orange light and interior (TP)	**£18-20**
	Same but with 'Ambulance' labels	**£18-20**
80	Blue body, UB, yellow 'Paris-Dakar 81' stripe, (French issue blister pack)	**£40-45**
81	White body, UB, blue 'County Sheriff' labels, blue light and interior	**£12-15**
	Same but '017', 'Sheriff', blue roof	**£15-18**
81-83	White body, UB, yellow 'Police' and 'shield' stripe above chequered stripe	**£8-10**
	Same but with black base	**£8-12**
	White body, UB, black 'Police' on sides, yellow light and interior	**£12-15**
83	Light brown or beige body, UB, yellow 'Securite-Rallye Paris-Dakar 83'	**£12-15**

MB 21d   Foden Concrete Truck

70-73	Dark yellow cab, yellow barrel, red body and shute, green base	**£18-20**
	Same but bright yellow cab, green or dark green base	**£25-30**

MB 21e   Rod Roller

73-78	Yellow body, black wheels with metallic red hubs, GB, 'flame' label	**£18-20**
	Same but with matt red hubs	**£15-20**
	Yellow or darker yellow body, black wheels, GB or BB, 'flame' or no label	**£8-10**

MB 21f   Renault 5TL

78-79	Metallic blue, red interior, BB or SB	**£15-20**
	Metallic blue body, tan interior, black, dark grey or silver base	**£8-10**
	Yellow body, red interior, BB or SB, 'Le Car' and stripe prints	**£12-15**
	Yellow body, tan interior, BB or SB or dark grey base, 'Le Car' prints	**£8-10**
79-81	Silver body, red interior, BB or SB, 'A5' and stripe prints	**£12-15**
	Same but no tampo prints	**£8-10**
	Silver body, tan interior, SB	**£15-20**
81-82	Silver body, red interior, dark grey or BB or SB, 'Le Car' and stripe prints	**£8-10**
82-83	White body, tan interior, BB, 'Renault' and '4' on green prints	**£8-10**
	Same but 'Renault' roof prints	**£8-10**
	White body, tan interior, BB, 'Renault' and '4' on green prints	**£8-10**
	White body, tan interior, BB, 'Roloil' and '21' on yellow prints	**£8-10**

	Same but with orange base	**£20-25**
	White body, white interior, BB, 'Roloil' and '21' on yellow prints	**£8-10**

MB 22c   Pontiac GP Sports Coupé

70	Red body, grey interior, BB	**£2,000-2,500**
	Light purple, grey interior, BB	**£40-50**
	Dark purple, grey interior, BB	**£40-50**

MB 22d   Freeman Intercity

70-71	Metallic purple body, off-white interior, UB, yellow arrow labels on some	**£8-10**
71-72	Metallic gold body, off-white interior, UB, yellow arrow labels	**£15-18**
72-75	Metallic red body, off-white interior, UB or SB, arrow labels on some	**£8-10**

MB 22e   Blaze Buster

75-80	Red body, silver interior, UB, yellow ladder, 'Fire' labels	**£6-8**
	Same but with black ladder	**£20-30**
	Same but with white ladder	**£130-150**
	Red body, silver or white interior, black or dark grey base, yellow ladder	**£6-8**
80-82	Dark red body, white interior, grey or BB, yellow ladder, 'Fire' labels	**£6-8**
83	Light red body, white interior, BB, dark yellow ladder, 'Fire' labels	**£6-8**
	Same but 'No.32' on yellow labels	**£12-15**

MB 23e   Volkswagen Camper

70-72	Blue body, orange interior and hinged roof, UB, CG, rear sailboat side labels on some, petrol filler cap, NW	**£80-100**
	Same but no filler cap	**£20-25**
72-75	Orange body, orange interior and hinged roof, UB, CG, sailboat labels, NW	**£100-120**
	Light or dark orange body, white interior, orange hinged roof, UB, CG, sailboat labels on some, NW	**£18-20**
77-80	Military olive green, no interior, cast roof, BB, BG, Red Cross labels, WW (TP)	**£15-18**
80	White body, no interior, cast roof, BB, GG, 'PizzaVan', WW. US LE	**£30-35**

MB 23f   Atlas Truck

75-81	Metallic blue body, orange tipper with yellow and red arrow labels, chrome interior, AG, UB	**£10-12**
	Same but without tipper labels	**£6-8**
	Same but grey interior, CG, UB	**£4-6**
	Same but grey interior, AG, UB or UB	**£6-8**
	With grey interior, CG and SB	**£8-10**
81	Metallic blue body, silver tipper, grey interior, CG, SB	**£8-10**
81-82	Same but red body	**£8-10**
	Same but red body, black interior	**£12-14**

MB 24c   Rolls-Royce Silver Shadow

70-73	Light metallic red body, cream interior, black base	**£18-20**
	Same, but Dark metallic red body	**£10-15**
	Same but with pink base	**£20-25**
	Same but SB or grey base	**£15-18**
	Same but with metallic green base	**£30-40**
77-78	Light metallic gold body, cream interior, UB, (Japanese issue)	**£80-120**
	Same but BB (Japanese issue)	**£25-30**

MB 24d   Team Matchbox

73	Bright yellow body, white man, '4' (or '8') and 'Team Matchbox' bonnet label	**£180-200**
	Metallic blue body, white man, '1' and 'Team Matchbox' label	**£230-250**
	With '5' and 'Team Matchbox'	**£200-220**
73-75	Metallic green, white man, '5' (or '8'), 'Team Matchbox' label, (G4 set)	**£30-50**
73-78	Metallic red body, white man, '8' and 'Team Matchbox' label	**£8-10**
78-80	Metallic ruby-red body, white man, '44', 'Champion', 'Goodyear', black trailer (TP)	**£10-12**
82-83	Same but orange body, yellow man	**£60-70**

MB 24e   Diesel Shunter

78	Metallic dark green body, light brown control panel, 'Railfreight'	**£6-8**
	Same but with 'D1496-RF' labels	**£4-6**
78-83	Light or dark yellow body, light brown control panel (or none), 'D1496-RF'	**£3-5**

MB 25d   Ford Cortina GT

70	Metallic light brown body, off white interior, unpainted base	**£130-150**
70-72	Same but metallic light blue body	**£20-25**
	Same but metallic dark blue body	**£30-35**

MB 25e   Mod Tractor

72-78	Metallic purple body, BB, yellow seat, headlights cast on rear mudguards	**£40-50**
	Without lights on rear mudguards	**£8-10**
	Metallic purple body, BB, red seat	**£80-90**
	Metallic purple, UB, yellow seat	**£8-10**
76-79	Red body, BB, yellow seat (TP)	**£8-10**

MB 25f   Flat Car Container

78-80	Light beige container red roof, black flat car, 'United States Lines' labels	**£8-10**
	Same but with 'N.Y.K.' labels	**£4-5**
	Same but with 'Sealand' labels	**£5-7**
	Dark beige container, red roof, black flat car, 'N.Y.K.' or 'Sealand' labels	**£4-5**
	Same but with 'OCL' labels	**£10-12**
	Dark brown container, red roof, black flat car, 'N.Y.K.' labels	**£12-15**

MB 25g   Audi Quattro

82-83	White and black, 'Audi' and '20'	**£10-12**

MB 26c   GMC Tipper Truck

70-72	Red tipping cab, silver tipper, green chassis, green glass, wide wheels	**£15-18**

MB 26d   Big Banger

72-76	Red body, UB, 'Big Banger', dark blue glass	**£10-12**
	Same but with amber glass	**£14-18**
78	Dark brown, 'Brown Sugar', WB, amber, black or blue glass (USA)	**£20-25**
81-83	White body, BB, 'Cosmic Blues' clear or blue glass, (US issue)	**£12-15**

MB 26e   Site Dumper

76-78	Yellow body, yellow dumper, black seats, black base	**£5-7**
78-81	Same but with red dumper	**£4-6**
	Same but dark grey base	**£8-12**
	Same but brown base	**£12-15**
81-82	Orange-red body, silver dumper, white seats, black base	**£4-6**
	Same but wheels have yellow hubs	**£7-10**
	Orange-red body, silver dumper, white seats, dark grey base	**£4-6**
	Same but wheels have yellow hubs	**£7-10**

MB 26f   Cable Truck

82-83	Orange-yellow body, red base, blue glass, two light grey cable drums	**£15-18**
	Same but dark grey or BB	**£7-10**
83	Bright yellow body, BB, blue glass, two dark grey cable drums	**£40-50**
	Same but dark red body	**£12-15**

MB 27d   Mercedes 230sl

70-71	White body, red interior, clear glass, unpainted base, narrow wheels	**£25-30**
71	Same but yellow body	**£20-25**
71-73	Yellow body, black interior, CG, UB, NW or WW	**£12-15**

MB 27e   Lamborghini Countach

73-75	Yellow body, BB, red glass, '3'	**£6-8**
	Same but with amber glass	**£8-10**
	Same but with purple glass	**£10-12**
	Yellow body, UB, red glass, '3'	**£6-8**
	Same but with purple glass	**£10-12**

75 Orange body, UB, red glass, '3' £20-30
Same but with amber glass £20-30
75-81 **Lamborghini 'Streakers'**. All have green/black 'Streaker' prints and a red '8' on the bonnet.
Orange body, chrome interior, BB........£8-10
Same but with amber or green glass....£10-12
Orange body, grey interior, BB, GG £8-10
Same but with purple glass................£10-12
Orange body, grey interior, UB, green glass, red '8' on bonnet.........................£8-10
Same but with brown base................£10-12
Orange body, yellow interior, BB or dark grey base, green glass £8-10
Orange, chrome interior, UB, green or amber glass, red '8' on bonnet £10-12
Orange body, grey interior, dark grey base, green glass £8-10
Same but with purple glass................£10-12
Orange body, beige interior, dark grey base, green glass £8-10
Same but with purple glass................£10-12
Orange body, beige interior, BB, GG £8-10

MB 27f   Swing Wing

81-83 Red/white, red glass............................£6-8
Red/white, dark yellow-orange glass....£7-9
Red/white, red or black 'Jet Set' £7-10

MB 28d   Mack Dump Truck

70-73 Metallic lime green body and dumper, UB, cab steps cast closed...................£18-20
Same but with steps cast open............£18-24
77-79 Military olive drab green body/dumper, BB, cab steps cast closed (TP) £40-50
Military olive green (TP).....................£20-25

MB 28e   Stoat

73-76 Metallic gold body, UB or BB, dark brown man, (Rola-Matic issue) £3-6
77 Military olive drab green body, BB, dark brown man, (TP).........................£40-50
77-79 Military olive green body, BB, dark brown man, (TP).................................£18-20

MB 28f   Lincoln Continental

79 Light red body, white roof, beige interior, clear glass, UB £8-10
79-81 Dark red body, beige, dark brown or grey interior, clear glass, UB.............£8-10

MB 28g   Formula Racing Car

81-83 Metallic brown-grey body, BB or UB, white driver, 'Exxon' and '8' prints........£5-7

MB 29c   Fire Pumper Truck

70 Red body, white back and ladders, UB, blue glass, narrow wheels £35-40
81 Same but 'P1' and 'Los Angeles Fire Dept.', wide wheels ('Code Red')......£18-20

MB 29d   Racing Mini

70-72 Metallic bronze body, SB or UB, off-white interior, '29' on yellow labels (orange edges) £15-20
72-76 Orange body, SB or UB, cream or off-white interior, '29' on yellow labels (orange edges) £12-15
Same but with green label edges..........£12-15
76-81 Red body, SB or UB, off-white or cream interior, '29' on yellow labels (green edges) (TP) £15-20
Red body, SB, cream interior, '3' on white circle door labels (TP)...........£35-40
Same but with no labels......................£15-20

MB 29e   Tractor Shovel

76-78 Light yellow body, red shovel, silver engine and seat, yellow base £8-10
77 Lime green body, yellow shovel, silver engine and seat, yellow base (German PS1000 set issue)..................£60-70

78-81 Yellow body, red shovel, silver or black engine and seat, yellow base..........£6-8
Same but with cream base £8-10
Same but with black base......................£6-8
Yellow body, red shovel, black engine and seat, yellow base, yellow hubs..........£6-8
Yellow body, black shovel, black engine and seat, yellow base £6-8
Same but with cream base £8-10
Same but with black base......................£6-8
79 Yellow body, black shovel, black engine and seat, BB, black stripes, ('C' prints on some), (G5 Construction Set)............£6-8
81 Orange-red body, red shovel, dark grey engine and seat, black base, ...£20-25
82-83 Same but with black shovel................£10-12

MB 30c   8-wheel Crane

70 Red body, dark orange crane arm with yellow hook, UB...........................£240-280
Same but with gold crane arm............£18-20

MB 30d   Beach Buggy

70-76 Light metallic purple body, yellow spots, UB, white interior.......................£20-25
Same but with yellow interior £8-10
Same but dark metallic purple body......£8-10
NB The yellow spots on this model can vary from only a few spots to almost an entire body covering.

MB 30e   Swamp Rat

76-81 Military green deck, light brown hull, 'Swamp Rat' labels on some £6-8

MB 30f   Articulated Truck

81-83 Metallic steel-blue cab, WB, red glass, silver trailer...........................£6-8
Blue cab, WB or YB, silver trailer £5-7
83 Blue cab, pale yellow or WB, blue trailer with 'Pauls' white labels, (Ltd. blister-pack issue of 900)............£35-45
Blue cab, WB or YB, yellow trailer, 'International' labels...................£8-10
Red cab, YB, yellow trailer with 'International' labels............................£8-10
Red cab, YB, silver trailer £10-12

MB 31e   Lincoln Continental

70 Sea-green body, white interior, unpainted base, CG, NW...........£1,500-2,000
Metallic lime-green body, white interior, UB, CG, NW £15-20
Same but with wide wheels................£20-25

MB 31d   Volksdragon

71-77 Red body, PG, UB or SB, yellow or cream interior, 'eyes' label on some £10-12
Red body, purple glass, UB or SB, yellow interior, 'flower' label...............£15-20
78 Black body, purple glass, UB, yellow interior, 'bug'/ 'flames' (US issue)......£15-20

MB 31e   Caravan

77-83 White body, off-white or light brown interior, UB, AG, orange or yellow door, orange stripe with white bird labels £6-8
White body, light yellow interior, light blue, orange or yellow door, orange stripe with white bird labels on some......£6-8
Same but dark blue door, blue stripe with white bird labels on some...............£6-8

MB 32c   Leyland Petrol Tanker

70-73 Dark green cab and body, white tank, SB, blue glass, 'B.P.' labels in centre or front of tank, NW £18-20
Dark green cab and body, white tank, GB, 'B.P.' labels in centre of tank £35-40
Blue cab and body, white tanker, SB, 'Aral' labels in centre of tank, (German issue in Aral Tankwagen box)...........£90-110

Metallic purple cab and body, silver tank, SB, no labels £100-125
Same but with 'N.A.M.C.' labels £150-180
Red cab and body, white tank, SB, 'N.A.M.C.' labels.....................£300-400

MB 32d   Maserati Bora

73-78 Metallic crimson body, lime green base, yellow interior, stripe and '8' label........£8-10
Same but with dark green or UB........£10-12
Same but dark green base, '3' label....£15-20
Same but with no label £6-8
79 Metallic gold, SB, yellow interior, no bonnet label, tow hook, (TP)........£35-40

MB 32e   Field Gun

77-81 Military green body, light or dark brown base, 2 soldiers and 4 shells on sprue, black wide wheels.................................£6-8
Same but black wheels, silver hubs.....£30-40
78 Military olive green body, no base, soldiers or shells, black wheels (TP) £3-5

MB 32f   Excavator

81-82 Orange-red body, dark grey or black swivel base, silver-grey tracks................£6-8
82-83 Yellow body, black swivel base, black tracks, black stripes & 'CAT' prints £8-10
Same but with no 'CAT' print £6-8

MB 33c   Lamborghini Miura P400

69 Yellow body, red interior, UB, NW .£100-120
70 Light metallic bronze body, red interior, UB, NW £25-30
Dark metallic bronze body, red interior, UB, NW £100-120
70 -73 Light metallic gold body, off-white interior, UB, NW £18-20
Same but dark metallic gold body.......£18-20
Dark metallic gold body, red interior, UB, NW £25-30
Lt. met. gold body, off-white interior, red or pink-red base, NW or WW £25-30
77-78 Light gold body, off-white interior, UB or BB, WW (Japanese issue) £25-30

MB 33d   Datsun 126X

73-75 Yellow body, orange base, AG £6-8
Same but with unpainted base £30-40
75-77 Yellow body, orange base, AG, red/orange or red/black flame prints, ('Streakers' issue) £10-12
78 Yellow body, BB, AG, red/black flame prints, (US Roman Numeral issue)......£18-20
Gold plated body, BB, black glass, green prints, (US Roman Numeral).....£18-20

MB 33e   Police Motorcycle

77-79 White frame, chrome or black engine, white bars, UW, blue man, white or black seat and panniers, 'Police' £5-7
79 White frame, chrome engine, white bars, UW, green man, seat and panniers, 'Polizei' (German) £15-18
79 Same but cream frame, man has white helmet and gloves (King Size 71 German Polizei Patrol set)...................£15-18
79 All black bike and wheels, dark blue man, white helmet, 3 stripes and shield, white seat and panniers, 'Police', gold star tank (KS 66 set)................£20-25
79 White frame, black engine and wheels, white bars, blue man, white helmet and gloves, white seat and panniers, 'Police' labels......................................£8-10
79-81 White frame, black engine, white bars, black wheels, green man, seat and panniers, 'Polizei' labels (German) £10-12
79 Same but white helmet and gloves £12-15
79-81 Same but white helmet and gloves, UW, (KS 66 Police Patrol set).............£20-25

81	White frame, black engine white bars, black wheels, green man, white seat and panniers, 'LAPD' labels......**£20-25**
81	White frame, chrome engine, black bars, black wheels, no man, white seat and panniers, 'Police' labels.........**£10-12**
81-82	Black frame, chrome engine, white bars, black wheels, blue man, white seat/panniers, 'LAPD' (Code Red)......**£12-15**

MB 34d   Formula I Racing Car

71-72	Metallic purple body, UB, CG, yellow or blue stripe, '16' label, 4 NW..........**£12-15**
71	Same but yellow stripe, 'Wynns' labels (Promotional issue)..................**£60-70**
72-75	Yellow body, UB, CG, blue bonnet stripe, '16' label, 4 NW or WW..............**£6-8**
	Same but front NW, rear WW.........**£8-10**
	Yellow body, UB, CG, yellow stripe, '16' label, 4 NW........**£8-10**
	Yellow body, UB, AG, blue or yellow stripe, '16' label, 4 WW............**£12-15**
73-75	Metallic blue body, UB, CG, yellow or blue stripe, '15' label, 4 WW (or front NW, rear WW) (G4 set)....**£35-40**
	Orange body, UB, CG, blue or yellow stripe, '16', 4 WW (or front NW, rear WW) (G4 set)............**£30-35**
	Orange-yellow body, UB, CG, blue stripe, '16' label, 2 NW, 2 WW..........**£15-18**

MB 34e   Vantastic

75-78	Orange body, WB, GG, white interior, rear stripes labels **£6-8**
	Same but motif instead of stripes **£8-10**
	Same but with stripes and UB **£100-150**
78	Orange body, WB, GG, white interior, 'Jaffa Mobile', (Promotional)..........**£200-230**
78	Orange body, WB, GG or CG, white interior, bonnet 'Sun' label **£25-30**
78-81	Orange body, WB, GG, white interior, '34', rear stripes labels on some.............**£6-8**

MB 34f   Chevy Pro-Stocker

81-83	White body, UB, blue '34' prints.............**£6-8**
	Same but with no tampo prints...........**£6-8**
	White body, red base, blue '34'..........**£10-12**

MB 35c   Merryweather Fire Engine

69-71	Metallic red body, GB, white ladder, 'London Fire Service', NW **£18-20**
71-75	Red body, GB, white ladder, 'London Fire Service', NW or WW **£12-15**
	Red, GB, 'Flame-Proof Wool'........**£125-150**
	Same but in promotional box **£250-300**
	Red body, BB, ladder, 'London Fire Service', wide wheels **£20-25**
	Same but with tan base **£25-30**
	Red body, GB, different style ladder, 'London Fire Service', WW, (TP)......**£12-15**
81	Red body, GB, white ladder and man from 13f, 'Los Angeles City Fire Dept.' prints, WW, (Code Red)............**£18-20**

MB 35d   Fandango

75-77	White body, red interior, red base, red or silver rear disc, arrow and '35' bonnet label (Rola-Matic)......................**£6-8**
	White body, red interior, UB, red rear disc, arrow and '35' bonnet label **£25-30**
	White body, red interior and base, silver rear disc, stripe and '6' bonnet label from 41c.........................**£15-20**
77-82	Red body, red interior, red base, blue arrow and '35' bonnet label, blue or silver rear disc **£85-100**
	Red body, off-white interior, WB, blue arrow and '35' label, blue, silver or red rear disc **£6-8**
	Red body, off-white or white interior, UB, blue rear disc, arrow and '35' **£10-12**
	Red body, white interior, UB, blue rear disc, 'Sun' bonnet label from 47d........**£18-20**

MB 35e   Zoo Truck

82	Red body, blue cage, light brown lions, blue glass, black base..............**£5-7**
	Same but with red base......................**£25-30**
	Same but with grey base....................**£10-12**
83	Red body, silver cage, light or dark brown lions, blue glass, black base **£5-7**

MB 36c   Opel Diplomat

70	Metallic light or dark gold body, silver grille, white interior, BB..........**£20-25**
	Same but without silver grille.............**£18-20**

MB 36d   Hot Rod Draguar

70-73	Metallic dark red body, off-white or light yellow interior, silver 'Draguar' label............................**£12-15**
	Same but with orange interior **£18-20**
	Same but lemon or white interior **£8-10**
73-75	Metallic pink body, light yellow interior, silver 'Draguar' label **£12-15**
	Metallic pink body, cream interior, no boot label **£8-10**
	Metallic pink body, light or dark yellow interior, no boot label................**£8-10**
	Same but with amber glass..................**£8-10**

MB 36e   Formula 5000

75-77	Orange body, blue or yellow man, 'Formula 5000' and orange or yellow '3', '5000' on rear spoiler..............**£6-8**
77	Same but red body, yellow man **£6-8**
77-78	Red body, yellow man, 'Texaco 11' on bonnet, no spoiler label or 'Marlboro' **£8-10**
78-80	Same but 'Champion' on rear spoiler....**£8-10**

MB 36f   Refuse Truck

80-82	Metallic red cab, all-yellow container, red load, no labels **£6-8**
	Same but without 'Collectomatic' on container....................................**£50-75**
82-83	Blue cab, all-yellow or all-orange container, black or red load, 'Metro DPW66' on side labels **£5-7**
	Same but orange container with yellow opening back, red load..............**£8-10**

MB 37c   Cattle Truck

70-71	Orange-yellow cab and body, grey back and 2 white cattle **£15-20**
71	Same but orange cab and body...........**£30-40**
	Orange cab and body, silver back.........**£80-90**
72	Bright-yellow cab/body, grey back......**£70-80**

MB 37d   Soopa Coopa

72-75	Metallic light blue body, yellow interior, AG, unpainted or silver base....................**£6-8**
75-76	Metallic light purple body, yellow interior, AG, UB, 'flower' label....**£12-15**
	Same but with red base....................**£150-200**
77	Orange body, yellow interior, AG, SB, 'Jaffa Mobile' (Promotional) **£100-120**

MB 37e   Skip Truck

76-81	Red cab/body, yellow skip, chrome interior, AG, BB **£6-8**
	Same but grey interior, clear glass **£5-7**
	Same but with brown base....................**£6-8**
	Red cab/body, yellow skip, orange interior, CG, BB **£8-10**
	Red cab/body, blue skip, grey interior, CG, BB **£90-100**
77	Orange cab/body, yellow skip, grey interior, CG, BB (German issue).....**£90-100**
	Same but (German PS1000 set).........**£90-100**
81-82	Metallic blue cab/body, yellow skip, grey interior, CG, gloss or matt BB **£6-8**
	Same but with silver base....................**£10-12**

MB 37f   Matra Rancho

82	Blue body, blue base, black interior **£8-10**
83	Yellow body, yellow base, black interior, red side stripe prints....................**£15-20**

MB 38c   Honda Motorcycle and Trailer

70-71	Metallic blue-green bike, yellow trailer, 'Honda' labels.............**£20-25**
71	Same but metallic pink bike **£25-30**
72-73	Same but metallic purple bike **£25-30**
77	Metallic green bike, orange trailer with 'Honda' labels on some (TP)......**£18-20**
82	Same but yellow trailer (TP) **£15-18**

MB 38d   Stingeroo

73-76	First issue: Metallic purple body, purple forks, white horse's head.........**£10-12**
	Later issue with pale blue forks..........**£35-40**
	Same but with chrome forks..........**£600-700**

MB 38e   Jeep

76-80	Military green body, gun, BB/seats, '21*11' or 'star' label............................**£8-10**
77	Military olive drab green body, no gun, BB/seats, 'star' label, (TP) **£55-65**
	Same but military olive green body **£25-30**
	Same but with '21*11' label (TP)........**£20-25**
	Yellow body, BB/seats, 'Gliding Club', (TP with yellow glider trailer).............**£15-20**
	Same but with white base, (TP with yellow glider trailer)............**£35-40**
	Red body, BB/seats, 'Gliding Club', (TP with red glider trailer)..............**£450-550**

MB 38f   Ford Camper

80-82	Orange-red body, green glass, cream back with AG, UB with no.'35' **£90-110**
	Same but camper back with no glass **£7-10**

MB 38g   Ford Model 'A' Van

The 'collectable cut-off point' for this Catalogue is generally 1983. However, the MB38g casting was used well into the 1990s and proved popular as a promotional item. This section therefore includes issues up to the end of 1989 but excludes items likely to be priced below £5.

84	'TOY FAIR 84' (US), roof label.........**£70-85**
	Same but without roof label **£40-50**
84	'PEPSI COLA', 'COME ALIVE'.........**£5-8**
	Same but without 'COME ALIVE' **£8-10**
	'PEPSI COLA', 'Matchmates'.........**£6-9**
84	'BEN FRANKLIN' **£250-350**
84	'MATCHBOX USA'......................**£15-20**
86	'WEET-BIX'/'SANITARIUM' **£6-8**
86	'H.H. BRAIN'.................................**£6-8**
87	'W.H.SMITH & SON Ltd', Red.......**£7-10**
87	'MICA' 2nd CONVENTION.........**£100-125**
87	'SILVO 1912-1987' **£8-10**
87	'This Van Delivers', with phone no.......**£8-10**
	without phone no **£250-350**
87	'RICE KRISPIES', Dark Blue, (US).....**£8-10**
88	'MICA 3rd CONVENTION' **£7-9**
88	'MICA 1st N.A. CONVENTION'.........**£5-8**
	with black 'island' **£18-22**
88	'W.H. SMITH & SON Ltd', Yellow.....**£7-10**
88	'UNIROYAL' (Canada)..................**£8-10**
89	'MB US COLLECTORS CLUB'.........**£18-22**
89	'JACKY MAEDER' (Swiss) **£6-9**
89	'SWARFEGA'.................................**£8-10**
89	'CAMPERDOWN' (Australia)...........**£12-15**

MB 39d   Clipper

73-79	Metallic crimson body, yellow interior, AG, unpainted base, chrome or white exhausts, (Rola-Matic)............**£15-20**
	With green base and amber glass **£8-10**
	With green base and clear glass..........**£10-12**

MB 39e   Rolls-Royce Silver Shadow

79-81	Silver body, Red interior, SB or UB....**£10-12**	
81-82	Metallic red body, off-white or yellow interior, silver or unpainted base **£8-12**	
82-83	Metallic gold-brown body, white interior, silver or unpainted base **£8-10**	
83	Ruby red body, white interior, matt black or matt silver base **£8-12**	

MB 40c   Hay Trailer

67-70	Dark blue body, yellow sides, BPT with yellow hubs **£8-10**
79-79	Lt. yellow body, no sides, BPT (TP).......**£4-6**
	Same but with black fixed sides (TP)......**£4-6**
	Orange-yellow body, black fixed sides, black wheels (TP) **£8-10**
79	Same but with light blue body, (TP) **£10-12**
80	Same but with red body, (TP)............**£10-12**
81	Same but with beige body, (TP) **£50-60**

MB 40d   Vauxhall Guildsman

71-74	Pink body, GG, cream interior, UB, blue circle flame bonnet label................**£8-12**
	Same but with silver base **£15-20**
	With UB, black circle flame label **£8-12**
	Same but with silver base **£15-20**
75	Pink body, GG, cream interior, UB, blue '40' print (Streakers issue)......**£100-120**
75-76	Red body, AG or GG, cream interior, UB or SB, blue '40' (Streakers) **£12-15**
76	Red body, GG or AG, cream interior, unpainted base, Blue circle flame bonnet label, (TP) **£12-15**
	Red body, AG, UB, cream interior, no bonnet label, (TP) **£12-15**

MB 40e   Horse Box

77-80	Orange cab, cream box, light or dark brown door, BB, SB, GB or UB..........**£10-12**
80-83	Light metallic green cab, cream box, dark brown door, unpainted base...........**£8-10**
	Same but with white door...................**£8-10**
	Dark metallic green cab, cream box, dark brown door, UB, SB or BB..........**£8-10**
	Same but lime green door, SB or BB...**£12-15**
83	Dark metallic green cab, dark brown box, white door, unpainted base **£12-15**
	Yellow cab, dark brown box, lime green door, black base **£20-25**
	Same but with white door..................**£18-20**
	Orange cab, dark brown box, lime green door, BB, SB or UB..................**£10-12**
	Same but with white door...................**£8-10**

MB 41c   Ford GT

69-70	White body, light or dark green or BB, red interior, '6' on bonnet, NW **£25-30**
71-72	Metallic bronze body, dark green or BB, red interior, '6', NW or WW....**£15-18**
	Same but WW, cream base **£30-35**
	Same but WW, grey base....................**£18-20**
	WW, light or dark yellow base **£30-35**
	Blue body, Yellow interior..................**£40-45**
77	White body, red interior, 'Wildcat' or '6' label, BB, (Japanese issue) **£30-35**
79	Yellow body, red interior, BB, no bonnet label, MP1 Italian issue .**£2,000-2,500**

MB 41d   Siva Spyder

72-75	Metallic red body, cream interior, black band, unpainted base, clear glass...........**£8-10**
	Same but with chrome band **£15-18**
	Metallic red body, white interior, black band, unpainted base, clear glass............**£8-10**
75-78	Metallic dark blue body, white or cream interior, black band, UB, CG, stars & stripes, '8', (Streakers issue)................**£15-20**
77	Light blue body, off-white interior, black band, UB, black glass or CG, 'Spider' print, (US Roman Numeral issue) **£20-25**

MB 41e   Ambulance

78-81	White body, grey interior, side stripe with 'Ambulance', red cross labels **£7-10**
	Same but with yellow interior **£10-12**
	White body, grey interior, side stripe with 'Emergency Medical Services'....**£7-10**
	Same but with yellow interior **£10-12**
	White body, grey interior, no stripe - only 'Ambulance' in grey letters **£12-15**
80	Silver body, grey interior, 'Paris-Dakar 81' (French blistercard issue) **£35-40**
	Same but with white rear doors..........**£35-40**
81	Red body, grey interior, 'Notarzt' and red cross prints, (German issue) **£25-30**
	White body, grey interior, side stripe with 'Ambulance', Blue Cross labels **£7-10**
	Same but with 'Pacific Ambulance, Emergency, 101' prints (Code Red)....**£25-30**

MB 42c   Iron Fairy Crane

70	Red body, yellow boom/hook/base....**£90-100**
	Light or dark orange-red body, lime boom, yellow hook, yellow base **£20-25**

MB 42d   Tyre Fryer

72-77	Metallic light blue body, yellow interior, unpainted base...........**£20-25**
	Same but with black base **£8-12**
	Metallic dark blue body, orange-yellow interior, black base......**£18-20**
77	Orange body, yellow interior, BB, 'Jaffa Mobile' (Promotional) **£100-120**

MB 42e   Mercedes Container Truck

77	All-yellow body, BG, BB, 'Deutsche Bundespost' labels (German issue)......**£20-25**
77-80	Red cab/body, cream container with red doors and roof, BG, UB, 'Sealand' or 'NYK' labels **£5-7**
	Same but with black base **£7-10**
	Same but with UB, 'OCL' labels **£7-10**
81	Same but with 'Confern Mobeltransport-betriebe' labels, PG (German issue) **£18-20**
	Dark blue cab and body, blue container BG, UB, 'Karstadt'(German issue)....**£20-25**
81-82	Red/white, 'Matchbox', BG or PG.....**£6-8**
	Metallic green/yellow, BG or PG, 'Mayflower' and ship labels **£6-8**
	Same but with red glass **£8-10**
	Same but red/white body, BG or PG **£6-8**

MB 42   '57 Thunderbird

82-83	Red body, white interior, UB or SB **£7-10**

MB 43c   Pony Trailer

70-71	Yellow body, grey door, light green base, 2 white horses, NW **£25-30**
	Same but with dark green base............**£20-25**
76-79	Orange body, brown door, BB or GB, 2 horses, 'horse head' labels (TP).......**£10-15**
79-83	Same but light brown body................**£10-15**
83	Light brown body, brown door, BB, 2 horses, 'Silver Shoes' or no labels (TP)....................................**£10-15**

MB 43d   Dragon Wheels

72-77	Dark green, BB, 'Dragon Wheels' **£12-18**
	Same but with unpainted base **£18-20**
	Light green, BB, 'Dragon Wheels'......**£18-20**

MB 43e   Steam Locomotive

78-82	Red cab/sides, black engine, '4345' **£4-5**
	Same but with 'NP' labels **£5-7**
81	Green cab/sides, black engine,'4345'...**£8-10**
81-83	Same but with side 'NP' labels (TP) **£7-9**

MB 44c   Refrigerator Truck

70	Red cab and body, green back, grey rear door, green glass, UB, NW **£150-200**
70-71	Yellow cab and body, red back, grey rear door, green glass, UB, WW.........**£10-15**

MB 44d   Boss Mustang

72	Yellow body, black bonnet, UB, WW .**£10-15**
	Same but with silver base **£20-30**
80	Green, UB, 'Cobra', (US Ltd. Ed.) **£10-15**
82-83	Dark or light orange body, off-white interior, UB, 'The Boss' and '5' **£10-12**

MB 44e   Passenger Coach / Caboose

78-83	Red/black, off-white roof, green glass, red '431 432' side labels.....................**£6-8**
	Same but with clear glass **£8-10**
	Same but with no glass **£6-8**
	Red/black, off-white roof, no glass, red '5810 6102' side labels...................**£6-8**
	Same but with cream or tan roof **£6-8**
	Red/black, off-white roof, no glass, green '5810 6102' side labels...............**£6-8**
	Red/black, off-white or cream roof, no glass, green 'GWR' side labels........**£8-10**
81-83	Green/black, off-white raised roof, no glass, green '5810 6102' labels (TP) **£6-8**
	Red/black, off-white raised roof, no glass, red '431 432' labels (TP)............**£6-8**
	Same but red '5810 6102' labels (TP)....**£6-8**

MB 45c   Ford Group 6

70	Non-metallic green body, white interior CE, CG, UB, '7' label, NW **£300-400**
70-71	Dark metallic green body, CE, CG, UB or BB, '7' label, NW **£25-30**
	Same but 'Burmah' labels (G3 set) **£25-30**
	Dark metallic green body, CE, CG, BB or GB, '45' label, NW.............**£12-15**
	Same but with pink base **£18-20**
71-73	Metallic lime green body, CE, AG, BB, '45' label, WW **£10-15**
	Same + 'Burmah' labels, (G3 set) **£15-18**
	Metallic lime green body, grey engine, AG, BB, '45', NW **£10-15**
	Same but grey or CE, GB, WW **£10-15**
73-76	Metallic dark or light purple body, grey or CE, AG, BB, '45', WW.........**£10-12**
	Metallic dark purple body, CE, AG, BB, 'eyes' label from 31d, WW **£30-35**

MB 45d   BMW 3.0 CSL

76-81	Light or dark orange body, cream interior, GG, 'BMW' label on some ...**£10-12**
	Same but with clear glass **£12-15**
77	White body, cream interior, GG, 'BMW' and 'Manhalter' signature label, (Austrian 50,000 issue)..............**£30-35**
	White body, GG, 'Polizei 123', blue or yellow light, (German issue)...........**£50-60**
	Same but no light or 'Polizei 123' **£50-60**
82	Red body, GG, 'BMW' (G15)........**£80-100**

MB 45e   Kenworth Cabover

82-83	White body, AG, blue/brown stripes......**£7-10**

MB 46c   Mercedes 300se Coupé

70	Metallic blue body, white interior, UB, opening doors and boot, NW..........**£150-200**
70-71	Metallic light or dark gold body, opening doors and boot, NW...............**£45-50**
	Metallic light gold body, opening boot but doors cast shut, NW.....................**£20-25**
77	Military olive green body, boot and doors cast shut, 'Staff' labels (TP) **£18-20**
81	Silver body, WW, (Multi Pack) **£70-80**

MB 46d   Stretcha Fetcha

72-77	All-white body, red base, BG, 'Ambulance', large Red Cross labels **£6-8**
	Same but no 'Amulance', small RC....**£15-18**
	All-white body, UB, BG, 'Ambulance' and large Red Cross labels **£8-10**
	All-white body, red base, 'Ambulance', large Red Cross labels, AG.................**£15-20**
	Same but no 'Amulance', small RC....**£20-25**

77	All-red body, red base, BG, 'Unfall Rettung' labels (German issue)...........£40-50
80	Lime green/white, WB or BB, AG, 'Viper Van' prints (US Ltd. Ed.).........£20-25

MB 46e   Ford Tractor and Harrow

78-81	Blue body, yellow interior, UB, black wheels, yellow plastic harrow £5-7
	Same but black wheels, yellow hubs......£6-8
	Blue body, white interior, UB, black wheels, yellow hubs, yellow harrow £6-8
79	Blue body, yellow interior, UB, black wheels, no harrow (TP) £5-7
81	Metallic lime green, yellow interior, BW, yellow hubs, no harrow (TP) £6-8
81-83	Metallic green body, yellow interior, BW, yellow hubs, yellow harrow £5-7
83	Blue body, white interior, GB, BW with gold hubs, no harrow (TP) £6-8

MB 47c   DAF Container Truck

70-72	Silver cab/body, yellow tipper £12-15

MB 47d   Beach Hopper

73-78	Blue body with paint spots, light or dark pink base, orange interior, light brown man, clear or no windscreen, 'Sun' label, wide WW (Rola-Matic)....£8-10
	Same but UB, no windscreen £15-18
	With light pink base, yellow interior, no windscreen, dark brown man........£30-35

MB 47e   Pannier Locomotive

79-82	Dark green and black, BB, 'G.W.R.' £3-5
	Same but with unpainted base............£8-10
	Same but with brown or grey base £10-12

MB 47f   Jaguar SS100

82-83	Red body, light brown interior, BB £8-10
	Same but with grey base....................£10-12

MB 48c   Dodge Dumper Truck

69-71	Blue cab and body, yellow tipper, chrome base, NW or WW....................£12-15

MB 48d   Pie-Eyed Piper

72-77	Metallic blue body, silver engine and exhausts, BG, UB, '8' and stars £8-12
	Same but with amber glass £12-15
	Red body, 'Big Banger', CE and exhausts, BG, UB £150-200
78	White body, silver/black engine, black exhausts, glass and base, orange prints, (US Roman Numeral issue)......£12-15
81-83	Red body, SE, black exhausts, AG, BB, 'Red Rider' prints (USA) £12-15

MB 48e   Sambron Jack Lift

77-81	Yellow body, BB, red 'Sambron'.....£600-800
	Same but with no tampo prints...............£5-7
	Yellow body, BB, yellow hubs...............£6-8
	Same but grey or brown base........£7-10
81-83	Yellow body, black forks, BB or GB......£6-8

MB 49b   Unimog

70	Blue body, red base, green glass, silver or plain grille............................£25-30
70-71	Same but metallic steel-blue body......£20-25
71-72	Same but sky blue body, plain grille ...£18-20
78	Military olive green body, BB, GG, tan load, 'A' label in square (TP)........£35-40
	Same but 'star' circle label, tan load on some, (TP)...................................£35-40

MB 49c   Chop Suey

73-76	Metallic red-purple frame, chrome forks, CE, 'bull's head' £400-500
	Same but with red forks.......................£8-10
	With black or orange forks £35-40

MB 49d   Crane Truck

76-79	Yellow body and crane arm, red hook, black base, green glass....................£6-8
77	Red body, yellow crane arm, red hook, BB, CG (German PS1000 set)............£70-80
	Same but GG (German PS1000 set)....£60-70
80-82	Yellow body, black crane arm, red hook, black base, purple or red glass ..£10-12
	Same but green glass £6-8
82-83	Same but 'A1 Crane Service' on arm + 'Safety First', 'C', 'Cat' on some.....£10-12

MB 50c   Kennel Truck

70-71	Dark or light metallic green body, BB, silver grille, 4 white dogs, NW...........£18-20
	Dark Metallic Green body, Grey base, silver grille, 4 white dogs, NW...........£15-18
	Same but with yellow base £25-30
72-73	Lime Green body, BB or GB, silver grille, 4 white dogs, WW.............£20-25
	Same but white grille, BB or GB £30-35
	Same but with unpainted base £35-40

MB 50d   Articulated Truck

73-79	Yellow cab/body, BB, light blue trailer with yellow chevron side labels, yellow or orange trailer body, red or PG............£7-10
	Same but no labels £6-8
80	Red cab/body, BB, light blue trailer, no labels, red trailer body, PG £35-40
	Yellow cab/ body, light blue trailer, no labels, yellow trailer body, white tow hook, purple glass (TP)...........................£6-8
	Red cab/body, silver trailer (red body), white hook on some, PG (TP) £35-40
80	**Articulated Trailer** Light blue trailer (yellow body) (TP).......................£6-8
	Silver trailer, red trailer body (TP) £35-40

MB 50e   Harley-Davidson

80-82	Light gold frame, black handlebars.....£10-12
82-83	Dark bronze frame, black bars............£10-15

MB 51c   8-wheel Tipper

70-71	Yellow cab and body, silver tipper, BG, SB, 'POINTER' labels on some £20-25
	Same but with grey base....................£80-100

MB 51d   Citroën SM

72-74	Metallic bronze body, cream interior, unpainted base, NW.........................£12-15
	Same but with orange interior £80-100
	Same but with yellow interior £20-25
	With cream interior, silver base £12-15
75	Metallic blue body, yellow interior, unpainted base, WW £25-30
75-78	Same plus '8', UB (Streakers issue)....£12-14
	With '8', UB and off-white or orange interior (Streakers issue) £15-18
79	Metallic blue body, orange interior, UB, roof rack, 'Yamaha Shell STP' (TP)....£15-18

MB 51e   Combine Harvester

78-81	Red body, yellow blades/arm, BB, black 'regular wheels'.............................£6-8
	Same but with black Superfast wheels £6-8
	Same but with yellow hubs.................£8-10
	Red body, yellow blades/arm, no base, black Superfast wheels £8-10
	Same but with yellow hubs.................£12-14
	Yellow body, red blades/arm, no base, '2' print, Superfast wheels (Gift Set).....£8-10

MB 51f   Pontiac Firebird SE

82-83	Red body, tan interior, silver base £8-10

MB 51i   Motorcycle Trailer

79-82	Metallic blue body, 3 orange-yellow or yellow bikes (TP).............................£7-10
	Same but with 3 red bikes (TP)..........£10-12
82-83	Red body, 3 yellow bikes (TP) £12-15

MB 52c   Dodge Charger Mk.III

70-71	Metallic light or dark red body, black interior.......................................£8-12
	Same but with '5' labels (G3 set).......£25-30
71	Metallic purple body, black interior £8-12
71-75	Metallic lime body, black interior £8-12
	Same but with '5' labels (G3 set).......£25-30
	Same but with UB (G3 set) £25-30

MB 52d   Police Launch

76-80	White deck, light blue hull, light or dark BG, orange stripes, 'Police', 2 light blue men, 2 horns £8-10
81	Same but with no roof horns £6-8
	White deck, red hull, roof and rear, BG, 'Los Angeles Fire Department', 2 light blue men (Code Red issue)....£25-30
	Same but 2 yellow men (Code Red)....£18-20

MB 52e   BMW M1

81-83	Silver body, red interior, BB, CG, black stripes and '52' tampo prints £7-10
	Same but blue-grey base....................£10-12
	With BB, amber glass £25-30
	With BB, CG, no tampo prints...............£7-10

MB 53c   Ford Zodiac Mk.IV

70	Metallic light blue body, NW £450-500
70-71	Metallic light green body, NW £25-30
	Metallic dark green body, NW £20-25
	Metallic emerald green body £25-30
72	Lime green body, wide wheels £40-55

MB 53d   Tanzara

72-74	Orange body, SE, silver interior, UB, AG £7-10
	Same but with green glass £10-15
75-76	White body, SE, silver interior, UB, AG, blue/orange stripes/stars, '53' £12-15
	Same but with no tampo prints...........£18-20
	With blue/red stripes/stars, '53' £12-15
	Same but with green glass £18-20
	White body, red engine, red interior, UB, AG, blue/red stripes/stars, '53'....£80-90

MB 53e   CJ6 Jeep

77-80	Red body, yellow interior, light brown roof, UB, WW.................................£5-8
	Same but with black interior.................£8-10
	With yellow interior, silver base £5-8
81-82	Metallic green body, yellow interior, light brown roof, UB, WW £5-8
	Same but with black interior.................£8-10
	With yellow interior, silver base £5-8
	Pale yellow body, dark brown roof, black interior, BB or GB, 'CJ6' print...........£12-15

MB 53f   Flareside Pick-up

82-83	Blue body, '326' and 'Baja Bouncer'....£8-10
	Same but with some or prints or none...£8-10

MB 54b   Cadillac Ambulance

70	White body, silver grille, red roof lights, BB, small Red Cross door labels....£20-30
	Off-white body, plain grille, red roof lights, BIB, large Red Cross labels......£20-25

MB 54c   Ford Capri

71	Pink or orange body, black bonnet, UB, wide wheels..................................£20-25
72-75	Metallic crimson body UB or SB £20-25
76	Orange body, UB, (TP)......................£20-25

MB 54d   Personnel Carrier

76-79	Military green body, black base, green glass, light brown soldiers on some.......£8-10

MB 54e   Mobile Home

80-82	Cream or white body, brown door, side stripes on some, BB £6-8
	Same but with grey or brown base £7-9

MB 54f   NASA Tracking Vehicle

82-83   White/red/black, BB, 'US Space
Shuttle Command Centre', 'NASA' **£7-10**
Same but with grey base.....................**£10-12**

MB 55d   Mercury Police Car

70   White body, 2 men, blue roof light,
shields and 'Police' label **£60-70**
Same but with red roof light..............**£50-60**

MB 55e   Mercury Estate Police Car

71-74   White body, off-white interior, no men,
UB, 2 red roof lights, bonnet shield and
'Police' label and side shield labels.....**£25-30**
Same but UB or SB, bonnet and side
'Police' arrow labels **£12-15**
Same but UB or SB, bonnet 'Police'
arrow label, plain sides **£15-18**

MB 55f   Hellraiser

75-76   White body, red interior, UB,
'Stars and Stripes' bonnet label **£8-10**
77-78   Metallic blue body, red interior, SB,
'Stars and Stripes' bonnet label **£10-12**
Metallic blue body, off-white interior,
UB or SB, 'Stars and Stripes'...............**£8-10**
Metallic blue body, off-white interior,
SB, bonnet stripe and '3' label **£20-25**
Same but with no label **£8-10**

MB 55g   Ford Cortina

79-80   Metallic green body, red interior,
UB, clear glass, opening doors.............**£8-10**
Same but with light yellow interior.....**£12-15**
81   Metallic red body, light yellow interior,
UB, opening doors...............................**£12-15**
82-83   Metallic light brown body, white interior,
UB or SB, opening doors, black stripe..**£8-10**
Light red body, white interior,
UB or SB, doors cast shut **£8-10**
Same but with gloss black base...........**£18-20**
Bright red body, white interior, UB or
SB, opaque glass, doors cast shut
(Gift Set issue) **£20-25**
83   Light red body, light brown interior,
UB or SB, doors cast shut, black
side stripe prints (TP) **£20-25**
Same but white interior (TP) **£12-15**

MB 56c   BMC 1800 Pinifarina

69-70   Metallic gold body, UB, NW............**£12-15**
Same, with '17', 'Gulf' (G3 set) **£20-25**
71-73   Peach body, UB, NW.........................**£25-30**
Orange body, UB, NW or WW..........**£10-12**
With '17' and 'Gulf' (G3 set) **£20-25**

MB 56d   Hi-Tailer

74-78   White body, orange/blue stripes, UB,
'MB5 Team Matchbox', yellow man **£8-10**
Same but with silver or red base **£12-14**
Same but with blue man **£8-10**
79   Red base, 'Martini 7' (Gift Set)..........**£20-25**

MB 56e   Mercedes 450 SEL

79-80   Metallic blue body, red interior **£10-12**
Same but with light brown interior.......**£7-10**
81-83   Light brown body, light or dark brown
interior, red 'Taxi' sign, UB or SB **£7-10**

MB 57c   Land-Rover Fire Truck

70   Red body, 'Kent Fire Brigade' labels ..**£60-70**
Same but with 'Kent Fire Brigade'
labels cut around words **£60-70**

MB 57d   Eccles Trailer Caravan

70-71   Cream body, orange roof, green
interior, maroon side stripe labels **£12-15**
Same but brown side stripe labels **£15-18**
With brown stripe and flower labels ...**£12-15**
72   Pale Yellow body, orange roof, green
interior, brown stripe, flower labels.....**£18-20**

76-78   Yellow body, red-orange roof, white
interior, black stripe, flowers (TP).......**£12-15**
Same but with side red dots label from
K-27 Camping Cruiser set (TP).........**£25-30**
79-81   Light brown, red-orange roof, white
interior, black stripe, flowers (TP).......**£10-12**
Same but 'white bird' label (TP) **£20-25**
82   White body, red-orange roof, white
interior, 'Sunset', palm tree (TP)........**£15-18**

MB 57e   Wildlife Truck

73-80   Yellow body, clear back, red glass,
'Ranger' (Rola-Matic version)..............**£8-10**
Same but with amber back **£10-12**
81   White body, clear back, red glass, light
brown lion, black/white camouflage
prints, (Rola-Matic version)..................**£8-10**
Same but with amber glass **£10-12**
Same but with purple glass **£12-15**
Same but tinted detachable back **£12-15**

MB 57f   Carmichael Rescue Vehicle

82   White body, 'Police Rescue' **£12-15**
83   Red body, 'Fire' **£15-20**

MB 58c   DAF Girder Truck

70   Cream or off-white cab and body,
red base (with 'Pat App' on some) **£80-100**
70-71   Metallic lime green cab and body **£18-20**

MB 58d   Woosh 'n' Push

72-75   Yellow body, red interior, '2' label........**£7-9**
Same but pale yellow interior..............**£25-30**
With red interior, 'flower' label............**£12-15**
76   Metallic red body, pale yellow interior,
'2' label on roof.................................**£8-10**
Same but '8' and stars label................**£12-15**

MB 58e   Faun Dump Truck

76-81   Yellow body, yellow tipper.....................**£6-9**
79   Yellow body, red tipper (G5 set) **£25-30**
82-83   Yellow body, yellow tipper, 'CAT'......**£10-12**

MB 59e   Ford Galaxie Fire Chief

70   Red body, white interior, 'Fire Chief'
and side shield labels **£25-30**

MB 59d   Mercury Fire Chief

71-74   Red body, '59' or '73', 2 men, yellow
'Fire Chief' on bonnet, 'shield' labels
on sides **£20-25**
Same but 'helmet & axes' on sides **£12-15**
Same but yellow bonnet 'helmet and
axes' labels, plain sides......................**£10-12**
Same but yellow 'helmet and axes'
labels on bonnet and sides **£10-12**
With nothing or just '59' on base **£10-12**
78   Same but with no men (TP)................**£10-12**
Red body, CG, 'Fire', shield (TP).......**£10-12**
Same but with purple glass (TP) **£15-20**
79   White, CG, 'Police', shield (TP).........**£20-25**
81   Red body, 'Los Angeles Fire Dept'
tampo prints (Code Red).....................**£18-20**
White body, CG or BG, 'Los Angeles
Police' tampo prints, (Code Red) **£18-20**
82   White body, CG, PG or BG, 'Police'
and shield, black wing panel prints ...**£15-18**
White body, CG or BG, 'Metro Police',
black wing tampo prints as 10f...........**£8-10**
Same but with white wing panels........**£10-12**

MB 59e   Planet Scout

75-77   Metallic green and lime green **£5-7**
78-80   Metallic red and light brown **£8-10**
77   Avocado/black, PG or AG (Adventure
2000 K2005 Command Force set)......**£25-30**
80   Metallic blue/black, PG, (Adventure
2000 set)...**£50-60**

MB 59f   Porsche 928

80-81   Light metallic brown body, brown
interior, black base, clear glass..............**£8-10**
Same but cream or off-white interior ..**£10-12**

With brown interior, amber glass **£10-12**
Dark metallic brown body, brown
interior, black base..............................**£8-10**
Same but with amber glass **£10-12**
Same but with brown glass **£10-12**
With clear glass, brown or grey base.....**£8-10**
With AG, brown or grey base **£12-15**
81-82   Metallic blue body, brown interior,
clear glass, black base.............................**£7-9**
Same but with grey or silver base **£8-10**
82-83   Black body, brown interior, 'Porsche'....**£9-12**
Same but with red interior **£10-12**

MB 60b   Truck with Site Office

70   Blue truck, yellow/green office **£18-20**

MB 60c   Lotus Super 7

71-75   Orange body, black interior and boot,
bonnet 'flame' label **£12-15**
Same but with Yellow body.................**£15-20**
75-76   Same but blue stripe and check design
+ bonnet '60' prints, (Streakers).........**£15-20**

MB 60d   Holden Pick-up

77   Metallic ruby red body, yellow interior,
AG, yellow bikes, '500' label **£10-12**
77-80   Bright red body, yellow interior,
AG, yellow bikes, '500' label **£10-12**
Same but with orange glass **£10-12**
Bright red body, red interior, orange or
AG, olive green bikes, '500' label **£12-14**
Bright red body, red interior, orange or
AG, olive green bikes, 'Sun' label.......**£20-25**
Bright red body, yellow interior, AG,
yellow bikes, 'striped' bonnet label.....**£15-18**
80   Metallic blue body, yellow interior,
orange or amber glass, yellow bikes,
'Paris-Dakar 81' (French issue)...........**£20-25**
81-83   Cream body, red interior, orange or
AG, red bikes, stripes and Superbike' ...**£8-10**
Same but with yellow bikes..................**£8-10**
Cream body, red interior, AG,
red bikes, 'Honda' labels **£25-30**

MB 61b   Alvis Stalwart

66-71   White body, yellow detachable top,
clear glass, 'BP Exploration' labels,
regular black wheels, yellow hubs.......**£35-40**
78   Metallic olive green body, fixed top,
GG, black wide wheels **£20-25**

MB 61c   Blue Shark

71-77   Metallic blue, UB or SB, CG, '86' **£8-10**
Same but with '69' label from 69d......**£12-14**
Metallic blue body, SB, CG or AG,
'Scorpion' label on bonnet..................**£35-40**
Metallic blue body, UB or SB, AG,
bonnet arrows and '86' label **£12-14**
Same but with '69' label from 69d......**£12-15**

MB 61d   Wreck Truck

78-80   Red body, white arms, red hooks,
BB or GB, AG and 2 roof lights............**£5-7**
With red or white arms, black hooks.....**£5-7**
Red body, red arms, red hooks **£8-10**
Red body, white arms, red hooks,
BB, blue glass and 2 roof lights **£25-30**
81   Red body, off-white arms, red hooks,
BB, 'Radio Despatches 24 Hour
Towing' tampo prints (TP)..................**£12-14**
81-82   Light yellow body, red arms, black
hooks, AG, black or grey base **£5-7**
Same but with brown base....................**£8-10**
Same but with silver base **£8-10**
With red arms & hooks, BB or GB **£5-7**
Light yellow body, white arms, red
hooks, BB or GB, AG and lights........**£20-25**
Light yellow body, green arms, red
or black hooks, BB or GB, AG lights..**£10-12**

Dark yellow body, red arms, black
hooks, BB, AG..................................**£7-9**
Same but with brown base....................**£8-10**
Dark yellow body, red arms, red hooks,
BB or GB, AG and lights....................**£7-9**
Dark yellow body, white arms, red
hooks, BB and lights........................**£20-25**
Dark yellow body, green arms, red
or black hooks, BB, AG and lights.....**£12-15**
Same but with grey base......................**£15-20**

MB 61e   Peterbilt Wreck Truck

82-83   Red-orange, white 'Eddies Wrecker' **£6-8**
Same but with black tampo prints.........**£8-10**
Blue body, no tampo print, from
'Highway Express' Gift Set)...............**£20-25**

MB 62c   Mercury Cougar

70   Light metallic gold or gold-green body
red interior...................................**£20-25**

MB 62d Mercury Cougar Dragster

70   Light green body, red interior, UB,
'Rat Rod' labels.............................**£20-25**
70-73   Same but lime green body **£10-12**
Same but with silver base **£25-35**
Same but UB, 'Wild Cat' labels **£25-30**

MB 62e   Renault 17TL

74-78   Red body, white interior, '9' label **£8-10**
Red-orange body, white interior, '9'.....**£8-10**
Same but label reversed to read '6' **£10-12**
76   Red body, white interior, 'Fire'
labels, (from G12 Rescue set) **£20-25**

MB 62f   Chevrolet Corvette

79-81   Metallic ruby red body, grey interior,
UB, CG, white bonnet prints............**£8-10**
Same but with black interior..............**£10-12**
Same but white interior......................**£12-15**
Same but with black interior................**£8-10**
Same but with grey interior.................**£8-10**
81-83   Black body, grey interior, UB, CG,
orange/yellow bonnet stripes **£7-9**
Same but with silver base **£8-10**
83   Same but UB, opaque glass, (from
Streak Racing set) **£12-15**

MB 63c   Dodge Crane Truck

70-72   Yellow body, yellow crane, arm
and hook (orange hook on some) **£15-18**

MB 63d   Freeway Gas Tanker

73   Red/black/white, 'Castrol' labels.........**£60-70**
73-77   Red/black/white, 'Burmah' labels **£5-7**
Same but with tow hook hole in rear **£6-8**
76   Military olive drab green and black,
'Canadian' flag labels (TP).............**£300-400**
Same but with 'French' flag (TP).......**£70-80**
76-77   Military olive green cab black base,
'95 High Octane' labels (TP)...........**£18-20**
77   Light blue/black/white, 'Aral'
labels (German issue)....................**£30-35**
78-79   Red/black/white, 'Chevron' labels,
tow hook hole in rear of tanker **£6-8**
Same but with white tow hook (TP)........**£8-10**
Red/black/white, 'Burmah' labels,
cream tow hook (TP)........................**£8-10**
79-80   White/yellow, 'Shell' labels, PG...........**£8-10**
Same but with red glass **£10-12**
Yellow/black/white, 'Shell', PG **£15-18**
80-81   White/yellow, 'Exxon' labels..............**£15-18**
White/black, 'Exxon' labels...............**£15-18**
White/yellow, 'Shell' labels,
cream tow hook (TP) **£8-10**
White/yellow, 'Exxon' labels,
cream tow hook (TP) **£15-18**
81-82   White/black/green, 'BP Super'..........**£12-15**
White/yellow, 'BP Super' (TP)..........**£25-30**

MB 63dx   Freeway Gas Trailer

78-79   White/red, 'Chevron' labels (TP) **£8-10**
Same but with 'Burmah' labels (TP).....**£8-10**

80-81   White/yellow, 'Shell' labels (TP) **£6-8**
White/yellow, 'Exxon' labels (TP) **£15-18**
81-82   White/yellow, 'BP Super' (TP)..........**£20-25**

MB 63e 4x4 Open Back Truck

82-83   Orange or light orange body, '24' and
'FWD' or '4x4' prints **£6-8**

MB 64b   MG 1100

70   Green body, white interior with man and
dog, unpainted base, clear glass **£300-400**
70-71   Same but metallic light blue body **£18-20**
Same but metallic dark blue body **£25-30**

MB 64c   Slingshot Dragster

71-72   Metallic pink body, BB, black exhausts,
bonnet flame and '9' labels.................**£10-12**
73   Orange body, BB, black exhausts,
bonnet flame and '9' label...............**£100-120**
Same but red exhausts **£150-200**
73-75   Metallic blue-green body, UB, red
exhausts, bonnet flame, '9' label **£15-18**
Same but BB, front NW or WW **£6-8**
Same but with '3' **£18-20**

MB 64d   Fire Chief Car

76-79   Red body, 'Fire', some yellow shield
labels have black edging.........................**£6-8**
Same but with orange base.....................**£8-10**

MB 64e   Caterpillar D-9 Tractor

79-81   Yellow body, brown roof, yellow shovel,
black tracks, orange or yellow rollers ...**£7-10**
82   Yellow body, black roof, yellow shovel,
'C'on cab, black tracks, yellow rollers..**£8-10**
82-83   Same but black shovel, black or silver
tow hook, 'C' on cab **£7-10**
Same plus 'CAT' print, (black hook)....**£8-10**

MB 65c   Claas Combine Harvester

67-72   Red body, yellow cutters, black base,
black wheels with yellow hubs..............**£8-10**

MB 65d   Saab Sonnet III

73-76   Metallic blue body, yellow interior,
UB, AG, grey rear door.........................**£8-10**
79   White body, yellow interior, UB, AG,
grey rear door, (Multi Pack) **£200-220**

MB 65e   Airport Coach

NB All Airport Coach models have white roofs
77-81   Metallic blue body, off-white or
pale yellow interior, AG or CG, UB,
'British Airways'.................................**£7-9**
Same but with labels reversed **£10-12**
Metallic blue body, off-white interior,
UB, AG, 'American Airlines' labels ...**£8-10**
Same but with clear glass **£12-15**
Same but pale yellow interior, AG **£8-10**
Same but with clear glass **£12-15**
Metallic blue, off-white or pale yellow
interior, AG, 'Lufthansa' (German).......**£8-10**
Same but with clear glass **£12-15**
81   Orange body, pale yellow interior, UB,
AG, 'Schulbus' (German issue) **£25-35**
81-83   Red body, 'TWA' **£7-9**
Red body, 'Qantas'................................**£7-9**
82   Red body, 'Fly Braniff' **£25-35**
White body, 'Stork SB'(Australian) **£18-20**
Metallic Blue body, 'Girobank'
(Promotional issue)...........................**£18-20**
83   Metallic Blue body, UB or SB, AG,
'British' labels **£7-9**
Metallic Blue body, UB or SB, AG,
'Australian' labels **£12-14**
White body, UB or SB, 'Alitalia'........**£15-20**
White body, UB or SB, 'Lufthansa' ...**£25-30**

MB 66c   Greyhound Coach

70   Silver body, yellow interior, AG, matt
or gloss BB, 'Greyhound'...................**£18-20**
Same but with yellow or pink base **£25-35**

MB 66d   Mazda RX500

71-74   Orange body, SE, white base, PG...........**£7-9**
Same but with unpainted base **£15-20**
Orange body, SE, white base, AG **£12-15**
75-76   Red body, SE, WB, AG, white/green
'77' and stripes(Streakers version) **£7-9**
Same but with PG (Streakers) **£12-14**
Same but UB, AG (Streakers) **£12-14**
Red body, light brown engine, WB,
AG, '77' and stripes (Streakers)........**£12-14**
Same but with PG (Streakers) **£15-18**

MB 66e   Ford Transit

77-80   Orange body, green glass, UB,
brown load, green interior **£15-20**
Same but light brown interior..............**£12-15**
Same but light yellow interior..............**£7-9**
Orange body, amber glass, UB,
beige load, green interior **£15-20**
Light brown or light yellow interior....**£12-15**
81-82   Yellow-orange body, off-white or green
interior, UB, brown load, green glass....**£8-10**
Same but with beige load **£7-9**
Yellow-orange body, green interior, GB,
brown or beige load, green glass..........**£8-10**
Same but with black base **£15-20**

MB 66f   Tyrone Malone Superboss

82-83   White body, blue/red stripes on some,
'Tyrone Malone' on white aerofoil......**£8-10**
With plain white or cream aerofoil........**£6-8**

MB 67b   Volkswagen 1600TL

70   Dark or light red body,
white interior, UB, CG, NW **£120-150**
70-71   Metallic purple body (may be dark,
mid or light), white interior, UB, CG,
narrow or wide wheels......................**£30-40**
71-72   Metallic pink body, white interior,
UB, CG, NW or WW **£30-40**

MB 67c   Hot Rocker

73-74   Metallic green-gold body, white interior,
UB, CG (Rola-Matic version) **£12-15**
Same but with silver base **£20-30**
Same but metallic green body, UB **£12-15**
Same but with silver base **£20-30**
75-77   Red body, UB, (Rola-Matic version) **£9-12**
Same but with silver base **£20-30**

MB 67d   Datsun 260Z 2+2

78-80   Metallic crimson body, white interior,
clear glass, black base............................**£6-8**
Same but with grey base **£8-10**
79   Metallic blue body, pale yellow
interior, matt black base (TP) **£15-20**
Same but with red interior (TP)..........**£30-40**
Metallic blue body, red interior,
brown base (TP)................................**£40-50**
80   Metallic red body, pale yellow
interior, black base **£8-10**
81-83   Silver body, red interior, black base **£6-8**
Same but grey or blue-grey base **£8-10**
Same but with brown base **£8-10**
Silver body, white interior, GB or BB,
red stripes, black 'Datsun 2+2' (TP) **£8-10**
Silver body, black interior, BB, blue
stripes, black 'Datsun 2+2' (TP).......**£10-12**
83   Black body and interior, BB (TP).......**£20-30**

MB 68c   Porsche 910

70-74   Metallic red body, pale yellow interior,
UB, AG, '68' label on bonnet, NW........**£8-10**
Same + '68' side labels (G3 set).......**£25-30**
Metallic red body, pale yellow interior,
UB, AG, bonnet '68' label, WW........**£8-10**
Same but with '45' label from 45c **£25-30**
Silver body, White interior, UB **£140-160**
72   White body, pale yellow interior, UB,
AG, WW ('Brroom Stick' issue).........**£35-40**

MB 68d   Cosmobile

75-78	Metallic light blue body, yellow under, white or silver interior, AG.........................**£5-7**
77	Avocado body, black under, white interior, AG, (Adventure 2000 set) **£20-25**
	Same but with purple glass (set).........**£15-20**
	Same but with silver interior (set).....**£25-30**
78-79	Metallic red body, beige under, white or silver interior, AG..................**£8-10**
80	Metallic dark blue, black under, silver interior, PG (Adventure 2000 set) **£50-65**

MB 68e   Chevy Van

79-80	Orange body, UB, BG, blue/red or blue/white stripes.....................................**£8-10**
	Same but CG, blue/red stripes **£10-12**
	Same but BG, red/black stripes.............**£8-10**
	Same but with green or red glass **£8-10**
80-81	Orange body, 'Matchbox Collectors Club' labels, BG (Ltd. Edition) **£15-18**
81-82	White body, 'Adidas' (German) **£25-30**
	White body, 'USA-1' (US issue)........**£12-15**
	Green body, 'Chevy' with brown or yellow segmented stripes.........................**£7-9**
82-83	Yellow body, 'Collect Exciting Matchbox' (Australian issue)...............**£20-25**
	Silver body, blue glass, 'Vanpire'.........**£8-10**

MB 69c   Rolls-Royce Silver Shadow

69-70	Metallic blue body, brown interior, tan folded top, BB, AG, NW..............**£12-15**
	Same but dark or light yellow base **£20-25**
71-72	Metallic light gold body, brown interior, tan folded top, BB, AG, WW..............**£12-15**
	Same but dark or light yellow base **£20-25**
	Same but with silver base **£12-15**
	With black folded top, BB **£10-12**
	Same but with light yellow base..........**£20-25**
	Same but with silver or grey base **£12-15**
	With off-white interior, black folded top, black base, AG, WW.................**£12-15**
	Same but with grey base....................**£15-20**
	Metallic dark gold, AG, off-white interior, black folded top, BB, WW.....**£12-15**
	Same but with grey or silver base **£18-20**
	Metallic dark gold body, brown interior, black folded top, BB, AG, WW **£12-15**
	Same but with grey or silver base **£18-20**
72-73	Metallic lime gold body, off-white or brown interior, BB, AG, WW **£30-40**
	Same but with grey or silver base **£40-50**

MB 69d   Turbo Fury

73-77	Metallic red body, CG, '69' and arrows label, (Rola-Matic version).......**£8-10**
	Same but AG (Rola-Matic version).....**£10-12**
	Metallic red body, '86' and arrows label, (Rola-Matic version).................**£15-18**
	Same but 'Scorpion' (Rola-Matic) **£40-45**

MB 69e   Security Truck

78-83	Dark red body, cream roof, UB or SB, BG, '732 2031', 'Wells Fargo' **£8-10**
	Light red body, white roof, SB, CG, '732 2031' and 'Wells Fargo'............**£12-15**
	Same but BG, UB or SB **£5-7**
	Light red body, white roof, SB, BG, 'QZ 2031' and 'Wells Fargo'.............**£8-10**
81	Metallic dark green body, SB, BG, 'Dresdner Bank' (German promo).......**£20-25**

MB 70b   Grit Spreading Truck

70	Red cab and body, dark or pale yellow grit spreader, UB, GG, NW.................**£12-15**

MB 70c   Dodge Dragster

71-75	Dark pink body, BB, 'snake' labels.....**£10-12**
	With purple, cream, light green, light yellow, dark yellow or grey base........**£20-25**

	With brown or unpainted base............**£35-40**
	Dark pink body, BB, 'Wild Cat'.........**£40-50**
	Dark pink body, 'Rat Rod' labels **£40-50**
	Light pink body, BB, 'snake' labels **£15-18**
	Bright pink body,BB, 'snake' labels **£15-18**
78	Yellow body, red glass, GB or BB, side prints, (US Roman Numeral) **£18-20**

MB 70d   S.P. Gun

76-80	Military green body, black or brown tracks, (Rola-Matic version).................**£8-10**

MB 70e   Ferrari 308 GTB

81-83	Red body and base, black stripe, CG **£8-10**
	Red body and base, CG, 'Ferrari' **£8-10**
	Same but with AG..............................**£10-12**
83	Red body, silver base, no 'Ferrari' **£8-10**

MB 71c   Ford Heavy Wreck Truck

70-72	Red cab, white body, red crane and hook, BB, GG, 'Esso' **£18-20**
	Same but with yellow hook.................**£18-20**
79	Military olive green, black hook, BB, GG, '3LGS64' labels (TP)...........**£20-25**
81	Dark blue, blue crane, black hook, BB, GG, no labels (Multi Pack)..........**£80-90**

MB 71d   Jumbo Jet

73-75	Metallic blue frame, red elephant head, dark blue handlebars, black wheels **£8-10**
	Same but light blue handlebars...........**£20-25**

MB 71e   Cattle Truck

76-81	Metallic orange-red cab, dark yellow back, UB or SB, GG or BG, 2 black cattle **£8-10**
	With AG, PG or orange glass, SB..........**£8-10**
79-83	Dark red cab, off-white back, SB, BG, 2 black cattle (TP) **£8-10**
	Same but with red or PG (TP)...............**£8-10**
	Dark red cab, dark or light yellow back, SB, PG, 2 black cattle (TP)....................**£8-10**
81-83	Metallic light green cab, off-white back, SB, OG, 2 brown cattle **£6-8**
	Metallic light or dark green cab, yellow back, SB, red or OG, 2 brown cattle........**£6-8**
	Metallic dark green cab, dark brown back, SB, red or AG, 2 brown cattle........**£6-8**
83	Yellow cab, brown back, BB, UB or SB, red or AG, 2 light brown cattle **£6-8**
	Same but with black tow hook (TP)........**£6-8**

MB 71ex   Cattle Truck Trailer

79-83	Dark red body, off-white or light or dark yellow back, SB, 2 black cattle (TP).......**£5-7**
83	Yellow body, dark yellow back, SB, 2 light brown cattle (TP).........................**£5-7**

MB 72b   Standard Jeep

70-71	Dull yellow body, red interior, UB **£18-20**
	Bright yellow body, red interior **£50-60**

MB 72c   SRN Hovercraft

72-78	White body, BB, BG, 'R.N.L.I.' **£6-8**

MB 72d   Bomag Road Roller

79-82	Yellow/red, black roller, 2 wheels **£6-8**
	Same but 2 wheels have yellow hubs.....**£7-9**

MB 72e   Dodge Delivery Truck

82-83	Red cab, white back, 'Pepsi' **£6-8**
	Red cab, white back, 'Kelloggs'............**£6-8**
	Either of the above with gold hubs.........**£7-9**
	Red cab, white back, 'Smiths Crisps' (Promotional offer)...............................**£6-8**
	Same but with gold hubs (Promo).........**£7-9**

MB 73c   Mercury Commuter

70-71	Metallic lime green body, UB with '59', '55' or '73', NW or WW **£20-25**
71-73	Red body, UB, 'Bull head' label on bonnet of some, wide wheels..............**£10-12**

MB 73d   Weasel

74-76	Metallic green body, metallic green and green base, (Rola-Matic)..................**£8-10**
76	Military olive drab green body, metallic green and green base, (Rola-Matic) (TP) **£35-40**
76-79	Same but with military olive green body (Rola-Matic) (TP) **£12-15**
	Military olive green body, olive green and green base, (Rola-Matic) (TP) **£12-15**
	Same but olive green and black base, (Rola-Matic) (TP) **£12-15**

MB 73e   Ford Model 'A' Car

79-80	Cream body, dark green wings, GG **£8-10**
	Same but no spare wheel or glass...........**£7-9**
80	White body, dark green wings, GG **£10-12**
80-82	Metallic green body, dark green wings, GG or no glass **£5-7**
82-83	Light brown body, dark brown wings, amber glass **£5-7**
	Same but with clear glass **£6-8**

MB 74b   Daimler Bus

70-72	Red body, white interior, 'Esso' **£18-20**
	Same but 'dayglo' pink body...............**£20-25**
72	Red body, 'Inn on the Park' labels ..**£130-150**
	Red body, 'The Baron of Beef' **£140-160**
	Red body, 'NAMC', 'The Miniature Vehicle' labels (Promotional) **£160-180**
	Red body, 'Kensington Hilton'........**£100-120**
	Red body, 'I.C.P. Interchemicals' **£250-300**

MB 74e   Tow Joe

72-77	Metallic green-gold body, UB, AG and roof light, green arms, Red hooks **£10-12**
	Same but with BB or SB **£10-12**
	With UB and black hooks...................**£12-15**
	Metallic green body, BB, AG and roof light, green arms, red hooks...........**£8-10**
76-81	Yellow body, BB, SB or UB, AG, red arms, black hooks (TP)........................**£8-10**
	With matt base, red or black hooks ...**£75-100**
	Metallic green body, BB, AG, red arms, black hooks (TP)..................**£25-30**
	Same, BB or SB, white arms (TP) **£90-100**
	Red body, BB, AG, red or green arms, red or black hooks (TP) **£150-170**
82	Yellow body, UB, AG, red arms, black hooks, 'Hitch Hiker' labels (TP) **£100-120**

MB 74d   Cougar Villager

78-81	Metallic light or dark green body, yellow interior, UB, AG....................**£10-12**
81-82	Metallic blue body, yellow or orange-yellow interior, UB, AG.....................**£15-20**

MB 74e   Fiat Arbath

82-83	White body, red interior, 'Matchbox'..**£10-12**
	Same but with black interior...............**£40-60**

MB 75b   Ferrari Berlinetta

70	Metallic green body, off-white interior, unpainted base, clear glass.............**£200-250**
70-71	Red body, off-white interior, UB, CG, silver grille on some **£60-75**

MB 75c   Alfa Carabo

71-75	Metallic Purple body, YB, NW.............**£8-10**
	Same but with unpainted base **£10-12**
75	Metallic light pink body, YB, WW.......**£15-20**
75-76	Metallic light pink or red body, WW, (Streakers) yellow/black/green prints ..**£10-12**

MB 75d   Seasprite Helicopter

77-81   White body, Red underside, BG or GG,
          black rotors, blue 'Rescue' labels..........**£8-10**
          Same but with red glass.......................**£12-15**
          Same but with purple glass.................**£15-18**

MB 75e   Helicopter

82-83   White/orange, black interior, black skids,
          AG, 'MBTV News' tampo prints.............**£6-8**
          White/black, black or grey interior, black
          skids, AG or CG, 'Police' and '36'..........**£6-8**
          White/black, black or grey interior,
          black or grey skids, AG, 'Rescue' **£8-10**

Matchbox Superfast and miscellaneous Sets

G 1	1968	**Service Station Set** Contains 13d, 56b, 32c, and 'BP' Service Station.....**£150-180**
G 1	1970	**Service Station Set** Contains 13d, 15d, 32c, and 'BP' Service Station...**£150-180**
G 1-8	1981	**Transporter Set** Contains Transporter and 5 Superfast Cars **£50-60**
G 1-9	1984	**Transporter Set** Contains K10 plus 4 cars.....**£40-50**
G 2-7	1970	**Transporter Set** Contains Transporter and 5 Superfast models **£85-100**
G 2-8	1973	**Transporter Set** Contains Transporter and 5 Superfast models **£85-100**
G 2-11	1981	**Railway Set** Contains 43e, 2 x 44e, 25f...................**£25-30**
G 3-7	1970	**Racing Specials Set** Contains 5e, 20c, 45c, 56c, 52c and 68c **£120-150**
G 3-8	1973	**'WILD ONES' Set.** Contains 5 Superfast Cars..........**£70-80**
G 3-9	1981	**Racing Car Set** Transporter and 4 Racing Cars........**£40-50**
G 4-7	1970	**Truck SuperSet** Contains 47c, 63c, 58c, 49b, 16d, 21d, 11d and 51c **£80-90**
G 4-8	1973	**Team Matchbox Set** Contains Racing Car Transporter and 4 Racing Cars **£60-70**
G 4-9	1981	**Military Assault** Landing Craft + 6 military models ...**£50-60**
G 5-9	1981	**Construction Set** Contains 5 construction models.....**£30-40**
G 6-6	1970	**Truck Set** Contains 1e, 10d, 21d, 26c, 30c, 60b, 70b and 49b...**£100-120**
G 6-7	1973	**Drag Race Set** Contains 6 Superfast Cars **£60-70**
G 6-8	1981	**Farm Set** Contains 6 farming models.........................**£35-40**
G 7-5	1973	**Ferry Boat** With Plastic Boat and 4 Superfast Cars....**£45-50**
G 7-8	1978	**Car Ferry Set** Contains 3 Cars and Sports Boat **£40-50**
G 7-6	1981	**Emergency Set** Contains 5 Rescue models **£40-50**
G 7-7	1984	**Emergency Set** With models 8, 12, 22, 57 and 75 .....**£40-50**
G 8-5	1984	**Turbo Charged Set** Contains Turbo Charger plus 7, 9, 52, 60 and 68 ....**£35-40**

G 10-5	1986	**'PAN-AM' Set** Contains 10, 54, 64, 65 and 'Sky-Buster' Boeing **£40-45**
G 11-1	1978	**Strike Force Set** Contains 6 Army Vehicles...............**£45-50**
G 11-2	1986	**'LUFTHANSA' Set** Contains 30, 54, 59, 65 and 'Sky-Buster' Airbus **£50-60**
G 12	1978	**Rescue Set** Contains 6 Rescue Vehicles.....................**£40-45**
G 13	1978	**Construction Set** Contains 6 Construction Vehicles..**£35-40**
G 14	1978	**Grand Prix Set** Transporter and 4 Racing Cars **£35-40**
G 15	1978	**Transporter Set** Transporter and 5 Superfast Cars **£35-40**
G 40	1988	**40 years Set** ('Made in China' cast under models). Aveling-Barford Road Roller, London Bus, Horse Drawn Milk Float, M-H Tractor, Dennis Fire Engine **£20-25**
C 6		**Emergency Gift Set** All Japanese Set **£25-30**
C 11		**Airport Gift Set** Japanese Foam Pump, Ikarus Coach and Aircraft **£30-35**
---	1971	**Matchbox Crash Game** With 4 assorted cars, racetrack, dice and instructions....**£50-60**
---		**Multi-Pack Gift Set** Contains 5 Superfast models.....**£20-25**
A1	70-73	**Service Ramp** 'CASTROL' **£30-35**
A2	1970	**'Superfast Auto Sales'** Plastic kit includes 'MATCHBOX SALES OFFICE', 'STAR VALUE' stand, 3 'M' flagpoles and 4 lamp posts, plus pink card base, signs and advert. stickers. 25 items in total..........**£150-200**
A2	71-73	**'Matchbox' Sales Park** Pink card sales park with four lampposts....................**£35-40**
A3	c1971	**'Brroooom Stick'** Blister-packed car with steering control. Contains No.20 Lamborghini Marzal in Yellow and No.68 Porsche in White................**£60-70**

We regret that it has not been possible to continue listing the Miniatures models produced from 1983 (with the exception of the important 'Londoner Bus' issues).

We would suggest that collectors requiring more information should contact: Nigel Cooper, Matchbox House, Alton Lane, Four Marks, Hants., GU34 5AL. Telephone: (01420) 568030. Also available from Nigel Cooper is a CD (priced at £15 ($25), post free) containing every known variation of Superfast model from 1969 to 2005. E-mail: coopertoys@hotmail.com.

Also see the MICA advertisement at the beginning of the Matchbox section.

Two fine collections of Models of Yesteryear showing various stages in the
early development of their box design.

Many variants of Yesteryears have resulted from long production runs which often required renewal or modification of worn dies. Considerable numbers of model variations have thus been issued over the years, some of them quite minor. The objective of this listing is to identify for the Yesteryear collector all those price-significant variations which really do matter. Collectors requiring details of the all the variations issued should contact:
The Matchbox International Collectors Association (M.I.C.A.)
PO Box 120, Deeside, CH5 3HE, UK.

This new listing has been extensively updated by Yesteryear authority Horace Dunkley.

Identification

Common features. Many models have common identifying features and these are shown below to avoid unnecessary repetition in the Features column.

Model name and number. Both 'Models of Yesteryear' and 'Made in England by Lesney' are cast underneath all models issued up to the end of 1982. With the change of ownership this was replaced by 'Matchbox Intl Ltd.' From 1987 'Made in Macau' appears on the base. All models have their 'Y' number shown underneath.

Wheels. All the wheels prior to 1970 were of metal construction. From 1972 (approximately), plastic wheels were used on all models. Nevertheless the models issued at this changeover period are to be found with either metal or plastic wheels.

Scale of models ranges from 1:34 to 1:130. The scale of each model is usually shown on its box.

Logos and designs. The early models had waterslide transfers. Labels have also been used and currently models are tampo printed.

Catalogue listings. Do not place too much reliance on the model colours shown in catalogues. Very often the pictures shown are from mock-ups in colours never actually issued. For example, the 1969 catalogue showed a picture of a blue Y-5 Peugeot that was issued in yellow. Similarly the 1973 catalogue showed a silver Hispano Suiza which was then issued in red.
Bumpers, dashboards, headlights, radiator shells and windscreens. All assumed to be of metal construction prior to 1974 (approx.), after which plastic was increasingly used.
Base plate and chassis are usually of metal construction.
Tyres are of treaded black plastic unless otherwise indicated.
Seats are all made of plastic unless otherwise indicated.

Boxes

1956-57	All card box with just a plain black number shown on box ends. Line drawing of model on the front of box.
1957-60	All card box with line drawing of model used for first 15 models issued, blue number shown on white circle on endflap.
1960-61	As first box but with a red number. All card box with coloured picture of the model (3 varieties of this box exist). All card box with model pictures on the box endflaps.
1968-69	Pink and yellow box with clear window.
1968-70	As previous box with hanging display card (developed in the US market and led to blister-pack design).
1969-70	Mauve and yellow box with window.
1974-78	'Woodgrain' window box in various colours
1979-83	'Straw' (light cream), window box.
1984-90	'Red' (maroon), window box.

MPR = Market Price Range   **GSP** = Gift Set price

Years of production; scale; other details	MPR

Y1-1 Allchin Traction Engine

1956-1965. Scale 1:80. Early issues have rear wheel treads with a straight-across pattern, second type are diagonal; third type has a smooth tread.

With straight-across treads to rear wheels.............................**£85-140**
Rear wheel treads in Red (as per spokes)...............................**£65-95**
Rear wheels with no tread pattern (smooth)...........................**£450-700**
Smoke box door in green (as per body) **£150-200**
Other versions **£25-50**

Y1-2 1911 Ford Model 'T'

1964-1984. Scale 1:42. All Y1-3 models have 'brass effect' finish wheels.

With twin brake lever (Dark Red models only) **£45-70**
Black textured roof (Dark Red or White/Red models) **£60-75**
Bright Red textured roof (White/Red models only)...........................**£85-120**
Other versions **£2-10**

Y1-3 1936 Jaguar SS100

1977-1994. Scale 1:38.

With small sidelights (Off-White model only).......................**£85-125**
Steel-Grey body and chassis.......................................**£150-175**
Other versions **£2-10**

Y2-1 1911 'B'-type London Bus

1956-1961. Scale 1:100. The diecast driver may be found in any shade of mid or dark blue, sometimes black.

With 4 over 4 side windows **£75-100**
With Black wheels **£50-75**
Other versions **£35-50**

Years of production; scale; other details	MPR

Y2-2 1911 Renault Two-Seater

1963-1968. Scale 1:40. Note that the red pigment used in the plastic seats is prone to fading in bright light.

All versions **£8-12**

Y2-3 1914 'Prince Henry' Vauxhall

1970-1979. Scale 1:47.

With Copper petrol tank (Red and Silver issue only) **£225-275**
Bright Red seats (Blue and Silver issue only)...................................**£450-650**
Other versions **£2-8**

Y3-1 1907 'E'-class Tramcar

1956-1965. Scale 1:130. All versions have a bright Red body with Yellow 'LONDON TRANSPORT' fleetname and 'NEWS OF THE WORLD' decals.

With thin (Grey) cow-catchers **£100-125**
Grey base (with thin or thick cowcatchers)................................**£125-175**
Other versions **£30-50**

Y3-2 1910 Benz Limousine

1965-1984. Scale 1:54.

With Cream body and chassis, Light Yellow roof..............................**£150-200**
Light Green body and chassis, Dark Green roof..............................**£150-200**
Light Green body and chassis, Light Yellow roof,
    separate rear wing supports............................**£200-275**
Light Green body and chassis, Black roof **£75-125**
Dark Metallic Green body and chassis, Light Yellow roof.................**£200-250**
As previous model, but without holes in base..............................**£300-350**
Other versions **£10-15**

Y3-3 1934 Riley MPH

1974-1979. Scale 1:35.

With Dark Purple body and chassis, Black seats and grille £135-185
Ruby Red body and chassis, Black seats and grille £135-185
Other versions £2-6

Y3-4 1912 Ford Model 'T' Tanker

1981-1989. Scale 1:35.

'BP', Green body, Red tank, with 'No. Y12' cast on base....................£75-125
'BP', other versions £2-4
'ZEROLENE', with 'No. Y12' cast on base £15-20
'ZEROLENE', other versions £2-4
'EXPRESS DAIRY', all versions..£2-6

Y4-1 1928 Sentinel Steam Wagon

1956 only. Scale 1:100. Blue body, **'SAND & GRAVEL SUPPLIES'**.

With Black plastic wheels £85-100
With Grey metal wheels £35-55

Y4-2 1905 Shand-Mason Fire Engine

1960-1965. Scale 1:63. Red metal body, two horses, three plastic firemen.

'KENT' Fire Brigade, Pale Grey Horses......................................£300-400
'KENT' Fire Brigade, White Horses £85-125
'LONDON' Fire Brigade, Bronze horses £150-175
'LONDON' Fire Brigade, White or Black horses £80-120

Y4-3 1909 Opel Coupé

1967-1984. Scale 1:38.

With Tan textured hood with rear window......................................£175-200
With Maroon grille and seats...£15-25
Other versions £2-8

Y4-4 1930 Duesenberg 'J' Town Car

1976-1997. Scale 1:43.

White body, Orange-Red or Red chassis, Yellow hood and seats..£1,000-1,500
White body, Orange-red or Red chassis, Black hood and seats.....£1,500-2,000
Dark Red body and chassis, Maroon hood and seats......................£175-200
Dark Red body and chassis, Dark Green hood and seats.................£75-100
Dark Red body and chassis, Dark Green hood, Light Brown seats.....£100-125
Light Green body and chassis, Lime Green side and rear body panels...£45-65
Other versions £2-5

Y5-1 1929 Le Mans Bentley

1958-1961. Scale 1:55. All are finished in British Racing Green.

With Grey folded hood, Silver radiator £85-125
With Grey folded hood, Gold radiator..£80-110
Other versions £35-55

Y5-2 1929 4½ litre Bentley

1962-1968. Scale 1:52. Model has Union Jacks and racing numbers on its sides, folded windscreen and silver 24-spoke wheels, (spare on nearside).

With Apple Green body, Dark Green or Dark Red seats £125-175
British Racing Green body, Red racing number '6'...............................£75-90
Other versions £10-15

Y5-3 1907 Peugeot

1969-1977. Scale 1:43. Except where noted, the model has 12-spoke wheels.

Yellow body and chassis, Black roof, no rib on rear edge of
     front seat side panels..£35-55
Yellow body and chassis, Black roof, clear windows £85-125
Yellow body and chassis, Gold roof..£100-150
Orange-Gold, or Light-Gold body, Black chassis and roof....................£65-85
Light-Gold body and roof, Black chassis,
     Chrome 12 or 24 spoke wheels, clear windows £100-105
Other versions £6-8

Y5-4 1927 Talbot Van

1978-1988. Scale 1:47.

'LIPTONS TEA' (1978), all versions £2-5
'CHOCOLAT MENIER' (1978-1979), all versions...............................£2-5
'TAYSTEE BREAD' (1980), all versions £2-5
'NESTLES' (1981), with Matt Black roof £175-225
     With Gloss Black roof...£200-250
     All other versions £2-5
'CHIVERS' (1982), all versions £2-5
'WRIGHTS' (1982), with Dark Brown roof £150-180
     All other versions £2-5
'EVER READY' (1983), all versions £2-5

Y6-1 1916 AEC 'Y' type Lorry

1957-1961. Scale 1:100. **'OSRAM LAMPS'**

Pale Blue or Mid Blue body, Grey metal wheels £1,250-1,750
Light Grey body, Grey metal wheels...£40-60
Dark Grey body, Grey metal wheels £60-100
Dark Grey body, Black plastic wheels £1,300-1,500

Y6-2 1935 Type 35 Bugatti

1961-1965. Scale 1:48. Model has a black baseplate and gold 8-spoke wheels with a spare on the nearside. Racing number '6' may be upside-down and appear as '9'.

Blue body, Grey tyres £45-65
Blue body, Blue radiator £80-100
Blue body, White dashboard £275-350
Red body, Red radiator £80-100
Red body, Black dashboard £300-375
Other versions £15-25

Y6-3 1913 Cadillac

1968-1975. Scale 1:48.

Gold body, Dark Red textured roof £80-110
All other Gold body versions £6-12
Green body, thin spare tyre carrier £45-65
All other Green body versions...£2-6

Y6-4 1920 Rolls-Royce Fire Engine

1977-1984. Scale 1:48.

Without locating lugs for side label..£75-100
With red front seats...£250-350
All other versions...£2-8

Y7-1 1918 Leyland 4-ton Van

1957-1960. Scale 1:100. **'W. & R. Jacob & Co. Ltd.'**

Dark Brown body £55-75
Dark Brown body with centre line of transfer omitted £600-800
Reddish Brown body £40-60
Reddish Brown body, Black plastic wheels £750-1,000

Y7-2 1913 Mercer Raceabout type 35J

1961-1965. Scale 1:46.

Lilac body and chassis £15-20
Lilac body and chassis, Grey tyres £60-85
Yellow body and chassis £10-15
Yellow body, chassis and radiator £15-20

Y7-3 1912 Rolls-Royce

1968-1970. Scale 1:48.

Silver body and bonnet, Dark Red chassis and smooth or
    ribbed roof £5-10
Silver body and bonnet, Dark Red chassis and smooth roof,
    Yellow seats and grille £550-800
Silver body and bonnet, Dark Red chassis, Grey ribbed roof.......£50-75
Gold body, Silver bonnet, Dark Red chassis and ribbed roof £75-100
Gold body and bonnet, Dark Red chassis and ribbed roof,
    thin brass 12-spoke wheels £50-75
Gold body and bonnet, Dark Red chassis and ribbed roof,
    wide chrome 12 or 24-spoke wheels £5-8
Gold body and bonnet, Dark Red chassis and ribbed roof, wide
    chrome 12-spoke wheels, Dark Green seats and grille.....£225-275
Yellow body and bonnet, Red chassis, Black ribbed roof.....£200-250
Yellow body and bonnet, Black chassis and ribbed roof £2-5

Y8-1 1926 Morris Cowley

1958 only. Scale 1:50.

Tan body, Dark Brown chassis, Silver or Light Copper wheels £30-45

Y8-2 1914 Sunbeam Motorcycle and Sidecar

1962-1967. Scale 1:34.

Chrome plated, Black m/cycle seat, Dark Green sidecar seat................£25-45
Chrome plated, Black m/cycle seat, Emerald Green sidecar seat.......£150-250
Chrome plated, Black m/cycle seat, Black sidecar seat £500-600
Light Gold plated...£550-750

Y8-3 1914 Stutz Roadster

1969-1973. Scale 1:48.

Dark Red body and bonnet, smooth Tan roof £6-10
Dark Red body and bonnet, brass petrol tank £75-95
Dark Red body and chassis, textured Tan roof £20-25
Dark Red body and chassis, textured Tan roof, Red grille.....................£30-50
Dark Red body and chassis, textured Tan roof, Pinky-Red seats
    or Maroon seats £50-75
Blue body and chassis, White seats and grille £3-5
Blue body and chassis, Bright Red seats and grille £35-45

Y8-4 1945 MG 'TC'

1978-1984. Scale 1:35.

Green body and chassis £5-10
Red body and chassis £3-5
Blue body and chassis £3-5

Y9-1 1924 Fowler Showman's Engine

1958-1965. Scale 1:80. **'Lesney's Modern Amusements'**.

Dark Maroon body...£70-80
Dark Maroon body, Gold cylinder block................................£85-125
Light Purple body, Gold or Light Purple cylinder block £350-400
Maroon body...£65-75
Bright Red body..£55-65
    NB Any of the above with a Black nameplate in the base usually
    adds a premium of approximately **£10**.

Y9-2 1912 Simplex

1968-1988. Scale 1:48.

Lime Green or Mid Green body £8-15
Dark Gold body, Dark Red chassis £10-15
Dark Gold body, Bright Red chassis £185-235
Red body, Red or Black chassis £5-10

Y10-1 1908 'Grand Prix' Mercedes

1958-1959. Scale 1:54.

Off-White/Pale Cream body, Light or Mid Green seats.........................£20-50
Pure White body, Light or Mid Green seats..£100-150

Y10-2 1928 Mercedes-Benz 36-220

1963 only. Scale 1:52

White body, Red seats and folded hood, single or twin spare wheels £10-20
White body, Black seats and folded hood, twin spare wheels £1,500-1,750

Y10-3 1906 Rolls-Royce Silver Ghost

1969-1983. Scale 1:51.

Lime Green body, Bronze chassis £8-12
White body, Purple or Dark Red chassis................................£4-7
White body, Silver chassis, Black seats £275-325
Silver body, Purple chassis £275-325
Silver body and chassis, Dark Red seats £2-4
Silver body and chassis, Yellow seats £4-6
Silver body and chassis, White or Ivory-White seats...........£300-350

Y11-1 1920 Aveling & Porter Steam Roller

1958 only. Scale 1:80.

Mid-Green body, boiler and roof; Black roof supports..........................£30-50
With Gold maker's plate (front of cylinder block), Black supports.....£200-250
With Gold maker's plate (front of cylinder block), Green supports £350-550

Y11-2 1912 Packard Landaulet

1964-1984. Scale 1:50.

Dark Red and Orange-Red versions £8-12
Cream version, only available in the 1984 'Connoisseur Collection' ....GSP

Y11-3 1938 Lagonda Drophead Coupé

1972-1985. Scale 1:43.

Gold body, Purple chassis..£650-750
Gold body, Dark Red chassis...£100-150
Gold body, Strawberry Red chassis £80-110
Gold body, Maroon chassis £15-20
Orange body, Gold chassis, brass (narrow) 24-spoke wheels.............£100-125
Orange or Copper body, Gold chassis, Chrome or Red (wide) wheels £4-15
Copper body, Gold chassis, Green or Bright Red seats,
    folded hood and grille £200-250
Orangey-Blood Red body, Gold chassis.................................£65-85
Copper body, Black chassis..£175-225
Dark Cream body, Gold chassis...£175-225
Dark Cream body, Black chassis £2-8
Maroon body version (in 1985 'Fathers Day' Set)...................GSP

Y12-1 1899 Horse-drawn Bus

1959 only. Scale 1:100.

Red body and chassis. All versions £35-55

Y12-2 1909 Thomas Flyabout

1967-1975. Scale 1:48.

Blue body and chassis, Yellow seats and grille......................£750-1,250
Blue body and chassis, Dark Red seats and grille..................£5-15
Purple-Red body and chassis, Off-White seats and grille.......£4-8

Matchbox 'Models of Yesteryear'

Y12-3 1912 Ford Model 'T' Van

1979-1986. Scale 1:35.

'COCA COLA' (1979)
    With 5 vertical Red printed coach lines..............................£200-300
    With 4 vertical Red printed coach lines..............................£10-25
'COLMANS MUSTARD' (1979-1981). All versions...............£2-4
'TAYSTEE' (1980)
    Yellow body, Black chassis and roof.................................£350-500
    NB There are known to be fakes which have the smaller labels as
    used on the Y5-4 Talbot Van. Genuine 'Taystee' labels for the
    Ford Model 'T' Van measure 29mm end to end of 'Taystee' oval
    and 11mm top to bottom of the oval.
'SUZE' (1980-1981)
    With Gloss Black roof, Red double lines on rear doors.............£85-125
    All other versions...£2-4
'SMITHS CRISPS' (1981)
    All versions...£2-4
'25 YEARS SILVER JUBILEE' (1981)
    With Silver printed single line on rear doors.....................£400-475
    With Yellow 24-spoke wheels..£45-65
    All other versions...£2-4
'BIRDS CUSTARD' (1982)
    With Metallic Blue body..£50-65
    All other (plain Blue) versions...£2-4
'CEREBOS' (1982)
    Light Blue body, Black chassis, Yellow roof.....................£175-225
    All other versions...£2-4
'ARNOTTS' (1982)
    Bright Red body, Black chassis, Gloss Black roof................£100-135
    Same but with Matt Black roof...£80-120
'HARRODS' (1982). All versions...................................£2-4
'SUNLIGHT SEIFE' (1983)
    Yellow body, Black chassis, matt Black roof.....................£45-65
    NB Models exist with fake labels. Genuine labels have a clothes
    line post to the right of the woman hanging out the washing.
'ROYAL MAIL' (1983)
    Bright Red body, Black chassis and roof, Yellow printed
    double lines on rear doors...£175-225
    All other versions (with cast rear door outline)....................£2-4
'CAPTAIN MORGAN' (1983-1984)
    Black body, with cast hole in rear base of body................£45-75
    All other versions...£2-4
'HOOVER' (1983). All versions.....................................£2-4
'MOTOR 100', world globe with blue land and white oceans........£700-£800

Y13-1 'Santa Fe' Locomotive (1862)

1959 only. Scale 1:112.

Mid-Green cab and boiler, Dark Red chassis and smokebox,
    Gold chimney rim and condenser tops.........................£700-800
Other versions (Dark Green)...£35-55

Y13-2 1911 Daimler

1966-1967 + 1984. Scale 1:45.

Yellow body, all versions..£6-8
Blue body, Powder Blue chassis, in 1984 'Connoisseur Collection'..........GSP

Y13-3 1918 Crossley Lorry

'RAF' Tender (1975-1976). Scale 1:47.
RAF Blue cab, body and chassis, no strengthening web between
    front mudguards and chassis...£175-200
With Dull Dark Red or Green seats...................................£75-100
With Olive Green canopy and grille..................................£8-15
With Black canopy and grille...£225-275
All other versions...£4-6

Y13-4 1918 Crossley Lorry

'EVANS Bros.' (1979-1982). Scale 1:47.
    Red cab and body, with two cast cleats on body sides.........£75-125
    All other versions...£2-4
'CARLSBERG' (1983-1984)
    Cream cab and body, 'Matchbox Toys Ltd' base.................£2-4
    With 'Lesney Products' cast on base.................................£40-50
    With Ice Blue canopy and tilt...£50-65

Y14-1 Duke of Connaught' Locomotive (1903)

1959 only. Scale 1:130.

Dark Green cab and boiler, with Gold sand boxes...................£45-60
With Silver smoke box door..£75-100
All other versions...£35-50

Y14-2 1911 Maxwell Roadster

1965 only (+1984). Scale 1:49.

Turquoise body and chassis, with Brass petrol tank...............£75-100
Any other versions...£4-8
Cream body, Dark Green chassis, in 1984 'Connoisseur Collection'..........GSP

Y14-3 1931 Stutz Bearcat

1974-1995. Scale 1:44.
All versions...£2-8

Y15-1 1907 Rolls-Royce Silver Ghost

1960 only. Scale 1:55.

Light Green body and chassis, Grey knobbly tyres, Silver rear
    number plate and Red rear light.....................................£20-35
With Dark Green seats..£40-50
Other versions...£4-8

Y15-2 1930 Packard Victoria

1969-1979 (+1984). Scale 1:46.

Lime Gold body, Dark Brown chassis, wide cast rear coach-line..........£20-30
Lime Gold body, Black chassis, thin or wide cast rear coach-line.....£235-285
Other versions...£2-8

Y16-1 1904 Spyker

1961-1968. Scale 1:45.

Pale Cream body and chassis, Grey knobbly tyres...............£275-350
Pale Lemon body and chassis, Grey knobbly tyres...............£30-40
With two cast holes in base..£45-75
Maroon body and chassis..£1,400-1,900
Other versions...£4-8

Y16-2 1928 Mercedes-Benz SS Coupé

1972- 1990. Scale 1:45.

Lime Green body, Dark Green chassis.................................£75-150
White body, Black chassis..£375-500
Blue body and chassis, Duck Egg Blue side panels...............£35-50
Blue body and chassis, Milky White side panels.................£75-90
Other versions...£2-8

Y17-1 1938 Hispano-Suiza

1975-1995. Scale 1:48.

Silver body (Powder Blue side panels on some),
    Silver or Black chassis..£135-175
Other versions...£2-6

Y18-1 1937 Cord 812

1979-1995. Scale 1:48.
All versions...£2-4

Y19-1 1936 Auburn Speedster

1979- 1990. Scale 1:42.

All versions...£2-4

Y20-1 1937 Mercedes-Benz 540K

1981-1995. Scale 1:45.

All versions...£2-6

Y21-1 1930 Ford Model 'A' Woody Wagon

1981-1985. Scale 1:40.

All versions £2-6

Y21-2 1930 Ford Model 'A' Woody Wagon

1983-1985. Scale 1:40

'A. & J. BOX'
With Yellow bonnet, 'Lesney' base £5-10
All other versions...£2-6

Y22-1 1930 Ford Model 'A' Van

1982-1991. Scale 1:41.

'OXO' (1982)
Red body, Red seats and interior, 'Lesney' base £75-125
Red body, Gloss Black van roof £10-15
All other versions £2-4

Y23-1 1922 AEC Omnibus

1983-1989. Scale 1:72.

'SCHWEPPES' (1983-1984)
Red body, with Red lettering on advertisement labels £30-45
All other versions £2-4

Y24-1 1928 Bugatti T44

1983-1995. Scale 1:72.

Black and Yellow body with Brown, Green or White seats.............£175-250
Black and Yellow body with Black seats £25-45
All other versions...£2-4

Y25-1 1910 Renault 'AG' Van

1983-1989. Scale 1:38.

'PERRIER' (1983)
Green body, Dark Green chassis, roof rack with 3 side struts ...£250-300
With closed grab handles £75-125
All other versions...£2-4

Models of Yesteryear Gift Sets

G 6	1960	**Gift Set**	Contains Nos. 1, 2, 5, 10 and 13. Lesney line-drawing box	**£325-375**
G 7	1960	**Gift Set**	Contains Nos 3, 8, 9, 12 and 14. Lesney line-drawing box	**£325-375**
G 6	1962	**Veteran & Vintage Car Set**	Contains Nos 5, 6, 7, 15 and 16. Lesney picture box.	**£325-375**
G 7	1962	**Gift Set**	Contains Nos 3, 4, 11, 12 and 13. Lesney picture box	**£325-375**
G 7	1965	**Veteran & Vintage Set**	Contains Y2, Y5, Y10, Y15 and Y16. Picture box	**£100-125**
G 7	1966	**Gift Set**	Y1-2 Model T Ford, Y3-2 Benz, Y11-2 Packard, Y14-2 Maxwell. Picture box	**£75-100**
G 5	1968	**Gift Set**	Y4-3 Opel, Y6-3 Cadillac, Y9-2 Simplex, Y9-2 Simplex	**£55-65**
G 5	1970-72	**Gift** Set	Contains Y8-3 Stutz Red, Y14 Maxwell, Y16-1 Spyker (Dark Yellow), Y7-3 Rolls-Royce Silver and Red. Picture box	**£45-55**
Y-50	1982	**Gift Set**	Contains Y3-4 'BP' Tanker, Y5-4 Talbot Van 'Chivers', Y10-3 Rolls Royce, Y12-3 Model 'T' Van, Y13-3 Crossley Coal Lorry	**£20-30**
	1984	**'Connoisseur Collection'**	Contains Y1-2 Black 1911 Model 'T' Ford, Y4-3 Red/Beige 1909 Opel, Y3-2 Blue/Black 1910 Benz Limousine, Y11-2 White/Black 1912 Packard Landaulet, Y13-2 Blue 1911 Daimler, Y14-2 Beige/Black 1911 Maxwell. 30,000 certificated and numbered sets issued in beechwood display case	**£80-100**

Models of Yesteryear plated souvenirs and giftware

Models specially plated to adorn giftware (e.g., cigarette boxes, ashtrays, penstands, boxes and pipestands. Non-plated versions of the models listed will also be found with the two baseplate holes used for fixing the plated models to the various items.
Prices (dependent on type of giftware):
Unboxed, not mounted on original giftware.....**£2-3**
Unboxed, still mounted on giftware **£5-20**
In original box, still on original giftware.....**£30-85**

SILVER-EFFECT PLATED MODELS
Y1-2	1911	Model 'T' Ford ....
Y2-2	1911	Renault 2 seater ....
Y2-3	1914	Prince Henry Vauxhall ....
Y3-3	1934	Riley MPH ....
Y4-3	1909	Opel Coupé ....
Y5-2	1929	4½ Litre Bentley ....

Y6-2	1926	Type 35 Bugatti ....
Y7-2	1913	Mercer Raceabout ....
Y7-3	1912	Rolls-Royce ....
Y10-2	1928	Mercedes-Benz 36-220 ....
Y10-3	1906	Rolls-Royce ....
Y12-2	1909	Thomas Flyabout...........................
Y13-2	1911	Daimler...
Y13-3	1918	Crossley ....
Y14-2	1911	Maxwell Roadster ....
Y15-1	1907	Rolls-Royce Silver Ghost ....
Y16-1	1904	Spyker ....

GOLD-EFFECT PLATED MODELS
Y1-2	1911	Model 'T' Ford ....
Y2-3	1914	Prince Henry Vauxhall ....
Y3-2	1910	Benz Limousine ....
Y4-3	1909	Opel Coupé ....

Y5-2	1929	4½ Litre Bentley ....
Y7-2	1913	Mercer Raceabout ....
Y7-3	1912	Rolls-Royce..................................
Y10-2	1928	Mercedes-Benz 36-220 ....
Y10-3	1906	Rolls-Royce..................................
Y12-2	1909	Thomas Flyabout...........................
Y13-2	1911	Daimler...
Y13-3	1918	Crossley ....
Y14-2	1911	Maxwell Roadster ....
Y15-1	1907	Rolls-Royce Silver Ghost ....

GOLD PLATED SETS
Golden Veteran Set with 3 models:
Y7-3, Y13-2, Y14-2 ....**£50-65**
Heritage Gifts, 2 models: Y7-3, Y10-3 ......**£35-50**

Lesney 'Pub Signs'

A series of plated figurines made for attachment to giftware. The base of each is marked 'Lesney Co. Ltd. 1975'. They have 'spurs' underneath to aid fixing to such items as ashtrays, etc. The Editor would be pleased to receive more details. NGPP.

'The Cock'	'The Unicorn'	'The Pig & Whistle'	'The Sherlock Holmes'	'The Mermaid'........................
'The Lion'	'The Bull'	'The George & Dragon'	'The Volunteer'.......................	'The Royal Standard' ....
'The Swan'	'The Rose & Crown'	'The Dick Turpin'...................	'The Britannia'	

Models of Yesteryear 'Codes 1 and 2' special issues

A system of categorising models has evolved among collectors to distinguish between authentic manufacturers' output and acceptable but unauthorised alteration of their models for later resale. The explanation which follows refers to a coding system adopted generally (but not officially) throughout the model collecting fraternity in the UK and elsewhere, and may he applied to models produced by any manufacturer.
CODE 1 Applies to models which have been originated and totally produced by an established manufacturer.
CODE 2 As CODE 1, but labelled or finished outside the factory WITH the manufacturer's permission.
CODE 3 Same as CODE 2, but model re-labelled, altered or re-worked WITHOUT authorisation or permission from the manufacturer.

Y1-2 76 **1911 Ford Model 'T' Car.** Black body, textured roof, grille and seats, Chrome 12-spoke wheels, brass trim, bare windscreen frame. 900 models made for the USA **£325-400**

Y5-4 78 **1927 Talbot Van** with 12-spoke wheels and Chrome trim.
'2nd AIM CONVENTION', Dark Green body and wheels, 'Toy Show, Harrisburgh PA May 27/28, 1978' **£75-125**
81 'CRAWLEY SWAPMEET 1981', Royal Blue body, Black roof and chassis, 'Follow Us To Crawley'...........**£125-175**
81 'VARIETY CLUB', 'Sunshine Coach Appeal'
1: Yellow body and chassis, Black roof, Red wheels......**£125-165**
2: As 1 but with Black chassis.................................**£150-175**
80 'MERITA BREAD', Yellow body, Red wheels **£20-40**
80 'LANGENDORF', Yellow body, Red wheels....................**£20-40**
80 'TAYSTEE BREAD', Yellow body, Black roof, Red wheels and Pale Yellow 'Taystee' on Red oval.................**£70-80**
81 'IRONBRIDGE' 1: Yellow body, matt Black roof, Red wheels, 'The World's First Iron Bridge' **£125-165**
2: As 1 with gloss Black chassis and mudguards...........**£140-180**

81 'BEES' 1: Yellow body, Black roof, Red wheels, plain or White-wall tyres, 'Bees Art & Model Service'.........**£100-150**
2: As 1 but Black chassis and mudguards **£90-110**
81 'DUTCH MATCHBOX MEET'.
'1st Matchbox meeting in Holland on 4th October 1981'.
1: Blue and Grey body, Black roof and chassis, 'Stoevclaar', with Certificate.................................**£175-225**
2: Yellow and Red body, Black roof and chassis, 'Stoevclaar', 72 only presented to stallholders **£400-500**
81 LAWRENCE FRASER TOYS', Blue body..................**£200-250**

Y7-3 82 **1912 Rolls-Royce.** Wedding of Prince Charles and Princess Diana. Bright Yellow and Black, Red wheels, 600 ....**£145-185**

Y12-3 81 **Ford Model 'T' Van**
1: 'BANG & OLUFSEN', White/Red, certificate **£275-325**
2: Without certificate **£165-185**
81 'RAYLEIGH SWAPMEET', Yellow body, Black roof....**£75-125**
82 'CADA TOYS Have Moved', Yellow/Black, 600 ....**£180-200**
82 'DEANS of LEEDS', Yellow body, Black roof, Red 'Deans for Toys', telephone no. on some, 800 ......**£125-150**
80 'CAMBERLEY NEWS', Yellow/Black, '75th', 750 ......**£155-185**
83 'HOOVER', Blue body, White roof, Black chassis,
1: With certificate, 500 ....**£500-600**
2: Without certificate, 50 ....**£350-400**

Y13-3 1918 Crossley
79 'UK MATCHBOX CLUB', Red/Yellow, 800................**£125-175**
81 'ASPECTS and IMAGES', Red/Light Brown **£125-150**
81 'SURREY MODEL FAIR', Red body, 'Tangley Model Workshop' on rear of Grey canopy only, 500 ....**£125-150**

Collectors notes

These Auction Results are provided to support the Market Price Range guidance throughout the Catalogue.

Vectis Auctions Ltd.
Fleck Way, Thornaby, Stockton -on-Tees TS17 9JZ.

Abbreviations: M = Mint, **NM** = Near Mint, **EP** = Excellent Plus,
E = Excellent, **GP** = Good Plus, **G** = Good, **F** = Fair.
Wheels: BPW = Black Plastic Wheels, **GPW** = Grey Plastic Wheels,
SPW = Silver Plastic Wheels, **MW** = metal wheels, **PH** - plastic hubs.
KG(B)PW = Knobbly Grey (Black) Plastic Wheels.
Components: int' - interior, **s'w** - steering wheel.

MATCHBOX 1 - 75 SERIES, REGULAR WHEELS
1. **Diesel Road Roller**, green, red MW, M in E box £160
5. **London Bus**, dark red, 'Matchbox Series', M in E box £160
4. **Massey Tractor**, no mudguards, GPW, M in EP box £150
5. **London Bus 'Players Please'**, red, GPW, NM in box £120
6. **Quarry Truck**, orange/grey, dark GPW, M, boxed £5,000
7. **Horsedrawn Milk Float**, orange, M in E box £80
7. **Ford Anglia**, pale blue, GPW, M in NM box £80
11. **ERF Petrol Tanker 'Esso'**, NM in NM box £140
12. **Land Rover**, green, fine tread GPW, M in E box £240
14. **Bedford Ambulance**, off-white, SPW, M in E box £260
17. **Removals Truck 'Matchbox'**, maroon, M, boxed £340
17. **Removals Truck 'Matchbox'**, light blue, M in E box £240
17. **Removals Truck 'Matchbox'**, light green, M in E box £160
17. **Removals Truck 'Matchbox'**, dark green, M in NM b box £280
18. **Field Car**, white/black, bonnet flag, M, boxed £320
19. **MGA Sports Car**, off-white, GPW, M, boxed £140
21. **Bedford Coach**, dark green, GPW, M in NM box £80
22. **Vauxhall Cresta**, brown/green, GPW, M in E box £160
26. **Foden Cement Truck**, orange/grey barrel, M, boxed £1,000
26. **ERF Cement Mixer**, all orange, GPW £90
27. **Bedford Low Loader**, green/beige, GPW, M, boxed £110
27. **Cadillac Sixty**, mauve/pink, GPW, M in GP box £80
30. **Ford Prefect**, light blue, GPW, M in E box £220
31. **Ford Wagon**, metallic green/pink, GPW, NM in E box £120
31. **Ford Station Wagon**, yellow, SPW, M, boxed £260
32. **Jaguar XK140**, red, GPW, NM in EP box £120
33. **Lamborghini Miura**, gold, off white int', chrome hubs, M in E box .£380
34. **VW Van 'Matchbox'**, blue, SPW, M in E box £280
36. **Lambretta Motorcycle and Sidecar**, green, BPW, M in E box £80
39. **Pontiac**, metallic purple, red s'w, SPW, M in NM box £130
39. **Ford Zodiac**, peach, sea green base, GPW, M, boxed £130
41. **Jaguar D-type**, green, metal wheels, M in GP box £80
41. **Jaguar D-type**, green, w'w, beige driver, No. '6', M, boxed £900
41. **Ford GT Racer**, white, red inter'/hubs, No. '6', M, boxed £440
44. **Morris Minor 1000**, blue, GPW, M in E box £120
50. **Commer Pick-up**, red/grey, GPW, M in NM box £260
53. **Aston-Martin**, metallic red, knobbly BPW, M boxed £220
55. **Ford Fairlane Police**, metallic blue, GPW, M in E box £110
59. **Ford Fairlane 'Fire Chief's Car'**, KGPW, M in E box £380
59. **Ford Thames Van 'Singer'**, dark green, GPW, M, boxed £200
65. **Jaguar 3.4**, metallic blue, GPW, M in E box £120
71. **Austin Water Truck** with badge, EP in F box £30
74. **Mobile Canteen**, white, light blue base, NM in M box £220
75. **Ford Thunderbird**, white/peach, SPW, E in GP box £70

Superfast Issues
8. **Ford Mustang**, orangey red, deep red interior, M, boxed £320
12. **Land Rover**, green, fine tread GPW, M in E box £240
17. **Londoner Bus 'Berger Paints'**, silver/red, grey base, M £60
31. **Lincoln Continental**, sea green, cream interior, NM in M box £600
38. **Stingeroo**, purple body, chrome engine/handlebars, NM, boxed £750
53. **Ford Zodiac**, blue, cream interior, Mint boxed £440
64. **MG 1100** green, cream interior, NM, boxed £90
67. **VW** - red, cream interior, NM in E box £45
75. **Ferrrari**, green, off white interior, silver base, M, boxed £180

Pre-Production Colour Trials
1. **Dodge Charger** - white/red/black £90
10. **Piston Popper** - black, amber tinted windows £130
13. **Baja Buggy** - orange, black exhaust stacks, big cat decal £100
19. **Road Dragster** - black, chrome engine £110

23. **VW Camper** - Pink, white roof and interior £160
34. **Formula 1 Racing Car** - pale blue body, RN '15' £110
35. **Fire Engine 'London Fire Service'**, white, blue windows £240
36. **Refuse Truck** - cream/yellow £90

38. **Ford 'Model' Van 'Champion Spark Plugs'**, red, '73' £170
46. **Stretcha-Fetcha**, lime green, blue windows/roof light £100
62. **Rat Rod Dragster** - silver with orange/green side decal £130
71. **Heavy Wreck Truck** - white, blue, amber windows/light £110
73. **Weasel** - metallic purple, black turret/gun £110
75. **Alpha Carabo** - orange, black engine cover yellow base £110

Models of Yesteryear
Y1 Allchin Traction Engine isues:
(i)   Green, red, silver boiler door, M in GP box £110
(ii) Green, red copper boiler door, straight treads NM in GP box £220
(iii) Green, gold boiler door, all red wheels, NM in E box £300
(iv) Green, gold boiler door, red, smooth rear wheels, NM in G box ... £620
Y1 Ford Model 'T', black including seats and textured roof,
     silver 12 spoke wheels, M in E woodgrain box £320
Y2 - **Prince Henry Vauxhall**, blue body, silver bonnet,
     bright blue seats, copper petrol tank, M boxed £660
Y4 Opel Coupé - white, red seats and grille, textured roof with
     rear window, E in NM box £130
Y5 Talbot Van issues:
'Lawrence Fraser' - Mint £220
'Dutch Matchbox Meet', Mint £160
'Bees', yellow, black roof and chassis, red wheels, Mint £150
'Crawley International Toy and Collectors Fair', M, boxed £200
'Taystee', yellow body/chassis, black roof, red wheels, M in NM box ... £50

Y8 Sunbeam Motor Cycle with Milford Sidecar, chrome,
     black seat with emerald green side seat, M in E box £220
Y8 Sunbeam Motor Cycle with Milford Sidecar, chrome finish
     with black seats, M in E window box £460
Y11 Lagonda Drophead Coupé, gold, purple chassis,
     black interior, M in EP box £900
Y12 Ford Model 'T' Van issues:
'Bang & Olufsen', Mint £280
'Dean's for Toys', Mint £180
'Cada Toys', Mint £220
'Hoover', Mint £380
'Rayleigh Model Collector's Extravaganza', Near Mint £130
'Camberley News', Mint £170

Y12 Thomas Flyabout, metallic blue, yellow seats and radiator,
     beige canopy, Mint, boxed £950
Y13 Crossley 'Aspects & Images', Mint £150
Y13 Crossley 'UK Matchbox', M in E box £220
Y13 Santa-Fe Locomotive, light green body, maroon chassis
     (without gold trim) E in E box £750
Y21 Ford Model TT Van 'Antiques Roadshow The Next Generation'
     black, red, gold, Mint, in special box £620
Y47 Morris Light Commercial Van
     'Antiques Roadshow Going Live',
     black, yellow, Mint, in special box £380

PREPRODUCTION MODELS OF YESTERYEAR
Y1 Ford Model 'T', orange, cream seats, green chassis £130
Y4 Duesenberg, brown body, metallic brown chassis £120
Y6 Cadillac, grey with red seat and grille, gold wheels £200
Y7 Rolls-Royce Silver Ghost, green, yellow chassis £200
Y10 Rolls-Royce Silver Ghost, blue, red seat and grille £200
Y12 Thomas Flyabout, white/black, cream seats £110
Y12 Thomas Flyabout, beige, white seats, orange canopy £130
Y12 Ford Model 'T' Van 'Nestles', blue, white roof £80
Y12 Ford Model 'T' Van 'Captain Morgan', yellow £90
Y12 Ford Model 'T' Van 'Postes Canada Post', red body £80

'MOKO' SERIES ISSUES
Prime Mover, orange, green engine covers, blue trailer,
     yellow bulldozer, GP - E overall in GP box £850
No. 2 Farm Wagon, blue/yellow/red, 2 horses in brown, E in GP box ... £320
No. 3 Bull Cart in green, red wheels, 2 brown horses, M in GP box ... £400

Vectis U.S.A Auctions
405 Carlisle Avenue, York, PA 17404, U.S.A.

Abbreviations:
BPW = Black Plastic Wheels, **GPW** = Grey Plastic Wheels,
SPW = Silver Plastic Wheels, **MW** = metal wheels, **PH** - plastic hubs.
KG(B)PW - Knobbly Grey (Black) Plastic Wheels.
Condition (A/A, A/B, B/A, etc.):
1st letter indicates model, 2nd indicates the box.

MATCHBOX 1-75 SERIES (REGULAR WHEELS)

1-1 Diesel Road Roller, light green, MW, A/A £335
2-1 Dumper Truck, green/red, green painted MW £265
4-1 Massey-Harris Tractor, Red, metal wheels, A/A...............£120
5-2 London Bus 'Viscostatic', KGPW, A/A...............................£500
7-1 Ford Anglia, pale blue, knobbly GPW, A/A..........................£65
8-1 Caterpillar Tractor, Silver plastic rollers/replaced treads, MW, A/B .£240
8-5 Ford Mustang, orange, red interior, correct 'F' box, A/B ...$360
9-2 Dennis Fire Truck, gold front bumper/KGPW, B/A $440
11-1 Road Tanker, green, MW, B/A £250
11-2 Tanker, red, small 11-1 'Esso' rear decal, MW, A/B.........£520
14-2 Daimler Ambulance, rare SPW £215
14-3 Lomas Ambulance, off-white, knobbly SPW, A/A............£340
15-1 Prime Mover, yellow, MW, B/A £325
15-1 Prime Mover, orange, 10 knobbly GPW, B/A...................£325
17-1 'Matchbox Removals Service', Maroon, MW, A/A.............£285
19-2 MGA Sports Car, white, silver trim, SPW, B/A £210
20-2 ERF 68G 'Ever Ready', knobbly GPW, A/A £145
22-2 Vauxhall Cresta, creamy pink, KGPW, A/A £220
22-2 Vauxhall Cresta, Turquoise/bronze, knobbly GPW, A/A ...£310
22-2 Vauxhall Cresta, lilac / grey, knobbly GPW, A/B £150
25-2 VW 1200 Sedan, green windows, fine GPW, A/A..............£410
25-3 'ARAL' Petrol Tanker, blue/white, A/B.............................£115
27-1 Bedford Low Loader, TT blue, MW, C unboxed.................£130
30-1 Ford Prefect, blue, KGPW, A/A £260
31-2 Ford Fairlane, clear windows, black base, A/A £340
33-3 Lamborghini Miura, metallic gold, white interior, A/A £255
38-1 Karrier Refuse, no decal lines (1st issue), MW, A/A £190
39-1 Ford Zodiac, peach, turquoise interior, KSPW, A/A £160
39-2 Ford Zodiac, dark peach, cream interior, KSPW, A/A £320
39-2 Pontiac, purple, cream interior, red SW, KSPW, A/A £165
41-2 D-Type Jaguar, rare red plastic hubs, B/B £190
41-3 Ford GT Race Car, rare red hubs, A/A £450
41-3 Ford GT Race Car, yellow plastic hubs, A/B £480
43-1 Hillman Minx, apple green, MW, B/A...............................£160
44-2 Rolls-Royce Phantom, unusual GPW, A/A £275
45-1 Vauxhall Victor, RED body, MW, A/B............................£2,700

46-1 Morris Minor, dark blue, KGPW, A/A £430
46-2 Removals Van, tan, 'Beales Bealsons', A, unboxed..........£400
46-2 'Pickfords' Van, dark blue, 2 line decal, KGPW, A/A £160
47-2 Commer Ice Cream Van, white interior, KBPW, A/A £200
48-1 Meteor Sports Boat, tan/blue, black trailer, SPW, A/A £170
49-1 Carrier, GPW on front/rare grey plastic rollers, A/A £340
50-1 Commer Pick-up, rare red/white, KSPW, A/A £130
52-1 Maserati, red, rare wire wheels, A/A £430
53-1 Aston-Martin, red, KGPW, A/A £340
55-1 Ford Fairlane Police Car, dark blue, KBPW, B/A £255
56-1 London Trolley Bus, red poles, KGPW, A/A £440
57-3 Land Rover, 'Kent Fire Brigade', fine GPW, A/A £455
58-1 BEA Coach, blue, rare SPW, 'BEA' to front,, A/A £180
59-1 Ford Thames 'Singer', Kelly green, KGPW, A/A £270
59-1 Ford Thames 'Singer', Kelly green, KSPW, A/A £455
59-2 Ford Fairlane 'Fire Chief' Car, KGPW, A/A £420
59-2 Ford Fairlane 'Fire Chief' Car, BPW, unusual shields, A/A ...£215
62-2 TV Van 'Rentaset', rare knobbly GPW, A/A £500
62-3 Mercury Cougar, cream in correct picture box, C/A £755
65-1 Jaguar 3.4 lt, metallic blue, KGPW, A/B £100
66-1 Citroën DS 19, yellow, KSPW, A/A £430
67-2 Volkswagen 1600TL, purple, A/A.....................................£235
72-1 Fordson Tractor, yellow plastic hubs, A/A £675
74-1 Mobile Canteen, cream, blue base, fine GPW, A/A £275
74-1 Canteen, silver-grey, turquoise base, KSPW, A/A £350
75-1 Ford T'bird, cream/pink, turquoise base, KSPW, A/A £420
75-1 Ford T'bird, cream/pink, black base, KGPW, A/A £265

GIFT SETS

G-1 Motorway Set, A/A..£750
G-2 Car Transporter Set with 7 pieces, A/A £460
G-4 Farm Set 1960, B/A £940
G-4 Grand Prix Race Track Set, A/A £835
G-6 Truck Set (late 1960's), A/A..£135
G-7 Military Gift Set, A/B £275
G-8 Construction Set, A/A £200

SERVICE STATION/GARAGE ISSUES

MG-1 'BP' Service Station, A/A..£95
MG-1 'BP' Double Decker, green/white, B/B £110
MG-1 Single 'Matchbox Garage', yellow base, A/B £165
MG-1 Single 'Matchbox Garage', red base, A/A £170
MF-1 'Matchbox Fire Station', rare white/green,
with unusual cream sides, A/A £365
MF-1 'Matchbox Fire Station', red and white, A/A £110
MF-1 'Matchbox Fire Station', green and white, A/A £200

MATCHBOX PAINTING BOOKS, Set of 4, A...............................£835

A selection of 'Superfast' models from Matchbox showing the development in 1970s box design.

Photo:
Vectis Auctions Ltd.

SUPERFAST ISSUES
7 Hairy Hustler, rare '137' side labels, A/A £55
8 Wild Cat Dragster, orange, black base, A/A £50
8 Ford Mustang Fastback, white, red interior, A/B....................£100
8 Ford Mustang US issue, red/orange, red interior, A/A................£165
10 Mustang Piston Popper, white, A/A.................................£105
12-A Safari Land Rover, blue, correct box £500
20 Lanborghini Marzal, pink, (gift set labels), A/A £40
20 Lamboghini Marzal, yellow, A/A.....................................£30
22 Pontiac Sports Car, red, rivets, excellent, A/A £2,650
22 Pontiac Gran Prix Sports Coupé, light purple, A/A £170
24 'Team Matchbox', yellow, with '4' hood label, A/A £200
24 'Team Matchbox', metallic blue, with '5' hood label, A/A £215
25 Ford Cortina GT, light brown in correct box, A/A £60
25 Ford Cortina GT, light blue, A/B..................................£150
32 Leyland 'Aral' Tanker, blue/white, A/A £120
32-A Leyland Tanker, 'Matchbox Collector's' label etc., A, unboxed £65
37 Skip Truck, red, blue plastic dump, A/A £65
41-A Ford GT, white, black base £30
41-A Ford GT, (Italian), yellow, 'England' base, A/A £1,350
42 Iron Fairy Crane, red, dark yellow boom, A/B £105
46 Mercedes 300 SE, blue, A/A..£70
49 Chop Suey, chrome handlebars, A/A.................................£200
53-A Ford Zodiac, apple green, A/A.....................................£35
55-A Mercury Police Car, white, red dome light, A/A £65
55-A Mercury Police Car, white, blue dome light, A/A £25
74 Daimler Bus, red, 'N.A.M.C.' labels etc., A, unboxed £150
75 Ferrari Berlinetta, metallic green, A/A £100

MAJOR PACKS
A-2 Bedford Transporter, KBPW, B/A....................................£210
M-1 'BP' Petrol Tanker, fine BPW, late picture box, A/A £110
M-2 Bedford 'Walls' Truck, KGPW, A/A..................................£80
M-2 Bedford T/T, 'Davies Tyres', KBPW, A/B £70
M-2 Bedford T/T 'LEP', etc., fine BPW, A/B.............................£65
M-3 Tank Transporter, KBPW plus Tank..................................£50
M-4 GMC 'Fruehof' Train, red PH, grey PT, A/B £235
M-5 Massey-Ferguson Combine Harvester, silver metal SW,
    yellow plastic front hubs/solid BPW at rear, B/B...............£550
M-5 Massey Ferguson Combine, yellow plastic SW and front
    hubs, solid BPW at rear, late picture box, A/A................£975
M-6 'Pickfords' Transporter, red/dark blue, KBPW, B/A................£180
M-7 Jennings Cattle Truck, tan rear door/KGPW, A/A.....................£60
M-9 'Cooper Jarrett', BPW, orange side labels, A/A.....................£85
M-9 'Cooper Jarrett', red PH, yellow side labels, A/A £180

MOKO AND EARLY LESNEY
Heavy Tractor, driver, orange, clockwork, key, A/A £1,560
Covered Wagon, red barrels, A/A.......................................£340
Orange **Hay Rake** c. 1947-50, A/B......................................£120
Motor Scooter, maroon with girl driver, A/A...........................£755
Massey Harris Tractor (large), red, original stacks, B U/B £755
Farm Tractor /driver and wagon, c. 1947-50, blue, A/A.................£810
Coronation Coach, (1952), gold, Queen figure only, A/A...............£200
Prime Mover, orange/blue, red/yellow M in E box £1,400
Bread Press, unpainted wing nut, green inner fixture, A/A.............£130
Caterpillar Excavator, (large) orange/green, NM......................£700
Muffin the Mule, GP in F box...£120
Cement Mixer (large), green, red metal wheels.........................£80

KING SIZE ISSUES
K-2 Wreck Truck 'Esso', gold, amber windows, A/A....................£140
K-3 D9 Bulldozer, yellow, red plastic rollers, A/A....................£105
K-4 McCormick Tractor, red, green PH, B/A.............................£65
K-4 McCormick Tractor, red axle ings/orange PH, B/A...................£80
K-5 Foden Dump Truck, metal hubs, A/B.................................£45
K-6 Mercedes Ambulance, off-white, patient/stretcher, A/A £65
K8 Laing T/T, orange/yellow, red PH, green treads, B/A £235
K-8 Transporter, aqua/orange, red axle springs, orange PH, B/A £80
K-8 Prime Mover, orange, orange plastic rollers, green treads, A/A £220
K-9 Road Roller, grey driver, A/A.....................................£60
K-10 Tractor Shovel, metal hubs, A/B..................................£65
K-11 'DAF' Transporter, red plastic hubs, A/A.........................£80
K-11 Fordson Tractor/Trailer, red PH, B/A.............................£90
K-12 'BP' Breakdown Truck, red plastic hubs, B/B......................£20
K-13 'Readymix' Concrete Truck, metal hubs, A/A.......................£65
K-17 Low Loader/Bulldozer, 'Taylor Woodrow', A/B......................£85

K-18 Horse Box, red/tan, red PH, A/B..................................£80
K-20 Tractor Transporter, 3 x MB 39 blue/yellow tractors, A/A £85

BATTLE KINGS
MM-2 Armoured Car Transporter, olive drab, with '7' label.
    Plus olive drab 73 Weasel (blisterpack) £155

MODELS OF YESTERYEAR
Y-1 Model 'T' Ford, all black, A/A...................................£165
Y-8 1914 Stutz Roadster, metallic red-brown, A/B.....................£135
Y-4 Fire Engine 'Kent Fire Brigade', gold boiler, A/B................£220
Y-6 1916 AEC 'Osram Lamps', KBPW, B/B..............................£1,150

Matchbox International Collectors Association
(Members bi-monthly club auctions results)
MICA UK, PO BOX 120, Deeside, CH5 3HE, UK.

Abbreviations: **M** = Mint, **NM** = Near Mint, **E** = Excellent,
G = Good, **F** = Fair, **UB** = Unoxed.

MOKO LESNEY
Mechanical Drummer Boy, 97% mint, in ageing box £1,117
Motor Scooter and Rider, 95% - 98% mint, G box £411
Excavator, 97%, good tracks and box..................................£509
Bulldozer, 98% Mint, clean original box..............................£226
Heavy Tractor, good driver, 95% mint, complete box...................£476
Railway Timekeeper Watch which houses matches.......................£280

EARLY LESNEY
Large Coronation Coach, gold, Queen only, M in G box.................£225
Massey-Harris Tractor, dark red, mostly mint, unboxed................£239
Jumbo The Walking Elephant, working, E in G box......................£999
Rag and Bone Merchant's Cart, complete, 96% M, box poor............£2,211
Large Coronation Coach, King and Queen, 98% M, fair box..............£689
Milk Float, orange, 98% mint, driver and 6 crates....................£451
Prime Mover, yellow/red bulldozer, 95% mint, Fair box................£888

MODELS OF YESTERYEAR
Y1 Allchin, mid-green boiler door, M, damaged box....................£421
Y1 Allchin with smooth rear wheels, E in F box.......................£601
Y2 Prince Henry Vauxhall, red and silver, blue seats, UB £752
Y3 Tram with open recess, clean box..................................£121
Y3 Benz, dark green, chartreuse roof, E in F box.....................£283
Y3 Benz with rare open wheel webs....................................£402
Y3 Riley in ruby red with black plastics, Mint boxed.................£403
Y4-3 Opel, textured tan hood, rear window, M in G box................£151
Y4 Sentinel with black plastics wheels, mint boxed...................£139
Y4 Opel, white with dark grey hood, red seats........................£111
Y4 Shand Mason Fire Engine, rare bronze horses, M, boxed.............£462
Y4 Shand Mason with white horses, 'LONDON' logo......................£252
Y5 Talbot Van 'Nestles' with black roof..............................£241
Y6 Bugatti with grey tyres...£111
Y5 Bentley with gold radiator shell, crisp box........................£78
Y8 Sunbeam Motorcycle, emerald green seat, F box.....................£222
Y11 Aveling, gold makers plate, black supports, M in G box...........£583
Y12 Ford Model T 'Coca-Cola', red vertical lines, boxed..............£482
Y12 GMC Van 'Singer Sewing Machines', Mint, unboxed..................£331
Y12 Ford Model 'T' Van, 'Sunlight', boxed............................£121
Y13 RAF Crossley with black plastics, M, boxed.......................£489
G7 Gift Set (1960) virtually mint in good box........................£272

MINIATURES 1-75 SERIES
G7 Gift Set, models virtually mint in very good box..................£272
G5 Construction Set, five models in shrinked wrap box................£171
72 Jeep CJ5, orange-yellow body/hubs, white interior, near M, boxed.....£891

MAJOR SERIES
G-9 1963-MP2, MP4, MP6 (red loader) virtually M, boxed...............£522
M6 'Pickford's Transporter, dark blue/red, 97% M in G box £175
M9 'Cooper-Jarrett', yellow labels, G in G box........................£70

A selection of Automobile Association models by Budgie Toys   Photo: Vectis Auctions Ltd.

A Budgie Toys Supercar   Photo: Swapmeet Publications

Budgie Toys 'Tonibell' Ice Cream Van by Budgie Toys

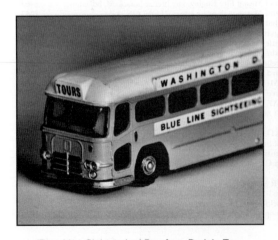

'Blue Line Sightseeing' Bus from Budgie Toys
Photo: Swapmeet Publications

Morestone No.3 Foden 14 ton Milk Delivery Wagon
Photo: Vectis Auctions Ltd.

Morestone, Modern Products, Budgie Toys and Seerol

The following history and listings have been provided by Robert Newson.

The history of these makes is a fascinating story of inter-linked companies, take-overs and bankruptcies reflecting the ups and downs of the toy trade. In the late 1940s Morris & Stone was a toy wholesaler selling the products of many small toy manufacturers including those from Modern Products who had started as die-casters. Morris and Stone decided to have their own exclusive 'Morestone' branded lines and some were made by Modern Products, who increasingly relied on Morestone for the sole marketing and distribution of their toys. Morestone continued to use several suppliers but in 1954 set up a die-casting company jointly with Rodney Smith (one of the founders of Lesney Products).

From the mid-1950s to 1966 the Morestone and Budgie ranges contained models that came either from the in-house factory or from Modern Products. Morestone's production expanded with new ranges of models, such as the 'Noddy' and 'Big-Ears' vehicles in 1956 and the Esso Petrol Pump Series of miniatures, launched at Christmas of that year. In 1958, the 'Trucks of the World International Series' was introduced, but only ran to three models.

Some of the earlier Morestone and Modern Products models were re-issued as part of the Budgie range which was introduced in 1959. Model numbers were allocated in 1960 and new additions to the range continued every year up to 1966. During 1961, Morris & Stone was taken over by S. Guiterman & Co. Ltd., who changed the name of their new subsidiary to Budgie Models Ltd. Although the range included many interesting and unusual subjects, they failed to compete with Corgi, Dinky and Matchbox, and losses in Budgie Models Ltd. contributed to losses in the Guiterman group. In March 1966 these companies went into voluntary liquidation.

Modern Products was badly hit by this but eventually were able to set up a new company called Budgie Models (Continuation) Ltd and purchase the Budgie trade mark from the receiver. They wanted the Budgie dies as well, but these were destroyed in a fire while negotiations were in progress. The only dies to survive were those in their own factory.

Thus the main range of Budgie commercial vehicles came to an end in 1966. Modern Products continued to produce the Budgie miniatures, mainly for the USA, until 1969 when the stronger competition this time was from Mattel's 'Hot Wheels'. Modern Products direction for the 1970s was to produce models for H. Seener Ltd., distributors of toys and souvenirs to London's tourist shops. The old Budgie Routemaster bus was reintroduced for Seener, followed by a new FX4 Taxi and Rolls-Royce Silver Cloud.

In 1983, following the death of one of the partners in Modern Products, the business was sold to a neighbouring engineering company called Starcourt Ltd (some boxes say Merracroft Ltd - an associated company of Starcourt). The new owners reintroduced several models from the original moulds, starting with the Aveling Barford Road Roller. However, a disagreement developed with Seener who withdrew the dies for the Taxi and Rolls-Royce (which he had paid for), and arranged for these to be made by Corgi together with a completely new Routemaster bus. These 'Seerol' models appeared in 1985 and are still available. Starcourt ceased toy production in 1985.

Some unpainted castings for no.204 Volkswagen Pick-Up and some empty boxes were sold to a Dutch firm and have since appeared in various liveries. These are classed as 'Code 3' models and have not been listed. The die-casting moulds were sold to Autocraft (Dave Gilbert) in 1988, and these include most of the 1950s Modern Products and part of the 1960s Budgie range. Autocraft are now in the process of adapting dies for a range of some 35 various models. Only one model has so far been reintroduced - a run of 1000 of no.258 Daimler Ambulance in kit form.

A complete history of these companies and their products is contained in the book 'Budgie Models' by Robert Newson. This hardback book also has full descriptions of all the models, 58 pages of colour photographs illustrating over 180 models, and reproductions of Budgie leaflets.

NB See the 'Miscellaneous Models' colour section for pictures.

Morestone and Modern Products

Ref	Year(s)	Model name	Colours, features, details	Market Price Range
-	c.1946	**Racing Car**	Red, Dark Blue, Dark Green or Light Brown. One piece casting including driver. No identification on model. 135 mm	£30-40
-	c.1947	**Stage Coach with Four Horses**	English mail coach with driver and trunk, Yellow body, Red wheels, 173 mm. 'Ye Olde Coach and Four' on box	£100-200
-	c.1948-56	**Fire Escape** (large)	Brass bell and wheel hubs. Base consists of sump and prop shaft only. Extending wheeled escape ladder. 108 mm. (excluding ladder)	£100-125
-	c.1950	**Fire Escape** (smaller)	Plain flat base, wheeled escape ladder, 66 mm. (excluding ladder)	£60-80
-	c.1948	**Fire Engine**	Clockwork motor and bell underneath, 'Morestone Series' cast-in, 135 mm	£100-200
-	c.1948-58	**0-6-0 Tank Locomotive**	Green or Red, 'British Railways' cast in, re-issued as Budgie 224, 119 mm	£25-35
-	1949-51	**Horse Drawn Snack Bar**	'SAM'S' cast on side below counter, removable roof, separate man, tea urn and two mugs, 117mm. Wide range of colours	£100-125
-	1949-59	**Horse Drawn Hansom Cab**	Black / Yellow, driver, elastic band for reins, 118 mm. (re-issued as Budgie 100)	£50-70
-	1949-?	**Gypsy Caravan**	Yellow, Green and Red caravan, step to seat, Grey or Brown horse, Gypsy	£200-300
-	c.1948-61	**Horse Drawn Covered Wagon with Four Horses**	Green, Red or Orange, driver, cloth canopy plain or printed with *'Thundering Hooves and Blazing Guns on the Western Trail'*, or *'Walt Disney's Davy Crockett Frontier Wagon'* or *'Last of the Mohicans Chingachgook Hawkeye'*, later with two barrels, 'Made in England' cast transversely under, 190 mm. (Budgie 404).	£100-200
-	1949	**'Wells Fargo' Stage Coach with two 'Galloping' Horses**	Brown / Yellow, driver and guard, eccentric wheel for 'galloping' effect, some with 'Copyright F.W. Birch & Co.' cast inside, 164 mm	£100-150
-	c.1950	**'Wells Fargo' Stage Coach**	Various colours, four horses, driver, 172 mm	£100-150
-	1952-58	**Stage Coach with Two Horses**	Red or Orange (no lettering), Black plastic horses, wheels and figures,165 mm	£100-150
-	1954-59	**Horse Drawn Covered Wagon with Six Horses**	Red, Yellow wheels, printed cloth canopy *'The Wild West Land of Buffalo and Covered Wagon'*, driver, two barrels, 'Made in England' cast transversely underneath, 265mm	£100-125
-	1950-51	**Mechanical Road Sweeper**	Metallic Green/Black, 'City Cleansing Dept.' cast-in, clockwork motor in some, 91 mm	£200-300
-	c.1950	**Compressor**	With man and pneumatic drill. No identification cast on model. 76 mm	£40-50

Morestone and Modern Products

-	1953	**State Landau with Six Horses**	Coronation souvenir, three figures cast-in. No identification on model. 111 mm	**£40-60**
-	1953	**Prime Mover with Trailer**	Red prime mover, 'British Road Services', 'NO 311' and 'MAX 20 MPH' cast-in, Black plastic wheels, 83 mm. Orange plastic trailer, 136 mm	**£150-175**
-	1953	**Sleigh with Father Xmas**	One reindeer. No identification on model. About 140 mm	**£175-225**
-	1953-55	**RAC Motorcycle and Sidecar**	Cast wheels / tyres and rider, no windscreen, hinged lid on sidecar, 70 mm	**£150-175**
-	1954-55	**A.A. Motorcycle and Sidecar**	Cast wheels / tyres and rider, windscreen, non-opening sidecar, separate rails	**£150-175**
-	1956-57	**RAC Motorcycle and Sidecar**	Cast rider, windscreen, separate rails and hinged lid on sidecar, steering front forks, rubber tyres, plain number plates, 82 mm	**£150-175**
-	1956-57	**A.A. Motorcycle and Sidecar**	Cast rider, windscreen, separate rails and hinged lid on sidecar, steering front forks, rubber tyres, plain number plates, 82 mm	**£150-175**
-	1956-57	**Solo Motorcycle**	Cast rider, steering front forks, rubber tyres, plain number plates, 82 mm. There are four versions: Police Patrol, Despatch Rider, GPO Messenger and TT Rider. Each	**£75-100**
-	?	**Police Motorcycle and Sidecar**	Black machine, Dark Blue sidecar, Black uniformed figures, cast wheels	**£75-100**
-	1954-55	**Horse Drawn Gipsy Caravan**	Yellow / Green, tinplate roof and base, separate driver and rear steps, 190 mm	**£300-350**
-	1954-56	**Bedford Dormobile**	Red or Green body. 90 mm	**£100-125**
-	1955-58	**Leyland Double Deck Bus**	'Finest Petrol - ESSO - in the World', Red or Green, route '7', 103 mm	**£70-80**
			'ESSO - for Happy Motoring - ESSO', Red body, route '7', 103 mm	**£70-80**
			'Motor Oil - ESSO - Petrol', Red body, route '7', 103 mm	**£70-80**
-	1955-56	**Aveling-Barford Road Roller**	Green, Yellow or Red, with driver, 117 mm. Re-issued as Budgie 701	**£40-50**
-	1955-59	**Wolseley 6/80 Police Car**	Black, loudspeaker, aerial, 113 mm. No maker's name. (Budgie 246)	**£50-60**
1	1955-57	**Foden 8-wheel Petrol Tanker**	Red body, 'Motor Oil Esso Petrol' transfers, leaflet, 136 mm	**£175-200**
2	1955-56	**Foden 8-wheel Open Lorry**	Light brown cab and chassis, Red truck body, leaflet, 138 mm	**£150-200**
3	1955-56	**Foden Flat Lorry with Chains**	Green cab and 8-wheel chassis, Beige flatbed, brass chain, leaflet, 138 mm	**£150-200**
4	1955-57	**Foden 8-wheel Flat Lorry**	Yellow or Orange cab and chassis, Grey flatbed, leaflet, 138 mm	**£150-200**
-	1956-57	**Bedford Car Transporter**	Orange cab, Grey trailer, collapsible top deck, two loading ramps, 243 mm	**£150-200**
-	1956	**Daimler Ambulance**	White or Cream body (no transfers), Silver base, opening rear doors, no maker's name, 110 mm. Re-issued as Budgie 258	**£110-130**
-	1955-57	**A.A. Land Rover** (large)	Yellow / Black, 'AA ROAD SERVICE' cast-in, opening rear doors, driver, passenger, 108 mm	**£500-600**
-	1957-58	**A.A. Land Rover** (medium)	Yellow / Black, driver, 79 mm. 'AA ROAD SERVICE' transfers, no rear windows	**£150-200**
			Same but 'AA ROAD SERVICE' cast-in, two rear windows	**£150-200**
-	1958	**Military Police Land Rover**	Olive Green, driver, 'MP Military Police' cast on sides, 79 mm	**£150-200**
-	1958	**Breakdown Service Land Rover**	Red body, driver, 'Breakdown Service Unit' cast on sides, 79 mm	**£125-150**
-	1958	**Foden Dumper**	Orange cab and chassis, Grey dumper, 108 mm. Re-issued as Budgie 226	**£40-50**

Morestone 'Trucks of the World International' Series

-	1958	**Klöckner Side Tipper**	Red cab, Black chassis, Cream tipper, 81 mm. (with 'Driving Licence')	**£40-50**
-	1958	**Scammell Articulated Tanker**	Orange cab, Cream tank. 'LIQUID IN BULK' cast on sides, 114 mm	**£35-45**
-	1958	**International Articulated Refrigerator Lorry**	Red / Blue cab, Silver trailer, 'COAST to COAST REFRIGERATION' transfers, 153 mm. Re-issued as Budgie 202	**£40-50**

'Noddy' items by Morestone and Budgie

The 'Noddy' items were given numbers when incorporated in the Budgie range around 1960.

301	1956-61	**Noddy and his Car** (large)	Yellow/Red, windscreen, solid rubber wheels, metal or plastic 'Noddy', 98 mm	**£150-200**
-	1957-58	**Big Ears on Bicycle** (large)	Red bicycle (64 mm.), metal 'Big Ears' with legs that move as the model is pushed along. No maker's name on model	**£150-200**
-	c.1959	**Clown on Bicycle** (large)	Metallic Light Brown bicycle (64 mm. as previous model), metal clown figure with moving legs. No maker's name on model	**£150-200**
-	1958	**Noddy's Garage Set**	331 Noddy's Car and 'Esso' series nos. 7, 13, 16 and 20. Box folds into garage	**£150-200**
303	c.1961	**Noddy and his Car** (large) with Big Ears	As 301 but with additional metal Big Ears Figure	**£150-200**
305	1959-61	**Noddy's Gift Box**	Contains numbers 331, 333 and plastic Mr. Plod the Policeman	**£600-800**
307	1959-61	**Locomotive and Wagon with Noddy and Big Ears**	Yellow loco with red cab. Red wagon. Plastic figures, 104 mm	**£125-150**
309	c.1961	**Noddy and Locomotive**	As no.307 but without wagon, 57 mm	**£80-100**
311	1960-61	**Noddy on Bicycle with Trailer**	Yellow bicycle, red trailer, plastic figure, 81 mm	**£100-125**
331	1958-61	**Noddy and his Car** (small)	Yellow car, red base and wheels, plastic figure, 52 mm	**£100-125**
333	1958-61	**Big Ears on Bicycle** (small)	Red. No maker's name on model, plastic figure, 48 mm	**£100-125**

Packed in 'Esso' Petrol Pump boxes from 1956 to around 1959, then in Budgie bubble packs (yellow backing card) till 1964, and from 1965 in bubble packs with 'The Esso Petrol Pump Series' blue backing card. In the early 1960s, conventional boxes marked 'Mobile Vehicle Series' or 'Modern Vehicle Series' were also used.

1	1956-58	**A.A. Motorcycle and Sidecar**	Yellow/Black motorcycle and sidecar, Blue uniformed rider, 46 mm	£40-50
2	1956-58	**RAC Motorcycle and Sidecar**	Black motorcycle, Mid-Blue sidecar, Dark Blue uniformed rider, 46 mm	£40-50
3	1956-58	**A.A. Land Rover**	'AA ROAD SERVICE' cast-in, spare wheel (on bonnet) on some, 54 mm	£45-55
4	1956-58	**A.A. Bedford Van**	AA badge and 'ROAD SERVICE' cast-in, 57 mm	£45-55
5	1956-70	**Wolseley 6/80 Police Car**	Black or green body, 65 mm	£40-50
6	1956-58	**Cooper-Bristol Racing Car**	Blue or Dark Blue body, Off-White base and driver, 58 mm	£15-20
7	1956-65	**Mercedes-Benz Racing Car**	Silver body, Red base and driver, 60 mm	£15-20
8	1956-70	**Volkswagen 1200 Saloon**	Metallic Light Blue body, 58 mm	£15-20
9	1956-58	**Maudslay Horse Box**	Red body, 'HORSE BOX SERVICE' cast-in, 57 mm	£40-50
10	1956-58	**Karrier GPO Telephones Van**	Dark green body, 57 mm	£50-60
11	1957-65	**Morris Commercial Van**	Red body, 'ROYAL MAIL' and 'E-II-R' cast-in, 58 mm	£50-60
12	1957-70	**Volkswagen Microbus**	Light Brown, Pale Blue or Metallic Dark Blue, 61 mm	£15-20
13	1957-64	**Austin FX3 Taxi**	Black body, Silver base and driver, 58 mm	£15-20
14	1957-70	**Packard Convertible**	Beige or Metallic Lt.Blue body, Red base/seats, Lt. Brown or Gold driver	£15-20
15	1957-70	**Austin A95 Westminster Countryman**	Blue or Orange, (Silver flash on some); or Metallic Mauve, 66 mm	£40-50
16	1957-64	**Austin-Healey 100**	Red body, Off-White base and driver, 57 mm	£50-65
17	1957-58	**Ford Thames 5 cwt. Van**	Blue body, 60 mm	£50-60
18	1957-66	**Foden Dumper**	Red cab and chassis, Lemon-Yellow or Grey dumper, 60 mm	£50-60
19	1957-70	**Rover 105R**	Green or Gold body, 65 mm	£30-35
20	1957-64	**Plymouth Belvedere Convertible**	Pale Pink or White body, Red base and driver, 64 mm	£20-30
20	1968-70	**Austin A95 Emergency Vehicle**	As 15 but White with Orange beacon, 'EMERGENCY' transfer, Red base	£40-50
21	1963-66.	**Bedford TK Tipper Lorry**	Dark Green tipper. Yellow, Off-White or Orange cab, 58 mm	£25-35
21	1968-70	**Oldsmobile Town Sedan**	Gold body, 66 mm	£20-25
22	1963-66	**Bedford TK Crane Lorry**	Dark Green cab, Orange crane, Orange or Dark Green platform, 56 mm	£20-30
22	1968-70	**Cattle Transporter**	Adapted from no.58. Light Brown body, Dark Brown rear door, 61 mm	£20-30
23	1963-66	**Bedford TK Cement Mixer**	Off-White mixer. Green, Yellow, Red or Orange cab and chassis, 59 mm	£20-30
24	1963-66	**Bedford TK Refuse Lorry**	Green, Orange, Red or Yellow cab, Silver back, 59 mm	£20-30
25	1963-66	**Bedford TK Cattle Lorry**	Light brown body. Off-White, Orange or Yellow cab, 58 mm	£20-30
26	1963-66	**Aveling-Barford Road Roller**	Similar to Lesney Matchbox no.1c. Green body, Red wheels, 55 mm	£20-25
27	1963-70	**Wolseley 6/80 Fire Chief Car**	Same as no.5 with altered base lettering. Red body, 65 mm	£40-50

Models 50 - 55 were designated the 'Road Tanker Series'.

50	1963-66	**'BP Racing Service' Tanker**	Green with White tank, 61 mm	£30-40
51	1963-66	**'Shell' Tanker**	Yellow, 61 mm	£30-40
52	1963-64	**'Shell BP' Tanker**	Green or Yellow; White tank, 61 mm	£30-40
53	1963-66	**'National' Tanker**	Blue with Yellow tank, 61 mm	£30-40
54	1963-66	**'BP' Tanker**	Green with White tank, 61 mm	£30-40
55	1963-66	**'Mobil' Tanker**	Red body, 61 mm	£30-40
56	1966-70	**GMC Box Van**	'HERTZ TRUCK RENTAL' transfers and 'TRUCK RENTAL' cast-in. Light Green or Pale Blue body, 61 mm	£30-40
57	1966-70	**International Parcels Van**	Green, sliding door. 'REA EXPRESS' transfers, 67 mm	£30-40
58	1966-70	**'Modern Removals' Van**	'MODERN REMOVALS' transfers. Light Brown or Metallic Green, 61 mm	£30-40
59	1967-70	**AEC Merryweather Fire Engine**	Copied from Lesney Matchbox no.9c. Red body, Gold ladder, 65 mm	£30-40
60	1966-70	**Rover 105R Squad Car**	As no.19 but with altered base lettering. Black or Red body, 65 mm	£30-40
61	1966-70	**Austin A95 'Q Car'**	As no.15 but with altered base lettering. Black or Metallic Dark Blue body	£30-40

Sets of three vehicles (bubble-packed)

94	1966	**Interpol Set**	Intended to contain no.5 Police Car, 60 Squad Car, 61 'Q' Car. Not issued	NPP
95	1966	**Road Haulage Set**	Intended to contain 56 Hertz Van, 57 REA Van, 58 Removals Van. Not issued	NPP
96	1965-66	**Road Construction Set**	Contains no.18 Dumper, 23 Cement Mixer, 26 Road Roller	£75-125
97	1965-66	**Truck Set**	Contains no.21 Tipper, 22 Crane, 25 Cattle Lorry	£75-125
98	1965-66	**Utility Vehicle Set**	Contains no.12 VW Microbus, 24 Refuse Lorry, 55 Mobil Tanker	£75-125
99	1965-66	**Traffic Set**	Contains no.8 Volkswagen, 15 Austin, 27 Fire Chief	£75-125
95	1968-70	**Town Set**	Contains no.20 Emergency Vehicle, 21 Oldsmobile, 56 Hertz Van	£75-125
96	1967-70	**Service Set**	Contains no.5 Police Car, 19 Rover, 59 Fire Engine	£75-125
97	1967-70	**Truck Set**	Contains no.12 VW Microbus, 57 REA Van, 58 Removals Van	£75-125
98	1967-70	**Utility Vehicle Set**	Contains no.27 Fire Chief, 60 Squad Car, 61 Q Car	£75-125
99	1967-70	**Traffic Set**	Contains no.8 Volkswagen, 14 Packard, 15 Austin	£75-125

Gift Sets

	1962	**Gift Set No.8**	Contains numbers 5, 8, 11, 12, 13, 15, 18 and 19	£200-300
	1962	**Gift Set No.12**	Contains 5, 7, 8, 11, 12, 13, 14, 15, 16, 18, 19 and 20 (Plymouth)	£200-300

Ref	Year(s)	Model name	Colours, features, details	Market Price Range
100	1972-84	**Horse Drawn Hansom Cab**	With driver, elastic band for reins. Re-issue of a Morestone/Modern Products model. 'Gold' plated or Metallic Light Brown, 118 mm	£25-30
101	1977-84	**Austin FX4 Taxi**	Also issued as no.703. Re-issued by Seerol. Black or Maroon. 106 mm	£25-30
101	1984	**Austin FX4 Taxi**	Silver body, 'LONDON VINTAGE TAXI ASSOCIATION'. Limited (1,000) commemorative marking 25 years of the FX4. Normal box	£25-30
102	1981-84	**Rolls-Royce Silver Cloud**	Re-issued by Seerol. Gold (painted or 'plated'), Black, Silver, Cream, Red, Blue, Metallic Lt.Blue, Metallic Turquoise or Metallic Dark Pink, 107 mm	£25-30
202	1959-66	**International Articulated Refrigerator Lorry**	Re-issued 'Trucks of the World' model. Red / Blue or Red cab (windows later). Silver trailer, 'COAST TO COAST REFRIGERATION', 153 mm	£50-75
204	1959-64	**Volkswagen Pick-Up**	Blue body, Cream base, cloth tilt 'EXPRESS DELIVERY', 92 mm	£50-75
206	1959-64	**Leyland Hippo Coal Lorry**	Green or Orange cab, Light Brown body, 'COAL AND COKE' cast-in, coal load, 92 mm	£65-85
208	1959-61	**RAF Personnel Carrier**	RAF blue, roundels, White tilt. 'A MORESTONE PRODUCT', 104 mm	£90-120
210	1959-61	**US Army Personnel Carrier**	As 208 but Army brown body with star, Light Brown tilt, 104 mm	£90-120
212	1959-61	**British Army Personnel Carrier**	As 208 but Dark Green with Red / Yellow square, Light Brown tilt	£90-120
214	1959-64	**Thornycroft Mobile Crane**	Red cab and chassis, Yellow crane engine, Light Blue crane, 100 mm	£50-60
216	1959-64	**Renault Truck**	Yellow cab, Red body. Cloth tilt, 'FRESH FRUIT DAILY', 103 mm	£40-50
218	1959-63	**Seddon 'Jumbo' Mobile Traffic Control Unit**	Yellow cab and trailer with Black flash and catwalk. 'AUTOMOBILE ASSOCIATION' and AA badge transfers, 168 mm	£125-175
220	1959-66	**Leyland Hippo Cattle Transporter**	Orange cab, Light Brown body, Dark Brown base and ramp, 97 mm	£35-45
222	1959-65	**International Tank Transporter with Centurion Tank**	Army brown with star transfers. Cab as no.202. 155 mm. (with ramps up)	£45-55
224	1959-66	**0-6-0 Tank Locomotive**	As Modern Products model. Red, 'BRITISH RAILWAYS' cast-in, 119 mm	£25-35
224	1971-84	**0-6-0 Tank Locomotive**	Red, Metallic Brown, Black or Dark Green, 'BRITISH RAILWAYS' on transfers or labels	£10-15
226	1959-66	**Foden Dumper**	Re-issue of a Morestone model. Orange cab and chassis, Grey dumper. 'BUD 123' number plate transfers, 108 mm	£30-40
228	1959-64	**Karrier Bantam Bottle Lorry**	Orange-Yellow, 12 maroon plastic crates. 'DRINK COCA-COLA' transfers, 'COMMER LOW LOADER' cast underneath, 134 mm	£300-400
230	1959-66	**Seddon Timber Transporter**	Orange cab (no windows), or Green cab (with windows), Yellow trailer, five 'logs', 178 mm	£200-250
232	1960-66	**Seddon Cable Drum Transporter**	Red prime mover (windows later), Orange trailer, 3 wooden cable drums 'STANDARD'	£150-200
234	1960-65	**International Low Loader with Caterpillar Tractor**	Orange cab, Light Brown trailer, Orange tractor, 155 mm. (with ramps up)	£140-180
236	1960-66 and 1969-84	**AEC Routemaster Bus**	Also issued as nos.704, 705 and 706. All models have destination transfers for route '9' and and 'LONDON TRANSPORT' transfers or labels. They were available with or without windows. 108 mm.	
			Red, 'Esso GOLDEN Esso'	£25-35
			Red, 'Esso UNIFLO - the tuned motor oil'	£25-35
			Red, 'GO ESSO - BUY ESSO - DRIVE ESSO'	£25-35
			Red, 'UNIFLO sae 10W/50 Motor Oil'	£25-35
			Red, Green or Gold, 'Houses of Parliament Tower Bridge'	£15-20
236	1973	Promotional issue:	Red body (with windows), 'Sheraton-Heathrow Hotel' on sides, 'OPENING 1st FEBRUARY 1973' on roof, Special box	£70-80
238	1960-63	**Scammell Scarab Van**	Crimson / Cream body. 'BRITISH RAILWAYS' and 'CADBURYS', 150mm. Note: Chocolate Bar picture may be vertical or horizontal	£120-140
238	1964-66		Yellow cab, Black chassis, Yellow trailer. 'Railfreight', 'CADBURYS'	£120-140
238	1985		Maroon cab, Maroon / Cream trailer. 'BRITISH RAILWAYS' and 'CADBURYS'	£25-35
			Yellow cab and trailer. 'Railfreight' and 'CADBURYS' transfers. Most of these were issued in original 1960s boxes. 150 mm	£25-35
240	1960-64	**Scammell Scarab Wagon**	Red / Cream cab, Yellow chassis, Red trailer, Green cloth tilt, 150 mm	£55-65
242	1960-66	**Euclid Dumper**	Red cab, Orange chassis and dumper. 114 mm	£55-65
244	1961-65	**Morris Breakdown Lorry**	Blue body, Yellow base, tool box and jib. 'BUDGIE SERVICE', 120 mm	£70-80
246	1960-63	**Wolseley 6/80 Police Car**	Re-issued Modern Products model. Black, loudspeaker, aerial, 'BUDGIE TOYS' cast under, 'POLICE' transfers on grille and boot, 113 mm	£40-50
246	1983	**Wolseley 6/80 Police Car**	Light Blue, 'POLICE' labels, spotlights and roof sign replace the loudspeaker and aerial. Trial run only - did not go into full production	£40-50
248	1961	**Stage Coach with Four Horses**	Listed on this number as 'available later', but issued as no. 434.	
250	------	Pack reference only	This number was used for packs of one dozen of the Budgie miniatures.	
252	1961-63	**Austin Articulated Lorry with Railway Container**	Crimson / Cream cab, windows, Crimson trailer / container, 'BRITISH RAILWAYS' transfers	£100-125
252	1964		Crimson cab / trailer, windows, Blue container, 'Door to Door' transfers	£100-125
254	1961-64	**AEC Merryweather Fire Escape**	Red, windows, Silver extending turntable ladder. 97 mm. (excl. ladder)	£100-130
256	1961-64	**Foden Aircraft Refuelling Tanker 'Pluto'**	Red, with windows. 'ESSO AVIATION PRODUCTS' transfers, 149 mm	£150-200
258	1961-63	**Daimler Ambulance**	Re-issued Modern Products model. Cream with Red base ('BUDGIE TOYS' cast-in), 'AMBULANCE' and 'EMERGENCY' transfers, 110 mm	£80-100

258	1991	Daimler Ambulance Kit	Re-issued as a kit of unpainted castings (by Autocraft)	£10-20
260	1962	Ruston-Bucyrus Excavator	Yellow / Red cab, '10-RB', Beige or Olive-Green base and jib, 73 mm	£300-400
262	1962-64	Racing Motorcycle	No maker's name. Unpainted cycle, tinplate fairing in Metallic Blue, Metallic Lilac, Metallic Brown or Lime Green, Black plastic rider, 104 mm	£75-100
264	1962-64	Racing Motorcycle and Sidecar	Cycle as 262, sidecar and fairing in Metallic Blue, Metallic Pinkish-Red, Metallic Green, Metallic Lilac, Metallic Brown or Lime Green. Black plastic rider / passenger, no maker's name, 104 mm	£75-100
266	1962-64	Motorcycle and Delivery Sidecar	Blue cycle as 262, Red sidecar, 'EXPRESS DELIVERY' cast-in, no maker's name, Black plastic rider. 108 mm	£100-125
268	1962-64	A.A. Land Rover	Different from Morestone AA Land Rovers. Yellow body, Black roof, windows, opening rear doors, 'AA ROAD SERVICE' transfers, 97 mm	£125-150
270	1962-66	Leyland Articulated Tanker	Red, windows, 'ESSO PETROLEUM COMPANY LTD' labels, 132 mm	£100-125
272	1962-64	Supercar	From TV series. Red / Silver body, Red wings (or colours reversed), clear plastic canopy, 'SUPERCAR' transfers, 122 mm	£400-500
274	1962-66	Ford Thames Refuse Lorry	Blue cab / Silver body, or Yellow cab / Metallic blue body, windows	£45-55
276	1962-66	Bedford LWB Tipper	Red cab with windows, Yellow tipper, 'HAM RIVER GRIT', 128 mm	£40-80
278	1963-64	RAC Land Rover	Casting as 268, Blue, windows, 'RAC RADIO RESCUE' transfers, 97 mm	£125-150
280	1963-64	AEC Super Fueller Tanker	White cab and trailer, windows, Green base and canopy, 'AIR BP', 219 mm	£300-400
282	1963-66	Euclid Scraper	Yellow or Lime Green, windscreen, 'EUCLID', Black plastic wheels, 163 mm	£35-45
284	1962	Euclid Crawler Tractor	Not issued	NPP
286	1962	Euclid Bulldozer	Not issued	NPP
288	1963-66	Leyland Bulk Flour Tanker	Red cab, windows, Off-White silos, Yellow hopppers, 'BULK FLOUR', 107 mm	£45-55
290	1963-64	Bedford Ice Cream Van	No maker's name on model. Blue body and base, windows, 'Tonibell' transfers, Pink plastic cow on roof, 103 mm	£125-150
292	1963-66	Leyland Bulk Milk Tanker	Blue or Red cab, windows, White tank, 'MILK', 107 mm	£45-55
294	1963-66	Bedford TK Horse Box	Off-White cab, windows, Brown body, Light Brown doors. two Brown plastic horses. 'EPSOM STABLE' transfer, 109 mm	£80-100
296	1963-66	Motorway Express Coach	Midland Red livery: Red body, Black roof, 'BIRMINGHAM-LONDON MOTORWAY EXPRESS' transfers, windows, 121 mm	£100-125
		USA livery:	Light Blue body, Cream roof, 'WASHINGTON D.C.' and 'BLUE LINE SIGHTSEEING CO.' transfers, phone number 'LA9-7755' at rear	£300-400
298	1963-66	Alvis Salamander Crash Tender	Red body, windows, Silver plastic ladder, Yellow engine cover at rear, Black plastic wheels. 'FIRE SERVICE' transfers, 92 mm.	£100-125
300	1963-65	Lewin Sweepmaster	Blue / Silver, windows, Black plastic wheels, Black sweeping brush	£60-75
302	1963-66	Commer Cabin Service Lift Truck	Blue cab, windows, Silver body, 'BOAC CABIN SERVICES', 104 mm	£75-95
304	1964-66	Bedford TK Glass Transporter	Off-white cab and chassis, windows, Green body. 'TOWER GLASS CO.' transfers. Four clear plastic 'glass' sheets, 108 mm	£45-55
306	1964-66	Fiat Tractor with Shovel	Orange tractor, Metallic Blue shovel, 108 mm	£75-100
308	1964-66	Seddon Pitt Alligator Low Loader	Green cab, windows, Yellow trailer with Black ramp, 163 mm	£45-55
310	1964-66	Leyland Cement Mixer	Orange cab, windows, Silver mixer, 'INVICTA Construction Co.', 98 mm	£60-80
312	1964-66	Bedford Super Tipmaster	Dark Green cab, windows, Silver tipper. 'SUPER TIP-MASTER', 127mm	£60-80
314	1965-66	Fiat Tractor with Dozer Blade	As 306 but enclosed cab, Orange tractor, Metallic Blue blade, 81 mm	£45-55
316	1965-66	Albion Overhead Maintenance Vehicle	Green body, windows, Silver / Black boom assembly, 107 mm	£40-50
318	1965-66	Euclid Mammoth Articulated Dumper	Modified from no.242. Green cab, Yellow chassis, Orange tipper, 201 mm	£75-95
322	1965-66	Scammell Routeman Pneumajector Transporter	Light Blue cab, Cream or White tank, 'THE ATLAS CARRIER CO.', 111 mm	£60-80
324	1965-66	Douglas Prospector Duomatic Tipper	Tips in two directions. Blue cab and chassis, windows, Grey tipper, 112 mm	£55-65
326	1965-66	Scammell Highwayman Gas Transporter	Green cab, windows, Dark Green trailer, 6 White / Red gas cylinders, 146 mm	£125-150
328	1966	Scammell Handyman Artic	Planned but not issued	NPP
330	1966	Land Rover	Modified 268, planned but not issued	NPP
332	1966	'Kenning' Breakdown Lorry	Planned but not issued	NPP
334	1966	Austin Gipsy Fire Tender	Planned but not issued	NPP
404	1960-61	Horse Drawn Covered Wagon	with Four Horses. For details see Morestone and Modern Products entry.	
410	1961	Stage Coach with Four Horses	Blue or 'Gold' plated coach, no lettering cast on sides but 'WELLS FARGO STAGE COACH' and 'A BUDGIE TOY' cast underneath, plastic horses and driver, bubble-packed, 118 mm	£100-150
430	1960-61	Wagon Train Set	Contains 3 of no. 432 plus two more horses with riders, bubble-packed	£150-200
432	1960-61	Horse Drawn Covered Wagon with Two Horses	Red wagon, ('A BUDGIE TOY' on floor), Grey, White or Lemon metal canopy, 2 barrels, plastic horses, driver, passenger, bubble packed, 82 mm	£35-45
434	1961	Stage Coach with Four Horses	'WELLS FARGO' above windows, 'STAGE LINES' on doors, luggage cast on roof, Red or Blue, plastic horses and driver, 189 mm	£100-150
452	1958-63	A.A. Motorcycle and Sidecar	Initially in Morestone box. Windscreen, plastic rider, integral rails and hinged lid on sidecar, steerable, rubber tyres, plain number plates, 82 mm	£100-150
452	1964-66	A.A. Motorcycle and Sidecar	New design. Sidecar with transfers and 'BUDGIE' underneath, plastic rider, windscreen and leg guards, plain number plates, 84 mm	£100-150
454	1958-63	RAC Motorcycle and Sidecar	Initially in Morestone box. Windscreen, plastic rider, integral rails and hinged lid on sidecar, steerable, rubber tyres, plain number plates, 82 mm	£100-150
454	1964-66	RAC Motorcycle and Sidecar	New design. Sidecar with transfers and 'BUDGIE' underneath, plastic rider, windscreen and leg guards, plain number plates, 84 mm	£100-150

Budgie Toys and Models

456	1958-66	**Solo Motorcycle**	Initially in Morestone boxes. Two casting versions as 452 and 454 but 'Silver plated'. Plastic riders:	
			Police Patrol (Blue uniform)	**£40-50**
			Despatch Rider (Light Brown uniform)	**£40-50**
			GPO Messenger (Light Blue uniform)	**£40-50**
			'Tourist Trophy' Rider (White racing overalls)	**£40-50**
701	1983	**Aveling-Barford Road Roller**	Re-issued Modern Products model. Dark Green body, Silver / Red wheels, Dark Blue driver	**£10-15**
702	1984-85	**Scammell Scarab Vans**	Re-issue of 238. Very Dark Blue cab and trailer, White 'RN' on doors, 'ROYAL NAVY' on tilt	**£15-25**
			Very Dark Blue cab and trailer, 'HALLS MENTHO-LYPTUS' labels	**£15-25**
			Maroon cab and trailer, 'LMS LIVERPOOL ROAD' transfers	**£15-25**
			Maroon cab and trailer, 'SPRATTS BONIO' transfers	**£15-25**
			Maroon cab and trailer, 'REA EXPRESS' transfers	**£15-25**
703	1984	**Austin FX4 Taxi**	As no.101 but in window box. Black, Silver, Met.Dk.Pink, Gold, Dark Green, Grey or White	**£15-25**
704	1984	**AEC Routemaster Bus**	Yellow / Red body with windows, 'SHOP LINKER' labels, casting as 236	**£15-25**
705	1984	**AEC Routemaster Bus**	Silver body with windows, '25 FAITHFUL YEARS' labels, casting as 236	**£15-25**
706	1984	**AEC Routemaster Bus**	Yellow / Red with windows, 'Watford FA Cup Final 84' labels, 236 casting	**£15-25**

Budgie Gift Sets

No. 4	1961	**Gift Set No.4**	Contains four models. Price depends on contents which vary	**£125-165**
No. 5	1961	**Gift Set No.5**	Contains five models. Price depends on contents which vary	**£150-200**

Seerol Models

-	1985	**Austin FX4 Taxi**	Re-issue of Budgie no.101 with amended base lettering and low friction wheels. Black body, 106mm. Still available	**£15-25**
-	1985	**Rolls-Royce Silver Cloud**	Re-issued Budgie 102, amended lettering, low friction wheels. Black, Silver, White, Yellow, Dark Blue, Pink or Maroon, 107 mm. Still available	**£15-25**
-	1985	**AEC Routemaster Bus**	New design, 1:76 scale, 108 mm. Was available from London souvenir outlets till the late 1990s.	
-			Red, Light Green or Dark Green, 'Houses of Parliament Tower Bridge' labels	**£15-25**
-			Red, 'The Original London Transport Sightseeing Tour' labels	**£15-25**
-			Red, 'Greetings from London' tampo print	**£15-25**
-			Red, 'Tower of London' tampo print	**£15-25**
-			Red, 'Petticoat Lane' tampo print	**£15-25**
-			Red, 'Buckingham Palace' tampo print	**£15-25**

Budgie Leaflets and Catalogues

A leaflet was included in the box with most Budgie Toys. Dates are not shown on any except the 1963 and 1964 catalogues.

-	1959	**Leaflet**	Printed on one side only. 'Budgie Toys Speak for Themselves' at top.	
		1st version:	Includes the Six-horse Covered Wagon	**£20-30**
		2nd version:	Timber Transporter replaces the Covered Wagon	**£20-30**
-	1960	**Leaflet**	'Budgie Toys Speak for Themselves' on front, 'Budgie Toys for Girls and Boys' on reverse	**£20-30**
-	1961	**Leaflet**	'Budgie Toys Speak for Themselves' on Black background	**£20-30**
	1961	**Trade catalogue**	Fold-out leaflet showing Noddy items, Wagon Train and Budgie miniatures as well as the main Budgie range. Separate price list marked 'Price List 1961' showing wholesale and retail prices	**£40-50**
-	1962	**Leaflet**	'Die-Cast Models by Budgie They Speak for Themselves' on Black background.	
		1st version:	268 AA Land Rover on front, 258 Daimler Ambulance on reverse	**£10-15**
		2nd version:	214 Mobile Crane on front, 266 Express Delivery Motorcycle on reverse	**£10-15**
-	1963	**Leaflet**	'Die-Cast Models by Budgie They Speak for Themselves' on Black background.	
		1st version:	278 RAC Land Rover on front, 258 Daimler Ambulance on reverse	**£10-15**
		2nd version:	278 RAC Land Rover on front, 266 Express Delivery Motorcycle on reverse	**£10-15**
-	1963	**Trade Catalogue** (8 pages)	Landscape format, includes retail price list	**£30-40**
-	1964	**Trade Catalogue** (8 pages)	'Budgie Models' on cover (portrait format). Includes retail price list	**£30-40**

Sales aids

Shop Display Unit: Five tiers, yellow / blue / red, with 'BUDGIE DIECAST MODELS' plus perching 'Budgie' logo **£200-250**

Shop Display Unit: 'The ESSO Petrol Pump Series': '1/6d each', 'A MORESTONE PRODUCT'. Features twenty models on four shelves .... NGPP

The 'River Series'

A trademark owned by M/s Jordan and Lewden of Homerton, London E9. Note that, while 'River Series' models were cast using tools supplied by DCMT, they had no other connection with DCMT. The Jordan and Lewden company started to offer diecast toys to the toy trade from about 1953 and continued to do so for only a few years. Dies were eventually sold to the Habonim firm in Israel and models subsequently appeared in the 'Gamda' series of toys. Some examples are known to have been produced in New Zealand by Lincoln Industries (who were also responsible for some 'lookalike' Matchbox models). Only 'Made in England' and the car name appear on the diecast

base of each model. None of the models acquired window glazing while made as 'River Series' – some did when produced as 'Gamda' toys.

These car models came in various colours and had cast hubs / rubber tyres where friction-motor fitted, otherwise one-piece rubber wheels.

Ford Prefect ....NGPP
American Buick ....NGPP
Daimler Conquest..NGPP
Austin Somerset ....NGPP
Standard Vanguard II Saloon ....NGPP
Standard Vanguard Estate.............................NGPP

These larger items were also available in various colours, some have clockwork motor, most have one-piece cast wheels, and some were boxed.

Cattle Truck...NGPP
Car Carrier ....NGPP
Excavator Truck ....NGPP
Tower Wagon ....NGPP
Cattle Truck...NGPP

The Editor would welcome any additional information on the 'River Series'.

'River Series' American Buick

'River Series' Austin Somerset

Scale Models Ltd. (Scamold)

Manufactured between 1939 and 1950 by Scale Models Ltd from whose title the model name was obtained. The models are extremely accurate 1/35 scale diecast models, with their original measurements being taken from the real racing cars at the famous Brooklands race track. Pre-war boxes state 'MANUFACTURED BY SCALE MODELS LTD, BROOKLANDS TRACK, WEYBRIDGE, ENG.'. This was dropped after the war. The proprietor of Scale Models Ltd was a Mr Tilley who wound up the business in the 1960s.

The model detail and castings are outstanding, with features such as removeable exhausts, spring suspension, steering wheels and dashboards. In addition the back axle could be exchanged for one containing a clockwork motor which was

wound up by a long starting handle. The wheel axles were crimped and the hubs were either brass (early) or aluminium (later) with black treaded rubber tyres.

Scamold kits were also available. The kit models had detailed features similar to the production issues including a working differential gear. In addition, it was also possible to fit a flywheel type motor which was activated by turning a 'starting handle'.

This information on Scamold models and kits has been kindly provided by Mr R.N. Eason-Gibson.The Editor would welcome additional information on this small but fascinating range.

SCAMOLD PRODUCTION MODELS

101	1939-50	**ERA Racing Car** ....Blue (Light or Dark), Green (Light or Dark), Yellow, White or Black body...................................**£150-200**
103	1939-50	**Maserati Racing Car** ....Red, Blue, Green (Mid or Dark), Silver body **£150-200**
105	1939-50	**Alta Racing Car** ....Green (Mid or Dark), Silver, White or Blue..**£150-200**

SCAMOLD KITS

Austin 7 Single-seater 750cc, Bugatti Type 35, 'E'-type E.R.A. (prototype only), Brooklands Riley, MG (planned type not known), Bentley LeMans Tourer and Maserati Racing Car.

Mobil Midget Fun-Ho! Series

Manufactured and distributed by the Underwood Engineering Co. Ltd, Mamaku Street, Inglewood, New Zealand.

Market Price Range. Most small cars and trucks etc. **£20-30.** Exceptions: No.7 BOAC Observation Coach **£40-50,** No.9 VW Beetle **£40-50,** No.11 Morris Mini Minor **£80-90,** No.2 Vauxhall Velox **£30-40,** No.? Morris 1100 **£40-50,** No.17 Austin Mini **£80-90,** No.23 Mark 10 Jaguar **£80-90,** No.25 MG Sports **£80-100**; No.43 E Type Jaguar **£80-90.**
Larger Commercials/Emergency vehicles etc.:
Nos.18, 21, 22, 27, 31, 35, 36, 40 **£30-40.**

Technical Information. Models from No.10 are 1:80 scale. Early models 1-32 1963-66 were all either chrome or copper plated. Painted finishes were introduced in 1966. Boxed models 1-18 include a folded leaflet in black and white giving details of the first 18 models and all have Black plastic wheels. Similarly the later issues contained leaflets showing the complete 1-46 model range as per the above leaflet.

'Fun Ho!' Mighty Mover Sets
1 Army Construction Battalion Kit Set: Contains six Military models, Bulldozer, Cement Mixer, Road Roller, Earth Mover, JCB, Land Rover, Brown display box **£50-60**
2 Civilian Road Construction Set: Yellow/Silver Bulldozer, Red/Silver Bedford Lorry, Green Aveling Road Roller, Blue Earth Mover, Red/Blue Ford Sand Dumper, Yellow JCB, Red window display box **£50-60**
3 Fire Service Kit Set: Contains six Red models, 21 Fire Engine, Jeep, Pick Up, Artic Lorry, Rescue Truck, Fire Van with Blue light, Red window display box **£50-60**

Later issues (c.1965?) Window Boxes
48 Ford, Brown/Green, Two-tone Green or Maroon White body **£10-15,** 49 Ford Sand Dumper, Red/Blue body **£10-15,** 50 Ford Dumper **£10-15,** 51 Ford Articulated Truck **£15-20,** 52 Sand Dumper Trailer **£5-10**

Shackleton Models

The company was formed by Maurice Shackleton and traded as James Shackleton & Sons Ltd. from 1939 to 1952. They had premises in Cheshire and originally produced wooden toys such as lorries and dolls houses. The toy lorries were only made pre-war and had four wheels, a simple wooden chassis and body with a green name badge on the rear of the cab, and were fitted with a highly detailed aluminium radiator grille. Known models are a Chain Lorry, Breakdown Lorry and a Sided Wagon. Their price today is around £100 each.

In 1948 having expanded its staff to nearly 40 people, the company started to produce diecast constructional models based on the Foden FG six-wheel platform lorry. The models consisted of separate parts all of which were, incredibly, made 'in house', including the clockwork motor, its key, and the wheels and tyres. The models were advertised in the 'Meccano Magazine' with the slogan 'You can dismantle it - Just like the real thing', and they were originally priced at £2/19/6. Eventually the range was extended to include a Dyson Drawbar Trailer and a Foden Tipper. Each model was packed in its own distinctive box which displayed a black and white picture of the model inside.

In 1952, whilst in the midst of producing the David Brown Trackmaster 30, Tractor, a shortage of materials coupled with difficult trading conditions brought about the end of the company. Some remaining models from this period were acquired and distributed by Chad Valley. The unique models produced by the Shackleton company are now highly collectable and difficult to find.

Note: It is known that some prototype models of Ploughs and Harrows were made, though it is not known if any were produced for sale.

---	1948-52	**Foden FG 6-wheel Platform Lorry**	Yellow, Blue, Grey or Green body with Red wings, Grey chassis and Red or Grey fuel tanks, 12½ inches (305 mm.) long, initially in Blue/Yellow box, later in mottled Green box, (20,000 made)	**£300-400**
			Same colours as above but with Grey or Black wings and Red chassis	**£500-600**
			Same casting but with Red, Orange or Brown cab	**£500-600**
		NB Box difficult to find:	Blue box with paper label having picture of chassis.	
---	1949-52	**Dyson 8-ton Drawbar Trailer**	Yellow, Blue, Grey or Green body, packed in Red and Yellow box, (15,000)	**£150-200**
---	1950-52	**Foden FG 6-wheel Tipper Lorry**	Yellow, Blue, Grey or Green body with Red wings, Grey chassis and Red or Grey fuel tanks, Silver wheels, (5,000)	**£500-600**
			As previous models but with Grey wings and Red chassis	**£500-600**
			As previous models but with Blue wings, Grey chassis, Grey wheels	**£500-600**
			Orange or Red body	**£500-600**
---	1952	**David Brown Trackmaster 30 Tractor**	Red body, Black rubber tracks, 10 inches long, boxed. Only 50 models thought to exist	**£1,000-1,250**
---	1958-60	**Foden S21 8-wheel Platform Lorry**	Dark Blue, Dark Green or Light Turquoise fibreglass cab with Red metal chassis and wheels, wooden flatbed, length overall 18½ inches (470 mm), plastic injection moulded springs and axle parts, powered by 'Minimax' electric motor. (250 made as a promotional for Foden)	**£1,000-1,250**

The information in this listing has been taken from an original article written by John Ormandy in the 'Modellers World' magazine, Volumes 12 and 13, and is used by kind permission of the Editors, Mike and Sue Richardson. Robert Taylor provided additional information. Gary Irwin contributed information on the DB Trackmaster.

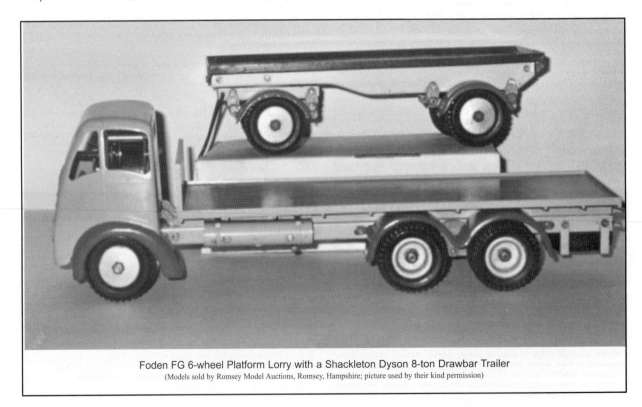

Foden FG 6-wheel Platform Lorry with a Shackleton Dyson 8-ton Drawbar Trailer
(Models sold by Romsey Model Auctions, Romsey, Hampshire; picture used by their kind permission)

Taylor and Barrett Lead Vehicles and the Postwar Re-issues

by Mike Richardson

The firm of Taylor and Barrett dates from the early 1920s when they started producing mainly figures but with a few odd carts. The vehicles themselves were only introduced in about 1935. These were rather crude by comparison with the Dinky Toys of the day as the lead gravity casting process was incapable of working to the fine limits possible with pressure diecasting as used by Meccano Ltd. The majority of the vehicles use a basic chassis incorporating the bonnet and wings. Different bodies are attached to this base unit by tabs and a radiator is plugged into the front. Some versions have the grille cast integrally with the bonnet, and most of these use plain metal wheels instead of having rubber tyres. These vehicles have a tremendous amount of charm as toys while they are only a generic representation of the types of vans and small trucks of the time.

A wide variety of types were made including petrol tankers, a pick-up truck and a couple of mail vans. The breakdown truck is particularly attractive with a working crane on the rear. These toys were made until the production was halted in 1940 when the factory was bombed out of existence. All salvageable tools, moulds and stock was moved to a new location in North Finchley but production stopped very soon after because of the munitions requirements of the war effort.

During the war the tools were split between the Taylors and the Barretts for safe keeping but they did not join up again afterwards and two separate companies, F.G.Taylor & Sons and A.Barrett & Sons, started up in 1945. The main part of the range, the small commercial vehicles and the cars, does not seem to have survived the War, only the trolley buses, which became Barretts, and the Leyland coach which appeared in one-piece casting form as a Taylor. It is interesting to note that the trolleybus carries a route board '621 Finchley' which probably means that they went past the factory.

A range of very nice fire engines came along in the late 1930s with a super turntable ladder appliance as the top of the range. These were longer than the main range and had many parts. To mark the advent of the Home Office Fire Precautions scheme (where fire appliances were made available to local areas by central government), Taylor and Barrett painted their range in grey as well as the more traditional red. These grey models are highly sought after now.

Personnel were also available to go with these fire engines. A 'Decontamination Squad' being a particular favourite with their gas masks and chemical-proof overalls. There is also a less impressive fire engine in the short chassis range.

The trolley buses came in two sizes. The large one has a separate driver figure (and conductor as well in the T & B version but not the later Barrett), and the body is in two pieces, upper and lower decks. The small one is in one piece and has no driver. Needless to say there is a vast difference in the values of the two sizes.

There are generic cars, roadster, coupé, saloon, on the short base but there is also quite a good model of the 1935 Singer Airstream saloon. This is also the poor man's Chrysler Airflow but never really caught on, the styling made the car look too tall to be appealing. A rather crude one-piece Austin Seven racer was the final car but this was to a larger scale.

Dinky Toys were not the only factory to make a model of the Air Mail Service Car based on the Morris Commercial chassis. T & B also made one and a nice chunky toy it is too. A couple of aeroplanes, a De Havilland Comet and an air liner, completed the range of powered vehicles. A modified version of the Comet seems to have been made by Barrett later but it differs a lot from the T & B, which is a much better model.

Some of the moulds were still around a few years ago and some attempts were made to make models again. These were fairly unsuccessful as casting techniques had changed and the new metals did not have the same flow characteristics as the early lead. Some models are definitely known to have been re-made as they have been seen at a swapmeet some time back, so collectors are advised to be wary.

Editor's note: All the models are rare - any auction prices that become available will be published in subsequent editions of this Catalogue.

The following listing is of models issued by Taylor and Barrett between 1920 and 1939. Post war production was split between F. G. Taylor & Sons and A. Barrett & Sons, each firm inheriting some moulds and continuing to make some but not all of the models until about 1952.
(FGT) = produced by F. G. Taylor after 1945, **(AB)** = produced by A. Barrett after 1945, **(-)** = date and company not known for certain,
NGPP = no price grading possible at present.

14	**Trotting Pony Racer** (FGT)	**£80-100**
15	**Turntable Fire Escape and 3 Firemen** (AB)	**£200-300**
16	**Fire Engine and Escape and 3 Firemen** (FGT)	**£200-300**
17	**Fire Engine and 3 Firemen** (FGT)	**£200-300**
20	**Horse Drawn Water Cart** (FGT)	**£300-400**
21	**Horse Drawn Brewer's Cart** (FGT)	**£100-200**
22	**Horse Drawn Window Cleaner's Cart** (FGT)	**£100-200**
23	**Horse Drawn Baker's Cart** (FGT)	**£100-200**
26	**Roman Chariot** (FGT)	**£25-35**
27	**Donkey Drawn Coster Cart with Dog and Boy** (FGT)	**£80-100**
28	**Donkey Drawn Coster Cart, Plants load, Walking Coster** (FGT)	**£80-100**
28a	**Donkey Drawn Coster Cart, Vegetable load, Walking Coster** (FGT)	**£80-100**
29	**Ice Cream Bicycle, 'ICE BRICKS'** (FGT)	**£200-300**
36	**Milk Float and Milkman, 'EXPRESS DAIRY'** (AB)	**£250-350**
42	**Fire Escape and Team of Firemen** (FGT)	**£200-300**
43	**Air and Land Postal Service Set** (-)	**£300-400**
45	**Road and Traffic Set** (-) Traffic island with bollards and street lamp, 2 swivelling traffic lights, school and 30mph signs, 2 Belisha beacons, pavement sections (2 straight, 2 corners). 45mm figures of lady and gentleman, 2 children (on base), mounted policeman, traffic policeman. Boxed	**£200-250**
49	**Street Cleaning Barrow with two Bins** (FGT)	**£80-100**
92	**Llama Cart** (FGT)	**£40-60**
92a	**Donkey Cart** (FGT)	**£40-60**
109	**Pony Drawn Governor's Cart** (AB)	**£40-60**
109a	**Pony Drawn Cart** (AB)	**£40-60**
111	**Saloon Car** (-)	**£80-100**
112	**Transport Lorry** (-)	**£80-100**
113	**'ROYAL MAIL' Van** (-)	**£150-200**
114	**'AMBULANCE', Grey (Wartime civilian)** (-)	**£150-200**
114a	**'AMBULANCE', Khaki (Army)** (-)	**£150-200**
115	**Sports Car** (-)	**£100-200**
116	**Coupé** (-)	**£100-200**
117	**'AMBULANCE', (Street, civilian)** (-)	**£80-100**
119	**Racer** (AB)	**£40-60**
120	**Fire Engine** (AB)	**£60-80**
123	**Atlanta Touring Plane** (AB)	**£100-125**
124	**'AIR MAIL' Van** (AB)	**£100-125**
128	**Petrol Tanker** (-)	**£100-125**
129	**Breakdown Lorry** (-)	**£80-100**
137	**DH 'Comet' Aeroplane** (AB)	**£80-100**
138	**'AIR MAIL' Streamline Van** (-)	**£175-225**
139	**Saloon Car** (-)	**£50-60**
152	**Streamline Motor Coach** (-)	**£100-150**
163	**Streamline Fire Engine** (-)	**£100-125**
197	**Trolley Bus** (small) (AB)	**£100-200**
204	**Trolley Bus** (large) (AB)	**£300-400**
302	**Horse Drawn Covered Wagon** (-)	**£60-80**
304	**Sledge and Dogs** (FGT)	**£60-80**
306	**Aeroplane Set** (Comet, Atlanta and pilots) (FGT)	**£120-150**
307	**Fire Brigade Set** (-)	**£300-400**
310	**Rickshaw pulled by Chinese Coolie** (FGT)	**£100-150**
311	**Light Trailer Fire Pump in Action Set** (-)	**£100-150**
?	**Space Ship** (-)	**NGPP**
?	**Coronation Coach** (small) (AB)	**£30-50**
?	**State Landau Coach** (-)	**£40-60**
?	**Farmer's Gig** (FGT)	**£80-100**
?	**Farm Cart with Trotting Horse** (-)	**£80-100**
?	**Mobile Animal Trailer and Vet** (-)	**£80-100**
---	**Racing Car**, Red body with 'MG Magnette' cast into side, 110 mm. 'FGT & SONS'	**£100-125**
---	**Petrol Pumps**, Black/White with rubber hoses (T&B)	**£80-100**
---	**'CASTROL' Oil Pump**, Green/Red, sliding cover (AB)	**£20-30**
---	**Village Blacksmith Set**, contains blacksmith, forge with hood, anvil, Shire horse. In 2-part card box	**£150-175**
---	**Fire Car**, Red, with 3 figures	**£175-200**

The listing has been compiled from original manufacturer's records by Mr Norman Joplin to whom the Editor would like to express his gratitude.
Thanks are also due to Mr J.R. Anderson of Queensland, Australia and Ross Kennett of Roscoes Relics, South Australia, Australia for kindly sending new model information.

Robert Newson has provided this history and listing of cast metal Timpo motor vehicles.

The name Timpo comes from 'Toy Importers Ltd'. It was only with the outbreak of war in 1939 that Timpo started to manufacture their own lines, when importing became impossible. A few vehicles were made in 1940-41, but the main Timpo range started in 1946. The models were cheap and sturdy, if somewhat crude, and many have survived. Relatively few suffer from metal deterioration. In 1949 Timpo advertised 'faithful replicas of famous delivery services' and introduced several vans with attractive advertising liveries. An AEC Monarch lorry in the livery of Vaux brewery was introduced around 1950, and this

was a far better model than the earlier toys. Sadly it was not the first of a new range - the 1951-2 ban on the use of zinc meant that Timpo discontinued all their diecast vehicles. Some of the dies were subsequently sold to Benbros, including the AEC lorry.

Timpo Toys are very rarely seen in mint condition, and prices are therefore quoted for good original condition. Dates given are the approximate year of introduction.

NB See the 'Miscellaneous Models' colour section for a picture of a Timpo model.

Intro	Model name	Details	MPR
1940	MG Record Car	Hollow-cast lead. Red, 'TIMPO TOYS' cast on side, 98 mm	£50-75
1940	Streamlined Saloon	Separate body and chassis. 'Timpo' in script underneath. 99 mm	£30-40
1940	Pick-Up Truck	Separate body and chassis. 'Timpo' in script underneath. Re-issued post-war with name blanked out. 99 mm	£30-40
1940	Four-light Saloon	Possibly re-issue of a Goody Toy	NGPP
1946	MG Record Car	Zinc diecast. 'TIMPO TOYS' cast at rear on offside. 97 mm	£50-75
1946	'American Star' Racer	Star transfer on each side, 101 mm	£40-50
1946	'Timpo Saloon'	Vaguely like a Morris 8. 93 mm	£40-50
1946	Austin 16 Saloon	Black. 'TIMPO TOYS' underneath. 96 mm. Re-issued by Betal in four versions:	£40-50
		1. No name on model, brass wheel hubs	£30-40
		2. 'A BETAL PRODUCT' under roof, tin base with friction motor, brass wheel hubs	£30-40
		3. As 2. but with plastic body	£30-40
		4. As 3. but with clockwork motor and solid metal wheels	£30-40
1946	MG Midget	Composition wheels. 82 mm	£30-40
1946	Packard Saloon	Fitted with aluminium baseplate and friction motor from 1948. 113 mm	£30-40
1946	'Speed of the Wind' Record Car	Similar to the Dinky Toy. 99 mm	£40-50
1946	No.1 'Arctic' Set	Sledge and dog team, Eskimo with whip, another with rifle, walking stick, 2 penguins, 2 seals, polar bear, snowy hedge and igloo. Boxed	£400-600
1947	Alvis 14 Saloon	A big four-light saloon. 106 mm	£30-40
1947	Utility Van	With aluminium baseplate and friction motor from 1948. (Early casting 102mm, later 104mm).	
		1. No transfers, plain colours, without motor	£10-15
	'TYRESOLES'	2. Black, 'TYRESOLES SERVICE' transfers, no motor	£200-300
	'HMV'	3. 'HIS MASTER'S VOICE' transfers, pale Yellow, Orange-Yellow, pale Blue or Green, with or without motor	£200-300
1947	Artic. Petrol Tanker	No transfers. Re-issued by Benbros. 149 mm	£30-40
		Red/white body, 'ESSO' logo	£80-120
1947	Lincoln Convertible	Vaguely like a 1942 Lincoln. Aluminium baseplate and windscreen. Usually single colours. Late version in cream with blue seats. 115 mm	£30-40
1947	Armstrong-Siddeley Hurricane	A coupé with top up. 105 mm	£30-40
1947	Streamlined Fire Engine	Red, 2 yellow aluminium ladders. Aluminium baseplate + friction motor from '49. 105 mm	£30-40
1947	Artic. Box Van	Re-issued by Benbros. 146 mm. Boxed.	
		1. Green, Blue or Red trailer with	
	'TIMPO'	'TIMPO TOYS' transfers	£160-190
		2. Black cab and trailer with Grey roof,	
	'PICKFORDS'	Red wheel hubs, 'PICKFORDS' transfers	£140-170
		3. Orange cab and trailer, Black roof,	
	'UNITED DAIRIES'	'UNITED DAIRIES' transfers	£140-170
		4. Light Blue cab, Light Blue and Cream	
	'WALL'S'	trailer, 'WALL'S ICE CREAM' transfers	£140-170
		5. Dark Blue cab and trailer with off-White	
		roof, 'LYONS TEA' transfers	£140-170
		6. Pale Yellow cab and trailer, transfers with	
	'BISHOPS'	'BISHOPS MOVE' logo and 'BISHOP & SONS DEPOSITORIES LTD. 10-12 BELGRAVE ROAD LONDON, S.W.1'	£140-170
		7. Same, but transfers with 'BISHOPS MOVE'	
	'BISHOPS/LUNN'	logo and 'JOHN H. LUNN LTD. 6 HOPE CRESCENT EDINBURGH'	£140-170
1947	London Taxi	Cast in two parts. 94 mm	£20-25

Intro	Model name	Details	MPR
1947	Alvis 14 Police Car	Police sign and loudspeakers at front of roof, wire aerial behind. Black. 106 mm	£50-75
1947	Artic. Low Loader	Re-issued by Benbros. 168 mm	£10-15
1947	Buick Saloon	Crude model, composition wheels. 99 mm	£10-15
1947	Pick-Up Truck	With eight cast-in barrels. 104 mm	£15-20
1947	Forward Control Tipper Lorry	Cream cab and chassis, Red tipper. 101 mm	£15-20
1947	Forward Control Luton Van	Same chassis as the tipper. 97 mm. boxed.	
		1. No transfers, black lower, light blue upper	£15-20
	'SMITH'S'	2. Dark blue, 'SMITH'S CRISPS' transfers	£120-150
	'WILLS'	3. Brown, 'W.D. & H.O. WILLS' transfers	£120-150
1949	Forward Control Box Van	Same chassis as above. Re-issued by Benbros.	
	'CHIVERS'	Dark blue, 'CHIVERS JELLIES' transfers	£120-150
1949	Normal Control Box Van	Later models with aluminium baseplate and friction motor. 105 mm. Models were boxed.	
	'EVER READY'	1. Dark Blue with White roof, 'EVER READY' transfers, motor in some	£120-150
	'GOLDEN SHRED'	2. Green, 'GOLDEN SHRED', with motor	£120-150
	'MELTONIAN'	3. Green, 'MELTONIAN SHOE CREAM' transfers, with motor	£120-150
1949	Normal Control Petrol Tanker 'ESSO'	Red, 'MOTOR OIL ESSO PETROL' on paper labels. Re-issued by Benbros. 116 mm	£120-150
1950	AEC Monarch Brewery Lorry	Red. 'VAUX' cast on headboard behind cab, 'SUNDERLAND' cast on cab sides. Boxed. Brown hollow-cast barrels with 'VAUX' cast on ends. Re-issued by Benbros without the headboard + other changes. 129 mm	£120-150
1940s	Bomber Station Set	3 x twin-fuselage aircraft, 2 x twin-engined, single-fuselage aircraft and a single-engined fighter. Box has a pictorial label on its lift-off lid	£150-200
No.249	Hopalong Cassidy Series Set	Contains 7 cowboys including Hopalong Cassidy, Lucky, California, etc. Boxed	£800-1,000
	Petrol Station No.2 Set	Saloon Car and Racing Car plus 3 Personnel and 5 Pumps. Pictorial box lid states: 'THE FAMOUS TIMPO CARS'	£150-200
	Station Figures Set	Contains Station Master, Porter with trolley, Porter with luggage, Signalman with flag, Signalman with whistle, Railwayman with lamps, Mr Brown, boy hiker, lady with bag, girl in red coat. Boxed	£500-750
	Tiger Hunt Set	Contains elephant, elephant with mahouts, Maharaja, hunter, 2 tigers, 4 bears. Boxed	£500-750
	Farm Series Set	15 piece dairy / poultry set	£300-350
	Gypsy Organ Grinder with Dancing Bear		£50-70

Timpo figures.

Knights of the Round Table and Ivanhoe figures. Each		£15-20
Policeman, Policewoman, Zoo Keeper, Farm Girls. Each		£15-20
Station Passengers (as in set), Soldier with Kitbag. Each		£15-20
Super heroes: Captain Marvel, Mary Marvel, Marvel Junior. Each		£15-20
Wild West: Seated cowboys with guitars, Indian chief, squaw with papoose. Each		£15-20

MARKET PRICE RANGE   Please note that for MPR purposes, the models have been assumed to be boxed where appropriate and in good condition.

Tri-ang Minic Ships

Minic ships are accurately detailed waterline models made between 1958 and 1964 to a scale of 1:1,200 (1in to 100ft).
Six sales catalogues were published which nowadays are quite hard to find.
No single catalogue shows the full range.
Minic ships re-introduced in 1976 were fitted with wheels and have 'Hong Kong' on the base.

Ocean Liners

Ref	Model name	Colours, features, details	Market Price Range
M701	RMS 'Caronia'	Green body, one plain Red/Black or detailed funnel, one mast, 178 mm. 'Painted in the correct Cunard green she is a most striking vessel'.	£55-75
M702	RMS 'Queen Elizabeth'	Black/White, 2 plain Red/Black or detailed funnels, 2 masts, 262 mm. 'The worlds largest ship and the pride of the Cunard fleet'.	£65-85
M703	RMS 'Queen Mary'	Black/White, plain Red/Black or detailed funnels, 2 masts, 259 mm. 'Her three funnels make her the most easily recognisable'.	£55-75
M704	SS 'United States'	Black/White body, two Red/White/Blue funnels, 252 mm. 'The present holder of the Blue Riband of the Atlantic'.	£55-75
M705	RMS 'Aquitania'	Black/White body, four Red/Black funnels, two masts, 231 mm.	£150-200
M706	SS 'Nieuw Amsterdam'	Grey/White body, two Yellow funnels, two masts, 192 mm.	£55-75
M707	SS 'France'	Black/White, 2 Red/Black funnels, 5 masts, 262 mm. 'The longest ship in the world – 1035ft, being 4ft longer than Queen Elizabeth'.	£125-150
M708	RMS 'Saxonia'	Black/White body, one Red/Black or detailed funnel, nine masts, cargo handling gear on stern	£50-75
M708/2	RMS 'Franconia'	Green body, one Red/Black funnel, nine Green masts, 155 mm, swimming pool on stern. 480 made.	£500-750
M709	RMS 'Ivernia'	Black/White or Green body, 155mm, cargo handling gear on stern.	£50-75
M709/2	RMS 'Carmania'	Green body, one Red/Black funnel, nine Green masts, 155 mm, swimming pool on stern. 480 made.	£500-750
M710	RMS 'Sylvania'	Black/White, one Red/Black funnel, nine masts, 155 mm.	£45-55
M711	RMS 'Carinthie'	Black/White, one Red/Black funnel, nine masts, 155 mm.	£45-55
M712	NS 'Savannah'	White, no funnels (nuclear powered), four masts, 149 mm.	£55-75
M713	SS 'Antilles'	Black/White, one Red/Black funnel, ten masts, 152 mm. All White body, one Red/Black funnel, ten masts	£60-80 / £70-90
M714	'Flandre'	Black/White, one Red/Black funnel, ten masts, 152 mm. All White body, one Red/Black funnel, ten masts	£45-65 / £55-75
M715	RMS 'Canberra'	White body, one Yellow funnel, three masts, 189 mm.	£65-85
M716	MS 'Port Brisbane'	Grey/White, one Red/Black funnel, eight masts, 140 mm.	£110-140
M717	SS 'Port Auckland'	Grey/White, one Red/Black funnel, seven masts, 140 mm.	£110-140
M718	RMS 'Amazon'	White, Yellow funnel, 19 masts, 10 lifeboats, 149 mm.	£125-150
M719	RMS 'Arlanza'	White, Yellow funnel, 19 masts, 149 mm.	£125-150
M720	RMS 'Aragon'	White, Yellow funnel, 19 masts, 149 mm.	£125-150
M721	RMS 'Britannia'	The Royal Yacht. Blue/White body, Yellow/Black funnel, 3 masts, 105 mm.	£50-75
M721/H	RMS 'Britannia'	Hospital Ship. White body, three masts, 105 mm.	£50-75

Smaller craft

CHANNEL ISLANDS STEAMERS (78mm long)

M722	'Isle of Jersey'	Black/White, 2 Yellow/Black funnels, 2 masts	£25-35
M723	'Isle of Guernsey'	Black/White, 2 Yellow/Black funnels, 2 masts	£25-35
M724	'Isle of Sark'	Black/White body, 2 Yellow/Black funnels, 2 masts	£25-35
M726	'PILOTS' Boat	Black/White/Yellow, 45 mm.	£75-95
M727	Lifeboat	Blue body	£25-35

PADDLE STEAMERS (all are 78 mm long)

M728	'Britannia'	Black/white, 2 funnels (black/blue, red/black or yellow/black), 2 masts	£25-35
M729	'Bristol Queen'	Black/white, 2 funnels (black/blue, red/black or yellow/black), 2 masts	£25-35
M730	'Cardiff Queen'	Black/White, 2 funnels (Black/Blue, Red/Black or Yellow/Black), 2 masts	£25-35

OIL TANKER

M732	SS 'Varicella'	Black/White body, Black/Yellow funnel ('SHELL' logo), 2 masts, 169 mm.	£40-60

WHALE FACTORY SHIPS

M733	TSS 'Vikingen'	Grey body, six masts, 125 mm.	£30-50
M734	Whale Chaser	Grey, Yellow/Black funnel, 39 mm.	£25-35

TUGBOATS (all except 'Turmoil' are 38mm long)

M731	Tugboat	Black/Grey/Red, Red/Black funnel	£10-15
M731	Tugboat	Black/Grey/Red, Yellow/Black funnel	£10-15
M731	Tugboat	Black/Blue/Red, Yellow/Black funnel	£10-15
M731	Tugboat	Black/Grey/Yellow, Yellow/Black funnel	£10-15
M740	Barge	Intended to match M731, but not issued	NPP
M810	Navy Tug HMS 'Turmoil'	Black/Blue or Grey, Black funnel, 50 mm.	£25-35

LIGHTSHIPS (all are 33mm long)

M735	'SUNK'	Red body, White logo/name	£25-35
M736	'SHAMBLES'	Red body, White logo/name	£25-35
M737	'CORK'	Red body, White logo/name	£25-35
M738	'VARNE'	Red body, White logo/name	£25-35
M739	'St GOWAN'	Red body, White logo/name, no number on base	£25-35

Tri-ang Minic Warships

BATTLESHIP
M741 HMS 'Vanguard' .....Grey or Blue, two masts, 206 mm **£35-55**

AIRCRAFT CARRIERS
M751 HMS 'Bulwark' ....Grey or Blue, one mast, 186 mm **£35-55**
M752 HMS 'Centaur' ....Grey or Blue body with one mast **£35-55**
M753 HMS 'Albion'..........Grey or Blue body with one mast **£35-55**

COMMANDO SHIP
M754 HMS 'Albion'..........Grey ship with 12 Cream or Brown plastic
          helicopters. 1,000 models issued and given to H.M.S. 'Albion'
          crew members (Capt. Adams in command)............................**£500-750**

CRUISERS
M761 HMS 'Swiftsure' ......Blue or Grey, one crane jib, 145 mm **£25-35**
M762 HMS 'Superb' ....Blue or Grey, one crane jib, 145 mm **£25-35**

DESTROYERS, FLEET ESCORT, 'DARING' CLASS
M771 HMS 'Daring' ....Blue or Grey, one mast, 98 mm **£25-35**
M772 HMS 'Diana' ....Blue or Grey, one mast, 98 mm **£25-35**
M773 HMS 'Dainty'..........Blue or Grey, one mast, 98 mm **£25-35**
M774 HMS 'Decoy' ....Blue or Grey, one mast, 98 mm **£25-35**

DESTROYERS, FLEET, 'BATTLE' CLASS
M779 HMS 'Alamein'.......Blue or Grey, one mast, 97 mm **£25-35**
M780 HMS 'Jutland' ....Blue or Grey, one mast, 97 mm **£25-35**
M781 HMS 'Anzac'..........Blue or Grey, one mast, 97 mm **£25-35**
M782 HMS 'Tobruk'.........Blue or Grey, one mast, 97 mm **£25-35**

DESTROYERS, GUIDED MISSILE, 'COUNTY' CLASS
M783 HMS 'Hampshire' ...Grey body with two masts, 136 mm **£45-55**

M784 HMS 'Kent'..............Grey body with two masts, 136 mm **£40-50**
M785 HMS 'Devonshire' ...Grey body with two masts, 136 mm **£40-50**
M786 HMS 'London'.........Grey body with two masts, 136 mm **£40-50**

FRIGATES, FAST ANTI-SUBMARINE, 'V' CLASS
M787 HMS 'Vigilant'........Blue or Grey, one mast, 92 mm **£25-35**
M788 HMS 'Venus'...........Blue or Grey, one mast, 92 mm **£25-35**
M789 HMS 'Virago'..........Blue or Grey, one mast, 92 mm **£25-35**
M790 HMS 'Volage'..........Blue or Grey, one mast, 92 mm **£25-35**

FRIGATES, ANTI-SUBMARINE, 'WHITBY' CLASS
M791 HMS 'Whitby' ....Blue or Grey body, 94 mm......................**£25-35**
M792 HMS 'Torquay'.......Blue or Grey body, 94 mm......................**£25-35**
M793 HMS 'Blackpool' .....Blue or Grey body, 94 mm......................**£25-35**
M794 HMS 'Tenby' ....Blue or Grey body, 94 mm......................**£25-35**

MINESWEEPERS, 'TON' CLASS
M799 HMS 'Repton'........Blue or Grey body **£25-35**
M800 HMS 'Dufton' ....Blue or Grey body **£25-35**
M801 HMS 'Ashton' ....Blue or Grey body **£25-35**
M802 HMS 'Calton' ....Blue or Grey body **£25-35**
M803 HMS 'Picton' ....Blue or Grey body **£25-35**
M804 HMS 'Sefton' ....Blue or Grey body **£25-35**
M805 HMS 'Upton'...........Blue or Grey body **£25-35**
M806 HMS 'Weston'........Blue or Grey body **£25-35**

SUBMARINES, 'A' CLASS
M817 Sub 'A' Class ....Blue or Grey body, 61 mm.....................**£10-15**
M818 Sub Recon...............Blue or Grey body, 61 mm.....................**£10-15**

Accessories, Gift Sets, Hong Kong issues and Catalogues

DOCKSIDE ACCESSORIES
M827   **Breakwater Straights**, Grey **£5**
M828/L   **Breakwater Angle**, Left, Grey **£1**
M828/R   **Breakwater Angle**, Right, Grey **£1**
M829   **Breakwater End**, Grey...................................**£1**
M836   **Quay Straights**,Tan **£5**
M837   **Crane Units**, Tan, Brown or Green cargo **£5**
M838   **Storage Tanks**, Grey/Silver and Red................**£5**
M839   **Customs Shed**, Green.....................................**£5**
M840   **Warehouse**, Brown **£5**
M841   **Ocean Terminal**, White with Black windows **£10**
M842   **Swing Bridge**, Red, no description on base **£8**
M843   **Terminal Extension**, White with Black windows **£10**
M844   **Lock Gates** (pair), Brown..............................**£3**
M845   **Landing Stages**, Cream 'L' shaped, 1in long **£3**
M846   **Lift Bridge**, Silver/Tan **£5**

M847   **Pier centre section**, White...............................**£5**
M848   **Pier entrance section**, White **£5**
M849   **Pier head**, White...**£20**
M850   **Pier Shelter**, Green, 35 mm **£10**
M851   **Pier archways** **£5**
M852   **Pier Building**, White/Blue/Green, Silver Cupola,
             'RESTAURANT' plus 'DANCING TONIGHT' **£15-20**

M853   **Factory Unit**, Pink and Buff, Black chimneys **£30-40**
M854   **Tanker Wharf Straight**, Cream and Red...............**£65-75**
M855   **Tanker Wharf Berth**, Red and Green or
             Cream and Green, Black plastic pipeline.................**£5**
M857   **26in Sea**, Blue plastic **£25-35**
M857   **52in Sea**, Blue plastic **£40-50**

M861   **Lifeboat set**, Grey, Blue shed, one lifeboat **£45-55**
M878   **Lighthouse**, White **£5**
M880   **Whales**, White or plain Grey **£15-20**
M882   **Beacon**, White/Red or Green............................**£5**
M884   **Statue of Liberty**, Green/Grey..........................**£30-40**
M885   **Floating Dock**, Grey, 4 Black plastic cranes **£25-35**
M -   **Helicopter**, Cream or Brown plastic **£30-35**

GIFT SETS and SPECIAL PRESENTATION PACKS
M891   'Queen Elizabeth' Gift Set...............................**£125-175**
M892   'United States' Gift Set.................................**£200-250**
M893   'Task Force' Gift Set......................................**£45-65**
M894   'Royal Yacht' Gift Set..................................**£125-150**
M895   'Nieuw Amsterdam' Gift Set.............................**£750-1,000**
M702s   'Queen Elizabeth' Presentation Set....................**£100-125**
M703s   'Queen Mary' Presentation Set.........................**£125-150**
M704s   SS 'United States' Presentation Set...................**£125-150**
M705s   RMS 'Aquitania' Presentation Set.....................**£150-200**
M707s   SS 'France' Presentation Set...........................**£150-200**
M741s   HMS 'Vanguard' Presentation Set **£75-100**

HONG KONG 'BLUE BOX' MODELS (1976-80)
These models are slightly larger than original issues, e.g., Canberra is 207mm.
'Queen Mary', 'Queen Elizabeth', 'United States', 'Canberra',
HMS 'Vanguard', HMS 'Bulwark', 'Missouri', 'Bismark',
'Scharnhorst', 'Yamato'. Each, boxed **£20-30**
RMS 'Canberra', boxed **£30-40**

HONG KONG SETS of MODELS
1   **Fleet Anchorage Set**, dockyard entrance scene on lid **£30-40**
2   **Quay Set**..**£**
3a   **Ocean Terminal**, lid shows stern of RMS 'Queen Mary'.....**£50-65**
3b   **Ocean Terminal**, lid shows bow of RMS 'Queen Mary'......**£40-50**
4   **Naval Task Force**, with HMS 'Bulwark' and 'Vanguard'....**£40-50**
5   **Naval Task Force**, with 'Bismark' and 'Scharnhorst'..........**£70-90**

MINIC CATALOGUES 1958-64
1   **Leaflet** ....with first Minic Ships listed....................**£100-125**
2   **Booklet** ....with first Minic Ships listed.....................**£25-30**
3   **Booklet** ....with Ships and other Tri-ang products........**£60-75**
4   **Booklet** ....with Minic Ships only............................**£25-30**
5   **Booklet** ....with Minic Ships only............................**£25-30**
6   **Booklet** ....with Tri-ang range...............................**£30-35**
M862   **Leaflet** ....Minic illustrated leaflet............................**£10-15**

Introduction

Spot-On Models were introduced in 1959 by Tri-ang Toys to gain a foothold in the diecast market dominated at the time by Dinky Toys and their recently established rivals Corgi Toys.

Tri-ang realised that they had to offer not only a range of features similar to those of their competitors' products but something more besides. They decided that collectors would appreciate models that were all made to the same precise scale right across the range.

The models would thus look right together and qualify as such rather than toys. Much of the Dinky and Corgi cars range was made to a scale of around 1:45 (with a few exceptions).

Tri-ang advertised the precise nature of their (larger) chosen scale as being 'spot-on' at 1:42.

A large modern factory was set up in Belfast, Northern Ireland to produce the models. A coloured picture of the real vehicle was included in the box of most early issues.

Well over a hundred different models were designed, the range being extended to include scale buildings and road signs. Production continued till the time that Tri-ang bought up Dinky Toys in 1967. After the cessation of UK production, some of the Spot-On dies went to New Zealand where some interesting versions were produced for a couple of years.

All Spot-On models are highly collectable today particularly commercial vehicles, buses and the Presentation and Gift Sets.

NB See the 'Miscellaneous Models' colour section for pictures.

Spot-On model identification

Makers Name and Trade Mark are clearly marked on base of the model ('SPOT-ON' and 'Models by Tri-ang'). Some New Zealand produced versions have nothing at all on the base.

Model Name is shown on the base (except some New Zealand versions) while the **Model Number** is usually shown on box but not always on the model.

Baseplates can be any of a variety of colours: black, silver, grey - even green has been observed on the base of a maroon version of No. 155 Taxi !

Scale of models is 1:42 (with very few exceptions) and is usually (but not always) shown on the base.

Wheel hubs on cars are usually turned aluminium with a raised 'hub cap'. Truck models usually have diecast and more accurate representations of real hubs. **Tyres** are mostly black rubber (occasionally plastic) on all the vehicle models. Rear twin wheels have special 'double tyres'.

Number plates are represented on most Spot-On models with the exception of those having plastic chassis (such as 266 Bull Nose Morris and 279 MG Midget). A large range of registration numbers were available to factory production staff and were applied randomly to most models. Different number plates are therefore to be expected on different examples of the same model and do not have any effect on the price.

Windscreens and windows are included in all vehicle models.
Other features include seats and steering wheel on most models, suspension on most cars, driver, other figures and lorry loads with some. Very few 'decals' or 'frills' is the norm.

Colours are all listed where known though different and previously unknown colours still come to light occasionally.

Prices shown in the 'Market Price Range' column are for mint models in pristine boxes. These models are rare, hence their high market prices. The condition of models generally encountered tends towards the average and consequently command lower prices. Similarly, rare colours or combinations of colours puts the price into the higher part of the range with common colours achieving a more moderate price level.

Spot-On Collector's Lapel Badge
Photo: Unique Collections of Chipstead

Ref	Model, year introduced	MPR

100 Ford Zodiac (without lights) (1959)
Red / Cream £80-100
Blue / Cream £80-100
Red body..£80-100
Cream body..£80-100
Yellow body £110-140
Light Blue £80-100
Salmon-Pink...£80-100
Green body..£80-100
Bluish-Grey/Brownish-Pink body .£100-125
Lt. Blue over Grey, Red interior....£100-120

100sl Ford Zodiac (with lights) (1959)
Grey/Turquoise £100-120
Grey/Pink body £100-120
Grey/White.......................................£100-120
Grey/Light Blue...............................£100-120
Green/White body.............................£100-120
Yellow/White...................................£100-120
Grey/Green.......................................£100-120
Two-tone Blue body £100-120

101 Armstrong Siddeley 236 Sapphire (1959)
Blue / Grey..£150-200
Turquoise / Black.............................£150-200
Blue / Black £150-200
Pink body..£150-200
Mauve body £150-200
Salmon body, Black roof £150-200
Mid-Green body, Dark Green roof
  Cream interior...............................£150-200
Light Blue body, Dark Blue roof...£150-175
Powder Green body £150-175
Metallic Green / Black.....................£150-175
Bluish-Grey.......................................£150-175
Light Blue body................................£150-175
Light Blue / Black £150-175
Grey / Black £150-175
Pale Green / Metallic Charcoal.....£150-175
Deep Lilac / Black roof £150-175
Cream / Metallic Charcoal..........£150-175
Metallic Blue / Black.....................£150-175
Yellow body, Black roof £150-175

102 Bentley Continental 4-door Sports (1959)
Metallic Green / Silver £140-180
Metallic Grey / Blue £140-180
Metallic Maroon / Silver £150-175
Two-tone Grey £140-180
Silver / Grey....................................£140-180
Green / Grey £140-180
Silver / Light Blue £120-150
Grey / Light Blue body.................£120-150

103 Rolls Royce Silver Wraith (1959)
Metallic Silver / Maroon,
  (White seats) £200-300
Metallic Silver / Metallic Lt. Blue,
  (Cream seats) £175-225
Metallic Silver / Metallic Green £175-225

104 M.G. 'MGA' Sports Car (1959)
Beige body £150-200
Red body (Grey seats) £150-200
Mid-blue (White seats) £150-200
Pale Blue body (White seats) £150-200
Turquoise (White seats)...............£150-200
Cream body (White seats) £150-200
Salmon Pink (Grey seats) £150-200
Bluish-Green (Lemon seats)........£150-200
Greenish-Grey (Turquoise seats) ..£150-200
Deep Green body (White seats)....£150-200
Metallic Steel Blue (Grey seats)....£150-200

105 Austin-Healey 100/6 (1959)
Yellow (White or Grey seats) £200-250
Grey (Red seats) £200-250
Beige (Grey seats) £200-250
Red / Cream £300-400
Metallic Blue / Cream £300-400
Blue body £150-200
Green body £150-200
Cream body £150-200
Turquoise body £150-200
Metallic Blue body £150-200
Metallic Green body £150-200
Pink body £150-200
Light Blue (Royal Blue seats) £150-200
Turquoise (Light Grey seats)........£150-200

107 Jaguar XK-SS (top down) (1960)
Metallic Blue body,
  (Lemon seats, Black hood)..........£150-200
Cream body......................................£150-200
Beige body £150-200
Red body £150-200
Light Green body £150-200
Dark Olive body,
  (Light Grey seats / hood)............£150-200
Pale Blue body,
  (Pale Grey seats / hood)..............£150-200
Lilac body,
  (Grey seats, Black hood) £150-200
Light Blue body,
  (Dark Blue seats and hood) £150-200
Light Grey body,
  (Pale Blue seats and hood) £150-200
Fawn body, cast hubs have 'stick-on'
  wheel trims that create a spoked
  wheel and white-wall tyre effect ....NGPP

108 Triumph TR3a Sports (1960)
Light Blue with Dark Blue seats ...£150-200
Cream body, Dark Brown seats.....£150-200
Light Brown (White seats) £150-200
Pale Green (Off-White seats) £150-200
Apple Green (Cream seats) £150-200
Red body with Grey seats.............£150-200
Sea Green body with Grey seats...£150-200
Grey body (White seats)...............£150-200
Metallic Green (Lemon seats) £150-200
Pale Blue body, Pale Grey seats ...£150-200
Mid-Blue body, Mid-Grey seats ...£150-200
NB Two baseplate castings are
known with this model. One exposes
the axle ends near to the wheels, while
the other completely hides the axles.

112 Jensen 541 (1960)
Grey body £125-150
Mauve body £125-150
Pink body £125-150
Maroon / Black £125-150
Metallic Green body £125-150
Light Blue body £125-150
Pale Green body £125-150
Metallic Blue body £125-150
Lemon body (Black roof)...............£125-150
Yellow body (Red seats)...............£125-150

113 Aston-Martin DB3 Saloon (1960)
Light Blue body £140-160
Grey body £140-160
Red body £140-160
Light Green body £140-160
Dark Green body £140-160
Maroon body....................................£200-250
Very Pale Pink, Cream interior......£160-190
Deep Pink body, Cream interior ...£160-190
Deep Lilac body...............................£160-190
Light Brown body £160-190
White body.......................................£160-190
Metallic Dark Green body £160-190
Metallic Silver Blue body £160-190
Yellow body, (Lemon interior,
  Red steering wheel) £160-190

114 Jaguar 3.4 Mark 1 Saloon (1960)
Metallic Blue body £150-175
Maroon body....................................£150-175
Mauve body £150-175
Metallic Green body £150-175
Pink body £150-175
Light Grey body...............................£140-180
Mid-Green body...............................£140-180
Light Blue body £110-150
Yellow body £110-150
White body.......................................£150-180
Dark Red body.................................£150-180
Very Pale Pink body £150-200
Deep Pink body £150-200

115 Bristol 406 Saloon (1960)
Orange body.....................................£150-175
Red body £150-175
Metallic Dark Steel body £150-175
Yellow body £150-175
Metallic Green body £150-175
Grey, Black roof, Cream seats......£150-175

118 BMW Isetta Bubble Car (1960)
Pale Blue body £100-125
Beige body £100-125
Grey body £100-125
Turquoise body £100-125
Green body £100-125
Metallic Green body £100-125
Red body £100-125
Pink body £100-125
Yellow body £120-160

Photo: Vectis Auctions Ltd.

119 Meadows Frisky Sport (1960)
Orange / Grey £80-100
Blue / Grey £80-100
Turquoise / Black......................£80-100
Red / Light Grey £80-100
Red / Black £80-100
Light Blue / White £80-100
Pale Blue / Black £100-125
Red / White £100-125

120 Fiat Multipla Estate (1960)
Blue (Cream seats)....................£80-100
Mauve (Red seats) £80-100
Pink body £100-125
Light Blue body £100-125
Yellow body £100-125
Red body £100-125
Dark Red body £100-125
Sea Green body £100-125
Pale Green body £100-125
White (Off-White seats) £100-125

131 Goggomobil Super Regent (1960)
Grey / Black...............................£80-100
Yellow / Black £80-100
Mauve / Black £80-100
Blue / Grey £80-100
Blue body £80-100
Green body £80-100
Grey body £80-100
Metallic Green body £80-100
Beige body £80-100
Light Grey body £80-100
Pink body £80-100
Deep Salmon Pink body £80-100
Red body £80-100
Turquoise body £80-100
Light Blue / Black £80-100
Red / Black £80-100
Dark Blue / Black £80-100
Green / Black £80-100

154 Austin A40 Farina Saloon (1961)
Green body £80-100
White body................................£80-100
Light Blue / White £80-100
Grey / Blue £80-100
Light Grey body £80-100
Metallic Blue body £80-100
Beige body £80-100
Light Blue body £80-100
Navy body £80-100
Turquoise body £80-100
Pale Grey body, White interior £100-125
Metallic Green, Cream interior........£80-100
Red / Black £80-100
Blue / Black £80-100
Green / Black £80-100
Lavender / Black.........................£80-100
'MAGGI' Promotional (1966),
Red body, Cream interior, 'MAGGI'
in yellow on front doors. Special
red / yellow box with leaflet.........£200-300

157 Rover 3-litre (without lights) (1963)
Mid Blue body £150-175
Mauve body £150-175
Beige body £150-175
Yellow body £150-175
Mid-Grey body £90-120
Dark Grey body £90-120
Pale Grey body £90-120
Sea Green body £90-120
Dark Green body £90-120
Light Blue body £90-120
Deep Pink body £90-120
Dark Blue body..........................£150-175
White body................................£95-125

157sl Rover 3-litre (with lights) (1963)
Light Blue body £150-175
Mid Blue body £90-120
Dark Blue body £120-150
Mauve body £90-120
Beige body £90-120
Red body £90-120
Yellow body £90-120
Pale Grey body £150-175
Grey body £150-175
Dark Grey body £120-150
Sea Green body £150-175
Dark Green body, Cream interior ..£150-175
White body.................................£95-125

165/1 Vauxhall PA Cresta Saloon (1961)
Beige body £100-130
Red body £100-130
Maroon body £100-130
Pink body £100-130
Turquoise body £100-130
Yellow body £100-130
Blue body £90-120
Light Blue body £90-120
Grey body £90-120
Light Grey body £90-120
Plum Red body £175-200
Sea Green body, Red interior........£175-200

165/2 Vauxhall PA Cresta with roof rack (1961)
Beige body £100-125
Red body £100-125
Maroon body £100-125
Pink body £100-125
Turquoise body £100-125
Yellow body £100-125
Blue body £90-120
Light Blue body £90-120
Grey body £90-120
Light Grey body £90-120
Plum Red body £110-150
Sea green body £110-150

166 Renault Floride Convertible (1962)
Blue body £80-100
Green body £80-100
Grey body £80-100
Dark Red body £80-100
White body £80-100
Yellow body £80-100

183 Humber Super Snipe Estate (1963)
Beige body £100-140
Beige/White £100-140
Blue/White £100-140
Green/White £100-140
Blue/Black £100-140
Blue body £100-140
Metallic Bronze body £100-140
Two-tone Blue............................£100-140
NB Some examples exist fitted
with wing mirrors.

184 Austin A60 (1963)
(with 2 figures, skis on roof rack)
Beige body £110-140
Green body £110-140
White body £110-140
Red (Grey rack) £100-125
Light Blue (Grey rack) £100-125
Light Grey (Grey rack)................£100-125
Lime Green................................£90-120
Greyish-Blue (Black or Grey rack) .£90-120

185 Fiat 500 (1963)
Light Blue body £80-100
Green body................................£80-100
Red body £80-100
Grey body £80-100
Yellow body £120-150
Dark Blue body..........................£120-150

191 Sunbeam Alpine Convertible (1963)
Beige body £120-140
Mid-Blue body £120-140
Green body £120-140
Red body £120-140
Mauve body £120-140
Pink body £120-140
Turquoise (Cream seats) £120-140
Grey (Cream seats) £120-140
Light Blue (White seats)..............£120-140
Deep Salmon Pink (Red seats) £120-140
White with Red seats £120-140
Yellow with Cream seats £120-140

191/1 Sunbeam Alpine Hardtop (1963)
Red / White £175-225
Turquoise / White £175-225
Blue / Black £175-225
Blue / Cream £175-225
White / Black £175-225
Beige / White £175-225
Grey / Black £175-225
Dark Green (Red seats) £175-225
Metallic Green / Black £175-225
Pink (Cream seats).....................£175-225
Mauve (Cream seats) £175-225
Yellow body (Cream seats)..........£175-225
Light Blue body £175-225
Light Blue/White £175-225
Pale Blue/White £175-225

193 N.S.U. Prinz (1963)
Turquoise body £50-70
Beige body £50-70
Pale Blue body £50-70
Light Blue body £50-70
Dark Blue body £50-70
Cream body £50-70
Grey body £50-70
Red body £50-70
White body £80-90

195 Volkswagen Rally Car (1963)
With roof light, bonnet flags,
racing number '6', '9' or '23'.
Beige body £200-250
Cream body £200-250
Maroon body £200-250
Orange body £200-250
Red body, racing number '11' £200-300
Metallic Bronze body £200-300
Light Blue body £150-175
Turquoise body £150-175

210 Morris Mini Minor (1960)
Shown in catalogue but not issued ....NPP

211 Austin Seven (Mini) (1963)
Light Blue body £125-150
Grey body £125-150
Red body £125-150
Yellow body £125-150
Pink body £200-250
White body £160-180

213 Ford Anglia Saloon (1963)
Beige body £130-160
Grey body £130-160
Yellow body £130-160
White body £130-160
Turquoise body £130-160
Light Blue body £130-160
Dark Blue body £130-160
Red body £130-160
Pink body £130-160

215 Daimler Dart SP250 (1961)
Beige body £120-150
Green body (Red seats) £160-190
Yellow body £120-150
White (Red seats).......................£160-190
Light Blue (Blue seats)................£160-190

Turquoise (White seats)................£100-125
Red (Cream seats)......................£100-125
Grey (Cream seats) £150-200

216 Volvo 122s (with sliding roof) (1963)
Red body.....................................£90-120
Orange body................................£90-120
Blue body....................................£90-120
Turquoise body £90-120
Grey body £100-125
Bright Yellow body......................£100-125
Dark Green body £100-125
Lime Green, White interior £125-150

217 Jaguar 'E' Type (1963)
Beige body..................................£150-175
Cream body..................................£150-175
Light Green body £150-175
Dark Green body £150-175
White body..................................£150-175
Yellow / Black £150-175
Mid-Blue body.............................£150-175
Light Blue body £150-175
Light Grey body £150-175
Red body, Cream interior..............£175-200

218 Jaguar Mk.10 (1963)
Metallic Brown body £90-120
Blue body....................................£90-120
Dark Green body £120-150
Mid-Green body............................£120-150
Bronze body.................................£120-150
White body..................................£120-150

219 Austin-Healey Sprite Mk.III
(with driver figure) (1963)
Red (White seats)..........................£125-150
Blue (Red seats)............................£125-150
Beige (White seats).......................£125-150
Off-White body £125-150
Light Blue body £125-150

259 Ford Consul Classic (1963)
White (Blue seats) £80-100
Beige (White seats)........................£80-100
Blue body.....................................£80-100
Light Blue body £80-100
Red body......................................£80-100
Grey body £80-100
Green body...................................£80-100

260 Royal Rolls-Royce Phantom V (1963)
Maroon body, Blue interior, 2 flags on
roof, Queen and Prince Philip in rear
seats, driver + attendant in front....£700-900

261 Volvo P1800 (1963)
Two versions of this model exist
(no price difference):
1: the bonnet and boot can be opened,
   and a spare wheel is supplied;
2: only the bonnet can be opened.
Light Blue body £100-130
Mid-Blue body £100-130
Red body......................................£100-130
Turquoise body £100-130
Grey body £100-130
Metallic Bronze body....................£100-130
Tan body......................................£100-130
Red body, Grey interior £125-150

262 Morris 1100 (1963)
Dark Blue (Grey seats) £70-90
Red (Grey seats) £70-90
Green (Red seats)..........................£70-90
Beige (Red seats)..........................£70-90
Lime Green body £70-90
Light Blue body £70-90

263 Bentley 4½ Litre (Supercharged) (1964)
Green body, Union Jack,
number '27', '11' or '15' £80-100

266 'Bull Nose' Morris 1923
(Scale 1:48) (1965)
Red / Black, Brown driver................£70-80
Yellow / Black, Brown driver.......£70-80

267 M.G. 1100 Saloon (1964)
White / Dark Green (Red seats) £150-175
Red (Cream seats)........................£150-175
Green (Red seats)..........................£150-175
Red / White (Red seats) £150-175
Royal Blue / White (Red seats) £350-450
Royal Blue / Off-White,
   (Grey seats)...............................£200-250
Cream / Beige (Red seats) £140-160

268 Vauxhall PB Cresta. (1965).
Shown in catalogue but not issued
under this number, see 280 ....NPP

270 Ford Zephyr 6 Mk.III
(with poodle) (1965)
Pale Blue (Red seats)....................£140-160
Cream body..................................£140-160
Green body...................................£140-160
Greyish-Green body.......................£140-160
Grey (Red seats) £140-160
Red (Grey seats) £140-160
Off-White (Red seats)..................£140-160

274 Morris 1100 and Canoe (1965)
Green body...................................£100-125
Grey body £100-125
Light Blue body (Red canoe) £100-125
Dark Blue body............................£100-125
Red car, Brown canoe on roof......£100-125
Two-tone Blue (Red canoe)...........£100-125
Red (Red / White canoe) £100-125
Light Blue car with Blue / Red canoe,
Orange paddle (Set 703)........................GSP

276 Jaguar 'S' type (with 2 figures) (1964)
Metallic Bronze body £150-200
Metallic Blue £150-200
Metallic Green body, Red interior .£150-200
Silver body..................................£200-250
Greyish Green body, Red interior..£200-250

278 Mercedes-Benz 230 SL
(with 2 figures) (1965)
Metallic Red body £100-150
Cream body..................................£100-150
Maroon body...............................£100-150
Metallic Blue body £100-150
Metallic Bronze body £100-150

279 M.G. PB Midget 1935 (scale 1:48) (1965)
Dark Blue body,
   Black wings / seats...................£100-125
Red body, Black wings and seats ..£100-125

280 Vauxhall PB Cresta (1963)
Beige / Red body, Red interior £140-160
Dark Blue / White body.................£140-160
Grey / Green body £140-160

281 M.G. Midget Mk.II,
(plus policeman figure) (1966)
Blue body, White interior, driver..£150-200
Red body, White interior, driver £150-200

286 Austin 1800 (1965)
Light Blue body (Red seats)..........£100-125
Dark Blue body (Red seats)...........£100-125
Cream body (Red seats)................£100-125
Green body (Red seats) £100-125
Beige body (Red seats) £100-125
Red body (Grey seats) £100-125

287 Hillman Minx (with Roof Rack and
2 brown suitcases) (1965)
Pale Green body (Red seats) £125-150
Beige body (Red seats).................£125-150
Cream body (Red seats)................£125-150
Green body (Red seats) £125-150
Red (Grey seats) £125-150
Greyish-Green body £125-150
NB This model is also known
   with the reference '287/1'.

289 Morris Minor 1000 (1963)
Metallic Blue body, Red seats £150-200
Light Blue body £150-200
Red body......................................£200-250
Metallic Green body £200-250

304 VW Variant Estate Car (1967)
Mid-Blue body and plastic
opening tailgate. See also 401/1 ....£500-750

306 Humber Super Snipe Estate (1964)
Same casting as 183 but with
roof-rack and two suitcases.
Beige body...................................£150-175
Blue body.....................................£150-175
Green body...................................£150-175
Red body......................................£150-175
Metallic Bronze body £150-175
Light Blue (White roof-rack).......£100-125
Turquoise (White roof-rack).........£100-125
White / Turquoise, Grey rack £100-125
Blue body, White roof £100-125

307 Volkswagen Beetle 1200 (1965)
Metallic Blue body £200-250
Metallic Dark Red body £200-250

308 Land Rover and Trailer (1965)
Green (Tan canopy), trailer
has Brown plastic body £80-100

401/1 VW Variant Estate Car (1967)
Dark Blue body, White plastic
opening tailgate.............................£300-500

405 'BEA' Vauxhall Cresta (1966)
Dark Grey body, Red 'BEA' logo,
   Red interior £175-200

407 Mercedes-Benz 230 SL (1966)
Brown body, Red interior,
boot rack and luggage.......................£70-80

408 Renault Caravelle. ('66). Not issued ...NPP

410 Austin 1800 and Rowboat (on roof) (1965)
Green car, Red or Orange boat........£80-100
Blue car with Red or Orange boat...£80-100
Red car with Red or Orange boat....£80-100
Beige car, Red or Orange boat £80-100

'Magicar' series

501	1965	**Jaguar Mk.10,** Blue or Green body..................£70-90
502	1965	**Rolls-Royce Silver Cloud Mk.III,** Blue or Red body.................£100-125
503	1965	**Bentley S3 Saloon,** Blue or Red body £80-110
504		**Ferrari Superfast,** Blue or Red £80-110
505	1966	**Batmobile,** Black body with Batman and Robin figures £150-175
?	**?**	**Tric-Trac car,** Plastic bodied racing car........£80-110

MG1, MG2, MG3 Magicar Sets
See 'Presentation and Gift Sets.

106a/0c 1960 **Austin Articulated Flatbed Lorry**
with MGA in Crate
Light Blue, Dark Blue, Red or Orange cab £250-400

106a/1 1959 **Austin Articulated Dropside Lorry**
Light Blue, Green or Orange cab and body............£200-250

106a/1c 1960 **Austin Articulated Flatbed Lorry**
with Crate Load
Light Blue, Light Green or Orange cab,
seven black plastic crates £200-250
Turquoise or Dark Blue body £300-350

CB106 1961 **Four Wheel Trailer**
Turquoise or Red body......................................£90-110

109/2 1960 **E.R.F. 68g Flatbed Lorry**
Turquoise, Light Grey or Blue body.....................£160-190
Maroon body...£350-400

109/2p 1960 **E.R.F. 68g Flatbed Lorry with Planks**
Turquoise (Black cab roof on some) £200-250
Yellow body £300-400

109/3 1960 **E.R.F. 68g Dropside Lorry**
Dark Blue cab with Pale Blue body £300-400
Dark Blue cab with Silver body £300-400
Yellow body (Metallic Grey roof) £160-190
Light Green body (Green roof)............................£160-190
Blue body (Black roof) £160-190
Green body (Black roof) £160-190
Deep Blue body, Silver chassis..........................£250-350
Orange-Red body, Light Grey chassis £350-450
Lemon body, Silver chassis £190-225
Pale Green body, Silver chassis..........................£190-225
Turquoise body, Silver chassis............................£190-225

109/3b 1960 **E.R.F. Dropside Lorry with Barrel load**
Turquoise, Light Blue or Red body (Silver truck
bed on some), ten Brown plastic barrels £250-350

110/2 1960 **A.E.C. Mammoth Major 8 Flatbed Lorry**
Red body (with or without Black roof) £200-250
Maroon or Dark Blue body................................£450-500

110/2b 1960 **A.E.C. Lorry 'London Brick Co Ltd'**
Red body, Black cab roof, 'brick' load,
'Phorpes Bricks'..£300-400

110/3 1960 **A.E.C. Lorry 'British Road Services'**
Red body, Black cab roof on some,
Silver chassis and back, barrels load £400-500

110/3d 1962 **A.E.C. Lorry with Oil Drums Load**
Red body, Black cab roof, Silver trim £500-600

110/4 1961 **A.E.C. Tanker 'SHELL-BP'**
Green cab, Red tank, Black chassis and catwalk £400-500
Yellow cab, White/Yellow tank,
Silver chassis / catwalk £500-750

111/30g 1962 **Ford Thames with Garage Kit**
Orange cab and truck body, Silver chassis £400-500
Light Blue cab and truck body, White garage £400-500

111/a0t 1961 **Ford Thames Trader with Three Log Load**
Dark Blue or Red cab and truck body, 3 logs..........£300-400
Light Blue cab and truck body £300-400
Light Yellow cab and truck body..........................£300-400

111a/1 1959 **Ford Thames Trader 'British Railways'**
Maroon and White body, '4884 BGM',
'M 1741 GT6'..£300-400

111a/1 1960 **Ford Thames Trader 'R.Hall & Son'**
Green body, logo on door. Doubtful if model issued ......NPP

111a/1s 1960 **Ford Thames with Sack Load**
Light Blue and Silver, twelve brown plastic sacks..£300-400
Dark Green body...£300-350
Two-tone Blue body..£300-400
Strawberry and Cream body £300-400

116 1959 **'CATERPILLAR' Tractor D9**
Dark Yellow / Silver body, Black rubber tracks,
'CAT D9', information leaflet £800-1,000

117 1963 **'JONES' Mobile Crane**
Cream cab and jib, Red body and wheels,
Black chassis, Grey base...................................£200-300
Dark Red cab / body, White jib,
Light Grey chassis, Silver wheels........................£300-400

122 1961 **'UNITED DAIRIES' Milk Float**
Red / White body, chains,
'Lada and New Yoghurt'......................................£125-150

123 1959 **Bamford Excavator**
Red / Yellow, 'J.C.B.'. Intended model but not issued....NPP

137 1962 **'MASSEY FERGUSON 65' Tractor**
Red engine cover, Grey chassis/engine,
Yellow hubs, Black tyres, plastic seat £500-700

158a/2 1961 **Bedford 'S' Type 2000 Gallon 'SHELL-BP' Tanker**
Green cab, Red tank, Black chassis, 'P33A37'.......£400-500
Yellow cab, White tank, 'P33A37' £700-1,000
Dark Metallic Green cab, Red tank, Black chassis .£500-600

158a/2C 1961 **Bedford Low Loader**
Red low-loader with cable drum. Doubtful if issued ......NPP

161 1961 **Land Rover (long wheel base)**
Grey / White..£100-125
Light Grey / White...£100-125
Blue / White...£100-125

210 1961 **Morris Mini Van**
Bright Yellow, seats / steering wheel, suspension ...£120-140

210/1 1962 **Morris Mini Van 'Royal Mail'**
Red body, Post Office crest, 'E-II-R', suspension...£150-200

210/2 1962 **Mini Van 'P.O. Telephones'**
Olive-Green body, White interior,
Gold crown logo, 'TELEPHONE MANAGER' £150-200

258 1963 **'R.A.C.' Land Rover**
Dark Blue body, 'RADIO RESCUE' £100-125

265 1964 **'TONIBELL' Ice Cream Van**
Blue body, thick Red flash, attendant....................£150-200

271 1965 **'EXPRESS DAIRIES' Milk Float**
Blue / White, 3 wheels, driver,
'Drink Express Milk'...£125-150

273 1965 **Commer Van 'SECURITY EXPRESS'**
Green / Gold, driver, seated guard,
coin slot in roof..£130-160

308 1965 **Land Rover and Trailer**
Green (Tan plastic canopy),
trailer has Brown plastic body £80-100

315 1965 **'GLASS & HOLMES' Commer Van**
Blue / Yellow, ladder, figures,
'Window Cleaning Co. Est 1891'........................£200-250

402 1966 **Crash Service Land Rover**
Orange body,
'MOTORWAYS CRASH SERVICE' in Blue £100-150

404 1966 **Morris Mini Van**
Yellow body, suspension, ladder, figure £500-700

404/1 1966 **Morris Mini Van 'SHELL'**
As previous model but without ladder and figure ...£500-700

404/2 1966 **Morris Mini Van 'AA'**
Shown in 1966 catalogue but never seen.....................NGPP

Photo: Bruce Sterling, New York

Buses, Coaches and Taxis

145	1963	**Routemaster Bus**, Red 'London Transport' bus, route '284', 'Ovaltine - The Worlds Best Nightcap'.
		1st type has chrome moulded radiator **£300-400**
		2nd type has transfer print on plastic background **£300-400**
155	1961	**Austin FX4 Taxi**, Maroon body, Cream steering wheel,
		Green base, tin-plate hubcaps..**£300-400**
		Black body, Red steering wheel, Grey base..........................**£65-80**
156	1961	**Mulliner Luxury Coach**, Pale Blue / Grey, Red flash,
		'Tri-ang Tours' rear logo, 213 mm **£200-300**
		Yellow / White body, Brown side flash......................**£900-1,200**
		Sea Green / Cream, Red flash **£800-1,000**
		Silver / Red / Dark Blue **£600-800**
		Sky Blue / White body, Red flash **£600-800**

Boats, Caravans and Scooter

135	1961	**14ft Sailing Dinghy and Trailer**,
		Blue / Grey, Dark Blue / Red, Dark Blue / White, or
		Red / White boat (with or without cover), plastic trailer **£60-80**
135	1964	**14ft GP Sailing Dinghy**,
		Brown or Yellow boat on trailer **£60-80**
139	1960	**Eccles E.16 Caravan**, Blue body, White roof, 146 mm.........NPP
229	1966	**Lambretta**, Pale Grey body,
		Red or White side panels, Black seat **£175-225**
264	1962	**Tourist Caravan**, Blue body, White roof, 152 mm.........**£90-120**
		Yellow body, White roof...**£70-90**
		Tan body, White roof..**£80-125**

Road Signs and Accessories

L208/B	**Road Traffic Signs:**	20 different signs issued, each **£5-10**
L1271/	**Road Direction Signs:**	/1 Portsmouth, /2 Guildford, /3 Bristol,
	/4 Birmingham, /5 Biggar, /6 Dumfries..................................**£10-15**
	Bus Stops: No details available.....................................**£10-15**
	Road sections: Straights, curves, T-junctions. Each **£6-8**
	Plastic Figures: In groups set on a card. Figures include:
	Garage Personnel, Newspaperman/Milkman/Postman,
	Doctor/Parson/Schoolmaster, 2 Policeman and an RAC
	Man, 3 Schoolboys, 2 Children and a Man (in country
	clothes), 3 Roadmen and Brazier or
	3 Roadmen and Road Drill/Planks/Walls
	Per card **£5-10**
	Retailer's sheet of any six cards of figures......................**£100-125**

Military models

415	1965	**R.A.F. Land Rover**, Blue/Grey, R.A.F. roundel,
		hose/pump/attendant, 111 mm....................................**£100-125**
416	1965	**Leyland Army Ambulance**. Not issued..................................NPP
417	1965	**Military 'FIELD KITCHEN'**, Olive Green body,
		squadron markings, suspension, 108 mm **£150-200**
418	1965	**Leyland Military Bus**, 'Army Personnel'. Not issued ....NPP
419	1965	**Land Rover and Missile Carrier**,
		Olive Green body, three White missiles.........................**£200-250**

Emergency vehicles

207	1964	**Wadham Ambulance**,
		Cream body, no Red crosses, with stretcher and patient ..**£300-400**
		White body with Red crosses, stretcher and patient **£400-500**
256	1966	**Jaguar 3.4 'POLICE' Car**, White or Black.
		Very few exist with undamaged aerial or roof sign **£200-275**
258	1963	**'R.A.C.' Land Rover**, Dark Blue body,
		'RADIO RESCUE', 108 mm **£100-125**
309	1965	**Police 'Z' Car**,
		Ford Zephyr police car from the BBC-TV series 'Z-Cars'.
		1st type with aerial and 'POLICE' sign, White body **£160-200**
		2nd type with no aerial or police sign. Black body **£300-400**
		2nd type (no aerial or police sign), White body **£300-400**
316	1966	**'FIRE DEPT' Land Rover**,
		Red body, suspension, two firemen, 112 mm **£150-200**
402	1966	**Land Rover 'MOTORWAYS'**, Orange / Blue body,
		hook, Blue 'CRASH SERVICE' logo.............................**£150-200**
409	1966	**Leyland 'Black Maria'**, Blue body, 'Police',
		policeman and villain. Not issued...NPP

Garages and Equipment

L146	'SHELL' lamp standard...**£20-25**
L147	'SHELL' sign **£15-20**
L148	'SHELL' petrol pump..**£15-20**
L148	Trade pack, Blue card box of 6 of L148 pumps...............**£100-150**
L149	Oil Dispenser Rack **£10-15**
L159	'BP' Lamp Standard...**£20-25**
162	'BP' or 'SHELL' Filling Station **£60-70**
162/1/2/3	Garages, each **£20-30**
163	'BP' Petrol Pump...**£15-20**
164	'BP' Forecourt Sign **£15-20**
172a	'SHELL' Garage Set..**£75-100**
172b	'BP' Garage Set..**£75-100**

Catalogues, Leaflets and Pictures

Ref	Issued	Publication	Cover, features, contents	Market Price Range
---	1959	**Early issue**	Red cover featuring a Target plus the dividers and diagram of Rolls Royce 'LTP 103'. Wording: '1/42' and 'SPOT-ON MODELS BY TRI-ANG'. Contains 8 pages	**£40-50**
---	1959	**'1st Edition'**	Village scene with Spot-On buildings and models, 'Tri-ang' logo in bright red, '6d', 'dividers' mark, 'SCALE 1/42'. Thick numbered pages with superb pictures	**£40-50**
---	1960	**'2nd Edition'**	As 1st Edition but 'Tri-ang' logo in maroon and pages not numbered	**£30-40**
100M/C.P.C./6.61	1961	**'3rd Edition'**	Same as 2nd Edition	**£25-35**
5a7383/DP	1963	**'4th Edition'**	Royal Rolls-Royce on cover, '3d', Page 19 shows the new Presentation Sets 5-10 and 14	**£20-30**
	1964	**'5th Edition'**	Blue Austin 1800 (286) on cover, '2d', concertina type leaflet featuring new type of Black/Red window boxes for Gift Sets and single models	**£20-£30**
---	1965	**'6th Edition'**	Cover again features 286 Austin 1800 plus 289 Morris Minor, '2d', concertina type leaflet which includes 'Tommy Spot' and 'Magicar' listings and pictures	**£20-30**
---	1966	**'7th Edition'**	Booklet type featuring 407 Mercedes 230 SL and 287 Hillman Minx, '6d', 'Tommy Spot' featured with 'Royal Occasion' set and Car Spotters guide	**£20-30**

Leaflets and Model Pictures The early 'blue boxes' for cars and small commercial vehicles and the early card boxes for the large commercial vehicles contained a model picture and a yellow / blue / white leaflet listing the models available. Prices of model picture cards can vary depending on the rarity of the model itself within a price range from **£5** to **£25**. Spot-On 'Picture wallets' are to be found at **£15-20**. It should be noted that no 'blue box' model or early large commercial boxed model is complete without the model picture. Leaflets are not uncommon and may be obtained for **£2-3**.

Trade Display Material

---	---	Electric revolving Trade Display Unit...**£300-400**
---	---	Glass shop-sign with 'SPOT-ON MODELS' in red/black/yellow design, 25 inches long.............................**£150-200**

Collector's Lapel Badge 'Spot-On by Tri-ang', Blue/Gold/Red, 2.5cm..**£80-100**

Spot-On Presentation and Gift Sets

Ref	Year(s)	Set name	Contents	Market Price Range

Colours of individual items are not listed. It is possible to find virtually any factory colour that was available at the time of manufacture in Spot-On Gift Sets. Early sets should contain Picture Cards, Fleet Owners leaflets and Magazine Club leaflets.

Ref	Year(s)	Set name	Contents	Market Price Range
A	1960	Presentation Set 'A'	102 Bentley, 108 Triumph TR3, 114 Jaguar 3.4, 118 BMW Isetta, 154 Austin A40	£500-750
No.0	1960	Presentation Set	106a/1 Austin Articulated Dropside Lorry, 100 Ford Zodiac, 103 Rolls-Royce Silver Wraith, 104 MGA and 113 Aston Martin	£500-750
No.1	1960	Presentation Set	100 Ford Zodiac, 101 Armstrong-Siddely, 103 Rolls-Royce and 104 MGA	£800-1,000
No.2	1960	Presentation Set	109/3 ERF Dropside Lorry, 101 Armstrong-Siddely, 102 Bentley Continental and 105 Austin-Healey 100/6	£800-1,000
No.3	1960	Presentation Set	Contains 111a/1 Ford Thames Trader, 101 Armstrong-Siddely, 104 MGA, 108 Triumph TR3a, 112 Jensen 541, 113 Aston Martin, 114 Jaguar 3.4	£800-1,000
No.4	1960	Presentation Set	106a/1 Austin Articulated Dropside Lorry, 109/3 ERF Dropside Lorry, 100 Ford Zodiac, 107 Jaguar XK-SS, 112 Jensen 541	£800-1,000
No.4a	1963	Presentation Set	104 MGA, 105 Austin-Healey, 107 Jaguar XK-SS and 108 Triumph TR3a	£400-500
No.5		Presentation Set	118 BMW Isetta, 119 Meadows Frisky Sport and 131 Goggomobil Super Regent	£400-600
No.6		'Miniature' Presentation Set	131 Goggomobil, 185 Fiat 500, 193 NSU Prinz and 211 Austin Seven	£400-600
			Variation with 210/1 'ROYAL MAIL' Van instead of 193 NSU Prinz	£400-600
No.6a		'Miniature' Presentation Set	131 Goggomobil, 185 Fiat 500, 119 Meadows Frisky and 211 Austin Seven	£400-600
No.7		Rally Presentation Set	Contains 166 Renault Floride, 191 Sunbeam Alpine, 211 Austin Seven, 213 Ford Anglia, 215 Daimler Dart, 217 Jaguar 'E'-type	£600-800
No.8		Presentation Set	157 Rover, 191 Sunbeam, 213 Ford Anglia, 216 Volvo, 258 RAC Land Rover	£600-800
No.9		Presentation Set	122 Milk Float, 145 Routemaster Bus, 193 NSU Prinz, 207 Wadham Ambulance, 211 Austin Seven, 256 Jaguar Police Car	NGPP
No.10		Presentation Set	122 Austin Seven, 145 Routemaster Bus, 157 Rover 3 litre, 158a/2 Bedford Tanker, 185 Fiat 500, 165 Vauxhall Cresta, 166 Renault Floride, 211 Austin Seven, 215 Daimler Dart and 262 Morris 1100	£500-750
No.14		Presentation Set	211 Austin 7 Mini, 154 Austin A40, 156 Mulliner Coach, 191/1 Sunbeam (Hardtop), 122 'UNITED DAIRIES' Milk Float, 157sl Rover 3 Litre with lights	£600-800
173		Terrapin Building Set	A constructional set	£35-45
208/a		Road Construction Set	4 workmen, brazier, hut, poles, road sections and 18 other small items	£200-250
259		Garage Set	A constructional set	£35-45
701		'His, Her's, Junior's' Set	219 Austin-Healey Sprite, 267 MG 1100, 280 Vauxhall Cresta, in 'window' box	£200-250
702		Gift Set 702	270 Zephyr Six, 274 Morris 1100 and canoe, 286 Austin 1800 and 135 Dinghy	£300-400
702(a)	1963	Gift Set 702	195 VW Rally, 217 Jaguar 'E' type, 261 Volvo P1800, 287 Hillman Minx	£400-500
212	1963	Car, Dinghy and Trailer Set	Contains 165 Vauxhall PA Cresta and 135 GP Dinghy	£150-200
269	1965	Ford Zephyr and Caravan	Contains 270 plus 264 Caravan	£200-300
308	1965	Land Rover and Trailer	Green bodywork, Fawn cover, 170 mm	£100-150
406	1966	Hillman Minx and Dinghy	Contains 287 Hillman Minx and 135 GP Dinghy and trailer	£100-150
MG1	1966	'Magicar Motoring' Set	501 Jaguar Mk.10 and 502 Rolls-Royce, roadway sections and traffic cones	NGPP
MG2		'Magicar Motoring' Set	503 Bentley S3 and 504 Ferrari Superfast, roadway sections and traffic cones	NGPP
MG3		'Magicar Motoring' Set	No details	NGPP

'Tommy Spot' Gift Sets

All include a building kit and Tommy Spot figure.

Ref	Set name	Contents	Market Price Range
801	'Home with Tommy Spot'	287 Hillman Minx (with Mr Spot), 270 Ford Zephyr Six with driver, pictorial stand	£350-400
802	'Cops 'n' Robbers with Tommy Spot'	309 BBC-TV 'Z-Car' with driver and criminal, 276 Jaguar and driver, pictorial stand	£350-450
803	'Superville Garage with Tommy Spot'	286 Austin 1800 with driver, 279 MG Midget, two garage workers, pictorial stand	£350-450
804	'Sailing with Tommy Spot'	280 Vauxhall PB Cresta and sailing dinghy with Tommy and Mr Spot, pictorial stand	£300-400
805	'Fire with Tommy Spot'	316 Fire Dept Land Rover and trailer, two firefighters, pictorial stand	£300-400
806	'Royal Occasion with Tommy Spot'	260 Royal Rolls-Royce with chauffeur and royal passengers, 6 guardsmen, pictorial stand	£1,400-1,500
807	'Pit stop with Tommy Spot'	Mercedes-Benz 230 SL and Jaguar 'S', two racing drivers, pictorial stand	£400-500
808	'Motorway Rescue with Tommy Spot'	402 'Crash Service' Land Rover and mechanic, A.A. van and man, pictorial stand	£500-600

The 'Cotswold Village' series

The 'Cotswold Village' items are rare and it is suggested that larger buildings (church, shop, etc) are likely to be in the region of **£100 - £150**, while smaller items might be anything from **£10 - £50** depending on size, complexity, etc.

These price levels can only be applied to pristine items in perfect original boxes.

1	School
2a	Haystack
3	'Cornerstones' Cottage
4	'Fourways' Cottage
4b	'The Cot' Cottage
5	Antiques Shop
6	General Store
7	Bourton Town Hall
8	Barn
9	'The King's Head' Public House
10	Farm House
11	Manor House
12	Post Office
13	Church
14	Forge
15	Memorial Stone
16	Water Well
16a	Stocks
-	Set of Trees
-	Bridge Sides

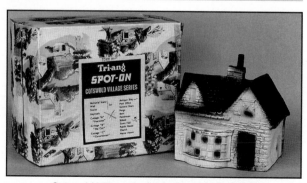

Cotswold Village Series No.5, Antiques Shop

Spot-On models 155 Taxi and 184 Austin A60 Cambridge with Skis.
The Taxi is shown with an early box; the Austin is on a later design of box that has illustrations of the model contained.

Spot-On New Zealand issues

When Tri-ang took over the production of Dinky Toys in 1967 they stopped production of Spot-On Models in the United Kingdom. Fourteen models were subsequently produced by the Tri-ang Pedigree company of New Zealand from the original dies sent out from the U.K.

New Zealand production lasted just two years and ceased in 1969 / 70. The New Zealand model reference numbers were different to their UK counterparts

as listed in the Spot-On 7th Edition catalogue. Extras such as roof racks and luggage were not included with NZ issues and the models were housed in New Zealand yellow cellophane 'window' boxes. The following listing first appeared in 'Mini Cars' ('The News Sheet for Caledonian Autominologists'), dated September 1972 and was prepared by Eric Brockie in New Zealand. Thanks are due to James McLachlan (Club Secretary) for his kind permission to reproduce the listing.

UK no.	NZ no.	Model name	Difference from UK version	NZ colour	Market Price Range
289	101	**Morris Minor 1000**	Not manufactured in New Zealand	-	NPP
219	102	**Austin-Healey Sprite**	Colour only	White body, Red seats	**£300-400**
281	103	**MG Midget**	No Policeman included	Dark Green or Red, White seats	**£300-400**
404	104	**Morris Mini Van**	No 'Shell' logo, ladder or mechanism	Yellow	**£200-300**
267	105	**MG 1100**	Single colour only	Green	**£200-300**
262	106	**Morris 1100**	Same as UK issue	Blue	**£200-300**
287/406	107	**Hillman Minx**	No roof rack or dinghy	Green	**£200-300**
280	108	**Vauxhall Cresta**	Single colour only	Blue	**£200-300**
276	109	**Jaguar 'S' type**	Same as UK issue	Blue	**£300-400**
286	110	**Austin 1800**	No lady driver or schoolboy	Light Brown	**£200-300**
270	111	**Ford Zephyr 6**	Same as UK issue	White	**£200-300**
308	112	**Land Rover**	No trailer included	Olive Green body, Pale Green tilt	**£200-300**
407	114	**Mercedes-Benz 230 SL**	Not manufactured in New Zealand	-	NPP
401	115	**Volkswagen Variant**	No roof rack or skis	Dark Blue, Red int., White hatchback	**£300-400**
279	116	**MG PB Midget**	Same as UK issue	Blue, Black	**£200-300**
265	117	**'TONIBELL' Ice Cream Van**	Same as UK issue	Turquoise	**£300-400**
402	118	**Crash Service Land Rover**	Same as UK issue	Orange, Blue	**£200-300**
316	119	**Fire Dept Land Rover**	No Firemen	Red	**£200-300**
415	120	**RAF Land Rover**	Not manufactured in New Zealand	-	NPP

These Auction Results are provided to support the Market Price Range guidance throughout the Catalogue.

Collectoys
BP 22 - 18001 Bourges Cedex, France
Condition Grading System: Models shown as A. B. C. & D.
Boxes - a. b. c. d. Unboxed o.

CARS
101 Armstrong Siddeley- red/black, cream interior, A.c..................£95
101 Armstrong Siddeley - lilac/grey, A.c.................................£95
102 Bentley - sky blue/silver. B.c...£95
102 Bentley - maroon/silver, A.d..£130
103 Rolls-Royce Silver Wraith - silver/blue, A.o....................£160
103 Rolls-Royce Silver Wraith - silver/green, A.o..................£135
104 MGA - sky blue, A.b..£100
104 MGA - pale blue, A.a..£170
105 Austin-Healey 100-6 - pale blue, red interior, A.a...........£170
105 Austin-Healey 100-6 - mid blue, red interior, A.c.............£95
105 Austin-Healey 100-6 - yellow, A.c.................................£110
105 Austin-Healey 100-6 (duotone) mid-blue, cream interior, B.b..........£170
105 Austin-Healey 100-6 (duotone) - grey, blue interior, B.c..........£135
105 Austin-Healey 100-6 (duotone) turquoise, grey interior, B.c..........£100
107 Jaguar XK SS - pale green, cream interior, A.a................£235
108 Triumph TR3 - blue, grey interior, A.b...........................£100
108 Triumph TR3 - pale green, lemon interior, A.o.................£115
108 Triumph TR3 - grey, sky blue interior, A.d.....................£110
112 Jensen 541 - lilac, cream interior, A.b...........................£130
113 Aston-Martin DB3 - prairie green, cream interior, A.o.....£200
113 Aston-Martin DB3 - beige, cream interior, B.b................£250
114 Jaguar 3.4 litre Mk.II - pale green, cream interior, B.c.....£115
115 Bristol 406 - green, red interior, B.d............................£100
217 Jaguar 'E' type - sky blue, red interior, A.o...................£145
260 Rolls-Royce Phantom V - maroon, working electrics, A.b..........£310
289 Morris 1000 - metallic green, red interior, A.b...............£210
289 Morris 1000 - red, grey interior, B.b............................£120
102 Austin-Healey Sprite Mk.II, white, red int, A.b. NZ issue..........£110
Set 4a Sports Cars - 104/105/107/108, A-C in set box b..........£420

COMMERCIAL VEHICLES
106A/1 Austin Flat Truck - orange/grey, C.c.........................£143
106A/OC Austin Transporter with (108) TR3 on board, A.b..........£420
109/2 ERF 68g - pale green, C.o...£110
109/3 ERF 68g - pale yellow, black cab roof, B.c...................£200
110/2 AEC Mammoth Flat Truck - red/grey, B.a.....................£200
110/4 AEC Mammoth Tanker 'SHELL-BP', B.b.......................£500
158A/2 Bedford 'S' Tanker 'SHELL-BP', B.c.........................£500
Ford Thames Timber Truck - pale blue, B.o..........................£160

Wallis & Wallis
West Street Auction Galleries, Lewes, Sussex, BN7 2NJ

Abbreviations: M = Mint, E = Excellent,
VGC = Very Good Condition, GC = Good Condition, F = Fair.

106 A/OC Austin Truck with MGA in crate, GC-VG, boxed..........£270
109/2 ERF 68g (Wood load) - pale green/black, GC.................£75
110/2b AEC Mammoth 'London Brick Co', GC boxed..........£160
111 a/1 'British Railways', GC, boxed (minor wear)................£200
116 D9 Caterpillar Bulldozer, boxed GC ·.............................£750
145 Routemaster Bus 'Ovaltine', VGC , boxed......................£220
157/SL - grey, battery lights, VGC in Fair box......................£40
207 Wadham Morris Ambulance - data sheet, GC, boxed..........£225
269 Car and Caravan - excellent condition...........................£250
271 Express Dairy Milk Cart - complete, boxed in VGC..........£110
Presentation Set A - boxed GC-VGC in GC box....................£280
111a/1 Thames Trader 'British Railways', E in E...................£235
'A' Presentation Set – five models, E in E box.....................£330
D9 Caterpillar Bulldozer – very good, boxed with data sheet.........£750
110/2b AEC 'London Brick Company Ltd', VGC boxed..........£160
110a/1 Ford Thames Trader 'British Railways', GC boxed..........£200
1-6 A/OC Prime Mover – 'BMC', crated MGA, boxed, GC..........£270
207 Wadham Ambulance with patient, GC boxed, some wear..........£225
308 LWB Land Tover & Trailer - green/beige, VGC boxed..........£70
315 Window Cleaner's Van – 'Glass & Holmes', VGC boxed..........£100

Vectis Auctions Ltd.
Fleck Way, Thornaby, Stockton -on-Tees TS17 9JZ
Abbreviations: M = Mint, NM = Near Mint, EP = Excellent Plus,
E = Excellent, GP = Good Plus, G = Good, F = Fair, P = Poor.

CARS
100 Ford Zodiac - pink, dark red interior, E in F box..............£140
100sl Ford Zodiac - white/turquoise, EP in G box.................£160
103 Rolls-Royce Silver Wraith - silver/blue, EP in F box..........£180
105 Austin-Healey - cream, light grey, E in F box.................£190
112 Jensen 541 - green, cream interior, E in GP box...............£120
118 BMW Isetta - turquoise, cream interior, E in F box...........£80
131 Goggomobil - turquoise, GP in G box...........................£70
157sl Rover 3 litre - green, cream interior, NM in G box..........£160
165/1 Vauxhall PA Cresta - lilac, red interior, EP in P - F box..........£120
166 Renault Floride - pale yellow, red interior, NM in F box..........£120
183 Humber Super Snipe - green/white, E in G (crushed) box..........£100
191/1 Sunbeam Alpine Hardtop, red/white interior, NM in E box..........£240
213 Ford Anglia – red, cream interior, EP in F box................£170
215 Daimler Dart SP250 - green, red interior, NM in F box..........£180
263 Vintage Bentley 4.5 ltr - EP in GP window box...............£90
267 MG 1100 - cream, beige, red interior, EP in E window box..........£160
270 Ford Zephyr - off white, red interior, figure/dog, EP in E box..........£160
276 Jaguar 'S' Type - metallic blue, red interior, E in F box..........£90
280 Vauxhall PB Cresta - cream, red interior, M in G box..........£160

COMMERCIAL VEHICLES
109/2P ERF 68g with plank load - green/black, E in GP box..........£190
110/3 AEC Mammoth 'British Road Services', E in GP box..........£240
117 Jones Crane - red/white, E in GP box...........................£170
122 'United Dairies' Milk Float, NM in F box.......................£100
158A – 2 Bedford S Type Tanker - 'Shell/BP', E in F box..........£500

MISCELLANEOUS
137 Massey Ferguson 65 Tractor - Excellent unboxed..............£380
207 Wadham Ambulance - E but no patient/stretcher, Unboxed..........£200
229 Lambretta Scooter -blue, red, NM in E box.....................£80
Lapel badge - 'Spot -On by Tri-ang', blue/gold/red...............£100

SETS
Presentation Set A, 5 models, GP - E in a G card set box..........£320
Presentation Set 0, 4 models, E - NM in GP - E window box..........£520
Presentation Set 0- with five models E overall, in F box..........£460
Presentation Set 4 - models, E - EP in F box.......................£900
Plastic wallet with 24 picture cards, GP- E........................£190
801 Tommy Spot at Home - 2 models, E - NM in G box..........£130
Presentation Set 2 - models, G - E in E box........................£600

Lacy, Scott & Knight
The Auction Centre, 10 Risbygate Street, Bury St Edmunds, IP33 3AA.

107 Jaguar XK SS – red body cream seat, Mint, box near mint..........£110
112 Jensen 541 – lemon body, black roof, Mint, box mint..........£100
113 Aston Martin DB3 – metallic silver blue, Mint, box mint..........£100
115 Bristol 406 – metallic green, Near Mint, box mint.............£75
118 BMW Isettta Bubble Car – metallic green, red seats, Mint boxed..........£80
166 Renault Floride – dark red body, cream interior, Mint boxed..........£55
213 Ford Anglia – turquoise/grey, near mint boxed................£78
AEC Mammoth Lorry – 'Express Brick' with load..................£85

Bonhams
Montpelier Street, Knightsbridge, London SW7 1HH

115 Bristol 406 – E in G box...£100
102 Bentley Saloon – E in G box.......................................£110
103 Rolls Royce Silver Wraith - E in G box..........................£160
104 MGA – E in G box..£130
105 Austin-Healey 100-Six – E in G box.............................£360
108 Triumph TR3 – E in G box...£140
118 BMW Isetta – E in G box...£95
195 VW Rally Car - light blue No. 8 - E in G box..................£130
213 Ford Anglia – light blue, G in F box..................Estimate £100
229 Lambretta Scooter – E in G box..................................£130
Presentation Set No 1. – four models and accessories good overall..........£240
L162B Filling Station – BP Garage - Good in torn box.............£380

Many toys and models exist about which we know very little. The 1940s in particular saw a proliferation of small manufacturers (often only a one-man operation in a North London shed). In this post-wartime period the established manufacturers were engaged in an export drive that meant shortages of products at home. Not surprisingly, enterprising ex-servicemen and others turned their hands to toy production on a scale that they could manage. Their range was small (sometimes only one product) and they were often in business for only a year or two.

One outcome of this is that some toys and models discovered in attics or at swapmeets present us with a puzzle. Who made the item? When were they in production? Where was the maker's workshop? Very often there is no information at all on the product or simply a statement to the fact that it was 'Made in England'. Identification is sometimes diffcult – but is it impossible?

Since the 10th Edition was published, some very interesting additional information has been obtained and we are delighted to be able to pass on the details below. However, our lists below are far from complete and we do still require your help, so if you have any information on any of the manufacturers mentioned, please write to: The Editor, Swapmeet Publications, PO Box 47, Felixstowe, Suffolk, IP11 9HE.

Arbur	Condon	Johillco	Knight	Salco	Toby
Baxtoys	W.H.Cornelius	John Hill & Co.	Louis Marx	Scaledown	Toy Products
Betal	Cursor	Jolly Roger	Mafwo	Slikka	Tractoys
BMC	Denzil Skinner	Kenbo	Millbo	Sundaw	Trent Products
Bren L Toys	Eaglewall Plastics	Kenbro	Millbro	Tal Developments	Tudor Rose
Cherilea	Empro	Kemlow	Model Toys	Teddy Toys	Wardie
City Toys	Goody Toys	Kitmaster	Moultoys Ltd	Industries	

Betal (see picture opposite)
Saloon Car. Clockwork motor in some ...**£15-20**

Bradcars (c1950-55)
Bradshaws Model Products. 1:75 scale. One-piece castings, no interiors. Boxed models: **Austin A30, Riley 1.5 litre, Austin 7, Morris 6.**

Brimtoy (diecast issues)
1948-50 **Vauxhall Saloon**. Yellow body, cast wheels, plain card box with picture **£100-150**

Cherilea
Set 1001 'Spacemen'. With rocket, 3 robots, 6 spacemen, 2 space animals **£500-600**

Condon (see picture opposite)
These were based on the same chassis casting:
Dumper Truck, various colours...............**£20-30**
Site Crane, various colours......................**£20-30**
Elevator Loader, various colours...........**£20-30**

Denzil Skinner
Nuffield Tractor............................**£1,000-1,250**

Gaiety Toys (late 1940s)
Castle Art Products Ltd., Birmingham. Models may be found painted in various colours, often chromed, sometimes motorised. Models in boxes are rare. Products known:
Morgan 3-wheel Sports Car, 4.75in.........NGPP
Racing Car, single driver, 5in. long..........NGPP
Racing Car, driver/co-driver, 4in. long.....NGPP
Racing Car, single driver, 3.25in. long.....NGPP
Fire Engine...NGPP

Gilco
No. 1 Traffic Sign Set. Ten items **£30-40**
No. 4 Traffic Sign Set. Contains 24 items inc. Road Signs, Traffic Lights, Telegraph Poles, 2 Belisha Beacons. Pictorial card box. ...**£80-100**

John Hill & Co. (Johilco)
Roman Gladiator Set: Gold Chariot and Charioteer, 2 horses, 5 Centurion Gladiators + Officer in pale cream toga. Boxed........**£125-150**
Roman Chariot: Gold Chariot with 2 horses and Gold Charioteer.................**£80-100**
Coronation (1935 Jubilee) **Coach Set**, 4 white horses + 2 riders, 6 'Beefeaters', 6 Footmen. The coach is 23cm long and contains figures of King George V & Queen Mary. Blue box marked 'Jubilee' ....NGPP

Jubilee Coach, King George V and Queen Mary in a 'coronation'-style coach with 4 white horses, 2 riders, 6 mounted Life Guards, 6 Beefeaters, 6 footmen, blue box ....NGPP
Mack Mail Van. Red, Grey wheels **£70-90**
Racing Car. Red......................................**£40-50**
Tank. Light Khaki, rubber tracks **£100-125**
Mack Gun Lorry. Khaki / Black...........**£90-110**
Searchlight Lorry. Khaki / Black.........**£90-110**
Mack Stake Truck. Green / Yellow........**£40-50**
Mack Concrete Truck. Mustard Yellow .**£30-40**
Ford 'T' Truck. Dk. Blue, Gold screen...**£60-70**
Fargo Single Deck Coach. Lt. Green......**£30-40**

Jolly Roger
Made c1946/7 by Tremo Mouldings, Cardiff.
Racing Car (boxed)...................................NGPP
Saloon Car (boxed) (picture opposite)......NGPP

Kembo
Articulated Lorry. Heavy lorry cab (tinplate base), open semi-trailer with curved front board and 'KEMBO TRANSPORT' paper labels. Minic-style tinplate wheels, rubber tyres...NGPP
Saloon Car Cast wheels, no base **£20-30**

Kemlow (1950s)
Kemlow's Diecasting Products Ltd., Wood Green, London. Distributors B.J. Ward Ltd. (trading as 'Wardie Products').
'PICKFORDS' Removal Van, 1:60 ....NGPP
Articulated Timber Truck, 1:50 ....NGPP
Farm Tractor and Trailer, 1:60...............NGPP
Caravan. 1:43 ....NGPP
Ford Zephyr Mk.I, 1:43 ....NGPP
Thornycroft Mighty Antar, 1:43 & 1:60.NGPP
Flat Truck, 1:50 ....NGPP
Armoured Car, 1:60 ....NGPP
Field Gun, 1:60 ....NGPP

Milton Toys
Made in India from old Corgi dies.
Routemaster Bus. Red, 'MILTON' logo .**£35-45**

Minitoy
Racing Car. Single piece casting includes cast stub axles for the cast wheels. 90mm. ....NGPP

Sacul
'Rob Roy' Set. This film-related boxed set contains Rob Roy in full tartan with sword and an English Redcoat with sword **£1,000-1,250**
'Bill and Ben' Set. TV-related set with Bill, Ben, Little Weed, 2 flower pots **£100-200**

Scaledown Models
Fordson Major Roadless Halftrack
Blue body **£100-125**

Skybirds (1930s)
Army Truck **£80-100**
Anti-Aircraft Gun, 4 Gunners, box ...**£400-500**
Lanchester Armoured Car, box **£500-600**
Tanker, 6 wheels, rubber tyres ....NGPP

Sundaw Products (c1950)
H130 Single-deck Motor Bus. Red body, 'TRANSPORT SERVICES', rubber wheels. Red/white end-flap box (picture)..........**£250-350**
H131 Double-deck Motor Bus. Green body, 'TRANSPORT SERVICES', rubber wheels. Green/white end-flap box (picture).......**£400-600**
NB Similar models were sold by Vectis Auctions Ltd in December 2000 for **£180** (H130) and **£600** (H131).

Tractoys Models
Ferguson 25 Tractor...........................**£175-200**

True-to-Type Models (similar in size to Matchbox 1:75s; all have unpainted cast wheels)
Cable-Layer Truck.
Green truck, Grey/Cream cable drum.......**£25-35**
Tip Cart Truck. Red body and tipper......**£25-35**
Excavator Truck.
Green body, Blue back **£25-35**
NB The three models listed above were sold by Vectis Auctions Ltd in 2000 for **£800**!

Tremo Models See also 'Jolly Roger'.
Set No.2 'Famous Fighting Ships of the Royal Navy'. Contains 5 ships: 'Resolution', 'Defender', 'Dauntless', Grimsby Escort Veassel + 'Shark' Submarine. Green presentation box / packing.
(picture opposite) **£250-300**

Tudor Rose
Heavy Duty Farm Tractor Red / Yellow / Silver, Green driver, boxed.....**£100-150**

Photo: John King

ARBUR PRODUCTS   BREN L TOYS   TOBY   JOLLY ROGER

Photo: Peter Brighty

The Kembo Articulated Lorry listed on the opposite page. Its tinplate base has 'KEMBO' impressed into it.

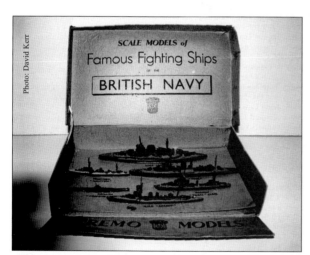

Photo: David Kerr

Tremo Models 'Famous Fighting Ships' set

Photo: John King

Condon Dump Truck

Kembo Saloon Car (left).

The Betal Saloon Car (right) has been observed with and without a clockwork motor.

Photographs: Swapmeet Publications.

VECTIS MODEL AUCTIONS

Stockton-on-Tees. TS17 9JZ. **Condition abbreviations**:
M = Mint, **NM** = Near Mint, **NMB** = Near Mint Boxed, **EP** = Excellent Plus,
E = Excellent, **EB** = Excellent Boxed, **GP** = Good Plus, **VG** = Very Good,
G = Good, **GB** = Good Box, **F** = Fair, **P** = Poor, **UB** = unboxed, **IB** =
Illustrated box, **CW** = Clockwork, **PC** = Petrol can, **PP** = Plated parts,
LTG = lithographed.

WELLS

Saloon Car, green with tan roof, upper body and wings, chauffeur,
electric lights, 'Dunlop Cord' tin tyres, GB and triangle transfers
to rear wings, 'MS 3516' number plate, PC/CW/PP (probably for
Marks & Spencer, VG, UB..**£520**

Police Patrol Car, black with blue and silver lining, blue running
boards, loudspeaker, 3 figures, bell, CW/PP, VG UB.........................**£340**

No. 68, 'Express Transport' Van , green with cream roof and sides,
red wings and RB's, CW, VG, UB..**£100**

Trolleybus, red, tin white 'tyres', LTG passengers, CW, 8", VG, UB **£100**

Coupé, 2 doors, light blue, mauve lining, plated radiator, CW, VG UB.....**£125**

Army Searchlight Lorry, camouflaged open lorry with searchlight,
5 figures, electric lights, (14" long) E in VG box..............................**£540**

1934 Double Decker Bus, red with grey roof, LTG passenger detail,
'Thanks for Buying British' on sides, balloon tyres, G **£180**

Double Decker Bus, grey roof, red body, lithographed passenger
detail, balloon tyres, (18cm long), Excellent Plus **£260**

Single Decker Bus, 'Greenline', lithographed passenger detail,
plastic tyres, Excellent **£140**

Saloon Car, pale olive with cream coach sides and lining,
plated radiator, driver, beige wings and running boards, CW, F, G........**£140**

Sunshine Saloon Car, green with cream lining, tin 'tyres', plated
radiator and bumpers, electric, (14" long), G, UB............................**£260**

Saloon Car, 4 doors, light brown and red, cream wings, yellow lining,
tinplate balloon tyres, driver, electric, E in G box.............................**£460**

WELLS-BRIMTOY

Routemaster Bus, red, lithographed passengers, 'Esso' adverts,
No. 25, 'High St and City Road', friction drive, E in VG....................**£280**

WELLS-BRIMTOY 'POCKETOYS'

Covered Lorry, mid blue, 'Lyons Tea' to sides, CW, NM in E box.............**£80**

Mechanical Bus, red with grey roof lithograhed details, G in IB **£60**

Single Deck Bus, green, yellow outlining, litho detail, VG in F box **£60**

506 Petrol Tanker, 'Regent' both sides, blue with red tank, E in VG box.....**£90**

508 Removal Van, red, yellow detail, 'All over the Globe', E in G box.......**£90**

Long Wheelbase Truck, red cab/chassis, green tin open body, E, VG box..**£80**

514 Breakdown Lorry, green/red/black, red tin wheels, E in G box............**£110**

516 Trolley Bus, red, black plastic wheels, LTG detail, CW, E in G box.....**£110**

9/520 Bedford Prime Mover, red, 'Transport' on sides, NM in NM..........**£140**

526 Lorry and Glider, red/green LTG detail, tinplate glider, E in G box......**£120**

537 Ambulance, white cab, ltg detail, black plastic wheels, E in VG box.....**£80**

540 Cleansing Lorry, Bedford 'S', 'Cleansing Department', Mint/GP **£100**

544 Lorry with Aeroplane, blue cab and trailer, tinplate glider, VG in G ..**£80**

546 Milk Lorry, cream tank with 'Pocketoy Dairies' on sides, E in VG....**£130**

551 Bulldozer, yellow / red, lithographed engine detail, CW, E in G box....**£80**

BETAL

Double Decker Bus, red and cream roof, TBT, 'General Transport',
'Palm Toffee' and 'Bisto' to sides, CW, (28cm long) GP, E.................**£280**

MINIMODELS

Goldie Gardener MB Land Record Car, red with silver cockpit,
'MG' to front and sides, (10" long) G **£130**

'John Cobb' Racing Car, silver with red, Union Jack and
US flags to front, CW, (10.5" long), VG in P box.............................**£120**

CHAD VALLEY

No. 10060 Saloon Car, cream with black wings and running boards,
green hubs, grey 'tin' tyres, PP/CW, VG UB **£160**

'Games' Van, green/cream/black, various games on sides,
'Tiddlywinks' etc, balloon tin tyres, (25cm long) GP, E **£260**

CHAD VALLEY (Clockwork - Wee-Kin Toys)

Humber Super Snipe – metallic blue, GP in P box **£110**

Humber Hawk – turquoise, Good unboxed...**£110**

Razor Edge Saloon – red, silver trim, GP in F box...............................**£160**

Tractor – yellow, Good (retouched) **£90**

Routemaster Bus – green, unboxed...**£60**

Commer Avenger Coach – blue, silver, GP unboxed **£100**

Truck & Trailer - red and black, 'Commer Hands', GP /UB.....................**£100**

Petrol Tanker – red, grey, 'Petrol' , EP unboxed **£90**

Tower Repair Wagon – green, red, EP unboxed **£60**

Milk Float – red, blue, 7 churns, E unboxed.......................................**£40**

Double Decker Bus – powder blue, Excellent in good box.....................**£160**

Guy Van – 'Lyons Ice Cream', dark blue/silver, E in F box **£140**

Guy Van 'Guy Motors Limited', green/black, E in F box **£620**

Refuse Van – green/grey, Excellent...**£80**

Low Loader Lorry – Green cab, red flatbed, 3 cases, G in G **£80**

Milk Float – green/cream 'MILK', 8 churns, GP in P box **£50**

Timber Lorry – red cab, blue flatbed with load, GP.............................**£50**

Fire Engine – red with gold trim, NM in GP box **£200**

Petrol Tanker – red and grey, 'Regent' to sides, E in F box.....................**£110**

Track Racer Car – green, silver trim, No. 2, E in F box **£140**

Sunbeam Talbot – light metallic green, GP......................................**£100**

Humber Hawk – green body, NM..**£90**

Fordson Major Tractor - mid blue, orange hubs, GP in F box **£340**

Motor Bus- 'National' Single Decker, 'CV10071', E in G......................**£240**

Commer Artic. Lorry – 'Commer Hands', red/black, NM in G box **£800**

Humber Super Snipe – very dark metallic olive, GP **£70**

Hillman Minx – red, Mint in Excellent box.......................................**£420**

Traffic Control Car (CW) – dark blue, E in G box **£130**

Police Car – black, silver trim, 'Police', NM in F box **£110**

Sunbeam Talbot – metallic blue body, EP.......................................**£90**

MIDGET SERIES

Coach – red with tin wheels, silver trim, EP in GP box **£120**

Royal Mail Van – 'GR' to sides, tin wheels ....(Estimate) £30 - £50

BURNETT

Open Tourer, cream and blue body, black hood, wings, and running
boards, tin grey 'tyres', BL 11224 number plate, CW, E **£300**

1920's 4 door Saloon Car, grey/blue, driver, blue spoked wheels,
'Whitanco' trade mark, B4 number plate, E.....................................**£360**

MORESTONE

No. 1 Foden Petrol Tanker 'Esso', E in E box..................................**£240**

No. 2 Long Distance Wagon – NM in E box **£140**

No. 3 Foden 14 ton Chain Lorry – NM in E box................................**£150**

Articulated Car Transporter – orange/grey, E in GP box **£26**

Land Rover 'AA Road Service', yellow/black, E in G box **£140**

RAC Motor Cycle & Sidecar – (small version), VG in VG box **£175**

AA Land Rover (large version) – Excellent boxed **£610**

Father Christmas, Sleigh & Reindeer - E in E box............................**£235**

Noddy Gift Set – Noddy with car, Big Ears with bicycle, plus
Big Ears riding his bicycle, NM in EP box......................................**£140**

Mr Plod the Policeman, NM in GP box.......................................**£1,000**

Mechanical Road Sweeper 'City Cleaning Dept', GP in F box.............**£260**

Gypsy Caravan – yellow/green/red, grey horse, E in G box **£250**

MORESTONE sold by VECTIS USA

Morestone 'Esso' Petrol Pump Series (All boxed)

No 11 'Royal Mail' Van, Excellent boxed **£50**

Cooper Bristol, blue, white driver, Excellent boxed..............................**£53**

Foden Dump Truck, red cab/chassis, yellow back, E boxed **£57**

Austin Westminster Countryman – red, silver flash, E boxed...............**£47**

BUDGIE

204 VW Pickup Truck – 'Express Delivery', blue, M/G box **£80**

Noddy on his bicycle with trailer, yellow/red, M in E+ box **£260**

Noddy with his train including Big Ears, M in NM box **£320**

Noddy and his Car, Mint in Near Mint box......................................**£280**

232 Seddon Low-loader - 3 'Standard' Cable Drums - NM in GP...........**£295**

238 Scammell Van - yellow, 'Railfreight', NM in E box **£35**

238 Scammell Van – maroon/cream, 'Railfreight', E in E **£130**

Renault Truck 'Fresh Fruit Daily', GP in G box **£50**

452 Motor Cycle & Sidecar – 'R.A.C.', figure, EP in G box **£100**

Display Stand – yellow/blue/red, boxed, near mint **£140**

240 'British Railways' Delivery Van – maroon, E in F-G box **£160**

254 Merryweather Fire Escape – red/silver, E in G box.......................**£130**

260 Ruston Bucyrus Excavator – red/grey, Excellent........................**£400**

Motor Cycle & Sidecar, 'Fire Service' livery, 2 figures, G/UB................**£160**

Land Rover 'AA Road Service', yellow/black, E in G box **£140**

282 Yard Scraper – Lime green, black wheels, VG in VG box **£70**

316 Overhead Maintenance Truck – 'Public Words Dept', E/VG...........**£70**

SHACKLETON

Foden FG6 Tipper – dark grey, red wings, E in F box **£400**

FG6 Flat Truck – apple green cab and back, GP in GP box **£460**

Foden FG6 Flat Truck – violet-blue /grey, G in G box **£460**

FG6 Tipper – dark grey with red wings/chassis, G in G box **£600**

Dyson Trailer – dark green, E in G box **£150**

Foden FG6 Flat Lorry – grey, red mudguards, E in F box **£1,150**

WARDIE PRODUCTS

Garage Accessories Set – Mobilgas, Shell, Castrol Oil bin, Dunlop
Tyre Rack, BP/National signs, E in VG box **£140**

CRESCENT TOYS

1809 Dextra Tractor – orange, red plastic wheels, EP /UB **£250**

Dodgem Car –dark green, child passenger **£130**

1269 Mobile Crane – red/green/yellow, EP in E **£110**

ARMSTRONG TOYS

Vauxhall Saloon – yellow, metal wheels, M in GP box........................**£340**

TIMPO
Van 'Radio Telivision Records' – green/yellow, EP/UB £160
London Taxi Cab – mid blue/black, E in GP box £90
Super Heroes – Capt. Marvel, Mary Marvel & Frogman VG £240
Articulated Lorry – dark blue, 'PICKFORDS', GP in E box....................£145
JOHILCO
Mail Van – red cab and body, Excellent..£90
Ford Model T Open Truck – dark blue, gold screen, Excellent.................£70

CHARBENS
British Paratrooper on Motor Cycle issued 1959, Good UB £210
Set 519 'Hikers Camp' – tent plus 4 hikers etc, G-VG in G box £380
Milk Float 'Express Dairy', VG in G box £565
KEMLOW
'Pickford's' Delivery Van – blue/white, EP/UB.................................£140
RIVER SERIES
Daimler Conquest – purple, Mint in Good Plus box..................................£380

TAYLOR AND BARRETT
London Coach – cream, green, Good Plus , unboxed £120
Streamline 'Royal Air Mail Service' – blue, GP unboxed £220
Saloon Car – brown with 4 doors, Good unboxed £160
Trolley Bus 'Champions Malt Vinegar' on sides, G unboxed £100
Ambulance (Large Scale) – grey/black, GP unboxed £90
Fire Car – red with 3 figures, EP unboxed £280
A Barrett & Son – 'Air Mail' Van, dark blue ....estimate £100
Fire Station Set – 2 Engines & 2 Escapes plus firemen, E/F £1,000
127 Gas Cooker Set – cream cooker, kettle etc, E in VG box £130
Fire Engine – grey 'AFS' paint, 4 firemen, prewar, VG...........................£180
Set 30 – 'Zoo Visitors at Tea', 3 adults, 2 children etc, VG £480

BENBROS
Motor Cycle and Sidecar 'AA' - bright yellow, GP in G box £80
Motor Cycle and Sidecar 'Express Window Service', EP/GP £170
10 Bulldozer – metallic blue, yellow hubs, black tracks, E/UB.............£117
Rear Dump Truck (large) – blue/yellow, VG in E box............................£175
Army Covered Truck – green, cloth canopy, GP in GP box.....................£100
'Sunderland' Wagon – green with dark green hubs, GP in E box £130
Ferguson Tractor with Log Carrier Trailer – VG in G box....................£140

SACUL – (Sacul items sold were made in London 1950-54)
Walt Disney, Film & TV Related Figures
Mickey Mouse (red), Minnie (blue) & Goofy (red), E £560
TV figures: Rag, Tag and Bobtail, VG..£220
1954 – Rob Roy and a Redcoat with swords,VG.....................................£360
1951 – Andy Pandy, Teddy and Looby Loo, E/VG £580
1951 - Bill & Ben , Little Weed – The Flower Pot Men, E/G £800
1953 – Peter Pan Set with Captain Hook, E in VG box £1,000

SALCO
Mickey Mouse Barrel Organ plus Mickey and Minnie, G in F.............£200

LUNTOY (Manufactured by Barrett & Sons in 1952)
Diecast TV Characters
Sooty with Xylophone, Prudence Kitten & Billy Bean, E/UB................£220
Perigrine/Penguin, Muffin/Mule, Mr Turnip, Prudence, F-G...............£300

EXCELLA (London -1935 - Film Related Characters)
Big Bad Wolf Set – with the wolf and 3 pigs, Excellent £750

LONESTAR
Dodge Dart –metallic blue, bright hubs, EP in GP box £140
Ford Sunliner Convertible – white, bright hubs, EP/GP box..................£120
Rambler Station Wagon – blue, cream, chrome hubs, M/GP £160
Chevrolet Corvair – red, chrome hubs, EP in E box £100
Chevrolet Corvair 'Feuerwehr' – red, blue roof light, EP/ E.................£130
Crane & Transporter – orange/black, VG in E box £35

METTOY
Open Lorry, red cab and rear tipping body, cream lining/detail,
6 wheels, clockwork G , VG...£50
Rolls-Royce, blue with cream lower body/front/rear, R.R. plated radiator,
AA and RAC badges, CW, (13.5" long), G...£170
Delivery Lorry, 'Royal Mail', 'GRV 1' to sides, 'Dunlop 90' to
tinplate balloon tyres, (24 cm long), Excellent......................................£180
Vanwall Racing Car made for Marks & Spencer, red, GP £420

RANLITE (Bakelite)
Singer Saloon, dark brown with black roof, wings and running boards,
black wheels and treaded pneumatic tyres, brown seating,
sliding roof, plated radiator/bumpers, excellent in F, G box £1,000
5 Wheel Set for Singer Saloon, dark green hubs,
black pneumatic tyres contained in a VG red box.................................£150
Radiator and Bonnet Set for Singer Saloon, dark green with plated
radiator, Excellent in a VG red box...£150
Petrol Pump, dark green with globe marked 'Petrol', wire hose with
nozzle, 5.5" high, Excellent UB...£300
SUTCLIFFE BOATS
Sea Wolf Atomic Submarine, yellow hull, red plastic conning tower
and missile, VG in G box..£70
Bluebird II Speedboat, cream with gold exhausts and windscreen,
red cockpit, bluebird and Union Jack transfers, E in G IB...................£270
Ocean Pilot 'Jupiter' in red and white, Mint Boxed £80
'Speed Hawk' in green and white, Mint Boxed...£80
'Sea Wolf' Atomic Submarine, yellow, clockwork, Mint Boxed £180
Diving Submarine 'Unda Wunda' in pale blue, unused, Mint Boxed.......£280
Cruiser 'Commodore' with red hull and white top, with flag,
clockwork, Near Mint Boxed..£80

VICTORY INDUSTRIES, ENGLAND
L.3010 Coles Diesel Electric Crane, yellow plastic body and crane,
electric, VG in VG IB £200

TRI-ANG STEEL TOYS
Long Nose Tipping Lorry, red cab with blue rear tippng body,
'Tri-ang Pedal Motors' transfers to sides, VG.......................................£200
Articulated Pantecnicon, Forward Control Cab, red/blue with
'Pedigree Dolls' and 'Minic Cars' etc. transfers (25" long), G.............£300
Short NoseTipping Lorry, red and blue, 'Triang Transport',
made in 'South Africa' transfers to sides, VG...£80
Routemaster Double Decker Bus, red, 'London Transport' livery,
'Pedigree Prams' adverts on sides, white interior, F.............................£120
Gyro Cycle, boy riding a red framed cycle on Tri-ang Cord tin wheels,
Gyro mechanism, VG in G box..£160

Aeroplane
Constructor Set
No.OO
in camouflage
finish sold by
Christie's
South Kensington

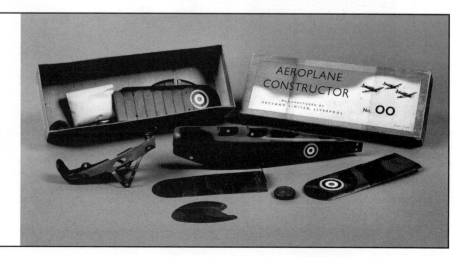

MECCANO CONSTRUCTOR OUTFITS
Abbreviations:
'MP' = 'Meccano Products', PW = Pre-War WB = Wood Box
BOXED SETS
No. 1 (1925), nickel, brass components, 7.25, E in GP box £50
No. 1A (1926), nickel and green, plus empty box for Set OOA....................£80
No 2 (1926), nickel/red/green, 'The New Meccano', GP £70
Inventor's Accessory Outfit c. 1917, nickel, E in G..................................£130
Inventor's Accessory Outfit c. 1920, nickel, E in G..................................£150
No. 2A (1929), red/green, factory strung, 5.29 M, G boxed........................£160
No. 1 (1931), red/green, factory strung, 6.31 manual £100
No. 5A (1927), red/green/nickel, Handbook 1.27, GP in F £150
No. 1 (1937), blue/gold, 6.36 M, plus 4A empty box £240
Accessory Outfit AA, blue/gold, and box 4A, 12.38 manual, G £240
Simplified Mechanics A (1907), not marked Meccano, Good £750
1912 'Royal Meccano' empty tinplate box, Good.........................estimate £225
No. 1C 'Mechanics Made Easy' (1907/08), nickel.....................................£340
Windmill Set c.1913, rarest Meccano outfit, E in G box.........................£1,100
Electrical Outfit (1922), complete with manual, Good Plus £600
Mechanical Demonstration Set c.1912, nickel, manual, G £800
No. 8A Accessory Outfit, blue/gold, 9/10 M, Excellent............................£480
No. 6 (1927/28), dark red/green in 6A oak cabinet, GP £1,400
No. 6 (1920), nickel, outfit in oak cabinet, manual is fair, E.......................£300
H. 1935 Outfit, blue/gold, yellow inner tray, manuals, G in E WB £440
No. 6 (1929), dark green/red in green cabinet, Good Plus £520
No. 10 (1939/40), blue/gold, complete set,Good boxed £4,200
Mechanised Army Set MA, instructions dated 1.40, GP boxed £620
No. 2, Elektron, c.1937, complete, GP boxed...£420
Post war No. 6A Accessory Set, red/green, factory strung MB £45
Post war No. 6 Outfit c.1951, red/green, factory strung, E.......................£160

DEALERS DISPLAY CABINETS
Display Cabinet c.1920 with parts, 'Meccano', Excellent £1,950
Display Cabinet, 1930's, blue/gold parts, 6 drawers, Good £2,100
Display Cabinet, 1930's, maroon, drawers 'A, F', G £420

SHOP DISPLAY SIGNS
Lantern (PW), 'Meccano' and 'Hornby Trains' adverts, GP..................£3,600
'Meccano' Shop sign, black/yellow/blue/gold, Good £390
'Meccano' wood/metal sign, c.1939, 'Toys of Quality', G £220
'Meccano' Dockyard Crane, 1950's on plinth, red/green, G....................£190
Glass colour slide, 'They All Want Meccano' etc., Excellent....................£460
Show Card, post war - Sydney Harbour Bridge, 8.5"x13", E £125

FACTORY BUILT DISPLAY MODELS
Blackpool Tower, 1950's factory built display model, EP £2,500

Big Wheel - 1950's factory built display model, red/green, GP.................£520
'Meccano' Jet Aeroplanes Roundabout - 1950's on base, GP £950
Cable Car, c.1960, factory built on green wood base, NM £1,300
1912 Meccano Butter Churn on box base, rare leaflet, GP £520
1921 Meccano Saw Bench, chrome top, 'M L LTD', E Boxed £460
Steam Excavator built up model, 1930's red/green, GP...........................£660
No. 1 Radio Receiving Set on Meccano oak base, Rare, G £4,600

MECCANO LITERATURE
'Meccano Products' Catalogue, blue/gold line, GP...................................£110
1921 'MP' Catalogue, train on Forth Bridge picture, G............................£90
1922 'MP' Catalogue, 'The Magic Carpet' train layout, E, ...£60
1923 'MP' Catalogue, full colour cover, 'O' gauge, G...............................£45
'The Story of Meccano', c.1920, Meccano boy, buff , G £220
'The Story of Meccano', c.1920, Meccano boy, red, G £180
'Adventures in Meccano Land', 1927, booklet (Dick), G..........................£160
'Dick's Visit to Meccano Land', 1935 booklet, Excellent.........................£190
'Meccano Book of Products', 1935, No. 2 car/speed boat, E...................£320

MECCANO MOTOR CARS and CONSTRUCTOR OUTFITS
Abbreviations: A = Assembled, AB = Alternative body, CW = Clockwork,
  D = Driver, FF = French Factory, IB = Illustrated Box,
  PP = Plated parts, RB = Running Board/s, WT = White tyres,
No. 1 Two-Seater Sports Car (Non Constructional),
  red with blue wings and seats, red hubs, WT/PP, E in E IB..............£,1900
No. 1 Two-Seater Sports Car (Non Constructional),
  all mid-blue with dark blue seats, PP/WT, E in G IB.......................£1,400
No. 1 Two-Seater Sports Car (Non Constructional),
  Blue and cream with red seat, E in G box with red dot on end £1,000
No. 1 Car Constructor Outfit, cream with red roof and wings,
  cream hubs, PP/WT, A/AB, E in E green IB......................................£640
No. 1 Car Constructor Outfit (Factory assembled), green with
  yellow roof and wings, green hubs, PP/WT, E in G IB....................£1,600
No. 1 Car Constructor Outfit, green with yellow wings and
  windscreen, red seats, green hubs, WT/PP, FF, E in VG.................£1,600
No. 1 Car Constructor Outfit, unassembled boxed set comprised of
  black bodies, red roof and wing parts, tools, E in E box.......................£950
No. 2 Car Constructor Outfit, black with red wings and seats,
  black hubs, PP/WT/D, E in VG IB £1,600
No. 2 Car Constructor Outfit, red with blue wings, red hubs,
  PP/WT/D, FF, E in E green IB...£1,700

Empty box for No. 2 Motor Car Garage, green cardboard,
  slightly worn, one end crushed £750
No. 2 Car Constructor Outfit (rare factory-assembled model) in
  cream and red, with 21/- price ticket in green £950

Chad Valley Fordson Dexta Tractor sold by Lacy Scott & Knight

Pre-war Dealer's Shop Display Card, 'Meccano,
Motor Car Constructor' with red car on yellow/blue background **£240**
Motor Car Lighting Set, 2.34 on lid, strung onto card with
multilingual instructions. Excellent in green box **£440**

MECCANO AEROPLANE CONSTRUCTOR OUTFITS
Abbreviation: **OBC** = Original backing card.
No. OO Outfit, blue and cream, instructions dated 12.39,
factory strung, U.S.A Export Box, superb **£460**
No. O Outfit, grey with R.A.F. roundels, floats, pilot etc.,
factory strung on OBC, instructions dated 11.39, GP in Good box **£560**
No. 1 Outfit, blue and cream with R.A.F. roundels, pilot etc.,
factory strung, instructions dated 4.33, Good Plus in Good Plus box....**£440**
No. 1A Accessory Outfit, manual dated 7.32,
strung to original backing card, Good Plus, boxed....................**£130**
No. 2 Outfit, early 1st type 1931 straight cut fuselage in silver.
Strung to OBC, manual dated 9.31, Good to Good Plus Boxed..... **£220**
No. 2 Outfit, silver and blue with flat wings, complete and strung to
original backing card, manual dated 7.32, GP boxed **£170**
No. 2 Outfit, red, cream and blue complete with all components in
display cabinet, Good Plus in excellent cabinet **£440**
No. 2 Outfit, green and cream and made up as a Tri Motor High Wing
Biplane with floats. Manual dated 3.39, G, GP **£560**
No. 0 Aeroplane Pilots, a box of six in different colours, most still in
original tissue wrap, box worn, NM boxed **£260**
No. 1 Aeroplane Pilots in various colours still in original tissue wrap,
box a little scuffed, Near Mint Boxed................................**£340**
No.O1P Aeroplane Hanger Outfit, red roof, green doors in original
base, Good Plus **£560**
Pre-war Dealer's Show Card, 'Meccano, AeroplaneConstructor,
The No. 2 Special Outfit Builds 44 Fine Models', E **£220**

MECCANO HORNBY SPEEDBOATS
No. 1 'Racer 1', cream and green, guarantee dated 2.36, GP boxed **£100**
No. 1 'Hawk', green hull and cream deck, Good boxed........................**£60**
No. 1 Naval Launch 'X46', 2 tone grey, post war, Fair boxed **£100**
No. 1 'Martin', red hull and deck, yellow motor cover, GP boxed **£130**
No. 2 'Swift', yellow hull, cream deck and blue trim, Good Plus boxed........**£100**
No. 2 'Swift', red hull, cream deck and blue trim, Good Plus Boxed..........**£160**
No. 3 'Racer III', cream with red trim, Good Boxed **£200**
No. 3 'Condor', red hull, cream deck and blue trim, Good Plus Boxed **£180**
No. 4 'Venture', blue hull, white deck, Good Plus, unboxed **£130**
Hornby Water Duck with lilac hull, rarest speedboat, GP in F box **£1,200**
'Hornby Speed Boats' Shop Display Card, shows 3 boats, Excellent **£150**
Shop Paper Display Poster, 'Hornby Speed Boat Week' 24"x18", NM **£400**

MAMOD LIVE STEAM MODELS
Steam Roadster SA1 in cream and red with instructions, E boxed..............**£45**
Steam Roadster SA2, cream / red, unused with all components, NMB **£60**
Steam Wagon SW1 in green, red and cream, unfired, E boxed **£70**
Steam Linousine SA1-L, silver, in black window box, MB....................**£100**
Fire Engine in red, never used, Near Mint boxed **£110**

SCALEXTRIC CARS and SETS
B2 Hurricane Racing Motor Cycle and Sidecar, yellow, '6', E/E **£100**
C1 Super Javelin 'Race Tuned' – blue, '9' E in GP box.......................**£60**
C5 Europa Vee 'Race Tuned' – yellow, '8', M in GP box **£60**
C14 Matra Grand Prix Car – blue, '6', GP in E box **£35**
C15 Ford Mirage – green, '2', E in F box **£35**
C16 Ferrari P4 – red, '4', 'You Steer', E in GP box **£35**
C34 (SpanishIssue) Jaguar E-type – green/chrome, NM UB **£120**
C54 Lotus Racing Car – yellow, '9', E in E box **£50**
C55 Vanwall R.C. – large head, blue, '8', E in E box **£110**
C56 Lister Jaguar – blue, '5', large head driver, EP in E box **£60**
C57 Aston-Martin – yellow, '4', large head driver, GP in GP **£150**
C57 Aston-Martin Racer – dark green, '5', E in EP box **£130**
C58 Cooper Racing Car – blue, '2', E in E box **£100**
C59 BRM Racing Car – green, '2', EP in E box **£120**
C60 Jaguar D type – green, '17', E in G box **£40**
C61 Porsche 'Race Tuned' – green, '12', E in repro box **£60**
C62 Ferrari Racing Car – yellow, '13', E in G box **£40**
C64 Bentley Racing Car (1929) – black, '6', figure, E in G **£130**
C65 Alfa Romeo Racing Car (1933) – blue, '10', G in GP **£140**
C66 Cooper Racing Car – blue, yellow wheels, '5' EP/GP **£30**
C67 Lotus Racing Car – red, yellow wheels, '3', EP/GP....................**£30**
C68 Aston-Martin DB4 – red, gold wheels, '6', EP in G box **£70**
C69 Ferrari Berlinetta – red, '6', Mint in E box **£110**
C71 Auto Union – yellow, green wheels, '3', E in E box **£380**
C74 Austin-Healey Sports 3000 – red, '5', M in NM box **£110**
C75 Mercedes-Benz 190SL – blue/white, NM in GP box **£130**
C76 Mini Cooper – red, '9', E in GP box **£45**
C77 Ford GT – pale blue, dark blue engine, '12', GP in E **£45**

C78 AC Cobra Sports Car – red, '66', E in GP box **£60**
C83 Sunbeam Tiger Sports Car – yellow/black, '7', E in E **£130**
C84 Triumph TR4 Sports Car – blue, '8', EP in E box **£120**
C87 Vanwall (Race Tuned) – dark green, '6', GP in F box **£45**
C93 Austin-Healey (Raced Tuned) – red, M in NM box **£160**
C94 Mercedes 190SL (Race Tuned) – white, NM/G.......................**£130**
C96 Auto Union – white, red wheels, '5', EP in G box **£240**
C97 James Bond Aston-Martin – white, red interior, GP /UB **£300**
C99 Fiat 600 – red, '16', E with folded leaflet in E box....................**£160**
C360 6R4 Metro 'Ternco' – blue/yellow, E in G box.......................**£140**
C562 'Batman Chase' Set – 2 cars with track, M in NM **£60**
C563 'Batman's Leap Set' – 2 cars plus track etc, M in E box **£70**
Cars from the James Bond set: Aston-Martin DB3 without sunroof and
Mercedes-Benz – black (missing 1 figure) G-E, unboxed **£680**

Scalextric Pin Badges (8) – blue/chrome/black E on Card **£90**
CK/1AC Cobra Kit – original unmade condition, NM in E **£200**
1/24 scale 24C/101 E-type Jaguar – green, '1', E in E box **£260**
E1 Lister Jaguar with Lights – blue, GP in GP box **£45**
E2 Aston-Martin with Lights – green, '8', E in GP box **£120**
E3 Aston-Martin DB4 with Lights (French) – NM in G box **£140**
E4 Ferrari 250 with Lights (French) - red, E in E box **£130**
Marshall's Car – black, 2 flags, unsold ....estimate **£350-£450**
K1 Go-Kart – blue, cream driver, black helmet, E in GP box **£130**
4050 Chevrolet Corvette (Spanish) – green, '52', GP, UB **£60**
4054 (Spanish) - Tyrrell P34 'Elf'- green, '8', M in G box **£40**
4059 (Spanish) - Lotus Mk. 4, 'John Player Special', M/GP **£50**
A221 Lap Recorder plus F302 TV Camera/Crew, both E/E...............**£130**
A239 Track and Pit Lights – black/green, EPin E box **£60**
French issue – Aston Martin DB4 GT 'Marshalls Car', E **£700**
G91 Scalestric Set - 2 x C8 and 2 x C9, near mint boxed..................**£300**
Set No. 80 with 2 x C81 Cooper and 2 x C82 Lotus, NM boxed **£300**
James Bond Set with Mercedes 190SL & Aston Martin DB4,
complete with figures, Good Plus in Fair box **£950**
VIP Raceway Models
Raceway Set No. A - MG Sports Car and Austin-Healey, E/E..............**£100**
R67S Lotus Indianapolis – green, red wheels, '8', EP in GP **£45**
Scalex Austin-Healey- red, and Aston-Martin DB2 - red, GP-E.............**£130**
MGTF – metallic blue, orange interior, Good Plus..........................**£90**
Airfix No. MR7 Motor Racing Set – overall M in GP box **£35**

WALLIS & WALLIS
West Street Auction Galleries, Lewes, Sussex, BN7 2NJ.
Condition abbreviations: VG = Very Good, **G** = Good, **UB** = Unboxed.

SUTCLIFFE SPEEDBOATS
Unda Wanda Diving Submarine, blue, Mint boxed with key...................**£70**
Jupiter Ocean Pilot Cruiser, red hull, cream deck, VG/UB **£50**
Sprite Day Cruiser, blue green hull, cream deck/cabin, M/UB **£90**
Valiant Battleship, black and grey, Mint Boxed............................**£95**
Commodore Cruiser, red hull, cream/blue deck area, M/UB **£60**
Victor Motor Torpedo Boat, pale blue/white, GC-VGC boxed **£40**
No. 1 'Martin', mid-blue hull, white cover, VG in VG box **£320**

MISCELLANEOUS TINPLATE
Mettoy Wells-style Tipping Lorry, tinplate wheels, VGC/UB **£210**
Mettoy Wells-style Military Lorry, camouflaged, VGC/UB **£150**
Mettoy Articulated AEC 'Queen Mary' Lorry, WW11 period
camouflaged with RAF aircraft 'WZF', roundels, GC-VGC **£500**
Scalex Aston Martin DB2, red in original box, GC for age....................**£80**
Wells delivery truck 'Express Transport', red/green, VGC...................**£95**
Wells-style 'Police' Van, dark blue, 'W417', VGC..........................**£110**
Camtoy Tipper Lorry, orange, blue/grey rear, 'PT669', VGC **£50**

TRI-ANG MINIC
8M Open Tourer, grey/cream, G/UB......................................**£75**
48M Transport Van, green/red, G boxed **£130**
81M 'LNER' Delivery Van, dark blue, GC -VGC **£80**
29M 'Police' Traffic Control Car, early, GC boxed.........................**£85**
48M Breadown Lorry, 2nd series, red/green, G boxed **£300**
53M Single Deck Bus, 'Greenline', G/UB **£150**
60M DD Bus, 1st version, red/cream, 'LBL174', G boxed **£250**
32M Dustcart, green cab, red back, VGC.................................**£130**

MECCANO
No. 6 Set dated 6/3/39, gold and blue in two layer box, Mint **£780**
1932 Aeroplane Sets 1 and 1A, silver finish, G-VG for age **£430**
1919 Inventors Outfit - various parts in original box, GC-VG................**£55**
Meccano 1970s shop display model 'Star Wheel', VGC **£160**
Meccano 1970s shop display model 'Windmill', GC – VGC **£150**

CHRISTIE'S, SOUTH KENSINGTON

Condition Abbreviations used in Christie's catalogues:
E = Excellent, **VG** = Very Good, **G** = Good, **F** = Fair.
MECCANO
Clockwork No.2 Constructor Car – red and blue, Good......................£418
No. 6 Outfit – nickel, in original oak case – G in F-G case.................£454
No. 5 Outfit – nickel in wooden case – F-G in F-G case....................£334
Trade Fair Model of 'Titanic' style liner, pitching action, VG............£1,116
Retail Display model of Two Tower Suspension Bridge, G-F.............£528
Outfit No. 7, 1st type (1927) red and green, oak case, VG/VG...............£3,172
Counter Display Chest, (1950's) red andgreen, VG overall.................£3,390
Outfit No. 10, red and green, original oak case, E-VG /VG...................£1,762
No. 1 Constructor Car, red/blue. Instructions/key, G/G......................£352
MISCELLANEOUS
Doll's House – 'Dingley Hall', 15 fully furnished rooms £127,750
Wells – 106 R.R.Town Coupé - blue/cream, E in VG box £382

LACY SCOTT & KNIGHT

10, Risbygate Street, Bury St Edmunds, Suffolk, IP33 3AA.
Condition abbreviations used in their catalogues:
E = Excellent, **VG** = Very good, **G** = Good, **F** = Fair, **UB** = Unboxed,
BM = Boxed/Mint, **NMB** = Near Mint, Boxed.

BUDGIE
Budgie Gift Set with four models issued in 1961, VG boxed £140
Budgie 218 Seddon 'Jumbo' Truck – 'AA', NMB £70
Budgie 238 Scammell Scarab Wagon – yellow 'Railfreight', BM............£48
Budgie 240 Scammell Scarab Wagon – crimson trailer, NMB..............£48

SHACKLETON MODELS
Foden FG6 Tipper Lorry – red/grey, E in F box £580
Foden FG6 Tipper Lorry – green/red, G in F box. £565
Foden FG6 Flatbed Lorry – blue/red, NM boxed............................£300
Foden FG6 Flatbed Lorry– green/red, G in G box £350

BRITAINS
20F Farmers Gig – green/red, farmer in grey, NM in E box...............£110
127F Fordson Major Tractor – G - E in E box £250
128F Fordson Major E27N Tractor – Fair in Good box £140
142F Single Horse Plough with Ploughman – E in G box £140
587 Village Idiot in pink smock, yellow socks, etc. – Good £145
9321 Ford Tractor TW35 – battery operated, MB...........................£90
9527 Ford Super Major 5000 Diesel Tractor – M in G box £205
Large quantity of Miniature Garden items, Good..........................£260
Britains Hunting Set 'Full Cry' (235)..£570
Britains – Fordson Tractor & Dump Truck, NM boxed £1,270

CHAD VALLEY
Fordson Major Tractor – G in NM box £240
9321 Ford Tractor TW35 – battery operated, MB...........................£90
9527 Ford Super Major 5000 Diesel Tractor – M in G box £205
Chad Valley London Bus Biscuit Tin, Mint boxed............................£700
Chad Valley Games Delivery Van, F-G in original box £680
Chad Valley No. 10003 Racing Car, green, aluminium, Mint £250
Chad Valley – 'Wee-Kin' Commer Avenger Coach £110
Chad Valley – Fordson Tractor (steering mechanism) £310

MISCELLANEOUS DIECAST
Benbros – Police Patrol, Reg No. 'TTC 147', E in E box...................£95
LoneStar – 'RAC' Land Rover, E in VG box £117
John Hill & Co – Dennis Fire Engine, G in VG box..........................£117
Charbens – Walking Barrow Boy – clockwork, VG in E box...............£110
Charbens – Steam Roller – green, red wheels, VG boxed £350
Scamold Alta Racing Car – silver, E boxed £175
Wells pre-war Rolls-Royce, cream/black, chauffeur, Mint £150
Wells Town Car, cream orange, lithographed, F-G £100
Kingsbury 'Bluebird' Record Car c.1929, blue, repaint £180
Kingsbury Seagrave's 'Golden Arrow' Record Car, repaint £130

MECCANO
No. 1 Sports Tourer M245, red/blue, Mint in good box £680
No. 1 Sports Car, green/yellow with red seats, G/UB.......................£220
No. 2 Constructor Car, red/blue, VG in VG box..............................£700
No. 2 Constructor Set, yellow/green, F.......................................£650
M250 Motor Car Garage, 'Meccano' on roof, VG /VG box £550
M251 Lighting Set for use with Constructor Set No.2, boxed.................£150

COLLECTOYS

BP22, 18001 Bourges Cedex, France.

Morestone – Wolseley Police Car, M in Ebox......................£90
Chad Valley – Fordson Tractor (1/16 scale) VG in VG box £570
Chad Valley – Guy Van, 'Chad Valley', G unboxed............................£180
Chad Valley – Guy Van, 'Guy Motors Ltd', E unboxed.......................£570
Chad Valley – Fordson Major Tractor – Mint in Good box £2,090
Britains – Two Seater Coupé, green/black, G in G box £370
Britains – 1499 Army Staff Car, VG in VG box £650
Lone Star – RAF Lorry, roundels on doors, E unboxed......................£325
Crescent – 1276 Scammell 'Esso' Tanker, VG in VG box £90
Crescent – 1272 Scammell Scarab Artic., G in VG box £57
Budgie – VW Pick-Up – 'Budgie Service', M in E box £98
Budgie – VW Pick-Up – yellow 'Kodak Films', M in E box £80
Benbros – AEC Lorry – Khaki, M in G box.....................................£65
Benbros – Foden Chain Lorry, M in E box £90
Benbros No 8. Foden Ballast Tractor with Log, VG in E.....................£82
Benbros – Euclid Rear Dump Truck (Qualitoy), VG in box £260
Dinky Toys 28b 'PICKFORDS' Van – very good condition £3,800
Skybirds – Lanchester Armoured Car, M in G box £650
Skybirds – Anti-Aircraft Gun, 4 soldiers, E in E box..........................£530
Spot-On – VW Variant Estate – NZ issue - VGC, unboxed...................£195
Spot-On – 402 Land Rover Breakdown Truck, G in G box..................£100
Spot-On – 114 Mk.I Jaguar – metallic green, E in E box £130

SPECIAL AUCTION SERVICES,

Kennetholme, Midgham, RG7

Timpo No.1 Car Set – tourer, attendant , pumps, etc., VG boxed £320
Timpo Farm Set – fifteen pieces in pink box – VG-E £260
Budgie Bulk Flour Tanker – G in G box.......................................£45
Budgie Commer Service Lorry – 'B.O.A.C.', E in G box....................£95
TINPLATE
Wells Tinplate Ambulance with driver, Reg No. W1929....................£240
Wells 'BP' Tanker with driver – green/yellow/black G £240
Wells DD Bus – 'Stirling Road, Walthamstow', 'AWW 130', G............£70
Betal (W Glasman Ltd) clockwork – Lithographed tinplate:
Betal Trolleybus –'Betal always the Winner', route '691', G-VG...........£100
Betal Trolleybus – 'Betal Toys for Girls and Boys, route '693', VG-E....£130
Betal Q Type Bus – 'General Transport Company', route '25', VG.........£220
Betal Q Type Trolleybus – 'Haymarket Station', route '25', VG............£240

CHAD VALLEY
DD Bus – 'Carrs Biscuits' Tin Bus, 'Victoria Station' G-VG................£320
Luxury Coach – blue/cream, 'CV 10005', VG in F box......................£380
Ford Dexta Tractor, VG in G box...£375

TRI-ANG MINIC
107M Short bonnet Lorry – 'British Railways', G £80
74M Forward Control Log Carrier – VG £65
32M pre-war Dust Cart with petrol can – E in VG box £180
32M post-war Dust Cart – red plastic hubs, E in G box £140
8M pre-war Open Touring Car – grey/chrome, G in F box £110
7M pre-war Town Coupé in reproduction box, G £90
34M pre-war Tourer with passengers, F in reproduction box £120
48M Brerakdown Lorry – Tri-ang transfers, G in F box £100
30M Articulated Pantechnicon - 'B Honess & Co Engineers from
 Marden in Kent' transfers (unrecorded promotional), Fair.................£90
21M Transport Van – pre war, 'Minic Transport',VG/F.....................£200
35M Taxi Cab – dark blue, F-G in reproduction box £65
60M pre-war 1st type DD Bus – 'Ovaltine', etc. adverts, VG/G............£420
60M pre-war 2nd type DD Bus, 'Ovaltine' etc adverts, E/F.................£240

Tri-ang Minic Toys

Minic Tinplate Model Toys
An introduction by Mike Richardson

Minic road vehicles and accessories were introduced in June 1935 by the famous English 'Lines Bros.', company of, by then, Morden Road, Merton, Surrey. The name 'Minic' had been registered as a trademark a few months earlier and was derived from the words MINIature Clockwork - which accurately described the toys.

The tinplate material used for the models was always painted and never lithographed as had been the usual method before. Radiator grilles were plated, as were the front wings on many of the models. In a manner similar to the contemporary Dinky Toys, the first issues were not badged as being a model of any particular car or truck, they were just named 'Limousine', 'Tourer', etc. The first car to carry the name of the manufacturer came along in 1936, the Ford £100 Saloon and the Ford Light Van built on the same chassis. These were really delightful little models and over the production run, which continued after 1945, appeared in many colours.

1937 was the year when Minic brought out the named Vauxhall, Rolls-Royce, Bentley and Daimler models. The Vauxhalls were the previous 'Limousine' and others but with the grille and bonnet modified to represent the flutes of the full-size cars. The Rolls, Bentley and Daimler were totally new models and were known as the 'Quality Cars'. These were also offered, with a very few other models, with electric headlights.

Some of the rarest models were produced for only a very short time in 1940-1941 in camouflage colours. Except for one item, these were otherwise normal issue models except for the colouring. The green paint was sprayed all over the assembled model and then the brown shading was brushed on by hand. This of course means that probably no two models are exactly alike. The most desirable is the Balloon Barrage Wagon and Trailer (76) which had a large balloon supplied with it. Once the three pieces of the balloon had been sewn together the toy could not be put back in its box, which has made a boxed version extremely valuable now. Petrol companies were under government control during the war and the petrol was known as 'POOL'. Tri-ang issued both of their petrol tankers, the rigid and the articulated, in grey with 'POOL' on the tanks in white.

When production resumed in 1946 not all of the range was re-introduced. Restrictions on the supply of metal for toys affected all toy factories badly. The colours of paint post-war were generally much harsher in shade — gone were the soft blues, browns, beiges and greys, and in their place were red, green and dark blue. By 1948 over 40 models had been re-issued, but by the middle of 1948 the first plastic Minics had appeared. Plastic of course allowed for more realistic shapes to be made. This applied particularly to private car models as the real car manufacturers had introduced curves into their new models. There were no new tinplate Minic cars after the war.

The generic truck models all featured a 'normal control' cab and bonnet layout left over from the pre-war era until 1950 to 1951.

Minic followed the full-size trucks by changing to the more modern looking 'forward control' configuration. This was known in the US as 'cabover', where the driver sat high up alongside the engine rather than behind it. Both the articulated and the rigid trucks were treated this way, but many people feel that Minic trucks lost a lot of their charm at this time. Motors changed from clockwork to 'push and go' about this time also.

Probably the most attractive models of the post-war era were the Delivery Vans (model nos. 79 - 82) painted in the colours of the four independent railway operators. These were only sold from 1947 to 1949 and were correctly coloured and decalled. They also had advertising posters stuck on the van sides. They were replaced by a similar 'British Railways' van (107) in 1950, but this was only sold for one year before being replaced by the short bonnet version. For some unknown reason the G.W.R. and L.M.S. vans are more difficult to find than the other two. The long bonnet B.R. van is also very scarce.

Pre-war Minic also made a wide range of wooden garages, fire stations and other accessories to go with the models. The construction of these was similar to the Tri-ang dolls' houses and other wooden toys.

1936 saw the appearance of the No. 1 Construction Set which was supplied in a fitted wooden case with a lovely colour poster on the lid showing six models and a parts list. The models were supplied unpainted and unassembled but with all the necessary axles, wheels, grilles, decals etc., even including small pots of paint. A lovely toy and one which could, and probably did, provide some unusual colour combinations once the children, or more likely, their fathers got at them.

As all Minic vehicles can be carefully disassembled by loosening the tin tabs, many odd variations have appeared over the years. One well known batch of G.W.R. vans appeared on the short bonnet van. These were done openly to use up a batch of old shop stock which had got a bit rusty. When they were sold in about 1978 everyone knew they were repaints, but do all collectors around today, some 25 years later, know this? Remember the Construction Set models as well.

Some cars, taxis and trucks have been very carefully 'restored' by skilful operators and have been seen in collections, sold in auctions and at swapmeets. Just take the usual care and do not jump at a 'yes, it's a rare colour variation' without giving it a very good look.

Minic also illustrated proposed models in their advertising which never went into production. Three of these spring to mind immediately, the Trolley Bus (77M), the Coal Lorry (70M) and the long-bodied Ambulance (75M). Some collectors and artisans have made replicas of these to show what they would have looked like. They are lovely pieces in their own right but just remember they were not made by Tri-ang.

Ref	Year(s), Model, details	Market Price Range
1M	**Ford £100 Saloon**	
	1936-41 Blue, green, beige, grey, red	£150-200
1MCF	1940-41 Camouflage finish	£400-500
1M	1946-49 As pre-war civilian version	£75-100
2M	**Ford Light Van**	
	1936-41 Blue, green, beige, red	£200-300
	1946-49 As pre-war version	£100-125
3M	**Ford Royal Mail Van**	
	1936-41 'Royal Mail'	£150-200
	1946-49 'E.R.', later 'G.R.' decals	£100-125
4M	**Sports Saloon**	
	1935-41	£200-300
5M	**Limousine**	
	1935-41	£200-300
6M	**Cabriolet**	
	1935-40	£300-400
7M	**Town Coupé**	
	1935-41 Brown / beige	£300-400
	1946-47 As pre-war version	£100-125
8M	**Open Touring Car**	
	1935-41 Green / cream	£200-300
	1946-47 As pre-war version	£100-125
9M	**Streamline Saloon**	
	1935-41 Based on the Chrysler Airflow sedan	£200-300
	1946-51 As pre-war version	£100-150
10M	**Delivery Lorry**	
	1935-41 Green / cream	£150-200
	1946-51 As pre-war version	£130-160
11M	**Tractor**	
	1935-40 See also 83M	£200-300
11MCF	1940-41 Camouflage finish	£500-600
12M	**Learner's Car**	
	1936-41 The pre-war version was based on 8M	£250-350
	1946-50 The post-war version was based on 17M	£150-200

Ref	Year(s), Model, details	Market Price Range
13M	**Racing Car**	
	1936-40 Open cockpit	£150-200
	1947-55 Closed cockit	£50-75
14M	**Streamline Sports**	
	1935-41 Open version of 9M	£250-350
	1946-51	£100-150
15M	**Petrol Tank Lorry / Petrol Tanker**	
	1936-41 Long bonnet cab, 'Shell' or 'B P' decals	£200-300
	1950-58 Short bonnet cab, 'Shell' or 'B P' decals	£100-150
NB	Some early post-war versions have Tri-ang triangle decal only.	
15MCF	**Petrol Tanker**	
	1940-41 Camouflage finish	£700-800
16M	**Caravan**	
	1936-41 Non-electric	£150-200
	1947-55 Non-electric	£50-75
17M	**Vauxhall Tourer**	
	1937-41 8M but with Vauxhall grille and bonnet	£250-350
	1947-55	£150-200
18M	**Vauxhall Town Coupé**	
	1937-41 Green / beige	£250-350
	1947-55 As pre-war version	£150-200
19M	**Vauxhall Cabriolet**	
	1937-41 Green body, plated wings	£300-400
19MCF	1940-41 Camouflage finish	£500-700
19M	1947-55 As pre-war version	£150-200
20M	**Light Tank**	
	1935-41	£400-500
20MCF	1940-41 Camouflage finish	£500-700
21M	**Tri-ang Transport Van / Delivery Van**	
	1935-41	£400-500
	1946-50 Replaced by 85M in 1951	£100-125
	'ATCO' version	£1,000-1,500

Tri-ang Minic

1M

'£100 Ford Saloon'

Photo:
Vectis Auctions Ltd.

21MCF **Delivery Van**
1940-41 Camouflage finish £600-800

22M **'Carter Paterson & Co' Van**
1936-41 ....£350-450
1946-51 ....£200-250
NB Early issues had 'Carter Paterson' decals,
later: 'Carter Paterson & Pickfords'.

23M **Tip Lorry**
1935-41 ....£200-250
1946-50 Replaced by 86M £100-150

24M **Luton Transport Van**
1936-41 Green / red £400-500
24MCF 1940-41 Camouflage finish £800-1,000
24M 1946-51 As pre-war version £150-200

25M **Delivery Lorry with Cases**
1936-41 Long bonnet cab, 6 wooden cases.......................£300-400
1946-50 Long bonnet cab, 6 wooden cases.......................£150-200
1950-56 Short bonnet cab, 6 wooden cases......................£150-200

26M **Tractor and Trailer with Cases**
1936-41 11M Tracked Tractor £300-400
1946-51 11M Tracked Tractor £150-200
1951-55 67M Farm Tractor, 6 wooden cases £150-200

27M, 28M Numbers not allocated.

29M **Traffic Control Car**
1938-41 As 4M, with driver, passenger,
single horn loudspeaker on roof........................£200-300
1947-52 With single horn loudspeaker on roof................£150-200
With later smaller 2-horn speaker £100-150

30M **Mechanical Horse & Pantechnicon**
1935-41 With 2-axle trailer, no decals.............................£150-200
1946-51 With 'Minic Transport' decals........................£150-200
1951-55 With single-axle trailer, 'Minic Transport' decals,
short bonnet cab £150-200
NB Rare 'BROCKHURST' issue £2,000-2,500

31M **Mechanical Horse & Fuel Oil Trailer**
1936-41 Long bonnet cab, 'Shell BP Fuel Oil' decals
(Mechanical Horse & Petrol Trailer)..................£300-400
1946-51 'Shell', 'BP', 'Shell Fuel Oils', or 'BP Fuel Oil' decals.
Long bonnet cab £150-200
1951-58 Same, but with short bonnet cab £150-200

32M **Dust Cart / Refuse Lorry**
1936-41 With long bonnet £200-300
1946-50 With long bonnet £100-150
1950-56 With short bonnet £100-150

33M **Steam Roller**
1935-41 Wooden wheels £175-225
1946-55 Plastic wheels £70-80

34M **Tourer with Passengers**
1937-40 8M with four cast lead figures £600-800

35M **Rolls Tourer**
1937-41 Sometimes numbered 118M.......................£1,000-1,200
1946-52 Sometimes numbered 118M.......................£150-200

36M **Daimler Tourer**
1937-41 Red with black hood.................................£1,000-1,200
1946-52 As pre-war version £150-200

37M **Bentley Tourer**
1938-41 Sometimes numbered 39M.......................£1,000-1,200
1946-52 Sometimes numbered 39M.......................£150-200

38M **Caravan Set (non-electric)**
1936-40 5M Limousine with 16M Caravan
(see 113M for post-war version)..........................£500-750

39M **Taxi / London Taxi**
1938-41 ....£1,500-2,000
1946-52 Post-war sometimes numbered 35M..................£100-150

40M **Mechanical Horse & Trailer with Cases**
1941-41 Long bonnet cab (very few made in 1941).........£300-400
1946-51 Long bonnet cab £150-200
1951-56 Short bonnet £100-150

41ME **Caravan with Electric Light & Battery**
1936-40 Battery not included, 16M with light bulb..........£300-400

42M **Rolls Sedanca**
1937-41 Orange/beige or beige/black.........................£1,000-1,500
1947-52 As pre-war version £150-200

43M **Daimler Sedanca**
1937-41 Red/black or beige/dark blue £1,000-1,500
1947-52 As pre-war version £150-200

44M **Traction Engine**
1938-41 ....£200-300
1946-55 ....£70-90

45M **Bentley Sunshine Saloon**
1938-41 Green/beige or dark green/black £1,250-1,750

46M **Daimler Sunshine Saloon**
1938-41 Green / beige £1,250-1,750
1946-52 As pre-war version £500-700

47M **Rolls Sunshine Saloon**
1938-41 Beige / black £1,250-1,750
1946-52 As pre-war version £500-700

48M **Breakdown Lorry with Mechanical Crane**
1936-41 Long bonnet..£300-400
1946-50 Long bonnet..£150-250
1950-56 Short bonnet £150-250

48MCF **Breakdown Lorry**
1940-41 Camouflage finish £500-700

49ME **Searchlight Lorry with Electric Searchlight**
1936-41 Battery not included £500-700

49MECF 1940-41 Camouflage finish, battery not included £700-900

50ME **Rolls Sedanca with Electric Headlamps**
1937-41 See also 42M. Red / black...........................£1,000-1,500

51ME **Daimler Sedanca with Electric Headlamps**
1937-41 See also 43M. Green / black £1,000-1,500

52M **Single Deck Bus / London Bus 'Red'**
1936-41 Duo-tone green, 'Green Line',
'London Transport' decals...............................£350-450
1946-58 Duo-tone green, early issues have 'Green Line'
decals, later: red 'London Transport' decals £350-450
Blue / Grey, 'Tri-ang Transport' decals....................NGPP
1958-60 Same model but with 'Routemaster' front £350-450

53M **Single Deck Bus**
1936-41 Red / stone livery, 'London Transport' decals £350-450

54M **Traction Engine & Trailer with Cases**
1939-41 44M with 2-axle Trailer, 6 wooden cases £150-200
1946-56 44M with 2-axle Trailer, 6 wooden cases £125-150

55ME **Bentley Tourer with Electric Headlamps**
1938-40 See also 37M. Beige / black..........................£1,500-2,000

56ME **Rolls Sunshine Saloon with Electric headlamps**
1938-40 See also 47M. Duotone green £1,500-2,000

57ME **Bentley Sunshine Saloon with Electric Headlamps**
1938-40 See also 45M. Apple green / black band........£1,500-2,000

58ME **Daimler Sunshine Saloon with Electric Headlamps**
1938-40 See also 46M. £1,500-2,000

59ME **Caravan Set (Tourer with Passengers)**
1937-40 34M Tourer with Passengers with
41ME Caravan with Electric Lights................£900-1,100

60M   **Double Deck Bus / London Bus**
1935-41   Red, maroon / stone, 'London Transport' **£400-500**
1946-58   All-red, red/cream roof,
     red / cream / red / cream / red roof,
     red with cream lower windows,
     red with cream upper windows;
     all with 'London Transport' decals **£250-350**
     Blue / cream **£300-400**
1958-60   Routemaster front, red, London transport or
     Tri-ang Transport decals......................................**£250-350**

61M   **Double Deck Bus**
1935-41   Green **£400-500**

62M   **London Fire Engine**
1936-41   ....**£200-300**
1946-56   ....**£175-225**

62ME   **Fire Engine with Electric Headlamps**
1936-38   ....**£350-450**

63M   **Presentation Set No. 1**
1936-40   Contains 1M, 4M, 5M, 6M and 8M..............**£1,500-2,000**

64M   **Presentation Set No. 2**
1936-40   Contains 1M, 2M, 5M, 13M, 15M, 20M,
     21M, 22M and 23M **£1,500-2,000**

65M   **Construction Set No. 1**
1936-40   Wooden case containing unpainted parts to
     assemble 5M, 6M, 9M, 10M, 11M and 21M
     models, including paint, decals and tools **£1,500-2,000**

66M   **Six-wheel Army Lorry**
1939-41   Model as 9M with 2 rear axles............................**£400-500**
66MCF   1940-41   Same model but in camouflage finish................**£400-500**

67M   **Farm Lorry**
1939-47   Model as 9M with stake frame **£600-800**

68M   **Timber Lorry**
1939-41   long bonnet cab, front ladder / plank rack **£250-350**
1946-51   long bonnet cab, front ladder / plank rack **£150-200**
1951-56   short bonnet, front ladder / plank rack...............**£100-150**

69M   **Canvas Tilt Lorry**
1939-41   Model as 9M with 2 rear axles and canvas tilt **£500-600**
69MCF   1940-41   Same model but in camouflage finish..............**£800-1,000**

70M   **Coal Lorry**   ---   Shown in catalogue but not issued.

71M   **Mechanical Horse & Milk Tanker**
1939-41   Long bonnet cab,
     'Minic Dairies 3150 Gallons' decals...................**£400-500**
1946-51   Long bonnet cab **£300-400**
1951-58   Short bonnet **£300-400**

72M   **Mechanical Horse & Lorry with Barrrels / Brewer's Trailer**
1939-41   Long bonnet cab **£400-500**
1946-51   Long bonnet cab **£400-500**
1951-56   Short bonnet **£300-400**

73M   **Mechanical Horse & Cable Drum Trailer / Cable Lorry**
1939-41   Long bonnet cab **£400-500**
1946-51   Long bonnet cab **£150-200**
1951-56   Short bonnet **£100-150**

74M   **Mechanical Horse & Log Trailer / Log Lorry**
1939-41   Long bonnet cab ....NGPP
1946-51   Long bonnet cab **£150-200**
1951-56   Short bonnet **£100-150**

75M   **Ambulance**
1939   Long bonnet cab shown in 1939/40 trade
     catalogue but model not issued.
1952-56   Short bonnet cab, based on 103M,
     red cross and 'LCC' decals **£200-250**

76M   **Balloon Barrage Wagon and Trailer**
1940-41   Truck chassis as 66M with winch,
     trailer with 'gas' cylinders,
     3-piece balloon in stiffened fabric.................**£3,000-4,000**

77M   **Trolley Bus** --- Shown in catalogue but not issued.

78M   **'POOL' Petrol Tanker**
1940-41   As 15M, grey only, white 'POOL' decals **£1,000-1,500**

78M   **Jeep No. 1**
1946-56   Olive green, gloss or matt **£70-90**

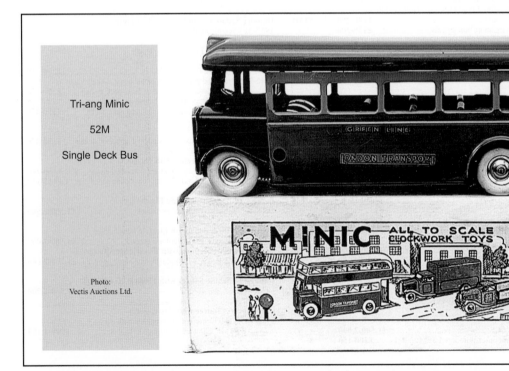

Tri-ang Minic

52M

Single Deck Bus

Photo:
Vectis Auctions Ltd.

79M   **Mechanical Horse & 'POOL' Tanker**
1940-41   As 31M, grey only, white 'POOL' decals **£1,000-1,500**

79M   **G.W.R. Railway Van**
1947-49   Model as 21M...**£1,000-1,200**

80M   **L.M.S. Railway Van**
1947-49   Model as 21M...**£500-750**

81M   **L.N.E.R. Railway Van**
1947-49   Model as 21M...**£400-500**

82M   **S.R. Railway Van**
1947-49   Model as 21M...**£400-500**

83M   **Farm Tractor**
1947-56   Main body as 11M..**£75-100**

84M   ---   See Plastic Models.

85M   **Forward Drive Van**
1951-55   Replaced 21M, short bonnet version....................**£100-150**

86M   **Forward Drive Tip Lorry**
1951-56   Replaced 23M...**£75-95**

87M - 92M   ---   Numbers not allocated.

93M   **'O' Saloon**
1952-56   Small scale car...**£150-200**

94M - 102M   ---   See Plastic Models.

103M   **Shutter Van**
1951-56   One piece lift-up rear door; see 75M **£100-150**

104M - 106M   See Plastic Models / No.2 Series.

107M   **British Railways Van**
1950-51   Model as 21M with British Railways decals **£150-200**
1951-55   Model based on 85M...**£100-150**

108M - 112M   ---   See Plastic Models.

113M   **Vauxhall Cabriolet and Caravan**
1950-51   19M + 16M...**£200-250**

114M   **Mechanical Horse & Trailer with Cruiser**
1950-51   Plastic Penguin boat **£150-200**
1951-56   Short bonnet cab, plastic Penguin boat **£150-200**

119M   **Watney's Barrel Lorry**
1952-56   Long bonnet tractor unit with barrel on roof, wooden
barrel artic. trailer; late models had short
bonnet cab without barrel on roof......................**£250-300**

123M   **British Road Services Lorry**
1951-56   Short bonnet 25M in red with B.R.S. decals **£250-300**

124M   **British Road Services Van**
1952-56   85M in green with B.R.S decals **£250-300**

145M   **Cement Mixer Lorry**
1951-56   Plastic mixer drum on short bonnet truck
chassis / cab **£100-125**

30M base Mechanical Horse & Pantechnicon
1937   'Brockhouse' promotional based on 30M **£1,500-2,000**

21M base Atco Mowers Van
1951?   'ATCO' promotional based on 21M..............**£1,000-1,500**

21M base Winstone Tiles / Furniture Van
1951?   New Zealand assembled model, based on 21M...**£500-750**

Other New Zealand issues

1M   **Ford Saloon**
1948?-51?   Red..NGPP
2M   **Ford Van**
1948?-51?   Blue ....NGPP
11M   **Tractor**
1948?-51?   Unpainted ....NGPP
15M   **Petrol Tank Lorry**
1948?-51?   Red / yellow, Shell decals **£500-750**
23M   **Tip Lorry**
1948?-51?   Red / purple-grey...NGPP
16M   **Caravan**
1948?-51?   Red / white ....NGPP
18M   **Vauxhall Town Coupé**
1948?-51?   Purple-grey / red wings ....NGPP
19M   **Vauxhall Cabriolet**
1948?-51?   Duotone blue ....NGPP

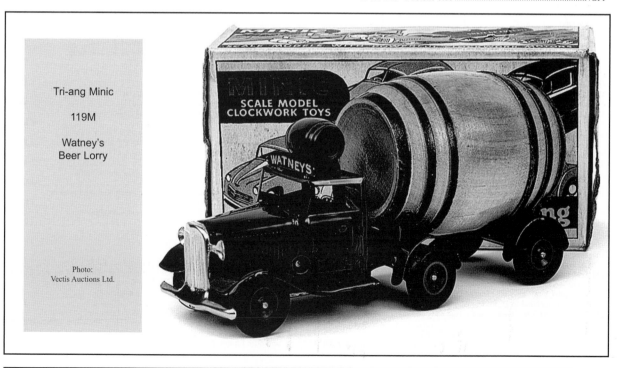

Tri-ang Minic

119M

Watney's
Beer Lorry

Photo:
Vectis Auctions Ltd.

These Auction Results are provided to support the Market Price Range guidance throughout the Catalogue.

**Results from the sale of the
Gates-Willard Tri-ang Minic Collection 2003/04**
sold by
Vectis Auctions Ltd.
Fleck Way, Thornaby, Stockton -on-Tees TS17 9JZ

Condition abbreviations:
M = Mint, **NM** = Near Mint, **EP** = Excellent Plus, **E** = Excellent,
GP = Good Plus, **G** = Good, **F** = Fair, **P** = Poor, **UB** = Unboxed.

Abbreviations for model features:
BH = Black Hubs, **BO** = Battery Operated, **BT** = Black Tyres,
BRW = Black Rounded Wings, **CH** = Cast Hubs,
C/M/F/2G/P = Chauffeur, Male, Female and 2 girl Passengers,
PFW = Plated Flared wings, **PRW** = Plated Round Wings,
'MT' = 'MINIC TRANSPORT, ROAD RAIL AIR SEA, EXPRESS
SERVICES' transfer, **PC** = Petrol Can, **PP** = Plated parts,
RPH = Red Plastic Hubs, **'TDH'** = 'Tri-ang Dolls Houses',
'TPM' = 'Tri-ang Pedal Motors', **'TT'** - 'Tri-ang Tricycles',
TNP = Transfer number Plate, **WT** = White Tyres, **WS** = Wooden seats

---

PRE-WAR ISSUES

1M Ford £100 Saloon, beige, PP/PC/WT, Excellent, UB £150
1M Ford £100 Saloon, green, no PC/PP/BT, E, UB £150
1MCF Ford Saloon, camouflage, BH/BT, E in G box £480
2M Ford Light Van, blue, 'Minic Transport Express Services'
transfer on sides, PC/PP/WT, E/UB £260
2M Ford Light Van, green, 'Minic Transport Express Services'
transfer on sides, PC (on offside), PP/WT, E/UB £280
2M Ford Light Van - red body, petrol can,white tyres,
'Lines Bros' triangle transfer on sides, excellent UB £270
2M Ford Light Van - beige, 'Minic Transport Express Services'
transfer on sides, petrol can, white tyres, VG in VG box £220
3M Ford 'Royal Mail', 'ER', PC/PP/WT, E /VG box £240
3M Ford 'Royal Mail' (LI) - 'GR' to sides, BH/BT, E/UB, ...£150
4M Sports Saloon, beige, flared wings, PP/TH/BT, E in VG £300
5M Limousine - new blue PRW/PP/WT/PC, VG/UB £220
6M Cabriolet - red/beige, PRW/PP/WT,VG /G £260
6M Cabriolet - dark brown, PFW/PP/BT, E/VG £380
7M Town Coupé - brown/beige, PFW/PP/WT, F-G/F £300
8M Open Tourer - blue/beige, PRW/PC/BT, E/UB £280
9M Streamline Saloon - red body, PP/WT, E/VG £320
10M Delivery Van -green/blue, PRW/PC/BT, E/VG £160
11MCF Tractor - Camouflage, BH/BT, E/E box £560
12M Learner's Car - green/beige, PRW/BT/PC/WS, E/UB £340
13M Racing Car -green, NO.'6', WT, E in F box £170
14M Streamline Sports, tan/ black, WS/WT,VG/G £360
15M Petrol Tanker, 'Shell & BP', white tyres, PP/PC/WT
'Lubricate with Shell Oil' logo on rear ....Estimate £200
15MCF Petrol Tanker - camouflage, BT, E, UB £700
17M Vauxhall Tourer - blue/stone, PRW/BT/PC, E/UB £240
18M Vauxhall Town Coupé, green/beige, PRW/PC/WT, G/UB £280
18M Vauxhall Town Coupé - dark blue, PFW/BT/PP, VG/G £320
19M Vauxhall Cabriolet - green body, plated rounded wings,
PP/BT/PC, Excellent unboxed £250
19MCF Vauxhall Cabriolet - all camouflage body, black hubs,
rounded wings, BT, Good unboxed £420
20M Light Tank - gloss olive green, wooden wheels, E, UB £440
20M Light Tank - camouflage, wooden wheels, E, UB £560
21M Transport Van - new blue cab , dark red body, CP,
WT, no decals on sides/rear, VG in G box £320
21M Transport Van - beige/green 'Minic' on
rear and front, 'MT' on sides, PP/BH/BT, E in G box £300
21M Transport Van - stone/brown, 'MT' and 'Triang' on sides,
'Minic' on rear and front, PP/WT/PC, E/VG £560
21M Transport Van - tan /red, 'Triang' and 'MT' on sides,
'Minic' on rear and front, PP/PC/WT, E/VG £520
21MCF Transport Van - brown camouflage body and hubs,
Excellent, unboxed £540
21M Transport Van - dark brown and beige, PP/BT,
'MG and Safety Fast', Promotional, Excellent UB £560

22M Transport Van - deep red cab, dark green body. 'Carter Paterson'
and Elephant design transfers, with 'Send your Trunk in Advance'
logo, PC/PP/WT, E/F...£320
23M Tip Lorry - green cab, deep red tipping body, chromed wing and
hubs, petrol can, black tyres, No result available, E/UB ....Estimate £175
24MCF Luton Van - all camouflage including radiator and hubs,
black tyres, VG in G box £800
24M Luton Van - green cab, red body, 'Minic' to rear,
'MT' on sides, PC/PP/WT..£420
30M Mechanical Horse & Pantechnicon - green/tan,
'Minic' & 'MT' on sides, PP/WT,VG red box £580
30M Mechanical Horse & Pantechnicon - red/gold fransfer with
'BROCKHOUSE TRAILERS OF ALL KINDS'.
Light grey cab, red back, chromed wings/hubs, PC/WT.
Promotional - E in red picture box - sold in 2001 for......................£1,200
31M Mechanical Horse & Fuel Oil Trailer/Petrol Tanker,
PC, 'SHELL - BP FUEL OIL', PC/CP/WT, E/UB £300
34M Open Tourer with C/M/F/2G/P - dark green with stone
interior, PP/BT, Excellent in VG red box £950
35M Rolls-Royce Tourer - red with black hood and wings,
plated rounded wings, CP/WT/PC, E/UB £900
39M Taxi - mid green, black roof/wings, beige interior,
'Taxi'to front, PC/PP/WT, TNP, VG ,UB £1,100
39M Taxi - new blue, black roof/ wings, beige interior,
'Taxi' to front, PC/PP/WT, TNP, E in VG box £1,700
39M Taxi - blue body, black roof, stone luggage area with PC,
PP/BT 'Taxi' sign, sold at 2001 auction, EP unboxed £500
39M Taxi - red body, black roof and wings, stone luggage area
with PC, Good Plus boxed - sold in 6/02 for £360
42M Rolls-Royce Sedanca - beige with black hood and wings,
red interior, PP/BT, Excellent in Good red box £1,100
42M Rolls-Royce Sedanca - orange with beige hood/wings,
red interior, PP/BT, mainly VG in VG red box £1,500
43M Daimler Sedanca - dark blue with black hood and wings,
white interior, PP/BT, Excellent U/B £1,300
44M Traction Engine - no auction details available.
..............................Estimate - for Excellent unboxed example £200
45M Bentley Sunshine Saloon - green with beige windows,
PP/BT, Excellent, UB £1,100
46M Daimler Sunshine Saloon - green with beige windows.
PP/BT, Excellent in VG blue/grey box £1,400
48M Breakdown Lorry - red cab/jib, green back, PC/PP/BT,
'Lines Bros'triangle, plus 'Minic Motor Service Co' and
'BreakdownLorry' transfers, E/F red box ....Estimate £400
48MCF Breakdown Lorry with Crane - green and brown
camouflage, painted hubs, PP/BT, Excellent unboxed......................£380
49ME Searchlight Lorry - dark green with dark red rear body,
PC/CP/WT, BO, Excellent in VG red box £520
49 MCF Searchlight Lorry - camouflage finish, painted hubs,
black tyres, battery operated searchlight, VG unboxed £620
50ME Rolls-Royce Sedanca - beige with green hood and wings,
PP/BT, battery in boot, BO,VG, unboxed..£800
51ME Daimler Sedanca (E) - green with beige hood and wings,
PP/BT, Excellent in VG red box £1,000
52M Single Deck Bus - red, stone roof, 'London Transport',
'Dorking', 'Bisto'advert to rear, PP/WT, E/F box £420
53M Single Deck Bus - duo green, 'Greenline', PP/WT,
'Bisto' advert to rear, VG in VG box £360
55ME Bentley Tourer - beige with black wings and running
boards, PP/BT, BO, VG in G grey box £1,600
56ME Rolls-Royce Sunshine Saloon - duo green body and running
boards, PP/BT, BO, VG in G grey box £1,600
57ME Bentley Sunshine Saloon - apple green with black hood
and wings, PP/BT/BO, Excellent in F green box.............................£1,700
58ME Daimler Sunshine Saloon - PP/BT, BO,
No results details available, Estimate, E /G £1,500
59ME Caravan Set (34M Tourer with passengers), PP/BO.
No auction results details available, Estimate for Excellent boxed ...£1,000
60M DD Bus - deep red, stone roof and windows, 'London Transport'
plus 'Ovaltine Bovril & Bisto' advert. transfers,
PP/WT, 'Mitcham', '177', E/F unboxed £480
61M Double Decker Bus - duo green, 'London Transport', 'Ovaltine',
'Bovril' and 'Bisto' transfers, 'Mitcham', '177', PP/WT, E, unboxed .£280
62ME London Fire Engine - red body with black wings, brass bell
and hose fittings, plated parts, black tyres, BO, E in E red box £340

62ME London Fire Engine (E) - red with black wings, BO/ PP/BT, brass bell and hose fittings, E in E box............£340

63M Presentation Set 1 - Limousine, Cabriolet, Sports Saloon, Open Tourer, Ford Saloon, E, boxed.................Estimate **£1,500**

64M Presentation Set 2 - for contents please refer to the tables. Models VG - E in F box (illustrated lid)............**£1,600**

65M Construction Set: Transport Van, Cabriolet, Super Saloon, Limousine and Tractor all in a dismantled, unpainted condition. Instructions, 4 tins 'Minic Paint' contained in oak box with cardboard outer.......**£1,600**

66M Six Wheel Army Lorry - gloss dark green cab and rear body, PH/BT, PC, Excellent, unboxed............£340

66MCF Six Wheel Army Lorry - brown and green camouflage body, plain white box, NMB £400

67M Farm Lorry - beige cab, green body, black R/H, plated wings and hubs with black tyres. E in F box **£680**

68M Timber Lorry - green cab, blue rear body, 12 wooden plank load, PP/BT, E in F printed box £240

68M Timber Lorry - light green/dark green, timber load, rounded wings, PP/BT, E in G box £280

69MCF Canvas Tilt Lorry (6 wheels) - Camouflage version including hubs with black tyres, E in VG box £800

72M Mechanical Horse & Lorry with Barrels - green with red trailer chrome parts, black tyres, Excellent in Fair box £240

76M Balloon Barrage Wagon and Trailer - camouflage, 12 wood 'cylinders', BT, VG in F blue box............**£3,000**

78M Petrol Tanker - all grey including the radiator with white 'POOL' on tank, CP/BT, Excellent unboxed............£900

POST WAR ISSUES

1M Ford Saloon - dark green, PP/BPW, Excellent, UB £50

2M Ford Van - green, 'MT' transfers to sides, E, unboxed............£70

3M Ford Post Office Van - 'Royal Mail GR', NM in GP box £100

10M Delivery Lorry - red/blue, tin hubs, PP, E in P box £130

15M Petrol Tanker - green/red, 'BP', PP/BT, NM in E box............£120

17M Vauxhall Tourer - mid green/black, PP/BT, EP/E £160

19M Vauxhall Cabriolet - green, flared wings, E in GP box £170

21M Transport Van - red/green, 'MT', VG, UB £80

22M 'Carter Paterson & Pickfords' Van - red cab, green body, 'Send It By' and Elephant transfers, PP/BT, E unboxed............£170

24M Luton Van - red cab with green back 'MT' on sides, PP/BT, VG in G box £130

30M Mechanical Horse & Pantechnicon - red/green, 'Triang & 'MT' transfers, PP/BT, VG /G............£130

31M Mechanical Horse & Fuel Oil Trailer - green cab, red tank, 'SHELL BP FUEL OIL', E/UB............no result, Estimate **£200**

39M Taxi Cab - dark blue/black, PP, (no headlights), GP £100

42M Rolls Sedanca - green body, black hood, Good Boxed............£125

48M Breakdown Lorry - red cab, green rear, 'Minic Motors Breakdown Service', NM in G box £240

47M Rolls-Royce Sunshine Saloon - red/black, GP, unboxed............£170

52M Single Deck Bus - deep red with stone roof, 'London Transport' and 'Dorking', PP/BT, E in illustrated box £420

52M Single Deck Bus - light blue, grey roof, cream stripe, 'London Transport' in gold on red, PP/BT, E/UB............£300

52M Single Deck Bus - 'Greenline'- two tone dark green sides, light green including roof, black trim, NM in blue box............£170

52M Single Deck Bus - 'Greenline' - Routemaster tin front, green, cream trim, 'Spot On' style tyres, GP unboxed............£80

53M Single Deck Bus (Routemaster front) - red, 'Tri-ang Pedal Motors', 'Pedigree Prams' posters plus 'Tri-ang Toys' decals, PP/BT, E, UB...£280

54M Traction Engine/Trailer, green and brass, Near Mint in Good box...£100

60M DD Bus - 1st issue - orangey-red with cream window surrounds to lower/upper decks, diecast hubs, 'Bovril', 'Ovaltine' and 'Bisto' adverts. Near Mint in Poor box £220

60M DD Bus 2nd issue - orangey-red, cream upper deck, windows, 'Minic Cars' and 'Penguin' adverts on sides, 'PedigreePrams' on rear, 'London Transport' to sides, Excellent Plus in Fair box............**£150**

60M DD Bus - later issue, all red with cream dividing line, 'Tri-ang Pedal Motors', 'Penguin Boats' and 'Frog Model Aircraft' poster adverts, CH/BT E/F **£320**

60M DD Bus - red lower deck, cream upper deck, grey roof, 'Tri-ang Pedal Motors', 'Penguin Boats' and 'Frog Model Aircraft' poster adverts, PP/BT, GP UB **£320**

60M Double Decker Bus - blue lower deck, cream upper deck, adverts for 'Pedigree Prams' and 'Penguin Boats', BT, Good Plus unboxed **£150**

60M Double Decker Bus - Routemaster tin front- red bdy, 'London Transport' on sides, 'Spot-On' style tyres, PP/BT, Good Plus unboxed............**£80**

60M Routemaster DD Bus 2nd version - two tone deep red, stone window surrounds to upper and lower deck 'Triang Pedal Motors, Pedigree Prams' adverts., 'Tri-ang Transport' to sides, PP/BT, GP - E, UB......**£280**

62M 'London Fire' Engine - red/black, RPH/BT, Near Mint Boxed............**£200**

68M Timber Lorry - green/red, red hubs, VG in G box **£120**

71M Mechanical Horse & Milk Tanker - 'Minic Dairies', dark blue/off white, '3150 gallons', PP/CH/BT, E in E **£220**

72M Mechanical Horse & Brewery Trailer - red and green, red 'Minic Brewery' logo, PP/BT, E in F box **£320**

73M Mechanical Horse & Cable Trailer - red/green , PP/BT, 'British Insulated Callenders Cables', GP in E box **£90**

74M Mechanical Horse & Log Lorry, red/green, log load, E in VG box ...**£90**

79M Delivery Van - dark brown/cream, 'B 4157' on bonnet, 'G.W.R - Express Cartage Service' plus 'Tri-ang Tricycles' and 'Pedigree Prams' poster adverts on sides, PP/BT, E in VG box.........**£900**

80M Delivery Van - maroon and black, '5147 G' on the bonnet, white 'L.M.S Express Parcels Service' on sides, 'L.M.S.' on front and right hand rear door, 'Tri-ang Tricycles' and 'Pedigree Prams' posters on sides, PP/BT, G boxed............**£450**

81M Delivery Van - all dark blue, 'BB 1374' on bonnet, 'L.N.E.R. Express Parcels Service' on sides, 'Pedigree Prams' and 'Fairycycles' poster adverts on sides, PP/BT, Excellent unboxed......**£280**

82M Delivery Van - all green , '241M' on bonnet and sides, 'Southern Railway' on sides and rear, 'Tri-ang Pedal Motors' and 'Tri-ang Dolls Houses' poster adverts on sides, PP/BT, E in VG box..**£340**

85M Forward DriveVan - red cab, blue back, cast hubs, PP/BT, 'MT' on gold background, E, unboxed **£100**

86M Forward Drive Tip Lorry - red cab with blue back, cast hubs, PP/BT, Excellent, unboxed **£55**

107M 'British Railways' Delivery Van - maroon/cream, 'Cheap Tickets and Excursions by British Railways' poster advert, PP/BT, GP - E, UB **£100**

114M Mechanical Horse & Boat Trailer, green, red/cream boat, VG, UB **£130**

119M Mechanical Horse & Trailer - white 'Watney's' logo, dark green with wood barrel with 'Watneys Red Barrel Ale' on end of barrel, red plastic barrel on cab roof with black 'Watney's' logo, RPH, Estimate E in VG box **£200**

124M Open Lorry - dark red, yellow British Railways 'Lion' emblem on doors white 'British Road Services' logo on sides, Near Mint in Good Plus box **£260**

New Zealand Issue 'Shell' Tanker - red cab, yellow tanker, plated wings and hubs, plated grille, black tyres, very good unboxed............**£520**

New Zealand Issue 24M-style 'Winstone' Luton Van, CP/BT, red/green, 'Winstone Tiles - Make Homes Beautiful' and 'Winstone Ltd - Furniture Van' logos, F-G, UB **£240**

Early post-war
Tri-ang Minic toys

15M
Petrol Tank Lorry

25M Delivery Lorry

Photo:
Vectis Auctions Ltd.

Meccano Cars and Constructor Outfits

In 1932, Meccano introduced their 'Motor Car Constructor Outfit'. With its special parts (not compatible with standard Meccano), a small range of very sporty looking car models could be built. A year later, a smaller set, designated 'Motor Car Constructor Outfit No.1' appeared and the first set was given the superior 'No.2' tag. Features abounded: stylishly shaped mudguards and body panels, alternative radiators, working Ackermann steering, a driver; even working brakes! The kits included a powerful clockwork motor as standard and the whole lot could be driven 'at night' with the addition of the Motor Car Lighting Set that came along as early as 1933.

In addition, spare parts were available from Meccano dealers that enabled young builders to achieve different colour schemes. Body Sections were available in Orange and in Yellow, Wings in Orange and in Green, and Wheels in Orange or Yellow.

Ready-built models were available and are listed below. These were made up from parts relevant to the No.1 Outfit. A non-constructional Meccano Sports Car was also marketed at the time, as was a Motor Car Garage to house the vehicles, whether ready made or owner constructed.

Production quantities of the Outfits appear to have been somewhat limited in the latter half of the 1930s decade, thus surviving items are quite rare nowadays, especially in good and complete condition. All the Car Constructor Outfits were withdrawn from the Meccano Products Catalogue around 1940 and were never reintroduced.

Motor Car Constructor Outfit.
Made from 1932 to 1933. No driver figure. Supplied in a strong green carton with a colourful label on the lid. In 1933, this set was promoted to 'Motor Car Constructor Outfit No.2'. Three colour options were available:
Red main components **£400-500**
Blue main components **£400-500**
Green main components **£400-500**

Motor Car Constructor No. 1 Outfit.
Made from 1933 to 1940. No driver figure. Supplied in a strong green and yellow carton on the lid of which was a colourful label with an artist's impression of the Road Racer at speed. Outfits were supplied complete with a powerful clockwork motor. Four colour options were available:
Red and Light Blue main components................................**£300-400**
Light Blue and Cream main components...............................**£300-400**
Green and Yellow main components.....................................**£300-400**
Cream and Red main components..**£300-400**

Ready-built models were also available, made up from the No.1 Outfit:
1/1	**Sports Tourer** (with Hood), blue box, instruction sheet ...	**£500-700**
1/2	**Saloon Coupé**, blue box with instruction sheet	**£500-700**
1/3	**Road Racer**, blue box with instruction sheet	**£500-700**
1/4	**Sports Tourer**, blue box with instruction sheet	**£500-700**

Meccano Two-seater Sports Car (non-constructional)
Length 8½". Clockwork motor. Available in three different colours:
Red, patterned green box has lift-off lid with full-colour label......**£1,200-1,500**
Blue, patterned green box has lift-off lid with full-colour label......**£1,000-1,200**
Cream, patterned green box has lift-off lid with full-colour label...**£1,000-1,200**

Motor Car Constructor No. 2 Outfit.
Made from 1933 to 1941. Presentation and colours of parts were identical to those of the No.1 Outfit. As this set was developed from the 1932 Outfit, early versions have no driver figure. This enhancement (plus a few other minor modifications) appeared a few months later. The separately available spare parts also came in the same choices as for the No.1 set. However, it is very important to note that parts for the No.1 Outfit were **not compatible** with the No.2 Outfit (nor with standard Meccano parts).
Red and Light Blue main components...**£700-900**
Light Blue and Cream main components..**£700-900**
Green and Yellow main components...**£700-900**
Cream and Red main components...**£700-900**

Ready-built models were also available, made up from the No.2 Outfit:
2/1	**Sports Tourer** (with Hood), blue box, instruction sheet ...	**£700-900**
2/2	**Saloon Coupé**, blue box with instruction sheet	**£700-900**
2/3	**Road Racer**, blue box with instruction sheet	**£700-900**
2/4	**Sports Tourer**, blue box with instruction sheet	**£700-900**

Motor Car Lighting Set
Introduced in 1933. This set enabled the headlights in the No.2 Outfit to be illuminated using a 3 volt battery (not supplied).
Green box with lift-off lid ('M251'), instruction sheet..........................**£150-300**

Meccano Motor Car Garage
designed to accommodate Meccano Motor Cars (or others of a suitable size). Inside dimensions: H 5in., L 13in., W 7 3/4in. Green box, lift-off lid ..**£200-400**

See pages 44, 45 and 48 for colour illustrations of Meccano Cars, Car Constructor Outfits, Aeroplane Constructor Outfits, accessories, and other Meccano Products.

Meccano Aeroplane Constructor Outfits

Meccano Aeroplane Constructor Outfits were introduced in October 1931 and were available in two varieties simply called Outfits No.1 and No.2. Unlike the Car Constructor Outfits, there was compatability between the No.1 and No.2 Aeroplane sets. This allowed the inclusion of a further set - No.1A Accessory Outfit which could convert the smaller one into the larger. Early wheels were actually standard Meccano pulleys painted red. There were a few other conventional Meccano parts in these Outfits (originally sprayed in silver paint) but the major components were specially designed for the purpose.
For the No.1 set, the manual described three biplanes and three monoplanes that could be constructed. With its extra parts, which included diecast engine and seaplane floats, the No.2 manual suggested sixteen additional potential models.
Early in 1932, two clockwork motors were introduced for use with these Outfits. The smaller of them just rotated the propeller, while the larger one actually provided sufficient motive power to the landing wheels to cause the model aircraft to taxi along the carpet runway.

A year later, much development work had produced better components. Special wheels complete with stylish spats, for instance, replaced the unsuitable pulley wheels. Wing edges had become realistically rounded and wing tips and fuselages were enamelled in red.
1933 saw the introduction of Outfits No.OO and No.O as cheaper, simpler sets aimed at younger builders, and not interchangeable with Nos. 1 and 2. In the same year, the range was enlarged to include No.1 Special Outfit (twenty models) and No.2 Special Outfit (forty-four models). Available in various bright and attractive colours, the Special Outfits were very well endowed with new purpose-made components such as workable ailerons and rudders, passenger window panels, pilot's cabins, tail elevators, etc. There was even a model pilot for insertion into the open-cockpit model. Both civilian and military liveries were from time to time available in the late 1930s.
As with most Meccano items, the War brought production to a halt around 1940. Aeroplane Constructor Outfits were officially withdrawn in 1941 and sadly were never made again.

No.00 Aeroplane Constructor Outfit
Made from 1932 to 1940. Designed for the younger builder, this set had a one-piece fuselage plus a few simple parts that were not compatible with Outfits No. 1 and 2. Supplied in a stout box with a two-colour label on the lid.
Red and cream components. Blue box with instructions.......................**£200-300**
Green and cream components. Blue box with instructions **£200-300**
Blue and white components. Blue box with instructions.......................**£200-300**

No.0 Aeroplane Constructor Outfit
Made from 1932 to 1940. As the No.0 Outfit but with more parts (also not compatible with Outfits No. 1 and 2). Supplied in a stout box with a full-colour label on the lid.
Red and cream components. Blue box with instructions.......................**£250-400**
Green and cream components. Blue box with instructions **£250-400**
Blue and white components. Blue box with instructions.......................**£250-400**
Seville Grey components, RAF markings. Blue box + instructions......**£250-400**

No.0P Aeroplane Hangar Outfit
Made from 1933 to 1940. The complete range of parts from Outfit No. 0, packed into a No.01 Aeroplane Hangar, then into a stout carton.
Red and cream components, blue box with lift-off lid, instructions **£350-500**
Green and cream components, blue box with lift-off lid, instructions ..**£350-500**
Blue and white components, blue box with lift-off lid, instructions **£350-500**

No.01 Aeroplane Hangar
Made from 1933 to 1940. To house a model aircraft made from Outfits No. 00, 0 or 01P. Single door, size (mm): 292(L) x 260(D) x 108(H).......NGPP

No.02 Aeroplane Hangar
Made from 1933 to 1940. To house two models made from Outfits No. 00, 0 or 01P. Single door, size (mm): 546(L) x 279(D) x 159(H).......NGPP

No.1 Aeroplane Constructor Outfit
Made from 1931 to 1932. Silver coloured components, standard Meccano pulley wheels (red). Wings and tailplanes have 'RAF markings. Manual shows 6 examples of mono- and biplanes that can be built. Supplied in a strong carton with a colourful label on the lid. **£100-200**

No.1 Aeroplane Constructor Outfit
Made from 1932 to 1940. Purpose-made wheels with enveloping spats replaced the Meccano pulley wheels. Wing and tailplanes edges were more rounded and realistic. Civilian as well as 'Military' models could also be built. Supplied in a strong blue carton with a colourful label on the lid.
Silver components (early production)....................................**£150-250**
Cream components, RAF roundels **£250-400**
Blue and cream components, RAF roundels.......................................**£250-400**
Red and cream components...**£250-400**
Green and cream components **£250-400**

No.1A Aeroplane Constructor Accessory Outfit
Made from 1931 to 1932. Silver components, sufficient to convert the No.1 Outfit into a No.2. Supplied in a strong carton with a colourful label on the lid..**£100-200**

No.1A Aeroplane Constructor Accessory Outfit
Made from 1932 to 1940. As the earlier set, but in the colours of the main Outfits available at the time Supplied in a strong carton with a colourful label on the lid. **£100-200**

No. 2 Aeroplane Constructor Outfit
Made from 1931 to 1932. Silver coloured components, red standard Meccano pulley wheels. Additional parts included seaplane floats and diecast engines. Wings and tailplanes have RAF markings. Manual shows 22 examples of mono-, bi- and seaplanes that can be built. Supplied in a strong carton with a colourful label on the lid. .**£100-200**

No. 2 Aeroplane Constructor Outfit
Made from 1932 to 1940. As with the No. 1 Outfit, purpose-made wheels with spats replaced the original pulley wheels. Wing and tailplanes edges were more rounded and realistic. A much larger range of models could be built, including 'planes with 1, 2 or 3 engines, a Racing Seaplane, and a Giant Italian Bomber. Supplied in a strong blue carton with a colourful label on the lid.
Silver and blue components (early production) **£100-200**
Cream components, RAF roundels **£250-400**
Blue and white components, RAF roundels...**£250-400**
Red and Cream components **£250-400**
Green and Cream components **£250-400**

No.1 Special Aeroplane Constructor Outfit
Made from 1933 to 1940. In addition to the improved parts in the standard Outfits, new components in the 'Special' sets included engine cowlings, a pilot figure, passenger windows, moving ailerons and rudders. The manual (that covered both Outfits 1 and 2) showed twenty example models. Supplied in a strong blue carton with a colourful label on the lid.
Silver components (early production)....................................**£300-450**
Cream components, RAF roundels **£300-450**
Blue and white components, RAF roundels...**£300-450**
Red and Cream components **£300-450**
Green and Cream components **£300-450**

No.1AS Special Aeroplane Constructor Accessory Outfit
Made from 1933 to 1940. This set provided sufficient parts to convert the No.1 Special Outfit into a No.2. Supplied in a strong blue carton with a colourful label on the lid. **£100-200**

No.2 Special Aeroplane Constructor Outfit
Made from 1933 to 1940. As the No.1 Special Outfit, but with many additional parts that allowed the construction of the forty-four models shown in the manual, plus many others. Supplied in a strong blue carton with a colourful label on the lid.
Silver components (early production)....................................**£300-500**
Cream components, RAF roundels **£300-500**
Blue and white components, RAF roundels...**£300-500**
Red and Cream components **£300-500**
Green and Cream components **£300-500**

Meccano Aero Motor No.1
Produced from early 1932. Designed to fit in the fuselage component of Outfit Nos. 1 or 2, the clockwork motor would 'rotate the propeller at high speed, thus greatly adding to the realism of the model.' **£30-40**

Meccano Aero Motor No.2
Produced from early 1932. Suitable for use with Outfit Nos. 1 or 2, this was a more powerful clockwork motor that would spin the propeller and drive the landing wheels 'making the machines taxi along the floor in a most realistic manner.' An Adjustable Tailwheel was included with Aero Motor No.2 ....**£60-80**

Hornby Speed Boats

Hornby toy boats were introduced in the summer of 1932. In that year, only one model was available; it was simply called Speed Boat 'Hornby', having no reference number. A year later it was promoted to Speed Boat No.3, four new models having been designed to provide a range costing between 2/6 and 17/6 each. Hornby Racing Boats followed in 1934 along with a 'water toy' in the shape of a duck. This, like all the Hornby pre-war boats was operated by a clockwork motor. Also available were Pennants, Motors,

Propellers and Shafts for the customisation or scratch-building of model boats. Production of the original tinplate products ceased at the outbreak of war in 1939. In 1960, Hornby Speed Boats made a reappearance, but only as a small new range of plastic mouldings with extra detail and clockwork motors until 1965. A battery-operated model continued in production up to 1969, the range being dropped by Lines Brothers five years after their aquisition of Meccano.

1932-32	**Speed Boat 'Hornby'**, Red, Green or Blue, open cockpit, 16in long	NGPP
1933-34	**Speed Boat No. 3, 'Hornby'**, Red, Green or Blue, open cockpit, 16in long	NGPP
1934-39	**Speed Boat No.2, 'Condor'**, Red/Cream, 16½in long	**£90-120**
	Speed Boat No.3, 'Gannet', Blue/White	NGPP
	Speed Boat No.3, 'Curlew', Green/Ivory	NGPP
1934-39	**Speed Boat No.1 'Hawk'**, Red/cream, Blue/White or Green/Ivory 9¼in long	**£60-80**
1947-??	**Speed Boat No.1 'Gleam'**, Green/White, picture box	**£60-80**
1947-??	**Speed Boat No.1 'Naval Launch X46'**, Grey, picture box	**£60-80**
1934-39	**Speed Boat No.2 'Swift'**, (blue box, full-colour label), Red/Cream, Blue/White or Yellow/White, 12½in long	**£100-150**
1934-39	**Limousine Boat No.4, 'Venture'**, Red/Cream, Blue/White or Green/Ivory, 16½in long	**£120-170**
1934-39	**Cabin Cruiser No.5 'Viking'**, Red/Cream, Blue/White or Green/Ivory, 16½in long	NGPP
1934-39	**Racing Boat No.1 'Racer I'**, Cream/Green, 8½in long	**£60-80**
1934-39	**Racing Boat No.2 'Racer II'**, Blue/Cream, 12½in long	**£90-120**
1934-39	**Racing Boat No.3 'Racer III'**, Red/Cream, 16½in long	**£130-180**

1934-39	**Hornby Water Toy (Duck)**, Superstructure is a tinplate pressing in the shape of a duck fitted to a 'Hawk' hull. 9¼in long	**£800-1,000**
1960-62	**Speed Boat No.3 River Launch**, Plastic moulding, 10in. long, clockwork motor	**£30-50**
1960-62	**Speed Boat No.4, Fast Patrol Launch**, plastic moulding, White hull, 'mahogany' deck, 10in. long, clockwork motor	**£40-60**
1960-65	**Speed Boat No.5 RAF Range Safety Launch**, plastic moulding, Black hull, Brown deck, 10in. long, clockwork	**£40-60**
1963-69	**Speed Boat**, plastic moulding, battery-operated motor	**£30-50**

See page 48 for colour illustrations of Hornby and Sutcliffe boats

Sutcliffe Model Boats

Sutcliffe Pressings was started in 1885, initially producing domestic and photographic sheet metal goods. Their famous oil cans came later, followed in 1920 by the first of their tinplate boats, the Valiant Battleship, the hulls of which were made as two pressings soldered together. In 1932 Sutcliffe

pioneered the production of hulls made from a single pressing. A variety of sizes of model boats were made but the majority were based on the 9 inch and 12 inch hulls. Production, mainly of boats, plus a smaller quantity of oil cans and other sheet metal work continued up to 1984.

1920	**'The Valiant Battleship'**. The first boat produced by Sutcliffe. Originally powered by a water circulatory boiler with the coil heated by methylated spirits.	NGPP
1928	**'The Valiant Battleship'**. Clockwork	NGPP
1978-80	**'The Valiant Battleship'**, 12" hull. Modified re-issue with moveable rudder and gun turrets. Three decals: 'Sutcliffe Models', 'Valiant', Union Jack	**£150-200**

1978-80	**'The Valiant Battleship'**. Electric powered (only 6 made)	NGPP
1935	**'Zip' Speedboat**, 9" hull with large clockwork motor	NGPP
c1978	**'Zip' Speedboat**, 9" hull, (A batch of 100 were made)	NGPP
1959-68	**'Noddy'**, 9" hull	NGPP
1963-80	**'Merlin'** electric, 12" hull	NGPP
1950-59	**'Viking' Liner**, 9" hull	NGPP
c1978	**'Viking' Liner**, 9" hull. (A batch of 100 were made)	NGPP
?	**'Victor'**	NGPP
?	**'Zodiac'**, large electric boat, plastic hull, wood deck	NGPP
?	**'Zodiac'**, a very few were factory modified to clockwork	NGPP
?	**'Minx' Cruiser** was smaller with a clockwork motor	NGPP
?	**'Jupiter' Ocean Pilot Cruiser**	NGPP
?	**'Racer'**	**£80-120**
?	**'Grenville' Destroyer**	**£200-300**
?	**'Snappy' Gunboat**	NGPP
?	**'Sprite'**	**£90-130**
?	**'Bluebird'**, single-hulled speedboat	**£150-250**
?	**'Bluebird'**, tri-hulled speedboat (picture at left)	**£150-250**

SUBMARINES
These were boxed with a winding key and a 'periscope' rubber plug.

?	**'Sea Wolf'**. A submarine	**£120-160**
?	**'Unda-Wunda'**. A submarine	**£170-230**
c1960s	**'Nautilus'**, clockwork submarine. "Nautilus, copyright Walt Disney Productions" transfer	**£120-180**
?	**'Sutcliffe' Oil Cans**. Numerous types and sizes, each:	**£25-50**

SUTCLIFFE INFORMATION. The listing above represents all the information we currently have on Sutcliffe. The Editors would welcome any contributions or new information that you may have for future inclusion.

Photo: Wallis & Wallis